HYGRADE®

CATALOG & PRICE GUIDE OF
TOPPS, DONRUSS, FLEER, SCORE,
SPORTFLICS, UPPER DECK AND BOWMAN

BASEBALL CARDS

Features card values of virtually every
baseball card issued by these manufacturers:

- TOPPS—years 1951 to 1990
- DONRUSS—years 1981 to 1990
- FLEER—years 1981 to 1990
- SCORE—years 1988 to 1990
- SPORTFLICS—years 1986 to 1990
- UPPER DECK—years 1989 to 1990
- BOWMAN—year 1989

All cards are copyrighted by Topps Chewing Gum, Fleer, Donruss, Score, Sportflics and Upper Deck.

Published annually in March— every year since 1986.

Fifth Edition (1)

Publisher: **HYGRADE SPORTS CARD CO., 5 East 17th Street, New York, N.Y. 10003**

General Information

Card values in this catalog represent approximate retail values as of **Feb., 1990.** Due to high demand, the values of popular cards (especially rookie cards of star players from the past five years) have been fluctuating every few weeks. Keep up-to-date on the latest market values with a monthly price guide.

Information on card values was compiled from various sources including dealer ads in card magazines, dealer catalogs, card auctions, offers at card conventions, etc. **The card values in this catalog do not represent an offer to buy or sell by the publisher. We are not responsible for typographical errors.**

What Makes a Card Valuable?

The value of a baseball card is determined by *supply* (how many cards are offered for sale at a certain price), and *demand* (how many cards buyers are willing and able to purchase at a certain price). When the demand is greater than the supply, the card's value *increases*; when supply exceeds demand, the card's value *decreases*. However, as with stamps and coins, the *condition* of a card also affects its value. Cards which have been preserved in *mint* condition are much more in demand by collectors, and therefore worth more than the same cards in worn condition. If the card shows *very light wear*, its value is usually about 65% to 80% of the price for the same card in mint condition. The more wear or damage the card shows, the less it is worth. So if you eventually hope to sell your collection for a profit, try to buy cards in the best possible condition.

Rookie Cards

A *rookie* card is a player's first card from the *main* card set of a major card manufacturer. Today the major card manufacturers are Topps, Donruss, Fleer, Score, Upper Deck and Bowman. Sometimes several players are shown on one rookie card. For example, Pete Rose is pictured with three other players on his 1963 rookie card. Occasionally a rookie card is issued one or more years after the player's actual rookie season. Each of the major manufacturers issues a main card set each year, as well as several special card sets. But in order for a card to qualify as the *rookie* card it must appear in the main card set, which is universally distributed. Sometimes special card sets, like the Topps *Traded Update*, include a player's first card, but this card is not generally considered to be a rookie card. Traded cards are mainly distributed through card hobby dealers, unlike cards from the main set which are sold everywhere. From 1956 to 1980 Topps was the only major card manufacturer, so each player had only one rookie card. Today there are six major card sets—so each player can have up to six rookie cards.

Complete Sets

The total cost of the individual cards in a set is always much greater than the complete set price—which makes the complete set an economical purchase. This is because a complete set includes many common cards, and minor-star cards which a dealer will sell at a reduced price when sold as a group. The complete set value does not include any error or variety cards. Donruss factory-sealed sets issued from 1983 to date sell at a premium over hand-collated sets.

Double-Printed Cards

Baseball cards are not printed individually, but are printed on big sheets that have space for up to 132 cards. Once printed, these sheets are cut apart, and the cards are sorted and packaged. If the number of cards on a sheet is the same as the number of cards in a set, or divides evenly into that set number, then each of the cards on the sheet shows a different player. From 1973 to 1977, Topps issued baseball sets of 660 cards. These were printed on five sheets, each with 132 different cards. But beginning in 1978 and continuing until 1981, Topps changed the number of cards in its sets from 660 to 726, an increase of 66 cards. Rather than print a sixth sheet only half filled, Topps decided to *double-print* (print twice the quantity) 66 cards in each set.

Common Cards

Common cards are the lowest valued cards in a set. They are cards that feature ordinary players, not stars or popular personalities. There is very little demand by collectors for individual common cards. They are often sold in lots and used primarily to assemble card sets. A typical Topps card set includes about 60% *common* cards, 25% *minor star* cards and 15% *star* cards.

High-Numbers

During the period from 1952 to 1973 Topps released their annual card sets in series, rather than issuing the complete set at one time as they do now. Most Topps sets consisted of six or seven card series, each released a few weeks or months apart. For example, the first series of the 1970 Topps card set had 132 cards, numbers 1 to 132; the second series contained numbers 133 to 263, etc. Since sales of the cards tended to become less and less as the season progressed, Topps usually printed fewer of the later card series, which contained the high number cards. Because the high number cards are scarcer today, they are generally more valuable as a group, than the low number cards of the same set. If the last series is not scarce, compared to other series in the same set, it is not a high number series. Every Topps set issued from 1952 to 1973 has a high number series except years 1954, 1956, 1957, 1958 and 1969.

Several Topps card sets from 1952 to 1973 also have a *semi-high-number* series. This is the next to the last series of a card set in which there is also a high number series, and the semi-high number cards are scarce. Semi-high number cards as a group are generally worth less than high numbers, but more than low numbers. Beginning in 1974 and continuing until today, Topps changed their policy and distributed their card sets all at one time, thus eliminating high numbers.

TOPPS® SPECIAL CARD SETS

ALL STAR GLOSSY "INSERT" (2½″ x 3½″)

22 card set features the starting players, managers, and captains of the previous year's All-Star Game. One random card was inserted in rack packs.

1984-$4, 1985-$4, 1986-$4, 1987-$4, 1988-$4, 1989-$3

ALL STAR GLOSSY "MAIL-IN" (2½″ x 3½″)

From 1983 to 1985 the set consisted of 40 cards; 1986 to date—60 cards. The set was offered by Topps directly to the consumer through the mail.

1983-$13, 1984-$12, 1985-$12, 1986-$15, 1987-$13, 1988-$13, 1989-$13

ROOKIES GLOSSY (2½″ x 3½″)

22 card set features the top rookies from the previous season. One random card was inserted in supermarket jumbo rack packs.

1987—$10, 1988-$8, 1989—$8

WAX BOX CARDS

Printed on the bottom of wax boxes of the main card set (except 1987 printed on the side of the box). Printed in panels of four cards per box. All sets include 16 cards (2½″ x 3½″) except 1987 has 8 cards (2⅛″ x 3″). Values are for full panels—cut cards are worth 60% less.

1986-$9, 1987-$3, 1988-$3, 1989-$3

MINI LEAGUE LEADERS (2⅛″ x 2¹⁵/₁₆″)

Features the highest rated players statistically from the previous year. All sets include 77 cards except 1986 has 66 cards.

1986-$7, 1987-$6, 1988-$6, 1989-$6

BIG BASEBALL (2⅝″ x 3¾″)

The design was styled after the Topps 1956 card set. Each set was distributed in wax packs and released in three different series.

1988 (264 cards)-$36, 1989 (330 cards)-$30

CHAIN STORE SETS (2½″ x 3½″)

Topps sold each card set exclusively to the chain stores listed below. Each set features a high gloss finish and is individually boxed. All sets include 33 cards—unless otherwise noted. Worth about $4. each.

AMES—1989 20/20 club

BOARDWALK & BASEBALL—1987 Run Makers

CIRCLE K—1985 Home Run Kings

CUMBERLAND FARMS—1989 Superstars

HILLS—1989 Team MVP's

K-MART—1982 MVP (44 cards). 1987 Stars of Decade, 1988 Memorable Moments, 1989 Dream Team

KAY BEE—1986 Young Superstars, 1987 to 1989 Superstars

REVCO—1988 League Leaders

RITE AID—1988 Team MVP's

TOYS R US—1987 to 1989 Rookies

WOOLWORTH—1985 All-Time Record Holders (44 cards). 1986 Champion Superstars, 1987 to 1989 Baseball Highlights

MISCELLANEOUS (1984 to 1989)

1989 Double Header All-Star (24 cards)-$18
1989 Heads Up (24 cards)
1988 United Kingdom (88 cards, size 2⅛″ x 3″)-$8
1986 Three Dimensional (30 cards, size 4½″ x 6″)-$10
1986 Supers (60 cards, 4⅞″ x 6⅞″)-$10
1985 Three Dimensional (30 cards, size 4½″ x 6″)-$10
1985 Supers (60 cards, size 4⅞″ x 6⅞″)-$15
1984 Supers (30 cards, size 4⅞″ x 6⅞″)-$10

DONRUSS® SPECIAL SETS

ACTION ALL STARS (3½" x 5")
Each 60 card set features an action shot of an All Star Player. The cards were sold in wax packs.

1983-$7, 1984-$7, 1985-$7

ALL STARS
Issued in conjunction with Donruss Pop-Up cards. Each wax pack includes one Pop-Up and three All Star Cards.

1986 (60 cards, 3½" x 5")—$7
1987 60 cards (3½" x 5")—$7,
1988 (64 cards, 2½" x 3½")—$5
1989 (64 cards, 2½" x 3½")—$5

POP-UPS
Issued in conjunction with Donruss All Star cards. Each wax pack includes one Pop-Up and three All Star Cards. Features the starting lineup of the previous year's All Star Game. The cards are die-cut and fold out to stand up.

1986 (18 cards, 2½" x 5")—$7,
1987 (20 cards, 2½" x 5")—$7,
1988 (20 cards, 2½" x 3½")—$6,
1989 (20 cards, 2½" x 3½")—$6

SUPER DIAMOND KINGS (4¾" x 6¾")
These are enlarged versions of the Diamond King cards of the main card set. All sets include 28 cards. Available through the mail directly from Perez Steele Galleries.

1985-$9, 1986-$9, 1987-$9, 1988-$8, 1989-$7

BONUS MVP's (2½" x 3½")
26 card set features Donruss' selection of MVP for each team. One card was inserted in wax and rack packs.

1988-$9, 1989-$9

BASEBALLS BEST (2½" x 3½")
Cards look like the main card set except they have a different color border. The 336 card set is packaged in a plastic gift tray.

1988—$20, 1989—$20

HIGHLIGHTS (2½" x 3½")
56 card glossy set features highlights of the season and Player of the Month. Packaged in a printed box.

1985-$20, 1986-$7, 1987-$7

WAX BOX CARDS (2½" x 3½")
Four cards were printed in panels on the bottom of wax and cello boxes of the main card set. All sets include four cards. Values are for panels—cut cards are worth 60% less.

1985-$7, 1986-$2, 1987-$3

"ALL STAR" WAX BOX CARDS (2½" x 3½")
Four cards were printed in panels on the bottom of wax boxes of All Star cards. All sets include four cards. Values are for full panels—cut cards are worth 60% less.

1986-$2, 1987-$2

MISCELLANEOUS (1981 to 1989)
1983 Hall of Fame Heroes (44 cards, 2½" x 3½")—$4
1984 Grand Champions (60 cards, size 3½" x 5")—$6
1987 Opening Day (272 cards, size 2½" x 3½")—$20

FLEER® SPECIAL SETS

ALL STAR TEAM (2½" x 3½")

12 card set features Fleer's selection of players for an All Star team. One card was inserted in wax and cello packs.

1986-$16, 1987-$15, 1988-$13, 1989-$10

FUTURE HALL OF FAMERS (2½" x 3½")

6 card set features Fleer's selection of players who would probably enter the Hall of Fame. One random card was inserted in three-pack racks.

1986-$8

HEADLINERS (2½" x 3½")

6 card set features players who made news headlines the previous season. One card was inserted in rack packs.

1987-$7, 1988-$7

FOR THE RECORD (2½" x 3½")

6 card set features players who broke records in the previous season. One card was inserted in rack packs.

1989-$5

WORLD SERIES (2½" x 3½")

12 card set features highlights from the previous year's World Series. The complete set was packaged as a bonus with the Fleer factory sealed sets.

1987-$4, 1988-$4, 1989-$4

WAX BOX CARDS (2½" x 3½")

Printed on the bottom of wax and cello boxes in panels of four cards per box. Values are for full panels—cut cards are worth 60% less.

1986-(8 cards)—$3, 1987—(16 cards)—$6, 1988 (16 cards)—$5, 1989 (28 cards)—$8

CLASSIC MINI (1⅞" x 2⅝")

120 card glossy coated set sold as a complete set and packaged in a printed box.

1986-$10, 1987-$10, 1988-$9

CHAIN STORE SETS (2½" x 3½")

Fleer sold each card set exclusively to the chain stores listed below. Each set features a high gloss finish and is individually boxed. All sets include 44 cards—worth about $4 each

BEN FRANKLIN—1987 to 1989 All Stars
CUMBERLAND FARMS—1987 to 1988 Exciting Stars
ECKERD DRUG—1987 to 1988 Record Setters
KAYBEE—1988 Team Leaders

McCRORY—1985 to 1989 Superstars, 1986 to 1988 Sluggers vs. Pitchers (some store display boxes feature cards printed on the bottom)
McCRORY—1985 to 1989 Superstars (from 1987 to 1989 six cards are printed on store display boxes); 1986 to 1988 Sluggers vs. Pitchers (six cards are printed on store display boxes).
PAY 'N SAVE—1987 Game Winners.
REVCO DRUG—1987 to 1988 Hottest Stars
7-ELEVEN—1987 to 1988 Award Winners
TOYS R US—1988 to 1989 MVP's
WALGREEN—1986 to 1989 League Leaders

SCORE® SPECIAL SETS

YOUNG SUPERSTARS (2½" x 3½")
Each set features a high gloss finish and is packaged in a printed box.

1988 Series No. 1 (40 cards)—$7, 1988 Series No. 2 (40 cards)—$7, 1989 Series No. 1 (42 cards)—$7, 1989 Series No. 2 (42 cards)—$7.

WAX BOX CARDS (2½" x 3½")
Four cards were printed in panels on the bottom of wax boxes. Values are for panels—cut cards are worth 60% less.

1988 (24 cards)—$6

HOTTEST ROOKIES (2½" x 3½")
100 card set was sold with a 48 page book featuring information about each player.

1989-$7

HOTTEST PLAYERS (2½" x 3½")
100 card set was sold with a 48 page book featuring information about each player.

1989-$7

SPORTFLICS® SPECIAL SETS

ROOKIES (2½ x 3½")
Each set was packaged in a printed box.

1986 (50 cards)-$15, 1987 series 1 (25 cards)-$8, 1987 Series 2 (25 cards)-$5

ROOKIE PROSPECTS (2½" x 3½")
Offered to hobby dealers who purchased Team Preview sets.

1987 (10 cards)-$8

TEAM PREVIEW (2½" x 3½")
Features a card for each team with outlook for the season.

1987 (26 cards)-$7

DECADE GREATS (2½" x 3½")
Features the best players at each position for each decade.

1986 (75 cards)-$15

LEGEND

R—the player's rookie card. Only rookie cards of "star" players are noted.

RR—the manufacturer's first card for that player, which is in the Traded Update or Rookie set.

*—there is a special feature of this card, which can be determined by referring to the headline for the set.

AS—a card featuring a player who was on the previous year's all-star team.

DK—abbreviation for Diamond King, which is a Donruss card with artwork by the Perez-Steele Gallery.

Mgr.—a card featuring the manager of a baseball team.

MVP—Most Valuable Player award

1951 Topps "Red Backs" . . . Complete Set of 52 Cards—Value $250.00 (Exc.); $400.00 (Mint)

This set, as well as the 1951 "Blue Backs", was Topps' first baseball card issue. The backs of the 2" x 2⅝" cards can be used to play a baseball card game. Card 36 was issued as either White Sox or Athletics. Card 52 was issued as either Hartford or Braves.

NO.	PLAYER	NR. MT.
1	Yogi Berra	55.00
2	Sid Gordon	5.00
3	Ferris Fain	5.00
4	Verne Stephens	5.00
5	Phil Rizzuto	18.00
6	Allie Reynolds	9.00
7	Howie Pollet	5.00
8	Early Wynn	15.00
9	Roy Sievers	5.00
10	Mel Parnell	5.00
11	Gene Hermanski	5.00
12	Jim Hegan	5.00
13	Dale Mitchell	5.00
14	Wayne Terwilliger	5.00
15	Ralph Kiner	18.00
16	Preacher Roe	8.00
17	Dave Bell	5.00
18	Gerry Coleman	5.00
19	Dick Kokos	5.00
20	Dominick DiMaggio	9.00
21	Larry Jansen	5.00
22	Bob Feller	20.00
23	Ray Boone	5.00
24	Hank Bauer	10.00
25	Cliffe Chambers	5.00
26	Luke Easter	5.00
27	Wally Westlake	5.00
28	Elmer Valo	5.00
29	Bob Kennedy	5.00
30	Warren Spahn	20.00
31	Gil Hodges	20.00
32	Henry Thompson	5.00
33	William Werle	5.00
34	Grady Hatton	5.00
35	Al Rosen	9.00
36	Gus Zernial*	15.00
37	Wes Westrum	5.00
38	Duke Snider	50.00
39	Ted Kluszewski	8.00
40	Mike Garcia	5.00
41	Whitey Lockman	5.00
42	Ray Scarborough	5.00
43	Maurice McDermott	5.00
44	Sid Hudson	5.00
45	Andy Seminick	5.00
46	Billy Goodman	5.00
47	Tom Glaviano	5.00
48	Ed Stanky	5.00
49	Al Zarilla	5.00
50	M. Irvin	20.00
51	Eddie Robinson	5.00
52	Tommy Holmes*	18.00

1951 Topps "Blue Backs" . . . Complete Set of 52 Cards—Value $800.00 (Exc.); $1350.00 (Mint)

Similar in format to the 1951 "Red Backs." The backs of the 2" x 2⅝" cards can be used to play a baseball card game.

NO.	PLAYER	NR. MT.
1	Eddie Yost	22.00
2	Hank Majeski	20.00
3	Richie Ashburn	40.00
4	Del Ennis	20.00
5	Johnny Pesky	20.00
6	Al Schoendienst	28.00
7	Gerald Staley	20.00
8	Dick Sisler	20.00
9	Johnny Sain	35.00
10	Joe Page	30.00
11	Johnny Groth	20.00
12	Sam Jethroe	20.00
13	Mickey Vernon	20.00
14	George Munger	20.00
15	Eddie Joost	20.00
16	Murry Dickson	20.00
17	Roy Smalley	20.00
18	Ned Garver	20.00
19	Phil Masi	20.00
20	Ralph Branca	20.00
21	Bill Johnson	20.00
22	Bob Kuzava	20.00
23	Dizzy Trout	20.00
24	Sherman Lollar	20.00
25	Sam A. Mele	20.00
26	Chico Carrasquel	20.00
27	Andy Pafko	20.00
28	Harry Brecheen	20.00
29	Granville Hamner	20.00
30	Enos Slaughter	50.00
31	Lou Brissie	20.00
32	Bob Elliott	20.00
33	Don Lenhardt	20.00
34	Earl Torgeson	20.00
35	Tom Byrne (R)	20.00
36	Cliff Fannin	20.00
37	Bobby Doerr	50.00
38	Irv Noren	20.00
39	Ed Lopat	30.00
40	Vic Wertz	20.00
41	Johnny Schmitz	20.00
42	Bruce Edwards	20.00
43	Willie Jones	20.00
44	Johnny Wyrostek	20.00
45	Bill Pierce (R)	30.00
46	Gerry Priddy	20.00
47	Herman Wehmeier	20.00
48	Billy Cox	20.00
49	Hank Sauer	20.00
50	John Mize	60.00
51	Ed Waitkus	20.00
52	Sam Chapman	20.00

1952 Topps . . . Complete Set of 407 Cards—Value $17,000.00 (Exc.); $40,000.00 (Mint)

Features the rookie cards of Hoyt Wilhelm, Billy Martin and Eddie Mathews. This is Topps' first *major* baseball card set. Cards 1 to 80 were printed with *black* or *red* backs. The high number series is 311 to 407. Semi-high numbers are 251 to 310. Topps introduced a new card size—2⅝" x 3¾", used until 1956. Cards 48 and 49 exist with each other's backs transposed—worth $275.00 each.

NO. PLAYER	NR. MT.	NO. PLAYER	NR. MT.	NO. PLAYER	NR. MT.	NO. PLAYER	NR. MT.
1 Andy Pafko (Exc. $50.00)	900.00	69 Virgil Stallcup	50.00	137 Roy McMillan	20.00	205 Clyde King	20.00
2 James Runnels	70.00	70 Al Zarilla	50.00	138 Bill MacDonald	20.00	206 Joe Ostrowski	20.00
3 Hank Thompson	50.00	71 Tom Upton	50.00	139 Ken Wood	20.00	207 Mickey Harris	20.00
4 Donald Lenhardt	50.00	72 Karl Olson	50.00	140 John Antonelli	20.00	208 Marlin Stuart	20.00
5 Larry Jansen	50.00	73 William Werle	50.00	141 Clint Hartung	20.00	209 Howie Fox	20.00
6 Grady Hatton	50.00	74 Andy Hansen	50.00	142 Harry Perkowski	20.00	210 Dick Fowler	20.00
7 Wayne Terwilliger	50.00	75 Wes Westrum	50.00	143 Les Moss	20.00	211 Ray Coleman	20.00
8 Fred Marsh	50.00	76 Eddie Stanky	50.00	144 Edward Blake	20.00	212 Ned Garver	20.00
9 Bob Hogue	50.00	77 Bob Kennedy	50.00	145 Joe Haynes	20.00	213 Nippy Jones	20.00
10 Al Rosen	60.00	78 Ellis Kinder	50.00	146 Frank House	20.00	214 Johnny Hopp	20.00
11 Phil Rizzuto	150.00	79 Gerald Staley	50.00	147 Bob Young	20.00	215 Hank Bauer	45.00
12 Monty Basgall	50.00	80 Herman Wehmeier	50.00	148 John Klippstein	20.00	216 Richie Ashburn	65.00
13 Johnny Wyrostek	50.00	81 Vernon Law	20.00	149 Dick Kryhoski	20.00	217 George Stirnweiss	20.00
14 Bob Elliott	50.00	82 Duane Pillette	20.00	150 Ted Beard	20.00	218 Clyde McCullough	20.00
15 Johnny Pesky	50.00	83 Billy Johnson	20.00	151 Wally Post	20.00	219 Bobby Shantz	30.00
16 Gene Hermanski	50.00	84 Vern Stephens	20.00	152 Al Evans	20.00	220 Joe Presko	20.00
17 Jim Hegan	50.00	85 Bob Kuzava	20.00	153 Bob Rush	20.00	221 Granny Hamner	20.00
18 Merrill Combs	50.00	86 Teddy Gray	20.00	154 Joe Muir	20.00	222 Walter Evers	20.00
19 John Bucha	50.00	87 Dale Coogan	20.00	155 Frank Overmire	20.00	223 Del Ennis	20.00
20 Billy Loes	85.00	88 Bob Feller	115.00	156 Frank Hiller	20.00	224 Bruce Edwards	20.00
21 Ferris Fain	50.00	89 Johnny Lipon	20.00	157 Bob Usher	20.00	225 Frank Baumholtz	20.00
22 Dom DiMaggio	75.00	90 Mickey Grasso	20.00	158 Eddie Waitkus	20.00	226 Dave Philley	20.00
23 Billy Goodman	50.00	91 Al Schoendienst	50.00	159 Saul Rogovin	20.00	227 Joe Garagiola	75.00
24 Luke Easter	50.00	92 Dale Mitchell	20.00	160 Owen Friend	20.00	228 Al Brazle	20.00
25 Johnny Grothe	50.00	93 Al Sima	20.00	161 Bud Byerly	20.00	229 Gene Bearden	20.00
26 Monte Irvin	100.00	94 Sam Mele	20.00	162 Del Crandall	20.00	230 Matt Batts	20.00
27 Sam Jethroe	50.00	95 Ken Holcombe	20.00	163 Stan Rojek	20.00	231 Sam Zoldak	20.00
28 Jerry Priddy	50.00	96 Willard Marshall	20.00	164 Walt Dubiel	20.00	232 Billy Cox	20.00
29 Ted Kluszewski	85.00	97 Earl Torgeson	20.00	165 Ed Kazak	20.00	233 Bob Friend	20.00
30 Mel Parnell	50.00	98 Bill Pierce	20.00	166 Paul LaPalme	20.00	234 Steve Souchock	20.00
31 Gus Zernial	50.00	99 Gene Woodling	40.00	167 Bill Howerton	20.00	235 Walt Dropo	20.00
32 Eddie Robinson	50.00	100 Del Rice	20.00	168 Charlie Silvera	20.00	236 Ed Fitzgerald	20.00
33 Warren Spahn	160.00	101 Max Lanier	20.00	169 Howie Judson	20.00	237 Jerry Coleman	20.00
34 Elmer Valo	50.00	102 Bill Kennedy	20.00	170 Gus Bell	20.00	238 Art Houtteman	20.00
35 Hank Sauer	50.00	103 Cliff Mapes	20.00	171 Ed Erautt	20.00	239 Rocky Bridges	20.00
36 Gil Hodges	125.00	104 Don Kolloway	20.00	172 Eddie Miksis	20.00	240 Jack Phillips	20.00
37 Duke Snider	240.00	105 John Pramesa	20.00	173 Roy Smalley	20.00	241 Tommy Byrne	20.00
38 Wally Westlake	50.00	106 Mickey Vernon	20.00	174 Clarence Marshall	20.00	242 Tom Poholsky	20.00
39 Dizzy Trout	50.00	107 Connie Ryan	20.00	175 Billy Martin (R)	225.00	243 Larry Doby	45.00
40 Irv Noren	50.00	108 Jimmy Konstanty	20.00	176 Hank Edwards	20.00	244 Vic Wertz	20.00
41 Bob Wellman	50.00	109 Ted Wilks	20.00	177 Bill Wight	20.00	245 Sherry Robertson	20.00
42 Lou Kretlow	50.00	110 Dutch Leonard	20.00	178 Cass Michaels	20.00	246 George Kell	65.00
43 Ray Scarborough	50.00	111 Harry Lowrey	20.00	179 Frank Smith	20.00	247 Randy Gumpert	20.00
44 Con Dempsey	50.00	112 Henry Majeski	20.00	180 Charley Maxwell	20.00	248 Frank Shea	20.00
45 Ed Joost	50.00	113 Dick Sisler	20.00	181 Bob Swift	20.00	249 Bobby Adams	20.00
46 Gordon Goldsberry	50.00	114 Willard Ramsdell	20.00	182 Bill Hitchcock	20.00	250 Carl Erskine	45.00
47 Willie Jones	50.00	115 George Munger	20.00	183 Erv Dusak	20.00	251 Chico Carrasquel	35.00
48 Joe Page*	75.00	116 Carl Scheib	20.00	184 Bob Ramazzotti	20.00	252 Vern Bickford	35.00
49 Johnny Sain*	75.00	117 Sherman Lollar	20.00	185 Bill Nicholson	20.00	253 Johnny Berardino	35.00
50 Marv Rickertt	50.00	118 Ken Raffensberger	20.00	186 Walt Masterson	20.00	254 Joe Dobson	35.00
51 Jim Russell	50.00	119 Maurice McDermott	20.00	187 Bob Miller	20.00	255 Clyde Vollmer	35.00
52 Don Mueller	50.00	120 Bob Chakales	20.00	188 Clarence Podbielan	20.00	256 Pete Suder	35.00
53 Chris Van Cuyk	50.00	121 Gus Niarhos	20.00	189 Harold Reiser	20.00	257 Bob Avila	35.00
54 Leo Kiely	50.00	122 Jack Jensen	50.00	190 Don Johnson	20.00	258 Steve Gromek	35.00
55 Ray Boone	50.00	123 Eddie Yost	20.00	191 Yogi Berra	275.00	259 Bob Addis	35.00
56 Tom Glaviano	50.00	124 Monte Kennedy	20.00	192 Myron Ginsberg	20.00	260 Pete Castiglione	35.00
57 Eddie Lopat	90.00	125 Bill Rigney	20.00	193 Harry Simpson	20.00	261 Willie Mays	1100.00
58 Bob Mahoney	50.00	126 Fred Hutchinson	20.00	194 Joe Hatten	20.00	262 Virgil Trucks	35.00
59 Robin Roberts	125.00	127 Paul Minner	20.00	195 Orestes Minoso (R)	45.00	263 Harry Brecheen	35.00
60 Sid Hudson	50.00	128 Don Bollweg	20.00	196 Solly Hemus	20.00	264 Roy Hartsfield	35.00
61 Tookie Gilbert	50.00	129 Johnny Mize	80.00	197 George Strickland	20.00	265 Chuck Diering	35.00
62 Chuck Stobbs	50.00	130 Sheldon Jones	20.00	198 Phil Haugstad	20.00	266 Murry Dickson	35.00
63 Howie Pollett	50.00	131 Morris Martin	20.00	199 George Zuverink	20.00	267 Sid Gordon	35.00
64 Roy Sievers	50.00	132 Clyde Klutz	20.00	200 Ralph Houk (R)	60.00	268 Bob Lemon	150.00
65 Enos Slaughter	110.00	133 Al Widmar	20.00	201 Alex Kellner	20.00	269 Willard Nixon	35.00
66 Preacher Roe	75.00	134 Joe Tipton	20.00	202 Joe Collins	20.00	270 Lou Brissie	35.00
67 Allie Reynolds	80.00	135 Dixie Howell	20.00	203 Curt Simmons	20.00	271 Jim Delsing	35.00
68 Cliff Chambers	50.00	136 Johnny Schmitz	20.00	204 Ron Northey	20.00	272 Mike Garcia	35.00

NO. PLAYER	NR. MT.	NO. PLAYER	NR. MT.	NO. PLAYER	NR. MT.	NO. PLAYER	NR. MT.
273 Erv Palica	35.00	307 Frank Campos	35.00	341 Hal Jeffcoat	150.00	375 Jack Merson	150.00
274 Ralph Branca	60.00	308 Luis Aloma	35.00	342 Clem Labine	150.00	376 Faye Throneberry	150.00
275 Pat Mullin	35.00	309 Jim Busby	35.00	343 Dick Gernert	150.00	377 Chuck Dressen	175.00
276 Jim Wilson	35.00	310 George Metkovich	35.00	344 Ewell Blackwell	150.00	378 Les Fusselman	150.00
277 Early Wynn	175.00	311 M. Mantle (Exc. $3000.00)	6750.00	345 Sammy White	150.00	379 Joe Rossi	150.00
278 Al Clark	35.00	312 Jackie Robinson	900.00	346 George Spencer	150.00	380 Clem Koshorek	150.00
279 Ed Stewart	35.00	313 Bobby Thomson	180.00	347 Joe Adcock	150.00	381 Milton Stock	150.00
280 Cloyd Boyer	35.00	314 Roy Campanella	1500.00	348 Bob Kelly	150.00	382 Samuel Jones	150.00
281 Tom Brown	45.00	315 Leo Durocher (Mgr)	250.00	349 Bob Cain	150.00	383 Del Wilber	150.00
282 Birdie Tebbetts	45.00	316 Dave Williams	150.00	350 Cal Abrams	150.00	384 Frank Crosetti	250.00
283 Phil Masi	45.00	317 Connie Marrero	150.00	351 Alvin Dark	200.00	385 Herman Franks	150.00
284 Hank Arft	45.00	318 Hal Gregg	150.00	352 Karl Drews	150.00	386 Eddie Yuhas	150.00
285 Cliff Fannin	45.00	319 Al Walker	150.00	353 Robert Del Greco	150.00	387 Bill Meyer	150.00
286 Joe DeMaestri	45.00	320 John Rutherford	150.00	354 Fred Hatfield	150.00	388 Bob Chipman	150.00
287 Steve Bilko	45.00	321 Joe Black (R)	175.00	355 Bobby Morgan	150.00	389 Ben Wade	150.00
288 Chet Nichols	45.00	322 Randy Jackson	150.00	356 Toby Atwell	150.00	390 Glenn Nelson	150.00
289 Tommy Holmes	45.00	323 Bubba Church	150.00	357 Smokey Burgess	175.00	391 Ben Chapman	150.00
290 Joe Astroth	45.00	324 Warren Hacker	150.00	358 John Kucab	150.00	(photo of Sam Chapman)	
291 Gil Coan	45.00	325 Bill Serena	150.00	359 Dee Fondy	150.00	392 Hoyt Wilhelm (R)	550.00
292 Floyd Baker	45.00	326 George Shuba	150.00	360 George Crowe	150.00	393 Ebba St. Claire	150.00
293 Sibby Sisti	45.00	327 Archie Wilson	150.00	361 Bill Posedel	150.00	394 Billy Herman	200.00
294 Walker Cooper	45.00	328 Bob Borkowski	150.00	362 Kenny Heintzelman	150.00	395 Jake Pitler	150.00
295 Phil Cavarretta	45.00	329 Ivan Delock	150.00	363 Dick Rozek	150.00	396 Dick Williams (R)	200.00
296 Red Rolfe	45.00	330 Turk Lown	150.00	364 Clyde Sukeforth	150.00	397 Forrest Main	150.00
297 Andy Seminick	45.00	331 Tom Morgan	150.00	365 Cookie Lavagetto	150.00	398 Hal Rice	150.00
298 Bob Ross	45.00	332 Anthony Bartirome	150.00	366 Dave Madison	150.00	399 Jim Fridley	150.00
299 Ray Murray	45.00	333 Pee Wee Reese	700.00	367 Bob Thorpe	150.00	400 Bill Dickey	500.00
300 Barney McCosky	45.00	334 Wilmer Mizell	150.00	368 Ed Wright	150.00	401 Bob Schultz	150.00
301 Bob Porterfield	35.00	335 Ted Lepcio	150.00	369 Dick Groat (R)	275.00	402 Earl Harrist	150.00
302 Max Surkont	35.00	336 Dave Koslo	150.00	370 Bill Hoeft	150.00	403 Bill Miller	150.00
303 Harry Dorish	35.00	337 Jim Hearn	150.00	371 Bob Hofman	150.00	404 Dick Brodowski	150.00
304 Sam Dente	35.00	338 Sal Yvars	150.00	372 Gil McDougald (R)	250.00	405 Eddie Pellagrini	150.00
305 Paul Richards	35.00	339 Russ Meyer	150.00	373 Jim Turner	150.00	406 Joseph Nuxhall (R)	200.00
306 Lou Sleater	35.00	340 Bob Hooper	150.00	374 Al Benton	150.00	407 E. Mathews (R)	1600.00
						(Exc. $300.00)	

1953 Topps . . . Complete Set of 274 Cards—Value $3750.00 (Exc.); $10,000 (Mint)

Features the rookie cards of Johnny Padres and Jim Gilliam. Although the cards are numbered up to 280, there are only 274 cards in the set. Six cards were not issued—numbers 253, 261, 267, 268, 271 and 275. The high number series is 221 to 280. Card size 2⅝" x 3¾".

MICKEY MANTLE
NEW YORK YANKEES

WILLIE MAYS
NEW YORK GIANTS

JIM GILLIAM
BROOKLYN DODGERS

JOHN PODRES
BROOKLYN DODGERS

MILT BOLLING
BOSTON RED SOX

NO. PLAYER	NR. MT.	NO. PLAYER	NR. MT.	NO. PLAYER	NR. MT.	NO. PLAYER	NR. MT.
1 J. Robinson (Exc. $135.00)	500.00	23 Toby Atwell	20.00	45 Grady Hatton	20.00	67 Roy Sievers	20.00
2 Luke Easter	20.00	24 Ferris Fain	20.00	46 John Klippstein	20.00	68 Del Rice	20.00
3 George Crowe	20.00	25 R. Boone	20.00	47 Bubba Church	20.00	69 Dick Brodowski	20.00
4 Benjamin Wade	20.00	26 Dale Mitchell	20.00	48 Bob Del Greco	20.00	70 Eddie Yuhas	20.00
5 Joe Dobson	20.00	27 Roy Campanella	175.00	49 Faye Throneberry	20.00	71 Tony Bartirome	20.00
6 Sam Jones	20.00	28 Eddie Pellagrini	20.00	50 Chuck Dressenn	20.00	72 Fred Hutchison	20.00
7 Bob Borkowski	15.00	29 Hal Jeffcoat	20.00	51 Frank Campos	20.00	73 Eddie Robinson	20.00
8 Clem Koshorek	15.00	30 Willard Nixon	20.00	52 Ted Gray	20.00	74 Joe Rossi	20.00
9 Joe Collins	15.00	31 Ewell Blackwell	30.00	53 Sherman Lollar	20.00	75 Mike Garcia	20.00
10 Smokey Burgess	25.00	32 Clyde Vollmer	20.00	54 Bob Feller	80.00	76 Pee Wee Reese	100.00
11 Sal Yvars	20.00	33 Bob Kennedy	20.00	55 Maurice McDermott	20.00	77 John Mize	60.00
12 Howie Judson	15.00	34 George Shuba	20.00	56 Gerald Staley	20.00	78 Al Schoendienst	40.00
13 Connie Marrero	20.00	35 Irv Noren	20.00	57 Carl Scheib	20.00	79 Johnny Wyrostek	20.00
14 Clem Labine	15.00	36 Johnny Groth	20.00	58 George Metkovich	20.00	80 Jim Hegan	20.00
15 Bobo Newsom	15.00	37 Ed Mathews	75.00	59 Karl Drews	20.00	81 Joe Black	35.00
16 Harry Lowrey	14.00	38 Jim Hearn	20.00	60 Cloyd Boyer	20.00	82 Mickey Mantle	1800.00
17 Billy Hitchcock	18.00	39 Eddie Miksis	20.00	61 Early Wynn	60.00	83 Howie Pollett	20.00
18 Ted Lepcio	15.00	40 Johnny Lipon	20.00	62 Monte Irvin	35.00	84 Bob Hooper	20.00
19 Melvin Parnell	20.00	41 Enos Slaughter	60.00	63 Gus Niarhos	15.00	85 Bobby Morgan	20.00
20 Hank Thompson	20.00	42 Gus Zernial	20.00	64 David Philley	20.00	86 Billy Martin	65.00
21 Billy Johnson	20.00	43 Gil McDougald	35.00	65 Earl Harrist	20.00	87 Ed Lopat	25.00
22 Howie Fox	20.00	44 Ellis Kinder	20.00	66 Orestes Minoso	30.00	88 Willie Jones	15.00

NO. PLAYER	NR. MT.
89 Chuck Stobbs	16.00
90 Hank Edwards	16.00
91 Ebba St. Claire	16.00
92 Paul Minner	16.00
93 Hal Rice	16.00
94 William Kennedy	16.00
95 Willard Marshall	16.00
96 Virgil Trucks	16.00
97 Don Kolloway	16.00
98 Cal Abrams	16.00
99 Dave Madison	16.00
100 Bill Miller	16.00
101 Ted Wilks	16.00
102 Connie Ryan	16.00
103 Joe Astroth	16.00
104 Yogi Berra	175.00
105 Joe Nuxhall	20.00
106 John Antonelli	20.00
107 Danny O'Connell	20.00
108 Bob Porterfield	20.00
109 Alvin Dark	25.00
110 Herman Wehmeier	16.00
111 Hank Sauer	16.00
112 Ned Garver	16.00
113 Jerry Priddy	16.00
114 Phil Rizzuto	70.00
115 George Spencer	20.00
116 Frank Smith	20.00
117 Sidney Gordon	20.00
118 Gus Bell	20.00
119 Johnny Sain	30.00
120 Davey Williams	20.00
121 Walt Dropo	20.00
122 Elmer Valo	20.00
123 Tommy Byrne	20.00
124 Sibby Sisti	20.00
125 Dick Williams	18.00
126 Billy Connelly	16.00
127 Clint Courtney	16.00
128 Wilmer Mizell	16.00
129 Keith Thomas	16.00
130 Turk Lown	16.00
131 Harry Byrd	16.00
132 Tom Morgan	16.00
133 Gil Coan	16.00
134 Rube Walker	16.00
135 Al Rosen	27.00

NO. PLAYER	NR. MT.
136 Ken Heintzelman	20.00
137 John Rutherford	20.00
138 George Kell	40.00
139 Sammy White	18.00
140 Tommy Glaviano	18.00
141 Allie Reynolds	30.00
142 Vic Wertz	16.00
143 Billy Pierce	16.00
144 Bob Schultz	16.00
145 Harry Dorish	16.00
146 Granville Hamner	16.00
147 Warren Spahn	80.00
148 Mickey Grasso	16.00
149 Dom DiMaggio	25.00
150 Harry Simpson	16.00
151 Hoyt Wilhelm	50.00
152 Bob Adams	16.00
153 Andy Seminick	16.00
154 Dick Groat	25.00
155 Dutch Leonard	16.00
156 Jim Rivera	16.00
157 Bob Addis	16.00
158 Jim Logan	16.00
159 Wayne Terwilliger	16.00
160 Bob Young	16.00
161 Vern Bickford	16.00
162 Ted Kluszewski	30.00
163 Fred Hatfield	16.00
164 Frank Shea	16.00
165 Billy Hoeft	16.00
166 Bill Hunter	15.00
167 Art Schult	15.00
168 Willard Schmidt	15.00
169 Dizzy Trout	15.00
170 Bill Werle	15.00
171 Bill Glynn	15.00
172 Rip Repulski	15.00
173 Preston Ward	15.00
174 Billy Loes	15.00
175 Ronald Kline	15.00
176 Don Hoak	15.00
177 Jim Dyck	15.00
178 Jim Waugh	15.00
179 Gene Hermanski	15.00
180 Virgil Stallcup	15.00
181 Al Zarilla	15.00
182 Robert Hofman	15.00

NO. PLAYER	NR. MT.
183 Stuart Miller	15.00
184 Hal Brown	15.00
185 Jim Pendleton	15.00
186 Charles Bishop	15.00
187 Jim Fridley	15.00
188 Andy Carey	15.00
189 Ray Jablonski	15.00
190 Dixie Walker	15.00
191 Ralph Kiner	50.00
192 Wally Westlake	15.00
193 Mike Clark	15.00
194 Eddie Kazak	15.00
195 Eddie McGhee	15.00
196 Bob Keegan	15.00
197 Del Crandall	15.00
198 Forrest Main	15.00
199 Marion Fricano	15.00
200 Gordon Goldsberry	15.00
201 Paul LaPalme	15.00
202 Carl Sawatski	15.00
203 Cliff Fannin	15.00
204 Dick Bokelmann	15.00
205 Vern Benson	15.00
206 Ed Bailey	15.00
207 Whitey Ford	90.00
208 Jim Wilson	15.00
209 Jim Greengrass	15.00
210 Bob Cerv	15.00
211 J.W. Porter	15.00
212 Jack Dittmer	15.00
213 Ray Scarborough	15.00
214 Bill Bruton	15.00
215 Gene Conley	15.00
216 Jim Hughes	15.00
217 Murray Wall	15.00
218 Les Fusselman	15.00
219 Pete Runnels	15.00
(Photo of Don Johnson)	
220 Satchell Paige	300.00
221 Bob Milliken	70.00
222 Vic Janowicz	70.00
223 John O'Brien	70.00
224 Lou Sleater	70.00
225 Bobby Shantz	75.00
226 Edward Erautt	70.00
227 Morris Martin	70.00
228 Hal Newhouser	100.00

NO. PLAYER	NR. MT.
229 Rocky Krsnich	70.00
230 Johnny Lindell	70.00
231 Solly Hemus	70.00
232 Dick Kokos	70.00
233 Al Aber	70.00
234 Ray Murray	70.00
235 John Hetki	70.00
236 Harold Perkowski	70.00
237 Clarence Podbielan	70.00
238 Cal Hogue	70.00
239 Jim Delsing	70.00
240 Fred Marsh	70.00
241 Al Sima	70.00
242 Charlie Silvera	70.00
243 Carlos Bernier	70.00
244 Willie Mays	1350.00
245 Bill Norman	70.00
246 Roy Face (R)	80.00
247 Mike Sandlock	70.00
248 Gene Stephens	70.00
249 Ed O'Brien	70.00
250 Bob Wilson	70.00
251 Sid Hudson	70.00
252 Henry Foiles	70.00
254 Preacher Roe	90.00
255 Dixie Howell	70.00
256 Les Peden	70.00
257 Bob Boyd	70.00
258 Jim Gilliam (R)	260.00
259 Roy McMillan	70.00
260 Sam Calderone	70.00
262 Bob Oldis	70.00
263 John Podres (R)	275.00
264 Gene Woodling	75.00
265 Jackie Jensen	100.00
266 Bob Cain	70.00
269 Duane Pillette	70.00
270 Vern Stephens	70.00
272 Bill Antonello	70.00
273 Harvey Haddix (R)	95.00
274 John Riddle	70.00
276 Ken Raffensberger	70.00
277 Don Lund	70.00
278 Willie Miranda	70.00
279 Joe Coleman	70.00
280 M. Boling (R) (Exc. $45.00)	300.00

1954 Topps . . . Complete Set of 250 Cards—Value $2400.00 (Exc.); $6000.00 (Mint)

Features the rookie cards of Hank Aaron, Al Kaline and Ernie Banks. Card size 2⅝" x 3¾". Topps' signed Ted Williams to a special contract for this set, and he appears on two cards.

NO. PLAYER	NR. MT.
1 Ted Williams (Exc. $100.00)	500.00
2 Gus Zernial	10.00
3 Monte Irvin	30.00
4 Hank Sauer	9.00
5 Ed Lopat	20.00

NO. PLAYER	NR. MT.
6 Pete Runnels	9.00
7 Ted Kluszewski	16.00
8 Bobby Young	9.00
9 Harvey Haddix	9.00
10 Jackie Robinson	200.00

NO. PLAYER	NR. MT.
11 Paul Smith	9.00
12 Del Crandall	9.00
13 Billy Martin	50.00
14 Preacher Roe	15.00
15 Al Rosen	13.00

NO. PLAYER	NR. MT.
16 Vic Janowicz	9.00
17 Phil Rizzuto	50.00
18 Walt Dropo	9.00
19 Johnny Lipon	9.00
20 Warren Spahn	65.00

NO. PLAYER	NR. MT.	NO. PLAYER	NR. MT.	NO. PLAYER	NR. MT.	NO. PLAYER	NR. MT.
21 Bobby Shantz	10.00	79 Andy Pafko	9.00	137 Wally Moon	15.00	193 Johnny Hopp	10.00
22 Jim Greengrass	9.00	80 Jackie Jensen	13.00	138 Bob Borkowski	10.00	194 Bill Sarni	10.00
23 Luke Easter	9.00	81 Dave Hoskins	9.00	139 The O'Brien's:	15.00	195 Bill Consolo	10.00
24 Granny Hamner	9.00	82 Milt Bolling	9.00	Johnny O'Brien,		196 Stan Jok	10.00
25 Harv. Kuenn (R)	20.00	83 Joe Collins	9.00	Eddie O'Brien		197 L. Rowe	10.00
26 Ray Jablonski	9.00	84 Dick Cole	9.00	140 Tom Wright	10.00	198 Carl Sawatski	10.00
27 Ferris Fain	9.00	85 Bob Turley (R)	16.00	141 Joe Jay	10.00	199 Glenn Nelson	10.00
28 Paul Minner	9.00	86 Billy Herman	15.00	142 Tom Poholsky	10.00	200 Larry Jansen	10.00
29 Jim Hegan	9.00	87 Roy Face	9.00	143 Rollie Hemsley	10.00	201 Al Kaline (R)	650.00
30 Ed Mathews	50.00	88 Matt Batts	9.00	144 Bill Werle	10.00	202 Bob Purkey	10.00
31 John Klippstein	9.00	89 Howie Pollet	9.00	145 Elmer Valo	10.00	203 Harry Brecheen	10.00
32 Duke Snider	110.00	90 Willie Mays	260.00	146 Don Johnson	10.00	204 Angel Scull	10.00
33 Johnny Schmitz	9.00	91 Bob Oldis	9.00	147 John Riddle	10.00	205 Johnny Sain	20.00
34 Jim Rivera	9.00	92 Wally Westlake	9.00	148 Bob Trice	10.00	206 Ray Crone	10.00
35 Junior Gilliam	15.00	93 Sid Hudson	9.00	149 Jim Robertson	10.00	207 Tom Oliver	10.00
36 Hoyt Wilhelm	25.00	94 Ernie Banks (R)	650.00	150 Dick Kryhoski	10.00	208 Grady Hatton	10.00
37 Whitey Ford	65.00	95 Hal Rice	10.00	151 Alex Grammas	10.00	209 Charlie Thompson	10.00
38 Eddie Stanky	9.00	96 Charlie Silvera	10.00	152 Mike Blyzka	10.00	210 Bob Buhl	10.00
39 Sherm Lollar	9.00	97 Jerry Lane	10.00	153 Albert Walker	10.00	211 Don Hoak	10.00
40 Mel Parnell	9.00	98 Joe Black	12.00	154 Mike Fornieles	10.00	212 Bob Micelotta	10.00
41 Willie Jones	9.00	99 Bob Hofman	10.00	155 Bob Kennedy	10.00	213 John Fitzpatrick	10.00
42 Don Mueller	9.00	100 Bob Keegan	10.00	156 Joe Coleman	10.00	214 A. Portocarrero	10.00
43 Dick Groat	11.00	101 Gene Woodling	12.00	157 Don Lenhardt	10.00	215 Ed McGhee	10.00
44 Ned Garver	9.00	102 Gil Hodges	60.00	158 Peanuts Lowrey	10.00	216 Al Sima	10.00
45 Richie Ashburn	20.00	103 Jim Lemon	10.00	159 Dave Philley	10.00	217 Paul Schreiber	10.00
46 Ken Raffensberger	9.00	104 Mike Sandlock	10.00	160 Red Kress	10.00	218 Fred Marsh	10.00
47 Ellis Kinder	9.00	105 Andy Carey	10.00	161 John Hetki	10.00	219 Charles Kress	10.00
48 Bill Hunter	9.00	106 Dick Kokos	10.00	162 Herman Wehmeier	10.00	220 Ruben Gomez	10.00
49 Ray Murray	9.00	107 Duane Pillette	10.00	163 Frank House	10.00	221 Dick Brodowski	10.00
50 Y. Berra	160.00	108 Thornton Kipper	10.00	164 Stuart Miller	10.00	222 Bill Wilson	10.00
51 Johnny Lindell	18.00	109 Bill Bruton	10.00	165 Jim Pendleton	10.00	223 Joe Haynes	10.00
52 Vic Power	18.00	110 Harry Dorish	10.00	166 Johnny Podres	20.00	224 Dick Weik	10.00
53 Jack Dittmer	18.00	111 Jim Delsing	10.00	167 Don Lund	10.00	225 Don Liddle	10.00
54 Vern Stephens	18.00	112 Bill Renna	10.00	168 Morrie Martin	10.00	226 Jehosie Heard	10.00
55 Phil Cavarretta	18.00	113 Bob Boyd	10.00	169 Jim Hughes	10.00	227 Buster Mills	10.00
56 Willie Miranda	18.00	114 Dean Stone	10.00	170 Jim Rhodes	10.00	228 Gene Hermanski	10.00
57 Luis Aloma	18.00	115 Rip Repulski	10.00	171 Leo Kiely	10.00	229 Bob Talbot	10.00
58 Bob Wilson	18.00	116 Steve Bilko	10.00	172 Hal Brown	10.00	230 Bob Kuzava	10.00
59 Gene Conley	18.00	117 Solly Hemus	10.00	173 Jack Harshman	10.00	231 Roy Smalley	10.00
60 Frank Baumholtz	18.00	118 Carl Scheib	10.00	174 Tom Qualters	10.00	232 Lou Limmer	10.00
61 Bob Cain	18.00	119 John Antonelli	10.00	175 Frank Leja	10.00	233 Augie Galan	10.00
62 Eddie Robinson	18.00	120 Roy McMillan	10.00	176 Robert Kelley	10.00	234 Jerry Lynch	10.00
63 Johnny Pesky	18.00	121 Clem Labine	10.00	177 Bob Milliken	10.00	235 Vernon Law	10.00
64 Hank Thompson	18.00	122 Johnny Logan	10.00	178 Bill Glynn	10.00	236 Paul Penson	10.00
65 Bob Swift	18.00	123 Bobby Adams	10.00	179 Gair Allie	10.00	237 Mike Ryba	10.00
66 Thad Lepcio	18.00	124 Marion Fricano	10.00	180 Wes Westrum	10.00	238 Al Aber	10.00
67 Jim Willis	18.00	125 Harry Perkowski	10.00	181 Mel Roach	10.00	239 Bill Skowron (R)	40.00
68 Sammy Calderone	18.00	126 Ben Wade	10.00	182 Chuck Harmon	10.00	240 Sam Mele	10.00
69 Bud Podbielan	18.00	127 Steve O'Neill	10.00	183 Earle Combs	15.00	241 Bob Miller	10.00
70 Larry Doby	35.00	128 Hank Aaron (R)	950.00	184 Ed Bailey	10.00	242 Curt Roberts	10.00
71 Frank Smith	18.00	129 Forrest Jacobs	10.00	185 Chuck Stobbs	10.00	243 Ray Blades	10.00
72 Preston Ward	18.00	130 Hank Bauer	18.00	186 Karl Olson	10.00	244 Leroy Wheat	10.00
73 Wayne Terwilliger	18.00	131 Reno Bertoia	10.00	187 Heinie Manush	15.00	245 Roy Sievers	12.00
74 Bill Taylor	18.00	132 Tommy Lasorda (R)	130.00	188 Dave Jolly	10.00	246 Howie Fox	10.00
75 Fred Haney	18.00	133 Del Baker	10.00	189 Bob Ross	10.00	247 Ed Mayo	10.00
76 Bob Scheffing	9.00	134 Cal Hogue	10.00	190 Ray Herbert	10.00	248 Al Smith	10.00
77 Ray Boone	9.00	135 Joe Presko	10.00	191 Dick Schofield	10.00	249 Wilmer Mizell	10.00
78 Ted Kazanski	9.00	136 Connie Ryan	10.00	192 Ellis Deal	10.00	250 Ted Williams (Exc. $100.00)	500.00

1955 Topps . . . Complete Set of 206 Cards—Value $1900.00 (Exc.); $4800.00 (Mint)

Features the rookie cards of Roberto Clemente, Sandy Koufax and Harmon Killebrew. Topps' switched to a horizontal format in 1955. Card size 2⅝" x 3¾". Four cards originally intended to be issued—175, 186, 203 and 209 were withdrawn. The high number series is 161 to 210.

NO. PLAYER	NR. MT.	NO. PLAYER	NR. MT.	NO. PLAYER	NR. MT.	NO. PLAYER	NR. MT.
1 Dusty Rhodes (Exc. $6.00)	.30.00	53 Bill Taylor	.5.00	104 Jack Harshman	.5.00	155 Eddie Mathews	. 65.00
2 Ted Williams	250.00	54 Lou Limmer	.5.00	105 Chuck Diering	.5.00	156 Joe Black	. 20.00
3 Art Fowler	5.00	55 Eldon Repulski	.5.00	106 Frank Sullivan	.5.00	157 Bob Miller	. 9.00
4 Al Kaline	160.00	56 Ray Jablonski	.5.00	107 Curt Roberts	5.00	158 Tommy Carroll	. 9.00
5 Jim Gilliam	9.00	57 Bill O'Dell	.5.00	108 Rube Walker	5.00	159 Johnny Schmitz	. 9.00
6 Stan Hack	5.00	58 Manuel Rivera	.5.00	109 Ed Lopat	12.00	160 Raymond Narleski	. 9.00
7 Jim Hegan	.5.00	59 Gair Allie	.5.00	110 Gus Zernial	.5.00	161 Chuck Tanner (R)	. 25.00
8 Hal Smith	.5.00	60 Dean Stone	.5.00	111 Bob Milliken	.5.00	162 Joe Coleman	. 12.50
9 Bob Miller	.5.00	61 Forrest Jacobs	.5.00	112 Nelson King	.5.00	163 Faye Throneberry	. 12.50
10 Bob Keegan	.5.00	62 Thornton Kipper	.5.00	113 Harry Brecheen	.5.00	164 Roberto Clemente (R)	.750.00
11 Ferris Fain	.5.00	63 Joe Collins	.6.00	114 Louie Ortiz	.5.00	165 Don Johnson	. 12.50
12 Vernon Thies	.5.00	64 Gus Triandos	.6.00	115 Ellis Kinder	.5.00	166 Hank Bauer	. 27.00
13 Fred Marsh	.5.00	65 Ray Boone	.5.00	116 Tom Hurd	.5.00	167 Tom Casagrande	. 12.50
14 Jim Finigan	.5.00	66 Ron Jackson	.5.00	117 Mel Roach	.5.00	168 Duane Pillette	. 12.50
15 Jim Pendleton	.5.00	67 Wally Moon	.5.00	118 Bob Purkey	.5.00	169 Bob Oldis	. 12.50
16 Roy Sievers	.5.00	68 Jim Davis	.5.00	119 Bob Lennon	.5.00	170 Jim Pearce	. 12.50
17 Bobby Hofman	.5.00	69 Ed Bailey	.5.00	120 Ted Kluszewski	12.00	171 Dick Brodowski	. 12.50
18 Russ Kemmerer	.5.00	70 Al Rosen	9.00	121 Bill Renna	4.00	172 Frank Baumholtz	. 12.50
19 Billy Herman	10.00	71 Ruben Gomez	.5.00	122 Carl Sawatski	4.00	173 Bob Kline	. 12.50
20 Andy Carey	5.00	72 Karl Olson	5.00	123 Sandy Koufax (R)	.550.00	174 Rudy Minarcin	. 12.50
21 Alex Grammas	5.00	73 Jack Shepard	.5.00	124 Harmon Killebrew (R)	.250.00	176 Norm Zauchin	. 12.50
22 Bill Skowron	11.00	74 Bob Borkowski	.5.00	125 Ken Boyer (R)	35.00	177 Jim Robertson	. 12.50
23 Jack Parks	5.00	75 Sandy Amoros (R)	9.00	126 Dick Hall	.5.00	178 Bobby Adams	. 12.50
24 Hal Newhouser	8.00	76 Howie Pollet	.5.00	127 Dale Long	.5.00	179 Jim Bolger	. 12.50
25 Johnnie Podres	11.00	77 Arnold Portocarrero	.5.00	128 Ted Lepcio	.5.00	180 Clem Labine	. 12.50
26 Dick Groat	5.00	78 Gordon Jones	.5.00	129 Elvin Tappe	.5.00	181 Roy McMillan	. 12.50
27 Billy Gardner	5.00	79 Clyde Schell	.5.00	130 Mayo Smith	.5.00	182 Humberto Robinson	. 12.50
28 Ernie Banks	90.00	80 Bob Grim (R)	.7.50	131 Grady Hatton	.5.00	183 Anthony Jacobs	. 12.50
29 Herman Wehmeier	5.00	81 Gene Conley	5.00	132 Bob Trice	.5.00	184 Harry Perkowski	. 12.50
30 Vic Power	5.00	82 Chuck Harmon	5.00	133 Dave Hoskins	.5.00	185 Don Ferrarese	. 12.50
31 Warren Spahn	50.00	83 Thomas Brewer	5.00	134 Joe Jay	.5.00	187 Gil Hodges	.115.00
32 Ed McGhee	5.00	84 Camilo Pascual (R)	6.00	135 Johnny O'Brien	.5.00	188 Charlie Silvera	. 12.50
33 Tom Qualters	5.00	85 Don Mossi (R)	7.50	136 Bunky Stewart	.5.00	189 Phil Rizzuto	.120.00
34 Wayne Terwilliger	5.00	86 Bill Wilson	.5.00	137 Harry Elliott	.5.00	190 Gene Woodling	. 12.50
35 Dave Jolly	5.00	87 Frank House	.5.00	138 Ray Herbert	.5.00	191 Eddie Stanky	. 12.50
36 Leo Kiely	5.00	88 Bob Skinner	.5.00	139 Steve Kraly	.5.00	192 Jim Delsing	. 12.50
37 Joe Cunningham	5.00	89 Joe Frazier	.5.00	140 Mel Parnell	.5.00	193 Johnny Sain	. 22.00
38 Bob Turley	8.00	90 Karl Spooner	.5.00	141 Tom Wright	.5.00	194 Willie Mays	.375.00
39 Billy Glynn	5.00	91 Milton Bolling	.5.00	142 Jerry Lynch	.5.00	195 Eddie Roebuck	. 12.50
40 Don Hoak	5.00	92 Don Zimmer (R)	.25.00	143 Dick Schofield	.5.00	196 Gale Wade	. 12.50
41 Chuck Stobbs	5.00	93 Steve Bilko	5.00	144 Joe Amalfitano	.5.00	197 Al Smith	. 12.50
42 John McCall	5.00	94 Reno Bertoia	5.00	145 Elmer Valo	.5.00	198 Yogi Berra	.175.00
43 Harvey Haddix	6.00	95 Preston Ward	5.00	146 Dick Donovan	.5.00	199 Bert Hamrick	. 12.50
44 Harold Valentine	5.00	96 Charlie Bishop	5.00	147 Laurin Pepper	.5.00	200 Jack Jensen	. 35.00
45 Hank Sauer	5.00	97 Carlos Paula	5.00	148 Hal Brown	.5.00	201 Sherman Lollar	. 12.50
46 Ted Kazanski	5.00	98 Johnny Riddle	5.00	149 Ray Crone	.5.00	202 Jim Owens	. 12.50
47 Hank Aaron	225.00	99 Frank Leja	5.00	150 Michael Higgins	.5.00	204 Frank Smith	. 12.50
48 Bob Kennedy	5.00	100 Monte Irvin	.20.00	151 Ralph Kress	8.00	205 Gene Freese	. 12.50
49 J.W. Porter	5.00	101 Johnny Gray	.5.00	152 Harry Agganis (R)	45.00	206 Pete Daley	. 12.50
50 Jack Robinson	150.00	102 Wally Westlake	.5.00	153 Bud Podbielan	9.00	207 Bill Consolo	. 12.50
51 Jim Hughes	5.00	103 Charlie White	.5.00	154 Willie Miranda	9.00	208 Ray Moore	. 12.50
52 Bill Tremel	5.00					210 Duke Snider (Exc. $90.00)	450.00

1956 Topps . . . Complete Set of 340 Cards—Value $2200.00 (Exc.); $5000.00 (Mint)

In 1956 Topps bought its competitor—Bowman Card Co., including all of its player contracts. Topps card sets would now be larger and more complete. Card size 2⅝" x 3¾". Features the rookie card of Luis Aparicio. Card numbers 1 to 180 were printed with *gray* or *white* backs. The six team cards indicated by an *asterisk* were issued with three different *face* designs. The team card dated *1955* is worth about four times the value of the other team cards. The two checklists are not included in the complete set price.

NO. PLAYER	NR. MT.	NO. PLAYER	NR. MT.	NO. PLAYER	NR. MT.	NO. PLAYER	NR. MT.
1 W. Harridge (Exc. $7.50)	.75.00	3 Elmer Valo	4.00	7 Ron Negray	4.00	11 Chicago Cubs*	.11.00
(AL President)		4 Carlos Paula	4.00	8 Walter Alston (Mgr)	20.00	12 Andy Carey	4.00
2 Warren Giles	.10.00	5 Ted Williams	200.00	9 Ruben Gomez	4.00	13 Roy Face	4.00
(NL President)		6 Ray Boone	4.00	10 Warren Spahn	35.00	14 Ken Boyer	9.00

NO.	PLAYER	NR. MT.
15	Ernie Banks	60.00
16	Hector Lopez	4.00
17	Gene Conley	4.00
18	Dick Donovan	4.00
19	Chuck Diering	4.00
20	Al Kaline	50.00
21	Joe Collins	5.00
22	Jim Finigan	4.00
23	Freddie Marsh	4.00
24	Dick Groat	5.00
25	Ted Kluszeski	10.00
26	Grady Hatton	4.00
27	Nelson Burbrink	4.00
28	Bobby Hofman	4.00
29	Jack Harshman	4.00
30	Jackie Robinson	135.00
31	Hank Aaron	175.00
32	Frank House	4.00
33	Roberto Clemente	200.00
34	Tom Brewer	4.00
35	Al Rosen	8.00
36	Rudy Minarcin	4.00
37	Alex Grammas	4.00
38	Bob Kennedy	4.00
39	Don Mossi	4.00
40	Bob Turley	7.00
41	Hank Sauer	4.00
42	Sandy Amoros	5.00
43	Ray Moore	4.00
44	Windy McCall	4.00
45	Gus Zernial	4.00
46	Gene Freese	4.00
47	Art Fowler	4.00
48	Jim Hegan	4.00
49	Pedro Ramos	4.00
50	Dusty Rhode	4.00
51	Ernie Oravetz	4.00
52	Bob Grim	4.00
53	Arnold Portocarrero	4.00
54	Bob Keegan	4.00
55	Wally Moon	4.00
56	Dale Long	4.00
57	Duke Maas	4.00
58	Ed Roebuck	4.00
59	Jose Santiago	4.00
60	Mayo Smith	4.00
61	Bill Skowron	10.00
62	Hal Smith	4.00
63	Roger Craig (R)	13.00
64	Luis Arroyo	4.00
65	Johnny O'Brien	4.00
66	Bob Speake	4.00
67	Vic Power	4.00
68	Chuck Stobbs	4.00
69	Chuck Tanner	4.00
70	Jim Rivera	4.00
71	Frank Sullivan	4.00
72	Philadelphia Phillies*	10.00
73	Wayne Terwilliger	4.00
74	Jim King	4.00
75	Roy Sievers	5.00
76	Ray Crone	4.00
77	Harvey Haddix	5.00
78	Herman Wehmeier	4.00
79	Sandy Koufax	200.00
80	Gus Triandos	5.00
81	Wally Westlake	4.00
82	Bill Renna	4.00
83	Karl Spooner	4.00
84	Babe Birrer	4.00
85	Cleveland Indians*	10.00
86	Ray Jablonski	4.00
87	Dean Stone	4.00
88	Johnny Kucks	4.00
89	Norm Zauchin	4.00
90	Cincinnati Redlegs*	10.00
91	Gail Harris	4.00
92	Red Wilson	4.00
93	George Susce Jr.	4.00
94	Ronald Kline	4.00
95	Milwaukee Braves*	10.00
96	Bill Tremel	4.00
97	Jerry Lynch	4.00
98	Camilo Pascual	4.00
99	Don Zimmer	8.00
100	Baltimore Orioles*	10.00
101	Roy Campanella	120.00
102	Jim Davis	5.00
103	Willie Miranda	5.00
104	Bob Lennon	5.00
105	Al Smith	5.00
106	Joe Astroth	5.00
107	Ed Mathews	40.00
108	Laurin Pepper	5.00
109	Enos Slaughter	20.00
110	Yogi Berra	90.00
111	Boston Red Sox	15.00
112	Dee Fondy	5.00
113	Phil Rizzuto	30.00
114	Jim Owens	5.00
115	Jackie Jensen	9.00
116	Eddie O'Brien	5.00
117	Virgil Trucks	5.00
118	Nellie Fox	15.00
119	Larry Jackson	5.00
120	Richie Ashburn	15.00
121	Pittsburgh Pirates	12.00
122	Willard Nixon	5.00
123	Roy McMillan	5.00
124	Don Kaiser	5.00
125	Minnie Minoso	10.00
126	Jim Brady	5.00
127	Willie Jones	5.00
128	Eddie Yost	5.00
129	Jake Martin	5.00
130	Willie Mays	200.00
131	Bob Roselli	5.00
132	Bobby Avila	5.00
133	Ray Narleski	5.00
134	St. Louis Cardinals	12.00
135	Mickey Mantle	750.00
136	Johnny Logan	5.00
137	Al Silvera	5.00
138	Johnny Antonelli	5.00
139	Tommy Carroll	5.00
140	Herb Score (R)	12.00
141	Joe Frazier	5.00
142	Gene Baker	5.00
143	Jimmy Piersall	8.00
144	Leroy Powell	5.00
145	Gil Hodges	30.00
146	Washington Nat'l	11.00
147	Earl Torgeson	5.00
148	Alvin Dark	5.00
149	Dixie Howell	5.00
150	Duke Snider	100.00
151	Spook Jacobs	5.00
152	Billy Hoeft	5.00
153	Frank Thomas	5.00
154	David Pope	5.00
155	Harvey Kuenn	7.00
156	Wes Westrum	5.00
157	Dick Brodowski	5.00
158	Wally Post	5.00
159	Clint Courtney	5.00
160	Billy Pierce	6.00
161	Joe DeMaestri	5.00
162	Gus Bell	5.00
163	Gene Woodling	5.00
164	Harmon Killebrew	75.00
165	Red Schoendienst	12.00
166	Brooklyn Dodgers	125.00
167	Harry Dorish	5.00
168	Sammy White	5.00
169	Bob Nelson	5.00
170	Bill Virdon	7.50
171	Jim Wilson	5.00
172	Frank Torre	5.00
173	Johnny Podres	10.00
174	Glen Gorbous	5.00
175	Del Crandall	5.00
176	Alex Kellner	5.00
177	Hank Bauer	10.00
178	Joe Black	5.00
179	Harry Chiti	5.00
180	Robin Roberts	25.00
181	Billy Martin	45.00
182	Paul Minner	8.00
183	Stan Lopata	8.00
184	Don Bessent	8.00
185	Bill Bruton	8.00
186	Ron Jackson	8.00
187	Early Wynn	25.00
188	Chicago White Sox	12.00
189	Ned Garver	8.00
190	Carl Furillo	16.00
191	Frank Lary	9.00
192	Smokey Burgess	8.00
193	Wilmer Mizell	8.00
194	Monte Irvin	22.00
195	George Kell	24.00
196	Tom Poholsky	8.00
197	Granny Hamner	8.00
198	Ed Fitzgerald	8.00
199	Hank Thompson	8.00
200	Bob Feller	65.00
201	Rip Repulski	8.00
202	Jim Hearn	8.00
203	Bill Tuttle	8.00
204	Arthur Swanson	8.00
205	Whitey Lockman	8.00
206	Erv Palica	8.00
207	Jim Small	8.00
208	Elston Howard	20.00
209	Max Surkont	8.00
210	Mike Garcia	8.00
211	Murry Dickson	8.00
212	Johnny Temple	8.00
213	Detroit Tigers	25.00
214	Bob Rush	8.00
215	Tommy Byrne	8.00
216	Jerry Schoonmaker	8.00
217	Billy Klaus	8.00
218	Joe Nuxhall	8.00
219	Lew Burdette	11.00
220	Del Ennis	8.00
221	Bob Friend	8.00
222	Dave Philley	8.00
223	Randy Jackson	8.00
224	Bud Podbielan	8.00
225	Gil McDougald	16.00
226	New York Giants	45.00
227	Russ Meyer	8.00
228	Mickey Vernon	8.00
229	Harry Brecheen	8.00
230	Chico Carrasquel	8.00
231	Bob Hale	8.00
232	Toby Atwell	8.00
233	Carl Erskine	15.00
234	Pete Runnels	8.00
235	Don Newcombe	25.00
236	Kansas C. Athletics	12.00
237	Jose Valdivielso	8.00
238	Walt Dropo	8.00
239	Harry Simpson	8.00
240	Whitey Ford	65.00
241	Don Mueller	8.00
242	Hershell Freeman	8.00
243	Sherm Lollar	8.00
244	Bob Buhl	8.00
245	Billy Goodman	8.00
246	Tom Gorman	8.00
247	Bill Sarni	8.00
248	Bob Porterfield	8.00
249	Johnny Klippstein	8.00
250	Larry Doby	12.00
251	New York Yankees	125.00
252	Vernon Law	8.00
253	Irv Noren	8.00
254	George Crowe	8.00
255	Bob Lemon	25.00
256	Tom Hurd	8.00
257	Bobby Thomson	12.00
258	Art Ditmar	8.00
259	Sam Jones	8.00
260	Pee Wee Reese	95.00
261	Bobby Shantz	6.00
262	Howie Pollett	6.00
263	Bob Miller	6.00
264	Ray Monzant	6.00
265	Sandy Consuegra	6.00
266	Don Ferrarese	6.00
267	Bob Nieman	6.00
268	Dale Mitchell	6.00
269	Jack Meyer	6.00
270	Billy Loes	6.00
271	Foster Castleman	6.00
272	Danny O'Connell	6.00
273	Walker Cooper	6.00
274	Frank Baumholtz	6.00
275	Jim Greengrass	6.00
276	George Zuverink	6.00
277	Daryl Spencer	6.00
278	Chet Nichols	6.00
279	Johnny Groth	6.00
280	Jim Gilliam	10.00
281	Art Houtteman	6.00
282	Warren Hacker	6.00
283	Hal Smith	6.00
284	Ike Delock	6.00
285	Eddie Miksis	6.00
286	Bill Wight	6.00
287	Bobby Adams	6.00
288	Bob Cerv	7.50
289	Hal Jeffcoat	6.00
290	Curt Simmons	6.00
291	Frank Kellert	6.00
292	Luis Aparicio (R)	75.00
293	Stu Miller	6.00
294	Ernie Johnson	6.00
295	Clem Labine	6.00
296	Andy Seminick	6.00
297	Bob Skinner	6.00
298	Johnny Schmitz	6.00
299	Charley Neal	6.00
300	Vic Wertz	6.00
301	Marv Grissom	6.00
302	Eddie Robinson	6.00
303	Jim Dyck	6.00
304	Frank Malzone	10.00
305	Brooks Lawrence	6.00
306	Curt Roberts	6.00
307	Hoyt Wilhelm	25.00
308	Charles Harmon	6.00
309	Don Blasingame	6.00
310	Steve Gromek	6.00
311	Hal Naragon	6.00
312	Andy Pafko	6.00
313	Gene Stephens	6.00
314	Hobie Landrith	6.00
315	Milt Bolling	6.00
316	Jerry Coleman	6.00
317	Al Aber	6.00
318	Fred Hatfield	6.00
319	Jack Crimian	6.00
320	Joe Adcock	6.00
321	Jim Konstanty	6.00
322	Karl Olson	6.00
323	Willard Schmidt	6.00
324	Rocky Bridges	6.00
325	Don Liddle	6.00
236	Connie Johnson	6.00
327	Bob Wiesler	6.00
328	Preston Ward	6.00
329	Lou Berberet	6.00
330	Jim Busby	6.00
331	Dick Hall	6.00
332	Don Larsen	15.00
333	Rube Walker	6.00
334	Bob Miller	6.00
335	Don Hoak	6.00
336	Ellis Kinder	6.00
337	Bobby Morgan	6.00
338	Jim Delsing	6.00
339	Rance Pless	6.00
340	M. McDermott (Exc. $5.00)	20.00
—	Checklist 1/3	175.00
—	Checklist 2/4	175.00

1957 Topps . . . Complete Set of 407 Cards—Value $2100.00 (Exc.); $5800.00 (Mint)

Topps' switched to a 2½″ x 3½″ card size. The 1957 set features the rookie cards of Don Drysdale, Frank Robinson, Tony Kubek and Brooks Robinson. The four checklists are not included in the complete set price.

NO. PLAYER	NR. MT.
1 Ted Williams (Exc. $75.00)	400.00
2 Yogi Berra	120.00
3 Dale Long	4.00
4 Johnny Logan	4.00
5 Sal Maglie	5.00
6 Hector Lopez	4.00
7 Luis Aparicio	20.00
8 Don Mossi	4.00
9 Johnny Temple	4.00
10 Willie Mays	160.00
11 George Zuverink	4.00
12 Dick Groat	5.00
13 Wally Burnette	4.00
14 Bob Nieman	4.00
15 Robin Roberts	20.00
16 Walt Moryn	4.00
17 Billy Gardner	4.00
18 Don Drysdale (R)	175.00
19 Bob Wilson	4.00
20 Hank Aaron	225.00
(negative reversed)	
21 Frank Sullivan	4.00
22 Jerry Snyder	4.00
(photo of Ed Fitzgerald)	
23 Sherm Lollar	4.00
24 Bill Mazeroski (R)	20.00
25 W. Ford	50.00
26 Bob Boyd	4.00
27 Ted Kazanski	4.00
28 Gene Conley	4.00
29 Whitey Herzog	18.00
30 Pee Wee Reese	45.00
31 Ron Northey	4.00
32 Hersh Freeman	4.00
33 Jim Small	4.00
34 Tom Sturdivant	4.00
35 Frank Robinson (R)	175.00
36 Bob Grim	4.00
37 Frank Torre	4.00
38 Nellie Fox	10.00
39 Al Worthington	4.00
40 Early Wynn	16.00
41 Hal Smith	4.00
42 Dee Fondy	4.00
43 Connie Johnson	4.00
44 Joe DeMaestri	4.00
45 Carl Furillo	8.00
46 Bob Miller	4.00
47 Don Blasingame	4.00
48 Bill Bruton	4.00
49 Daryl Spencer	4.00
50 Herb A. Score	5.00
51 Clint Courtney	4.00
52 Lee Walls	4.00
53 Clem Labine	4.00
54 Elmer Valo	4.00
55 Ernie Banks	70.00
56 Dave Sisler	4.00
57 Jim Lemon	4.00
58 Ruben Gomez	4.00
59 Dick Williams	4.00
60 Billy Hoeft	4.00
61 Dusty Rhodes	4.00
62 Billy Martin	35.00
63 Ike Delock	4.00
64 Pete Runnels	4.00

NO. PLAYER	NR. MT.
65 Wally Moon	4.00
66 Brooks Lawrence	4.00
67 Chico Carrasquel	4.00
68 Ray Crone	4.00
69 Roy McMillan	4.00
70 Richie Ashburn	10.00
71 Murry Dickson	4.00
72 Bill Tuttle	4.00
73 George Crowe	4.00
74 Vito Valentinetti	4.00
75 Jim Piersall	5.00
76 Roberto Clemente	140.00
77 Paul Foytack	4.00
78 Vic Wertz	4.00
79 Lindy McDaniel	4.00
80 Gil Hodges	30.00
81 Herman Wehmeier	4.00
82 Elston Howard	10.00
83 Lou Skizas	4.00
84 Moe Drabowsky	4.00
85 Larry Doby	7.00
86 Bill Sarni	4.00
87 Tom Gorman	4.00
88 Harvey Kuenn	7.00
89 Roy Sievers	4.00
90 Warren Spahn	40.00
91 Mack Burk	3.00
92 Mickey Vernon	3.00
93 Hal Jeffcoat	3.00
94 Bobby Del Greco	3.00
95 Mickey Mantle	750.00
96 Hank Aguirre	3.00
97 New York Yankees	32.00
98 Alvin Dark	5.00
99 Bob Keegan	3.00
100 Giles and Harridge	6.00
(League Presidents)	
101 Chuck Stobbs	3.00
102 Ray Boone	3.00
103 Joe Nuxhall	3.00
104 Hank Foiles	3.00
105 Johnny Antonelli	3.00
106 Ray Moore	3.00
107 Jim Rivera	3.00
108 Tommy Byrne	3.00
109 Hank Thompson	3.00
110 Bill Virdon	5.00
111 Hal Smith	3.00
112 Tom Brewer	3.00
113 Wilmer Mizell	3.00
114 Milwaukee Braves	8.00
115 Jim Gilliam	8.00
116 Mike Fornieles	3.00
117 Joe Adcock	6.00
118 Bob Porterfield	3.00
119 Stan Lopata	3.00
120 Bob Lemon	16.00
121 Cletis Boyer	10.00
122 Ken Boyer	8.00
123 Steve Ridzik	3.00
124 Dave Philley	3.00
125 Al Kaline	55.00
126 Bob Wiesler	3.00
127 Bob Buhl	3.00
128 Ed Bailey	3.00
129 Saul Rogovin	3.00

NO. PLAYER	NR. MT.
130 Don Newcombe	8.00
131 Milt Bolling	3.00
132 Art Ditmar	3.00
133 Del Crandall	3.00
134 Don Kaiser	3.00
135 Bill Skowron	10.00
136 Jim Hegan	3.00
137 Bob Rush	3.00
138 Minnie Minoso	7.00
139 Lou Kretlow	3.00
140 Frank Thomas	3.00
141 Al Aber	3.00
142 Charley Thompson	3.00
143 Andy Pafko	3.00
144 Ray Narleski	3.00
145 Al Smith	3.00
146 Don Ferrarese	3.00
147 Al Walker	3.00
148 Don Mueller	3.00
149 Bob Kennedy	3.00
150 Bob Friend	3.00
151 Willie Miranda	3.00
152 Jack Harshman	3.00
153 Karl Olson	3.00
154 Red Schoendienst	12.00
155 Jim Brosnan	3.00
156 Gus Triandos	3.00
157 Wally Post	3.00
158 Curt Simmons	3.00
159 Solly Drake	3.00
160 Billy Pierce	7.00
161 Pittsburgh Pirates	8.00
162 Jack Meyer	3.00
163 Sammy White	3.00
164 Tommy Carroll	3.00
165 Ted Kluszewski	12.00
166 Roy Face	4.00
167 Vic Power	3.00
168 Frank Lary	3.00
169 Herb Plews	3.00
170 Duke Snider	85.00
171 Boston Red Sox	10.00
172 Gene Woodling	4.00
173 Roger Craig	7.00
174 Willie Jones	3.00
175 Don Larsen	9.00
176 Gene Baker	3.00
177 Eddie Yost	3.00
178 Don Bessent	3.00
179 Ernie Oravetz	3.00
180 Dave Bell	3.00
181 Dick Donovan	3.00
182 Hobie Landrith	3.00
183 Chicago Cubs	8.00
184 Tito Francona	3.00
185 Johnny Kucks	3.00
186 Jim King	3.00
187 Virgil Trucks	3.00
188 Felix Mantilla	3.00
189 Willard Nixon	3.00
190 Randy Jackson	3.00
191 Joe Margoneri	3.00
192 Gerry Coleman	3.00
193 Del Rice	3.00
194 Hal Brown	3.00
195 Bobby Avila	3.00

NO. PLAYER	NR. MT.
196 Larry Jackson	3.00
197 Hank Sauer	3.00
198 Detroit Tigers	10.00
199 Vernon Law	3.00
200 Gil McDougald	9.00
201 Sandy Amoros	3.00
202 Dick Gernert	3.00
203 Hoyt Wilhelm	16.00
204 Kansas C. Athletics	7.00
205 Charlie Maxwell	3.00
206 Willard Schmidt	3.00
207 Bill Hunter	3.00
208 Lew Burdette	7.00
209 Bob Skinner	3.00
210 Roy Campanella	90.00
211 Camilo Pascual	3.00
212 Rocco Colavito (R)	35.00
213 Les Moss	3.00
214 Philadelphia Phillies	7.00
215 Enos Slaughter	18.00
216 Marv Grissom	3.00
217 Gene Stephens	3.00
218 Ray Jablonski	3.00
219 Tom Acker	3.00
220 Jackie Jensen	7.00
221 Dixie Howell	3.00
222 Alex Grammas	3.00
223 Frank House	3.00
224 Marv Blaylock	3.00
225 Harry Simpson	3.00
226 Preston Ward	3.00
227 Jerry Staley	3.00
228 Smokey Burgess	3.00
229 George Susce	3.00
230 George Kell	16.00
231 Solly Hemus	3.00
232 Whitey Lockman	3.00
233 Art Fowler	3.00
234 Dick Cole	3.00
235 Tom Poholsky	3.00
236 Joe Ginsberg	3.00
237 Foster Catleman	3.00
238 Eddie Robinson	3.00
239 Tom Morgan	3.00
240 Hank Bauer	9.00
241 Joe Lonnett	3.00
242 Charlie Neal	3.00
243 St. Louis Cardinals	3.00
244 Billy Loes	3.00
245 Rip Repulski	3.00
246 Jose Valdivielso	3.00
247 Turk Lown	3.00
248 Jim Finigan	3.00
249 Dave Pope	3.00
250 Ed Mathews	24.00
251 Baltimore Orioles	8.00
252 Carl Erskine	7.50
253 Gus Zernial	3.00
254 Ron Negray	3.00
255 Charlie Silvera	3.00
256 Ronnie Kline	3.00
257 Walt Dropo	3.00
258 Steve Gromek	3.00
259 Eddie O'Brien	3.00
260 Del Ennis	3.00
261 Bob Chakales	3.00

NO. PLAYER	NR. MT.
262 Bobby Thomson	6.00
263 George Strickland	3.00
264 Bob Turley	6.00
265 Harvey Haddix	16.00
266 Kenny Kuhn	13.00
267 Danny Kravitz	13.00
268 Jackie Collum	13.00
269 Bob Cerv	13.00
270 Washington Senators	25.00
271 Danny O'Connell	13.00
272 Bobby Shantz	25.00
273 Jim Davis	13.00
274 Don Hoak	13.00
275 Cleveland Indians	25.00
276 Jim Pyburn	13.00
277 Johnny Podres	55.00
278 Fred Hatfield	13.00
279 Bob Thurman	13.00
280 Alex Kellner	13.00
281 Gail Harris	13.00
282 Jack Dittmer	13.00
283 Wes Covington	13.00
284 Don Zimmer	25.00
285 Ned Garver	12.00
286 Bobby Richardson (R)	90.00
287 Sam Jones	13.00
288 Ted Lepcio	13.00
289 Jim Bolger	13.00
290 Andy Carey	13.00
291 Windy McCall	13.00
292 Bill Klaus	13.00
293 Ted Abernathy	13.00
294 Rocky Bridges	13.00
295 Joe Collins	13.00
296 Johnny Klippstein	13.00
297 Jack Crimian	13.00
298 Irv Noren	13.00
299 Chuck Harmon	13.00
300 Mike Garcia	13.00

NO. PLAYER	NR. MT.
301 Sam Esposito	13.00
302 Sandy Koufax	325.00
303 Billy Goodman	13.00
304 Joe Cunningham	13.00
305 Chico Fernandez	13.00
306 Darrell Johnson	13.00
307 Jack Phillips	13.00
308 Dick Hall	13.00
309 Jim Busby	13.00
310 Max Surkont	13.00
311 Al Pilarcik	13.00
312 Tony Kubek (R)	120.00
313 Mel Parnell	13.00
314 Ed Bouchee	13.00
315 Lou Berberet	13.00
316 Billy O'Dell	13.00
317 New York Giants	40.00
318 Mickey McDermott	13.00
319 Gino Cimoli	13.00
320 Neil Chrisley	13.00
321 Red Murff	13.00
322 Cincinnati Redlegs	45.00
323 Wes Westrum	13.00
324 Brooklyn Dodgers	80.00
325 Frank Bolling	13.00
326 Pedro Ramos	13.00
327 Jim Pendleton	13.00
328 Brooks Robinson (R)	350.00
329 Chicago White Sox	25.00
330 Jim Wilson	13.00
331 Ray Katt	13.00
332 Bob Bowman	13.00
333 Ernie Johnson	13.00
334 Jerry Schoonmaker	13.00
335 Granny Hamner	13.00
336 Haywood Sullivan	13.00
337 Rene Valdes	13.00
338 Jim Bunning (R)	100.00

NO. PLAYER	NR. MT.
339 Bob Speake	13.00
340 Bill Wight	13.00
341 Don Gross	13.00
342 Gene Mauch	17.00
343 Taylor Phillips	13.00
344 Paul LaPalme	13.00
345 Paul Smith	13.00
346 Dick Littlefield	13.00
347 Hal Naragon	13.00
348 Jim Hearn	13.00
349 Nelson King	13.00
350 Eddie Miksis	13.00
351 Dave Hillman	13.00
352 Ellis Kinder	13.00
353 Cal Neeman	4.00
354 Rip Coleman	4.00
355 Frank Malzone	4.00
356 Faye Throneberry	4.00
357 Earl Torgeson	4.00
358 Jerry Lynch	4.00
359 Tom Cheney	4.00
360 Johnny Groth	4.00
361 Curt Barclay	4.00
362 Roman Mejias	4.00
363 Eddie Kasko	4.00
364 Cal McLish	4.00
365 Ossie Virgil	4.00
366 Ken Lehman	4.00
367 Ed Fitzgerald	4.00
368 Bob Purkey	4.00
369 Milt Graff	4.00
370 Warren Hacker	4.00
371 Bob Lennon	4.00
372 Norm Zauchin	4.00
373 Pete Whisenant	4.00
374 Don Cardwell	4.00
375 Jim Landis	4.00
376 Don Elston	4.00

NO. PLAYER	NR. MT.
377 Andre Rodgers	4.00
378 Elmer Singleton	4.00
379 Don Lee	4.00
380 Walker Cooper	4.00
381 Dean Stone	4.00
382 Jim Brideweser	4.00
383 Juan Pizarro	4.00
384 Bobby Smith	4.00
385 Art Houtteman	4.00
386 Lyle Luttrell	4.00
387 Jack Sanford (R)	6.00
388 Pete Daley	4.00
389 Dave Jolly	4.00
390 Reno Bertoia	4.00
391 Ralph Terry (R)	7.50
392 Chuck Tanner	4.00
393 Raul Sanchez	4.00
394 Luis Aroyo	4.00
395 Bubba Phillips	4.00
396 Casey Wise	4.00
397 Roy Smalley	4.00
398 Al Cicotte	4.00
399 Billy Consolo	4.00
400 Dodgers' Sluggers:	165.00
Carl Furillo, Gil Hodges	
Duke Snider	
Roy Campanella	
401 Earl Battey	4.00
402 Jim Pisani	4.00
403 Dick Hyde	4.00
404 Harry Anderson	4.00
405 Duke Maas	4.00
406 Bob Hale	4.00
407 Yanks' Power Hitters:	250.00
M. Mantle, Y. Berra (Exc. $50.00)	
— Checklist 1/2	90.00
— Checklist 2/3	200.00
— Checklist 3/4	275.00
— Checklist 4/5	400.00

1958 Topps . . . Complete Set of 494 Cards—Value $1400.00 (Exc.); $3600.00 (Mint)

Features the rookie cards of Roger Maris and Orlando Cepeda. 33 cards exist with the player's name or team in *yellow* type. These cards are worth more than the cards with *white* type. Card 145 was not issued. Prices for team checklists (377, 397, 408 and 428) are with the teams listed in alphabetical order. Team checklists with the teams in numerical order are worth about $12.00 each.

NO. PLAYER	NR. MT.
1 Ted Williams (Exc. $50.00)	300.00
2 Bob Lemon	16.00
2 Bob Lemon	32.00
(yellow type)	
3 Alex Kellner	3.00
4 Hank Foiles	3.00
5 Willie Mays	120.00
6 George Zuverink	3.00
7 Dale Long	3.50
8 Eddie Kasko	3.50
8 Eddie Kasko	22.00
(yellow type)	
9 Hank Bauer	6.00
10 Lou Burdette	5.00
11 Jim Rivera	3.00

NO. PLAYER	NR. MT.
11 Jim Rivera	16.00
(yellow type)	
12 George Crowe	3.00
13 Billy Hoeft	3.00
13 Billy Hoeft	18.00
(yellow type)	
14 Rip Repulski	3.00
15 Jim Lemon	3.00
16 Charley Neal	3.00
17 Felix Mantilla	3.00
18 Frank Sullivan	3.00
19 New York Giants	13.00
20 Gil McDougald	7.00
20 Gil McDougald	25.00
(yellow type)	

NO. PLAYER	NR. MT.
21 Curt Barclay	3.00
22 Hal Naragon	3.00
23 Bill Tuttle	3.00
23 Bill Tuttle	18.00
(yellow type)	
24 Hobie Landrith	3.00
24 Hobie Landrith	18.00
(yellow type)	
25 Don Drysdal	35.00
26 Ron Jackson	3.00
27 Bud Freeman	3.00
28 Jim Busby	3.00
29 Ted Lepcio	3.00
30 Hank Aaron	120.00
30 Hank Aaron	240.00
(yellow letters)	

NO. PLAYER	NR. MT.
31 Tex Clevenger	3.00
32 J.W. Porter	3.00
32 J.W. Porter	18.00
(yellow letters)	
33 Cal Neeman	3.00
33 Cal Neeman	15.00
(yellow letters)	
34 Bob Thurman	3.00
35 Don Mossi	3.00
35 Don Mossi	15.00
(yellow letters)	
36 Ted Kazanski	3.00
37 Mike McCormick	5.00
(photo of Ray Monzant)	
38 Dick Gernert	3.00

NO.	PLAYER	NR. MT.
39	Bob Martyn	3.00
40	George Kell	13.00
41	Dave Hillman	3.00
42	John Roseboro (R)	6.00
43	Sal Maglie	6.00
44	Wash Senators	6.00
45	Dick Groat	5.00
46	Lou Sleater	3.00
46	Lou Sleater (yellow letters)	18.00
47	Roger Maris (R)	300.00
48	Chuck Harmon	3.00
49	Smokey Burgess	3.00
50	Billy Pierc	3.00
50	Billy Pierc (yellow letters)	15.00
51	Del Rice	3.00
52	Bob Clemente	65.00
52	Bob Clemente (yellow letters)	120.00
53	Morrie Martin	3.00
53	Morrie Martin (yellow letters)	18.00
54	Norm Siebern	3.00
55	Chico Carrasquel	3.00
56	Bill Fischer	3.00
57	Tim Thompson	3.00
57	Tim Thompson (yellow letters)	18.00
58	Art Schult	3.00
58	Art Schult (yellow letters)	15.00
59	Dave Sisler	3.00
60	Del Ennis	3.00
60	Del Ennis (yellow letters)	18.00
61	Darrell Johnson	3.00
61	Darrell Johnson (yellow letters)	18.00
62	Joe DeMaestri	3.00
63	Joe Nuxhall	3.00
64	Joe Lonnett	3.00
65	Von McDaniel	3.00
65	Von McDaniel (yellow letters)	18.00
66	Lee Walls	3.00
67	Joe Ginsberg	3.00
68	Daryl Spencer	3.00
69	Wally Burnette	3.00
70	Al Kaline	35.00
70	Al Kaline (yellow letters)	85.00
71	Brooklyn Dodgers	15.00
72	Bud Byerly	3.00
73	Pete Daley	3.00
74	Roy Face	3.00
75	Gus Bell	3.00
76	Dick Farrell	3.00
76	Dick Farrell (yellow letters)	15.00
77	Don Zimmer	3.00
77	Don Zimmer (yellow letters)	15.00
78	Ernie Johnson	3.00
78	Ernie Johnson (yellow letters)	18.00
79	Dick Williams	3.00
79	Dick Williams (yellow letters)	15.00
80	Dick Drott	3.00
81	Steve Boros	3.00
81	Steve Boros (yellow letters)	15.00
82	Ronnie Kline	3.00
83	Bob Hazle	3.00
84	Billy O'Dell	3.00
85	Luis Aparicio	15.00
85	Luis Aparicio (yellow letters)	30.00
86	Valmy Thomas	3.00
87	Johnny Kucks	3.00
88	Duke Snider	50.00
89	Bill Klaus	3.00
90	Robin Roberts	15.00
91	Chuck Tanner	3.00
92	Clint Courtney	3.00
92	Clint Courtney (yellow letters)	18.00
93	Sandy Amoros	3.00
94	Bob Skinner	3.00
95	Frank Bolling	3.00
96	Joseph Durham	3.00
97	Larry Jackson	3.00
97	Larry Jackson (yellow letters)	18.00
98	Bill Hunter	3.00
98	Bill Hunter (yellow letters)	18.00
99	Bobby Adams	3.00
100	Early Wynn	15.00
100	Early Wynn (yellow letters)	30.00
101	Bob Richardson	10.00
101	Bob Richardson (yellow letters)	32.00
102	George Strickland	3.00
103	Jerry Lynch	3.00
104	Jim Pendleton	3.00
105	Billy Gardner	3.00
106	Dick Schofield	3.00
107	Ossie Virgil	3.00
108	Jim Landis	3.00
108	Jim Landis (yellow letters)	15.00
109	Herb Plews	3.00
110	Johnny Logan	3.00
111	Stu Miller	2.50
112	Gus Zernial	2.50
113	Jerry Walker	2.50
114	Irv Noren	2.50
115	Jim Bunning	10.00
116	Dave Philley	2.50
117	Frank Torre	2.50
118	Harvey Haddix	2.50
119	Harry Chiti	2.50
120	Johnny Podres	5.00
121	Ed Miksis	2.50
122	Walter Moryn	2.50
123	Dick Tomanek	2.50
124	Bobby Usher	2.50
125	Al Dark	2.50
126	Stan Palys	2.50
127	Tom Sturdivant	2.50
128	Willie Kirkland	2.50
129	Jim Derrington	2.50
130	Jackie Jensen	7.00
131	Bob Henrich	2.50
132	Vernon Law	2.50
133	Russ Nixon	3.00
134	Philadelphia Phillies	6.00
135	Mike Drabowsky	2.50
136	Jim Finigan	2.50
137	Russ Kemmerer	2.50
138	Earl Torgeson	2.50
139	George Brunet	2.50
140	Wes Covington	2.50
141	Ken Lehman	2.50
142	Enos Slaughter	15.00
143	Billy Muffett	2.50
144	Bobby Morgan	2.50
146	Dick Gray	2.50
147	Don McMahon	2.50
148	Billy Consolo	2.50
149	Tom Acker	2.50
150	Mickey Mantle	500.00
151	Buddy Pritchard	2.50
152	Johnny Antonelli	2.50
153	Les Moss	2.50
154	Harry Byrd	2.50
155	Hector Lopez	2.50
156	Dick Hyde	2.50
157	Dee Fondy	2.50
158	Cleveland Indians	7.00
159	Taylor Phillips	2.50
160	Don Hoak	2.50
161	Don Larsen	6.00
162	Gil Hodges	18.00
163	Jim Wilson	2.50
164	Bob Taylor	2.50
165	Bob Nieman	2.50
166	Danny O'Connell	2.50
167	Frank Baumann	2.50
168	Joe Cunningham	2.50
169	Ralph Terry	2.50
170	Vic Wertz	2.50
171	Harry Anderson	2.50
172	Don Gross	2.50
173	Eddie Yost	2.50
174	Kansas C. Athletics	7.00
175	Marv Throneberry (R)	7.00
176	Bob Buhl	2.50
177	Al Smith	2.50
178	Ted Kluszewski	7.00
179	Willy Miranda	2.50
180	Lindy McDaniel	2.50
181	Willie Jones	2.50
182	Joe Caffie	2.50
183	Dave Jolly	2.50
184	Elvin Tappe	2.50
185	Ray Boone	2.50
186	Jack Meyer	2.50
187	Sandy Koufax	110.00
188	Milt Bolling (photo of Lou Berberet)	2.50
189	George Susce	2.50
190	Red Schoendienst	10.00
191	Art Ceccarelli	2.50
192	Milt Graff	2.50
193	Jerry Lumpe	2.50
194	Roger Craig	5.00
195	Whitey Lockman	2.50
196	Mike Garcia	2.50
197	Haywood Sullivan	2.50
198	Bill Virdon	3.00
199	Don Blasingame	2.00
200	Bob Keegan	2.00
201	Jim Bolger	2.00
202	Woody Held	2.00
203	Al Walker	2.00
204	Leo Kiely	2.00
205	Johnny Temple	2.00
206	Bob Shaw	2.00
207	Solly Hemus	2.00
208	Cal McLish	2.00
209	Bob Anderson	2.00
210	Wally Moon	2.00
211	Pete Burnside	2.00
212	Bubba Phillips	2.00
213	Red Wilson	2.00
214	Willard Schmidt	2.00
215	Jim Gilliam	6.00
216	St. Louis Cardinals	7.00
217	Jack Harshman	2.00
218	Dick Rand	2.00
219	Camilo Pascual	2.00
220	Tom Brewer	2.00
221	Jerry Kindall	2.00
222	Bud Daley	2.00
223	Andy Pafko	2.00
224	Bob Grim	2.00
225	Billy Goodman	2.00
226	Bob Smith	2.00
227	Gene Stephehs	2.00
228	Duke Maas	2.00
229	Frank Zupo	2.00
230	Richie Ashburn	9.00
231	Lloyd Merritt	2.00
232	Reno Bertoia	2.00
233	Mickey Vernon	2.00
234	Carl Sawatski	2.00
235	Tom Gorman	2.00
236	Ed Fitzgerald	2.00
237	Bill Wight	2.00
238	Bill Mazeroski	8.00
239	Chuck Stobbs	2.00
240	Moose Skowron	7.00
241	Dick Littlefield	2.00
242	Johnny Klippstein	2.00
243	Larry Raines	2.00
244	Don Demeter	2.00
245	Frank Lary	2.00
246	New York Yankees	25.00
247	Casey Wise	2.00
248	Herm Wehmeier	2.00
249	Ray Moore	2.00
250	Roy Sievers	2.00
251	Warren Hacker	2.00
252	Bob Trowbridge	2.00
253	Don Muefler	2.00
254	Alex Grammas	2.00
255	Bob Turley	6.00
256	Chicago White Sox	5.00
257	Hal Smith	2.00
258	Carl Erskine	5.00
259	Alan Pilarcik	2.00
260	Frank Malzone	2.00
261	Turk Lown	2.00
262	John Groth	2.00
263	Ed Bressoud	2.00
264	Jack Sanford	2.00
265	Pete Runnels	2.00
266	Connie Johnson	2.00
267	Sherm Lollar	2.00
268	Granny Hamner	2.00
269	Paul Smith	2.00
270	Warren Spahn	25.00
271	Billy Martin	10.00
272	Ray Crone	2.00
273	Hal Smith	2.00
274	Rocky Bridges	2.00
275	Elston Howard	7.00
276	Bobby Avila	2.00
277	Virgil Trucks	2.00
278	Mack Burk	2.00
279	Bob Boyd	2.00
280	Jim Piersall	5.00
281	Sam Taylor	2.00
282	Paul Foytack	2.00
283	Ray Shearer	2.00
284	Ray Katt	2.00
285	Frank Robinson	45.00
286	Gino Cimoli	2.00
287	Sam Jones	2.00
288	Harmon Killebrew	35.00
289	Hurling Rivals: Lou Burdette, Bobby Shantz	6.00
290	Dick Donovan	2.00
291	Don Landrum	2.00
292	Ned Garver	2.00
293	Gene Freese	2.00
294	Hal Jeffcoat	2.00
295	Minnie Minoso	5.00
296	Ryne Duren	6.00
297	Don Buddin	2.00
298	Jim Hearn	2.00
299	Harry Simpson	2.00
300	Harridge and Giles League Presidents	5.00
301	Randy Jackson	2.00
302	Mike Baxes	2.00
303	Neil Chrisley	2.00
304	Tigers' Big Bats: Harvey Kuenn, Al Kaline	7.50
305	Clem Labine	2.50
306	Whammy Douglas	2.00
307	Brooks Robinson	55.00
308	Paul Giel	2.00
309	Gail Harris	2.00
310	Ernie Banks	50.00
311	Bob Purkey	2.00
312	Boston Red Sox	8.00
313	Bob Rush	2.00
314	Boss and Power Duke Snider, Walt Alston	15.00
315	Bob Friend	2.00
316	Tito Francona	2.00
317	Albie Pearson	2.50
318	Frank House	2.00

NO. PLAYER	NR. MT.	NO. PLAYER	NR. MT.	NO. PLAYER	NR. MT.	NO. PLAYER	NR. MT.
319 Lou Skizas	2.00	362 Ray Jablonski	2.00	407 Carlton Willey	2.00	450 Preston Ward	4.00
320 Whitey Ford	35.00	363 Don Elston	2.00	408 Baltimore Orioles*	7.00	451 Joe Taylor	2.00
321 Sluggers Supreme:	16.00	364 Earl Battey	2.00	409 Frank Thomas	2.00	452 Roman Mejias	2.00
Ted Kluszewski,		365 Tom Morgan	2.00	410 Murray Wall	2.00	453 Tom Qualters	2.00
Ted Williams		366 Gene Green	2.00	411 Tony Taylor	2.00	454 Harry Hanebrink	2.00
322 Harding Peterson	2.00	367 Jack Urban	2.00	412 Jerry Staley	2.00	455 Hal Griggs	2.00
323 Elmer Valo	2.00	368 Rocky Colavito	9.00	413 Jim Davenport	2.00	456 Dick Brown	2.00
324 Hoyt Wilhelm	15.00	369 Ralph Lumenti	2.00	414 Sammy White	2.00	457 Milt Pappas (R)	5.00
325 Joe Adcock	2.50	370 Yogi Berra	50.00	415 Bob Bowman	2.00	458 Julio Becquer	2.00
326 Bob Miller	2.00	371 Marty Keough	2.00	416 Foster Castleman	2.00	459 Ron Blackburn	2.00
327 Chicago Cubs	7.00	372 Don Cardwell	2.00	417 Carl Furillo	6.00	460 Chuck Essegian	2.00
328 Ike Delock	2.00	373 Joe Pignatano	2.00	418 W. Series Batting Foes:	125.00	461 Ed Mayer	2.00
329 Bob Cerv	2.00	374 Brooks Lawrence	2.00	Mickey Mantle, Hank /		462 Gary Geiger	4.00
330 Ed Bailey	2.00	375 Pee Wee Reese	35.00	419 Bobby Shantz	2.50	463 Vito Valentinetti	2.00
331 Pedro Ramos	2.00	376 Charley Rabe	2.00	420 Vada Pinson	13.00	464 Curt Flood (R)	9.00
332 Jim King	2.00	377 Milwaukee Braves*	7.00	421 Dixie Howell	2.00	465 Arnie Portocarrero	2.00
333 Andy Carey	2.00	378 Hank Sauer	2.00	422 Norm Zauchin	2.00	466 Pete Whisenant	2.00
334 Mound Aces:	3.00	379 Ray Herbert	2.00	423 Phil Clark	2.00	467 Glen Hobbie	2.00
Bob Friend, Billy Pierce		380 Charley Maxwell	2.00	424 Larry Doby	4.00	468 Bob Schmidt	2.00
335 Ruben Gomez	2.50	381 Hal Brown	2.00	425 Sam Esposito	2.00	469 Don Ferrarese	2.00
336 Bert Hamric	2.50	382 Al Cicotte	2.00	426 Johnny O'Brien	2.00	470 R.C. Stevens	2.00
337 Hank Aguirre	2.50	383 Lou Berberet	2.00	427 Al Worthington	2.00	471 Lenny Green	2.00
338 Walter Dropo	2.50	384 John Goryl	2.00	428 Cincinnati Redlegs*	7.00	472 Joe Jay	2.00
339 Fred Hatfield	2.50	385 Wilmer Mizell	2.00	429 Gus Triandos	2.00	473 Bill Renna	2.00
340 Don Newcombe	5.00	386 Young Sluggers:	6.00	430 Bobby Thomson	4.00	474 Roman Semproch	2.00
341 Pittsburgh Pirates	7.00	Ed Bailey, Birdie Tebbetts,		431 Gene Conley	2.00	475 All-Star Managers:	13.00
342 Jim Brosnan	2.50	Frank Robinson		432 John Powers	2.00	Stengel, Haney	
343 Orlando Cepeda (R)	35.00	387 Wally Post	2.00	433 Pancho Herrera	3.00	476 Stan Musial (AS)	20.00
344 Bob Porterfield	2.00	388 Billy Moran	2.00	433 Pancho Herrer	200.00	477 Bill Skowron (AS)	3.00
345 Jim Hegan	2.00	389 Bill Taylor	2.00	(name spelled wrong)		478 Johnny Temple (AS)	3.00
346 Steve Bilko	2.00	390 Del Crandall	2.00	434 Harvey Kuenn	5.00	479 Nellie Fox (AS)	4.00
347 Don Rudolph	2.00	391 Dave Melton	2.00	435 Ed Roebuck	5.00	480 Eddie Mathews (AS)	12.00
348 Chico Fernandez	2.00	392 Bennie Daniels	2.00	436 Rival Fence Busters:	40.00	481 Frank Malzone (AS)	3.00
·349 Murry Dickson	2.00	393 Tony Kubek	11.00	Willie Mays, Duke Snid		482 Ernie Banks (AS)	15.00
350 Ken Boyer	5.00	394 Jim Grant	2.00	437 Bob Speake	2.00	483 Luis Aparicio (AS)	7.00
351 Braves Fence Busters:	17.00	395 Willard Nixon	2.00	438 Whitey Herzog	2.00	484 Frank Robinson (AS)	11.00
Del Crandall, Eddie Mathews,		396 Dutch Dotterer	2.00	439 Ray Narleski	2.00	485 Ted Williams (AS)	35.00
Hank Aaron, Joe Adcock		397 Detroit Tigers*	7.00	440 Eddie Mathews	22.00	486 Willie Mays (AS)	25.00
352 Herb Score	3.00	398 Gene Woodling	2.00	441 Jim Marshall	2.00	487 Mickey Mantle (AS)	60.00
353 Stan Lopata	2.00	399 Marv Grissom	2.00	442 Phil Paine	2.00	488 Hank Aaron (AS)	25.00
354 Art Ditmar	2.00	400 Nellie Fox	7.00	443 Billy Harrell	4.00	489 Jackie Jensen (AS)	4.00
355 Billy Bruton	2.00	401 Don Bessent	2.00	444 Danny Kravitz	2.00	490 Ed Bailey (AS)	3.00
356 Bob Malkmus	2.00	402 Bobby Gene Smith	2.00	445 Bob Smith	2.00	491 Sherm Lollar (AS)	3.00
357 Danny McDevitt	2.00	403 Steve Korcheck	2.00	446 Carroll Hardy	4.00	492 Bob Friend (AS)	3.00
358 Gene Baker	2.00	404 Curt Simmons	2.00	447 Ray Monzant	2.00	493 Bob Turley (AS)	3.00
359 Billy Loes	2.00	405 Ken Aspromonte	2.00	448 Charlie Lau	4.00	494 Warren Spahn (AS)	11.00
360 Roy McMillan	2.00	406 Vic Power	2.00	449 Gene Fodge	2.00	495 H. Score (AS) (Exc. $1.50)	5.00
361 Mike Fornieles	2.00						

1959 Topps . . . Complete Set of 572 Cards—Value $1400.00 (Exc.); $3600.00 (Mint)

Includes Bob Gibson's rookie card. The high numbers are 507 to 572. Cards 199 to 286 were issued with *white* or *gray* backs. Cards 316, 321, 322, 336 and 362 exist without the *option* or *traded* line—worth $75.00 each.

NO. PLAYER	NR. MT.	NO. PLAYER	NR. MT.	NO. PLAYER	NR. MT.	NO. PLAYER	NR. MT.
1 BB Commissioner	30.00	10 Mickey Mantle	350.00	18 Jack Urban	2.50	28 Red Worthington	2.50
Ford Frick (Exc. $5.00)		11 Billy Hunter	2.50	19 Ed Bressoud	2.50	29 Jim Bolger	2.50
2 Eddie Yost	2.50	12 Vern Law	3.00	20 Duke Snider	40.00	30 Nellie Fox	7.00
3 Don McMahon	2.50	13 Dick Gernert	2.50	21 Connie Johnson	2.50	31 Ken Lehman	2.50
4 Albie Pearson	2.50	14 Pete Whisenant	2.50	22 Al Smith	2.50	32 Don Buddin	2.50
5 Dick Donovan	2.50	15 Dick Drott	2.50	23 Murry Dickson	2.50	33 Ed Fitzgerald	2.50
6 Alex Grammas	2.50	16 Joe Pignatano	2.50	24 Red Wilson	2.50	34 Pitchers Beware:	7.00
7 Al Pilarcik	2.50	17 Danny's All-Stars:	4.00	25 Dan Hoak	2.50	Al Kaline, Charley Maxwell	
8 Philadelphia Phillies	6.00	Frank Thomas, Danny		26 Chuck Stobbs	2.50	35 Ted Kluszewski	5.00
9 Paul Giel	2.50	Murtaugh, Ted Kluszewski		27 Andy Pafko	2.50	36 Hank Aguirre	2.50

NO.	PLAYER	NR. MT.
37	Gene Green	2.50
38	Morrie Martin	2.50
39	Ed Bouchee	2.50
40	Warren Spahn	25.00
41	Bob Martyn	2.50
42	Murray Wall	2.50
43	Steven Bilko	2.50
44	Vito Valentinetti	2.50
45	Andy Carey	2.50
46	Bill Henry	2.50
47	Jim Finigan	2.50
48	Baltimore Orioles	5.00
49	Bill Hall	2.50
50	Willie May	95.00
51	Rip Coleman	2.50
52	Coot Veal	2.50
53	Stan Williams	2.50
54	Mel Roach	2.50
55	Tom Brewer	2.50
56	Carl Sawatski	2.50
57	Al Cicotte	2.50
58	Eddie Miksis	2.50
59	Irv Noren	2.50
60	Bob Turley	4.00
61	Dick Brown	2.50
62	Tony Taylor	2.50
63	Jim Hearn	2.50
64	Joe DeMaestri	2.50
65	Frank Torre	2.50
66	Joe Ginsberg	2.50
67	Brooks Lawrence	2.50
68	Dick Schofield	2.50
69	San F. Giants	5.00
70	Harvey Kuenn	4.00
71	Don Bessent	2.50
72	Bill Renna	2.50
73	Ron Jackson	2.50
74	Directing the Power:	3.00
	Jim Lemon, Cookie	
	Lavagetto, Roy Sievers	
75	Sam Jones	2.50
76	Bobby Richardson	6.00
77	John Goryl	2.50
78	Pedro Ramos	2.50
79	Harry Chiti	2.50
80	Minnie Minoso	4.00
81	Hal Jeffcoat	2.50
82	Bob Boyd	2.50
83	Bob Smith	2.50
84	Reno Bertoia	2.50
85	Harry Anderson	2.50
86	Bob Keegan	2.50
87	Danny O'Connell	2.50
88	Herb Score	3.00
89	Billy Gardner	2.50
90	Bill Skowron	7.00
91	Herb Moford	2.50
92	David Philley	2.50
93	Julio Becquer	2.50
94	Chicago White Sox	5.00
95	Carl Willey	2.50
96	Lou Berberet	2.50
97	Jerry Lynch	2.50
98	Arnie Portocarrero	2.50
99	Ted Kazanski	2.50
100	Bob Cerv	2.50
101	Alex Kellner	2.50
102	Felipe Alou (R)	6.00
103	Billy Goodman	2.50
104	Del Rice	2.50
105	Lee Walls	2.50
106	Hal Woodeshick	2.50
107	Norm Larker	2.50
108	Zack Monroe	2.50
109	Bob Schmidt	2.50
110	George Witt	2.50
111	Cincinnati Redlegs	6.00
112	Billy Consolo	2.00
113	Taylor Phillips	2.00
114	Earl Battey	2.00
115	Mickey Vernon	2.00

No. 116 to 146 Rookie Stars

NO.	PLAYER	NR. MT.
116	Bob Allison	5.00
117	John Blanchard	2.00
118	John Buzhardt	2.00
119	John Callison	4.00
120	Chuck Coles	2.00
121	Bob Conley	2.00
122	Bennie Daniels	2.00
123	Donald Dillard	2.00
124	Dan Dobbek	2.00
125	Ron Fairly	4.00
126	Eddie Haas	2.00
127	Kent Hadley	2.00
128	Bob Hartman	2.00
129	Frank Herrera	2.00
130	Lou Jackson	2.00
131	Deron Johnson	2.00
132	Don Lee	2.00
133	Bob Lillis	2.00
134	Jim McDaniel	2.00
135	Gene Oliver	2.00
136	Jim O'Toole	2.00
137	Dick Ricketts	2.00
138	John Romano	2.00
139	Ed Sadowski	2.00
140	Charlie Secrest	2.00
141	Joe Shipley	2.00
142	Dick Stigman	2.00
143	Willie Tasby	2.00
144	Jerry Walker	2.00
145	Dom Zanni	2.00
146	Jerry Zimmerman	2.00
147	Cubs' Clubbers:	7.00
	Dale Long, Ernie Banks,	
	Walt Moryn	
148	Mike McCormick	2.00
149	Jim Bunning	7.00
150	Stan Musial	100.00
151	Bob Malkmus	2.00
152	Johnny Klippstein	2.00
153	Jim Marshall	2.00
154	Ray Herbert	2.00
155	Enos Slaughter	12.00
156	Ace Hurlers:	5.00
	Billy Pierce, Robin Roberts	
157	Felix Mantilla	2.00
158	Walt Dropo	2.00
159	Bob Shaw	2.00
160	Dick Groat	4.00
161	Frank Baumann	2.00
162	Bobby Smith	2.00
163	Sandy Koufax	80.00
164	Johnny Groth	2.00
165	Bill Bruton	2.00
166	Destruction Crew:	3.00
	Minnie Minoso, Rocky	
	Colavito, Larry Doby	
167	Duke Maas	2.00
168	Carroll Hardy	2.00
169	Ted Abernathy	2.00
170	Gene Woodling	2.00
171	Willard Schmidt	2.00
172	Kansas C. Athletics	5.00
173	Bill Monbouquette	2.00
174	Jim Pendleton	2.00
175	Dick Farrell	2.00
176	Preston Ward	2.00
177	John Briggs	2.00
178	Ruben Amaro	2.00
179	Don Rudolph	2.00
180	Yogi Berra	45.00
181	Bob Porterfield	2.00
182	Milt Graff	2.00
183	Stu Miller	2.00
184	Harvey Haddix	3.00
185	Jim Busby	2.00
186	Mudcat Grant	2.00
187	Bubba Phillips	2.00
188	Juan Pizarro	2.00
189	Neil Chrisley	2.00
190	Bill Virdon	4.00

NO.	PLAYER	NR. MT.
191	Russ Kemmerer	2.00
192	Charley Beamon	2.00
193	Sammy Taylor	2.00
194	Jim Brosnan	2.00
195	Rip Repulski	2.00
196	Billy Moran	2.00
197	Ray Semproch	2.00
198	Jim Davenport	2.00
199	Leo Kiely	2.00
200	NL President:	
	Warren Giles	4.00
201	Tom Acker	2.00
202	Roger Maris	90.00
203	Ozzie Virgil	2.00
204	Casey Wise	2.00
205	Don Larsen	4.00
206	Carl Furillo	5.00
207	George Strickland	2.00
208	Willie Jones	2.00
209	Lenny Green	2.00
210	Ed Bailey	2.00
211	Bob Blaylock	2.00
212	Fence Busters:	20.00
	Hank Aaron, Eddie Mathews	
213	Jim Rivera	2.00
214	Marcelino Solis	2.00
215	Jim Lemon	2.00
216	Andre Rodgers	2.00
217	Carl Erskine	4.00
218	Roman Mejias	2.00
219	George Zuverink	2.00
220	Frank Malzone	2.00
221	Bob Bowman	2.00
222	Bobby Shantz	2.00
223	St. Louis Cardinals	6.00
224	Claude Osteen (R)	4.00
225	Johnny Logan	2.00
226	Art Ceccarelli	2.00
227	Hal Smith	2.00
228	Don Gross	2.00
229	Vic Power	2.00
230	Bill Fischer	2.00
231	Ellis Burton	2.00
232	Eddie Kasko	2.00
233	Paul Foytack	2.00
234	Chuck Tanner	3.00
235	Valmy Thomas	2.00
236	Ted Bowsfield	2.00
237	Run Preventers:	3.00
	Gil McDougald, Bob Turley,	
	Bobby Richardson	
238	Gene Baker	2.00
239	Bob Trowbridge	2.00
240	Hank Bauer	5.00
241	Billy Muffett	2.00
242	Ron Samford	2.00
243	Marv Grissom	2.00
244	Dick Gray	2.00
245	Ned Garver	2.00
246	J.W. Porter	2.00
247	Don Ferrarese	2.00
248	Boston Red Sox	7.00
249	Bobby Adams	2.00
250	Billy O'Dell	2.00
251	Cletis Boyer	4.00
252	Ray Boone	2.00
253	Seth Morehead	2.00
254	Zeke Bella	2.00
255	Del Ennis	2.00
256	Jerry Davie	2.00
257	Leon Wagner	2.00
258	Fred Kipp	2.00
259	Jim Pisoni	2.00
260	Early Wynn	12.00
261	Gene Stephens	2.00
262	Hitters' Foes:	4.00
	Johnny Podres, Clem	
	Labine, Don Drysdale	
263	Buddy Daley	2.00
264	Chico Carrasquel	2.00
265	Ron Kline	2.00

NO.	PLAYER	NR. MT.
266	Woody Held	2.00
267	John Romonosky	2.00
268	Tito Francona	2.00
269	Jack Mayer	2.00
270	Gil Hodges	12.00
271	Orlando Pena	2.00
272	Jerry Lumpe	2.00
273	Joey Jay	2.00
274	Jerry Kindall	2.00
275	Jack Sanford	2.00
276	Pete Daley	2.00
277	Turk Lown	2.00
278	Chuck Essegian	2.00
279	Ernie Johnson	2.00
280	Frank Bolling	2.00
281	Walt Craddock	2.00
282	R.C. Stevens	2.00
283	Russ Heman	2.00
284	Steve Korcheck	2.00
285	Joe Cunningham	2.00
286	Dean Stone	2.00
287	Don Zimmer	2.00
288	Dutch Dotterer	2.00
289	Johnny Kucks	2.00
290	Wes Covington	2.00
291	Pitching Partners:	3.00
	Pedro Ramos,	
	Camilo Pascual	
292	Dick Williams	2.00
293	Ray Moore	2.00
294	Hank Foiles	2.00
295	Billy Martin	6.00
296	Ernie Broglio	2.00
297	Jackie Brandt	2.00
298	Tex Clevenger	2.00
299	Billy Klaus	2.00
300	Richie Ashburn	7.00
301	Earl Averill	2.00
302	Don Mossi	2.00
303	Marty Keough	2.00
304	Chicago Cubs	6.00
305	Curt Raydon	2.00
306	Jim Gilliam	5.00
307	Curt Barclay	2.00
308	Norm Siebern	2.00
309	Sal Maglie	4.00
310	Luis Aparicio	11.00
311	Norm Zauchin	2.00
312	Don Newcombe	3.00
313	Frank House	2.00
314	Don Cardwell	2.00
315	Joe Adcock	2.50
316	Ralph Lumenti*	2.00
	(photo of Camilo Pascual)	
317	Hitting Kings:	15.00
	Willie Mays, Richie Ashburn	
318	Rocky Bridges	2.00
319	Dave Hillmann	2.00
320	Bob Skinner	2.00
321	Bob Giallombardo*	2.00
322	Harry Hanebrink*	2.00
323	Frank Sullivan	2.00
324	Donald Demeter	2.00
325	Ken Boyer	4.00
326	Marv Throneberry	3.00
327	Gary Bell	2.00
328	Lou Skizas	2.00
329	Detroit Tigers	6.00
330	Gus Triandos	2.00
331	Steve Boros	2.00
332	Ray Monzant	2.00
333	Harry Simpson	2.00
334	Glen Hobbie	2.00
335	Johnny Temple	2.00
336	Billy Loes*	2.00
337	George Crowe	1.25
338	Sparky Anderson (R)	12.00
339	Roy Face	3.00
340	Roy Sievers	3.00
341	Tom Qualters	2.00
342	Ray Jablonski	2.00

NO. PLAYER	NR. MT.	NO. PLAYER	NR. MT.	NO. PLAYER	NR. MT.	NO. PLAYER	NR. MT.
343 Billy Hoeft	2.00	401 Ron Blackburn	2.00	458 Gordon Jones	2.00	518 Mike Cueller (R)	12.00
344 Russ Nixon	2.00	402 Hector Lopez	2.00	459 Bill Tuttle	2.00	519 Infield Power:	7.50
345 Gil McDougald	5.00	403 Clem Labine	2.00	460 Bob Friend	2.00	Pete Runnels, Dick	
346 Batter Bafflers:	2.00	404 Hank Sauer	2.00	461 Mantle Hits 42nd HR	32.00	Gernert, Frank Malzone	
Tom Brewer, Dave Sisler		405 Roy McMillan	2.00	462 Colavito's Catch	3.50	520 Don Elston	7.50
347 Bob Buhl	2.00	406 Solly Drake	2.00	463 Kaline Bat Champ	7.00	521 Gary Geiger	7.50
348 Ted Lepcio	2.00	407 Moe Drabowsky	2.00	464 Mays' Series Catch	15.00	522 Gene Snyder	7.50
349 Hoyt Wilhelm	10.00	408 Keystone Combo:	6.00	465 Sievers HR Mark	3.00	523 Harry Bright	7.50
350 Ernie Banks	42.00	Nellie Fox, Luis Aparicio		466 Pierce All-Star	3.00	524 Larry Osborne	7.50
351 Earl Torgeson	2.00	409 Gus Zernial	2.00	467 Aaron Clubs Homer	15.00	525 Jim Coates	7.50
352 Robin Roberts	12.00	410 Billy Pierce	2.00	468 Snider's Play	10.00	526 Bob Speake	7.50
353 Curt Flood	4.00	411 Whitey Lockman	2.00	469 Banks MVP	9.00	527 Solly Hemus	7.50
354 Pete Burnside	2.00	412 Stan Lopata	2.00	470 Musial's 3000 Hits	10.00	528 Pittsburgh Pirates	16.00
355 Jim Piersall	3.00	413 Camillo Pascual	2.00	471 Tom Sturdivant	2.00	529 George Bamberger (R)	10.00
356 Bob Mabe	2.00	414 Dale Long	2.00	472 Gene Freese	2.00	530 Wally Moon	7.50
357 Dick Stuart (R)	3.00	415 Bill Mazeroski	5.00	473 Mike Fornieles	2.00	531 Ray Webster	7.50
358 Ralph Terry	2.00	416 Haywood Sullivan	2.00	474 Moe Thacker	2.00	532 Mark Freeman	7.50
359 Bill White (R)	10.00	417 Virgil Trucks	2.00	475 Jack Harshman	2.00	533 Darrell Johnson	7.50
360 Al Kaline	35.00	418 Gino Cimoli	2.00	476 Cleveland Indians	6.00	534 Faye Throneberry	7.50
361 Willard Nixon	2.00	419 Milwuakee Braves	4.00	477 Barry Latman	2.00	535 Ruben Gomez	7.50
362 Dolan Nichols*	2.00	420 Rocky Colavito	5.00	478 Bob Clemente*	65.00	536 Dan Kravitz	7.50
363 Bobby Avila	2.00	421 Herm Wehmeier	2.00	479 Lindy McDaniel	2.00	537 Rudolph Arias	7.50
364 Danny McDevitt	2.00	422 Hobie Landrith	2.00	480 Red Schoendienst	8.00	538 Chick King	7.50
365 Gus Bell	2.00	423 Bob Grim	2.00	481 Charlie Maxwell	2.00	539 Gary Blaylock	7.50
366 Humberto Robinson	2.00	424 Ken Aspromonte	2.00	482 Russ Meyer	2.00	540 Willie Miranda	7.50
367 Cal Neeman	2.00	425 Del Crandall	2.00	483 Clint Courtney	2.00	541 Bob Thurman	7.50
368 Don Mueller	2.00	426 Jerry Staley	2.00	484 Willie Kirkland	2.00	542 Jim Perry (R)	12.00
369 Dick Tomanek	2.00	427 Charlie Neal	2.00	485 Ryne Duren	2.00	543 Corsair Outfield Trio:	35.00
370 Pete Runnels	2.00	428 Buc Hill Aces:	4.00	486 Sammy White	2.00	Bob Skinner, Bill Virdon,	
371 Dick Brodowski	2.00	Ron Kline, Bob Friend,		487 Hal Brown	2.00	Roberto Clemente	
372 Jim Hegan	2.00	Vernon Law, Roy Face		488 Walt Moryn	2.00	544 Lee Tate	7.50
373 Herb Plews	2.00	429 Bobby Thomson	2.50	489 John Powers	2.00	545 Tom Morgan	7.50
374 Art Ditmar	2.00	430 Whitey Ford	30.00	490 Frank Thomas	2.00	546 Al Schroll	7.50
375 Bob Nieman	2.00	431 Whammy Douglas	2.00	491 Don Blasingame	2.00	547 Jim Baxes	7.50
376 Hal Naragon	2.00	432 Smokey Burgess	2.00	492 Gene Conley	2.00	548 Elmer Singleton	7.50
377 Johnny Antonelli	2.00	433 Billy Harrell	2.00	493 Jim Landis	2.00	549 Howie Nunn	7.50
378 Gail Harris	2.00	434 Hal Griggs	2.00	494 Don Pavletich	2.00	550 Symbol of Courage:	100.00
379 Bob Miller	2.00	435 Frank Robinson	28.00	495 Johnny Podres	4.00	Roy Campanella	
380 Hank Aaron	75.00	436 Granny Hamner	2.00	496 Wayne Terwilliger	2.00	551 F. Haney—Mgr.(AS)	8.00
381 Mike Baxes	2.00	437 Ike Delock	2.00	497 Hal R. Smith	2.00	552 C. Stengel—Mgr. (AS)	25.00
382 Curt Simmons	2.00	438 Sam Esposito	2.00	498 Dick Hyde	2.00	553 Orlando Cepeda (AS)	9.00
383 Words of Wisdom:	6.00	439 Brooks Robinson	35.00	499 Johnny O'Brien	2.00	554 Bill Skowron (AS)	8.00
Don Larsen, Casey Stengel		440 Lou Burdette	5.00	500 Vic Wertz	2.00	555 Bill Mazeroski (AS)	9.00
384 Dave Sisler	2.00	441 John Roseboro	2.00	501 Bobby Tiefenauer	2.00	556 Nellie Fox (AS)	10.00
385 Sherm Lollar	2.00	442 Ray Narleski	2.00	502 Al Dark	2.00	557 Ken Boyer (AS)	8.00
386 Jim Delsing	2.00	443 Daryl Spencer	2.00	503 Jim Owens	2.00	558 Frank Malzone (AS)	8.00
387 Don Drysdale	25.00	444 Ronnie Hansen	2.00	504 Ossie Alvarez	2.00	559 Ernie Banks (AS)	30.00
388 Bob Will	2.00	445 Cal McLish	2.00	505 Tony Kubek	7.50	560 Luis Aparicio (AS)	15.00
389 Joe Nuxhall	2.00	446 Rocky Nelson	2.00	506 Bob Purkey	2.00	561 Hank Aaron (AS)	65.00
390 Orlando Cepeda	7.50	447 Bob Anderson	2.00	507 Bob Hale	7.50	562 Al Kaline (AS)	25.00
391 Milt Pappas	2.00	448 Vada Pinson	4.00	508 Art Fowler	7.50	563 Willie Mays (AS)	60.00
392 Whitey Herzog	3.00	449 Tom Gorman	2.00	509 Norm Cash (R)	20.00	564 Mickey Mantle (AS)	160.00
393 Frank Lary	2.00	450 Ed Mathews	20.00	510 New York Yankees	35.00	565 Wes Covington (AS)	8.00
394 Randy Jackson	2.00	451 Jimmy Constable	2.00	511 George Susce	7.50	566 Roy Sievers (AS)	8.00
395 Elston Howard	6.00	452 Chico Fernandez	2.00	512 George Altman	7.50	567 Del Crandall (AS)	8.00
396 Bob Rush	2.00	453 Les Moss	2.00	513 Tommy Carroll	7.50	568 Gus Triandos (AS)	8.00
397 Washington Senators	6.00	454 Phil Clark	2.00	514 Bob Gibson (R)	250.00	569 Bob Friend (AS)	8.00
398 Wally Post	2.00	455 Larry Doby	4.00	515 Harmon Killebrew	75.00	570 Bob Turley (AS)	8.00
399 Larry Jackson	2.00	456 Jerry Casale	2.00	516 Mike Garcia	7.50	571 Warren Spahn (AS)	25.00
400 Jackie Jensen	3.00	457 Los Angeles Dodgers	15.00	517 Joe Koppe	7.50	572 B. Pierce (AS) (Exc. $5.00)	20.00

1960 Topps . . . Complete Set of 572 Cards—Value $1300.00 (Exc.); $3200.00 (Mint)

This set features the rookie cards of Willie McCovey and Carl Yastrzemski. The high numbers are 507 to 572. Semi-high numbers are 441 to 506. Topps' switched to a predominately horizontal format, and used it for the last time. Cards 375 to 440 exist with *gray* or *white* backs.

1960 Topps (Continued)

NO.	PLAYER	NR. MT.
1	E. Wynn (Exc. $6.00)	30.00
2	Roman Mejias	1.00
3	Joe Adcock	2.50
4	Bob Purkey	1.00
5	Wally Moon	1.00
6	Lou Berberet	1.00
7	Master & Mentor: Willie Mays, Bill Rigney	8.00
8	Bud Daley	1.00
9	Faye Throneberry	1.00
10	Ernie Banks	25.00
11	Norm Siebern	1.00
12	Milt Pappas	1.00
13	Wally Post	1.00
14	Jim Grant	1.00
15	Pete Runnels	1.00
16	Ernie Broglio	1.00
17	John Callison	1.00
18	Los Angeles Dodgers	9.00
19	Felix Mantilla	1.00
20	Roy Face	1.50
21	Dutch Dotterer	1.00
22	Rocky Bridges	1.00
23	Eddie Fisher	1.00
24	Dick Gray	1.00
25	Ray Sievers	1.00
26	Wayne Terwilliger	1.00
27	Dick Drott	1.00
28	Brooks Robinson	30.00
29	Clem Labine	1.00
30	Tito Francona	1.00
31	Sammy Esposito	1.00
32	Sophomore Stalwarts: Jim O'Toole, Vada Pinson	1.50
33	Tom Morgan	1.00
34	Sparky Anderson	4.00
35	Whitey Ford	22.00
36	Russ Nixon	1.00
37	Bill Bruton	1.00
38	Jerry Casale	1.00
39	Earl Averill	1.00
40	Joe Cunningham	1.00
41	Barry Latman	1.00
42	Hobie Landrith	1.00
43	Washington Senators	3.00
44	Bobby Locke	1.00
45	Roy McMillan	1.00
46	Jack Fisher	1.00
47	Don Zimmer	3.00
48	Hal Smith	1.00
49	Curt Raydon	1.00
50	Al Kaline	25.00
51	Jim Coates	1.00
52	Dave Philley	1.00
53	Jackie Brandt	1.00
54	Mike Fornieles	1.00
55	Bill Mazeroski	3.00
56	Steve Korcheck	1.00
57	Win Savers: Turk Lown, Jerry Staley	1.25
58	Gino Cimoli	1.00
59	Juan Pizarro	1.00
60	Gus Triandos	1.00
61	Eddie Kasko	1.00
62	Roger Craig	2.50
63	George Strickland	1.00
64	Jack Meyer	1.00
65	Elston Howard	4.00
66	Bob Trowbridge	1.00
67	Jose Pagan	1.00
68	Dave Hillman	1.00
69	Billy Goodman	1.00
70	Lou Burdette	3.00
71	Marty Keough	1.00
72	Detroit Tigers	4.00
73	Bob Gibson	27.00
74	Walt Moryn	1.00
75	Vic Power	1.00
76	Bill Fischer	1.00
77	Hank Foiles	1.00
78	Bob Grim	1.00
79	Walt Dropo	1.00
80	Johnny Antonelli	1.00
81	Russ Snyder	1.00
82	Ruben Gomez	1.00
83	Tony Kubek	5.00
84	Hal Smith	1.00
85	Frank Lary	1.00
86	Dick Gernert	1.00
87	John Romonosky	1.00
88	John Roseboro	1.00
89	Hal Brown	1.00
90	Bobby Avila	1.00
91	Bennie Daniels	1.00
92	Whitey Herzog	2.00
93	Art Schult	1.00
94	Leo Kiely	1.00
95	Frank Thomas	1.00
96	Ralph Terry	1.00
97	Ted Lepcio	1.00
98	Gordon Jones	1.00
99	Lenny Green	1.00
100	Nellie Fox	5.00
101	Bob Miller	1.00
102	Kent Hadley	1.00
103	Dick Farrell	1.00
104	Dick Schofield	1.00
105	Larry Sherry (R)	1.50
106	Billy Gardner	1.00
107	Carl Willey	1.00
108	Pete Daley	1.00
109	Cletis Boyer	1.25
110	Cal McLish	1.00
111	Vic Wertz	1.00
112	Jack Harshman	1.00
113	Bob Skinner	1.00
114	Ken Apromonte	1.00
115	Fork & Knuckler: Roy Face, Hoyt Wilhelm	4.00
116	Jim Rivera	1.00

No. 117 to 148—ROOKIE STARS

NO.	PLAYER	NR. MT.
117	Tom Borland	1.00
118	Bob Bruce	1.00
119	Chico Cardenas	1.00
120	Duke Carmel	1.00
121	Camilo Carreon	1.00
122	Don Dillard	1.00
123	Dan Dobbek	1.00
124	Jim Donohue	1.00
125	Dick Ellsworth	1.00
126	Chuck Estrada (R)	1.50
127	Ronnie Hansen	1.00
128	Bill Harris	1.00
129	Bob Hartman	1.00
130	Frank Herrera	1.00
131	Ed Hobaugh	1.00
132	Frank Howard (R)	10.00
133	Manuel Javier	1.00
134	Deron Johnson	1.00
135	Ken Johnson	1.00
136	Jim Kaat (R)	22.00
137	Lou Klimchock	1.00
138	Art Mahaffey	1.00
139	Carl Mathias	1.00
140	Julio Navarro	1.00
141	Jim Proctor	1.00
142	Bill Short	1.00
143	Al Spangler	1.00
144	Al Stieglitz	1.00
145	Jim Umbricht	1.00
146	Ted Wieand	1.00
147	Bob Will	1.00
148	Carl Yastrzemski (R)	300.00
149	Bob Nieman	1.00
150	Billy Pierce	1.50
151	San F. Giants	4.00
152	Gail Harris	1.00
153	Bobby Thomson	1.50
154	Jim Davenport	1.00
155	Charlie Neal	1.00
156	Art Ceccarelli	1.00
157	Rocky Nelson	1.00
158	Wes Covington	1.00
159	Jim Piersall	2.00
160	Rival All-Stars: Mickey Mantle, Ken Boyer	30.00
161	Ray Narleski	1.00
162	Sammy Taylor	1.00
163	Hector Lopez	1.00
164	Cincinnati Reds	4.00
165	Jack Sanford	1.00
166	Chuck Essegian	1.00
167	Valmy Thomas	1.00
168	Alex Grammas	1.00
169	Jake Striker	1.00
170	Del Crandall	1.00
171	Johnny Groth	1.00
172	Willie Kirkland	1.00
173	Billy Martin	5.00
174	Cleveland Indians	4.00
175	Pedro Ramos	1.00
176	Vada Pinson	3.00
177	Johnny Kucks	1.00
178	Woody Held	1.00
179	Rip Coleman	1.00
180	Harry Simpson	1.00
181	Billy Loes	1.00
182	Glen Hobbie	1.00
183	Eli Grba	1.00
184	Gary Geiger	1.00
185	Jim Owens	1.00
186	Dave Sisler	1.00
187	Jay Hook	1.00
188	Dick Williams	1.00
189	Don McMahon	1.00
190	Gene Woodling	1.00
191	Johnny Klippstein	1.00
192	Danny O'Connell	1.00
193	Dick Hyde	1.00
194	Bobby Gene Smith	1.00
195	Lindy McDaniel	1.00
196	Andy Carey	1.00
197	Ron Kline	1.00
198	Jerry Lynch	1.00
199	Dick Donovan	1.00
200	Willie Mays	75.00
201	Larry Osborne	1.00
202	Fred Kipp	1.00
203	Sammy White	1.00
204	Ryne Duren	1.00
205	Johnny Logan	1.00
206	Claude Osteen	1.00
207	Bob Boyd	1.00
208	Chicago White Sox	4.00
209	Ron Blackburn	1.00
210	Harmon Killebrew	20.00
211	Taylor Phillips	1.00
212	Walt Alston (Mgr.)	7.00
213	Chuck Dressen (Mgr.)	1.00
214	Jim Dykes (Mgr.)	1.00
215	Bob Elliott (Mgr.)	1.00
216	Joe Gordon (Mgr.)	1.00
217	Charley Grimm (Mgr.)	1.00
218	Solly Hemus (Mgr.)	1.00
219	Fred Hutchinson (Mgr.)	1.00
220	Billy Jurges (Mgr.)	1.00
221	Cookie Lavagetto (Mgr.)	1.00
222	Al Lopez (Mgr.)	5.00
223	Danny Murtaugh (Mgr.)	1.00
224	Paul Richards (Mgr.)	1.00
225	Bill Rigney (Mgr.)	1.00
226	Eddie Sawyer (Mgr.)	1.00
227	Casey Stengel (Mgr.)	14.00
228	Ernie Johnson	1.00
229	Joe Morgan	4.00
230	Mound Magicians: Lou Burdette, Warren Spahn, Bob Buhl	6.00
231	Hal Naragon	1.00
232	Jim Busby	1.00
233	Don Elston	1.00
234	Don Demeter	1.00
235	Gus Bell	1.00
236	Dick Ricketts	1.00
237	Elmer Valo	1.00
238	Danny Kravitz	1.00
239	Joe Shipley	1.00
240	Luis Aparicio	11.00
241	Albie Pearson	1.00
242	St. Louis Cardinals	4.00
243	Bubba Phillips	1.00
244	Hal Griggs	1.00
245	Eddie Yost	1.00
246	Lee Maye	1.00
247	Gil McDougald	4.00
248	Del Rice	1.00
249	Earl Wilson	1.00
250	Stan Musial	70.00
251	Bobby Malkmus	1.00
252	Ray Herbert	1.00
253	Eddie Bressoud	1.00
254	Arnie Portocarrero	1.00
255	Jim Gilliam	3.00
256	Dick Brown	1.00
257	Gordy Coleman	1.00
258	Dick Groat	4.00
259	George Altman	1.00
260	Power Plus: Rocky Colavito, Tito Francona	1.50
261	Pete Burnside	1.00
262	Hank Bauer	1.00
263	Darrell Johnson	1.00
264	Robin Roberts	10.00
265	Rip Repulski	1.00
266	Joe Jay	1.00
267	Jim Marshall	1.00
268	Al Worthington	1.00
269	Gene Green	1.00
270	Bob Turley	2.00
271	Julio Bequer	1.00
272	Fred Green	1.00
273	Neil Chrisley	1.00
274	Tom Acker	1.00
275	Curt Flood	3.00
276	Ken McBride	1.00
277	Harry Bright	1.00
278	Stan Williams	1.00
279	Chuck Tanner	1.00
280	Frank Sullivan	1.00
281	Ray Boone	1.00
282	Joe Nuxhall	1.00
283	John Blanchard	1.00
284	Don Gross	1.00
285	Harry Anderson	1.00
286	Ray Semproch	1.00
287	Felipe Alou	2.00
288	Bob Mabe	1.50
289	Willie Jones	1.50
290	Jerry Lumpe	1.50
291	Bob Keegan	1.50
292	Dodger Backstops: Joe Pignatano, John Roseboro	2.00
293	Gene Conley	1.50
294	Tony Taylor	1.50
295	Gil Hodges	12.00
296	Nelson Chittum	1.50
297	Reno Bertoia	1.50
298	George Witt	1.50
299	Earl Torgeson	1.50
300	Hank Aaron	75.00
301	Jerry Davie	1.50
302	Philadelphia Phillies	4.00
303	Billy O'Dell	1.50
304	Joe Ginsberg	1.50
305	Richie Ashburn	6.00
306	Frank Baumann	1.50
307	Gene Oliver	1.50
308	Dick Hall	1.50
309	Bob Hale	1.50
310	Frank Malzone	1.50
311	Raul Sanchez	1.50
312	Charlie Lau	1.50
313	Turk Lown	1.50
314	Chico Fernandez	1.50
315	Bobby Shantz	2.50

NO. PLAYER	NR. MT.
316 Willie McCovey (R)	125.00
317 Pumpsie Green	1.50
318 Jim Baxes	1.50
319 Joe Koppe	1.50
320 Bob Allison	1.50
321 Ron Fairly	1.50
322 Willie Tasby	1.50
323 Johnny Romano	1.50
324 Jim Perry	2.50
325 Jim O'Toole	1.50
326 Bob Clemente	85.00
327 Ray Sadecki	1.50
328 Earl Battey	1.50
329 Zack Monroe	1.50
330 Harvey Kuenn	3.00
331 Henry Mason	1.50
332 New York Yankees	17.00
333 Danny McDevitt	1.50
334 Ted Abernathy	1.50
335 Red Schoendienst	8.00
336 Ike Delock	1.50
337 Cal Neeman	1.50
338 Ray Monzant	1.50
339 Harry Chiti	1.50
340 Harvey Haddix	3.00
341 Carroll Hardy	1.50
342 Casey Wise	1.50
343 Sandy Koufax	75.00
344 Clint Courtney	1.50
345 Don Newcombe	1.75
346 J.C. Martin	1.50
(photo of Gary Peters)	
347 Ed Bouchee	1.50
348 Barry Shetrone	1.50
349 Moe Drabowsky	1.50
350 Mickey Mantle	350.00
351 Don Nottebart	1.50
352 Cincy Clouters:	4.00
Gus Bell, Frank	
Robinson, Jerry Lynch	
353 Don Larsen	2.00
354 Bob Lillis	1.50
355 Bill White	4.00
356 Joe Amalfitano	1.50
357 Al Schroll	1.50
358 Joe DeMaestri	1.50
359 Buddy Gilbert	1.50
360 Herb Score	2.00
361 Bob Oldis	1.50
362 Russ Kemmerer	1.50
363 Gene Stephens	1.50
364 Paul Foytack	1.50
365 Minnie Minoso	4.00
366 Dallas Green (R)	6.00
367 Bill Tuttle	1.50
368 Daryl Spencer	1.50
369 Billy Hoeft	1.50
370 Bill Skowron	5.00
371 Bud Byerly	1.50
372 Frank House	1.50
373 Don Hoak	1.50
374 Bob Buhl	1.50
375 Dale Long	1.50
376 Johnny Briggs	1.50
377 Roger Maris	90.00
378 Stu Miller	1.50
379 Red Wilson	1.50
380 Bob Shaw	1.50
381 Milwakee Braves	4.00
382 Ted Bowsfield	1.50
383 Leon Wagner	1.50
384 Don Cardwell	1.50
385 World Series Game 1	4.00
Neal Steals Second	

NO. PLAYER	NR. MT.
386 World Series Game 2	4.00
Neal Belts 2nd Homer	
387 World Series Game 3	4.00
Furillo Breaks Up Game	
388 World Series Game 4	4.00
Hodges' Winning Homer	
389 World Series Game 5	4.00
Luis Swipes Base	
390 World Series Game 6	4.00
Scrambling After Ball	
391 World Series	4.00
The Champs Celebrate	
392 Tex Clevenger	1.50
393 Smokey Burgess	1.75
394 Norm Larker	1.50
395 Hoyt Wilhelm	10.00
396 Steve Bilko	1.50
397 Don Blasingame	1.50
398 Mike Cuellar	1.50
399 Young Hill Stars:	1.50
Milt Pappas, Jack Fisher,	
Jerry Walker	
400 Rocky Colavito	3.50
401 Bob Duliba	1.50
402 Dick Stuart	1.50
403 Ed Sadowski	1.50
404 Bob Rush	1.50
405 Bobby Richardson	5.00
406 Billy Klaus	1.50
407 Gary Peters	1.50
(photo of J.C. Martin)	
408 Carl Furillo	3.00
409 Ron Samford	1.50
410 Sam Jones	1.50
411 Ed Bailey	1.50
412 Bob Anderson	1.50
413 Kansas C. Athletics	4.00
414 Don Williams	1.50
415 Bob Cerv	1.50
416 Humberto Robinson	1.50
417 Chuck Cottier (R)	1.75
418 Don Mossi	1.50
419 George Crowe	1.50
420 Ed Mathews	18.00
421 Duke Maas	1.50
422 Johnny Powers	1.50
423 Ed Fitzgerald	1.50
424 Pete Whisenant	1.50
425 Johnny Podres	2.50
426 Ron Jackson	1.50
427 Al Grunwald	1.50
428 Al Smith	1.50
429 Amer. League Kings:	3.00
Nellie Fox, Harvey Kuenn	
430 Art Ditmar	1.50
431 Andre Rodgers	1.50
432 Chuck Stobbs	1.50
433 Irv Noren	1.50
434 Brooks Lawrence	1.50
435 Gene Freese	1.50
436 Marv Throneberry	3.00
437 Bob Friend	1.50
438 Jim Coker	1.50
439 Tom Brewer	1.50
440 Jim Lemon	1.50
441 Gary Bell	2.50
442 Joe Pignatano	2.50
443 Charlie Maxwell	2.50
444 Jerry Kindall	2.50
445 Warren Spahn	24.00
446 Ellis Burton	2.50
447 Ray Moore	2.50
448 Jim Gentile	3.00

NO. PLAYER	NR. MT.
449 Jim Brosnan	2.50
450 Orlando Cepeda	6.00
451 Curt Simmons	3.00
452 Ray Webster	3.00
453 Vern Law	4.00
454 Hal Woodeschick	2.50
455 Orioles Coaches:	4.00
Robinson, Brecheen, Harris	
456 Red Sox Coaches:	4.00
York, Herman, Maglie, Baker	
457 Cubs Coaches:	4.00
Klein, Tappe, Root	
458 White Sox Coaches:	4.00
Cooney, Gutteridge,	
Cuccinello, Berres	
459 Reds Coaches:	4.00
Deal, Moses, Otero	
460 Indians Coaches:	4.00
White, Lemon, Harder, Kress	
461 Tigers Coaches:	4.00
Ferrick, Appling, Hitchcock	
462 Athletics Coaches:	4.00
Cooper, Fitzsimmons,	
Heffner	
463 Dodgers Coaches:	4.00
Bragan, Reiser,	
Becker, Mulleavy	
464 Braves Coaches:	4.00
Scheffing, Myatt,	
Wyatt, Pafko	
465 Yankees Coaches:	8.00
Dickey, Houk,	
Lopat, Crosetti	
466 Phillies Coaches:	4.00
Silvestri, Cohen, Carter	
467 Pirates Coaches:	4.00
Vernon, Oceak,	
Narron, Burwell	
468 Cardinals Coaches:	4.00
Keane, Pollet,	
Katt, Walker	
469 Giants Coaches:	4.00
Westrum, Parker, Posedel	
470 Senators Coaches:	4.00
Swift, Mele, Clary	
471 Ned Garver	2.50
472 Al Dark	3.00
473 Al Cicotte	2.50
474 Haywood Sullivan	2.50
475 Don Drysdale	22.00
476 Lou Johnson	2.50
477 Don Ferrarese	2.50
478 Frank Torre	2.50
479 Georges Maranda	2.50
480 Yogi Berra	50.00
481 Wes Stock	3.00
482 Frank Bolling	2.50
483 Camilo Pascual	2.50
484 Pittsburgh Pirates	11.00
485 Ken Boyer	5.00
486 Bobby Del Greco	2.50
487 Tom Sturdivant	2.50
488 Norm Cash	4.00
489 Steve Ridzik	2.50
490 Frank Robinson	30.00
491 Mel Roach	2.50
492 Larry Jackson	2.50
493 Duke Snider	35.00
494 Baltimore Orioles	7.00
495 Sherm Lollar	2.50
496 Bill Virdon	3.50
497 John Tsitouris	2.50
498 Al Pilarcik	2.50

NO. PLAYER	NR. MT.
499 Johnny James	2.50
500 Johnny Temple	2.50
501 Bob Schmidt	2.50
502 Jim Bunning	7.00
503 Don Lee	2.50
504 Seth Morehead	2.50
505 Ted Kluszewski	5.00
506 Lee Walls	2.50
507 Dick Stigman	7.00
508 Billy Consolo	7.00
509 Tommy Davis (R)	12.00
510 Jerry Staley	7.00
511 Ken Walters	7.00
512 Joe Gibbon	7.00
513 Chicago Cubs	18.00
514 Steve Barber	7.00
515 Stan Lopata	7.00
516 Marty Kutyna	7.00
517 Charley James	7.00
518 Tony Gonzalez	7.00
519 Ed Roebuck	7.00
520 Don Buddin	7.00
521 Mike Lee	7.00
522 Ken Hunt	7.00
523 Clay Dalrymple	7.00
524 Bill Henry	7.00
525 Marv Breeding	7.00
526 Paul Giel	7.00
527 Jose Valdivielso	7.00
528 Ben Johnson	7.00
529 Norm Sherry (R)	7.00
530 Mike McCormick	7.00
531 Sandy Amoros	7.00
532 Mike Garcia	7.00
533 L. Clinton	7.00
534 Ken Mackenzie	7.00
535 Whitey Lockman	7.00
536 Wynn Hawkins	7.00
537 Boston Red Sox	20.00
538 Frank Barnes	7.00
539 Gene Baker	7.00
540 Jerry Walker	7.00
541 Tony Curry	7.00
542 Ken Hamlin	7.00
543 Elio Chacon	7.00
544 Bill Monbouquette	7.00
545 Carl Sawatski	7.00
546 Hank Aguirre	7.00
547 Bob Aspromonte	7.00
548 Don Mincher	7.00
549 John Buzhardt	7.00
550 Jim Landis	7.00
551 Ed Rakow	7.00
552 Walt Bond	7.00
553 Bill Skowron (AS)	8.00
554 Willie McCovey (AS)	35.00
555 Nellie Fox (AS)	11.00
556 Charlie Neal (AS)	8.00
557 Frank Malzone (AS)	8.00
558 Eddie Mathews (AS)	20.00
559 Luis Aparicio (AS)	15.00
560 Ernie Banks (AS)	27.00
561 Al Kaline (AS)	25.00
562 Joe Cunningham (AS)	8.00
563 Mickey Mantle (AS)	200.00
564 Willie Mays (AS)	70.00
565 Roger Maris (AS)	50.00
566 Hank Aaron (AS)	65.00
567 Sherm Lollar (AS)	8.00
568 Del Crandall (AS)	8.00
569 Camilo Pascual (AS)	8.00
570 Don Drysdale (AS)	18.00
571 Billy Pierce (AS)	8.00
572 J. Antonelli (AS)	15.00
(Exc. $5.00)	

1961 Topps. . . . Complete Set of 587 Cards—Value $1600.00 (Exc.); $4250.00 (Mint)

Juan Marichal and Billy Williams' rookie cards are in this set. The high numbers are 523 to 589. Cards 587 and 588 were not issued. Card 426 (Braves team) was mistakenly numbered 463.

NO. PLAYER	NR. MT.
1 Dick Groat (Exc. $2.00) . . .	15.00
2 Roger Maris	90.00
3 John Buzhardt	1.00
4 Lenny Green	1.00
5 Johnny Romano	1.00
6 Ed Roebuck	1.00
7 Chicago White Sox	3.00
8 Dick Williams	1.00
9 Bob Purkey	1.00
10 Brooks Robinson	.25.00
11 Curt Simmons	1.50
12 Moe Thacker	1.00
13 Chuck Cottier	1.00
14 Don Mossi	1.00
15 Willie Kirkland	1.00
16 Billy Muffett	1.00
17 Checklist No. 1	4.00
18 Jim Grant	1.00
19 Cletis Boyer	3.00
20 Robin Roberts	11.00
21 Zorro Versalles	1.50
22 Clem Labine	1.25
23 Don Demeter	1.00
24 Ken Johnson	1.00
25 Reds' Heavy Artillery:	5.00
Vada Pinson, Gus Bell,	
Frank Robinson	
26 Wes Stock	1.00
27 Jerry Kindall	1.00
28 Hector Lopez	1.00
29 Don Nottebart	1.00
30 Nellie Fox	5.00
31 Bob Schmidt	1.00
32 Ray Sadecki	1.00
33 Gary Geiger	1.00
34 Wynn Hawkins	1.00
35 Ron Santo (R)	10.00
36 Jack Kralick	1.00
37 Charlie Maxwell	1.00
38 Bob Lillis	1.00
39 Leo Posada	1.00
40 Bob Turley	1.50
41 NL Batting Leaders:	3.00
Willie Mays, Dick Gorat,	
Norm Larker,	
Roberto Clemente	
42 AL Batting Leaders:	2.00
Pete Runnels,	
Minnie Minoso, Al Smith,	
Bill Skowron	
43 NL Home Run Leaders:	3.00
Ernie Banks, Ed Mathews,	
Hank Aaron, Ken Boyer	
44 AL Home Run Leaders:	13.00
Mickey Mantle, Roger Maris,	
Jim Lemon, Rocky Colavito	
45 NL ERA Leaders:	3.00
Mike McCormick, Ernie	
Broglio, Don Drysdale,	
Bob Friend, Stan Williams	
46 AL ERA Leaders:	3.00
Frank Baumann, Jim	
Bunning, Art Ditmar,	
Hal Brown	
47 NL Pitching Leaders:	3.00
E. Broglio, W. Spahn,	
Vern Law, Lou Burdette	

NO. PLAYER	NR. MT.
48 AL Pitching Leaders:	2.50
Chuck Estrada, Jim Perry,	
Bud Daley, Art Ditmar,	
Frank Lary, Milt Pappas	
49 NL Strikeout Leaders:	4.00
Don Drysdale, Sandy	
Koufax, Sam Jones,	
Ernie Broglio	
50 AL Strikeout Leaders:	2.50
Jim Bunning, Pedro Ramos,	
Early Wynn, Frank Lary	
51 Detroit Tigers	4.00
52 George Crowe	1.00
53 Russ Nixon	1.00
54 Earl Francis	1.00
55 Jim Davenport	1.00
56 Russ Kemmerer	1.00
57 Marv Throneberry	2.00
58 Joe Schaffernoth	1.00
59 Jim Woods	1.00
60 Woodie Held	1.00
61 Ron Piche	1.00
62 Al Pilarcik	1.00
63 Jim Kaat	7.00
64 Alex Grammas	.90
65 Ted Kluszewski	4.00
66 Bill Henry	1.00
67 Ossie Virgil	1.00
68 Deron Johnson	1.50
69 Earl Wilson	1.00
70 Bill Virdon	2.00
71 Jerry Adair	1.00
72 Stu Miller	1.00
73 Al Spangler	1.00
74 Joe Pignatano	1.00
75 Lindy Shows Larry:	2.00
Lindy McDaniel,	
Larry Jackson	
76 Harry Anderson	1.00
77 Dick Stigman	1.00
78 Lee Walls	1.00
79 Joe Ginsberg	1.00
80 Harmon Killebrew	20.00
81 Tracy Stallard	1.00
82 Joe Christopher	1.00
83 Bob Bruce	1.00
84 Lee Maye	1.00
85 Jerry Walker	1.00
86 Los Angeles Dodgers	4.00
87 Joe Amalfitano	1.00
88 Richie Ashburn	5.00
89 Billy Martin	5.00
90 Jerry Staley	1.00
91 Walt Moryn	1.00
92 Hal Naragon	1.00
93 Tony Gonzalez	1.00
94 John Kucks	1.00
95 Norm Cash	3.00
96 Bill O'Dell	1.00
97 Jerry Lynch	1.00
98 Checklist No. 2	4.00
99 Don Buddin	1.00
100 Harvey Haddix	3.00
101 Bubba Phillips	1.00
102 Gene Stephens	1.00
103 Ruben Amaro	1.00
104 John Blanchard	1.50

NO. PLAYER	NR. MT.
105 Carl Willey	1.00
106 Whitey Herzog	3.00
107 Seth Morehead	1.00
108 Dan Dobbek	1.00
109 Johnny Podres	3.00
110 Vada Pinson	3.00
111 Jack Meyer	1.00
112 Chico Fernandez	1.00
113 Mike Fornieles	1.00
114 Hobie Landrith	1.00
115 Johnny Antonelli	1.50
116 Joe DeMaestri	1.00
117 Dale Long	1.00
118 Chris Cannizzaro	1.00
119 A's Big Armor:	2.00
Norm Siebern, Hank Bauer,	
Jerry Lumpe	
120 Ed Mathews	15.00
121 Eli Grba	1.00
122 Chicago Cubs	3.00
123 Billy Gardner	1.00
124 J.C. Martin	1.00
125 Steve Barber	1.00
126 Dick Stuart	1.00
127 Ron Kline	1.00
128 Rip Repulski	1.00
129 Ed Hobaugh	1.00
130 Norm Larker	1.00
131 Paul Richards (Mgr.)	1.50
132 Al Lopez (Mgr.)	4.00
133 Ralph Houk (Mgr.)	3.00
134 Mickey Vernon (Mgr.)	1.50
135 Fred Hutchinson (Mgr.)	1.25
136 Walt Alston (Mgr.)	4.00
137 Chuck Dressen (Mgr.)	1.00
138 Danny Murtaugh (Mgr.)	1.00
139 Solly Hemus (Mgr.)	1.00
140 Gus Triandos	1.00
141 Billy Williams (R)	70.00
142 Luis Arroyo	1.00
143 Russ Snyder	1.00
144 Jim Coker	1.00
145 Bob Buhl	1.00
146 Marty Keough	1.00
147 Ed Rakow	1.00
148 Julian Javier	1.00
149 Bob Oldis	1.00
150 Willie Mays	65.00
151 Jim Donohue	1.00
152 Earl Torgeson	1.00
153 Don Lee	1.00
154 Bobby Del Greco	1.00
155 Johnny Temple	1.00
156 Ken Hunt	1.00
157 Cal McLish	1.00
158 Pete Daley	1.00
159 Baltimore Orioles	3.00
160 Whitey Ford	22.00
161 Sherman Jones	1.00
162 Jay Hook	1.00
163 Ed Sadowski	1.00
164 Felix Mantilla	1.00
165 Gino Cimoli	1.00
166 Danny Kravitz	1.00
167 San F. Giants	3.00
168 Tommy Davis	2.50
169 Don Elston	1.00

NO. PLAYER	NR. MT.
170 Al Smith	1.00
171 Paul Foytack	1.00
172 Don Dillard	1.00
173 Beantown Bombers:	1.50
Frank Malzone, Vic Wertz,	
Jackie Jensen	
174 Ray Semproch	1.00
175 Gene Freese	1.00
176 Ken Aspromonte	1.00
177 Don Larsen	1.50
178 Bob Nieman	1.00
179 Joe Koppe	1.00
180 Bobby Richardson	4.00
181 Fred Green	1.00
182 Dave Nicholson	1.00
183 Andre Rodgers	1.00
184 Steve Bilko	1.00
185 Herb Score	1.50
186 Elmer Valo	1.00
187 Billy Klaus	1.00
188 Jim Marshall	1.00
189 Checklist No. 3	4.00
190 Stan Williams	1.00
191 Mike De La Hoz	1.00
192 Dick Brown	1.00
193 Gene Conley	1.00
194 Gordy Coleman	1.00
195 Jerry Casale	1.00
196 Ed Bouchee	1.00
197 Dick Hall	1.00
198 Carl Sawatski	1.00
199 Bob Boyd	1.00
200 Warren Spahn	18.00
201 Pete Whisenant	1.00
202 Al Neiger	1.00
203 Eddie Bressoud	1.00
204 Bob Skinner	1.00
205 Bill Pierce	1.50
206 Gene Green	1.00
207 Dodger Southpaws:	11.00
Sandy Koufax, J. Podres	
208 Larry Osborne	1.00
209 Ken McBride	1.00
210 Pete Runnels	1.00
211 Bob Gibson	18.00
212 Haywood Sullivan	1.00
213 Bill Stafford	1.00
214 Danny Murphy	1.00
215 Gus Bell	1.00
216 Ted Bowsfield	1.00
217 Mel Roach	1.00
218 Hal Brown	1.00
219 Gene Mauch (Mgr.)	1.50
220 Al Dark (Mgr.)	1.25
221 Mike Higgins (Mgr.)	1.25
222 Jimmie Dykes (Mgr.)	1.25
223 Bob Scheffing (Mgr.)	1.25
224 Joe Gordon (Mgr.)	1.25
225 Bill Rigney (Mgr.)	1.25
226 Harry Lavagetto (Mgr.)	1.25
227 Juan Pizarro	1.00
228 New York Yankees	15.00
229 Rudy Hernandez	1.00
230 Don Hoak	1.00
231 Dick Drott	1.00
232 Bill White	3.00
233 Joe Jay	1.00

NO. PLAYER	NR. MT.
234 Ted Lepcio	1.00
235 Camilo Pascual	1.00
236 Don Gile	1.00
237 Billy Loes	1.00
238 Jim Gilliam	3.00
239 Dave Sisler	1.00
240 Ron Hansen	1.00
241 Al Cicotte	1.00
242 Hal Smith	1.00
243 Frank Lary	1.00
244 Chico Cardenas	1.00
245 Joe Adcock	1.25
246 Bob Davis	1.00
247 Billy Goodman	1.00
248 Ed Keegan	1.00
249 Cincinnati Reds	3.00
250 Buc Hill Aces:	1.50
Vern Law, Roy Face	
251 Bill Bruton	1.00
252 Bill Short	1.00
253 Sammy Taylor	1.00
254 Ted Sadowski	1.00
255 Vic Power	1.00
256 Billy Hoeft	1.00
257 Carroll Hardy	1.00
258 Jack Sanford	1.00
259 John Schaive	1.00
260 Don Drysdale	16.00
261 Charlie Lau	1.00
262 Tony Curry	1.00
263 Ken Hamlin	1.00
264 Glen Hobbie	1.00
265 Tony Kubek	5.00
266 Lindy McDaniel	1.00
267 Norm Siebern	1.00
268 Ike Delock	1.00
269 Harry Chiti	1.00
270 Bob Friend	1.00
271 Jim Landis	1.00
272 Tom Morgan	1.00
273 Checklist No. 4	4.00
274 Gary Bell	1.00
275 Gene Woodling	1.00
276 Ray Rippelmeyer	1.00
277 Hank Foiles	1.00
278 Don McMahon	1.00
279 Jose Pagan	1.00
280 Frank Howard	3.00
281 Frank Sullivan	1.00
282 Faye Throneberry	1.00
283 Bob Anderson	1.00
284 Dick Gernert	1.00
285 Sherm Lollar	1.00
286 George Witt	1.00
287 Carl Yastrzemski	125.00
288 Albie Pearson	1.00
289 Ray Moore	1.00
290 Stan Musial	75.00
291 Tex Clevenger	1.00
292 Jim Baumer	1.00
293 Tom Sturdivant	1.00
294 Don Blasingame	1.00
295 Milt Pappas	1.00
296 Wes Covington	1.00
297 Kansas C. Athletics	3.00
298 Jim Golden	1.00
299 Clay Dalrymple	1.00
300 Mickey Mantle	325.00
301 Chet Nichols	1.00
302 Al Heist	1.00
303 Gary Peters	1.00
304 Rocky Nelson	1.00
305 Mike McCormick	1.00
306 World Series Game 1	4.00
Virdon Saves Game	
307 World Series Game 2	22.00
Mantle Slams 2 Homers	
308 World Series Game 3	4.00
Richardson is Hero	
309 World Series Game 4	4.00
Cimoli Safe	

NO. PLAYER	NR. MT.
310 World Series Game 5	4.00
Face Saves the Day	
311 World Series Game 6	4.00
Ford Shutout	
312 World Series Game 7	4.00
Mazeroski's Homer	
313 W.S. Celebration	3.00
314 Bob Miller	1.00
315 Earl Battey	1.00
316 Bobby Gene Smith	1.00
317 Jim Brewer	1.00
318 Danny O'Connell	1.00
319 Valmy Thomas	1.00
320 Lou Burdette	3.00
321 Marv Breeding	1.00
322 Bill Kunkel	1.00
323 Sammy Esposito	1.00
324 Hank Aguirre	1.00
325 Wally Moon	1.00
326 Dave Hillman	1.00
327 Matty Alou (R)	4.00
328 Jim O'Toole	1.00
329 Julio Becquer	1.00
330 Rocky Colavito	3.00
331 Ned Garver	1.00
332 Dutch Dotterer	1.00
(photo of Tommy Dotterer)	
333 Fritz Brickell	1.00
334 Walt Bond	1.00
335 Frank Bolling	1.00
336 Don Mincher	1.00
337 Al's Aces:	3.00
Herb Score, Early Wynn,	
Al Lopez	
338 Don Landrum	1.00
339 Gene Baker	1.00
340 Vic Wertz	1.00
341 Jim Owens	1.00
342 Clint Courtney	1.00
343 Earl Robinson	1.00
344 Sandy Koufax	65.00
345 Jim Piersall	1.50
346 Howie Nunn	1.00
347 St. Louis Cardinals	3.00
348 Steve Boros	1.00
349 Danny McDevitt	1.00
350 Ernie Banks	24.00
351 Jim King	1.00
352 Bob Shaw	1.00
353 Howie Bedell	1.00
354 Billy Harrell	1.00
355 Bob Allison	1.00
356 Ryne Duren	1.50
357 Daryl Spencer	1.00
358 Earl Averill	1.00
359 Dallas Green	3.00
360 Frank Robinson	27.00
361 Checklist No. 5	6.00
362 Frank Funk	1.00
363 John Roseboro	1.00
364 Moe Drabowsky	1.00
365 Jerry Lumpe	1.00
366 Eddie Fisher	1.00
367 Jim Rivera	1.00
368 Bennie Daniels	1.00
369 Dave Philley	1.00
370 Roy Face	1.50
371 Bill Skowron	9.00
372 Bob Hendley	1.50
373 Boston Red Sox	3.00
374 Paul Giel	1.50
375 Ken Boyer	4.00
376 Mike Roarke	1.50
377 Ruben Gomez	1.50
378 Wally Post	1.50
379 Bobby Shantz	2.00
380 Minnie Minoso	4.00
381 Dave Wickersham	1.50
382 Frank Thomas	1.50
383 Frisco First Liners:	1.50
Mike McCormick, Jack	
Sanford, Billy O'Dell	

NO. PLAYER	NR. MT.
384 Chuck Essegian	1.50
385 Jim Perry	2.00
386 Joe Hicks	1.50
387 Duke Maas	1.50
388 Bob Clemente	65.00
389 Ralph Terry	2.00
390 Del Crandall	2.00
391 Winston Brown	1.50
392 Reno Bertoia	1.50
393 Batter Bafflers:	1.50
Don Cardwell, Glen Hobbie	
394 Ken Walters	1.50
395 Chuck Estrada	1.50
396 Bob Aspromonte	1.50
397 Hal Woodeschick	1.50
398 Hank Bauer	2.00
399 Cliff Cook	1.50
400 Vern Law	2.00
401 Ruth 60th Homer	15.00
402 Larsen—Perfect Game	7.00
403 26 Inning Tie	3.00
404 Honsby .424 Average	4.00
405 Gehrig—2,130 Games	9.00
406 Mantle 565 Ft. HR	25.00
407 Chesbro Wins 41	2.50
408 Mathewson 267 SO's	3.00
409 Johnson Shutouts	3.00
410 Haddix Perfect Game	2.00
411 Tony Taylor	1.50
412 Larry Sherry	1.50
413 Eddie Yost	1.50
414 Dick Donovan	1.50
415 Hank Aaron	80.00
416 Dick Howser (R)	7.00
417 Juan Marichal (R)	90.00
418 Ed Bailey	1.50
419 Tom Borland	1.50
420 Ernie Broglio	1.50
421 Ty Cline	1.50
422 Bud Daley	1.50
423 Charlie Neal	1.50
424 Turk Lown	1.50
425 Yogi Berra	50.00
426 Milwaukee Braves	6.00
(error—numbered 463)	
427 Dick Ellsworth	1.50
428 Ray Barker	1.50
429 Al Kaline	27.00
430 Bill Mazeroski	7.00
431 Chuck Stobbs	1.50
432 Coot Veal	1.50
433 Art Mahaffey	1.50
434 Tom Brewer	1.50
435 Orlando Cepeda	6.00
436 Jim Maloney (R)	5.00
437 Checklist No. 6	4.00
438 Curt Flood	3.00
439 Phil Regan	1.50
440 Luis Aparicio	10.00
441 Dick Bertell	1.50
442 Gordon Jones	1.50
443 Duke Snider	30.00
444 Joe Nuxhall	1.50
445 Frank Malzone	1.50
446 Bob Taylor	1.50
447 Harry Bright	1.75
448 Del Rice	1.75
449 Bobby Bolin	1.75
450 Jim Lemon	1.75
451 Power for Ernie:	1.75
Daryl Spencer, Bill White,	
Ernie Broglio	
452 Bob Allen	1.75
453 Dick Schofield	1.75
454 Pumpsie Green	1.75
455 Early Wynn	10.00
456 Hal Bevan	1.75
457 Johnny James	1.75
458 Willie Tasby	1.75
459 Terry Fox	1.75
460 Gil Hodges	10.00
461 Smoky Burgess	1.75

NO. PLAYER	NR. MT.
462 Lou Klimchock	1.75
463 Jack Fisher (see #426)	1.75
464 Leroy Thomas	1.75
465 Roy McMillan	1.75
466 Ron Moeller	1.75
467 Cleveland Indians	3.00
468 John Callison	1.75
469 Ralph Lumenti	1.75
470 Roy Sievers	1.75
471 Phil Rizzuto (MVP)	10.00
472 Yogi Berra (MVP)	25.00
473 Bobby Shantz (MVP)	2.00
474 Al Rosen (MVP)	2.00
475 Mickey Mantle (MVP)	80.00
476 Jackie Jensen (MVP)	2.00
477 Nellie Fox (MVP)	2.00
478 Roger Maris (MVP)	30.00
479 Jim Konstanty (MVP)	2.00
480 R. Campanella (MVP)	20.00
481 Hank Sauer (MVP)	2.00
482 Willie Mays (MVP)	25.00
483 Don Newcombe (MVP)	2.00
484 Hank Aaron (MVP)	28.00
485 Ernie Banks (MVP)	15.00
486 Dick Groat (MVP)	2.00
487 Gene Oliver	1.75
488 Joe McClain	1.75
489 Walt Dropo	1.75
490 Jim Bunning	7.00
491 Philadelphia Phillies	3.00
492 Ron Fairly	1.75
493 Don Zimmer	3.00
494 Tom Cheney	1.75
495 Elston Howard	5.00
496 Ken MacKenzie	1.75
497 Willie Jones	1.75
498 Ray Herbert	1.75
499 Chuck Schilling	1.75
500 Harvey Kuenn	3.00
501 John DeMerit	1.75
502 Clarence Coleman	1.75
503 Tito Francona	1.75
504 Billy Consolo	1.75
505 Red Schoendienst	8.00
506 Willie Davis (R)	6.00
507 Pete Burnside	1.75
508 Rocky Bridges	1.75
509 Camilo Carreon	1.75
510 Art Ditmar	1.75
511 Joe Morgan	3.00
512 Bob Will	1.75
513 Jim Brosnan	1.75
514 Jake Wood	1.75
515 Jackie Brandt	1.75
516 Checklist No. 7	4.00
517 Willie McCovey	45.00
518 Andy Carey	1.75
519 Jim Pagliaroni	1.75
520 Joe Cunningham	1.75
521 Brother Battery:	1.75
Norm Sherry, Larry Sherry	
522 Dick Farrell	1.75
523 Joe Gibbon	20.00
524 Johnny Logan	20.00
525 Ron Perranoski	20.00
526 R.C. Stevens	20.00
527 Gene Leek	20.00
528 Pedro Ramos	20.00
529 Bob Roselli	20.00
530 Bobby Malkmus	20.00
531 Jim Coates	20.00
532 Bob Hale	20.00
533 Jack Curtis	20.00
534 Eddie Kasko	20.00
535 Larry Jackson	20.00
536 Bill Tuttle	20.00
537 Bobby Locke	20.00
538 Chuck Hiller	20.00
539 John Klippstein	20.00
540 Jackie Jensen	25.00
541 Roland Sheldon	20.00
542 Minnesota Twins	35.00

NO. PLAYER	NR. MT.	NO. PLAYER	NR. MT.	NO. PLAYER	NR. MT.	NO. PLAYER	NR. MT.
543 Roger Craig	25.00	555 Sam Jones	20.00	566 P. Richards—Mgr. (AS)	20.00	577 Hank Aaron (AS)	150.00
544 George Thomas	20.00	556 Ken R. Hunt	20.00	567 D. Murtaugh—Mgr. (AS)	20.00	578 Mickey Mantle (AS)	350.00
545 Hoyt Wilhelm	50.00	557 Jose Valdivielso	20.00	568 Bill Skowron (AS)	20.00	579 Willie Mays (AS)	120.00
546 Marty Kutyna	20.00	558 Don Ferrarese	20.00	569 Frank Herrera (AS)	20.00	580 Al Kaline (AS)	70.00
547 Leon Wagner	20.00	559 Jim Gentile	20.00	570 Nellie Fox (AS)	30.00	581 Frank Robinson (AS)	75.00
548 Ted Wills	20.00	560 Barry Latman	20.00	571 Bill Mazeroski (AS)	20.00	582 Earl Battey (AS)	20.00
549 Hal R. Smith	20.00	561 Charley James	20.00	572 Brooks Robinson	70.00	583 Del Crandall (AS)	20.00
550 Frank Baumann	20.00	562 Bill Monbouquette	20.00	573 Ken Boyer (AS)	20.00	584 Jim Perry (AS)	20.00
551 George Altman	20.00	563 Bob Cerv	20.00	574 Luis Aparicio (AS)	35.00	585 Bob Friend (AS)	20.00
552 Jim Archer	20.00	564 Don Cardwell	20.00	575 Ernie Banks (AS)	70.00	586 Whitey Ford (AS)	70.00
553 Bill Fischer	20.00	565 Felipe Alou	20.00	576 Roger Maris (AS)	90.00	589 W. Spahn (AS) (Exc. $35.00)	120.00
554 Pittsburgh Pirates	35.00						

1962 Topps. . . . Complete Set of 598 Cards—Value $1250.00 (Exc.); $3750.00 (Mint)

The rookie cards of Lou Brock, Gaylord Perry and Bob Uecker are in this set. The high numbers are 523 to 598. Nine cards were reprinted with different photos. These are worth a premium. The value of the complete set does not include the *variety* cards.

NO. PLAYER	NR. MT.	NO. PLAYER	NR. MT.	NO. PLAYER	NR. MT.	NO. PLAYER	NR. MT.
1 Roger Maris (Exc. $20.00)	150.00	42 Jim King	.90	62 Steve Boros	.90	104 Ted Savage	.90
2 Jim Brosnan	.90	43 Los Angeles Dodgers	3.00	63 Tony Cloninger	.90	105 Don Mossi	.90
3 Pete Runnels	.90	44 Don Taussig	.90	64 Russ Snyder	.90	106 Carl Sawatski	.90
4 John DeMerit	.90	45 Brooks Robinson	20.00	65 Bobby Richardson	4.00	107 Mike McCormick	.90
5 Sandy Koufax	65.00	46 Jack Baldschun	.90	66 Cuno Barragan	.90	108 Willie Davis	.90
6 Marv Breeding	.90	47 Bob Will	.90	67 Harvey Haddix	.90	109 Bob Shaw	.90
7 Frank Thomas	.90	48 Ralph Terry	.90	68 Ken Hunt	.90	110 Bill Skowron	3.00
8 Ray Herbert	.90	49 Hal Jones	.90	69 Phil Ortega	.90	111 Dallas Green	3.00
9 Jim Davenport	.90	50 Stan Musal	55.00	70 Harmon Killebrew	18.00	112 Hank Foiles	.90
10 Bob Clemente	60.00	51 AL Batting Leaders:	1.50	71 Dick Le May	.90	113 Chicago White Sox	2.00
11 Tom Morgan	.90	Al Kaline, Norm Cash,		72 Bob's Pupils:	.90	114 Howie Koplitz	.90
12 Harry Craft (Mgr.)	.90	Jim Piersall, Elston Howard		Steve Boros, Bob		115 Bob Skinner	.90
13 Dick Howser	1.50	52 NL Batting Leaders:	1.50	Scheffing, Jake Wood		116 Herb Score	1.50
14 Bill White	2.00	Wally Moon, Bob Clemente,		73 Nellie Fox	4.00	117 Gary Geiger	.90
15 Dick Donovan	.90	Vada Pinson, Ken Boyer		74 Bob Lillis	.90	118 Julian Javier	.90
16 Darrell Johnson	.90	53 AL Home Run Leaders:	12.00	75 Milt Pappas	.90	119 Danny Murphy	.90
17 Johnny Callison	.90	Jim Gentile, Roger		76 Howie Bedell	.90	120 Bob Purkey	.90
18 Managers' Dream:	75.00	Maris, Mickey Mantle,		77 Tony Taylor	.90	121 Billy Hitchcock	.90
Mickey Mantle, Willie Mays		Harmon Killebrew		78 Gene Green	.90	122 Norm Bass	.90
19 Ray Washburn	.90	54 NL Home Run Leaders:	2.00	79 Ed Hobaugh	.90	123 Mike De La Hoz	.90
20 Rocky Colavito	2.50	Orlando Cepeda, Willie		80 Vada Pinson	2.50	124 Bill Pleis	.90
21 Jim Kaat	3.00	Mays, Frank Robinson		81 Jim Pagliaroni	.90	125 Gene Woodling	.90
22 Checklist No. 1	3.50	55 AL ERA Leaders:	1.50	82 Deron Johnson	.90	126 Al Cicotte	.90
23 Norm Larker	.90	Dick Donovan, Bill Stafford,		83 Larry Jackson	.90	127 Pride of A's:	.90
24 Detroit Tigers	3.00	Don Mossi, Milt Pappas		84 Lenny Green	.90	Norm Siebern, Hank Bauer,	
25 Ernie Bank	20.00	56 NL ERA Leaders:	1.50	85 Gil Hodges	10.00	Jerry Lumpe	
26 Chris Cannizzaro	.90	Warren Spahn, Jim		86 Donn Clendenon	.90	128 Art Fowler	.90
27 Chuck Cottier	.90	O'Toole, Curt Simmons,		87 Mike Roarke	.90	129 Lee Walls (faces right)	1.00
28 Minnie Minoso	2.00	Mike McCormick		88 Ralph Houk	1.50	129 Lee Walls (faces left)	12.00
29 Casey Stengel (Mgr.)	12.00	57 AL Win Leaders:	1.50	89 Barney Schultz	.90	130 Frank Bolling	.90
30 Ed Mathews	15.00	Frank Lary, Whitey Ford,		90 Jim Piersall	1.25	131 Pete Richert	.90
31 Tom Tresh (R)	7.50	Steve Barber, Jim Bunning		91 J.C. Martin	.90	132 Los Angeles Angels*	1.50
32 John Roseboro	.90	58 NL Win Leaders:	1.50	92 Sam Jones	.90	133 Felipe Alou	.90
33 Don Larsen	.90	Warren Spahn, Joe Jay,		93 John Blanchard	.90	134 Billy Hoeft (faces right)	1.00
34 Johnny Temple	.90	Jim O'Toole		94 Jay Hook	.90	134 Billy Hoeft (faces front)	12.00
35 Don Schwall	.90	59 AL Strikeout Leaders:	1.50	95 Don Hoak	.90	135 Babe Ruth Special:	6.00
36 Don Leppert	.90	Camilo Pascual, Whitey		96 Eli Grba	.90	Babe as a Boy	
37 Tribe Hill Trio:	.90	Ford, Jim Bunning,		97 Tito Francona	.90	136 Babe Ruth Special:	6.00
Barry Latman, Dick		Juan Pizarro		98 Checklist No. 2	3.50	Babe Joins Yanks	
Stigman, Jim Perry		60 NL Strikeout Leaders:	1.50	99 John Powell (R)	9.00	137 Babe Ruth Special:	6.00
38 Gene Stephens	.90	Sandy Koufax, Stan		100 Warren Spahn	20.00	Babe and Mgr. Huggins	
39 Joe Koppe	.90	Williams, Don Drysdale,		101 Carroll Hardy	.90	138 Babe Ruth Special:	6.00
40 Orlando Cepeda	4.00	Jim O'Toole		102 Al Schroll	.90	Famous Slugger	
41 Cliff Cook	.90	61 St. Louis Cardinals	1.50	103 Don Blasingame	.90		

NO.	PLAYER	NR. MT.
139	Babe Ruth Special	6.00
	Babe Hits 60	
	See Card no. 159	
140	Babe Ruth Special:	6.00
	Gehrig and Ruth	
141	Babe Ruth Special:	6.00
	Twilight Years	
142	Babe Ruth Special:	6.00
	Coaching for Dodgers	
143	Babe Ruth Special:	6.00
	Greatest Sports Hero	
144	Babe Ruth Special:	6.00
	Farewell Speech	
145	Barry Latman	.90
146	Don Demeter	.90
147	Bill Kunkel (head shot)	1.00
147	Bill Kunkel (pitching)	12.00
148	Wally Post	.90
149	Bob Duliba	.90
150	Al Kaline	20.00
151	Johnny Klippstein	.90
152	Mickey Vernon (Mgr.)	1.25
153	Pumpsie Green	.90
154	Lee Thomas	.90
155	Stu Miller	.90
156	Merritt Ranew	.90
157	Wes Covington	.90
158	Milwaukee Braves	2.00
159	Hal Reniff	1.25
159	Hal Reniff	10.00
	Error—reads no. 139	
159	Hal Reniff (pitching)	35.00
	Error—reads no. 139	
160	Dick Stuart	1.25
161	Frank Baumann	.90
162	Sammy Drake	.90
163	Hot Corner Guardians:	1.50
	Billy Gardner, Cletis Boyer	
164	Hal Naragon	.90
165	Jackie Brandt	.90
166	Don Lee	.90
167	Tim McCarver (R)	15.00
168	Leo Posada	.90
169	Bob Cerv	.90
170	Ron Santo	3.00
171	Dave Sisler	.90
172	Fred Hutchinson (Mgr.)	.90
173	Chico Fernandez	.90
174	Carl Willey (no hat)	1.00
174	Carl Willey (with hat)	12.00
175	Frank Howard	2.00
176	Eddie Yost (head shot)	1.00
176	Eddie Yost (with bat)	12.00
177	Bobby Shantz	1.25
178	Camilo Carreon	.90
179	Tom Sturdivant	.90
180	Bob Allison	1.25
181	Paul Brown	.90
182	Bob Nieman	.90
183	Roger Craig	1.25
184	Haywood Sullivan	.90
185	Roland Sheldon	.90
186	Mack Jones	.90
187	Gene Conley	.90
188	Chuck Hiller	.90
189	Dick Hall	.90
190	Wally Moon (head shot)	1.00
190	Wally Moon (with bat)	12.00
191	Jim Brewer	.90
192	Checklist No. 3	4.00
193	Eddie Kasko	.90
194	Dean Chance	1.50
195	Joe Cunningham	.90
196	Terry Fox	.90
197	Daryl Spencer	.90
198	Johnny Keane (Mgr.)	.90
199	Gaylord Perry (R)	75.00
200	Mickey Mantle	400.00
201	Ike Delock	.90
202	Carl Warwick	.90
203	Jack Fisher	.90
204	Johnny Weekly	.90

NO.	PLAYER	NR. MT.
205	Gene Freese	.90
206	Washington Senators	2.00
207	Pete Burnside	.90
208	Billy Martin	4.00
209	Jim Fregosi (R)	5.00
210	Roy Face	1.25
211	Midway Masters:	1.00
	Frank Bolling, Roy McMillan	
212	Jim Owens	.90
213	Richie Ashburn	4.00
214	Dom Zanni	.90
215	Woody Held	.90
216	Ron Kline	.90
217	Walt Alston (Mgr.)	3.00
218	Joe Torre (R)	11.00
219	Al Downing (R)	3.00
220	Roy Sievers	1.25
221	Bill Short	.90
222	Jerry Zimmerman	.90
223	Alex Grammas	.90
224	Don Rudolph	.90
225	Frank Malzone	.90
226	San F. Giants	2.50
227	Bobby Tiefenauer	.90
228	Dale Long	.90
229	Jesus McFarlane	.90
230	Camilo Pascual	.90
231	Ernie Bowman	.90
232	World Series Game 1:	2.50
	Yanks Win Opener	
233	World Series Game 2:	2.50
	Jay Ties It Up	
234	World Series Game 3:	6.00
	Maris Wins In 9th	
235	World Series Game 4:	4.00
	Ford Sets New Mark	
236	World Series Game 5:	2.50
	Yanks Crush Reds	
237	World Series	2.50
	Winners Celebrate	
238	Norm Sherry	1.25
239	Cecil Butler	.90
240	George Altman	.90
241	Johnny Kucks	.90
242	Mel McGaha (Mgr.)	.90
243	Robin Roberts	9.00
244	Don Gile	.90
245	Ron Hansen	.90
246	Art Ditmar	.90
247	Joe Pignatano	.90
248	Bob Aspromonte	.90
249	Ed Keegan	.90
250	Norm Cash	2.00
251	New York Yankees	10.00
252	Earl Francis	.90
253	Harry Chiti	.90
254	Gordon Windhorn	.90
255	Joan Pizarro	.90
256	Elio Chacon	.90
257	Jack Spring	.90
258	Marty Keough	.90
259	Lou Klimchock	.90
260	Bill Pierce	1.25
261	George Alusik	.75
262	Bob Schmidt	.75
263	The Right Pitch:	.75
	Bob Purkey, Jim Turner, Joe Jay	
264	Dick Ellsworth	.90
265	Joe Adcock	1.50
266	John Anderson	.90
267	Dan Dobbek	.90
268	Ken McBride	.90
269	Bob Oldis	.90
270	Dick Groat	2.00
271	Ray Rippelmeyer	.90
272	Earl Robinson	.90
273	Gary Bell	.90
274	Sammy Taylor	.90
275	Norm Siebern	.90
276	Hal Kolstad	.90
277	Checklist No. 4	4.00

NO.	PLAYER	NR. MT.
278	Ken Johnson	.90
279	Hobie Landrith	.90
280	Johnny Podres	2.00
281	Jake Gibbs	1.25
282	Dave Hillman	.90
283	Charlie Smith	.90
284	Ruben Amaro	1.25
285	Curt Simmons	1.25
286	Al Lopez (Mgr.)	2.50
287	George Witt	1.25
288	Billy Williams	15.00
289	Mike Krsnich	1.25
290	Jim Gentile	1.75
291	Hal Stowe	1.25
292	Jerry Kindall	1.25
293	Bob Miller	1.25
294	Philadelphia Phillies	2.00
295	Vern Law	2.00
296	Ken Hamlin	1.25
297	Ron Perranoski	1.25
298	Bill Tuttle	1.25
299	Don Wert	1.25
300	Willie Mays	90.00
301	Galen Cisco	1.25
302	John Edwards	1.25
303	Frank Torre	1.25
304	Dick Farrell	1.25
305	Jerry Lumpe	1.25
306	Redbird Rippers:	1.25
	Lindy McDaniel, Larry Jackson	
307	Jim Grant	1.25
308	Neil Chrisley	1.25
309	Moe Morhardt	1.25
310	Whitey Ford	20.00
311	Kubek Double Play	2.50
312	Spahn No-Hit	6.00
313	Maris Blasts 61 HR	12.00
314	Colavito's Power	2.50
315	Ford Curveball	6.00
316	Killebrew's Orbit	5.00
317	Musial's 21st Season	8.00
318	Switch Hitter Mantle	30.00
319	McCormick in Action	2.00
320	Hank Aaron	95.00
321	Lee Stange	1.25
322	Al Dark (Mgr.)	1.75
323	Don Landrum	1.25
324	Joe McClain	1.25
325	Luis Aparicio	9.00
326	Tom Parsons	1.25
327	Ozzie Virgil	1.25
328	Ken Walters	1.25
329	Bob Bolin	1.25
330	Johnny Romano	1.25
331	Moe Drabowsky	1.25
332	Don Buddin	1.25
333	Frank Cipriani	1.25
334	Boston Red Sox	3.00
335	Bill Bruton	1.25
336	Billy Muffett	1.25
337	Jim Marshall	1.50
338	Billy Gardner	1.50
339	Jose Valdivielso	1.50
340	Don Drysdale	18.00
341	Mike Hershberger	1.25
342	Ed Rakow	1.25
343	Albie Pearson	1.25
344	Ed Bauta	1.25
345	Chuck Schilling	1.25
346	Jack Kralick	1.25
347	Chuck Hinton	1.25
348	Larry Burright	1.25
349	Paul Foytack	1.25
350	Frank Robinson	21.00
351	Braves' Backstops:	2.00
	Joe Torre, Del Crandall	
352	Frank Sullivan	1.25
353	Bill Mazeroski	2.00
354	Roman Mejias	1.25
355	Steve Barber	1.25
356	Tom Haller	1.50

NO.	PLAYER	NR. MT.
357	Jerry Walker	1.25
358	Tommy Davis	2.00
359	Bobby Locke	1.25
360	Yogi Berra	35.00
361	Bob Hendley	1.25
362	Ty Cline	1.25
363	Bob Roselli	1.25
364	Ken Hunt	1.25
365	Charley Neal	1.25
366	Phil Regan	1.25
367	Checklist No. 5	3.50
368	Bob Tillman	1.25
369	Ted Bowsfield	1.25
370	Ken Boyer	3.00
371	Earl Battey	1.50
372	Jack Curtis	1.50
373	Al Heist	1.50
374	Gene Mauch (Mgr.)	1.50
375	Ron Fairly	1.50
376	Bud Daley	1.50
377	Johnny Orsino	1.50
378	Bennie Daniels	1.50
379	Chuck Essegian	1.50
380	Lou Burdette	2.00
381	Chico Cardenas	1.50
382	Dick Williams	3.00
383	Ray Sadecki	1.50
384	K.C. Athletics	5.00
385	Early Wynn	10.00
386	Don Mincher	1.50
387	Lou Brock (R)	100.00
388	Ryne Duren	1.50
389	Smoky Burgess	1.50
390	Orlando Cepeda (AS)	5.00
391	Bill Mazeroski (AS)	4.00
392	Ken Boyer (AS)	3.00
393	Roy McMillan (AS)	3.00
394	Hank Aaron (AS)	20.00
395	Willie Mays (AS)	20.00
396	Frank Robinson (AS)	.90
397	John Roseboro (AS)	1.50
398	Don Drysdale (AS)	7.00
399	Warren Spahn (AS)	7.00
400	Elston Howard	4.00
401	AL & NL Homer Kings:	18.00
	Roger Maris, O. Cepeda	
402	Gino Cimoli	1.25
403	Chet Nichols	1.25
404	Tim Harkness	1.25
405	Jim Perry	1.50
406	Bob Taylor	1.50
407	Hank Aguirre	1.50
408	Gus Bell	1.50
409	Pittsburgh Pirates	5.00
410	Al Smith	1.50
411	Danny O'Connell	1.50
412	Charlie James	1.50
413	Matty Alou	2.00
414	Joe Gaines	1.50
415	Bill Virdon	2.00
416	Bob Scheffing (Mgr.)	1.50
417	Joe Azcue	1.50
418	Andy Carey	1.50
419	Bob Bruce	1.50
420	Gus Triandos	1.50
421	Ken MacKenzie	1.50
422	Steve Bilko	1.50
423	Rival Relief Aces:	4.00
	Roy Face, Hoyt Wilhelm	
424	Al McBean	1.50
425	Carl Yastrzemski	120.00
426	Bob Farley	1.50
427	Jake Wood	1.50
428	Joe Hicks	1.50
429	Billy O'Dell	1.50
430	Tony Kubek	7.00
431	Bob Rodgers	2.00
432	Jim Pendleton	1.50
433	Jim Archer	1.50
434	Clay Dalrymple	1.50
435	Larry Sherry	1.50
436	Felix Mantilla	1.50

NO. PLAYER	NR. MT.	NO. PLAYER	NR. MT.	NO. PLAYER	NR. MT.	NO. PLAYER	NR. MT.
437 Ray Moore	1.50	480 Harvey Kuenn	3.00	527 Dick McAuliffe	8.00	574 Dean Stone	8.00
438 Dick Brown	1.50	481 Vic Wertz	3.00	528 Turk Lown	8.00	575 Red Schoendienst	25.00
439 Jerry Buchek	1.50	482 Sam Mele	3.00	529 John Schaive	8.00	576 Russ Kemmerer	8.00
440 Joe Jay	1.50	483 Don McMahon	3.00	530 Bob Gibson	100.00	577 Dave Nicholson	8.00
441 Checklist No. 6	3.50	484 Dick Schofield	3.00	531 Bobby G. Smith	8.00	578 Jim Duffalo	8.00
442 Wes Stock	1.50	485 Pedro Ramos	3.00	532 Dick Stigman	8.00	579 Jim Schaffer	8.00
443 Del Crandall	2.50	486 Jim Gilliam	5.00	533 Charley Lau	8.00	580 Bill Monbouquette	8.00
444 Ted Wills	1.50	487 Jerry Lynch	3.00	534 Tony Gonzalez	8.00	581 Mel Roach	8.00
445 Vic Power	1.50	488 Hal Brown	3.00	535 Ed Roebuck	8.00	582 Ron Piche	8.00
446 Don Elston	1.50	489 Julio Gotay	3.00	536 Dick Gernert	8.00	583 Larry Osborne	8.00
447 Willie Kirland	3.00	490 Clete Boyer	4.00	537 Cleveland Indians	15.00	584 Minnesota Twins	15.00
448 Joe Gibbon	3.00	491 Leon Wagner	3.00	538 Jack Sanford	8.00	585 Glen Hobbie	8.00
449 Jerry Adair	3.00	492 Hal Smith	3.00	539 Billy Moran	8.00	586 Sammy Esposito	8.00
450 Jim O'Toole	3.00	493 Danny McDevitt	3.00	540 Jim Landis	8.00	587 Frank Funk	8.00
451 Jose Tartabull	3.00	494 Sammy White	3.00	541 Don Nottebart	8.00	588 Birdie Tebbetts (Mgr.)	8.00
452 Earl Averill	3.00	495 Don Cardwell	3.00	542 Dave Philley	8.00	589 Bob Turley	12.00
453 Cal McLish	3.00	496 Wayne Causey	3.00	543 Bob Allen	8.00	590 Curt Flood	15.00
454 Floyd Robinson	3.00	497 Ed Bouchee	3.00	544 Willie McCovey	90.00	591 Rookie Pitchers:	25.00
455 Luis Arroyo	3.00	498 Jim Donohue	3.00	545 Hoyt Wilhelm	40.00	Sam McDowell, D. Radatz,	
456 Joe Amalfitano	3.00	499 Zoilo Versalles	3.00	546 Moe Thacker	8.00	Ron Taylor, Ron Nischwitz,	
457 Lou Clinton	3.00	500 Duke Snider	40.00	547 Don Ferrarese	8.00	Art Quirk	
458 Bob Buhl ("M" on hat)	4.00	501 Claude Osteen	3.00	548 Bobby Del Greco	8.00	592 Rookie Pitchers:	35.00
458 Bob Buhl	25.00	502 Hector Lopez	3.00	549 Bill Rigney (Mgr.)	8.00	D. Stenhouse, Dan Pfister,	
(without "M" on hat)		503 Danny Murtaugh (Mgr.)	3.00	550 Art Mahaffey	8.00	Bo Belinsky, Jim Bouton,	
459 Ed Bailey	3.00	504 Eddie Bressoud	3.00	551 Harry Bright	8.00	Joe Bonikowski	
460 Jim Bunning	6.00	505 Juan Marichal	30.00	552 Chicago Cubs	15.00	593 Rookie Pitchers:	15.00
461 Ken Hubbs (R)	7.00	506 Charley Maxwell	3.00	553 Jim Coates	9.00	Bob Moorhead, Jack	
462 Willie Tasby	3.00	507 Ernie Broglio	3.00	554 Bubba Morton	8.00	Lamabe, Jack Hamilton,	
("W" on hat)		508 Gordy Coleman	3.00	555 John Buzhardt	8.00	Bob Veale, Craig Anderson	
462 Willie Tasby	25.00	509 Dave Giusti	3.00	556 Al Spangler	8.00	594 Rookie Catchers:	125.00
(without "W" on hat)		510 Jim Lemon	3.00	557 Bob Anderson	8.00	Bob Uecker, Doc Edwards,	
463 Hank Bauer (Mgr.)	4.00	511 Bubba Phillips	3.00	558 John Goryl	8.00	Ken Retzer, Doug Camilli,	
464 Al Jackson	3.00	512 Mike Fornieles	3.00	559 Mike Higgins (Mgr.)	8.00	Don Pavletich	
465 Cincinnati Reds	5.00	513 Whitey Herzog	4.00	560 Chuck Estrada	8.00	595 Rookie Infielders:	15.00
466 Norm Cash (AS)	5.00	514 Sherm Lollar	3.00	561 Gene Oliver	8.00	Bob Sadowski, Marlan	
467 Chuck Schilling (AS)	3.00	515 Stan Williams	3.00	562 Bill Henry	8.00	Coughtry, Ed Charles,	
468 Brooks Robinson (AS)	10.00	516 Checklist No. 7	7.00	563 Ken Aspromonte	8.00	Felix Torres	
469 Luis Aparicio (AS)	6.00	517 Dave Wickersham	3.00	564 Bob Grim	8.00	596 Rookie Infielders:	25.00
470 Al Kaline (AS)	12.00	518 Lee Maye	3.00	565 Jose Pagan	8.00	Bernie Allen, Phil Linz,	
471 Mickey Mantle (AS)	70.00	519 Bob Johnson	3.00	566 Marty Kutyna	8.00	Rich Rollins, Joe Pepitone	
472 Rocky Colavito (AS)	4.00	520 Bob Friend	3.00	567 Tracy Stallard	8.00	597 Rookie Infielders:	15.00
473 Elston Howard (AS)	4.00	521 Jacke Davis	3.00	568 Jim Golden	8.00	Denis Menke, Jim	
474 Frank Lary (AS)	3.00	522 Lindy McDaniel	3.00	569 Ed Sadowski	8.00	McKnight, Rod Kanehl,	
475 Whitey Ford (AS)	10.00	523 Russ Nixon	8.00	570 Bill Stafford	8.00	Amado Samuel	
476 Baltimore Orioles	5.00	524 Howie Nunn	8.00	571 Billy Klaus	8.00	598 Rookie Outfielders:	35.00
477 Andre Rodgers	3.00	525 George Thomas	8.00	572 Bob Miller	8.00	Al Luplow, Danny Jimenez,	
478 Don Zimmer	5.00	526 Hal Woodeschick	8.00	573 Johnny Logan	8.00	Ed Olivares, Howie Gross,	
479 Joel Horlen	3.00					Jim Hickman	

1963 Topps. . . . Complete Set of 576 Cards—Value $1350.00 (Exc.); $3500.00 (Mint)

Pete Rose's rookie card is in this set. Cards 507 to 576 are the high numbers. Also includes the rookie cards of Willie Stargell, Tony Oliva, and Rusty Staub. Cards 29 and 54 exist with the error "1962 Rookie Stars" instead of "1963 Rookie Stars"—worth $5.00 each.

NO. PLAYER	NR. MT.	NO. PLAYER	NR. MT.	NO. PLAYER	NR. MT.	NO. PLAYER	NR. MT.
1 NL Bat Ldrs.: (Exc. $4.00)	15.00	3 NL Home Run Leaders:	6.00	5 NL ERA Leaders:	1.75	7 NL Pitching Leaders:	1.25
Frank Robinson, Stan		O. Cepeda, Hank Aaron,		Bob Purkey, Bob Shaw,		Don Drysdale, Billy O'Dell,	
Musial, Tommy Davis, Bill		Ernie Banks, Frank		Sandy Koufax, Bob Gibson,		Jack Sanford, Bob Purkey,	
White, Hank Aaron		Robinson, Willie Mays		Don Drysdale		Art Mahaffey, Joe Jay	
2 AL Batting Leaders:	8.00	4 AL Home Run Leaders:	1.50	6 AL ERA Leaders:	1.50	8 AL Pitching Leaders:	1.25
Norm Siebern, Pete		Roger Maris, R. Colavito,		Whitey Ford, Robin Roberts,		Dick Donovan, Ray Herbert,	
Runnels, Floyd Robinson,		Harmon Killebrew, Norm		Eddie Fisher, Hank Aguirre,		Ralph Terry, Jim Bunning,	
C. Hinton, Mickey Mantle		Cash, J. Gentile, L. Wagner		Dean Chance		Camilo Pascual	

NO. PLAYER	NR. MT.	NO. PLAYER	NR. MT.	NO. PLAYER	NR. MT.	NO. PLAYER	NR. MT.
9 NL Strikeout Leaders:	2.00	77 Al Spangler	.65	150 Johnny Podres	1.50	221 Cookie Rojas	1.75
Sandy Koufax, Bob Gibson,		78 Marv Throneberry	1.00	151 Pittsburgh Pirates	1.50	222 Chicago Cubs	1.00
Don Drysdale, Billy O'Dell,		79 Checklist No. 1	3.00	152 Ron Nischwitz	.65	223 Eddie Fisher	1.00
Dick Farrell		80 Jim Gilliam	2.00	153 Hal Smith	.65	224 Mike Roarke	1.00
10 AL Strikeout Leaders:	1.25	81 Jim Schaffer	.65	154 Walt Alston (Mgr.)	3.00	225 Joe Jay	1.00
Ralph Terry, Juan Pizarro,		82 Ed Rakow	.65	155 Bill Stafford	.65	226 Julian Javier	1.00
Camilo Pascual, Jim		83 Charley James	.65	156 Roy McMillan	.65	227 Jim Grant	1.00
Bunning, Jim Kaat		84 Ron Kline	.65	157 Diego Segui	.65	228 Rookie Stars:	25.00
11 Lee Walls	.65	85 Tom Haller	.65	158 Rookie Stars:	.60	Max Alvis, Bob Bailey,	
12 Steve Barber	.65	86 Charley Maxwell	.65	Bob Saverine, Rogelio		Pedro Oliva, Ed Kranepool	
13 Philadelphia Phillies	1.00	87 Bob Veale	.65	Alvarez, Dave Roberts,		229 Willie Davis	1.00
14 Pedro Ramos	.40	88 Ron Hansen	.65	Tommy Harper		230 Pete Runnels	1.00
15 Ken Hubbs	1.50	89 Dick Stigman	.65	159 Jim Pagliaroni	.65	231 Eli Grba	1.00
16 Al Smith	.65	90 Gordy Coleman	.65	160 Juan Pizarro	.65	(photo of Ryne Duren)	
17 Ryne Duren	.65	91 Dallas Green	1.75	161 Frank Torre	.65	232 Frank Malzone	1.00
18 Buc Blasters:	7.00	92 Hector Lopez	.65	162 Minnesota Twins	1.00	233 Casey Stengel (Mgr.)	13.00
Smoky Burgess, Dick Stuart,		93 Galen Cisco	.65	163 Don Larsen	.60	234 Dave Nicholson	1.00
Bob Clemente, Bob Skinner		94 Bob Schmidt	.65	164 Bubba Morton	.65	235 Bill O'Dell	1.00
19 Pete Burnside	.65	95 Larry Jackson	.65	165 Jim Kaat	3.00	236 Bill Bryan	1.00
20 Tony Kubek	3.00	96 Lou Clinton	.65	166 Johnny Keane (Mgr.)	.65	237 Jim Coates	1.00
21 Marty Keough	.65	97 Bob Duliba	.65	167 Jim Fregosi	1.00	238 Lou Johnson	1.00
22 Curt Simmons	.65	98 George Thomas	.65	168 Russ Nixon	.65	239 Harvey Haddix	1.00
23 Ed Lopat (Mgr.)	.75	99 Jim Umbricht	.65	169 Rookie Stars:	15.00	240 Rocky Colavito	3.00
24 Bob Bruce	.65	100 Joe Cunningham	.65	Gaylord Perry, Dick Egan,		241 Billy Smith	1.00
25 A. Kaline	20.00	101 Joe Gibbon	.65	Julio Navarro, Tommie Sisk		242 Power Plus:	17.00
26 Ray Moore	.65	102 Checklist No. 2	4.00	170 Joe Adcock	.65	Ernie Banks, Hank Aaron	
27 Choo Choo Coleman	.65	103 Chuck Essegian	.65	171 Steve Hamilton	.65	243 Don Leppert	1.00
28 Mike Fornieles	.65	104 Lew Krausse	.65	172 Gene Oliver	.65	244 John Tsitouris	1.00
29 Rookie Stars:*	1.25	105 Ron Fairly	.65	173 Bombers' Best:	30.00	245 Gil Hodges	10.00
Sammy Ellis, Jesse Gonder,		106 Bob Bolin	.65	Tom Tresh, Mickey Mantle,		246 Lee Stange	1.00
Ray Culp, John Boozer		107 Jim Hickman	.65	Bobby Richardson		247 New York Yankees	10.00
30 Harvey Kuenn	.75	108 Hoyt Wilhelm	7.50	174 Larry Burright	.65	248 Tito Francona	1.00
31 Cal Koonce	.65	109 Lee Maye	.65	175 Bob Buhl	.65	249 Leo Burke	1.00
32 Tony Gonzalez	.65	110 Rich Rollins	.65	176 Jim King	.65	250 Stan Musial	75.00
33 Bo Belinsky	.65	111 Al Jackson	.65	177 Bubba Phillips	.65	251 Jack Lamabe	1.00
34 Dick Schofield	.65	112 Dick Brown	.65	178 Johnny Edwards	.65	252 Ron Santo	2.50
35 John Buzhardt	.65	113 Don Landrum	.65	179 Ron Pich	.65	253 Rookie Stars;	1.00
36 Jerry Kindall	.65	(photo of Ron Santo)		180 Bill Skowron	1.50	Len Gabrielson, Pete	
37 Jerry Lynch	.65	114 Dan Osinski	.65	181 Sammy Esposito	.65	Jernigan, Deacon Jones,	
38 Bud Daley	.65	115 Carl Yastrzemski	65.00	182 Albie Pearson	.65	John Wojcik	
39 Los Angeles Angels	1.00	116 Jim Brosnan	.65	183 Joe Pepitone	2.00	254 Mike Hershberger	1.00
40 Vic Power	.65	117 Jacke Davis	.65	184 Vern Law	.65	255 Bob Shaw	1.00
41 Charlie Lau	.65	118 Sherm Lollar	.65	185 Chuck Hiller	.65	256 Jerry Lumpe	1.00
42 Stan Williams	.65	119 Bob Lillis	.65	186 Jerry Zimmerman	.65	257 Hank Aguirre	1.00
43 Veteran Masters:	3.00	120 Roger Maris	40.00	187 Willie Kirkland	.65	258 Alvin Dark (Mgr.)	1.00
C. Stengel, G. Woodling		121 Jim Hannan	.65	188 Eddie Bressoud	.65	259 Johnny Logan	1.00
44 Terry Fox	.65	122 Julio Gotay	.65	189 Dave Giusti	.65	260 Jim Gentile	1.00
45 Bob Aspromonte	.65	123 Frank Howard	1.50	190 Minnie Minoso	1.50	261 Bob Miller	1.00
46 Tommie Aaron	.65	124 Dick Howser	.65	191 Checklist No. 3	4.00	262 Ellis Burton	1.00
47 Don Lock	.65	125 Robin Roberts	9.00	192 Clay Dalrymple	.65	263 Dave Stenhouse	1.00
48 Birdie Tebbetts (Mgr.)	.65	126 Bob Uecker	30.00	193 Andre Rodgers	.65	264 Phil Linz	1.00
49 Dal Maxvill	.65	127 Bill Tuttle	.65	194 Joe Nuxhall	.65	265 Vada Pinson	2.50
50 Bill Pierc	.70	128 Matty Alou	.65	195 Manny Jimenez	.65	266 Bob Allen	1.00
51 George Alusik	.65	129 Gary Bell	.65	196 Doug Camilli	.65	267 Carl Sawatski	1.00
52 Chuck Schilling	.65	130 Dick Groat	.60	197 Roger Craig	1.00	268 Don Demter	1.00
53 Joe Moeller	.65	131 Washington Senators	1.00	198 Lenny Green	1.00	269 Don Mincher	1.00
54 Rookie Stars:*	3.50	132 Jack Hamilton	.65	199 Joe Amalfitano	1.00	270 Felipe Alou	1.00
N. Mathews, D. DeBusschere,		133 Gene Freese	.65	200 Mickey Mantle	350.00	271 Dean Stone	1.00
Harry Fanok, J. Cullen		134 Bob Scheffing (Mgr.)	.65	201 Cecil Butler	1.00	272 Danny Murphy	1.00
55 Bill Virdon	.75	135 Richie Ashburn	4.00	202 Boston Red Sox	2.50	273 Sammy Taylor	1.00
56 Dennis Bennett	.65	136 Ike Delock	.65	203 Chico Cardenas	1.00	274 Checklist No. 4	4.00
57 Billy Moran	.65	137 Mack Jones	.65	204 Don Nottebart	1.00	275 Ed Mathews	15.00
58 Bob Will	.65	138 Pride Of N.L.:	18.00	205 Luis Aparicio	10.00	276 Barry Shetrone	1.00
59 Craig Anderson	.65	Willie Mays, Stan Musial		206 Ray Washburn	1.00	277 Dick Farrell	1.00
60 Elston Howard	3.00	139 Earl Averill	.65	207 Ken Hunt	1.00	278 Chico Fernandez	1.00
61 Ernie Bowman	.65	140 Frank Lary	.65	208 Rookie Stars:	1.00	279 Wally Moon	1.00
62 Bob Hendley	.65	141 Manny Mota (R)	4.00	Ron Herbel, John Miller,		280 Bob Rodgers	1.00
63 Cincinnati Reds	1.25	142 World Series Game 1	3.00	Ron Taylor, Wally Wolf		281 Tom Sturdivant	1.00
64 Dick McAuliffe	.65	Ford Wins Opener		209 Hobie Landrith	1.00	282 Bob Del Greco	1.00
65 Jackie Brandt	.65	143 World Series Game 2	2.00	210 Sandy Koufax	95.00	283 Roy Sievers	1.00
66 Mike Joyce	.65	Sanford Shutout		211 Fred Whitfield	1.00	284 Dave Sisler	1.25
67 Ed Charles	.65	144 World Series Game 3	5.00	212 Glen Hobbie	1.00	285 Dick Stuart	1.25
68 Friendly Foes:	6.00	Maris Sparks Rally		213 Billy Hitchcock (Mgr.)	1.00	286 Stu Miller	1.25
Duke Snider, Gil Hodges		145 World Series Game 4	2.00	214 Orlando Pena	1.00	287 Dick Bertell	1.25
69 Bud Zipfel	.65	Hiller Grand Slam		215 Bob Skinner	1.00	288 Chicago White Sox	2.00
70 Jim O'Toole	.65	146 World Series Game 5	2.00	216 Gene Conley	1.00	289 Hal Brown	1.25
71 Bobby Wine	.65	Tresh's Homer		217 Joe Christopher	1.00	290 Bill White	3.00
72 Johnny Romano	.65	147 World Series Game 6	2.00	218 Tiger Twirlers:	1.50	291 Don Rudolph	1.25
73 Bob Bragan (Mgr.)	.65	Pierce Victory		Frank Lary, Don Mossi,		292 Pumpsie Green	1.25
74 Denver Lemaster	.65	148 World Series Game 7	2.00	Jim Bunning		293 Bill Pleis	1.25
75 Bobby Allison	.65	Yanks Celebrate		219 Chuck Cottier	1.00	294 Bill Rigney (Mgr.)	1.25
76 Earl Wilson	.65	149 Marv Breeding	.65	220 Camilo Pascual	1.00	295 Ed Roebuck	1.25

NO.	PLAYER	NR. MT.
296	Doc Edwards	1.25
297	Jim Golden	1.25
298	Don Dillard	1.25
299	Rookie Stars:	1.25
	Dave Morehead, Bob Dustal,	
	Dan Schneider, Tom Butters	
300	Willie Mays	100.00
301	Bill Fischer	1.25
302	Whitey Herzog	1.75
303	Earl Francis	1.25
304	Harry Bright	1.25
305	Don Hoak	1.25
306	Star Receivers:	1.75
	Earl Battey, Elston Howard	
307	Chet Nichols	1.25
308	Camilo Carreon	1.25
309	Jim Brewer	1.25
310	Tommy Davis	2.50
311	Joe McClain	1.25
312	Houston Colts	7.50
313	Ernie Broglio	1.25
314	John Goryl	1.25
315	Ralph Terry	1.25
316	Norm Sherry	1.25
317	Sam McDowell	1.50
318	Gene Mauch (Mgr.)	1.50
319	Joe Gaines	1.25
320	Warren Spahn	20.00
321	Gino Cimoli	1.25
322	Bob Turley	1.50
323	Bill Mazeroski	2.00
324	Rookie Stars:	2.00
	G. Williams, Vic Davalillo,	
	P. Ward, Phil Roof	
325	Jack Sanford	1.25
326	Hank Foiles	1.25
327	Paul Foytack	1.25
328	Dick Williams	1.25
329	Lindy McDaniel	1.25
330	Chuck Hinton	1.25
331	Series Foes:	1.25
	Bill Stafford, Bill Pierce	
332	Joel Horlen	1.25
333	Carl Warwick	1.25
334	Wynn Hawkins	1.25
335	Leon Wagner	1.25
336	Ed Bauta	1.25
337	Los Angeles Dodgers	8.00
338	Russ Kemmerer	1.25
339	Ted Bowsfield	1.25
340	Yogi Berra	45.00
341	Jack Baldschun	1.25
342	Gene Woodling	1.25
343	Johnny Pesky (Mgr.)	1.25
344	Don Schwall	1.25
345	Brooks Robinson	30.00
346	Billy Hoeft	1.25
347	Joe Torre	3.00
348	Vic Wertz	1.25
349	Zoilo Versalles	1.25
350	Bob Purkey	1.25
351	Al Luplow	1.25
352	Ken Johnson	1.25
353	Billy Williams	15.00
354	Dom Zanni	1.25
355	Dean Chance	1.25
356	John Schaive	1.25
357	George Altman	1.25
358	Milt Pappas	1.25
359	Haywood Sullivan	1.25
360	Don Drysdale	16.00
361	Clete Boyer	1.50
362	Checklist No. 5	4.00
363	Dick Radatz	1.25
364	Howie Goss	1.25
365	Jim Bunning	6.00
366	Tony Taylor	1.25
367	Tony Cloninger	1.25
368	Ed Bailey	1.25

NO.	PLAYER	NR. MT.
369	Jim Lemon	1.25
370	Dick Donovan	1.25
371	Rod Kanehl	1.25
372	Don Lee	1.25
373	Jim Campbell	1.25
374	Claude Osteen	1.25
375	Ken Boyer	3.00
376	John Wyatt	1.25
377	Baltimore Orioles	3.00
378	Bill Henry	1.25
379	Bob Anderson	1.25
380	Ernie Banks	35.00
381	Frank Baumann	1.25
382	Ralph Houk (Mgr.)	1.50
383	Pete Richert	1.25
384	Bob Tillman	1.25
385	Art Mahaffey	1.25
386	Rookie Stars:	1.50
	Ed Kirkpatrick, J. Bateman,	
	G. Roggenburk, L. Bearnarth	
387	Al McBean	1.25
388	Jim Davenport	1.25
389	Frank Sullivan	1.25
390	Hank Aaron	100.00
391	Bill Dailey	1.25
392	Tribe Thumpers:	1.25
	Johnny Romano,	
	Tito Francona	
393	Ken MacKenzie	1.25
394	Tim McCarver	5.00
395	Don McMahon	1.25
396	Joe Koppe	1.25
397	Kansas C. Athletics	2.50
398	Boog Powell	7.00
399	Dick Ellsworth	1.00
400	Frank Robinson	30.00
401	Jim Bouton	3.00
402	Mickey Vernon (Mgr.)	1.25
403	Ron Perranoski	1.25
404	Bob Oldis	1.25
405	Floyd Robinson	1.25
406	Howie Koplitz	1.25
407	Rookie Stars:	1.25
	Dick Simpson, Frank Kostro,	
	Chico Ruiz, Larry Elliot	
408	Billy Gardner	1.25
409	Roy Face	1.25
410	Earl Battey	1.25
411	Jim Constable	1.25
412	Dodger Big Three:	22.00
	Sandy Koufax, Johnny	
	Podres, Don Drysdale	
413	Jerry Walker	1.25
414	Ty Cline	1.25
415	Bob Gibson	25.00
416	Alex Grammas	1.25
417	San F. Giants	2.50
418	Johnny Orsino	1.25
419	Tracy Stallard	1.25
420	Bobby Richardson	5.00
421	Tom Morgan	1.25
422	Fred Hutchinson (Mgr.)	1.25
423	Ed Hobaugh	1.25
424	Charley Smith	1.25
425	Smokey Burgess	1.25
426	Barry Latman	1.25
427	Bernie Allen	1.25
428	Carl Boles	1.25
429	Lou Burdette	1.50
430	Norm Siebern	1.25
431	Checklist No. 6	4.00
432	Roman Mejias	1.25
433	Denis Menke	1.25
434	Johnny Callison	1.25
435	Woody Held	1.25
436	Tim Harkness	1.25
437	Bill Bruton	1.25
438	Wes Stock	1.25
439	Don Zimmer	2.50

NO.	PLAYER	NR. MT.
440	Juan Marichal	15.00
441	Lee Thomas	1.25
442	J.C. Hartman	1.25
443	Jim Piersall	1.50
444	Jim Maloney	1.25
445	Norm Cash	3.00
446	Whitey Ford	30.00
447	Felix Mantilla	6.00
448	Jack Kralick	6.00
449	Jose Tartabull	6.00
450	Bob Friend	6.00
451	Cleveland Indians	6.00
452	Barney Schultz	6.00
453	Jake Wood	6.00
454	Art Fowler	6.00
455	Ruben Amaro	6.00
456	Jim Coker	6.00
457	Tex Clevenger	6.00
458	Al Lopez (Mgr.)	10.00
459	Dick LeMay	6.00
460	Del Crandall	6.00
461	Norm Bass	6.00
462	Wally Post	6.00
463	Joe Schaffernoth	6.00
464	Ken Aspromonte	6.00
465	Chuck Estrada	6.00
466	Rookie Stars:	18.00
	Tony Martinez, Bill Freehan,	
	Jerry Robinson, Nate Oliver	
467	Phil Ortega	6.00
468	Carroll Hardy	6.00
469	Jay Hook	6.00
470	Tom Tresh	22.00
471	Ken Retzer	6.00
472	Lou Brock	85.00
473	New York Mets	25.00
474	Jack Fisher	6.00
475	Gus Triandos	6.00
476	Frank Funk	6.00
477	Donn Clendenon	6.00
478	Paul Brown	6.00
479	Ed Brinkman	6.00
480	Bill Monbouquette	6.00
481	Bob Taylor	6.00
482	Felix Torres	6.00
483	Jim Owens	6.00
484	Dale Long	6.00
485	Jim Landis	6.00
486	Ray Sadecki	6.00
487	John Roseboro	6.00
488	Jerry Adair	6.00
489	Paul Toth	6.00
490	Willie McCovey	75.00
491	Harry Craft (Mgr.)	6.00
492	Dave Wickersham	6.00
493	Walt Bond	6.00
494	Phil Regan	6.00
495	Frank Thomas	6.00
496	Rookie Stars:	6.00
	Steve Dalkowski, Carl	
	Bouldin, Fred Newman,	
	Jack Smith	
497	Bennie Daniels	6.00
498	Eddie Kasko	6.00
499	J.C. Martin	6.00
500	Harmon Killebrew	50.00
501	Joe Azcue	6.00
502	Daryl Spencer	6.00
503	Milwaukee Braves	10.00
504	Bob Johnson	6.00
505	Curt Flood	12.00
506	Gene Green	6.00
507	Roland Sheldon	5.00
508	Ted Savage	5.00
509	Checklist No. 7	13.00
510	Ken McBride	5.00
511	Charlie Neal	5.00
512	Cal McLish	5.00
513	Gary Geiger	5.00

NO.	PLAYER	NR. MT.
514	Larry Osborne	5.00
515	Don Elston	5.00
516	Purnal Goldy	5.00
517	Hal Woodeschick	5.00
518	Don Blasingame	5.00
519	Claude Raymond	5.00
520	Orlando Cepeda	13.00
521	Dan Pfister	5.00
522	Rookie Stars:	5.00
	Mel Nelson, Gary Peters,	
	Art Quirk, Jim Roland	
523	Bill Kunkel	5.00
524	St. Louis Cards	8.00
525	Nellie Fox	10.00
526	Dick Hall	5.00
527	Ed Sadowski	5.00
528	Carl Willey	5.00
529	Wes Covington	5.00
530	Don Mossi	5.00
531	Sam Mele (Mgr.)	5.00
532	Steve Boros	5.00
533	Bobby Shantz	5.00
534	Ken Walters	5.00
535	Jim Perry	5.00
536	Norm Larker	5.00
537	Rookie Stars:	600.00
	Pedro Gonzalez, Pete Rose,	
	Ken McMullen, Al Weis	
538	George Brunet	5.00
539	Wayne Causey	5.00
540	Bob Clemente	125.00
541	Ron Moeller	5.00
542	Lou Klimchock	5.00
543	Russ Snyder	5.00
544	Rookie Stars:	30.00
	Rusty Staub, Duke Carmel,	
	Bill Haas, Dick Phillips	
545	Jose Pagan	5.00
546	Hal Reniff	5.00
547	Gus Bell	5.00
548	Tom Satriano	5.00
549	Rookie Stars:	5.00
	Paul Ratliff, Marcelino	
	Lopez, Pete Lovrich,	
	Elmo Plaskett	
550	Duke Snider	65.00
551	Billy Klaus	5.00
552	Detroit Tigers	15.00
553	Rookie Stars:	175.00
	Brock Davis, Jim Gosger,	
	W. Stargell, J. Herrnstein	
554	Hank Fischer	5.00
555	John Blanchard	5.00
556	Al Worthington	5.00
557	Cuno Barragan	5.00
558	Rookie Stars:	5.00
	Bill Faul, Ron Hunt,	
	Bob Lipski, Al Moran	
559	Danny Murtaugh (Mgr.)	5.00
560	Ray Herbert	5.00
561	Mike De La Hoz	5.00
562	Rookie Stars:	8.00
	Don Rowe, Randy Cardinal,	
	Dave McNally, Ken Rowe	
563	Mike McCormick	5.00
564	George Banks	5.00
565	Larry Sherry	5.00
566	Clif Cook	5.00
567	Jim Duffalo	5.00
568	Bob Sadowski	5.00
569	Luis Arroyo	5.00
570	Frank Bolling	5.00
571	Johnny Klippstein	5.00
572	Jack Spring	5.00
573	Coot Veal	5.00
574	Hal Kolstad	5.00
575	Don Cardwell	5.00
576	Johnny Temple	5.00

Phil Niekro's rookie card is in this set. The high numbers are 523 to 587. For the first time a card was issued for a deceased player—Ken Hubbs.

    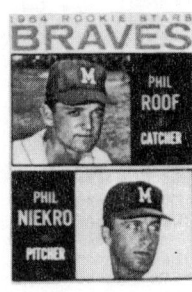

NO. PLAYER	NR. MT.
1 NL ERA Ldrs.:(Exc. $2.00) ..9.00	
Sandy Koufax, Dick	
Ellsworth, Bob Friend	
2 AL ERA Leaders: 1.50	
Gary Peters, Juan Pizarro,	
Camilo Pascual	
3 NL Pitching Leaders: 3.00	
S. Koufax, Juan Marichal,	
W. Spahn, Jim Maloney	
4 AL Pitching Leaders: 1.75	
Whitey Ford, Camilo	
Pascual, Jim Bouton	
5 NL Strikeout Leaders: ...3.00	
Sandy Koufax, Jim	
Maloney, Don Drysdale	
6 AL Strikeout Leaders:....1.75	
Camilo Pascual, Jim	
Bunning, Dick Stigman	
7 NL Batting Leaders: 1.75	
T. Davis, Bob Clemente,	
D. Groat, Hank Aaron	
8 AL Batting Leaders: 2.50	
Carl Yastrzemski, Al Kaline,	
Rich Rollins	
9 NL Home Run Leaders: ..7.00	
Hank Aaron, W. McCovey,	
W. Mays, Orlando Cepeda	
10 AL Home Run Leaders: ..1.75	
Harmon Killebrew, Dick	
Stuart, Bob Allison	
11 NL RBI Leaders:........1.75	
Hank Aaron, Ken Boyer	
Bill White	
12 AL RBI Leaders:........1.75	
Dick Stuart, Al Kaline,	
Harmon Killebrew	
13 Hoyt Wilhelm 7.00	
14 Dodgers Rookies:........60	
Dick Nen, Nick Willhite	
15 Zoilo Versalles 60	
16 John Boozer 60	
17 Willie Kirkland 60	
18 Bill O'Dell 60	
19 Don Wert 60	
20 Bob Friend 60	
21 Yogi Berra (Mgr.).......25.00	
22 Jerry Adair............60	
23 Chris Zachary 60	
24 Carl Sawatski 60	
25 Bill Monbouquett 60	
26 Gino Cimoli 60	
27 New York Mets 2.00	
28 Claude Osteen 60	
29 Lou Brock 25.00	
30 Ron Perranoski 60	
31 Dave Nicholson 60	
32 Dean Chance 1.00	
33 Reds Rookies:...........60	
Sammy Ellis, Mel Queen	
34 Jim Perry 60	
35 Ed Mathews...........10.00	
36 Hal Reniff...........60	
37 Smoky Burgess 60	
38 Jim Wynn (R) 1.50	
39 Hank Aguirre 60	
40 Dick Groat 1.00	

NO. PLAYER	NR. MT.
41 Friendly Foes:..........3.00	
W. McCovey, Leon Wagner	
42 Moe Drabowski 60	
43 Roy Sievers 70	
44 Duke Carmel 60	
45 Milt Pappas 60	
46 Ed Brinkman 60	
47 Giants Rookies: 1.00	
Jesus Alou, Ron Herbel	
48 Bob Perry 60	
49 Bill Henry 60	
50 M. Mantle 250.00	
51 Pete Richert 60	
52 Chuck Hinton 60	
53 Denis Menke 60	
54 Sam Mele 60	
55 Ernie Banks 18.00	
56 Hal Brown 60	
57 Tim Harkness 60	
58 Don Demeter 60	
59 Ernie Broglio 60	
60 Frank Malzone 60	
61 Angel Backstops:..........60	
Bob Rodgers, Ed Sadowski	
62 Ted Savage 60	
63 Johnny Orsino 60	
64 Ted Abernathy 60	
65 Felipe Alou 60	
66 Eddie Fisher 60	
67 Detroit Tigers 1.50	
68 Willie Davis 75	
69 Clete Boyer 60	
70 Joe Torre 2.00	
71 Jack Spring 60	
72 Chico Cardenas 60	
73 Jimmie Hall 60	
74 Pirates Rookies: 60	
Bob Priddy, Tom Butters	
75 Wayne Causey 60	
76 Checklist No. 1 ....3.00	
77 Jerry Walker 60	
78 Merritt Ranew 60	
79 Bob Heffner............60	
80 Vada Pinson 1.50	
81 All-Star Vets:...........4.00	
Nellie Fox, H. Killebrew	
82 Jim Davenport 60	
83 Gus Triandos 60	
84 Carl Willey 60	
85 Pete Ward 60	
86 Al Doning...............60	
87 St. Louis Cardinals 1.50	
88 John Roseboro 60	
89 Boog Powell 2.00	
90 Earl Battey 60	
91 Bob Bailey 60	
92 Steve Ridzik 60	
93 Gary Geiger 60	
94 Braves Rookies: 60	
Jim Britton, Larry Maxie	
95 George Altman 60	
96 Bob Buhl 60	
97 Jim Fregosi 60	
98 Bill Bruton 60	
99 Al Stanek 60	
100 Elston Howard 2.50	

NO. PLAYER	NR. MT.
101 Walt Alston (Mgr.) 3.00	
102 Checklist No. 2 ....3.00	
103 Curt Flood 1.50	
104 Art Mahaffey 60	
105 Woody Held 60	
106 Joe Nuxhall 60	
107 White Sox Rookies: 60	
B. Howard, F. Kreutzer	
108 John Wyatt 60	
109 Rusty Staub 6.00	
110 Albie Pearson 60	
111 Don Elston...............60	
112 Bob Tillman 60	
113 Grover Powell 60	
114 Don Lock 60	
115 Frank Bolling 60	
116 Twins Rookies:..........7.50	
Jay Ward, Tony Oliva	
117 Earl Francis 60	
118 John Blanchard 60	
119 Gary Kolb 60	
120 Don Drysdale 10.00	
121 Pete Runnels 60	
122 Don McMahon 60	
123 Jose Pagan 60	
124 Orlando Pena 60	
125 Pete Rose 150.00	
126 Russ Snyder 60	
127 Angels Rookies: 60	
Dick Simpson,	
Aubrey Gatewood	
128 Mickey Lolich (R) 8.00	
129 Amado Samuel 60	
130 Gary Peters 60	
131 Steve Boros 60	
132 Milwaukee Braves 1.50	
133 Jim Grant 60	
134 Don Zimmer 1.25	
135 Johnny Callison 60	
136 World Series Game 1 ....8.00	
Koufax Strikes Out 15	
137 World Series Game 2 ....2.00	
Davis Sparks Rally	
138 World Series Game 3 ...,2.00	
LA Takes 3 Straight	
139 World Series Game 4 ....2.00	
Sealing Yanks' Doom	
140 World Series 2.00	
Dodgers Celebrate	
141 Danny Murtaugh (Mgr.)....60	
142 John Bateman 60	
143 Bubba Phillips 60	
144 Al Worthington 60	
145 Norm Siebern 60	
146 Indians Rookies: 35.00	
Tommy John, Bob Chance	
147 Ray Sadecki 60	
148 J.C. Martin 60	
149 Paul Foytack 60	
150 Willie Mays 50.00	
151 K.C. Athletics 1.50	
152 Denver LeMaster 60	
153 Dick Williams 60	
154 Dick Tracewski...........60	
155 Duke Snider 18.00	
156 Bill Dailey 60	

NO. PLAYER	NR. MT.
157 Gene Mauch 60	
158 Ken Johnson.............60	
159 Charlie Dees 60	
160 Ken Boyer 4.00	
161 Dave McNally 60	
162 Hitting Area:...........60	
Dick Sisler, Vada Pinson	
163 Donn Clendenon 60	
164 Bud Daley 60	
165 Jerry Lumpe 60	
166 Marty Keough 60	
167 Senators Rookies: 20.00	
Mike Brumley, Lou Piniella	
168 Al Weis 60	
169 Del Crandall 60	
170 Dick Radatz 60	
171 Ty Cline 60	
172 Cleveland Indians 1.50	
173 Ryne Duren 60	
174 Doc Edwards 60	
175 Billy Williams 9.00	
176 Tracy Stallard 60	
177 Harmon Killebrew 11.00	
178 Hank Bauer (Mgr.) 60	
179 Carl Warwick 60	
180 Tommy Davis 75	
181 Dave Wickersham 60	
182 Sox Sockers: 8.00	
C. Schilling, C. Yastrzemski	
183 Ron Taylor...............60	
184 Al Luplow 60	
185 Jim O'Toole 60	
186 Roman Mejias.............60	
187 Ed Roebuck 60	
188 Checklist No. 3 ....3.00	
189 Bob Hendley 60	
190 Bobby Richardson 3.00	
191 Clay Dalrymple 60	
192 Cubs Rookies: 60	
J. Boccabella, B. Cowan	
193 Jerry Lynch 60	
194 John Goryl 60	
195 Floyd Robinson 60	
196 Jim Gentile 60	
197 Frank Lary 60	
198 Len Gabrielson 60	
199 Joe Azcue 60	
200 Sandy Koufax 55.00	
201 Orioles Rookies: 75	
Wally Bunker, Sam Bowens	
202 Galen Cisco 75	
203 John Kennedy 75	
204 Matty Alou 75	
205 Nellie Fox...............3.00	
206 Steve Hamilton 75	
207 Fred Hutchinson (Mgr.) 75	
208 Wes Covington 75	
209 Bob Allen 75	
210 Carl Yastrzemski 60.00	
211 Jim Coker 75	
212 Pete Lovrich 75	
213 L.A. Angels 1.50	
214 Ken McMullen 75	
215 Ray Herbert 75	
216 Mike De La Hoz 75	
217 Jim King 75	

NO. PLAYER	NR. MT.
218 Hank Fischer	.75
219 Young Aces:	1.25
Al Downing, Jim Bouton	
220 Dick Ellsworth	.75
221 Bob Saverine	.75
222 Bill Pierce	1.00
223 George Banks	.75
224 Tommie Sisk	.75
225 Roger Maris	35.00
226 Colts Rookies:	.75
Gerald Grote, Larry Yellen	
227 Barry Latman	.75
228 Felix Mantilla	.75
229 Charley Lau	.75
230 Brooks Robinson	24.00
231 Dick Calmus	.75
232 Al Lopez (Mgr.)	2.00
233 Hal Smith	.75
234 Gary Bell	.75
235 Ron Hunt	.75
236 Bill Faul	.75
237 Chicago Cubs	2.00
238 Roy McMillan	.75
239 Herm Starrette	.75
240 Bill White	1.50
241 Jim Owens	.75
242 Harvey Kuenn	1.00
243 Phillies Rookies (R)	10.00
Richie Allen, J. Herrnstein	
244 Tony LaRussa (R)	8.00
245 Dick Stigman	.75
246 Manny Mota	1.00
247 Dave DeBusschere	2.00
248 Johnny Pesky	.75
249 Doug Camilli	.75
250 Al Kaline	16.00
251 Choo Choo Coleman	.75
252 Ken Aspromonte	.75
253 Wally Post	.75
254 Don Hoak	.75
255 Lee Thomas	.75
256 Johnny Weekly	.75
257 San F. Giants	1.50
258 Garry Roggenburk	.75
259 Harry Bright	.75
260 Frank Robinson	16.00
261 Jim Hannan	.75
262 Cardinals Rookies:	3.00
Harry Fanok, Mike Shann	
263 Chuck Estrada	.75
264 Jim Lndis	.75
265 Jim Bunning	3.00
266 Gene Freese	.75
267 Wilbur Wood	1.00
268 Bill's Got It:	.75
Bill Virdon, D. Murtaugh	
269 Ellis Burton	.75
270 Rich Rollins	.75
271 Bob Sadowski	.75
272 Jake Wood	.75
273 Mel Nelson	.75
274 Checklist No. 4	3.00
275 John Tsitouris	.75
276 Jose Tartabull	.75
277 Ken Retzer	.75
278 Bobby Shantz	.75
279 Joe Koppe	.75
280 Juan Marichal	10.00
281 Yankees Rookies:	.75
Jake Gibbs, Tom Metcalf	
282 Bob Bruce	.75
283 Tommy McCraw	.75
284 Dick Schofield	.75
285 Robin Roberts	8.00
286 Don Landrum	.75
287 Red Sox Rookies:	8.00
T. Conigliaro, B. Spanswick	
288 Al Moran	.75
289 Frank Funk	.75
290 Bob Allison	.75
291 Phil Ortega	.75

NO. PLAYER	NR. MT.
292 Mike Roarke	.75
293 Philadelphia Phillies	1.00
294 Ken Hunt	.75
295 Roger Craig	.75
296 Ed Kirkpatrick	.75
297 Ken MacKenzie	.75
298 Harry Craft (Mgr.)	.75
299 Bill Stafford	.75
300 Hank Aaron	60.00
301 Larry Brown	.75
302 Dan Pfister	.75
303 Jim Campbell	.75
304 Bob Johnson	.75
305 Jack Lamabe	.75
306 Giant Gunners:	13.00
Willie Mays, O. Cepeda	
307 Joe Gibbon	.75
308 Gene Stephens	.75
309 Paul Toth	.75
310 Jim Gilliam	2.00
311 Tom Brown	.75
312 Tigers Rookies:	.75
Fred Gladding, Fritz Fisher	
313 Chuck Hiller	.75
314 Jerry Buchek	.75
315 Bo Belinsky	.75
316 Gene Oliver	.75
317 Al Smith	.75
318 Minnesota Twins	1.50
319 Paul Brown	.75
320 Rocky Colavito	2.00
321 Bob Lillis	.75
322 George Brunet	.75
323 John Buzhardt	.75
324 Casey Stengel (Mgr.)	9.00
325 Hector Lopez	.75
326 Ron Brand	.75
327 Don Blasingame	.75
328 Bob Shaw	.75
329 Russ Nixon	.75
330 Tommy Harper	.75
331 AL Bombers:	65.00
Mickey Mantle, R. Maris,	
Norm Cash, Al Kaline	
332 Ray Washburn	.75
333 Billy Moran	.75
334 Lew Krausse	.75
335 Don Mossi	.75
336 Andre Rodgers	.75
337 Dodgers Rookies:	1.50
Al Ferrara, Jeff Torborg	
338 Jack Kralick	.75
339 Walt Bond	.75
340 Joe Cunningham	.75
341 Jim Roland	.75
342 Willie Stargell	30.00
343 Washington Senators	1.25
344 Phil Linz	.75
345 Frank Thomas	.75
346 Joe Jay	.75
347 Bobby Wine	.75
348 Ed Lopat	1.00
349 Art Fowler	.75
350 Willie McCovey	16.00
351 Dan Schneider	.75
352 Eddie Bressoud	.75
353 Wally Moon	.75
354 Dave Giusti	.75
355 Vic Power	.75
356 Reds Rookies:	.75
Bill McCool, Chico Ruiz	
357 Charley James	.75
358 Ron Kline	.75
359 Jim Schaffer	.75
360 Joe Pepitone	1.25
361 Jay Hook	.75
362 Checklist No. 5	3.00
363 Dick McAuliffe	.75
364 Joe Gaines	.75
365 Cal McLish	.75
366 Nelson Mathews	.75

NO. PLAYER	NR. MT.
367 Fred Whitfield	.75
368 White Sox Rookies:	.75
Fritz Ackley, Don Buford	
369 Jerry Zimmerman	.75
370 Hal Woodeschick	.75
371 Frank Howard	2.00
372 Howie Koplitz	.90
373 Pittsburgh Pirates	1.50
374 Bobby Bolin	.90
375 Ron Santo	2.00
376 Dave Morehead	.90
377 Bob Skinner	.90
378 Braves Rookies:	.90
W. Woodward, Jack Smith	
379 Tony Gonzalez	.90
380 Whitey Ford	18.00
381 Bob Taylor	.90
382 Wes Stock	.90
383 Bill Rigney (Mgr.)	.90
384 Ron Hansen	.90
385 Curt Simmons	1.25
386 Lenny Green	.90
387 Terry Fox	.90
388 A's Rookies:	.90
G. Williams, J. O'Donoghue	
389 Jim Umbricht	.90
390 Orlando Cepeda	6.00
391 Sam McDowell	1.00
392 Jim Pagliaroni	.90
393 Casey Teaches:	4.00
C. Stengel, Ed Kranepool	
394 Bob Miller	.90
395 Tom Tresh	1.50
396 Dennis Bennett	.90
397 Chuck Cottier	.90
398 Mets Rookies:	.90
Bill Haas, Dick Smith	
399 Jackie Brandt	.90
400 Warren Spahn	16.00
401 Charlie Maxwell	.90
402 Tom Sturdivant	.90
403 Cincinnati Reds	2.50
404 Tony Martinez	.90
405 Ken McBride	.90
406 Al Spangler	.90
407 Bill Freehan	3.00
408 Cubs Rookies:	.90
Jim Stewart, Fred Burdette	
409 Bill Fischer	.90
410 Dick Stuart	1.25
411 Lee Walls	.90
412 Ray Culp	.90
413 Johnny Keane (Mgr.)	.90
414 Jack Sanford	.90
415 Tony Kubek	5.00
416 Lee Maye	.90
417 Don Cardwell	.90
418 Orioles Rookies:	1.50
Les Narum, D. Knowles	
419 Ken Harrelson (R)	5.00
420 Jim Maloney	.90
421 Camilo Carreon	.90
422 Jack Fisher	.90
423 Tops in N.L.:	35.00
Hank Aaron, Willie Mays	
424 Dick Bertell	.90
425 Norm Cash	2.50
426 Bob Rodgers	.90
427 Don Rudolph	.90
428 Red Sox Rookies:	.90
Archie Skeen, Pete Smith	
429 Tim McCarver	5.00
430 Juan Pizarro	.90
431 George Alusik	.90
432 Ruben Amaro	.90
433 New York Yankees	11.00
434 Don Nottebart	.90
435 Vic Davalillo	.90
436 Charlie Neal	.90
437 Ed Bailey	.90
438 Checklist No. 6	3.00

NO. PLAYER	NR. MT.
439 Harvey Haddix	1.25
440 Bob Clemente	55.00
441 Bob Duliba	.90
442 Pumpsie Green	.90
443 Chuck Dressen (Mgr.)	.90
444 Larry Jackson	.90
445 Bill Skowron	1.75
446 Julian Javier	.90
447 Ted Bowsfield	.90
448 Cookie Rojas	.90
449 Deron Johnson	.90
450 Steve Barber	.90
451 Joe Amalfitano	.90
452 Giants Rookies:	2.00
Gil Garrido, Jim Hart	
453 Frank Baumann	.90
454 Tommie Aaron	.90
455 Bernie Allen	.90
456 Dodgers Rookies:	2.00
John Werhas, Wes Parker	
457 Jesse Gonder	.90
458 Ralph Terry	.90
459 Red Sox Rookies:	.90
Pete Charton, D. Jones	
460 Bob Gibson	18.00
461 George Thomas	.90
462 Birdie Tebbetts	.90
463 Don Leppert	.90
464 Dallas Green	2.50
465 Mike Hershberger	.90
466 A's Rookies:	.90
D. Green, A. Monteagudo	
467 Bob Aspromonte	.90
468 Gaylord Perry	22.00
469 Cubs Rookies:	1.25
S. Slaughter, Fred Norman	
470 Jim Bouton	3.00
471 Gates Brown (R)	1.50
472 Vern Law	1.00
473 Baltimore Orioles	1.50
474 Larry Sherry	.90
475 Ed Charles	.90
476 Braves Rookies:	5.00
Rico Carty, Dick Kelley	
477 Mike Joyce	.90
478 Dick Howser	1.25
479 Cardinals Rookies:	.90
D. Bakenhaster, J. Lewis	
480 Bob Purkey	.90
481 Chuck Schilling	.90
482 Phillies Rookies:	1.00
John Briggs, Danny Cate	
483 Fred Valentine	.90
484 Bill Pleis	.90
485 Tom Haller	.90
486 Bob Kennedy	.90
487 Mike McCormick	.90
488 Yankees Rookies:	.90
Pete Mikkelsen, Bob Meyer	
489 Julio Navarro	.90
490 Ron Fairly	.90
491 Ed Rakow	.90
492 Colts Rookies:	.90
Jim Beauchamp, M. White	
493 Don Lee	.90
494 Al Jackson	.90
495 Bill Virdon	2.00
496 Chicago White Sox	1.50
497 Jeoff Long	.90
498 Dave Stenhouse	.90
499 Indians Rookies:	.90
Chico Salmon, G. Seyfried	
500 Camilo Pascual	.90
501 Bob Veale	.90
502 Angels Rookies:	.90
Bobby Knoop, Bob Lee	
503 Earl Wilson	.90
504 Claude Raymond	.90
505 Stan Williams	.90
506 Bobby Bragan (Mgr.)	.90
507 John Edwards	.90

NO. PLAYER	NR. MT.
508 Diego Segui	.90
509 Pirates Rookies:	1.50
Gene Alley, O. McFarlane	
510 Lindy McDaniel	.90
511 Lou Jackson	.90
512 Tigers Rookies:	5.00
Joe Sparma, Willie Horton	
513 Don Larsen	1.50
514 Jim Hickman	.90
515 Johnny Romano	.90
516 Twins Rookies:	.90
Dwight Siebler, Jerry Arrigo	
517 Checklist No. 7	4.00
518 Carl Bouldin	.90
519 Charlie Smith	.90
520 Jack Baldschun	.90
521 Tom Satriano	.90
522 Bobby Tiefenauer	.90
523 Lou Burdette	6.00
524 Reds Rookies:	4.00
Jim Dickson, Bobby Klaus	
525 Al McBean	4.00
526 Lou Clinton	4.00
527 Larry Bearnarth	4.00
528 A's Rookies:	4.00
D. Duncan, Tom Reynolds	

NO. PLAYER	NR. MT.
529 Al Dark	4.00
530 Leon Wagner	4.00
531 L.A. Dodgers	8.00
532 Twins Rookies:	4.00
Bud Bloomfield (wrong photo), Joe Nossek	
533 John Klippstein	4.00
534 Gus Bell	4.00
535 Phil Regan	4.00
536 Mets Rookies:	4.00
Larry Elliot, J. Stephenson	
537 Dan Osinski	4.00
538 Minnie Minoso	6.00
539 Roy Face	4.50
540 Luis Aparicio	15.00
541 Braves Rookies:	90.00
Phil Niekro, Phil Roof	
542 Don Mincher	4.00
543 Don Uecker	50.00
544 Colts Rookies:	4.00
Steve Hertz, Joe Hoerner	
545 Max Alvis	4.00
546 Joe Christopher	4.00
547 Gil Hodges (Mgr.)	10.00
548 NL Rookies:	4.00
W. Schurr, P. Speckenbach	

NO. PLAYER	NR. MT.
549 Joe Moeller	4.00
550 Ken Hubbs	9.00
(In Memoriam)	
551 Billy Hoeft	4.00
552 Indians Rookies:	4.00
Tom Kelley, Sonny Siebert	
553 Jim Brewer	4.00
554 Hank Foiles	4.00
555 Lee Stange	4.00
556 Mets Rookies:	4.00
Steve Dillon, Ron Locke	
557 Leo Burke	4.00
558 Don Schwall	4.00
559 Dick Phillips	4.00
560 Dick Farrell	5.00
561 Phillies Rookies:	5.00
Dave Bennett, Rick Wise	
562 Pedro Ramos	4.00
563 Dal Maxvill	4.00
564 AL Rookies:	4.00
Joe McCabe, J. McNertney	
565 Stu Miller	4.00
566 Ed Kranepool	4.00
567 Jim Kaat	8.00

NO. PLAYER	NR. MT.
568 NL Rookies:	4.00
Phil Gagliano, Cap Peterson	
569 Fred Newman	4.00
570 Bill Mazeroski	5.00
571 Gene Conley	4.00
572 AL Rookies:	4.00
Dave Gray, Dick Egan	
573 Jim Duffalo	4.00
574 Manny Jimenez	4.00
575 Tony Cloninger	4.00
576 Mets Rookies:	4.00
J. Hinsley, Bill Wakefield	
577 Gordy Coleman	4.00
578 Glen Hobbie	4.00
579 Boston Red Sox	8.00
580 Johnny Podres	7.00
581 Yankees Rookies:	4.00
P. Gonzalez, Archie Moore	
582 Rod Kanehl	4.00
583 Tito Francona	4.00
584 Joel Horlen	4.00
585 Tony Taylor	4.00
586 Jim Piersall	6.00
587 Bennie Daniels (Exc. $1.50)	6.00

1965 Topps. . . . Complete Set of 598 Cards—Value $1000.00 (Exc.); $2400.00 (Mint)

This set includes the rookie cards of Steve Carlton, Joe Morgan, Tony Perez and "Catfish" Hunter. Cards 523 to 598 are the high numbers. Semi-high numbers are 447 to 522.

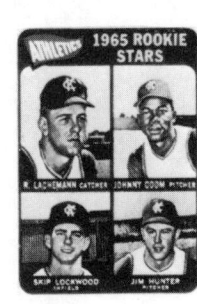

NO. PLAYER	NR. MT.
1 AL Bat Ldrs.: (Exc. $1.00)	8.00
Elston Howard, Tony Oliva, Brooks Robinson	
2 NL Batting Leaders:	4.00
Hank Aaron, Bob Clemente, Rico Carty	
3 AL Home Run Leaders:	7.50
Boog Powell, Harmon Killebrew, Mickey Mantle	
4 NL Home Run Leaders:	4.00
Willie Mays, Billy Williams, Johnny Callison, Jim Hart, Orlando Cepeda	
5 AL RBI Leaders:	7.00
Brooks Robinson, Dick Stuart, Harmon Killebrew, Mickey Mantle	
6 NL RBI Leaders:	2.50
Ken Boyer, Willie Mays, Ron Santo	
7 AL ERA Leaders:	1.50
Dean Chance, Joel Horlen	
8 NL ERA Leaders:	4.00
S. Koufax, Don Drysdale	
9 AL Pitching Leaders:	1.50
D. Chance, G. Peters, J. Pizarro, W. Bunker, D. Wickersham	
10 NL Pitching Leaders:	2.00
L. Jackson, Juan Marichal, Ray Sadecki	

NO. PLAYER	NR. MT.
11 AL Strikeout Leaders:	1.50
A. Downing, D. Chance, C. Pascual	
12 NL Strikeout Leaders:	2.00
Bob Gibson, B. Veale, Don Drysdale	
13 Pedro Ramos	.50
14 Len Gabrielson	.50
15 Robin Roberts	7.50
16 Houston Rookies:	60.00
Joe Morgan, Sonny Jackson	
17 John Romano	.50
18 Bill McCool	.50
19 Gates Brown	.50
20 Jim Bunning	3.00
21 Don Blasingame	.50
22 Charlie Smith	.50
23 Bob Tiefenauer	.50
24 Twins—6th Place	2.00
25 Al McBeane	.50
26 Bob Knoop	.50
27 Dick Bertell	.50
28 Barney Schultz	.50
29 Felix Mantilla	.50
30 Jim Bouton	1.50
31 Mike White	.50
32 Herman Franks	.50
33 Jackie Brandt	.50
34 Cal Koonce	.50
35 Ed Charles	.50
36 Bobby Wine	.50

NO. PLAYER	NR. MT.
37 Fred Gladding	.50
38 Jim King	.50
39 Gerry Arrigo	.50
40 Frank Howard	1.50
41 White Sox Rookies:	.50
Bruce Howard, Marv Staehle	
42 Earl Wilson	.50
43 Mike Shannon	.60
44 Wade Blasingame	.50
45 Roy McMillan	.50
46 Bob Lee	.50
47 Tommy Harper	.50
48 Claude Raymond	.50
49 Orioles Rookies:	1.00
John Miller, Curt Blefary	
50 Juan Marical	8.00
51 Billy Bryan	.50
52 Ed Roebuck	.50
53 Dick McAuliffe	.50
54 Joe Gibbon	.50
55 Tony Conigliaro	3.00
56 Ron Kline	.50
57 Cardinals—1st Place	1.25
58 Fred Talbot	.50
59 Nate Oiver	.50
60 Jim O'Toole	.50
61 Chris Cannizzaro	.50
62 Jim Kaat	4.00
63 Ty Cline	.50
64 Lou Burdette	1.25
65 Tony Kubek	3.00

NO. PLAYER	NR. MT.
66 Bill Rigney	.50
67 Harvey Haddix	.50
68 Del Crandall	.50
69 Bill Virdon	1.00
70 Bill Skowron	1.25
71 John O'Donoghue	.50
72 Tony Gonzalez	.50
73 Dennis Ribant	.50
74 Red Sox Rookies:	3.00
R. Petrocelli, J. Stephenson	
75 Deron Johnson	.50
76 Sam McDowell	.75
77 Doug Camilli	.50
78 Dal Maxvill	.50
79 Checklist No. 1	2.50
80 Turk Farrell	.50
81 Don Buford	.50
82 Braves Rookies:	.50
Santos Alomar, John Braun	
83 George Thomas	.50
84 Ron Herbel	.50
85 Willie Smith	.50
86 Les Narum	.50
87 Nelson Mathews	.50
88 Jack Lamabe	.50
89 Mike Hershberger	.50
90 Rich Rollins	.50
91 Cubs—8th Place	1.25
92 Dick Howser	1.00
93 Jack Fisher	.50
94 Charlie Lau	.50

NO.	PLAYER	NR. MT.
95	Bill Mazeroski	1.50
96	Sonny Siebert	.50
97	Pedro Gonzalez	.50
98	Bob Miller	.50
99	Gil Hodges	5.00
100	Ken Boyer	2.50
101	Fred Newman	.50
102	Steve Boros	.50
103	Harvey Kuenn	.75
104	Checklist No. 2	2.50
105	Chico Salmon	.50
106	Gene Oliver	.50
107	Phillies Rookies:	1.50
	C. Shockley, Pat Corrales	
108	Don Mincher	.50
109	Walt Bond	.50
110	Ron Santo	1.50
111	Lee Thomas	.50
112	Derrell Griffith	.50
113	Steve Barber	.50
114	Jim Hickman	.50
115	Bob Richardson	2.50
116	Cardinals Rookies:	1.00
	Dave Dowling, Bob Tolan	
117	Wes Stock	.50
118	Hal Lanier (R)	1.25
119	John Kennedy	.50
120	Frank Robinson	12.00
121	Gene Alley	.50
122	Bill Pleis	.50
123	Frank Thomas	.50
124	Tom Satriano	.50
125	Juan Pizarro	.50
126	Dodgers—6th Place	3.00
127	Frank Lary	.50
128	Vic Davalillo	.50
129	Bennie Daniels	.50
130	Al Kaline	15.00
131	Johnny Keane (Mgr.)	.50
132	World Series Game 1	2.50
	Cards Take Opener	
133	World Series Game 2	2.50
	Stottlemyre Wins	
134	World Series Game 3	18.00
	Mantle's Clutch Homer	
135	World Series Game 4	2.50
	Boyer's Grand-Slam	
136	World Series Game 5	2.50
	10th Inning Triumph	
137	World Series Game 6	2.50
	Bouton Wins Again	
138	World Series Game 7	4.00
	Gibson Wins Finale	
139	World Series	2.50
	The Cards Celebrate	
140	Dean Chance	.50
141	Charlie James	.50
142	Bill Monouquette	.50
143	Pirates Rookies:	.50
	John Gelnar, Jerry May	
144	Ed Kranepool	.50
145	Luis Tiant (R)	7.50
146	Ron Hansen	.50
147	Dennis Bennett	.50
148	Willie Kirkland	.50
149	Wayne Schurr	.50
150	Brooks Robinson	17.00
151	Athletics—10th Place	1.25
152	Phil Ortega	.50
153	Norm Cash	1.50
154	Bob Humphreys	.50
155	Roger Maris	35.00
156	Bob Sadowski	.50
157	Zoilo Versalles	1.00
158	Dick Sisler (Mgr.)	.50
159	Jim Duffalo	.50
160	Bob Clemente	40.00
161	Frank Baumann	.50
162	Russ Nixon	.50
163	John Briggs	.50
164	Al Spangler	.50
165	Dick Ellsworth	.50
166	Indians Rookies:	1.25
	G. Culver, Tommie Agee	
167	Bill Wakefield	.50

NO.	PLAYER	NR. MT.
168	Dick Green	.50
169	Dave Vineyard	.50
170	Hank Aaron	50.00
171	Jim Roland	.50
172	Jim Piersall	1.00
173	Tigers—4th Place	2.00
174	Joe Jay	.50
175	Bob Aspromonte	.50
176	Willie McCovey	13.00
177	Pete Mikkelsen	.50
178	Dalton Jones	.50
179	Hal Woodeschick	.50
180	Bob Allison	.75
181	Senators Rookies:	.50
	Don Loun, Joe McCabe	
182	Mike De La Hoz	.50
183	Dave Nicholson	.50
184	John Boozer	.50
185	Max Alvis	.50
186	Bill Cowan	.50
187	Casey Stengel (Mgr.)	9.00
188	Sam Bowens	.50
189	Checklist No. 3	2.50
190	Bill White	1.50
191	Phil Regan	.50
192	Jim Coker	.50
193	Gaylord Perry	10.00
194	Angels Rookies:	.50
	Rick Reichardt, Bill Kelso	
195	Bob Veale	.50
196	Ron Fairly	.50
197	Diego Segui	.50
198	Smoky Burgess	.50
199	Bob Heffner	.75
200	Joe Torre	2.00
201	Twins Rookies:	1.25
	S. Valdespino, Cesar Tovar	
202	Leo Burke	.75
203	Dallas Green	1.75
204	Russ Snyder	.75
205	Warren Spahn	14.00
206	Willie Horton	1.25
207	Pete Rose	160.00
208	Tommy John	8.00
209	Pirates—6th Place	1.50
210	Jim Fregosi	1.25
211	Steve Ridzik	.75
212	Ron Brand	.75
213	Jim Davenport	.75
214	Bob Purkey	.75
215	Pete Ward	.75
216	Al Worthington	.75
217	Walt Alston (Mgr.)	2.50
218	Dick Schofield	.75
219	Bob Meyer	.75
220	Billy Williams	8.00
221	John Tsitouris	.75
222	Bob Tillman	.75
223	Dan Osinski	.75
224	Bob Chance	.75
225	Bo Belinsky	.75
226	Yankees Rookies:	1.50
	Elvio Jimenez, Jake Gibbs	
227	Bobby Klaus	.75
228	Jack Sanford	.75
229	Lou Clinton	.75
230	Ray Sadecki	.75
231	Jerry Adair	.75
232	Steve Blass (R)	1.25
233	Don Zimmer	1.25
234	White Sox—2nd Place	1.25
235	Chuck Hinton	.75
236	Dennis McLain (R)	10.00
237	Bernie Allen	.75
238	Joe Moeller	.75
239	Doc Edwards	1.00
240	Bob Bruce	.75
241	Mack Jones	.75
242	George Brunet	.75
243	Reds Rookies:	1.50
	T. Helms, Ted Davidson	
244	Lindy McDaniel	.75
245	Joe Pepitone	1.25
246	Tom Butters	.75
247	Wally Moon	.75

NO.	PLAYER	NR. MT.
248	Gus Triandos	.75
249	Dave McNally	1.25
250	Willie Mays	65.00
251	Billy Herman (Mgr.)	2.00
252	Pete Richert	.75
253	Danny Cater	.75
254	Roland Sheldon	.75
255	Camilo Pascual	.75
256	Tito Francona	.75
257	Jim Wynn	1.00
258	Larry Bearnarth	.75
259	Tigers Rookies:	2.00
	Jim Northrup, Ray Oyler	
260	Don Drysdale	11.00
261	Duke Carmel	.75
262	Bud Daley	.75
263	Marty Keough	.75
264	Bob Buhl	.75
265	Jim Pagliaroni	.75
266	Bert Campaneris	2.50
267	Senators—9th Place	1.25
268	Ken McBride	.75
269	Frank Bolling	.75
270	Milt Pappas	.75
271	Don Wert	.75
272	Chuck Schilling	.75
273	Checklist No. 4	2.50
274	Lum Harris (Mgr.)	.75
275	Dick Groat	1.00
276	Hoyt Wilhelm	8.00
277	Johnny Lewis	.75
278	Ken Retzer	.75
279	Dick Tracewski	.75
280	Dick Stuart	.75
281	Bill Stafford	.75
282	Giants Rookies:	1.50
	Dick Estelle, M. Murakami	
283	Fred Whitfield	.75
284	Nick Willhite	.75
285	Ron Hunt	.75
286	Athletics Rookies:	.75
	J. Dickson, A. Monteagudo	
287	Gary Kolb	.75
288	Jack Hamilton	.75
289	Gordy Coleman	.75
290	Wally Bunker	.75
291	Jerry Lynch	.75
292	Larry Yellen	.75
293	Angels—5th Place	1.50
294	Tim McCarver	1.50
295	Dick Radatz	.75
296	Tony Taylor	.75
297	Dave Debusschere	2.50
298	Jim Stewart	.75
299	Jerry Zimmerman	.75
300	Sandy Koufax	75.00
301	Birdie Tebbetts	.75
302	Al Stanek	.75
303	John Orsino	.75
304	Dave Stenhouse	.75
305	Rico Carty	1.25
306	Bubba Phillips	.75
307	Barry Latman	.75
308	Mets Rookies:	.75
	Tom Parsons, Cleon Jones	
309	Steve Hamilton	.75
310	Johnny Callison	.75
311	Orlando Pena	.75
312	Joe Nuxhall	.75
313	Jim Schaffer	.75
314	Sterling Slaughter	.75
315	Frank Malzone	.75
316	Reds—2nd Place	1.50
317	Don McMahon	.75
318	Matty Alou	.75
319	Ken McMullen	.75
320	Bob Gibson	15.00
321	Rusty Staub	3.50
322	Rick Wise	.75
323	Hank Bauer (Mgr.)	.75
324	Bobby Locke	.75
325	Donn Clendenon	.75
326	Dwight Siebler	.75
327	Dennis Menke	.75
328	Eddie Fisher	.75

NO.	PLAYER	NR. MT.
329	Hawk Taylor	.75
330	Whitey Ford	15.00
331	Dodgers Rookies:	1.00
	Al Ferrara, John Purdin	
332	Ted Abernathy	.75
333	Tommie Reynolds	.75
334	Vic Roznovsky	.75
335	Mickey Lolich	2.00
336	Woody Held	.75
337	Mike Cuellar	1.00
338	Phillies—2nd Place	1.50
339	Ryne Duren	.75
340	Tony Oliva	5.00
341	Bobby Bolin	.75
342	Bob Rodgers	.75
343	Mike McCormick	.75
344	Wes Parker	.75
345	Floyd Robinson	.75
346	Bob Bragan (Mgr.)	.75
347	Roy Face	1.00
348	George Banks	.75
349	Larry Miller	.75
350	Mickey Mantle	400.00
351	Jim Perry	1.00
352	Alex Johnson	.75
353	Jerry Lumpe	.75
354	Cubs Rookies:	.75
	Billy Ott, Jack Warner	
355	Vada Pinson	1.50
356	Bill Spanswick	.75
357	Carl Warwick	.75
358	Albie Pearson	.75
359	Ken Johnson	.75
360	Orlando Cepeda	5.00
361	Checklist No. 5	2.50
362	Don Schwall	.75
363	Bob Johnson	.75
364	Galen Cisco	.75
365	Jim Gentile	.75
366	Dan Schneider	.75
367	Leon Wagner	.75
368	White Sox Rookies:	1.00
	Ken Berry, Joel Gibson	
369	Phil Linz	.75
370	Tommy Davis	1.25
371	Frank Kreutzer	.75
372	Clay Dalrymple	.75
373	Curt Simmons	.75
374	Angels Rookies:	.75
	J. Cardenal, D. Simpson	
375	Dave Wickersham	.75
376	Jim Landis	.75
377	Willie Stargell	22.00
378	Chuck Estrada	.75
379	Giants—4th Place	1.50
380	Rocky Colavito	2.50
381	Al Jackson	.75
382	J.C. Martin	.75
383	Felipe Alou	1.00
384	Johnny Klippstein	.75
385	Carl Yastrzemski	65.00
386	Cubs Rookies:	1.00
	Paul Jaeckel, Fred Norman	
387	Johnny Podres	1.25
388	John Blanchard	.75
389	Don Larsen	1.25
390	Bill Freehan	1.00
391	Mel McGaha	.75
392	Bob Friend	.75
393	Ed Kirkpatrck	.75
394	Jim Hannan	.75
395	Jim Hart	1.00
396	Frank Bertaina	.75
397	Jerry Buchek	.75
398	Reds Rookies:	.75
	Art Shamsky, Dan Neville	
399	Ray Herbert	.75
400	Harmon Killebrew	13.00
401	Carl Willey	.75
402	Joe Amalfitano	.75
403	Red Sox—8th Place	1.50
404	Stan Williams	.75
405	John Roseboro	.75
406	Ralph Terry	.75
407	Lee Maye	.75

NO. PLAYER	NR. MT.
408 Larry Sherry	.75
409 Astros Rookies:	1.00
Jim Beauchamp, L. Dierker	
410 Luis Aparicio	8.00
411 Roger Craig	.75
412 Bob Bailey	.75
413 Hal Reniff	.75
414 Al Lopez	2.50
415 Curt Flood	2.00
416 Jim Brewer	.75
417 Ed Brinkman	.75
418 Johnny Edwards	.75
419 Ruben Amaro	.75
420 Larry Jackson	.75
421 Twins Rookies:	.75
Gary Dotter, Jay Ward	
422 Aubrey Gatewood	.75
423 Jesse Gonder	.75
424 Gary Bell	.75
425 Wayne Causey	.75
426 Braves—5th Place	1.25
427 Bob Saverine	.75
428 Bob Shaw	.75
429 Don Demeter	.75
430 Gary Peters	.75
431 Cards Rookies:	1.00
Nelson Briles, W. Spiezio	
432 Jim Grant	.75
433 John Bateman	.75
434 Dave Morehead	.75
435 Willie Davis	1.00
436 Don Elston	.75
437 Chico Cardenas	.75
438 Harry Walker (Mgr.)	.75
439 Moe Drabowsky	.75
440 Tom Tresh	1.25
441 Denver LeMaster	.75
442 Vic Power	.75
443 Checklist No. 6	2.50
444 Bob Hendley	.75
445 Don Lock	.75
446 Art Mahaffey	.75
447 Julian Javier	2.00
448 Lee Stange	2.00
449 Mets Rookies:	2.00
Jerry Hinsley, Gary Kroll	
450 Elston Howard	4.00
451 Jim Owens	2.00
452 Gary Geiger	2.00
453 Dodgers Rookies:	3.00
W. Crawford, J. Werhas	
454 Ed Rakow	2.00
455 Norm Siebern	2.00
456 Bill Henry	2.00
457 Bob Kennedy—Coach	2.00
458 John Buzhardt	2.00
459 Frank Kostro	2.00
460 Richie Allen	5.00

NO. PLAYER	NR. MT.
461 Braves Rookies:	30.00
Clay Carroll, Phil Niekro	
462 Lew Krausse	2.00
(photo of Pete Lovrich)	
463 Manny Mota	2.00
464 Ron Piche	2.00
465 Tom Haller	2.00
466 Senators Rookies:	2.00
Pete Craig, Dick Nen	
467 Ray Washburn	2.00
468 Larry Brown	2.00
469 Don Nottebart	2.00
470 Yogi Berra	35.00
471 Billy Hoeft	2.00
472 Don Pavletich	2.00
473 Orioles Rookies:	9.00
Paul Blair, Dave Johnson	
474 Cookie Rojas	2.00
475 Clete Boyer	3.00
476 Billy O'Dell	2.00
477 Cards Rookies:	165.00
Fritz Ackley, Steve Carlton	
478 Wilbur Wood	2.00
479 Ken Harrelson	4.00
480 Joel Horlen	2.00
481 Indians—7th Place	4.00
482 Bob Priddy	2.00
483 George Smith	2.00
484 Ron Perranoski	2.50
485 Nellie Fox	4.00
486 Angels Rookies:	2.00
Pat Rogan Tom Egan	
487 Woody Woodward	2.00
488 Ted Wills	2.00
489 Gene Mauch (Mgr.)	2.00
490 Earl Battey	2.00
491 Tracy Stallard	2.00
492 Gene Freese	2.00
493 Tigers Rookies:	2.00
Bill Roman, Bruce Brubaker	
494 Jay Ritchie	2.00
495 Joe Christopher	2.00
496 Joe Cunningham	2.00
497 Giants Rookies:	2.00
Ken Henderson, Jack Hiatt	
498 Gene Stephens	2.00
499 Stu Miller	2.00
500 Ed Mathews	20.00
501 Indians Rookies:	2.00
Jim Rittwage, R. Gagliano	
502 Don Cardwell	2.00
503 Phil Gagliano	2.00
504 Jerry Grote	2.00
505 Ray Culp	2.00
506 Sam Mele	2.00
507 Sammy Ellis	2.00
508 Checklist No. 7	4.00
509 Red Sox Rookies:	2.00
Bob Guindon, G. Vezendy	

NO. PLAYER	NR. MT.
510 Ernie Banks	40.00
511 Ron Locke	2.00
512 Cap Peterson	2.00
513 Yankees—1st Place	10.00
514 Joe Azcue	2.00
515 Vern Law	2.00
516 Al Weis	2.00
517 Angels Rookies:	2.00
Paul Schaal, Jack Warner	
518 Ken Rowe	2.00
519 Bob Uecker	45.00
520 Tony Cloninger	2.00
521 Phillies Rookies:	2.00
Dave Bennett, M. Steevens	
522 Hank Aguirre	2.00
523 Mike Brumley	4.00
524 Dave Giusti	4.00
525 Ed Bressoud	4.00
526 Athletics Rookies:	75.00
S. Lockwood, R. Lachemann,	
Johnny Odom, Jim Hunter	
527 Jeff Torborg	4.00
528 George Altman	4.00
529 Jerry Fosnow	4.00
530 Jim Maloney	4.00
531 Chuck Hiller	4.00
532 Hector Lopez	4.00
533 Mets Rookies:	12.00
Dan Napoleon, Ron	
Swoboda, Jim Bethke,	
Tug McGraw	
534 John Herrnstein	4.00
535 Jack Kralick	4.00
536 Andre Rodgers	4.00
537 Angels Rookies:	4.00
Marcelino Lopez, Rudy	
May, Phil Roof	
538 Chuck Dressen (Mgr.)	4.00
539 Herm Starrette	4.00
540 Lou Brock	35.00
541 White Sox Rookies:	4.00
Bob Locker, Greg Bollo	
542 Lou Klimchock	4.00
543 Ed Connolly	4.00
544 Howie Reed	4.00
545 Jesus Alou	4.00
546 Indians Rookies:	4.00
Floyd Weaver, Bill Davis,	
Mike Hedlund, Ray Barker	
547 Jake Wood	4.00
548 Dick Stigman	4.00
549 Cubs Rookies:	5.00
R. Pena, Glenn Beckert	
550 Mel Stottlemyre (R)	13.00
551 Mets—10th Place	8.00
552 Julio Gotay	4.00
553 Astros Rookies:	4.00
Gene Ratliff, Dan Coombs,	
Jack McClure	

NO. PLAYER	NR. MT.
554 Chico Ruiz	4.00
555 Jack Baldschun	4.00
556 Red Schoendienst	8.00
557 Jose Santiago	4.00
558 Tommie Sisk	4.00
559 Ed Bailey	4.00
560 Boog Powell	6.00
561 Dodgers Rookies:	7.00
D. Daboll, Mike Kekich,	
H. Valle, Jim Lefebvre	
562 Billy Moran	4.00
563 Julio Navarro	4.00
564 Mel Nelson	4.00
565 Ernie Broglio	4.00
566 Yankees Rookies:	4.00
Art Lopez, Gil Blanco,	
Ross Moschitto	
567 Tommie Aaron	4.00
568 Ron Taylor	4.00
569 Gino Cimoli	4.00
570 Claude Osteen	4.00
571 Ossie Virgil	4.00
572 Orioles—3rd Place	5.00
573 Red Sox Rookies:	8.00
Jim Lonborg, Mike Ryan,	
G. Moses, Bill Schlesinger	
574 Roy Sievers	5.00
575 Jose Pagan	4.00
576 Terry Fox	4.00
577 AL Rookie Stars:	4.00
D. Knowles, R. Scheinblum,	
Don Buschhorn	
578 Camilo Carreon	4.00
579 Dick Smith	4.00
580 Jimmie Hall	4.00
581 NL Rookie Stars:	50.00
Tony Perez, Dave Ricketts,	
Kevin Collins	
582 Bob Schmidt	4.00
583 Wes Covington	4.00
584 Harry Bright	4.00
585 Hank Fischer	4.00
586 Tommy McCraw	4.00
587 Joe Sparma	4.00
588 Lenny Green	4.00
589 Giants Rookies:	4.00
Frank Linzy, B. Schroder	
590 Johnnie Wyatt	4.00
591 Bob Skinner	4.00
592 Frank Bork	4.00
593 Tigers Rookies:	4.00
Jackie Moore, John Sullivan	
594 Joe Gaines	4.00
595 Don Lee	4.00
596 Don Landrum	4.00
597 Twins Rookies:	4.00
Dick Reese, Joe Nossek,	
John Sevcik	
598 Al Downing (Exc. $1.50)	5.00

1966 Topps. . . . Complete Set of 598 Cards—Value $1100.00 (Exc.); $3000.00 (Mint)

Features the rookie cards of Jim Palmer, and Don Sutton. The high numbers are 523 to 598. Cards 62, 103 and 104 (worth $20.00) and card 91 (worth $50.00) exist without a *traded* or *sold* line. Card 101 (checklist) exists identifying card 115 as either Bill Henry—worth $3.00 or Warren Spahn—worth $7.50.

NO. PLAYER	NR. MT.
1 Willie Mays (Exc. $25.00)	125.00
2 Ted Abernathy	.50
3 Sam Mele (Mgr.)	.50
4 Ray Culp	.50
5 Jim Fregosi	1.00
6 Chuck Schilling	.50
7 Tracy Stallard	.50
8 Floyd Robinson	.50
9 Clete Boyer	1.25
10 Tony Cloninger	.50
11 Senators Rookies:	.50
Brant Alyea, Pete Craig	
12 John Tsitouris	.50
13 Lou Johnson	.50
14 Norm Siebern	.50
15 Vern Law	1.00
16 Larry Brown	.50
17 John Stephenson	.50
18 Roland Sheldon	.50
19 Giants—2nd Place	1.25
20 Willie Horton	1.25
21 Don Nottebart	.50
22 Joe Nossek	.50
23 Jack Sanford	.50
24 Don Kessinger (R)	1.50
25 Joe Ward	.50
26 Ray Sadecki	.50
27 Orioles Rookies:	1.00
D. Knowles, A. Etchebarren	
28 Phil Niekro	14.00
29 Mike Brumley	1.00
30 Pete Rose	60.00
31 Jack Cullen	.50
32 Adolfo Phillips	.50
33 Jim Pagliaroni	.50
34 Checklist No. 1	2.00
35 Ron Swoboda	1.00
36 Jim Hunter	15.00
37 Billy Herman	1.75
38 Ron Nischwitz	.50
39 Ken Henderson	.50
40 Jim Grant	.50
41 Don LeJohn	.50
42 Aubrey Gatewood	.50
43 Don Landrum	.50
44 Indians Rookies:	.50
Bill Davis, Tom Kelley	
45 Jim Gentile	.60
46 Howie Koplitz	.50
47 J.C. Martin	.50
48 Paul Blair	1.00
49 Woody Woodward	.50
50 Mick Mantle	225.00
51 Gordon Richardson	.50
52 Power Plus:	.75
W. Covington, J. Callison	
53 Bob Duliba	.50
54 Jose Pagan	.50
55 Ken Harrelson	1.00
56 Sandy Valdespino	.50
57 Jim Lefebvre	.50
58 Dave Wickersham	.50
59 Reds—4th Place	1.25
60 Curt Flood	1.25
61 Bob Bolin	.50
62 Merritt Ranew*	.50
63 Jim Stewart	.50
64 Bob Bruce	.50
65 Leon Wagner	.50
66 Al Weis	.50
67 Mets Rookies:	.50
Cleon Jones, Dick Selma	
68 Hal Reniff	.50
69 Ken Hamlin	.50
70 Carl Yastrzemski	45.00
71 Frank Carpin	.50
72 Tony Perez	10.00
73 Jerry Zimmerman	.50
74 Don Mossi	.75
75 Tommy Davis	1.00
76 R. Schoendienst (Mgr.)	4.00
77 Johnny Orsino	.50
78 Frank Linzy	.50
79 Joe Pepitone	1.25
80 Richie Allen	2.00

NO. PLAYER	NR. MT.
81 Ray Oyler	.50
82 Bob Hendley	.50
83 Albie Pearson	.50
84 Braves Rookies:	.50
J. Beauchamp, D. Kelley	
85 Eddie Fisher	.50
86 John Bateman	.50
87 Dan Napoleon	.50
88 Fred Whitfield	.50
89 Ted Davidson	.50
90 Luis Aparicio	7.00
91 Bob Uecker*	15.00
92 Yankees—6th Place	3.00
93 Jim Lonborg	1.00
94 Matty Alou	1.00
95 Pete Richert	.50
96 Felipe Alou	1.00
97 Jim Merritt	.50
98 Don Demeter	.50
99 Buc Belters:	3.00
W. Stargell, D. Clendenon	
100 Sandy Koufax	50.00
101 Checklist No. 2*	4.00
102 Ed Kirkpatrick	.50
103 Dick Groat*	1.00
104 Alex Johnson*	1.00
105 Milt Pappas	.75
106 Rusty Staub	1.50
107 A's Rookies:	.50
L. Stahl, Ron Tompkins	
108 Bobby Klaus	.50
109 Ralph Terry	.50
110 Ernie Banks	15.00
111 Gary Peters	.50
112 Manny Mota	.75
113 Hank Aguirre	.50
114 Jim Gosger	.50
115 Bill Henry*	.50
116 Walt Alston (Mgr.)	2.50
117 Jake Gibbs	.50
118 Mike McCormick	.50
119 Art Shamsky	.50
120 Harmon Killebrew	11.00
121 Ray Herbert	.50
122 Joe Gaines	.50
123 Pirates Rookies:	.50
Frank Bork, Jerry May	
124 Tug McGraw	3.00
125 Lou Brock	12.00
126 Jim Palmer (R)	90.00
127 Ken Berry	.50
128 Jim Landis	.50
129 Jack Kralick	.50
130 Joe Torre	1.25
131 Angels—7th Place	1.00
132 Orlando Cepeda	3.00
133 Don McMahon	.50
134 Wes Parker	.50
135 Dave Morehead	.50
136 Woody Held	.50
137 Pat Corrales	.75
138 Roger Repoz	.50
139 Cubs Rookies:	.50
Byron Browne, Don Young	
140 Jim Maloney	.75
141 Tom McCraw	.50
142 Don Dennis	.50
143 Jose Tartabull	.50
144 Don Schwall	.50
145 Bill Freehan	.75
146 George Altman	.50
147 Lum Harris (Mgr.)	.50
148 Bob Johnson	.50
149 Dick Nen	.50
150 Rocky Colavito	1.25
151 Gary Wagner	.50
152 Frank Malzone	.50
153 Rico Carty	1.00
154 Chuck Hiller	.50
155 Marcelino Lopez	.50
156 Double Play Combo:	.75
Dick Schofield, Hal Lanier	
157 Rene Lachemann	.50
158 Jim Brewer	.50
159 Chico Ruiz	.50

NO. PLAYER	NR. MT.
160 Whitey Ford	14.00
161 Jerry Lumpe	.50
162 Lee Maye	.50
163 Tito Francona	.50
164 White Sox Rookies:	.75
Tommie Agee, M. Staehle	
165 Don Lock	.50
166 Chris Krug	.50
167 Boog Powell	2.00
168 Dan Osinski	.50
169 Duke Sims	.50
170 Cookie Rojas	.50
171 Nick Willhite	.50
172 Mets—10th Place	1.50
173 Al Spangler	.50
174 Ron Taylor	.50
175 Bert Campaneris	1.00
176 Jim Davenport	.50
177 Hector Lopez	.50
178 Bob Tillman	.50
179 Cards Rookies:	.75
Dennis Aust, Bob Tolan	
180 Vada Pinson	1.25
181 Al Worthington	.50
182 Jerry Lynch	.50
183 Checklist No. 3	2.00
184 Denis Menke	.50
185 Bob Buhl	.50
186 Ruben Amaro	.50
187 Chuck Dressen (Mgr.)	.75
188 Al Luplow	.50
189 John Roseboro	.50
190 Jimmie Hall	.50
191 Darrell Sutherland	.50
192 Vic Power	.50
193 Dave McNally	.75
194 Senators—8th Place	.50
195 Joe Morgan	16.00
196 Don Pavletich	.50
197 Sonny Siebert	.50
198 Mickey Stanley	1.25
199 Chisox Clubbers:	.75
Bill Skowron, Johnny Romano, Floyd Robinson	
200 Ed Mathews	10.00
201 Jim Dickson	.50
202 Clay Dalrymple	.50
203 Jose Santiago	.50
204 Cubs—8th Place	1.25
205 Tom Tresh	1.00
206 Alvin Jackson	.75
207 Frank Quilici	.75
208 Bob Miller	.75
209 Tigers Rookies:	1.25
Fritz Fisher, John Hiller	
210 Bill Mazeroski	1.00
211 Frank Kreutzer	.50
212 Ed Kranepool	.75
213 Fred Newman	.50
214 Tommy Harper	.50
215 NL Batting Leaders:	10.00
Willie Mays, Bob Clemente, Hank Aaron	
216 AL Batting Leaders:	3.00
Tony Oliva, Carl Yastrzemski, Vic Davalillo	
217 NL Home Run Leaders:	3.00
Willie McCovey, Willie Mays, Billy Williams	
218 AL Home Run Leaders:	1.50
Norm Cash, Willie Horton, Tony Conigliaro	
219 NL RBI Leaders:	1.50
Frank Robinson, Deron Johnson, Willie Mays	
220 AL RBI Leaders:	1.25
Rocky Colavito, Willie Horton, Tony Oliva	
221 NL ERA Leaders:	2.50
Sandy Koufax, Vern Law, Juan Marichal	
222 AL ERA Leaders:	1.25
Sam McDowell, Sonny Siebert, Eddie Fisher	
223 NL Pitching Leaders:	2.50
Sandy Koufax, Tony Cloninger, Don Drysdale	

NO. PLAYER	NR. MT.
224 AL Pitching Leaders:	1.25
Mel Stottlemyre, Jim Grant, Jim Kaat	
225 NL Strikeout Leaders:	2.50
Bob Gibson, Sandy Koufax, Bob Veale	
226 AL Strikeout Leaders:	1.75
Sam McDowell, Mickey Lolich, Denny McLain, Sonny Siebert	
227 Russ Nixon	.50
228 Larry Dierker	.50
229 Hank Bauer	.75
230 Johnny Callison	.75
231 F. Weaver	.50
232 Glenn Beckert	.75
233 Dom Zanni	.50
234 Yankees Rookies:	4.00
Roy White, Rich Beck	
235 Don Cardwell	.50
236 Mike Hershberger	.50
237 Billy O'Dell	.50
238 Dodgers—1st Place	2.00
239 Orlando Pena	.50
240 Earl Battey	.50
241 Dennis Ribant	.50
242 Jesus Alou	.50
243 Nelson Briles	.50
244 Astros Rookies:	.50
C. Harrison, S. Jackson	
245 John Buzhardt	.50
246 Ed Bailey	.50
247 Carl Warwick	.50
248 Pete Mikkelsen	.50
249 Bill Rigney (Mgr.)	.50
250 Sam Ellis	.50
251 Ed Brinkman	.50
252 Denver Lemaster	.50
253 Don Wert	.50
254 Phillies Rookies:	20.00
Ferguson Jenkins, Bill Sorrell	
255 Willie Stargell	15.00
256 Lew Krausse	.50
257 Jeff Torborg	.50
258 Dave Giusti	.50
259 Red Sox—9th Place	1.50
260 Bob Shaw	.50
261 Ron Hansen	.50
262 Jack Hamilton	.50
263 Tom Egan	.50
264 Twins Rookies:	.50
Ted Uhlaender, Andy Kosco	
265 Stu Miller	.50
266 Pedro Gonzalez	.50
267 Joe Sparma	.50
268 John Blanchard	.50
269 Don Heffner (Mgr.)	.50
270 Claude Osteen	.75
271 Hal Lanier	.75
272 Jack Baldschun	.50
273 Astro Aces:	1.00
Bob Aspromonte, Rusty Staub	
274 Buster Narum	.50
275 Tim McCarver	2.00
276 Jim Bouton	1.50
277 George Thomas	.50
278 Calvin Koonce	.50
279 Checklist No. 4	2.00
280 Bobby Knoop	.50
281 Bruce Howard	.50
282 Johnny Lewis	.50
283 Jim Perry	1.00
284 Bobby Wine	.50
285 Luis Tiant	2.00
286 Gary Geiger	.50
287 Jack Aker	.50
288 Dodgers Rookies:	75.00
Bill Singer, Don Sutton	
289 Larry Sherry	.60
290 Ron Santo	1.50
291 Moe Drabowsky	.50
292 Jim Coker	.50

NO. PLAYER	NR. MT.
293 Mike Shannon	.50
294 Steve Ridzik	.50
295 Jim Hart	.50
296 Johnny Keane (Mgr.)	.50
297 Jim Owens	.50
298 Rico Petrocelli	1.00
299 Lou Burdette	1.25
300 Bob Clemente	55.00
301 Greg Bollo	.50
302 Ernie Bowman	.50
303 Indians—5th Place	1.00
304 John Herrnstein	.50
305 Camilo Pascual	.75
306 Ty Cline	.50
307 Clay Carroll	.50
308 Tom Haller	.50
309 Diego Segui	.50
310 Frank Robinson	22.00
311 Reds Rookies:	.60
D. Simpson, T. Helms	
312 Bob Saverine	.50
313 Chris Zachary	.50
314 Hector Valle	.50
315 Norm Cash	1.50
316 Jack Fisher	.50
317 Dalton Jones	.50
318 Harry Walker	.50
319 Gene Freese	.50
320 Bob Gibson	15.00
321 Rick Reichardt	.50
322 Bill Faul	.50
323 Ray Barker	.50
324 John Boozer	.50
325 Vic Davalillo	.75
326 Braves—5th Place	1.00
327 Bernie Allen	.50
328 Jerry Grote	.50
329 Pete Charton	.50
330 Ron Fairly	.75
331 Ron Herbel	.50
332 Billy Bryan	.50
333 Senators Rookies:	.50
Joe Coleman, Jim French	
334 Marty Keough	.50
335 Juan Pizarro	.50
336 Gene Alley	.50
337 Fred Gladding	.50
338 Dal Maxvill	.50
339 Del Crandall	.75
340 Dean Chance	.60
341 Wes Westrum	.50
342 Bob Humphreys	.50
343 Joe Christopher	.50
344 Steve Blass	.60
345 Bob Allison	.75
346 Mike De La Hoz	.50
347 Phil Regan	.50
348 Orioles—3rd Place	1.00
349 Cap Peterson	.50
350 Mel Stottlemyre	1.75
351 Fred Valentine	.50
352 Bob Aspromonte	.50
353 Al McBean	.50
354 Smoky Burgess	.50
355 Wade Blasingame	.50
356 Red Sox Rookies:	.50
Owen Johnson,	
Ken Sanders	
357 Gerry Arrigo	.50
358 Charlie Smith	.50
359 Johnny Briggs	.50
360 Ron Hunt	.50
361 Tom Satriano	.50
362 Gates Brown	.50
363 Checklist No. 5	3.00
364 Nate Oliver	.50
365 Roger Maris	35.00
366 Wayne Causey	.50
367 Mel Nelson	.50
368 Charlie Lau	.50
369 Jim King	.50
370 Chico Cardenas	.50
371 Lee Stange	1.00
372 Harvey Kuenn	1.25
373 Giants Rookies:	1.00
Jack Hiatt, Dick Estelle	

NO. PLAYER	NR. MT.
374 Bob Locker	1.00
375 Donn Clendenon	1.25
376 Paul Schaal	1.00
377 Turk Farrell	1.00
378 Dick Tracewski	1.00
379 Cardinal—7th Place	1.50
380 Tony Conigliaro	3.00
381 Hank Fischer	1.00
382 Phil Roof	1.00
383 Jack Brandt	1.00
384 Al Downing	1.50
385 Ken Boyer	2.50
386 Gil Hodges (Mgr.)	4.00
387 Howie Reed	1.00
388 Don Mincher	1.00
389 Jim O'Toole	1.00
390 Brooks Robinson	15.00
391 Chuck Hinton	1.00
392 Cubs Rookies:	1.00
Bill Hands, Randy Hundley	
393 George Brunet	1.00
394 Ron Brand	1.00
395 Len Gabrielson	1.00
396 Jerry Stephenson	1.00
397 Bill White	2.00
398 Danny Cater	1.00
399 Ray Washburn	1.00
400 Zoilo Versalles	1.00
401 Ken McMullen	1.00
402 Jim Hickman	1.00
403 Fred Talbot	1.00
404 Pirates—3rd Place	1.50
405 Elston Howard	2.50
406 Joe Jay	1.00
407 John Kennedy	1.00
408 Lee Thomas	1.00
409 Billy Hoeft	1.00
410 Al Kaline	15.00
411 Gene Mauch (Mgr.)	1.25
412 Sam Bowens	1.00
413 John Romano	1.00
414 Dan Coombs	1.00
415 Max Alvis	1.00
416 Phil Ortega	1.00
417 Angels Rookies:	1.00
Jim McGlothlin, Ed Sukla	
418 Phil Gagliano	1.00
419 Mike Ryan	1.00
420 Juan Marichal	9.00
421 Roy McMillan	1.00
422 Ed Charles	1.00
423 Ernie Broglio	1.00
424 Reds Rookies:	3.00
Lee May, Darrell Osteen	
425 Bob Veale	1.00
426 White Sox—2nd Place	1.50
427 John Miller	1.00
428 Sandy Alomar	1.00
429 Bill Monbouquette	1.00
430 Don Drysdale	10.00
431 Walt Bond	1.00
432 Bob Heffner	1.00
433 Alvin Dark (Mgr.)	1.25
434 Willie Kirkland	1.00
435 Jim Bunning	4.00
436 Julian Javier	1.00
437 Al Stanek	1.00
438 Willie Smith	1.00
439 Pedro Ramos	1.00
440 Deron Johnson	1.00
441 Tommie Sisk	1.00
442 Orioles Rookies:	1.00
Ed Barnowski, Eddie Watt	
443 Bill Wakefield	1.00
444 Checklist No. 6	3.00
445 Jim Kaat	4.00
446 Mack Jones	1.00
447 Dick Ellsworth	3.00
(photo of Ken Hubbs)	
448 Eddie Stanky	3.00
449 Joe Moeller	3.00
450 Tony Oliva	5.00
451 Barry Latman	2.50
452 Joe Azcue	2.50
453 Ron Kline	2.50
454 Jerry Buchek	2.50

NO. PLAYER	NR. MT.
455 Mickey Lolich	3.00
456 Red Sox Rookies:	2.50
Darrell Brandon, Joe Foy	
457 Joe Gibbon	2.50
458 Manny Jiminez	2.50
459 Bill McCool	2.50
460 Curt Blefary	2.50
461 Roy Face	3.00
462 Bob Rodgers	3.00
463 Phillies—6th Place	4.00
464 Larry Bearnarth	2.50
465 Don Buford	2.50
466 Ken Johnson	2.50
467 Vic Roznovsky	2.50
468 Johnny Podres	3.00
469 Yankees Rookies:	10.00
Bobby Murcer,	
Dooley Womack	
470 Sam McDowell	3.00
471 Bob Skinner	2.50
472 Terry Fox	2.50
473 Rich Rollins	2.50
474 Dick Schofield	2.50
475 Dick Radatz	2.50
476 Bobby Bragan	2.50
477 Steve Barber	2.50
478 Tony Gonzalez	2.50
479 Jim Hannan	2.50
480 Dick Stuart	2.50
481 Bob Lee	2.50
482 Cubs Rookies:	2.50
J. Boccabella, D. Dowling	
483 Joe Nuxhall	3.00
484 Wes Covington	2.50
485 Bob Bailey	2.50
486 Tommy John	8.00
487 Al Ferrara	2.50
488 George Banks	2.50
489 Curt Simmons	2.50
490 Bobby Richardson	7.50
491 Dennis Bennett	2.50
492 Athletics—10th Place	3.00
493 John Klippstein	2.50
494 Gordon Coleman	2.50
495 Dick McAuliffe	2.50
496 Lindy McDaniel	2.50
497 Chris Cannizzaro	2.50
498 Pirates Rookies:	2.50
Luke Walker, W. Fryman	
499 Wally Bunker	2.50
500 Hank Aaron	65.00
501 John O'Donoghue	2.50
502 Lenny Green	2.50
503 Steve Hamilton	2.50
504 Grady Hatton	2.50
505 Jose Cardenal	2.50
506 Bo Belinsky	2.50
507 John Edwards	2.50
508 Steve Hargan	2.50
509 Jake Wood	2.50
510 Hoyt Wilhelm	10.00
511 Giants Rookies:	2.50
Bob Barton, Tito Fuentes	
512 Dick Stigman	2.50
513 Camilo Carreon	2.50
514 Hal Woodeschick	2.50
515 Frank Howard	3.00
516 Eddie Bressoud	2.50
517 Checklist No. 7	9.00
518 Braves Rookies:	2.50
Arnie Umbach, H. Hippauf	
519 Bob Friend	2.50
520 Jim Wynn	2.50
521 John Wyatt	2.50
522 Phil Linz	2.50
523 Bob Sadowski	13.00
524 Giants Rookies:	13.00
Ollie Brown, Don Mason	
525 Gary Bell	13.00
526 Twins—1st Place	40.00
527 Julio Navarro	13.00
528 Jesse Gonder	13.00
529 White Sox Rookies:	13.00
Dennis Higgins, Lee Elia,	
Bill Voss	
530 Robin Roberts	37.00

NO. PLAYER	NR. MT.
531 Joe Cunningham	13.00
532 Aurelio Monteagudo	13.00
533 Jerry Adair	13.00
534 Mets Rookies:	13.00
Dave Eilers, Rob Gardner	
535 Willie Davis	18.00
536 Dick Egan	13.00
537 Herman Franks (Mgr.)	13.00
538 Bob Allen	13.00
539 Astros Rookies:	13.00
Bill Heath, Carroll Sembera	
540 Denny McLain	35.00
541 Gene Oliver	13.00
542 George Smith	13.00
543 Roger Craig	20.00
544 Cardinals Rookies:	13.00
J. Williams, J. Hoerner,	
George Kernek	
545 Dick Green	13.00
546 Dwight Siebler	13.00
547 Horace Clarke (R)	20.00
548 Gary Kroll	13.00
549 Senators Rookies:	13.00
Al Closter, Casey Cox	
550 Willie McCovey	100.00
551 Bob Purkey	13.00
552 Birdie Tebbetts	13.00
553 Rookie Stars:	13.00
Pat Garrett, Jackie Warner	
554 Jim Northrup	13.00
555 Ron Perranoski	13.00
556 Mel Queen	13.00
557 Felix Mantilla	13.00
558 Red Sox Rookies:	20.00
Pete Magrini, Guido Grilli,	
George Scott	
559 Roberto Pena	13.00
560 Joel Horlen	13.00
561 Choo Choo Coleman	20.00
562 Russ Snyder	13.00
563 Twins Rookies:	13.00
Pete Cimino, Cesar Tovar	
564 Bob Chance	13.00
565 Jimmy Piersall	25.00
566 Mike Cuellar	14.00
567 Dick Howser	15.00
568 Athletics Rookies:	13.00
Paul Lindblad, Ron Stone	
569 Orlando McFarlane	13.00
570 Art Mahaffey	13.00
571 Dave Roberts	13.00
572 Bob Priddy	13.00
573 Derrell Griffith	13.00
574 Mets Rookies:	13.00
Billy Hepler, Bill Murphy	
575 Earl Wilson	13.00
576 Dave Nicholson	13.00
577 Jack Lamabe	13.00
578 Chi Chi Olivo	13.00
579 Orioles Rookies:	15.00
F. Bertaina, G. Brabender,	
Dave Johnson	
580 Billy Williams	60.00
581 Tony Martinez	13.00
582 Garry Roggenburk	13.00
583 Tigers—3rd Place	65.00
584 Yankees Rookies:	13.00
F. Fernandez, F. Peterson	
585 Tony Taylor	13.00
586 Claude Raymond	13.00
587 Dick Bertell	13.00
588 Athletics Rookies:	13.00
Ken Suarez, Chuck Dobson	
589 Lou Klimchock	13.00
590 Bill Skowron	30.00
591 NL Rookie Stars:	13.00
Bart Shirley, Grant Jackson	
592 Andre Rodgers	13.00
593 Doug Camilli	13.00
594 Chico Salmon	13.00
595 Larry Jackson	13.00
596 John Sullivan	13.00
597 Astros Rookies:	13.00
Nate Colbert, Greg Sims	
598 G. Perry (Exc. $35.00)	200.00

1967 Topps. . . . Complete Set of 609 Cards—Value $1150.00 (Exc.); $3250.00 (Mint)

Features the rookie cards of Tom Seaver and Rod Carew. Cards 534 to 609 are high numbers. Cards 458 to 533 are semi-high numbers. Cards 26 and 86 exist without the *traded* line—worth $12.00 each. Card 191 exists identifying card 214 as either Dick Kelley—worth $5.00 or Tom Kelley—worth $1.50.

NO.	PLAYER	NR. MT.
1	The Champs: (Exc. $1.75)	10.00
	Frank Robinson, Hank	
	Bauer, Brooks Robinson	
2	Jack Hamilton	.50
3	Duke Sims	.50
4	Hal Lanier	.75
5	Whitey Ford	9.00
6	Dick Simpson	.50
7	Don McMahon	.50
8	Chuck Harrison	.50
9	Ron Hansen	.50
10	Matty Alou	.75
11	Barry Moore	.50
12	Dodgers Rookies:	.75
	J. Campanis, Bill Singer	
13	Joe Sparma	.50
14	Phil Linz	.50
15	Earl Battey	.75
16	Bill Hands	.50
17	Jim Gosger	.50
18	Gene Oliver	.50
19	Jim McGlothlin	.50
20	Orlando Cepeda	5.00
21	Dave Bristol (Mgr.)	.50
22	Gene Brabender	.50
23	Larry Elliot	.50
24	Bob Allen	.50
25	Elstan Howard	2.00
26	Bob Priddy*	.50
27	Bob Saverine	.50
28	Barry Latman	.50
29	Tom McCraw	.50
30	Al Kaline	10.00
31	Jim Brewer	.50
32	Bob Bailey	.50
33	Athletic Rookies:	1.50
	Sal Bando, R. Schwartz	
34	Pete Cimino	.50
35	Rico Carty	1.00
36	Bob Tillman	.50
37	Rick Wise	.75
38	Bob Johnson	.50
39	Curt Simmons	.75
40	Rick Reichardt	.50
41	Joe Hoerner	.50
42	Mets Team	2.00
43	Chico Salmon	.50
44	Joe Nuxhall	.75
45	Roger Maris	25.00
46	Lindy McDaniel	.50
47	Ken McMullen	.50
48	Bill Freehan	.75
49	Roy Face	1.00
50	Tony Olava	2.50
51	Astros Rookies:	.50
	Dave Adlesh, W. Bales	
52	Dennis Higgins	.50
53	Clay Dalrymple	.50
54	Dick Green	.50
55	Don Drysdale	7.50
56	Jose Tartabull	.50
57	Pat Jarvis	.50
58	Paul Schaal	.50
59	Ralph Terry	.50
60	Luis Aparicio	5.00
61	Gordy Coleman	.50

NO.	PLAYER	NR. MT.
62	Checklist No. 1	2.50
63	Cards Clubbers	5.00
	Lou Brock, Curt Flood	
64	Fred Valentine	.50
65	Tom Haller	.50
66	Manny Mota	1.00
67	Ken Berry	.50
68	Bob Buhl	.50
69	Vic Davalillo	.75
70	Ron Santo	1.25
71	Camilo Pascual	.50
72	Tigers Rookies:	.75
	George Korince (Photo of	
	John Brown), J. Matchick	
73	Rusty Staub	1.50
74	Wes Stock	.50
75	George Scott	.75
76	Jim Barbieri	.50
77	Dooley Womack	.50
78	Pat Corrales	.75
79	Bubba Morton	.50
80	Jim Maloney	.50
81	Eddie Stanky (Mgr.)	.75
82	Steve Barber	.50
83	Ollie Brown	.50
84	Tommie Sisk	.50
85	Johnny Callison	.75
86	Mike McCormick*	.75
87	George Altman	.50
88	Mickey Lolich	1.25
89	Felix Millan	.50
90	Jim Nash	.50
91	Johnny Lewis	.50
92	Ray Washburn	.50
93	Yankees Rookies:	3.00
	Stan Bahnsen, B. Murcer	
94	Ron Fairly	.75
95	Sonny Siebert	.75
96	Art Shamsky	.50
97	Mike Cuellar	.75
98	Rich Rollins	.50
99	Lee Stange	.50
100	Frank Robinson	10.00
101	Ken Johnson	.50
102	Phillies Team	1.50
103	Checklist No. 2	6.00
104	Minnie Rojas	.50
105	Ken Boyer	1.50
106	Randy Hundley	.50
107	Joel Horlen	.50
108	Alex Johnson	.50
109	Tribe Thumpers:	1.00
	R. Colavito, Leon Wagner	
110	Jack Aker	.50
111	John Kennedy	.65
112	Dave Wickersham	.65
113	Dave Nicholson	.65
114	Jack Baldschun	.65
115	Paul Casanova	.65
116	Herman Franks	.65
117	Darrell Brandon	.65
118	Bernie Allen	.65
119	Wade Blasingame	.65
120	Floyd Robinson	.65
121	Ed Bressoud	.65
122	George Brunet	.65

NO.	PLAYER	NR. MT.
123	Pirates Rookies:	.65
	Jim Price, L. Walker	
124	Jim Stewart	.65
125	Moe Drabowsky	.65
126	Tony Taylor	.65
127	John O'Donoghue	.65
128	Ed Spiezio	.65
129	Phil Roof	.65
130	Phil Regan	.65
131	Yankees Team	4.00
132	Ozzie Virgil	.65
133	Ron Kline	.65
134	Gates Brown	.65
135	Deron Johnson	.65
136	Carroll Sembera	.65
137	Twins Rookies:	.65
	Ron Clark, Jim Ollum	
138	Dick Kelley	.65
139	Dalton Jones	.65
140	Willie Stargell	12.00
141	John Miller	.65
142	Jackie Brandt	.65
143	Sox Sockers:	.65
	Don Buford, Pete Ward	
144	Bill Hepler	.65
145	Larry Brown	.65
146	Steve Carlton	65.00
147	Tom Egan	.65
148	Adolfo Phillips	.65
149	Joe Moeller	.65
150	Mickey Mantle	225.00
151	World Series Game 1:	2.00
	Moe Mows Down 11	
152	World Series Game 2:	3.00
	Palmer Blanks Dodgers	
153	World Series Game 3:	2.00
	Blair's Homer Defeats L.A.	
154	World Series Game 4:	2.00
	Orioles Win 4 Straight	
155	World Series:	2.00
	The Winners Celebrate	
156	Ron Herbel	.65
157	Danny Cater	.65
158	Jimmy Coker	.65
159	Bruce Howard	.65
160	Willie Davis	1.00
161	Dick Williams (Mgr.)	1.00
162	Billy O'Dell	.65
163	Vic Roznovsky	.65
164	Dwight Siebler	.65
165	Cleon Jones	.65
166	Ed Mathews	8.00
167	Senators Rookies:	.65
	Joe Coleman, Tim Cullen	
168	Ray Culp	.65
169	Horace Clarke	.65
170	Dick McAuliffe	.65
171	Calvin Koonce	.65
172	Bill Heath	.65
173	Cardinals Team	1.50
174	Dick Radatz	.65
175	Bobby Knoop	.65
176	Sammy Ellis	.65
177	Tito Fuentes	.65
178	John Buzhardt	.65
179	Braves Rookies:	.65
	C. Vaughan, Cecil Upshaw	

NO.	PLAYER	NR. MT.
180	Curt Blefary	.65
181	Terry Fox	.65
182	Ed Charles	.65
183	Jim Pagliaroni	.65
184	George Thomas	.65
185	Ken Holtzman (R)	1.50
186	Mets Maulers	1.00
	Ed Kranepool, R. Swoboda	
187	Pedro Ramos	.65
188	Ken Harrelson	1.25
189	Chuck Hinton	.65
190	Turk Farrell	.65
191	Checklist No. 3*	3.00
192	Fred Gladding	.65
193	Jose Cardenal	.65
194	Bob Allison	.65
195	Al Jackson	.65
196	Johnny Romano	.65
197	Ron Perranoski	.65
198	Chuck Hiller	.65
199	Billy Hitchcock	.65
200	Willie Mays	45.00
201	Hal Reniff	.65
202	Johnny Edwards	.65
203	Al McBean	.65
204	Orioles Rookies:	.75
	Mike Epstein, Tom Phoebus	
205	Dick Groat	.75
206	Dennis Bennett	.65
207	John Orsino	.65
208	Jack Lamabe	.65
209	Joe Nossek	.65
210	Bob Gibson	11.00
211	Twins Team	1.50
212	Chris Zachary	.65
213	Jay Johnstone	1.00
214	Tom Kelley	.65
215	Ernie Banks	12.00
216	Bengal Belters:	4.00
	Norm Cash, Al Kaline	
217	Rob Gardner	.65
218	Wes Parker	.65
219	Clay Carroll	.65
220	Jim Hart	.65
221	Woody Fryman	.65
222	Reds Rookies:	1.00
	Darrell Osteen, Lee May	
223	Mike Ryan	.65
224	Walt Bond	.65
225	Mel Stottlemyre	1.50
226	Julian Javier	.65
227	Paul Lindblad	.65
228	Gil Hodges (Mgr.)	4.00
229	Larry Jackson	.65
230	Boog Powell	2.00
231	John Bateman	.65
232	Don Buford	.65
233	AL ERA Leaders:	1.50
	Joel Horlen, Gary Peters,	
	Steve Hargan	
234	NL ERA Leaders:	4.00
	Sandy Koufax, Mike	
	Cuellar, Juan Marichal	
235	AL Pitching Leaders:	2.00
	Earl Wilson, Jim Kaat,	
	Denny McLain	

NO. PLAYER	NR. MT.
236 NL Pitching Leaders: Sandy Koufax, Juan Marichal, Gaylord Perry, Bob Gibson	7.50
237 AL Strikeout Leaders: Jim Kaat, Earl Wilson, Sam McDowell	1.50
238 NL Strikeout Leaders: Sandy Koufax, Jim Bunning, Bob Veale	2.00
239 AL Batting Leaders: Al Kaline, Frank Robinson, Tony Oliva	2.00
240 NL Batting Leaders: Matty Alou, Felipe Alou, Rico Carty	1.25
241 AL RBI Leaders: Frank Robinson, Boog Powell, Harmon Killebrew	2.00
242 NL RBI Leaders: Bob Clemente, Richie Allen, Hank Aaron	2.50
243 AL Home Run Leaders: Frank Robinson, Harmon Killebrew, Boog Powell	2.00
244 NL Home Run Leaders: Hank Aaron, Richie Allen, Willie Mays	3.00
245 Curt Flood	1.00
246 Jim Perry	1.00
247 Jerry Lumpe	.65
248 Gene Mauch (Mgr.)	1.00
249 Nick Willhite	.65
250 Hank Aaron	50.00
251 Woody Held	.65
252 Bob Bolin	.65
253 Indians Rookies: Bill Davis, Gus Gil	.65
254 Milt Pappas	.65
255 Frank Howard	1.25
256 Bob Hendley	.65
257 Charley Smith	.65
258 Lee Maye	.65
259 Don Dennis	.65
260 Jim Lefebvre	1.00
261 John Wyatt	.65
262 Athletics Team	1.50
263 Hank Aguirre	.65
264 Ron Swoboda	.75
265 Lou Burdette	1.00
266 Pitt Power: W. Stargell, D. Clendenon	4.00
267 Don Schwall	.65
268 John Briggs	.65
269 Don Nottebart	.65
270 Zoilo Versalles	.65
271 Eddie Watt	.65
272 Cubs Rookies: Bill Connors, Dave Dowling	.65
273 Dick Lines	.65
274 Bob Aspromonte	.65
275 Fred Whitfield	.65
276 Bruce Brubaker	.65
277 Steve Whitaker	.65
278 Checklist No. 4	2.50
279 Frank Linzy	.65
280 Tony Conigliaro	2.50
281 Bob Rodgers	.65
282 Johnny Odom	.65
283 Gene Alley	.65
284 Johnny Podres	1.00
285 Lou Brock	12.00
286 Wayne Causey	.65
287 Mets Rookies: Greg Goossen, Bart Shirley	.65
288 Denver Lemaster	.65
289 Tom Tresh	1.00
290 Bill White	1.50
291 Jim Hannan	.65
292 Don Pavletich	.65
293 Ed Kirkpatrick	.65
294 Walt Alston (Mgr.)	2.00
295 Sam McDowell	1.00
296 Glenn Beckert	.65
297 Dave Morehead	.65
298 Ron Davis	.65
299 Norm Siebern	.65
300 Jim Kaat	2.50
301 Jesse Gonder	.65
302 Orioles Team	1.50
303 Gil Blanco	.65
304 Phil Gagliano	.65
305 Earl Wilson	.65
306 Bud Harrelson	1.00
307 Jim Beauchamp	.65
308 Al Downing	.75
309 Hurlers Beware: J. Callison, Richie Allen	1.00
310 Gary Peters	.65
311 Ed Brinkman	.65
312 Don Mincher	.65
313 Bob Lee	.65
314 Red Sox Rookies: Mike Andrews, R. Smith	3.00
315 Billy Williams	6.00
316 Jack Kralick	.65
317 Cesar Tovar	.65
318 Dave Giusti	.65
319 Paul Blair	.65
320 Gaylord Perry	6.00
321 Mayo Smith (Mgr.)	.65
322 Jose Pagan	.65
323 Mike Hershberger	.65
324 Hal Woodeschick	.65
325 Chico Cardenas	.65
326 Bob Uecker	15.00
327 Angels Team	1.50
328 Clete Boyer	.75
329 Charlie Lau	.75
330 Claude Osteen	.65
331 Joe Foy	.65
332 Jesus Alou	.65
333 Ferguson Jenkins	5.00
334 Twin Terrors: Bob Allison, H. Killebrew	4.00
335 Bob Veale	.65
336 Joe Azcue	.65
337 Joe Morgan	8.00
338 Bob Locker	.65
339 Chico Ruiz	.65
340 Joe Pepitone	1.00
341 Giants Rookies: Dick Dietz, Bill Sorrell	1.00
342 Hank Fischer	.65
343 Tom Satriano	.65
344 Ossie Chavarria	.65
345 Stu Miller	.65
346 Jim Hickman	.65
347 Grady Hatton (Mgr.)	.65
348 Tug McGraw	1.50
349 Bob Chance	.65
350 Joe Torre	1.50
351 Vern Law	.65
352 Ray Oyler	.65
353 Bill McCool	.65
354 Cubs Team	1.50
355 Carl Yastrzemski	85.00
356 Larry Jaster	.65
357 Bill Skowron	1.00
358 Ruben Amaro	.65
359 Dick Ellsworth	.65
360 Leon Wagner	.65
361 Checklist No. 5	2.50
362 Darold Knowles	.65
363 Dave Johnson	1.25
364 Claude Raymond	.65
365 John Roseboro	.65
366 Andy Kosco	.65
367 Angels Rookies: Bill Kelso, Don Wallace	.65
368 Jack Hiatt	.65
369 Jim Hunter	8.00
370 Tommy Davis	.65
371 Jim Lonborg	1.50
372 Mike De La Hoz	1.00
373 White Sox Rookies: D. Josephson, F. Klages	1.00
374 Mel Queen	1.00
375 Jake Gibbs	1.00
376 Don Lock	1.00
377 Luis Tiant	2.00
378 Tigers Team	2.00
379 Jerry May	1.00
380 Dean Chance	1.00
381 Dick Schofield	1.00
382 Dave McNally	1.50
383 Ken Henderson	1.00
384 Cardinals Rookies: Dick Hughes, Jim Cosman	1.00
385 Jim Fregosi	1.50
386 Dick Selma	1.00
387 Cap Peterson	1.00
388 Arnold Earley	1.00
389 Al Dark (Mgr.)	1.25
390 Jim Wynn	1.00
391 Wilbur Wood	1.00
392 Tommy Harper	1.00
393 Jim Bouton	1.75
394 Jake Wood	1.00
395 Chris Short	1.00
396 Atlanta Aces: D. Meke, T. Cloninger	1.00
397 Willie Smith	1.00
398 Jeff Torborg	1.25
399 Al Worthington	1.00
400 Bob Clemente	45.00
401 Jim Coates	1.00
402 Phillies Rookies: Grant Jackson, Billy Wilson	1.25
403 Dick Nen	1.00
404 Nelson Briles	1.00
405 Russ Snyder	1.00
406 Lee Elia	1.00
407 Reds Team	2.00
408 Jim Northrup	1.00
409 Ray Sadecki	1.00
410 Lou Johnson	1.00
411 Dick Howser	1.50
412 Astros Rookies: Norm Miller, Doug Rader	2.00
413 Jerry Grote	1.00
414 Casey Cox	1.00
415 Sonny Jackson	1.00
416 Roger Repoz	1.00
417 Bob Bruce	1.00
418 Sam Mele (Mgr.)	1.00
419 Don Kessinger	1.50
420 Denny McLain	2.50
421 Dal Maxvill	1.00
422 Hoyt Wilhelm	7.00
423 Fence Busters: Willie Mays, Willie McCovey	11.00
424 Pedro Gonzalez	1.00
425 Pete Mikkelsen	1.00
426 Lou Clinton	1.00
427 Ruben Gomez	1.00
428 Dodgers Rookies: Tom Hutton, Gene Michael	1.50
429 Garry Roggenburk	1.00
430 Pete Rose	75.00
431 Ted Uhlaender	1.00
432 Jimmie Hall	1.00
433 Al Luplow	1.00
434 Eddie Fisher	1.00
435 Mack Jones	1.00
436 Pete Ward	1.00
437 Senators Team	2.00
438 Chuck Dobson	1.00
439 Byron Browne	1.00
440 Steve Hargan	1.00
441 Jim Davenport	1.00
442 Yankees Rookies: Bill Robinson, Joe Verbanic	1.50
443 Tito Francona	1.00
444 George Smith	1.00
445 Don Sutton	13.00
446 Russ Nixon	1.00
447 Bo Belinsky	1.00
448 Harry Walker (Mgr.)	1.00
449 Orlando Pena	1.00
450 Richie Allen	2.50
451 Fred Newman	1.00
452 Ed Kranepool	1.50
453 Aurelio Monteagudo	1.00
454 Checklist No. 6	2.50
455 Tommy Agee	1.00
456 Phil Niekro	7.50
457 Andy Etchebarren	1.00
458 Lee Thomas	3.00
459 Senators Rookies: Dick Bosman, Pete Craig	3.00
460 Harmon Killebrew	25.00
461 Bob Miller	3.00
462 Bob Barton	3.00
463 Hill Aces: Sam McDowell, S. Siebert	3.00
464 Dan Coombs	3.00
465 Willie Horton	3.00
466 Bobby Wine	3.00
467 Jim O'Toole	3.00
468 Ralph Houk (Mgr.)	4.00
469 Len Gabrielson	3.00
470 Bob Shaw	3.00
471 Rene Lachemann	3.00
472 Rookies Pirates: John Gelnar, G. Spriggs	3.00
473 Jose Santiago	3.00
474 Bob Tolan	3.00
475 Jim Palmer	40.00
476 Tony Perez	40.00
477 Braves Team	6.00
478 Bob Humphreys	3.00
479 Gary Bell	3.00
480 Willie McCovey	17.00
481 Leo Durocher (Mgr.)	4.00
482 Bill Monbouquette	3.00
483 Jim Landis	3.00
484 Jerry Adair	3.00
485 Tim McCarver	5.00
486 Twins Rookies: Rich Reese, Bill Whitby	3.00
487 Tom Reynolds	3.00
488 Gerry Arrigo	3.00
489 Doug Clemens	3.00
490 Tony Cloninger	3.00
491 Sam Bowens	3.00
492 Pirates Team	6.00
493 Phil Ortega	3.00
494 Bill Rigney (Mgr.)	3.00
495 Fritz Peterson	3.00
496 Orlando McFarlane	3.00
497 Ron Campbell	3.00
498 Larry Dierker	3.00
499 Indians Rookies: George Culver, Jose Vidal	3.00
500 Juan Marichal	12.00
501 Jerry Zimmerman	3.00
502 Derrell Griffith	3.00
503 Dodgers Team	6.00
504 Orlando Martinez	3.00
505 Tommy Helms	3.00
506 Smoky Burgess	3.00
507 Orioles Rookies: Ed Barnowski, Larry Haney	3.00
508 Dick Hall	3.00
509 Jim King	3.00
510 Bill Mazeroski	4.00
511 Don Wert	3.00
512 R. Schoendienst (Mgr.)	6.00
513 Marcelino Lopez	3.00
514 John Werhas	3.00
515 Bert Campaneris	4.00
516 Giants Team	6.00
517 Fred Talbot	3.00
518 Denis Menke	3.00
519 Ted Davidson	3.00
520 Max Alvis	3.00
521 Bird Bombers: Boog Powell, Curt Blefary	4.00
522 John Stephenson	3.00
523 Jim Merritt	3.00
524 Felix Mantilla	3.00
525 Ron Hunt	3.00
526 Tigers Rookies: Pat Dobson, G. Korince	4.00
527 Dennis Ribant	3.00
528 Rico Petrocelli	4.00
529 Gary Wagner	3.00
530 Felipe Alou	4.00
531 Checklist No. 7	6.00

NO. PLAYER	NR. MT.	NO. PLAYER	NR. MT.	NO. PLAYER	NR. MT.	NO. PLAYER	NR. MT.
532 Jim Hicks	3.00	552 Ted Savage	6.00	571 Larry Sherry	6.00	591 Ty Cline	6.00
533 Jack Fisher	3.00	553 Yankees Rookies:	18.00	572 Don Demeter	6.00	592 NL Rookies:	6.00
534 Hank Bauer (Mgr.)	8.00	Mike Hegan, Thad Tillotson		573 White Sox Team	18.00	Jim Shellenback, Ron Willis	
535 Donn Clendenon	7.00	554 Andre Rodgers	6.00	574 Jerry Buchek	6.00	593 Wes Westrum (Mgr.)	6.00
536 Cubs Rookies:	.20.00	555 Don Cardwell	6.00	575 Dave Boswell	6.00	594 Dan Osinski	6.00
Joe Niekro, Paul Popovich		556 Al Weis	6.00	576 NL Rookies:	6.00	595 Cookie Rojas	6.00
537 Chuck Estrada	6.00	557 Al Ferrara	6.00	R. Hernandez, Norm Gigon		596 Galen Cisco	6.00
538 J.C. Martin	6.00	558 Orioles Rookies:	24.00	577 Bill Short	6.00	597 Ted Abernathy	6.00
539 Dick Egan	6.00	Mark Belanger, Bill Dillman		578 John Boccabella	6.00	598 White Sox Rookies:	6.00
540 Norm Cash	22.00	559 Dick Tracewski	6.00	579 Bill Henry	6.00	Ed Stroud, Walt Williams	
541 Joe Gibbon	5.00	560 Jim Bunning	35.00	580 Rocky Colavito	25.00	599 Bob Duliba (Mgr.)	6.00
542 Athletics Rookies:	9.00	561 Sandy Alomar	6.00	581 Mets Rookies:	750.00	600 Brooks Robinson	200.00
Tony Pierce, Rick Monday		562 Steve Blass	6.00	Bill Denehy, Tom Seaver		601 Bill Bryan	6.00
543 Dan Schneider	5.00	563 Joe Adcock (Mgr.)	13.00	582 Jim Owens	6.00	602 Juan Pizarro	6.00
544 Indians Team	18.00	564 Astros Rookies:	6.00	583 Ray Barker	6.00	603 Athletics Rookies:	6.00
545 Jim Grant	6.00	Alonzo Harris, A. Pointer		584 Jim Piersall	22.00	Tim Talton, Ramon Webster	
546 Woody Woodward	6.00	565 Lew Krausse	6.00	585 Wally Bunker	6.00	604 Red Sox Team	65.00
547 Red Sox Rookies:	6.00	566 Gary Geiger	6.00	586 Manny Jimenez	6.00	605 Mike Shannon	30.00
Russ Gibson, Bill Rohr		567 Steve Hamilton	6.00	587 NL Rookies:	6.00	606 Ron Taylor	6.00
548 Tony Gonzalez	6.00	568 John Sullivan	6.00	Don Shaw, Gary Sutherland		607 Mickey Stanley	20.00
549 Jack Sanford	6.00	569 AL Rookies:	210.00	588 Johnny Klippstein	6.00	608 Cubs Rookies:	6.00
550 Vada Pinson	9.00	Rod Carew, Hank Allen		589 Dave Ricketts	6.00	John Upham, Rich Nye	
551 Doug Camilli	6.00	570 Maury Wills	80.00	590 Pete Richert	6.00	609 Tommy John (Exc. $20.00)	80.00

1968 Topps. . . . Complete Set of 598 Cards—Value $700.00 (Exc.); $1750.00 (Mint)

Features the rookie cards of Johnny Bench and Nolan Ryan. High numbers are 534 to 598. Card 66 exists with "Senators" in *white*—worth $.50 and "Senators" in *yellow*—$35.00. Card 518 (checklist) exists identifying card 539 as "Maj. L. Rookies"—worth $3.00 or "Am. L. Rookies"—worth $8.00.

NO. PLAYER	NR. MT.	NO. PLAYER	NR. MT.	NO. PLAYER	NR. MT.	NO. PLAYER	NR. MT.
1 NL Ldrs.: (Exc. $1.50)	7.50	13 Chuck Hartenstein	.50	47 Ralph Houk (Mgr.)	.75	81 Larry Jackson	.50
Bob Clemente, Matty Alou, Tony Gonzalez		14 Jerry McNertney	.50	48 Ted Davidson	.50	82 Sam Bowens	.50
2 AL Batting Leaders:	2.50	15 Ron Hunt	.50	49 Ed Brinkman	.50	83 John Stephenson	.50
Frank Robinson, Al Kaline, Carl Yastrzemski		16 Indians Rookies:	2.00	50 Willy Mays	40.00	84 Bob Tolan	.50
3 NL RBI Leaders:	2.50	Lou Piniella, R. Schienblum		51 Bob Locker	.50	85 Gaylord Perry	6.00
Hank Aaron, O. Cepeda, Bob Clemente		17 Dick Hall	.50	52 Hawk Taylor	.50	86 Willie Stargell	7.00
4 AL RBI Leaders:	2.50	18 Mike Hershberger	.50	53 Gene Alley	.50	87 Dick Williams (Mgr.)	.75
C. Yastrzemski, H. Killebrew, F. Robinson		19 Juan Pizarro	.50	54 Stan Williams	.50	88 Phil Regan	.50
5 NL Home Run Leaders:	2.50	20 Brooks Robinson	10.00	55 Felipe Alou	.75	89 Jake Gibbs	.50
Ron Santo, Hank Aaron, Jim Wynn, Willie McCovey		21 Ron Davis	.50	56 Orioles Rookies:	.60	90 Vada Pinson	1.00
6 AL Home Run Leaders:	2.50	22 Pat Dobson	.60	Dave May, Dave Leonhard		91 Jim Ollom	.50
C. Yastrzemski, H. Killebrew, F. Howard		23 Chico Cardenas	.50	57 Dan Schneider	.50	92 Ed Kranepool	.50
7 NL ERA Leaders:	1.25	24 Bobby Locke	.50	58 Ed Mathews	7.00	93 Tony Cloninger	.50
Jim Bunning, Chris Short, Phil Niekro		25 Jan Javier	.50	59 Don Lock	.50	94 Lee Maye	.50
8 AL ERA Leaders:	1.25	26 Darrell Brandon	.50	60 Ken Holtzman	.60	95 Bob Aspromonte	.50
Joe Horlen, Sonny Siebert, Gary Peters		27 Gil Hodges (Mgr.)	3.00	61 Reggie Smith	1.00	96 Senator Rookies:	.50
9 NL Pitching Leaders:	1.25	28 Ted Uhlaender	.50	62 Chuck Dobson	.50	Frank Coggins, Dick Nold	
C. Osteen, M. McCormick, F. Jenkins, J. Bunning		29 Joe Verbanic	.50	63 Dick Kenworthy	.50	97 Tom Phoebus	.50
10 AL Pitching Leaders:	1.25	30 Joe Torre	1.00	64 Jim Merritt	.50	98 Gary Sutherland	.50
Jim Lonborg, Earl Wilson, Dean Chance		31 Ed Stroud	.50	65 John Roseboro	.50	99 Rocky Colavito	1.00
11 NL Strikeout Leaders:	1.25	32 Joe Gibbon	.50	66 Casey Cox*	.50	100 Bob Gibson	10.00
Ferguson Jenkins, Gaylord Perry, Jim Bunning		33 Pete Ward	.50	67 Checklist No. 1	2.50	101 Glenn Beckert	.50
12 AL Strikeout Leaders:	1.25	34 Al Ferrara	.50	68 Ron Willis	.50	102 Jose Cardenal	.50
Jim Lonborg, Dean Chance, Sam McDowell		35 Steve Hargan	.50	69 Tom Tresh	.75	103 Don Sutton	6.00
		36 Pirates Rookies:	.65	70 Bob Veale	.75	104 Dick Dietz	.50
		Bob Moose, B. Robertson		71 Vern Fuller	.50	105 Al Downing	.75
		37 Billy Williams	7.00	72 Tommy John	3.00	106 Dalton Jones	.50
		38 Tony Pierce	.50	73 Jim Hart	.50	107 Checklist No. 2	2.50
		39 Cookie Rojas	.50	74 Milt Pappas	.75	108 Don Pavletich	.50
		40 Denny McLain	3.00	75 Don Mincher	.50	109 Bert Campaneris	.75
		41 Julio Gotay	.50	76 Braves Rookies:	.75	110 Hank Aaron	40.00
		42 Larry Haney	.50	Jim Britton, Ron Reed		111 Rich Reese	.50
		43 Gary Bell	.50	77 Don Wilson	.50	112 Woody Fryman	.50
		44 Frank Kostro	.50	78 Jim Northrup	.75	113 Tigers Rookies:	.50
		45 Tom Seaver	95.00	79 Ted Kubiak	.50	T. Matchick, D. Patterson	
		46 Dave Ricketts	.50	80 Rod Carew	55.00	114 Ron Swoboda	.75

NO. PLAYER	NR. MT.	NO. PLAYER	NR. MT.	NO. PLAYER	NR. MT.	NO. PLAYER	NR. MT.
115 Sam McDowell	.75	188 Cap Peterson	.50	268 Bob Humphreys	.50	348 Phillies Rookies:	.50
116 Ken McMullen	.50	189 Bill Landis	.50	269 Bob Tiefenauer	.50	Larry Colton, Dick Thoenen	
117 Larry Jaster	.50	190 Bill White	1.50	270 Matty Alou	1.00	349 Ed Spiezio	.50
118 Mark Belanger	1.00	191 Dan Frisella	.50	271 Bobby Knoop	.50	350 Hoyt Wilhelm	5.00
119 Ted Savage	.50	192 Checklist No. 3	2.50	272 Ray Culp	.50	351 Bob Barton	.50
120 Mel Stottlemyre	1.00	193 Jack Hamilton	.50	273 Dave Johnson	1.00	352 Jackie Hernandez	.50
121 Jimmie Hall	.50	194 Don Buford	.50	274 Mike Cuellar	.75	353 Mack Jones	.50
122 Gene Mauch (Mgr.)	.60	195 Joe Pepitone	1.00	275 Tim McCarver	1.50	354 Pete Richert	.50
123 Jose Santiago	.50	196 Gary Nolan	.50	276 Jim Roland	.50	355 Ernie Banks	10.00
124 Nate Oliver	.50	197 Larry Brown	.50	277 Jerry Buchek	.50	356 Checklist No. 5	2.50
125 Joe Horlen	.50	198 Roy Face	1.00	278 Checklist No. 4	2.50	357 Len Gabrielson	.50
126 Bobby Etheridge	.50	199 A's Rookies:	.50	279 Bill Hands	.50	358 Mike Epstein	.50
127 Paul Lindblad	.50	R. Rodriquez, D. Osteen		280 Mickey Mantle	200.00	359 Joe Moeller	.50
128 Astros Rookies:	.50	200 Orlando Cepeda	3.00	281 Jim Campanis	.50	360 Willie Horton	1.00
Alonzo Harris, Tom Dukes		201 Mike Marshall (R)	1.25	282 Rick Monday	1.25	361 Harmon Killebrew (AS)	4.00
129 Mickey Stanley	.50	202 Adolfo Phillips	.50	283 Mel Queen	.50	362 Orlando Cepeda (AS)	2.00
130 Tony Perez	5.00	203 Dick Kelley	.50	284 John Briggs	.50	363 Rod Carew (AS)	8.00
131 Frank Bertaina	.50	204 Andy Etchebarren	.50	285 Dick McAuliffe	.50	364 Joe Morgan (AS)	3.00
132 Bud Harrelson	.50	205 Juan Marichal	5.00	286 Cecil Upshaw	.50	365 Brooks Robinson (AS)	5.00
133 Fred Whitfield	.50	206 Cal Ermer	.50	287 White Sox Rookies:	.75	366 Ron Santo (AS)	1.25
134 Pat Jarvis	.50	207 Carroll Sembera	.50	Mickey Abarbanel,		367 Jim Fregosi (AS)	.75
135 Paul Blair	.50	208 Willie Davis	1.00	Cisco Carlos		368 Gene Alley (AS)	.75
136 Randy Hundley	.50	209 Tim Cullen	.50	288 Dave Wickersham	.50	369 Carl Yastrzemski (AS)	8.00
137 Minnesota Twins	1.50	210 Gary Peters	.50	289 Woody Held	.50	370 Hank Aaron (AS)	9.00
138 Ruben Amaro	.50	211 J.C. Martin	.50	290 Willie McCovey	8.00	371 Tony Oliva (AS)	1.50
139 Chris Short	.50	212 Dave Morehead	.50	291 Dick Lines	.50	372 Lou Brock (AS)	4.00
140 Tony Conigliaro	1.25	213 Chico Ruiz	.50	292 Art Shamsky	.50	373 Frank Robinson (AS)	4.00
141 Dal Maxvill	.50	214 Yankees Rookies:	1.00	293 Bruce Howard	.50	374 Bob Clemente (AS)	8.00
142 White Sox Rookies:	.50	S. Bahnsen, F. Fernandez		294 Red Schoendienst	3.00	375 Bill Freehan (AS)	.75
Bill Voss, B. Bradford		215 Jim Bunning	3.00	295 Sonny Siebert	.50	376 Tim McCarver (AS)	1.50
143 Pete Cimino	.50	216 Bubba Morton	.50	296 Byron Browne	.50	377 Joe Horlen (AS)	.75
144 Joe Morgan	5.00	217 Turk Farrell	.50	297 Russ Gibson	.50	378 Bob Gibson (AS)	5.00
145 Don Drysdale	6.00	218 Ken Suarez	.50	298 Jim Brewer	.50	379 Gary Peters (AS)	.75
146 Sal Bando	1.00	219 Rob Gardner	.50	299 Gene Michael	.75	380 Ken Holtzman (AS)	.75
147 Frank Linzy	.50	220 Harmon Killebrew	9.00	300 Rusty Staub	1.25	381 Boog Powell	1.50
148 Dave Bristol (Mgr.)	.50	221 Atlanta Braves	1.50	301 Twins Rookies:	.75	382 Ramon Hernandez	.50
149 Bob Saverine	.50	222 Jim Hardin	.50	G. Mitterwald, R. Renick		383 Steve Whitaker	.50
150 Bob Clemente	30.00	223 Ollie Brown	.50	302 Gerry Arrigo	.50	384 Reds Rookies:	4.00
151 World Series Game 1:	4.00	224 Jack Aker	.50	303 Dick Green	.50	Bill Henry, Hal McRae	
Brock Socks 4 Hits		225 Richie Allen	2.00	304 Sandy Valdespino	.50	385 Jim Hunter	7.00
152 World Series Game 2:	5.00	226 Jimmie Price	.50	305 Minnie Rojas	.50	386 Greg Goossen	.50
Yaz Smashes 2 Homers		227 Joe Hoerner	.50	306 Mike Ryan	.50	387 Joe Foy	.50
153 World Series Game 3:	2.00	228 Dodgers Rookies:	.75	307 John Hiller	.50	388 Ray Washburn	.50
Briles Cools Off Boston		Jack Billingham, Jim Fairey		308 Pittsburgh Pirates	1.50	389 Jay Johnstone	.50
154 World Series Game 4:	4.00	229 Fred Klages	.50	309 Ken Henderson	.50	390 Bill Mazeroski	1.25
Gibson Hurls Shutout		230 Pete Rose	55.00	310 Luis Aparicio	5.00	391 Bob Priddy	.50
155 World Series Game 5:	2.00	231 Dave Baldwin	.50	311 Jack Lamabe	.50	392 Grady Hatton (Mgr.)	.50
Lonborg Wins Again		232 Denis Menke	.50	312 Curt Blefary	.50	393 Jim Perry	.75
156 World Series Game 6:	2.00	233 George Scott	.75	313 Al Weis	.50	394 Tommie Aaron	.75
Petrocelli 2 Homers		234 Bill Monbouquette	.50	314 Red Sox Rookies:	.50	395 Camilo Pascual	.75
157 World Series Game 7:	2.00	235 Ron Santo	1.00	Bill Rohr, George Spriggs		396 Bobby Wine	.50
St. Louis Wins It		236 Tug McGraw	1.00	315 Zoilo Versalles	.50	397 Vic Davalillo	.50
158 World Series:	2.00	237 Alvin Dark (Mgr.)	.75	316 Steve Barber	.50	398 Jim Grant	.50
The Cardinal Celebrate		238 Tom Satriano	.50	317 Ron Brand	.50	399 Ray Oyler	.50
159 Don Kessinger	.75	239 Bill Henry	.50	318 Chico Salmon	.50	400 Mike McCormick	.50
160 Earl Wilson	.50	240 Al Kaline	12.00	319 George Culver	.50	401 New York Mets	1.50
161 Norm Miller	.50	241 Felix Millan	.50	320 Frank Howard	1.00	402 Mike Hegan	.50
162 Cardinals Rookies:	1.00	242 Moe Drabowsky	.50	321 Leo Durocher (Mgr.)	1.50	403 John Buzhardt	.50
Hal Gilson, Mike Torrez		243 Rich Rollins	.50	322 Dave Boswell	.50	404 Floyd Robinson	.50
163 Gene Brabender	.50	244 John Donaldson	.50	323 Deron Johnson	.50	405 Tommy Helms	.50
164 Ramon Webster	.50	245 Tony Gonzalez	.50	324 Jim Nash	.50	406 Dick Ellsworth	.50
165 Tony Oliva	3.00	246 Fritz Peterson	.50	325 Manny Mota	1.00	407 Gary Kolb	.50
166 Claude Raymond	.50	247 Reds Rookies:	300.00	326 Denny Ribant	.50	408 Steve Carlton	35.00
167 Elston Howard	2.00	Johnny Bench, R. Tompkins		327 Tony Taylor	.50	409 Orioles Rookies:	.50
168 Los Angeles Dodgers	1.50	248 Fred Valentine	.50	328 Angels Rookies:	.50	Frank Peters, Don Stone	
169 Bob Bolin	.50	249 Bill Singer	.50	Chuck Vinson, Jim Weaver		410 Ferguson Jenkins	4.00
170 Jim Fregosi	1.00	250 Carl Yastrzemski	30.00	329 Duane Josephson	.50	411 Ron Hansen	.50
171 Don Nottebart	.50	251 Manny Sanguillen (R)	2.00	330 Roger Maris	20.00	412 Clay Carroll	.50
172 Walt Williams	.50	252 Angels Team	1.50	331 Dan Osinski	.50	413 Tommy McCraw	.50
173 John Boozer	.50	253 Dick Hughes	.50	332 Doug Rader	.50	414 Mickey Lolich	2.00
174 Bob Tillman	.50	254 Cleon Jones	.50	333 Ron Herbel	.50	415 Johnny Callison	.50
175 Maury Wills	4.00	255 Dean Chance	.50	334 Baltimore Orioles	1.50	416 Bill Rigney (Mgr.)	.50
176 Bob Allen	.50	256 Norm Cash	1.50	335 Bob Allison	.50	417 Willie Crawford	.50
177 Mets Rookies:	900.00	257 Phil Niekro	5.00	336 John Purdin	.50	418 Eddie Fisher	.50
J. Koosman, Nolan Ryan		258 Cubs Rookies:	.75	337 Bill Robinson	.50	419 Jack Hiatt	.50
178 Don Wert	.50	J. Arcia, B. Schlesinger		338 Bob Johnson	.50	420 Cesar Tovar	.50
179 Bill Stoneman	.50	259 Ken Boyer	1.25	339 Rich Nye	.50	421 Ron Taylor	.50
180 Curt Flood	1.00	260 Jim Wynn	1.00	340 Max Alvis	.50	422 Rene Lachemann	.50
181 Jerry Zimmerman	.50	261 Dave Duncan	.50	341 Jim Lemon (Mgr.)	.50	423 Fred Gladding	.50
182 Dave Guisti	.50	262 Rick Wise	.50	342 Ken Johnson	.50	424 Chicago White Sox	1.50
183 Bob Kennedy	.50	263 Horace Clarke	.75	343 Jim Gosger	.50	425 Jim Maloney	.50
184 Lou Johnson	.50	264 Ted Abernathy	.50	344 Don Clendenon	.75	426 Hank Allen	.50
185 Tom Haller	.50	265 Tommy Davis	.75	345 Bob Hendley	.50	427 Dick Calmus	.50
186 Eddie Watt	.50	266 Paul Popovich	.50	346 Jerry Adair	.50	428 Vic Roznovsky	.50
187 Sonny Jackson	.50	267 Herman Franks (Mgr.)	.50	347 George Brunet	.50	429 Tommie Sisk	.50

NO. PLAYER	NR. MT.
430 Rico Petrocelli	1.00
431 Dooley Womack	.50
432 Indians Rookies:	.50
Bill Davis, Jose Vidal	.60
433 Bob Rodgers	.50
434 Ricardo Joseph	.60
435 Ron Perranoski	.75
436 Hal Lanier	.50
437 Don Cardwell	.50
438 Lee Thomas	.50
439 Luman Harris (Mgr.)	.60
440 Claude Osteen	.50
441 Alex Johnson	.50
442 Dick Bosman	.50
443 Joe Azcue	.50
444 Jack Fisher	.60
445 Mike Shannon	.50
446 Ron Kline	.50
447 Tigers Rookies:	.50
G. Korince, F. Lasher	
448 Gary Wagner	.50
449 Gene Oliver	.50
450 Jim Kaat	3.00
451 Al Spangler	.50
452 Jesus Alou	.50
453 Sammy Ellis	.50
454 Checklist No. 6	2.50
455 Rico Carty	1.25
456 John O'Donoghue	.50
457 Jim Lefebvre	.50
458 Lew Krausse	.75
459 Dick Simpson	.75
460 Jim Lonborg	1.00
461 Chuck Hiller	.75
462 Barry Moore	.75
463 Jimmie Schaffer	.75
464 Don McMahon	.75
465 Tommie Agee	.75
466 Bill Dillman	.75
467 Dick Howser	1.00
468 Larry Sherry	.75
469 Ty Cline	.75
470 Bill Freehan	.75
471 Orlando Pena	1.25
472 Walt Alston (Mgr.)	2.00
473 Al Worthington	.75

NO. PLAYER	NR. MT.
474 Paul Schaal	.75
475 Joe Niekro	1.50
476 Woody Woodward	.75
477 Philadelphia Phillies	1.50
478 Dave McNally	1.00
479 Phil Gagliano	.75
480 Manager's Dream:	10.00
Tony Oliva, Chico	
Cardenas, Bob Clemente	
481 John Wyatt	.75
482 Jose Pagan	.75
483 Darold Knowles	.75
484 Phil Roof	.75
485 Ken Berry	.75
486 Cal Koonce	.75
487 Lee May	1.00
488 Dick Tracewski	.75
489 Wally Bunker	.75
490 Super Stars:	40.00
Harmon Killebrew, Willie	
Mays, Mickey Mantle	
491 Denny LeMaster	.75
492 Jeff Torborg	.75
493 Jim McGlothlin	.75
494 Ray Sadecki	.75
495 Leon Wagner	.75
496 Steve Hamilton	.75
497 St. Louis Cardinals	2.00
498 Bill Bryan	.75
499 Steve Blass	.75
500 Frank Robinson	10.00
501 John Odom	.75
502 Mike Andrews	.75
503 Al Jackson	.75
504 Russ Snyder	.75
505 Joe Sparma	.75
506 Clarence Jones	.75
507 Wade Blasingame	.75
508 Duke Sims	.75
509 Dennis Higgins	.75
510 Ron Fairly	.75
511 Bill Kelso	.75
512 Grant Jackson	.75
513 Hank Bauer (Mgr.)	.75
514 Al McBean	.75
515 Russ Nixon	.75

NO. PLAYER	NR. MT.
516 Pete Mikkelsen	.75
517 Diego Segui	.75
518 Checklist No. 7*	2.50
519 Jerry Stephenson	.75
520 Lou Brock	10.00
521 Don Shaw	.75
522 Wayne Causey	.75
523 John Tsitouris	.75
524 Andy Kosco	.75
525 Jim Davenport	.75
526 Bill Denehy	.75
527 Tito Francona	.75
528 Detroit Tigers	7.00
529 Bruce Von Hoff	.75
530 Bird Belters:	5.00
Frank Robinson,	
Brooks Robinson	
531 Chuck Hinton	.75
532 Luis Tiant	1.50
533 Wes Parker	.75
534 Bob Miller	.75
535 Danny Cater	.75
536 Bill Short	.75
537 Norm Siebern	.75
538 Manny Jimenez	.75
539 Major League Rookies:	1.00
Jim Ray, Mike Ferraro	
540 Nelson Briles	.75
541 Sandy Alomar	.75
542 John Boccabella	.75
543 Bob Lee	.75
544 Mayo Smith (Mgr.)	.75
545 Lindy McDaniel	.75
546 Roy White	1.50
547 Dan Coombs	.75
548 Bernie Allen	.75
549 Orioles Rookies:	.75
Curt Motton, Roger Nelson	
550 Clete Boyer	1.00
551 Darrell Sutherland	.75
552 Ed Kirkpatrick	.75
553 Hank Aguirre	.75
554 Oakland A's	2.00
555 Jose Tartabull	.75
556 Dick Selma	.75
557 Frank Quilici	.75

NO. PLAYER	NR. MT.
558 John Edwards	.75
559 Pirates Rookies:	1.00
Carl Taylor, Luke Walker	
560 Paul Casanova	.75
561 Lee Elia	.75
562 Jim Bouton	1.50
563 Ed Charles	.75
564 Eddie Stanky	.75
565 Larry Dierker	.75
566 Ken Harrelson	1.50
567 Clay Dalrymple	.75
568 Willie Smith	.75
569 NL Rookies:	.75
Ivan Murrell, Les Rohr	
570 Rick Reichardt	.75
571 Tony LaRussa	1.00
572 Don Bosch	.75
573 Joe Coleman	.75
574 Cincinnati Reds	1.50
575 Jim Palmer	15.00
576 Dave Adlesh	.75
577 Fred Talbot	.75
578 Orlando Martinez	.75
579 NL Rookies:	1.25
Larry Hisle, Mike Lum	
580 Bob Bailey	.75
581 Garry Roggenburk	.75
582 Jerry Grote	.75
583 Gates Brown	.75
584 Larry Shepard	.75
585 Wilbur Wood	.75
586 Jim Pagliaroni	.75
587 Roger Repoz	.75
588 Dick Schofield	.75
589 Twins Rookies:	.75
Ron Clark, Moe Ogier	
590 Tommy Harper	.75
591 Dick Nen	.75
592 John Bateman	.75
593 Lee Stange	.75
594 Phil Linz	.75
595 Phil Ortega	.75
596 Charlie Smith	.75
597 Bill McCool	.75
598 Jerry May (Exc. $.75)	3.00

1969 Topps.... Complete Set of 664 Cards—Value $700.00 (Exc.); $1600.00 (Mint)

Includes the rookie cards of Reggie Jackson, Al Oliver and Rollie Fingers. The high numbers are 513 to 664. The values listed for the 23 cards with an *asterisk* are with the player's entire name in *yellow* letters. These cards also exist with the player's name in *white* letters—worth $12.50 each, except card no. 440—$70.00, no. 485—$40.00 and no. 500—$500.00.

NO. PLAYER	NR. MT.
1 AL Bat Ldrs. (Exc. $1.50)	7.00
Carl Yastrzemski, Tony	
Oliva, Danny Cater	
2 NL Batting Leaders:	3.00
Matty Alou, Felipe Alou,	
Pete Rose	
3 AL RBI Leaders:	1.25
Frank Howard, Ken	
Harrelson, Jim Northrup	

NO. PLAYER	NR. MT.
4 NL RBI Leaders:	1.25
Willie McCovey, Ron	
Santo, Billy Williams	
5 AL Home Run Leaders:	1.25
Frank Howard, Willie	
Horton, Ken Harrelson	
6 NL Home Run Leaders:	2.00
Willie McCovey, Richie	
Allen, Ernie Banks	

NO. PLAYER	NR. MT.
7 AL ERA Leaders:	1.25
Luis Tiant, Sam	
McDowell, Dave McNally	
8 NL ERA Leaders:	1.25
Bobby Bolin, Bob Gibson,	
Bob Veale	
9 AL Pitching Leaders:	1.25
Mel Stottlemyre, Denny	
McLain, Dave McNally,	
Luis Tiant	

NO. PLAYER	NR. MT.
10 NL Pitching Leaders:	2.50
Juan Marichal, Bob	
Gibson, Fergie Jenkins	
11 AL Strikeout Leaders:	1.25
Sam McDowell, Denny	
McLain, Luis Tiant	
12 NL Strikeout Leaders:	1.50
Bob Gibson, Fergie	
Jenkins, Bill Singer	

NO. PLAYER	NR. MT.
13 Mickey Stanley	.50
14 Al McBean	.35
15 Boog Powell	1.50
16 Giants Rookies:	.50
C. Gutierrez, R. Robertson	
17 Mike Marshall	.75
18 Dick Schofield	.35
19 Ken Suarez	.35
20 Ernie Banks	9.00
21 Jose Santiago	.35
22 Jesus Alou	.35
23 Lew Krause	.35
24 Walt Alston (Mgr.)	1.75
25 Ray White	.75
26 Clay Carroll	.35
27 Bernie Allen	.35
28 Mike Ryan	.35
29 Dave Morehead	.35
30 Bob Allison	.35
31 Mets Rookies:	1.50
Gary Gentry, Amos Otis	
32 Sammy Ellis	.35
33 Wayne Causey	.35
34 Gary Peters	.35
35 Joe Morgan	5.00
36 Luke Walker	.35
37 Curt Motton	.35
38 Zoilo Versalles	.35
39 Dick Hughes	.35
40 Mayo Smith (Mgr.)	.35
41 Bob Barton	.35
42 Tommy Harper	.35
43 Joe Niekro	.75
44 Danny Cater	.35
45 Maury Wills	2.00
46 Fritz Peterson	.35
47 Paul Popovich	.35
(without "C" on helmet)	
47 Paul Popovich	8.00
(with "C" on helmet)	
48 Brant Alyea	.35
49 Royals Rookies:	.35
Steve Jones, E. Rodriguez	
49 Royals Rookies:	8.00
Error—name misspelled	
"Rodriquez"	
50 Bob Clement	25.00
51 Woody Fryman	.35
52 Mike Andrews	.35
53 Sonny Jackson	.35
54 Cisco Carlos	.35
55 Jerry Grote	.35
56 Rich Reese	.35
57 Checklist No. 1	2.00
58 Fred Gladding	.35
59 Jay Johnstone	.35
60 Nelson Briles	.35
61 Jimmie Hall	.35
62 Chico Salmon	.35
63 Jim Hickman	.35
64 Bill Monbouquette	.35
65 Willie Davis	.60
66 Orioles Rookies:	.50
M. Adamson, M. Rettenmund	
67 Bill Stoneman	.35
68 Dave Duncan	.35
69 Steve Hamilton	.35
70 Tommy Helms	.35
71 Steve Whitaker	.35
72 Ron Taylor	.35
73 Johnny Briggs	.35
74 Preston Gomez (Mgr.)	.35
75 Luis Aparicio	5.00
76 Norm Miller	.35
77 Ron Perranoski	.35
(no team logo on hat)	
77 Ron Perranoski	8.00
(with team logo on hat)	
78 Tom Satriano	.35
79 Milt Pappas	.35
80 Norm Cash	1.25
81 Mel Queen	.35
82 Pirates Rookies:	8.00
Rich Hebner, Al Oliver	
83 Mike Ferraro	.35

NO. PLAYER	NR. MT.
84 Bob Humphreys	.35
85 Lou Brock	7.00
86 Pete Richert	.35
87 Horace Clarke	.35
88 Rich Nye	.35
89 Russ Gibson	.35
90 Jerry Koosman	1.50
91 Al Dark (Mgr.)	.50
92 Jack Billingham	.35
93 Joe Foy	.35
94 Hank Aguirre	.35
95 Johnny Bench	90.00
96 Denver LeMaster	.35
97 Buddy Bradford	.35
98 Dave Giusti	.35
99 Twins Rookies:	15.00
Danny Morris, Graig Nettles	
100 Hank Aaron	35.00
101 Daryl Patterson	.35
102 Jim Davenport	.35
103 Roger Repoz	.35
104 Steve Blass	.35
105 Rick Monday	.35
106 Jim Hannan	.35
107 Checklist No.2	1.50
(error—#161 Jim Purdin)	
107 Checklist No.2	5.00
(correct—#161 John Purdin)	
108 Tony Taylor	.35
109 Jim Lonborg	.35
110 Mike Shannon	.35
111 Johnny Morris	.35
112 J.C. Martin	.35
113 Dave May	.35
114 Yankees Rookies:	.35
A. Closter, J. Cumberland	
115 Bill Hands	.35
116 Chuck Harrison	.35
117 Jim Fairey	.35
118 Stan Williams (Mgr.)	.35
119 Doug Rader	.35
120 Pete Rose	35.00
121 Joe Grzenda	.35
122 Ron Fairly	.35
123 Wilbur Wood	.35
124 Hank Bauer (Mgr.)	.35
125 Ray Sadecki	.35
126 Dick Tracewski	.35
127 Kevin Collins	.35
128 Tommie Aaron	.35
129 Bill McCool	.35
130 Carl Yastrzemski	25.00
131 Chris Cannizzaro	.35
132 Dave Baldwin	.35
133 Johnny Callison	.35
134 Jim Weaver	.35
135 Tommy Davis	.75
136 Cards Rookies:	.35
Steve Huntz, Mike Torrez	
137 Wally Bunker	.35
138 John Bateman	.35
139 Andy Kosco	.35
140 Jim Lefebvre	.35
141 Bill Dillman	.35
142 Woody Woodward	.35
143 Joe Nossek	.35
144 Bob Hendley	.35
145 Max Alvis	.35
146 Jim Perry	.60
147 Leo Durocher (Mgr.)	1.25
148 Lee Stange	.35
149 Ollie Brown	.35
150 Denny McLain	2.00
151 Clay Dalrymple	.35
(Orioles Team)	
151 Clay Dalrymple	6.00
(Phillies Team)	
152 Tommie Sisk	.35
153 Ed Brinkman	.35
154 Jim Britton	.35
155 Pete Ward	.35
156 Houston Rookies:	.35
Hal Gilson, Leon McFadden	
157 Bob Rodgers	.35
158 Joe Gibbon	.35

NO. PLAYER	NR. MT.
159 Jerry Adair	.35
160 Vada Pinson	1.00
161 John Purdin	.35
162 World Series Game 1:	3.00
Gibson Fans 17	
163 World Series Game 2:	1.50
Tigers Deck Cards	
164 World Series Game 3:	1.50
McCarver's Homer	
165 World Series Game 4:	3.00
Brock Lead-Off HR	
166 World Series Game 5:	4.00
Kaline's Key Hit	
167 World Series Game 6:	1.50
Tigers 10-Run Inning	
168 World Series Game 7:	3.00
Lolich Outduels Gibson	
169 World Series:	1.50
Tigers Celebrate Victory	
170 Frank Howard	1.00
171 Glenn Beckert	.35
172 Jerry Stephenson	.35
173 White Sox Rookies:	.35
B. Christian, G. Nyman	
174 Grant Jackson	.35
175 Jim Bunning	2.00
176 Joe Azcue	.35
177 Ron Reed	.35
178 Ray Oyler	.35
179 Don Pavletich	.35
180 Willie Horton	.50
181 Mel Nelson	.35
182 Bill Rigney (Mgr.)	.35
183 Don Shaw	.35
184 Roberto Pena	.35
185 Tom Phoebus	.35
186 John Edwards	.35
187 Leon Wagner	.35
188 Rick Wise	.35
189 Red Sox Rookies:	.60
J. Lahoud, J. Thibadeau	
190 Willie Mays	32.00
191 Lindy McDaniel	.35
192 Jose Pagan	.35
193 Don Cardwell	.35
194 Ted Uhlaender	.35
195 John Odom	.35
196 Lum Harris (Mgr.)	.35
197 Dick Selma	.35
198 Willie Smith	.35
199 Jim French	.35
200 Bob Gibson	6.00
201 Russ Snyder	.35
202 Don Wilson	.35
203 Dave Johnson	.75
204 Jack Hiatt	.35
205 Rick Reichardt	.35
206 Phillies Rookies:	.50
Larry Hisle, Barry Lersch	
207 Roy Face	.50
208 Donn Clendenon	.35
(Astros Team)	
208 Donn Clendenon	9.00
(Expos Team)	
209 Larry Haney	.35
(negative reversed)	
210 Felix Millan	.35
211 Galen Cisco	.35
212 Tom Tresh	.50
213 Gerry Arrigo	.35
214 Checklist No. 3	2.00
215 Rico Petrocelli	.35
216 Don Sutton	5.00
217 John Donaldson	.35
218 John Roseboro	.35
219 Freddie Patek	.75
220 Sam McDowell	.75
221 Art Shamsky	.75
222 Duane Josephson	.75
223 Tom Dukes	.75
224 Angels Rookies:	.75
B. Harrelson, S. Kealey	
225 Don Kessinger	1.00
226 Bruce Howard	.75
227 Frank Johnson	.75

NO. PLAYER	NR. MT.
228 Dave Leonhard	.75
229 Don Lock	.75
230 Rusty Staub	1.50
231 Pat Dobson	.75
232 Dave Ricketts	.75
233 Steve Barber	.75
234 Dave Bristol (Mgr.)	.75
235 Jim Hunter	6.00
236 Manny Mota	1.00
237 Bobby Cox	1.00
238 Ken Johnson	.75
239 Bob Taylor	.75
240 Ken Harrelson	1.00
241 Jim Brewer	.75
242 Frank Kostro	.75
243 Ron Kline	.75
244 Indians Rookies:	1.00
R. Fosse, G. Woodson	
245 Ed Charles	.75
246 Joe Coleman	.75
247 Gene Oliver	.75
248 Bob Priddy	.75
249 Ed Spiezio	.75
250 Frank Robinson	12.00
251 Ron Herbel	.75
252 Chuck Cottier	.75
253 Jerry Johnson	.75
254 Joe Schultz (Mgr.)	.75
255 Steve Carlton	32.00
256 Gates Brown	.75
257 Jim Ray	.75
258 Jackie Hernandez	.75
259 Bill Short	.75
260 Reggie Jackson (R)	300.00
261 Bob Johnson	.75
262 Mike Kekich	.75
263 Jerry May	.75
264 Bill Landis	.75
265 Chico Cardenas	.75
266 Dodger Rookies:	1.00
Tom Hutton, Alan Foster	
267 Vicente Romo	.75
268 Al Spangler	.75
269 Al Weis	.75
270 Mickey Lolich	1.50
271 Larry Stahl	.75
272 Ed Stroud	.75
273 Ron Willis	.75
274 Clyde King (Mgr.)	.75
275 Vic Davalillo	.75
276 Gary Wagner	.75
277 Ron Hendricks	.75
278 Gary Geiger	.75
279 Roger Nelson	.75
280 Alex Johnson	.75
281 Ted Kubiak	.75
282 Pat Jarvis	.75
283 Sandy Alomar	.75
284 Expos Rookies:	.75
M. Wegener, J. Robertson	
285 Don Mincher	.75
286 Dock Ellis	1.00
287 Jose Tartabull	.75
288 Ken Holtzman	1.00
289 Bart Shirley	.75
290 Jim Kaat	3.00
291 Vern Fuller	.75
292 Al Downing	1.00
293 Dick Dietz	.75
294 Jim Lemon	.75
295 Tony Perez	5.00
296 Andy Messersmith (R)	1.50
297 Deron Johnson	.75
298 Dave Nicholson	.75
299 Mark Belanger	1.00
300 Felipe Alou	1.00
301 Darrell Brandon	.75
302 Jim Pagliaroni	.75
303 Cal Koonce	.75
304 Padres Rookies:	.75
Bill Davis, Clarence Gaston	
305 Dick McAuliffe	.75
306 Jim Grant	.75
307 Gary Kolb	.75
308 Wade Blasingame	.75

NO. PLAYER	NR. MT.
309 Walt Williams	.75
310 Tom Haller	.75
311 Sparky Lyle (R)	4.00
312 Lee Elia	.75
313 Bill Robinson	1.00
314 Checklist No. 4	2.00
315 Eddie Fisher	.75
316 Hal Lanier	1.00
317 Bruce Look	.75
318 Jack Fisher	.75
319 Ken McMullen	.75
320 Dal Maxvill	.75
321 Jim McAndrew	.75
322 Jose Vidal	.75
323 Larry Miller	.75
324 Tiger Rookies:	1.00
Les Cain, Dave Campbell	
325 Jose Cardenal	.75
326 Gary Sutherland	.75
327 Willie Crawford	.75
328 Joe Horlen	.35
329 Rick Joseph	.35
330 Tony Conigliaro	.75
331 Braves Rookies:	.50
Tom House, Gil Garrido	
332 Fred Talbot	.35
333 Ivan Murrell	.35
334 Phil Roof	.35
335 Bill Mazeroski	1.00
336 Jim Roland	.35
337 Marty Martinez	.35
338 Del Unser	.35
339 Reds Rookies:	.35
Steve Mingori, Jose Pena	
340 Dave McNally	.60
341 Dave Adlesh	.35
342 Bubba Morton	.35
343 Dan Frisella	.35
344 Tom Matchick	.35
345 Frank Linzy	.35
346 Wayne Comer	.35
347 Randy Hundley	.35
348 Steve Hargan	.35
349 Dick Williams (Mgr.)	.35
350 Richie Allen	1.00
351 Carroll Sembera	.35
352 Paul Schaal	.35
353 Jeff Torborg	.35
354 Nate Oliver	.35
355 Phil Niekro	4.00
356 Frank Quilici	.35
357 Carl Taylor	.35
358 Athletics Rookies:	.35
George Lauzerique, Roberto Rodriguez	
359 Dick Kelley	.35
360 Jim Wynn	.50
361 Gary Holman	.35
362 Jim Maloney	.35
363 Russ Nixon	.35
364 Tommie Agee	.35
365 Jim Fregosi	.75
366 Bo Belinsky	.35
367 Lou Johnson	.35
368 Vic Roznovsky	.35
369 Bob Skinner (Mgr.)	.35
370 Juan Marichal	5.00
371 Sal Bando	.75
372 Adolfo Phillips	.35
373 Fred Lasher	.35
374 Bob Tillman	.35
375 Harmon Killebrew	10.00
376 Royals Rookies:	.45
Mike Fiore, Jim Rooker	
377 Gary Bell	.35
378 Jose Herrera	.35
379 Ken Boyer	1.00
380 Stan Bahnsen	.35
381 Ed Kranepool	.35
382 Pat Corrales	.35
383 Casey Cox	.35
384 Larry Shepard	.35
385 Orlando Cepeda	2.50
386 Jim McGlothlin	.35

NO. PLAYER	NR. MT.
387 Bobby Klaus	.35
388 Tom McCraw	.35
389 Dan Coombs	.35
390 Bill Freehan	.50
391 Ray Culp	.35
392 Bob Burda	.35
393 Gene Brabender	.35
394 Pilots Rookies:	2.00
Lou Piniella, M. Staehle	
395 Chris Short	.35
396 Jim Campanis	.35
397 Chuck Dobson	.35
398 Tito Francona	.35
399 Bob Bailey	.35
400 Don Drysdale	6.00
401 Jake Gibbs	.35
402 Ken Boswell	.35
403 Bob Miller	.35
404 Cubs Rookies:	.50
Vic LaRose, Gary Ross	
405 Lee May	.50
406 Phil Ortega	.35
407 Tom Egan	.35
408 Nate Colbert	.35
409 Bob Moose	.35
410 Al Kaline	8.00
411 Larry Dierker	.35
412 Checklist No. 5	5.00
413 Roland Sheldon	.35
414 Duke Sims	.35
415 Ray Washburn	.35
416 Willie McCovey (AS)	3.00
417 Ken Harrelson (AS)	.50
418 Tommy Helms (AS)	.50
419 Rod Carew (AS)	5.00
420 Ron Santo (AS)	.50
421 Brooks Robinson (AS)	4.00
422 Don Kessinger (AS)	.50
423 Bert Campaneris (AS)	.50
424 Pete Rose (AS)	10.00
425 Carl Yastrzemski (AS)	7.00
426 Curt Flood (AS)	.50
427 Tony Oliva (AS)	.75
428 Lou Brock (AS)	4.00
429 Willie Horton (AS)	.50
430 Johnny Bench (AS)	10.00
431 Bill Freehan (AS)	.50
432 Bob Gibson (AS)	3.00
433 Denny McLain (AS)	.60
434 Jerry Koosman (AS)	.50
435 Sam McDowell (AS)	.50
436 Gene Alley	.35
437 Luis Alcaraz	.35
438 Gary Waslewski	.35
439 White Sox Rookies:	.50
Ed Herrmann, Dan Lazar	
440 Willie McCovey*	12.00
441 Dennis Higgins*	.35
442 Ty Cline	.35
443 Don Wert	.35
444 Joe Moeller*	.35
445 Bobby Knoop	.35
446 Claude Raymond	.35
447 Ralph Houk (Mgr.)*	.65
448 Bob Tolan	.35
449 Paul Lindblad	.35
450 Billy Williams	5.00
451 Rich Rollins*	.35
452 Al Ferrara*	.35
453 Mike Cuellar	1.00
454 Phillies Rookies:*	.50
Larry Colton, Don Money	
455 Sonny Siebert	.35
456 Bud Harrelson	.35
457 Dalton Jones	.35
458 Curt Blefary	.35
459 Dave Boswell	.35
460 Joe Torre	1.00
461 Mike Epstein*	.35
462 Red Schoendienst	2.00
463 Dennis Ribant	.35
464 Dave Marshall*	.35
465 Tommy John	3.00
466 John Boccabella	.35

NO. PLAYER	NR. MT.
467 Tom Reynolds	.35
468 Pirates Rookies:*	.50
Bruce Del Canton, Bob Robertson	
469 Chico Ruiz	.35
470 Mel Stottlemyre*	.65
471 Ted Savage*	.35
472 Jim Price	.35
473 Jose Arcia*	.35
474 Tom Murphy	.35
475 Tim McCarver	1.00
476 Boston Rookies:*	.50
Ken Brett, Gerry Moses	
477 Jeff James	.35
478 Don Buford	.35
479 Richie Scheinblum	.35
480 Tom Seaver	65.00
481 Bill Melton	.35
482 Jim Gosger*	.35
483 Ted Abernathy	.35
484 Joe Gordon	.35
485 Gaylord Perry*	5.00
486 Paul Casanova*	.35
487 Denis Menke	.35
488 Joe Sparma	.35
489 Clete Boyer	.50
490 Matty Alou	.50
491 Twins Rookies:*	.50
Jerry Crider, George Mitterwald	
492 Tony Cloninger	.35
493 Wes Parker*	.35
494 Ken Berry	.35
495 Bert Campaneris	.50
496 Larry Jaster	.35
497 Julian Javier	.35
498 Juan Pizarro	.35
499 Astro Rookies:	.50
Don Bryant, Steve Shea	
500 Mickey Mantle*	175.00
501 Tony Gonzalez*	.35
502 Minnie Rojas	.35
503 Larry Brown	.35
504 Checklist No. 6	2.00
505 Bobby Bolin*	.35
506 Paul Blair	.35
507 Cookie Rojas	.35
508 Moe Drabowsky	.35
509 Manny Sanguillen	.50
510 Rod Carew	35.00
511 Diego Segui*	.35
512 Cleon Jones	.35
513 Camilo Pascual	.60
514 Mike Lum	.50
515 Dick Green	.35
516 Earl Weaver (Mgr.)	4.00
517 Mike McCormick	.50
518 Fred Whitfield	.50
519 Yankees Rookies:	.75
G. Kenney, Len Boehmer	
520 Bob Veale	.65
521 George Thomas	.50
522 Joe Hoerner	.50
523 Bob Chance	.50
524 Expos Rookies:	.50
Jose Laboy, Floyd Wicker	
525 Earl Wilson	.50
526 Hector Torres	.50
527 Al Lopez (Mgr.)	2.50
528 Claude Osteen	.50
529 Ed Kirkpatrick	.50
530 Cesar Tovar	.50
531 Dick Farrell	.50
532 Bird Hill Aces:	.65
D. McNally, T. Phoebus, J. Hardin, M. Cuellar	
533 Nolan Ryan	250.00
534 Jerry McNertney	.50
535 Phil Regan	.50
536 Padres Rookies:	.60
D. Breeden, Dave Roberts	
537 Mike Paul	.50
538 Charlie Smith	.50
539 Ted Shows How:	3.00
Mike Epstein, Ted Williams	

NO. PLAYER	NR. MT.
540 Curt Flood	1.00
541 Joe Verbanic	.50
542 Bob Aspromonte	.50
543 Fred Newman	.50
544 Tigers Rookies:	.75
Mike Kilkenny, Ron Woods	
545 Willie Stargell	10.00
546 Jim Nash	.50
547 Billy Martin (Mgr.)	2.50
548 Bob Locker	.50
549 Ron Brand	.50
550 Brooks Robinson	12.00
551 Wayne Granger	.50
552 Dodgers Rookies:	.50
Ted Sizemore, Bill Sudakis	
553 Ron Davis	.50
554 Frank Bertaina	.50
555 Jim Hart	.50
556 A's Stars:	.75
Bert Campaneris, Sal Bando, Danny Cater	
557 Frank Fernandez	.50
558 Tom Burgmeier	.50
559 Cardinals Rookies:	.60
Joe Hague, Jim Hicks	
560 Luis Tiant	1.00
561 Ron Clark	.50
562 Bob Watson (R)	2.00
563 Marty Pattin	.50
564 Gil Hodges (Mgr.)	6.00
565 Hoyt Wilhelm	5.00
566 Ron Hansen	.50
567 Pirates Rookies:	.60
Elvio Jimenez, Jim Shellenback	
568 Cecil Upshaw	.50
569 Billy Harris	.50
570 Ron Santo	1.00
571 Cap Peterson	.50
572 Giants Heroes:	7.00
Willie McCovey, Juan Marichal	
573 Jim Palmer	13.00
574 George Scott	.50
575 Bill Singer	.50
576 Phillies Rookies:	.50
Ron Stone, Bill Wilson	
577 Mike Hegan	.50
578 Don Bosch	.50
579 Dave Nelson	.50
580 Jim Northrup	.50
581 Gary Nolan	.50
582 Checklist No. 7	2.00
583 Clyde Wright	.50
584 Don Mason	.50
585 Ron Swoboda	.50
586 Tim Cullen	.50
587 Joe Rudi (R)	1.50
588 Bill White	1.50
589 Joe Pepitone	1.00
590 Rico Carty	.75
591 Mike Hedlund	.75
592 Padres Rookies:	.75
R. Robles, Al Santorini	
593 Don Nottebart	.75
594 Dooley Womack	.75
595 Lee Maye	.75
596 Chuck Hartenstein	.75
597 AL Rookies:	25.00
Bob Floyd, Larry Burchart, Rollie Fingers	
598 Ruben Amaro	.75
599 John Boozer	.75
600 Tony Oliva	2.50
601 Tug McGraw	1.50
602 Cubs Rookies:	.75
Alec Distaso, Jim Qualls, Don Young	
603 Joe Keough	.75
604 Bobby Etheridge	.75
605 Dick Ellsworth	.75
606 Gene Mauch (Mgr.)	.75
607 Dick Bosman	.75
608 Dick Simpson	.75

1969 Topps (Continued)

NO. PLAYER	NR. MT.
609 Phil Gagliano	.75
610 Jim Hardin	.75
611 Braves Rookies:	.75
Bob Didier, Walt Hriniak, Gary Neibauer	
612 Jack Aker	.75
613 Jim Beauchamp	.75
614 Houston Rookies:	.75
Tom Griffin, Skip Guinn	
615 Len Gabrielson	.75
616 Don McMahon	.75
617 Jesse Gonder	.75
618 Ramon Webster	.75
619 Royals Rookies:	1.00
Pat Kelly, Juan Rios, Bill Butler	
620 Dean Chance	.75
621 Bill Voss	.75
622 Dan Osinski	.75
623 Hank Allen	.75

NO. PLAYER	NR. MT.
624 NL Rookies:	.75
Darrel Chaney, Duffy Dyer, Terry Harmon	
625 Mack Jones	.75
626 Gene Michael	.75
627 George Stone	.75
628 Red Sox Rookies:	1.00
Bill Conigliaro, Syd O'Brien, Fred Wenz	
629 Jack Hamilton	.75
630 Bobby Bonds (R)	7.50
631 John Kennedy	.75
632 Jon Warden	.75
633 Harry Walker (Mgr.)	.75
634 Andy Etchebarren	.75
635 George Culver	.75
636 Woodie Held	.75
637 Padres Rookies:	.75
Jerry DaVanon, Frank Reberger, Clay Kirby	

NO. PLAYER	NR. MT.
638 Ed Sprague	.75
639 Barry Moore	.75
640 Fergie Jenkins	3.00
641 NL Rookies:	.75
Bobby Darwin, John Miller, Tommy Dean	
642 John Hiller	.75
643 Billy Cowan	.75
644 Chuck Hinton	.75
645 George Brunet	.75
646 Expos Rookies:	.75
Carl Morton, Dan McGinn	
647 Dave Wickersham	.75
648 Bobby Wine	.75
649 Al Jackson	.75
650 Ted Williams (Mgr.)	6.00
651 Gus Gil	.75
652 Eddie Watt	.75
653 Aurelio Rodriguez	2.00
(Photo of Angels Batboy)	

NO. PLAYER	NR. MT.
654 White Sox Rookies:	.90
Carlos May, Don Secrist, Rich Morales	
655 Mike Hershberger	.75
656 Dan Schneider	.75
657 Bobby Murcer	1.50
658 AL Rookies:	.75
Tom Hall, Bill Burbach, Jim Miles	
659 Johnny Podres	1.00
660 Reggie Smith	1.50
661 Jim Merritt	.75
662 Royals Rookies:	1.00
Dick Drago, Bob Oliver, George Spriggs	
663 Dick Radatz	.75
664 Ron Hunt (Exc. $.50)	2.00

1970 Topps. . . . Complete Set of 720 Cards—Value $800.00 (Exc.); $1450.00 (Mint)

Features the rookie cards of Thurman Munson, Darrell Evans, Vida Blue, and Bill Buckner. The high numbers are 634 to 720. Card 588 (checklist) exists with *Adolpho* misspelled *Adolfo*—worth $5.00.

  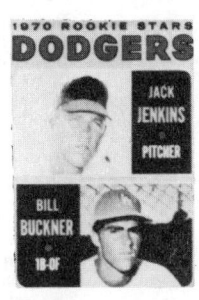  

NO. PLAYER	NR. MT.
1 Champ Mets (Exc $1.25)	6.00
2 Diego Segui	.25
3 Darrel Chaney	.25
4 Tom Egan	.25
5 Wes Parker	.25
6 Grant Jackson	.25
7 Indians Rookies:	.25
Gary Boyd, Russ Nagelson	
8 Jose Martinez	.25
9 Checklist No. 1	1.50
10 Carl Yastrzemski	25.00
11 Nate Colbert	.25
12 John Hiller	.25
13 Jack Hiatt	.25
14 Hank Allen	.25
15 Larry Dierker	.25
16 Charlie Metro	.25
17 Hoyt Wilhelm	4.00
18 Carlos May	.25
19 John Boccabella	.25
20 Dave McNally	.40
21 A's Rookies:	2.00
Gene Tenace, Vida Blue	
22 Ray Washburn	.25
23 Bill Robinson	.40
24 Dick Selma	.25
25 Cesaer Tovar	.25
26 Tug McGraw	.75
27 Chuck Hinton	.25
28 Billy Wilson	.25
29 Sandy Alomar	.25
30 Matty Alou	.50
31 Marty Pattin	.25
32 Harry Walker	.25
33 Don Wert	.25
34 Willie Crawford	.25
35 Joe Horlen	.25

NO. PLAYER	NR. MT.
36 Red Rookies:	.25
D. Breeden, B. Carbo	
37 Dick Drago	.25
38 Mack Jones	.25
39 Mike Nagy	.25
40 Rich Allen	.60
41 George Lauzerique	.25
42 Tito Fuentes	.25
43 Jack Aker	.25
44 Roberto Pena	.25
45 Dave Johnson	.75
46 Ken Rudolph	.25
47 Bob Miller	.25
48 Gil Garrido	.25
49 Tim Cullen	.25
50 Tommy Agee	.40
51 Bob Christian	.25
52 Bruce Dal Canton	.25
53 John Kennedy	.25
54 Jeff Torborg	.35
55 John Odom	.25
56 Phillies Rookies:	.25
Joe Lis, Scott Reid	
57 Pat Kelly	.25
58 Dave Marshall	.25
59 Dick Ellsworth	.25
60 Jim Wynn	.45
61 NL Batting Leaders:	3.00
Cleon Jones, Pete Rose, Bob Clemente	
62 AL Batting Leaders:	1.25
Rod Carew, Reggie Smith, Tony Oliva	
63 NL RBI Leaders:	1.25
Ron Santo, Tony Perez, Willie McCovey	

NO. PLAYER	NR. MT.
64 AL RBI Leaders:	1.25
Harmon Killebrew, Boog Powell, Reggie Jackson	
65 NL Home Run Leaders:	1.50
Hank Aaron, Willie McCovey, Lee May	
66 AL Home Run Leaders:	1.50
Harmon Killebrew, Frank Howard, Reggie Jackson	
67 NL ERA Leaders:	3.00
Bob Gibson, Juan Marichal, Steve Carlton	
68 AL ERA Leaders:	1.00
Dick Bosman, Jim Palmer, Mike Cuellar	
69 NL Pitching Leaders:	3.00
Phil Niekro, Tom Seaver, F. Jenkins, Juan Marichal	
70 AL Pitching Leaders:	.75
Dennis McLain, Mike Cuellar, Dave McNally, Jim Perry, Dave Boswell, Mel Stottlemyre	
71 NL Strikeout Leaders:	1.00
Fergie Jenkins, Bob Gibson, Bill Singer	
72 AL Strikeout Leaders:	.75
Andy Messersmith, Sam McDowell, Mickey Lolich	
73 Wayne Granger	.25
74 Angels Rookies:	.40
Greg Washburn, Wally Wolf	
75 Jim Kaat	2.00
76 Carl Taylor	.25
77 Frank Linzy	.25
78 Joe Lahoud	.25
79 Clay Kirby	.25

NO. PLAYER	NR. MT.
80 Don Kessinger	.25
81 Dave May	.25
82 Frank Fernandez	.25
83 Don Cardwell	.25
84 Paul Casanova	.25
85 Max Alvis	.25
86 Lum Harris (Mgr.)	.25
87 Steve Renko	.25
88 Pilots Rookies:	.25
Miguel Fuentes, Dick Baney	
89 Juan Rios	.25
90 Tim McCarver	1.00
91 Rich Morales	.25
92 George Culver	.25
93 Rick Renick	.25
94 Fred Patek	.25
95 Earl Wilson	.25
96 Cardinals Rookies:	2.00
Leron Lee, Jerry Reuss	
97 Joe Moeller	.25
98 Gates Brown	.25
99 Bobby Pfeil	.25
100 Mel Stottlemyre	.50
101 Bobby Floyd	.25
102 Joe Rudi	.50
103 Frank Reberger	.25
104 Gerry Moses	.25
105 Tony Gonzalez	.25
106 Darold Knowles	.25
107 Bobby Etheridge	.25
108 Tom Burgmeier	.25
109 Expos Rookies:	.35
Garry Jestadt, Carl Morton	
110 Bob Moose	.25
111 Mike Hegan	.25
112 Dave Nelson	.25
113 Jim Ray	.25

NO. PLAYER	NR. MT.
114 Gene Michael	.25
115 Alex Johnson	.25
116 Sparky Lyle	.50
117 Don Young	.25
118 George Mitterwald	.25
119 Chuck Taylor	.25
120 Sal Bando	.45
121 Orioles Rookies:	.40
Fred Beene, Terry Crowley	
122 George Stone	.25
123 Don Gutteridge (Mgr.)	.25
124 Larry Jaster	.25
125 Deron Johnson	.25
126 Marty Martinez	.25
127 Joe Coleman	.25
128 Checklist No. 2	1.50
129 Jimmie Price	.25
130 Ollie Brown	.25
131 Dodgers Rookies:	.40
Ray Lamb, Bob Stinson	
132 Jim McGlothlin	.25
133 Clay Carroll	.25
134 Danny Walton	.25
135 Dick Dietz	.25
136 Steve Hargan	.25
137 Art Shamsky	.25
138 Joe Foy	.25
139 Rich Nye	.25
140 Reggie Jackson	55.00
141 Pirates Rookies:	.40
Dave Cash, Johnny Jeter	
142 Fritz Peterson	.25
143 Phil Gagliano	.25
144 Ray Culp	.25
145 Rico Carty	.50
146 Danny Murphy	.25
147 Angel Hermoso	.25
148 Earl Weaver (Mgr.)	1.00
149 Billy Champion	.30
150 Harmon Killebrew	5.00
151 Dave Roberts	.25
152 Ike Brown	.25
153 Gary Gentry	.25
154 Senators Rookies:	.35
Jim Miles, Jan Dukes	
155 Denis Menke	.25
156 Eddie Fisher	.25
157 Manny Mota	.40
158 Jerry McNertney	.25
159 Tommy Helms	.35
160 Phil Niekro	4.00
161 Richie Scheinblum	.25
162 Jerry Johnson	.25
163 Syd O'Brien	.25
164 Ty Cline	.25
165 Ed Kirkpatrick	.25
166 Al Oliver	2.50
167 Bill Burbach	.25
168 Dave Watkins	.25
169 Tom Hall	.25
170 Billy Williams	4.00
171 Jim Nash	.25
172 Braves Rookies:	.75
Garry Hill, Ralph Garr	
173 Jim Hicks	.25
174 Ted Sizemore	.25
175 Dick Bosman	.25
176 Jim Hart	.35
177 Jim Northrup	.25
178 Denny Lemaster	.25
179 Ivan Murrell	.25
180 Tommy John	2.00
181 Sparky Anderson	.50
182 Dick Hall	.25
183 Jerry Grote	.25
184 Ray Fosse	.25
185 Don Mincher	.25
186 Rick Joseph	.25
187 Mike Hedlund	.25
188 Manny Sanguillen	.40
189 Yankees Rookies:	40.00
Thurman Munson,	
Dave McDonald	
190 Joe Torre	1.00
191 Vicente Romo	.25

NO. PLAYER	NR. MT.
192 Jim Qualls	.25
193 Mike Wegener	.25
194 Chuck Manuel	.25
195 NL Playoff Game 1:	2.50
Seaver Wins Opener	
196 NL Playoff Game 2:	1.00
Mets Show Muscle	
197 NL Playoff Game 3:	3.00
Ryan Saves the Day	
198 We're Number One	1.00
Mets Celebrate	
199 AL Playoff Game 1:	1.00
Orioles Win Squeaker	
200 AL Playoff Game 2:	1.00
Powell Scores Winning Run	
201 AL Playoff Game 3:	1.00
Birds Wrap it Up	
202 Sweep Twins in Three!	1.00
Orioles Celebrate	
203 Rudy May	.25
204 Len Gabrielson	.25
205 Bert Campaneris	.40
206 Clete Boyer	.25
207 Tigers Rookies:	.50
Norman McRae, Bob Reed	
208 Fred Gladding	.25
209 Ken Suarez	.25
210 Juan Marichal	5.00
211 Ted Williams (Mgr.)	6.00
212 Al Santorini	.25
213 Andy Etchebarren	.25
214 Ken Boswell	.25
215 Reggie Smith	1.00
216 Chuck Hartenstein	.25
217 Ron Hansen	.25
218 Ron Stone	.25
219 Jerry Kenney	.25
220 Steve Carlton	14.00
221 Ron Brand	.25
222 Jim Rooker	.25
223 Nate Oliver	.25
224 Steve Barber	.25
225 Lee May	.40
226 Ron Perranoski	.35
227 Astros Rookies:	1.00
J. Mayberry, B. Watkins	
228 Aurelio Rodriguez	.25
229 Rich Robertson	.25
230 Brooks Robinson	6.00
231 Luis Tiant	.75
232 Bob Didier	.25
233 Lew Krausse	.25
234 Tommy Dean	.25
235 Mike Epstein	.25
236 Bob Veale	.25
237 Russ Gibson	.25
238 Jose Laboy	.25
239 Ken Berry	.25
240 Fergie Jenkins	2.50
241 Royals Rookies:	.40
A. Fitzmorris, S. Northey	
242 Walter Alston (Mgr.)	1.50
243 Joe Sparma	.25
244 Checklist No. 4	1.00
245 Leo Cardenas	.25
246 Jim McAndrew	.25
247 Lou Klimchock	.25
248 Jesus Alou	.25
249 Bob Locker	.25
250 Willie McCovey	6.00
251 Dick Schofield	.25
252 Lowell Palmer	.25
253 Ron Woods	.25
254 Camilo Pascual	.25
255 Jim Spencer	.25
256 Vic Davalillo	.25
257 Dennis Higgins	.25
258 Paul Popovich	.25
259 Tommie Reynolds	.25
260 Claude Osteen	.25
261 Curt Motton	.25
262 Twins Rookies:	.35
Jerry Morales, Jim Williams	
263 Duane Josephson	.25
264 Rich Hebner	.50

NO. PLAYER	NR. MT.
265 Randy Hundley	.25
266 Wally Bunker	.25
267 Twins Rookies:	.35
Paul Ratliff, Herman Hill	
268 Claude Raymond	.25
269 Cesar Gutierrez	.25
270 Chris Short	.25
271 Greg Goossen	.25
272 Hector Torres	.25
273 Ralph Houk (Mgr.)	.40
274 Gerry Arrigo	.25
275 Duke Sims	.25
276 Ron Hunt	.25
277 Paul Doyle	.25
278 Tommie Aaron	.50
279 Bill Lee	.50
280 Donn Clendenon	.50
281 Casey Cox	.25
282 Steve Huntz	.25
283 Angel Bravo	.25
284 Jack Baldschun	.25
285 Paul Blair	.25
286 Dodgers Rookies:	6.00
Bill Buckner, Jack Jenkins	
287 Fred Talbot	.25
288 Larry Hisle	.40
289 Gene Brabender	.25
290 Rod Carew	15.00
291 Leo Durocher (Mgr.)	1.00
292 Eddie Leon	.25
293 Bob Bailey	.25
294 Jose Azcue	.25
295 Cecil Upshaw	.25
296 Woody Woodward	.25
297 Curt Blefary	.25
298 Ken Henderson	.25
299 Buddy Bradford	.25
300 Tom Seaver	35.00
301 Chico Salmon	.25
302 Jeff James	.25
303 Brant Alyea	.25
304 Bill Russell (R)	1.50
305 World Series Game 1	1.00
Buford's Leadoff Homer	
306 World Series Game 2	1.00
Clendenon's Homer	
307 World Series Game 3	1.00
Agee's Catch	
308 World Series Game 4	1.00
Martin's Bunt	
309 World Series Game 5	1.00
Koosman Shuts Door	
310 World Series Celebration	1.00
Mets Whoop it Up	
311 Dick Green	.25
312 Mike Torrez	.40
313 Mayo Smith (Mgr.)	.25
314 Bill McCool	.25
315 Luis Aparicio	3.00
316 Skip Guinn	.25
317 Red Sox Rookies:	.50
B. Conigliaro, L. Alvarado	
318 Willie Smith	.25
319 Clay Dalrymple	.25
320 Jim Maloney	.25
321 Lou Piniella	1.00
322 Luke Walker	.25
323 Wayne Comer	.25
324 Tony Taylor	.25
325 Dave Boswell	.25
326 Bill Voss	.25
327 Hal King	.25
328 George Brunet	.25
329 Chris Cannizzaro	.25
330 Lou Brock	5.00
331 Chuck Dobson	.25
332 Bobby Wine	.25
333 Bobby Murcer	1.00
334 Phil Regan	.25
335 Bill Freehan	.50
336 Del Unser	.25
337 Mike McCormick	.25
338 Paul Schaal	.25
339 Johnny Edwards	.25
340 Tony Conigliaro	.60

NO. PLAYER	NR. MT.
341 Bill Sudakis	.25
342 Wilbur Wood	.25
343 Checklist No. 4	1.50
344 Marcelino Lopez	.25
345 Al Ferrara	.25
346 Red Schoendienst	2.00
347 Russ Snyder	.25
348 Mets Rookies:	.45
M. Jorgensen, J. Hudson	
349 Steve Hamilton	.25
350 Roberto Clemente	25.00
351 Tom Murphy	.25
352 Bob Barton	.25
353 Stan Williams	.25
354 Amos Otis	.40
355 Doug Rader	.25
356 Fred Lasher	.25
357 Bob Burda	.25
358 Pedro Borbon	.25
359 Phil Roof	.25
360 Curt Flood	.50
361 Ray Jarvis	.25
362 Joe Hague	.25
363 Tom Shopay	.25
364 Dan McGinn	.25
365 Zoilo Versalles	.25
366 Barry Moore	.25
367 Mike Lum	.25
368 Ed Herrmann	.25
369 Alan Foster	.25
370 Tommy Harper	.25
371 Rod Gaspar	.25
372 Dave Guisti	.25
373 Roy White	.40
374 Tommie Sisk	.25
375 Johnny Callison	.25
376 Lefty Phillips (Mgr.)	.25
377 Bill Butler	.25
378 Jim Davenport	.25
379 Tom Tischinski	.25
380 Tony Perez	3.00
381 Athletics Rookies:	.35
Bobby Brooks, Mike Olivo	
382 Jack DiLauro	.25
383 Mickey Stanley	.35
384 Gary Neibauer	.25
385 George Scott	.35
386 Bill Dillman	.25
387 Baltimore Orioles	.75
388 Byron Browne	.25
389 Jim Shellenback	.25
390 Willie Davis	.60
391 Larry Brown	.25
392 Walt Hriniak	.25
393 John Gelnar	.25
394 Gil Hodges (Mgr.)	3.00
395 Walt Williams	.25
396 Steve Blass	.25
397 Roger Repoz	.25
398 Bill Stoneman	.25
399 New York Yankees	1.00
400 Denny McLain	1.00
401 Giants Rookies:	.40
John Harrell, B. Williams	
402 Ellie Rodriguez	.25
403 Jim Bunning	2.50
404 Rich Reese	.25
405 Bill Hands	.25
406 Mike Andrews	.25
407 Bob Watson	.40
408 Paul Lindblad	.25
409 Bob Tolan	.25
410 Boog Powell	2.00
411 L.A. Dodgers	1.25
412 Larry Burchart	.25
413 Sonny Jackson	.25
414 Paul Edmondson	.25
415 Julian Javier	.25
416 Joe Verbanic	.25
417 John Bateman	.25
418 John Donaldson	.25
419 Ron Taylor	.25
420 Ken McMullen	.25
421 Pat Dobson	.25
422 Kansas City Royals	.60

NO.	PLAYER	NR. MT.
423	Jerry May	.25
424	Mike Kilkenny	.25
425	Bobby Bonds	2.50
426	Bill Rigney (Mgr.)	.25
427	Fred Norman	.25
428	Don Buford	.25
429	Cubs Rookies:	.40
	Randy Bobb, Jim Cosman	
430	Andy Messersmith	.50
431	Ron Swoboda	.50
432	Checklist No. 5	1.00
433	Ron Bryant	.25
434	Felipe Alou	.40
435	Nelson Briles	.25
436	Philadelphia Phillies	1.00
437	Danny Cater	.25
438	Pat Jarvis	.25
439	Lee Maye	.25
440	Bill Mazeroski	.50
441	John O'Donoghue	.25
442	Gene Mauch (Mgr.)	.40
443	Al Jackson	.25
444	White Sox Rookies:	.35
	Billy Farmer, John Matias	
445	Vada Pinson	1.00
446	B. Grabarkewitz	.25
447	Lee Stange	.25
448	Houston Astros	.75
449	Jim Palmer	9.00
450	Willie McCovey (AS)	4.00
451	Boog Powell (AS)	.60
452	Felix Millan (AS)	.45
453	Rod Carew (AS)	5.00
454	Ron Santo (AS)	.45
455	Brooks Robinson (AS)	3.00
456	Don Kessinger (AS)	.45
457	Rico Petrocelli (AS)	.45
458	Pete Rose (AS)	10.00
459	Reggie Jackson (AS)	8.00
460	Matty Alou (AS)	.60
461	Carl Yastrzemski (AS)	6.00
462	Hank Aaron (AS)	6.00
463	Frank Robinson (AS)	4.00
464	Johnny Bench (AS)	5.00
465	Bill Freehan (AS)	.60
466	Juan Marichal (AS)	4.00
467	Denny McLain (AS)	.75
468	Jerry Koosman (AS)	.60
469	Sam McDowell (AS)	.60
470	Willie Stargell	6.00
471	Chris Zachary	.50
472	Atlanta Braves	.75
473	Don Bryant	.50
474	Dick Kelley	.50
475	Dick McAuliffe	.50
476	Don Shaw	.50
477	Orioles Rookies:	.60
	Roger Freed, Al Severinsen	
478	Bob Heise	.50
479	Dick Woodson	.50
480	Glen Beckert	.50
481	Jose Tartabull	.50
482	Tom Hilgendorf	.50
483	Gail Hopkins	.50
484	Gary Nolan	.50
485	Jay Johnstone	.60
486	Terry Harmon	.50
487	Cisco Carlos	.50
488	J.C. Martin	.50
489	Eddie Kasko (Mgr.)	.50
490	Bill Singer	.50
491	Graig Nettles	4.00
492	Astros Rookies:	.60
	K. Lampard, S. Spinks	
493	Lindy McDaniel	.50
494	Larry Stahl	.50
495	Dave Morehead	.50
496	Steve Whitaker	.50
497	Eddie Watt	.50
498	Al Weis	.50
499	Skip Lockwood	.50

NO.	PLAYER	NR. MT.
500	Hank Aaron	24.00
501	Chicago White Sox	1.50
502	Rollie Fingers	5.00
503	Dal Maxvill	.50
504	Don Pavletich	.50
505	Ken Holtzman	.50
506	Ed Stroud	.50
507	Pat Corrales	.50
508	Joe Niekro	1.00
509	Montreal Expos	1.00
510	Tony Oliva	1.50
511	Joe Hoerner	.50
512	Billy Harris	.50
513	Preston Gomez (Mgr.)	.50
514	Steve Hovley	.50
515	Don Wilson	.50
516	Yankees Rookies:	.75
	John Ellis, Jim Lyttle	
517	Joe Gibbon	.50
518	Bill Melton	.50
519	Don McMahon	.50
520	Willie Horton	.75
521	Cal Koonce	.50
522	California Angels	1.00
523	Jose Pena	.50
524	Alvin Dark (Mgr.)	.75
525	Jerry Adair	.50
526	Ron Herbel	.50
527	Don Bosch	.50
528	Elrod Hendricks	.50
529	Bob Aspromonte	.50
530	Bob Gibson	6.00
531	Ron Clark	.50
532	Danny Murtaugh (Mgr.)	.50
533	Buzz Stephen	.50
534	Minnesota Twins	1.00
535	Andy Kosco	.50
536	Mike Kekich	.50
537	Joe Morgan	4.00
538	Bob Humphreys	.50
539	Phillies Rookies:	4.00
	Larry Bowa, Dennis Doyle	
540	Gary Peters	.50
541	Bill Heath	.50
542	Checklist No. 6	1.50
543	Clyde Wright	.50
544	Cincinnati Reds	1.50
545	Ken Harrelson	.75
546	Ron Reed	.50
547	Rick Monday	1.50
548	Howie Reed	1.00
549	St. Louis Cardinals	1.50
550	Frank Howard	1.25
551	Dock Ellis	1.00
552	Royals Rookies:	1.00
	Dennis Paepke, Fred Rico, Don O'Riley	
553	Jim LeFebvre	1.00
554	Tom Timmermann	1.00
555	Orlando Cepeda	4.00
556	Dave Bristol	1.00
557	Ed Kranepool	1.00
558	Vern Fuller	1.00
559	Tommy Davis	1.00
560	Gaylord Perry	5.00
561	Tom McCraw	1.00
562	Ted Abernathy	1.00
563	Boston Red Sox	1.50
564	Johnny Briggs	1.00
565	Jim Hunter	5.00
566	Gene Alley	1.00
567	Bob Oliver	1.00
568	Stan Bahnsen	1.00
569	Cookie Rojas	1.00
570	Jim Fregosi	1.25
571	Jim Brewer	1.00
572	Frank Quilici	1.00
573	Padres Rookies:	1.00
	Mike Corkins, Rafael Robles, Ron Slocum	
574	Bobby Bolin	1.00

NO.	PLAYER	NR. MT.
575	Cleon Jones	1.00
576	Milt Pappas	1.00
577	Bernie Allen	1.00
578	Tom Griffin	1.00
579	Detroit Tigers	2.00
580	Pete Rose	80.00
581	Tom Satriano	1.00
582	Mike Paul	1.00
583	Hal Lanier	1.00
584	Al Downing	1.00
585	Rusty Staub	2.00
586	Rickey Clark	1.00
587	Jose Arcia	1.00
588	Checklist No. 7*	3.00
589	Joe Keough	1.00
590	Mike Cuellar	1.25
591	Mike Ryan	1.00
592	Daryl Patterson	1.00
593	Chicago Cubs	1.50
594	Jake Gibbs	1.00
595	Maury Wills	2.50
596	Mike Hershberger	1.00
597	Sonny Siebert	1.00
598	Joe Pepitone	2.00
599	Senators Rookies:	1.00
	Dick Such, Gene Martin, Dick Stelmaszek,	
600	Willie Mays	35.00
601	Pete Richert	1.00
602	Ted Savage	1.00
603	Ray Oyler	1.00
604	Clarence Gaston	1.00
605	Rick Wise	1.00
606	Chico Ruiz	1.00
607	Gary Waslewski	1.00
608	Pittsburgh Pirates	1.50
609	Buck Martinez	1.00
610	Jerry Koosman	2.00
611	Norm Cash	1.00
612	Jim Hickman	1.00
613	Dave Baldwin	1.00
614	Mike Shannon	1.00
615	Mark Belanger	1.00
616	Jim Merritt	1.00
617	Jim French	1.00
618	Billy Wynne	1.00
619	Norm Miller	1.00
620	Jim Perry	1.25
621	Braves Rookies:	12.00
	Darrell Evans, Mike McQueen, Rick Kester	
622	Don Sutton	6.00
623	Horace Clarke	1.00
624	Clyde King	1.00
625	Dean Chance	1.00
626	Dave Ricketts	1.00
627	Gary Wagner	1.00
628	Wayne Garrett	1.00
629	Merv Rettenmund	1.00
630	Ernie Banks	15.00
631	Oakland Athletics	2.00
632	Gary Sutherland	1.00
633	Roger Nelson	1.00
634	Bud Harrelson	3.00
635	Bob Allison	2.00
636	Jim Stewart	2.00
637	Cleveland Indians	4.00
638	Frank Bertaina	2.00
639	Dave Campbell	2.00
640	Al Kaline	30.00
641	Al McBean	2.00
642	Angels Rookies:	2.00
	Greg Garrett, Jarvis Tatum, Gordon Lund	
643	Jose Pagan	2.00
644	Gerry Nyman	2.00
645	Don Money	2.00
646	Jim Britton	2.00
647	Tom Matchick	2.00
648	Larry Haney	2.00
649	Jimmie Hall	2.00

NO.	PLAYER	NR. MT.
650	Sam McDowell	2.00
651	Jim Gosger	2.00
652	Rich Rollins	2.00
653	Moe Drabowsky	2.00
654	NL Rookies:	2.00
	Oscar Gamble, Boots Day, Angel Mangual	
655	John Roseboro	2.00
656	Jim Hardin	2.00
657	San Diego Padres	4.00
658	Ken Tatum	2.00
659	Pete Ward	2.00
660	Johnny Bench	120.00
661	Jerry Robertson	2.00
662	Frank Lucchesi	2.00
663	Tito Francona	2.00
664	Bob Robertson	2.00
665	Jim Lonborg	2.00
666	Adolfo Phillips	2.00
667	Bob Meyer	2.00
668	Bob Tillman	2.00
669	White Sox Rookies:	2.00
	Bart Johnson, Dan Lazar, Mickey Scott	
670	Ron Santo	4.00
671	Jim Campanis	2.00
672	Leon McFadden	2.00
673	Ted Uhlaender	2.00
674	Dave Leonhard	2.00
675	Jose Cardenal	2.00
676	Washington Senators	4.00
677	Woodie Fryman	2.00
678	Dave Duncan	2.00
679	Ray Sadecki	2.00
680	Rico Petrocelli	3.00
681	Bob Garibaldi	2.00
682	Dalton Jones	2.00
683	Reds Rookies:	3.00
	Wayne Simpson, Vern Geishert, Hal McRae	
684	Jack Fisher	2.00
685	Tom Haller	2.00
686	Jackie Hernandez	2.00
687	Bob Priddy	2.00
688	Ted Kubiak	2.00
689	Frank Tepedino	2.00
690	Ron Fairly	2.00
691	Joe Grzenda	2.00
692	Duffy Dyer	2.00
693	Bob Johnson	2.00
694	Gary Ross	2.00
695	Bobby Knoop	2.00
696	S.F. Giants	4.00
697	Jim Hannan	2.00
698	Tom Tresh	3.00
699	Hank Aguirre	2.00
700	Frank Robinson	25.00
701	Jack Billingham	2.00
702	AL Rookies:	2.00
	Bob Johnson, Ron Klimkowski, Bill Zepp	
703	Lou Marone	2.00
704	Frank Baker	2.00
705	Tony Cloninger	2.00
706	John McNamara (R)	4.00
707	Kevin Collins	2.00
708	Jose Santiago	2.00
709	Mike Fiore	2.00
710	Felix Millan	2.00
711	Ed Brinkman	2.00
712	Nolan Ryan	200.00
713	Seattle Pilots	9.00
714	Al Spangler	2.00
715	Mickey Lolich	4.00
716	Cardinals Rookies:	2.00
	Sal Campisi, R. Cleveland, Santiago Guzman	
717	Tom Phoebus	2.00
718	Ed Spiezio	2.00
719	Jim Roland	2.00
720	R. Reichardt (Exc. $1.00)	6.00

1971 Topps.... Complete Set of 752 Cards—Value $600.00 (Exc.); $1400.00 (Mint)

Features the rookie cards of Steve Garvey, Don Baylor and George Foster. The high numbers are 644 to 752. Semi-high numbers are 524 to 643. The cards in this set are more difficult to find in *mint* condition because the black border scratches easily.

NO. PLAYER	NR. MT.
1 World Champs (Exc. $1.50)	6.00
2 Dock Ellis	.35
3 Dick McAuliffe	.35
4 Vic Davalillo	.35
5 Thurman Munson	18.00
6 Ed Spiezio	.35
7 Jim Holt	.35
8 Mike McQueen	.35
9 George Scott	.35
10 Claude Osteen	.35
11 Elliott Maddox	.35
12 Johnny Callison	.35
13 White Sox Rookies:	.40
C. Brinkman, D. Moloney	
14 Dave Concepcion (R)	5.00
15 Andy Messersmith	.40
16 Ken Singleton (R)	2.50
17 Billy Sorrell	.35
18 Norm Miller	.35
19 Skip Pitlock	.35
20 Reggie Jackson	25.00
21 Dan McGinn	.35
22 Phil Roof	.35
23 Oscar Gamble	.45
24 Rich Hand	.35
25 Clarence Caston	.35
26 Bert Blyleven (R)	16.00
27 Pirates Rookies:	.40
Fred Cambria, Gene Clines	
28 Ron Klimkowski	.35
29 Don Buford	.35
30 Phil Niekro	4.00
31 Eddie Kasko	.35
32 Jerry Da Vanon	.35
33 Del Unser	.35
34 Sandy Vance	.35
35 Lou Piniella	1.00
36 Dean Chance	.35
37 Rich McKinney	.35
38 Jim Colborn	.35
39 Tiger Rookies:	.35
L. LaGrow, Gene Lamont	
40 Lee May	.35
41 Rick Austin	.35
42 Boots Day	.35
43 Steve Kealey	.35
44 Johnny Edwards	.35
45 Jim Hunter	4.00
46 Dave Campbell	.35
47 Johnny Jeter	.35
48 Dave Baldwin	.35
49 Don Money	.35
50 Willy McCovey	6.00
51 Steve Kline	.35
52 Braves Rookies:	.35
Oscar Brown, Earl Williams	
53 Paul Blair	.35
54 Checklist No. 1	2.00
55 Steve Carlton	12.50
56 Duane Josephson	.35
57 Von Joshua	.35
58 Bill Lee	.35
59 Gene Mauch (Mgr.)	.35
60 Dick Bosman	.35
61 AL Batting Leaders:	1.50
Alex Johnson, Carl Yastrzemski, Tony Oliva	

NO. PLAYER	NR. MT.
62 NL Batting Leaders:	1.00
Joe Torre, Rico Carty, Manny Sanguillen	
63 AL RBI Leaders:	1.25
Boog Powell, Frank Robinson, Tony Conigliaro	
64 NL RBI Leaders:	1.00
Johnny Bench, Billy Williams, Tony Perez	
65 AL HR Leaders:	1.25
Frank Howard, Harmon Killebrew, C. Yastrzemski	
66 NL HR Leaders:	1.25
Johnny Bench, Billy Williams, Tony Perez	
67 AL ERA Leaders:	1.00
Clyde Wright, Diego Segui, Jim Palmer	
68 NL ERA Leaders:	1.25
Wayne Simpson, Luke Walker, Tom Seaver	
69 AL Pitching Leaders:	1.00
Mike Cuellar, Dave McNally, Jim Perry	
70 NL Pitching Leaders:	1.50
Gaylord Perry, Bob Gibson, Fergie Jenkins	
71 AL Strikeout Leaders:	1.00
Sam McDowell, Mickey Lolich, Bob Johnson	
72 NL Strikeout Leaders:	1.50
Bob Gibson, Tom Seaver, Fergie Jenkins	
73 George Brunet	.35
74 Twins Rookies:	.40
Pete Hamm, Jim Nettles	
75 Gary Nolan	.35
76 Ted Savage	.35
77 Mike Compton	.35
78 Jim Spencer	.35
79 Wade Blasingame	.35
80 Bill Melton	.35
81 Felix Millan	.35
82 Casey Cox	.35
83 Met Rookies:	.45
Tim Foli, Randy Bobb	
84 Marcel Lachemann	.35
85 Bill Grabarkewitz	.35
86 Mike Kilkenny	.35
87 Jack Heidemann	.35
88 Hal King	.35
89 Ken Brett	.35
90 Joe Pepitone	.45
91 Bob Lemon (Mgr.)	1.25
92 Fred Wenz	.35
93 Senators Rookies:	.35
Norm McRae, Denny Riddleberger	
94 Don Hahn	.35
95 Luis Tiant	.75
96 Joe Hague	.35
97 Floyd Wicker	.35
98 Joe Decker	.35
99 Mark Belanger	.50
100 Pete Rose	45.00
101 Les Cain	.35

NO. PLAYER	NR. MT.
102 Astros Rookies:	1.00
Ken Forsch, Larry Howard	
103 Rich Severson	.35
104 Dan Frisella	.35
105 Tony Conigliaro	1.00
106 Tom Dukes	.35
107 Roy Foster	.35
108 John Cumberland	.35
109 Steve Hovley	.35
110 Bill Mazeroski	1.00
111 Yankee Rookies:	.45
L. Colson, B. Mitchell	
112 Manny Mota	.60
113 Jerry Crider	.35
114 Billy Conigliaro	.35
115 Donn Clendenon	.35
116 Ken Sanders	.35
117 Ted Simmons (R)	7.50
118 Cookie Rojas	.35
119 Frank Lucchesi (Mgr.)	.35
120 Willie Horton	.40
121 Cubs Rookies:	.40
J. Dunegan, R. Skidmore	
122 Eddie Watt	.35
123 Checklist No. 2	2.00
124 Don Gullett	.35
125 Ray Fosse	.35
126 Danny Coombs	.35
127 Danny Thompson	.35
128 Frank Johnson	.35
129 Aurelio Monteagudo	.35
130 Denis Menke	.35
131 Curt Blefary	.35
132 Jose Laboy	.35
133 Mickey Lolich	.75
134 Jose Arcia	.35
135 Rick Monday	.60
136 Duffy Dyer	.35
137 Marcelino Lopez	.35
138 Phillies Rookies:	.45
Joe Lis, W. Montanez	
139 Paul Casanova	.40
140 Gaylord Perry	3.00
141 Frank Quilici	.35
142 Mack Jones	.35
143 Steve Blass	.35
144 Jackie Hernandez	.35
145 Bill Singer	.35
146 Ralph Houk (Mgr.)	.40
147 Bob Priddy	.35
148 John Mayberry	.35
149 Mike Hershberger	.35
150 Sam McDowell	.60
151 Tommy Davis	.40
152 Angels Rookies:	.40
Lloyd Allen, Winston Llenas	
153 Gary Ross	.35
154 Cesar Gutierrez	.35
155 Ken Henderson	.35
156 Bart Johnson	.35
157 Bob Bailey	.35
158 Jerry Reuss	.65
159 Jarvis Tatum	.35
160 Tom Seaver	22.00
161 Coins Checklist	1.25
162 Jack Billingham	.35

NO. PLAYER	NR. MT.
163 Buck Martinez	.35
164 Reds Rookies:	.75
Frank Duffy, Milt Wilcox	
165 Cesar Tovar	.35
166 Joe Hoerner	.35
167 Tom Grieve	.60
168 Bruce Dal Canton	.35
169 Ed Herrmann	.35
170 Mike Cuellar	.60
171 Bobby Wine	.35
172 Duke Sims	.35
173 Gil Garrido	.35
174 Dave LaRoche	.35
175 Jim Hickman	.35
176 Red Sox Rookies:	.45
Bob Montgomery, Doug Griffin	
177 Hal McRae	.60
178 Dave Duncan	.35
179 Mike Corkins	.35
180 Al Kaline	8.00
181 Hal Lanier	.60
182 Al Downing	.35
183 Gil Hodges (Mgr.)	3.00
184 Stan Bahnsen	.35
185 Julian Javier	.35
186 Bob Spence	.35
187 Ted Abernathy	.35
188 Dodgers Rookies:	2.50
Mike Strahler, Bob Valentine	
189 George Mitterwald	.35
190 Bob Tolan	.35
191 Mike Andrews	.35
192 Billy Wilson	.35
193 Bob Grich (R)	2.00
194 Mike Lum	.35
195 AL Playoff Game 1	1.25
Powell Muscles Twins	
196 AL Playoff Game 2	1.25
McNally's Two Straight	
197 AL Playoff Game 3	2.00
Palmer Mows 'Em Down	
198 Orioles Celebrate	1.25
A Team Effort	
199 NL Playoff Game 1	1.25
Cline Pinch-Triple	
200 NL Playoff Game 2	1.25
Tolan Scores Third Time	
201 NL Playoff Game 3	1.25
Cline Scores Winning Run	
202 Reds Celebrate	1.25
World Series Bound	
203 Larry Gura (R)	1.00
204 Brewers Rookies:	.40
B. Smith, G. Kopacz	
205 Gerry Moses	.35
206 Checklist No. 3	2.00
207 Alan Foster	.35
208 Billy Martin	2.00
209 Steve Renko	.35
210 Rod Carew	15.00
211 Phil Hennigan	.35
212 Rich Hebner	.35
213 Frank Baker	.35
214 Al Ferrara	.35
215 Diego Segui	.35

NO. PLAYER	NR. MT.
216 Cards Rookies:	.40
Reggie Cleveland,	
Luis Melendez	
217 Ed Stroud	.35
218 Tony Cloninger	.35
219 Elrod Hendricks	.35
220 Ron Santo	.75
221 Dave Morehead	.35
222 Bob Watson	.50
223 Cecil Upshaw	.35
224 Alan Gallagher	.35
225 Gary Peters	.35
226 Bill Russell	.50
227 Floyd Weaver	.35
228 Wayne Garrett	.35
229 Jim Hannan	.35
230 Willie Stargell	7.00
231 Indians Rookies:	.45
Vince Colbert,	
John Lowenstein	
232 John Strohmayer	.35
233 Larry Bowa	2.00
234 Jim Lyttle	.35
235 Nate Colbert	.35
236 Bob Humphreys	.35
237 Cesar Cedeno (R)	1.50
238 Chuck Dobson	.35
239 R. Schoendienst (Mgr.)	1.25
240 Clyde Wright	.35
241 Dave Nelson	.35
242 Jim Ray	.35
243 Carlos May	.35
244 Bob Tillman	.35
245 Jim Kaat	2.00
246 Tony Taylor	.35
247 Royals Rookies:	.75
Jerry Cram, Paul Splittorff	
248 Hoyt Wilhelm	3.00
249 Chico Salmon	.35
250 Johnny Bench	25.00
251 Frank Reberger	.35
252 Eddie Leon	.35
253 Bill Sudakis	.35
254 Cal Koonce	.35
255 Bob Robertson	.35
256 Tony Gonzalez	.35
257 Nelson Briles	.35
258 Dick Green	.35
259 Dave Marshall	.35
260 Tommy Harper	.35
261 Darold Knowles	.35
262 Padres Rookies:	.40
D. Robinson, J. Williams	
263 John Ellis	.35
264 Joe Morgan	4.00
265 Jim Northrup	.35
266 Bill Stoneman	.35
267 Rich Morales	.35
268 Philadelphia Phillies	1.00
269 Gail Hopkins	.35
270 Rico Carty	.60
271 Bill Zepp	.35
272 Tommy Helms	.35
273 Pete Richert	.35
274 Ron Slocum	.35
275 Vada Pinson	1.00
276 Giants Rookies:	5.00
M. Davison, George Foster	
277 Gary Waslewski	.35
278 Jerry Grote	.35
279 Lefty Phillips (Mgr.)	.35
280 Fergie Jenkins	3.00
281 Danny Walton	.35
282 Jose Pagan	.35
283 Dick Such	.35
284 Jim Gosger	.35
285 Sal Bando	.50
286 Jerry McNertney	.35
287 Mike Fiore	.35
288 Joe Moeller	.35
289 Chicago White Sox	.75
290 Tony Oliva	2.00
291 George Culver	.35
292 Jay Johnstone	.35
293 Pat Corrales	.50

NO. PLAYER	NR. MT.
294 Steve Dunning	.35
295 Bobby Bonds	1.50
296 Tom Timmermann	.35
297 Johnny Briggs	.35
298 Jim Nelson	.35
299 Ed Kirkpatrick	.35
300 Brooks Robinson	7.50
301 Earl Wilson	.35
302 Phil Gagliano	.35
303 Lindy McDaniel	.35
304 Ron Brand	.35
305 Reggie Smith	.75
306 Jim Nash	.35
307 Don Wert	.35
308 St. Louis Cardinals	1.00
309 Dick Ellsworth	.35
310 Tommie Agee	.50
311 Lee Stange	.35
312 Harry Walker	.35
313 Tom Hall	.35
314 Jeff Torborg	.35
315 Ron Fairly	.50
316 Fred Scherman	.35
317 Athletic Rookies:	.35
Angel Mangual, Jim Driscoll	
318 Rudy May	.35
319 Ty Cline	.35
320 Dave McNally	.40
321 Tom Matchick	.35
322 Jim Beauchamp	.35
323 Billy Champion	.35
324 Graig Nettles	2.50
325 Juan Marichal	5.00
326 Richie Scheinblum	.35
327 World Series Game 1	1.25
Powell Homers	
328 World Series Game 2	1.25
Buford Goes 2 For 4	
329 World Series Game 3	2.00
F. Robinson Shows Muscle	
330 World Series Game 4	1.25
Reds Stay Alive	
331 World Series Game 5	2.00
B. Robinson Robbery	
332 World Series Celebratio.	1.25
Convincing Performance	
333 Clay Kirby	.35
334 Roberto Pena	.35
335 Jerry Koosman	1.00
336 Detroit Tigers	1.00
337 Jesus Alou	.35
338 Gene Tenace	.45
339 Wayne Simpson	.35
340 Rico Petrocelli	.50
341 Steve Garvey (R)	80.00
342 Frank Tepedino	.35
343 Pirates Rookies:	.40
Ed Acosta, M. May	
344 Ellie Rodriguez	.35
345 Joe Horlen	.35
346 Lum Harris	.35
347 Ted Uhlaender	.35
348 Fred Norman	.35
349 Rich Reese	.35
350 Billy Williams	5.00
351 Jim Shellenback	.35
352 Denny Doyle	.35
353 Carl Taylor	.35
354 Don McMahon	.35
355 Bud Harrelson	.50
356 Bob Locker	.35
357 Cincinnati Reds	1.00
358 Danny Cater	.35
359 Ron Reed	.35
360 Jim Fregosi	.60
361 Don Sutton	4.00
362 Orioles Rookies:	.40
Mike Adamson, R. Freed	
363 Mike Nagy	.35
364 Tommy Dean	.35
365 Bob Johnson	.35
366 Ron Stone	.35
367 Dalton Jones	.35
368 Bob Veale	.35
369 Checklist No. 4	2.00

NO. PLAYER	NR. MT.
370 Joe Torre	2.00
371 Jack Hiatt	.35
372 Lew Krausse	.35
373 Tom McCraw	.35
374 Clete Boyer	.50
375 Steve Hargan	.35
376 Expos Rookies:	.35
C. Mashore, E. McAnally	
377 Greg Garrett	.35
378 Tito Fuentes	.35
379 Wayne Granger	.35
380 Ted Williams (Mgr.)	4.00
381 Fred Gladding	.35
382 Jake Gibbs	.35
383 Rod Gaspar	.35
384 Rollie Fingers	3.00
385 Maury Wills	1.50
386 Boston Red Sox	1.00
387 Ron Herbel	.35
388 Al Oliver	2.00
389 Ed Brinkman	.35
390 Glenn Beckert	.35
391 Twins Rookies:	.35
Steve Brye, Cotton Nash	
392 Grant Jackson	.35
393 Merv Rettenmund	.35
394 Clay Carroll	.35
395 Roy White	.70
396 Dick Schofield	.50
397 Alvin Dark (Mgr.)	.65
398 Howie Reed	.50
399 Jim French	.50
400 Hank Aaron	22.00
401 Tom Murphy	.50
402 Los Angeles Dodgers	1.00
403 Joe Coleman	.50
404 Astros Rookies:	.50
B. Harris, R. Metzger	
405 Leo Cardenas	.50
406 Ray Sadecki	.50
407 Joe Rudi	.75
408 Rafael Robles	.50
409 Don Pavletich	.50
410 Ken Holtzman	.60
411 George Spriggs	.50
412 Jerry Johnson	.50
413 Pat Kelly	.50
414 Woodie Fryman	.50
415 Mike Hegan	.50
416 Gene Alley	.50
417 Dick Hall	.50
418 Adolfo Phillips	.50
419 Ron Hansen	.50
420 Jim Merritt	.50
421 John Stephenson	.50
422 Frank Bertaina	.50
423 Tigers Rookies:	.65
T. Marting, D. Saunders	
424 Roberto Rodriguez	.50
425 Doug Rader	.60
426 Chris Cannizzaro	.50
427 Bernie Allen	.50
428 Jim McAndrew	.50
429 Chuck Hinton	.50
430 Wes Parker	.60
431 Tom Burgmeier	.50
432 Bob Didier	.50
433 Skip Lockwood	.50
434 Gary Sutherland	.50
435 Jose Cardenal	.50
436 Wilbur Wood	.50
437 Danny Murtaugh (Mgr.)	.50
438 Mike McCormick	.50
439 Phillies Rookies:	2.00
Greg Luzinski, Scott Reid	
440 Bert Campaneris	.65
441 Milt Pappas	.50
442 California Angels	1.00
443 Rich Robertson	.50
444 Jimmie Price	.50
445 Art Shamsky	.50
446 Bobby Bolin	.50
447 Cesar Geronimo	.50
448 Dave Roberts	.50
449 Brant Alyea	.50

NO. PLAYER	NR. MT.
450 Bob Gibson	6.00
451 Joe Keough	.50
452 John Boccabella	.50
453 Terry Crowley	.50
454 Mike Paul	.50
455 Don Kessinger	.65
456 Bob Meyer	.50
457 Willie Smith	.50
458 White Sox Rookies:	.65
Ron Lolich, Dave Lemonds	
459 Jim LeFebvre	.50
460 Fritz Peterson	.50
461 Jim Hart	.70
462 Senators Team	1.00
463 Tom Kelley	.50
464 Aurelio Rodriguez	.50
465 Tim McCarver	1.25
466 Ken Berry	.50
467 Al Santorini	.50
468 Frank Fernandez	.50
469 Bob Aspromonte	.50
470 Bob Oliver	.50
471 Tom Griffin	.50
472 Ken Rudolph	.50
473 Gary Wagner	.50
474 Jim Fairey	.50
475 Ron Perranoski	.70
476 Dal Maxvill	.50
477 Earl Weaver (Mgr.)	1.00
478 Bernie Carbo	.50
479 Dennis Higgins	.50
480 Manny Sanguillen	.70
481 Daryl Patterson	.50
482 San Diego Padres	1.00
483 Gene Michael	.70
484 Don Wilson	.50
485 Ken McMullen	.50
486 Steve Huntz	.50
487 Paul Schaal	.50
488 Jerry Stephenson	.50
489 Luis Alvardao	.50
490 Deron Johnson	.50
491 Jim Hardin	.50
492 Ken Boswell	.50
493 Dave May	.50
494 Braves Rookies:	.75
Ralph Garr, Rick Kester	
495 Felipe Alou	.75
496 Woody Woodward	.60
497 Horacio Pina	.50
498 John Kennedy	.50
499 Checklist No. 5	2.00
500 Jim Perry	.75
501 Andy Etchebarren	.50
502 Chicago Cubs	1.00
503 Gates Brown	.50
504 Ken Wright	.50
505 Ollie Brown	.50
506 Bobby Knoop	.50
507 George Stone	.50
508 Roger Repoz	.50
509 Jim Grant	.50
510 Ken Harrelson	1.00
511 Chris Short	.50
512 Red Sox Rookies:	.65
Dick Mills, Mike Garman	
513 Nolan Ryan	75.00
514 Ron Woods	.50
515 Carl Morton	.50
516 Ted Kubiak	.50
517 Charlie Fox (Mgr.)	.50
518 Joe Grzenda	.50
519 Willie Crawford	.50
520 Tommy John	2.50
521 Leron Lee	.50
522 Minnesota Twins	1.00
523 John Odom	.50
524 Mickey Stanley	1.00
525 Ernie Banks	13.00
526 Ray Jarvis	1.00
527 Cleon Jones	1.00
528 Wally Bunker	1.00
529 NL Rookies:	3.00
Enzo, Hernandez, Bill	
Buckner, Marty Perez	

NO. PLAYER	NR. MT.
530 Carl Yastrzemski	28.00
531 Mike Torrez	1.00
532 Bill Rigney (Mgr.)	1.00
533 Mike Ryan	1.00
534 Luke Walker	1.00
535 Curt Flood	1.50
536 Claude Raymond	1.00
537 Tom Egan	1.00
538 Angel Bravo	1.00
539 Larry Brown	1.00
540 Larry Dierker	1.00
541 Bob Burda	1.00
542 Bob Miller	1.00
543 New York Yankees	2.50
544 Vida Blue	2.50
545 Dick Dietz	1.00
546 John Matias	1.00
547 Pat Dobson	1.00
548 Don Mason	1.00
549 Jim Brewer	1.00
550 Harmon Killebrew	12.00
551 Frank Linzy	1.00
552 Buddy Bradford	1.00
553 Kevin Collins	1.00
554 Lowell Palmer	1.00
555 Walt Williams	1.00
556 Jim McGlothlin	1.00
557 Tom Satriano	1.00
558 Hector Torres	1.00
559 AL Rookies:	1.00
Gary Jones, Terry Cox,	
Bill Gogolewski	
560 Rusty Staub	2.00
561 Syd O'Brien	1.00
562 Dave Giusti	1.00
563 Giants Team	2.00
564 Al Fitzmorris	1.00
565 Jim Wynn	1.00
566 Tim Cullen	1.00
567 Walt Alston (Mgr.)	2.00
568 Sal Campisi	1.00
569 Ivan Murrell	1.00
570 Jim Palmer	11.00
571 Ted Sizemore	1.00
572 Jerry Kenney	1.00
573 Ed Kranepool	1.00
574 Jim Bunning	2.50
575 Bill Freehan	1.25
576 Cubs Rookies:	1.00
Brock Davis, Adrian	
Garrett, Garry Jestadt	
577 Jim Lonborg	1.50
578 Ron Hunt	1.00
579 Marty Pattin	1.00
580 Tony Perez	3.00
581 Roger Nelson	1.00
582 Dave Cash	1.00
583 Ron Cook	1.00
584 Cleveland Indians	2.00
585 Willie Davis	1.00
586 Dick Woodson	1.00

NO. PLAYER	NR. MT.
587 Sonny Jackson	1.00
588 Tom Bradley	1.00
589 Bob Barton	1.00
590 Alex Johnson	1.00
591 Jackie Brown	1.00
592 Randy Hundley	1.00
593 Jack Aker	1.00
594 Cardinals Rookies:	1.50
Bob Chlupsa, Bob Stinson,	
Al Hrabosky	
595 Dave Johnson	2.00
596 Mike Jorgensen	1.00
597 Ken Suarez	1.00
598 Rick Wise	1.00
599 Norm Cash	1.50
600 Willie Mays	35.00
601 Ken Tatum	1.00
602 Marty Martinez	1.00
603 Pittsburgh Pirates	2.00
604 John Gelnar	1.00
605 Orlando Cepeda	3.00
606 Chuck Taylor	1.00
607 Paul Ratliff	1.00
608 Mike Wegener	1.00
609 Leo Durocher (Mgr.)	2.00
610 Amos Otis	1.25
611 Tom Phoebus	1.00
612 Indians Rookies:	1.00
Ted Ford, Steve Mingori,	
Lou Camilli	
613 Pedro Borbon	1.00
614 Billy Cowan	1.00
615 Mel Stottlemyre	1.50
616 Larry Hisle	1.00
617 Clay Dalrymple	1.00
618 Tug McGraw	1.50
619 Checklist No. 6	2.00
620 Frank Howard	1.50
621 Ron Bryant	1.00
622 Joe LaHoud	1.00
623 Pat Jarvis	1.00
624 Oakland Athletics	2.00
625 Lou Brock	10.00
626 Freddie Patek	1.00
627 Steve Hamilton	1.00
628 John Bateman	1.00
629 John Hiller	1.00
630 Roberto Clemente	25.00
631 Eddie Fisher	1.00
632 Darrel Chaney	1.00
633 AL Rookies:	1.00
Pete Koegel, Bobby Brooks,	
Scott Northey	
634 Phil Regan	1.00
635 Bobby Murcer	2.00
636 Denny LeMaster	1.00
637 Dave Bristol (Mgr.)	1.00
638 Stan Williams	1.00
639 Tom Haller	1.00
640 Frank Robinson	14.00
641 New York Mets	4.00

NO. PLAYER	NR. MT.
642 Jim Roland	1.00
643 Rick Reichardt	1.00
644 Jim Stewart	2.00
645 Jim Maloney	2.50
646 Bobby Floyd	2.00
647 Juan Pizarro	2.00
648 Mets Rookies:	4.00
Rich Folkers, Ted Martinez,	
John Matlack	
649 Sparky Lyle	2.50
650 Rich Allen	7.00
651 Jerry Robertson	2.00
652 Atlanta Braves	3.50
653 Russ Snyder	2.00
654 Don Shaw	2.00
655 Mike Epstein	2.00
656 Gerry Nyman	2.00
657 Jose Azcue	2.00
658 Paul Lindblad	2.00
659 Byron Browne	2.00
660 Ray Culp	2.00
661 Chuck Tanner (Mgr.)	2.50
662 Mike Hedlund	2.00
663 Marv Staehle	2.00
664 Rookies Pitchers:	2.00
Archie Reynolds, Bob	
Reynolds, K. Reynolds	
665 Ron Swoboda	2.00
666 Gene Brabender	2.00
667 Pete Ward	2.00
668 Gary Neibauer	2.00
669 Ike Brown	2.00
670 Bill Hands	2.00
671 Bill Voss	2.00
672 Ed Crosby	2.00
673 Gerry Janeski	2.00
674 Montreal Expos	3.50
675 Dave Boswell	2.00
676 Tommie Reynolds	2.00
677 Jack DiLauro	2.00
678 George Thomas	2.00
679 Don O'Riley	2.00
680 Don Mincher	2.00
681 Bill Butler	2.00
682 Terry Harmon	2.00
683 Bill Burbach	2.00
684 Curt Motton	2.00
685 Moe Drabowsky	2.00
686 Chico Ruiz	2.00
687 Ron Taylor	2.00
688 S. Anderson (Mgr.)	4.00
689 Frank Baker	2.00
690 Bob Moose	2.00
691 Bob Heise	2.00
692 AL Rookies Pitchers:	2.00
Hal Haydel, Rogelio Moret,	
Wayne Twitchell	
693 Jose Pena	2.00
694 Rick Renick	2.00
695 Joe Niekro	3.00
696 Jerry Morales	2.00

NO. PLAYER	NR. MT.
697 Rickey Clark	2.00
698 Milwaukee Brewers	4.00
699 Jim Britton	2.00
700 Boog Powell	4.50
701 Bob Garibaldi	2.00
702 Milt Ramirez	2.00
703 Mike Kekich	2.00
704 J.C. Martin	2.00
705 Dick Selma	2.00
706 Joe Foy	2.00
707 Fred Lasher	2.00
708 Russ Nagelson	2.00
709 Rookie Outfielders:	25.00
Don Baylor, Tom Paciorek,	
Dusty Baker	
710 Sonny Siebert	2.00
711 Larry Stahl	2.00
712 Jose Martinez	2.00
713 Mike Marshall	2.50
714 Dick Williams (Mgr.)	2.50
715 Horace Clarke	2.00
716 Dave Leonhard	2.00
717 Tommie Aaron	2.00
718 Billy Wynne	2.00
719 Jerry May	2.00
720 Matty Alou	2.00
721 John Morris	2.00
722 Houston Astros	4.00
723 Vicente Romo	2.00
724 Tom Tischinski	2.00
725 Gary Gentry	2.00
726 Paul Popovich	2.00
727 Ray Lamb	2.00
728 NL Rookie Outfielders:	2.00
Wayne Redmond, Keith	
Lampard, Bernie Williams	
729 Dick Billings	2.00
730 Jim Rooker	2.00
731 Jim Qualls	2.00
732 Bob Reed	2.00
733 Lee Maye	2.00
734 Rob Gardner	2.00
735 Mike Shannon	2.00
736 Mel Queen	2.00
737 Preston Gomez (Mgr.)	2.00
738 Russ Gibson	2.00
739 Barry Lersch	2.00
740 Luis Aparicio	11.00
741 Skip Guinn	2.00
742 Kansas City Royals	4.00
743 John O'Donoghue	2.00
744 Chuck Manuel	2.00
745 Sandy Alomar	2.00
746 Andy Kosco	2.00
747 NL Rookie Pitchers:	2.00
Al Severinsen, Scipio	
Spinks, Balor Moore	
748 John Purdin	2.00
749 Ken Szotkiewicz	2.00
750 Denny McLain	4.00
751 Al Weis	2.00
752 Dick Drago (Exc. $1.00)	5.00

1972 Topps. . . . Complete Set of 787 Cards—Value $550.00 (Exc.); $1300.00 (Mint)

Features the rookie cards of Carlton Fisk and Ben Oglivie. The high numbers are 657 to 787. Semi-high numbers are 526 to 656.

NO. PLAYER	NR. MT.
1 Pirates-Champs (Exc. $1.00)	5.00
2 Ray Culp	.25
3 Bob Tolan	.25
4 Checklist No. 1	1.00
5 John Bateman	.25
6 Fred Scherman	.25
7 Enzo Hernandez	.25
8 Ron Swoboda	.25
9 Stan Williams	.25
10 Amos Otis	.35
11 Bobby Valentine	.50
12 Jose Cardenal	.25
13 Joe Grzenda	.25
14 Phillies Rookies:	.30
Pete Koegel, Mike	
Anderson, W. Twitchell	
15 Walt Williams	.25
16 Mike Jorgensen	.25
17 Dave Duncan	.25
18 Juan Pizarro	.25
19 Billy Cowan	.25
20 Don Wilson	.25
21 Atlanta Braves	.75
22 Rob Gardner	.25
23 Ted Kubiak	.25
24 Ted Ford	.25
25 Will Singer	.25
26 Andy Etchebarren	.25
27 Bob Johnson	.25
28 Twins Rookies:	.30
Steve Brye, Bob Gebhard,	
Hal Haydel	
29 Bill Bonham	.25
30 Rico Petrocelli	.30
31 Cleon Jones	.25
32 C. Jones (In Action)	.25
33 Billy Martin	1.50
34 B. Martin (In Action)	.75
35 Jerry Johnson	.25
36 J. Johnson (In Action)	.25
37 Carl Yastrzemski	15.00
38 Yastrzemski (In Action)	7.50
39 Bob Barton	.25
40 B. Barton (In Action)	.25
41 Tommy Davis	.60
42 T. Davis (In Action)	.30
43 Rick Wise	.35
44 R. Wise (In Action)	.35
45 Glenn Beckert	.35
46 G. Beckert (In Action)	.35
47 John Ellis	.25
48 J. Ellis (In Action)	.25
49 Willie Mays	16.00
50 W. Mays (All Action)	8.00
51 Harmon Killebrew	5.00
52 H. Killebrew (In Action)	2.50
53 Bud Harrelson	.50
54 B. Harrelson (In Action)	.30
55 Clyde Wright	.25
56 Rich Chiles	.25
57 Bob Oliver	.25
58 Ernie McAnally	.25
59 Fred Stanley	.25
60 Manny Sanguillen	.35
61 Cubs Rookies:	1.00
Burt Hooton, Gene Hiser,	
Earl Stephenson	
62 Angel Mangual	.25
63 Duke Sims	.25
64 Pete Broberg	.25
65 Cesar Cedeno	.75
66 Ray Corbin	.25
67 Red Schoendienst	1.25
68 Jim York	.25
69 Roger Freed	.25
70 Mike Cuellar	.40
71 Angels Team	.50
72 Bruce Kison (R)	.50
73 Steve Huntz	.25
74 Cecil Upshaw	.25
75 Bert Campaneris	.50
76 Don Carrithers	.25
77 Ron Theobald	.25
78 Steve Arlin	.25

NO. PLAYER	NR. MT.
79 Red Sox Rookies:	35.00
Carlton Fisk, Mike Garman,	
Cecil Cooper	
80 Tony Perez	2.50
81 Mike Hedlund	.25
82 Ron Woods	.25
83 Dalton Jones	.25
84 Vince Colbert	.25
85 NL Batting Leaders:	1.00
Ralph Garr, Glenn Beckert,	
Joe Torre	
86 AL Batting Leaders:	1.00
Tony Oliva, Bobby Murcer,	
Merv Rettenmund	
87 NL RBI Leaders:	1.25
Joe Torre, Willie Stargell,	
Hank Aaron	
88 AL RBI Leaders:	1.00
Harmon Killebrew, Frank	
Robinson, Reggie Smith	
89 NL Home Run Leaders:	1.25
Willie Stargell, Lee May,	
Hank Aaron	
90 AL Home Run Leaders:	1.25
Reggie Jackson, Bill	
Melton, Norm Cash	
91 NL ERA Leaders:	1.00
Tom Seaver, Dave Roberts	
(wrong photo), D. Wilson	
92 AL ERA Leaders:	.75
Vida Blue, Wilbur Wood,	
Jim Palmer	
93 NL Pitching Leaders:	1.25
Tom Seaver, Fergie	
Jenkins, Steve Carlton,	
Al Downing	
94 AL Pitching Leaders:	.75
Mickey Lolich, Vida Blue,	
Wilbur Wood	
95 NL Strikeout Leaders:	1.00
Bill Stoneman, Tom Seaver,	
Fergie Jenkins	
96 AL Strikeout Leaders:	.75
Mickey Lolich, Vida Blue,	
Joe Coleman	
97 Tom Kelley	.25
98 Chuck Tanner	.35
99 Ross Grimsley	.25
100 Frank Robinson	5.00
101 Astros Rookies:	1.50
B. Greif, J.R. Richard,	
Ray Busse	
102 Lloyd Allen	.25
103 Checklist No. 2	1.00
104 Toby Harrah (R)	1.50
105 Gary Gentry	.25
106 Milwaukee Brewers	.75
107 Jose Cruz (R)	2.00
108 Gary Waslewski	.25
109 Jerry May	.25
110 Ron Hunt	.25
111 Jim Grant	.25
112 Greg Luzinski	1.00
113 Rogelio Moret	.25
114 Bill Buckner	1.25
115 Jim Fregosi	.35
116 Ed Farmer	.25
117 Cleo James	.25
118 Skip Lockwood	.25
119 Marty Perez	.25
120 Bill Freehan	.35
121 Ed Sprague	.25
122 Larry Biittner	.25
123 Ed Acosta	.25
124 Yankees Rookies:	.45
Alan Closter, Rusty	
Torres, R. Hambright	
125 Dave Cash	.25
126 Bart Johnson	.25
127 Duffy Dyer	.25
128 Eddie Watt	.25
129 Charlie Fox	.25
130 Bob Gibson	4.00
131 Jim Nettles	.25

NO. PLAYER	NR. MT.
132 Joe Morgan	2.50
133 Joe Keough	.25
134 Carl Morton	.25
135 Vada Pinson	.50
136 Darrel Chaney	.25
137 Dick Williams	.35
138 Mike Kekich	.25
139 Tim McCarver	.50
140 Pat Dobson	.35
141 Mets Rookies:	.60
Buzz Capra, Leroy Stanton,	
Jon Matlack	
142 Chris Chambliss (R)	2.00
143 Garry Jestadt	.25
144 Marty Pattin	.25
145 Don Kessinger	.30
146 Steve Kealey	.25
147 Dave Kingman (R)	4.00
148 Dick Billings	.25
149 Gary Neibauer	.25
150 Norm Cash	.35
151 Jim Brewer	.25
152 Gene Clines	.25
153 Rick Auerbach	.25
154 Ted Simmons	1.25
155 Larry Dierker	.30
156 Minnesota Twins	.50
157 Don Gullett	.35
158 Jerry Kenney	.25
159 John Boccabella	.25
160 Andy Messersmith	.35
161 Brock Davis	.25
162 Brewers Rookies:	1.00
Darrell Porter, Jerry Bell,	
Bob Reynolds (Bell and	
Porter photos switched)	
163 Tug McGraw	.60
164 T. McGraw (In Action)	.30
165 Chris Speier	.50
166 C. Speier (In Action)	.25
167 Deron Johnson	.25
168 D. Johnson (In Action)	.75
169 Vida Blue	.40
170 V. Blue (In Action)	1.25
171 Darrell Evans	.60
172 D. Evans (In Action)	.50
173 Clay Kirby	.25
174 C. Kirby (In Action)	.25
175 Tom Haller	.25
176 T. Haller (In Action)	.25
177 Paul Schaal	.25
178 P. Schaal (In Action)	.25
179 Dock Ellis	.25
180 D. Ellis (In Action)	.25
181 Ed Kranepool	.30
182 E. Kranepool (In Action)	.20
183 Bill Melton	.25
184 B. Melton (In Action)	.25
185 Ron Bryant	.25
186 R. Bryant (In Action)	.25
187 Gates Brown	.25
188 Frank Lucchesi	.25
189 Gene Tenace	.30
190 Dave Giusti	.25
191 Jeff Burroughs	.75
192 Chicago Cubs	.60
193 Kurt Bevacqua	.25
194 Fred Norman	.25
195 Orlando Cepeda	1.50
196 Mel Queen	.25
197 Johnny Briggs	.25
198 Dodgers Rookies:	1.50
Charlie Hough, Bob	
O'Brien, Mike Strahler	
199 Mike Fiore	.25
200 Lou Brock	4.00
201 Phil Roof	.25
202 Scipio Spinks	.25
203 Ron Blomberg	.25
204 Tommy Helms	.25
205 Dick Drago	.25
206 Dal Maxvill	.25
207 Tom Egan	.25
208 Milt Pappas	.35

NO. PLAYER	NR. MT.
209 Joe Rudi	.30
210 Denny McLain	1.00
211 Gary Sutherland	.25
212 Grant Jackson	.25
213 Angels Rookies:	.30
Tom Silverio, Billy Parker,	
Art Kusnyer	
214 Mike McQueen	.25
215 Alex Johnson	.25
216 Joe Niekro	.50
217 Roger Metzger	.25
218 Eddie Kasko	.25
219 Rennie Stennett	.30
220 Jim Perry	.30
221 NL Playoffs:	1.00
Bucs Champs	
222 AL Playoffs:	1.50
Orioles Champs	
223 World Series Game 1	.75
224 World Series Game 2	.75
225 World Series Game 3	.75
226 World Series Game 4	2.50
227 World Series Game 5	.75
228 World Series Game 6	.75
229 World Series Game 7	.75
230 World S. Celebration	.75
231 Casey Cox	.25
232 Giants Rookies:	.30
Chris Arnold, Jim Barr,	
Dave Rader	
233 Jay Johnstone	.30
234 Ron Taylor	.25
235 Merv Rettenmund	.25
236 Jim McGlothlin	.25
237 New York Yankees	1.00
238 Leron Lee	.25
239 Tom Timmerman	.25
240 Rich Allen	2.00
241 Rollie Fingers	2.50
242 Don Mincher	.25
243 Frank Linzy	.25
244 Steve Braun	.25
245 Tommie Agee	.40
246 Tom Burgmeier	.25
247 Milt May	.25
248 Tom Bradley	.25
249 Garry Walker	.25
250 Boog Powell	1.00
251 Checklist No. 3	1.00
252 Ken Reynolds	.25
253 Sandy Alomar	.25
254 Boots Day	.25
255 Jim Lonborg	.30
256 George Foster	1.50
257 Tigers Rookies:	.30
Paul Jata, Jim Foor,	
Tim Hosley	
258 Randy Hundley	.25
259 Sparky Lyle	.35
260 Ralph Garr	.25
261 Steve Mingori	.25
262 San Diego Padres	.50
263 Felipe Alou	.30
264 Tommy John	2.00
265 Wes Parker	.35
266 Bobby Bolin	.35
267 Dave Concepcion	1.50
268 A's Rookies:	.40
Dwain Anderson, C. Floethe	
269 Don Hahn	.35
270 Jim Palmer	4.50
271 Ken Rudolph	.35
272 Mickey Rivers	1.00
273 Bobby Floyd	.35
274 Al Severinsen	.35
275 Cesar Tovar	.35
276 Gene Mauch	.35
277 Eliott Maddox	.35
278 Dennis Higgins	.35
279 Larry Brown	.35
280 Willie McCovey	5.00
281 Bill Parsons	.35
282 Houston Astros	.75
283 Darrell Brandon	.35

NO.	PLAYER	NR. MT.
284	Ike Brown	.35
285	Gaylord Perry	5.00
286	Gene Alley	.35
287	Jim Hardin	.35
288	Johnny Jeter	.35
289	Syd O'Brien	.35
290	Sonny Siebert	.35
291	Hal McRae	.60
292	H. McRae (In Action)	.35
293	Danny Frisella	.35
294	D. Frisella (In Action)	.35
295	Dick Dietz (In Action)	.35
296	D. Dietz (In Action)	.35
297	Claude Osteen	.35
298	C. Osteen (In Action)	.35
299	Hank Aaron	16.00
300	H. Aaron (In Action)	8.00
301	George Mitterwald	.35
302	Mitterwald (In Action)	.35
303	Joe Pepitone	.60
304	J. Pepitone (In Action)	.35
305	Ken Boswell	.35
306	K. Boswell (In Action)	.35
307	Steve Renko	.35
308	S. Renko (In Action)	.35
309	Roberto Clemente	15.00
310	Clemente (In Action)	7.50
311	Clay Carroll	.35
312	C. Carroll (In Action)	.35
313	Luis Aparicio	3.00
314	L. Aparicio (In Action)	1.50
315	Paul Splittorff	.40
316	Cardinals Rookies:	.65
	Jim Bibby, Jorge Roque,	
	Santiago Guzman	
317	Rich Hand	.35
318	Sonny Jackson	.35
319	Aurelio Rodriguez	.35
320	Steve Blass	.35
321	Joe LaHoud	.35
322	Jose Pena	.35
323	Earl Weaver	.75
324	Mike Ryan	.35
325	Mel Stottlemyre	.50
326	Pat Kelly	.35
327	Steve Stone (R)	.60
328	Boston Red Sox	.75
329	Roy Foster	.35
330	Jim Hunter	3.00
331	Stan Swanson	.35
332	Buck Martinez	.35
333	Steve Barber	.35
334	Rangers Rookies:	.40
	Bill Fahey, Jim Mason,	
	Tom Ragland	
335	Bill Hands	.35
336	Marty Martinez	.35
337	Mike Kilkenny	.35
338	Bob Grich	.65
339	Ron Cook	.35
340	Roy White	.60
341	Joe Torre (Boyhood)	.45
342	Wilbur Wood (Boyhood)	.45
343	W. Stargell (Boyhood)	1.00
344	D. McNally (Boyhood)	.45
345	Rick Wise (Boyhood)	.45
346	Jim Fregosi (Boyhood)	.45
347	Tom Seaver (Boyhood)	1.50
348	Sal Bando (Boyhood)	.45
349	Al Fitzmorris	.35
350	Frank Howard	.75
351	Braves Rookies:	.40
	Tom House, Rick Kester,	
	Jimmy Britton	
352	Dave LaRoche	.35
353	Art Shamsky	.35
354	Tom Murphy	.35
355	Bob Watson	.50
356	Gerry Moses	.35
357	Woodie Fryman	.35
358	Sparky Anderson	.50
359	Don Pavletich	.35
360	Dave Roberts	.35
361	Mike Andrews	.35
362	New York Mets	1.00

NO.	PLAYER	NR. MT.
363	Ron Klimkowski	.35
364	Johnny Callison	.50
365	Dick Bosman	.35
366	Jimmy Rosario	.35
367	Ron Perranoski	.45
368	Danny Thompson	.35
369	Jim LeFebvre	.35
370	Don Buford	.35
371	Denny LeMaster	.35
372	Royals Rookies:	.35
	Lance Clemons,	
	Monty Montgomery	
373	John Mayberry	.45
374	Jack Heidemann	.35
375	Reggie Cleveland	.35
376	Andy Kosco	.35
377	Terry Harmon	.35
378	Checklist No. 4	1.00
379	Ken Berry	.35
380	Earl Williams	.35
381	Chicago White Sox	.75
382	Joe Gibbon	.35
383	Brant Alyea	.35
384	Dave Campbell	.35
385	Mickey Stanley	.35
386	Jim Colborn	.35
387	Horace Clarke	.35
388	Charlie Williams	.35
389	Bill Rigney	.35
390	Willie Davis	.45
391	Kan Sanders	.35
392	Pirates Rookies:	.75
	Fred Cambria, Richie Zisk	
393	Curt Motton	.35
394	Ken Forsch	.45
395	Matty Alou	.65
396	Paul Lindblad	.50
397	Philadelphia Phillies	1.25
398	Larry Hisle	.50
399	Milt Wilcox	.50
400	Tony Oliva	1.50
401	Jim Nash	.50
402	Bobby Heise	.50
403	John Cumberland	.50
404	Jeff Torborg	.50
405	Ron Fairly	.50
406	George Hendrick (R)	1.25
407	Chuck Taylor	.50
408	Jim Northrup	.50
409	Frank Baker	.50
410	Fergie Jenkins	2.00
411	Bob Montgomery	.50
412	Dick Kelley	.50
413	White Sox Rookies:	.60
	Don Eddy, Dave Lemonds	
414	Bob Miller	.50
415	Cookie Rojas	.50
416	Johnny Edwards	.50
417	Tom Hall	.50
418	Tom Shopay	.50
419	Jim Spencer	.50
420	Steve Carlton	12.00
421	Ellie Rodriguez	.50
422	Ray Lamb	.50
423	Oscar Gamble	.50
424	Bill Gogolewski	.50
425	Ken Singleton	.75
426	K. Singleton (In Action)	.50
427	Tito Fuentes	.50
428	T. Fuentes (In Action)	.50
429	Bob Robertson	.50
430	B. Robertson (In Action)	.50
431	Clarence Gaston	.50
432	C. Gaston (In Action)	.50
433	Johnny Bench	25.00
434	J. Bench (In Action)	12.50
435	Reggie Jackson	25.00
436	R. Jackson (In Action)	12.50
437	Maury Wills	1.25
438	M. Wills (In Action)	.60
439	Billy Williams	3.50
440	B. Williams (In Action)	1.75
441	Thurman Munson	10.00
442	T. Munson (In Action)	5.00
443	Ken Henderson	.50

NO.	PLAYER	NR. MT.
444	Henderson (In Action)	.50
445	Tom Seaver	15.00
446	T. Seaver (In Action)	7.50
447	Willie Stargell	5.00
448	W. Stargell (In Action)	2.50
449	Bob Lemon	1.00
450	Mickey Lolich	.75
451	Tony LaRussa	.60
452	Ed Herrmann	.50
453	Barry Lersch	.50
454	Oakland A's	1.50
455	Tommy Harper	.50
456	Mark Belanger	.60
457	Padres Rookies:	.65
	Darcy Fast, Derrel Thomas,	
	Mike Ivie	
458	Aurelio Monteagudo	.50
459	Rick Renick	.50
460	Al Downing	.50
461	Tim Cullen	.50
462	Rickey Clark	.50
463	Bernie Carbo	.50
464	Jim Roland	.50
465	Gil Hodges	2.00
466	Norm Miller	.50
467	Steve Kline	.50
468	Richie Scheinblum	.50
469	Ron Herbel	.50
470	Ray Fosse	.50
471	Luke Walker	.50
472	Phil Gagliano	.50
473	Dan McGinn	.50
474	Orioles Rookies:	2.00
	Johnny Oates, Don Baylor,	
	Roric Harrison	
475	Gary Nolan	.50
476	Lee Richard	.50
477	Tom Phoebus	.50
478	Checklist No. 5	1.00
479	Don Shaw	.50
480	Lee May	.75
481	Billy Conigliaro	.50
482	Joe Hoerner	.50
483	Ken Suarez	.50
484	Lum Harris	.50
485	Phil Regan	.50
486	John Lowenstein	.50
487	Detroit Tigers	1.25
488	Mike Nagy	.50
489	Expos Rookies:	.50
	T. Humphrey, K. Lampard	
490	Dave McNally	.50
491	Lou Piniella (Boyhood)	.40
492	M. Stottlemyre (Boyhood)	.40
493	Bob Bailey (Boyhood)	.40
494	Willie Horton (Boyhood)	.40
495	Bill Melton (Boyhood)	.40
496	B. Harrelson (Boyhood)	.40
497	Jim Perry (Boyhood)	.40
498	B. Robinson (Boyhood)	1.50
499	Vicente Romo	.50
500	Joe Torre	1.00
501	Pete Hamm	.50
502	Jackie Hernandez	.50
503	Gary Peters	.50
504	Ed Spiezio	.50
505	Mike Marshall	.50
506	Indians Rookies:	.50
	Terry Ley, Dick Tidrow,	
	Jim Moyer	
507	Fred Gladding	.50
508	Ellie Hendricks	.50
509	Don McMahon	.50
510	Ted Williams (Mgr.)	5.00
511	Tony Taylor	.50
512	Paul Popovich	.50
513	Lindy McDaniel	.50
514	Ted Sizemore	.50
515	Bert Blyleven	4.00
516	Oscar Brown	.50
517	Ken Brett	.50
518	Wayne Garrett	.50
519	Ted Abernathy	.50
520	Larry Bowa	1.25
521	Alan Foster	.50

NO.	PLAYER	NR. MT.
522	Los Angeles Dodgers	1.50
523	Chuck Dobson	.50
524	Reds Rookies:	.60
	Ed Armbrister, Mel Behney	
525	Carlos May	.50
526	Bob Bailey	1.00
527	Dave Leonhard	1.00
528	Ron Stone	1.00
529	Dave Nelson	1.00
530	Don Sutton	4.00
531	Freddie Patek	1.00
532	Fred Kendall	1.00
533	Ralph Houk (Mgr.)	1.00
534	Jim Hickman	1.00
535	Ed Brinkman	1.00
536	Doug Rader	1.00
537	Bob Locker	1.00
538	Charlie Sands	1.00
539	Terry Forster (R)	1.25
540	Felix Milan	1.00
541	Roger Repoz	1.00
542	Jack Billingham	1.00
543	Duane Josephson	1.00
544	Ted Martinez	1.00
545	Wayne Granger	1.00
546	Joe Hague	1.00
547	Cleveland Indians	1.50
548	Frank Reberger	1.00
549	Dave May	1.00
550	Brooks Robinson	12.00
551	Ollie Brown	1.00
552	O. Brown (In Action)	1.00
553	Wilbur Wood	1.25
554	W. Wood (In Action)	1.00
555	Ron Santo	1.25
556	R. Santo (In Action)	1.00
557	John Odom	1.00
558	J. Odom (In Action)	1.00
559	Pete Rose	60.00
560	P. Rose (In Action)	30.00
561	Leo Cardenas	1.00
562	L. Cardenas (In Action)	1.00
563	Ray Sadecki	1.00
564	R. Sadecki (In Action)	1.00
565	Reggie Smith	1.25
566	R. Smith (In Action)	1.00
567	Juan Marichal	5.00
568	J. Marichal (In Action)	2.50
569	Ed Kirkpatrick	1.00
570	Kirkpatrick (In Action)	1.00
571	Nate Colbert	1.00
572	N. Colbert (In Action)	1.00
573	Fritz Peterson	1.00
574	F. Peterson (In Action)	1.00
575	Al Oliver	2.00
576	Leo Durocher	1.50
577	Mike Paul	1.00
578	Billy Grabarkewitz	1.00
579	Doyle Alexander (R)	3.00
580	Lou Piniella	2.00
581	Wade Blasingame	1.00
582	Montreal Expos	1.50
583	Darold Knowles	1.00
584	Jerry McNertney	1.00
585	George Scott	1.00
586	Denis Menke	1.00
587	Billy Wilson	1.00
588	Jim Holt	1.00
589	Hal Lanier	1.00
590	Graig Nettles	2.00
591	Paul Casanova	1.00
592	Lew Krausse	1.00
593	Rich Morales	1.00
594	Jim Beauchamp	1.00
595	Nolan Ryan	40.00
596	Manny Mota	1.25
597	Jim Magnuson	1.00
598	Hal King	1.00
599	Billy Champion	1.00
600	Al Kaline	12.00
601	George Stone	1.00
602	Dave Bristol	1.00
603	Jim Ray	1.00
604	Checklist No. 6	4.00
605	Nelson Briles	1.00

NO.	PLAYER	NR. MT.
606	Luis Melendez	1.00
607	Frank Duffy	1.00
608	Mike Corkins	1.00
609	Tom Grieve	1.00
610	Bill Stoneman	1.00
611	Rich Reese	1.00
612	Joe Decker	1.00
613	Mike Ferraro	1.00
614	Ted Uhlaender	1.00
615	Steve Hargan	1.00
616	Joe Ferguson (R)	1.00
617	Kansas City Royals	1.50
618	Rich Robertson	1.00
619	Rich McKinney	1.00
620	Phil Niekro	5.00
621	Commissioners Award	1.25
622	MVP Award	1.25
623	Cy Young Award	1.25
624	Minor League Player of the Year	1.25
625	Rookie of the Year	1.25
626	Babe Ruth Award	1.25
627	Moe Drabowsky	1.00
628	Terry Crowley	1.00
629	Paul Doyle	1.00
630	Rich Hebner	1.00
631	John Strohmayer	1.00
632	Mike Hegan	1.00
633	Jack Hiatt	1.00
634	Dick Woodson	1.00
635	Don Money	1.25
636	Bill Lee	1.25
637	Preston Gomez	1.00
638	Ken Wright	1.00
639	J.C. Martin	1.00
640	Joe Coleman	1.00
641	Mike Lum	1.00
642	Dennis Riddleberger	1.00
643	Russ Gibson	1.00
644	Bernie Allen	1.00
645	Jim Maloney	1.25
646	Chico Salmon	1.00
647	Bob Moose	1.00
648	Jim Lyttle	1.00
649	Pete Richert	1.00
650	Sal Bando	1.25
651	Cincinnati Reds	1.50
652	Marcelino Lopez	1.00

NO.	PLAYER	NR. MT.
653	Jim Fairey	1.00
654	Horacio Pina	1.00
655	Jerry Grote	1.00
656	Rudy May	1.00
657	Bobby Wine	2.00
658	Steve Dunning	2.00
659	Bob Aspromonte	2.00
660	Paul Blair	2.25
661	Bill Virdon	2.50
662	Stan Bahnsen	2.00
663	Fran Healy	2.00
664	Bobby Knoop	2.00
665	Chris Short	2.00
666	Hector Torres	2.00
667	Ray Newman	2.00
668	Texas Rangers	4.00
669	Willie Crawford	2.00
670	Ken Holtzman	2.25
671	Donn Clendenon	2.25
672	Archie Reynolds	2.00
673	Dave Marshall	2.00
674	John Kennedy	2.00
675	Pat Jarvis	2.00
676	Danny Cater	2.00
677	Ivan Murrell	2.00
678	Steve Luebber	2.00
679	Astros Rookies: Bob Fenwick, Bob Stinson	2.00
680	Dave Johnson	3.00
681	Bobby Pfeil	2.00
682	Mike McCormick	2.00
683	Steve Hovley	2.00
684	Hal Breeden	2.00
685	Joe Horlen	2.00
686	Steve Garvey	80.00
687	Del Unser	2.00
688	St. Louis Cardinals	4.00
689	Eddie Fisher	2.00
690	Willie Montanez	2.00
691	Curt Blefary	2.00
692	C. Blefary (In Action)	2.00
693	Alan Gallagher	2.00
694	Gallagher (In Action)	2.00
695	Rod Carew	65.00
696	R. Carew (In Action)	32.50
697	Jerry Koosman	5.00
698	J. Koosman (In Action)	2.50
699	Bobby Murcer	5.00

NO.	PLAYER	NR. MT.
700	B. Murcer (In Action)	2.50
701	Jose Pagan	2.00
702	J. Pagan (In Action)	2.00
703	Doug Griffin	2.00
704	D. Griffin (In Action)	2.00
705	Pat Corrales	2.00
706	P. Corrales (In Action)	2.00
707	Tim Foli	2.00
708	T. Foli (In Action)	2.00
709	Jim Kaat	6.00
710	J. Kaat (In Action)	3.00
711	Bobby Bonds	5.00
712	B. Bonds (In Action)	2.50
713	Gene Michael	2.00
714	G. Michael (In Action)	2.00
715	Mike Epstein	2.00
716	Jesus Alou	2.00
717	Bruce Dal Canton	2.00
718	Del Rice	2.00
719	Cesar Geronimo	2.00
720	Sam McDowell	2.00
721	Eddie Leon	2.00
722	Bill Sudakis	2.00
723	Al Santorini	2.00
724	AL Rookie Pitchers: John Curtis, Rich Hinton, Mickey Scott	2.00
725	Dick McAuliffe	2.00
726	Dick Selma	2.00
727	Jose LaBoy	2.00
728	Gail Hopkins	2.00
729	Bob Veale	2.00
730	Rick Monday	2.50
731	Baltimore Orioles	3.00
732	George Culver	2.00
733	Jim Hart	2.25
734	Bob Burda	2.00
735	Diego Segui	2.00
736	Bill Russell	3.00
737	Lenny Randle	2.00
738	Jim Merritt	2.00
739	Don Mason	2.00
740	Rico Carty	2.50
741	Rookie Stars: Tom Hutton, John Milner, Rick Miller	2.50
742	Jim Rooker	2.00
743	Cesar Gutierrez	2.00

NO.	PLAYER	NR. MT.
744	Jim Slaton	2.00
745	Julian Javier	2.00
746	Lowell Palmer	2.00
747	Jim Stewart	2.00
748	Phil Hennigan	2.00
749	Walter Alston (Mgr.)	4.00
750	Willie Horton	2.50
751	S. Carlton (Traded)	36.00
752	Joe Morgan (Traded)	15.00
753	D. McLain (Traded)	4.00
754	F. Robinson (Traded)	15.00
755	Jim Fregosi (Traded)	3.00
756	Rick Wise (Traded)	3.00
757	J. Cardenal (Traded)	3.00
758	Gil Garrido	2.00
759	Chris Cannizzaro	2.00
760	Bill Mazeroski	3.50
761	Rookie Stars: Bernie Williams, Ben Oglivie, Ron Cey	12.50
762	Wayne Simpson	2.00
763	Ron Hansen	2.00
764	Dusty Baker	3.50
765	Ken McMullen	2.00
766	Steve Hamilton	2.00
767	Tom McCraw	2.00
768	Denny Doyle	2.00
769	Jack Aker	2.00
770	Jim Wynn	2.25
771	San Francisco Giants	4.00
772	Ken Tatum	2.00
773	Ron Brand	2.00
774	Luis Alvarado	2.00
775	Jerry Reuss	3.50
776	Bill Voss	2.00
777	Hoyt Wilhelm	10.00
778	Twins Rookies: Vic Albury, Rick Dempsey, Jim Strickland	2.00
779	Tony Cloninger	2.00
780	Dick Green	2.00
781	Jim McAndrew	2.00
792	Larry Stahl	2.00
783	Les Cain	2.00
784	Ken Aspromonte	2.00
785	Vic Davalillo	2.00
786	Chuck Brinkman	2.00
787	Ron Reed (Exc. $1.00)	4.00

1973 Topps. . . . Complete Set of 660 Cards—Value $300.00 (Exc.); $700.00 (Mint)

Includes the rookie cards of Mike Schmidt, Darrell Evans and Davey Lopes. The high numbers are 529 to 660. This was the last Topps' set to be issued in *series*. Starting in 1974 the entire set was issued at one time.

NO.	PLAYER	NR. MT.
1	All-Time HR Leaders Babe Ruth, Hank Aaron, Willie Mays (Exc. $4.00)	13.50
2	Rich Hebner	.30
3	Jim Lonborg	.30
4	John Milner	.30
5	Ed Brinkman	.30
6	Mac Scarce	.30
7	Texas Rangers	.30
8	Tom Hall	.30
9	Johnny Oates	.30

NO.	PLAYER	NR. MT.
10	Don Sutton	2.00
11	Chris Chambliss	.60
12	Don Zimmer (Mgr.)	.50
13	George Hendrick	.75
14	Sonny Siebert	.30
15	Ralph Garr	.30
16	Steve Braun	.30
17	Fred Gladding	.30
18	Leroy Stanton	.30
19	Tim Foli	.30
20	Stan Bahnsen	.30

NO.	PLAYER	NR. MT.
21	Randy Hundley	.30
22	Ted Abernathy	.30
23	Dave Kingman	1.25
24	Al Santorini	.30
25	Ray White	.40
26	Pittsburgh Pirates	.60
27	Bill Gogolewski	.30
28	Hal McRae	.50
29	Tony Taylor	.30
30	Tug McGraw	.75
31	Buddy Bell (R)	4.00

NO.	PLAYER	NR. MT.
32	Fred Norman	.30
33	Jim Breazeale	.30
34	Pat Dobson	.30
35	Willie Davis	.40
36	Steve Barber	.30
37	Bill Robinson	.30
38	Mike Epstein	.30
39	Dave Roberts	.30
40	Reggie Smith	.75
41	Tom Walker	.30
42	Mike Andrews	.30

NO.	PLAYER	NR. MT.
43	Randy Moffitt	.30
44	Rick Monday	.40
45	Ellie Rodriguez (wrong photo)	.30
46	Lindy McDaniel	.30
47	Luis Melendez	.30
48	Paul Splittorff	.35
49	Frank Quilici (Mgr.)	.50
50	Roberto Clement	13.00
51	Chuck Seelbach	.30
52	Denis Menke	.30
53	Steve Dunning	.30
54	Checklist No. 1	1.25
55	Jon Matlack	.45
56	Merv Rettenmund	.30
57	Derrel Thomas	.30
58	Mike Paul	.30
59	Steve Yeager (R)	.60
60	Ken Holtzman	.40
61	Batting Leaders: Billy Williams, Rod Carew	1.00
62	Home Run Leaders: Johnny Bench, Dick Allen	1.00
63	RBI Leaders: Johnny Bench, Dick Allen	1.00
64	Stolen Base Leaders: B. Campaneris, L. Brock	.60
65	ERA Leaders: Steve Carlton, Luis Tiant	.75
66	Victory Leaders: Wilbur Wood, Steve Carlton, Gaylord Perry	1.00
67	Strikeout Leaders: Steve Carlton, Nolan Ryan	3.50
68	Leading Firemen: Clay Carroll, Sparky Lyle	.45
69	Phil Gagliano	.30
70	Milt Pappas	.30
71	Johnny Briggs	.30
72	Ron Reed	.30
73	Ed Herrmann	.30
74	Billy Champion	.30
75	Vada Pinson	.50
76	Doug Rader	.30
77	Mike Torrez	.40
78	Richie Scheinblum	.30
79	Jim Willoughby	.30
80	Tony Oliva	1.00
81	Whitey Lockman (Mgr.)	.45
82	Fritz Peterson	.30
83	Leron Lee	.30
84	Rollie Fingers	2.00
85	Ted Simmons	1.25
86	Tom McCraw	.30
87	Ken Boswell	.30
88	Mickey Stanley	.30
89	Jack Billingham	.30
90	Brooks Robinson	4.00
91	Los Angeles Dodgers	.75
92	Jerry Bell	.30
93	Jesus Alou	.30
94	Dick Billings	.30
95	Steve Blass	.30
96	Doug Griffin	.30
97	Willie Montanez	.30
98	Dick Woodson	.30
99	Carl Taylor	.30
100	Hank Aaron	15.00
101	Ken Henderson	.30
102	Rudy May	.30
103	Celerino Sanchez	.30
104	Reggie Cleveland	.30
105	Carlos May	.30
106	Terry Humphrey	.30
107	Phil Hennigan	.30
108	Bill Russell	.30
109	Doyle Alexander	.50
110	Bob Watson	.40
111	Dave Nelson	.30
112	Gary Ross	.30
113	Jerry Grote	.30
114	Lynn McGlothen	.30
115	Ron Santo	.60
116	Ralph Houk (Mgr.)	.60
117	Ramon Hernandez	.30

NO.	PLAYER	NR. MT.
118	John Mayberry	.40
119	Larry Bowa	.75
120	Joe Coleman	.30
121	Dave Rader	.30
122	Jim Strickland	.30
123	Sandy Alomar	.30
124	Jim Hardin	.30
125	Ron Fairly	.30
126	Jim Brewer	.30
127	Milwaukee Brewers	.75
128	Ted Sizemore	.30
129	Terry Forster	.40
130	Pete Rose	18.00
131	Eddie Kasko (Mgr.)	.50
132	Matty Alou	.50
133	Dave Roberts	.30
134	Milt Wilcox	.40
135	Lee May	.40
136	Earl Weaver (Mgr.)	.75
137	Jim Beauchamp	.30
138	Horacio Pina	.30
139	Carmen Fanzone	.30
140	Lou Piniella	.75
141	Bruce Kison	.40
142	Thurman Munson	6.00
143	John Curtis	.30
144	Marty Perez	.30
145	Bobby Bonds	.60
146	Woodie Fryman	.30
147	Mike Anderson	.30
148	Dave Goltz	.30
149	Ron Hunt	.30
150	Wilbur Wood	.30
151	Wes Parker	.30
152	Dave May	.30
153	Al Hrabosky	.40
154	Jeff Torborg	.30
155	Sal Bando	.45
156	Cesar Geronimo	.30
157	Denny Riddleberger	.30
158	Houston Astros	.60
159	Clarence Gaston	.30
160	Jim Palmer	4.00
161	Ted Martinez	.30
162	Pete Broberg	.30
163	Vic Davalillo	.30
164	Monty Montgomery	.30
165	Luis Aparicio	2.50
166	Terry Harmon	.30
167	Steve Stone	.35
168	Jim Northrup	.30
169	Ron Schueler	.30
170	Harmon Killebrew	4.00
171	Bernie Carbo	.30
172	Steve Kline	.30
173	Hal Breeden	.30
174	Rich Gossage (R)	7.50
175	Frank Robinson	3.00
176	Chuck Taylor	.30
177	Bill Plummer	.30
178	Don Rose	.30
179	Dick Williams (Mgr.)	.50
180	Fergie Jenkins	1.25
181	Jack Brohamer	.30
182	Mike Caldwell (R)	.50
183	Don Buford	.30
184	Jerry Koosman	.50
185	Jim Wynn	.35
186	Bill Fahey	.30
187	Luke Walker	.30
188	Cookie Rojas	.30
189	Greg Luzinski	.75
190	Bob Gibson	3.00
191	Detroit Tigers	.75
192	Pat Jarvis	.30
193	Carlton Fisk	5.00
194	Jorge Orta	.30
195	Clay Carroll	.30
196	Ken McMullen	.30
197	Ed Goodson	.30
198	Horace Clarke	.30
199	Bert Blyleven	1.50
200	Billy Williams	3.50
201	AL Playoffs: Hendrick Scores	.75

NO.	PLAYER	NR. MT.
202	NL Playoffs: Foster's Run Decides It	.75
203	World Series Game 1 Tenace the Menace	.75
204	World Series Game 2 A's Make It Two Straight	.75
205	World Series Game 3 Reds Win Squeaker	.75
206	World Series Game 4 Tenace Singles In Ninth	.75
207	World Series Game 5 Odom Out at Plate	.75
208	World Series Game 6 Red's Ties Series	.75
209	World Series Game 7 Campy Stars Rally	.75
210	World Series A's— World Champions	.75
211	Balor Moore	.30
212	Joe LaHoud	.30
213	Steve Garvey	9.00
214	Steve Hamilton	.30
215	Dusty Baker	.75
216	Toby Harrah	.35
217	Don Wilson	.30
218	Aurelio Rodriguez	.30
219	St. Louis Cardinals	.50
220	Nolan Ryan	7.50
221	Fred Kendall	.30
222	Rob Gardner	.30
223	Bud Harrelson	.30
224	Bill Lee	.30
225	Al Oliver	1.25
226	Ray Fosse	.30
227	Wayne Twitchell	.30
228	Bobby Darwin	.30
229	Roric Harrison	.30
230	Joe Morgan	3.00
231	Bill Parsons	.30
232	Ken Singleton	.60
233	Ed Kirkpatrick	.30
234	Bill North	.30
235	Jim Hunter	3.00
236	Tito Fuentes	.30
237	Eddie Mathews (Mgr.)	1.00
238	Tony Muser	.30
239	Pete Richert	.30
240	Bobby Murcer	.75
241	Dwain Anderson	.30
242	George Culver	.30
243	California Angels	.75
244	Ed Acosta	.30
245	Carl Yastrzemski	13.00
246	Ken Sanders	.30
247	Del Unser	.30
248	Jerry Johnson	.30
249	Larry Biittner	.30
250	Manny Sanguillen	.40
251	Roger Nelson	.30
252	Charlie Fox (Mgr.)	.50
253	Mark Belanger	.35
254	Bill Stoneman	.30
255	Reggie Jackson	16.00
256	Chris Zachary	.30
257	Yogi Berra (Mgr.)	1.50
258	Tommy John	1.50
259	Jim Holt	.30
260	Gary Nolan	.30
261	Pat Kelly	.30
262	Jack Aker	.30
263	George Scott	.30
264	Checklist No. 2	1.00
265	Gene Michael	.50
266	Mike Lum	.30
267	Lloyd Allen	.30
268	Jerry Morales	.30
269	Tim McCarver	.75
270	Luis Tiant	.50
271	Tom Hutton	.30
272	Ed Farmer	.30
273	Chris Speier	.45
274	Darold Knowles	.30
275	Tony Perez	1.50
276	Joe Lovitto	.30
277	Bob Miller	.30

NO.	PLAYER	NR. MT.
278	Baltimore Orioles	.50
279	Mike Strahler	.30
280	Al Kaline	4.00
281	Mike Jorgensen	.30
282	Steve Hovley	.30
283	Ray Sadecki	.30
284	Glenn Borgmann	.30
285	Don Kessinger	.40
286	Frank Linzy	.30
287	Eddie Leon	.30
288	Gary Gentry	.30
289	Bob Oliver	.30
290	Cesar Cedeno	.65
291	Rogelio Moret	.30
292	Jose Cruz	1.00
293	Bernie Allen	.30
294	Steve Arlin	.30
295	Bert Campaneris	.45
296	Sparky Anderson (Mgr.)	.50
297	Walt Williams	.30
298	Ron Bryant	.30
299	Ted Ford	.30
300	Steve Carlton	7.50
301	Billy Grabarkewitz	.30
302	Terry Crowley	.30
303	Nelson Briles	.30
304	Duke Sims	.30
305	Willie Mays	15.00
306	Tom Burgmeier	.30
307	Boots Day	.30
308	Skip Lockwood	.30
309	Paul Popovich	.30
310	Dick Allen	.75
311	Joe Decker	.30
312	Oscar Brown	.30
313	Jim Ray	.30
314	Ron Swoboda	.30
315	John Odom	.30
316	San Diego Padres	.50
317	Danny Cater	.30
318	Jim McGlothlin	.30
319	Jim Spencer	.30
320	Lou Brock	4.00
321	Rich Hinton	.30
322	Garry Maddox (R)	.75
323	Billy Martin (Mgr.)	.75
324	Al Downing	.50
325	Boog Powell	.75
326	Darrell Brandon	.30
327	John Lowenstein	.30
328	Bill Bonham	.30
329	Ed Kranepool	.50
330	Rod Carew	7.50
331	Carl Morton	.30
332	John Felske	.30
333	Gene Clines	.30
334	Freddie Patek	.30
335	Bob Tolan	.30
336	Tom Bradley	.30
337	Dave Duncan	.30
338	Checklist No. 3	1.25
339	Dick Tidrow	.30
340	Nate Colbert	.30
341	Jim Palmer (Boyhood)	1.25
342	S. McDowell (Boyhood)	.45
343	B. Murcer (Boyhood)	.45
344	Jim Hunter (Boyhood)	1.25
345	Chris Speier (Boyhood)	.45
346	G. Perry (Boyhood)	1.25
347	Kansas City Royals	.75
348	Rennie Stennett	.30
349	Dick McAuliffe	.30
350	Tom Seaver	10.00
351	Jimmy Stewart	.30
352	Don Stanhouse	.30
353	Steve Brye	.30
354	Billy Parker	.30
355	Mike Marshall	.50
356	Chuck Tanner (Mgr.)	.60
357	Ross Grimsley	.30
358	Jim Nettles	.30
359	Cecil Upshaw	.30
360	Joe Rudi (photo of Gene Tenace)	.60
361	Fran Healy	.30

NO.	PLAYER	NR. MT.
362	Eddie Watt	.30
363	Jackie Hernandez	.30
364	Rick Wise	.30
365	Rico Petrocelli	.50
366	Brock Davis	.30
367	Burt Hooton	.30
368	Bill Buckner	.75
369	Lerrin LaGrow	.30
370	Willie Stargell	4.00
371	Mike Kekich	.30
372	Oscar Gamble	.40
373	Clyde Wright	.30
374	Darrell Evans	.60
375	Larry Dierker	.40
376	Frank Duffy	.30
377	Gene Mauch (Mgr.)	.50
378	Lenny Randle	.30
379	Cy Acosta	.30
380	Johnny Bench	15.00
381	Vicente Romo	.30
382	Mike Hegan	.30
383	Diego Segui	.30
384	Don Baylor	1.00
385	Jim Perry	.35
386	Don Money	.30
387	Jim Barr	.30
388	Ben Oglivie	.50
389	New York Mets	1.50
390	Mickey Lolich	.60
391	Lee Lacy (R)	.75
392	Dick Drago	.30
393	Jose Cardenal	.30
394	Sparky Lyle	.50
395	Roger Metzger	.30
396	Grant Jackson	.30
397	Dave Cash	.50
398	Rich Hand	.50
399	George Foster	1.50
400	Gaylord Perry	2.25
401	Clyde Mashore	.50
402	Jack Hiatt	.50
403	Sonny Jackson	.50
404	Chuck Brinkman	.50
405	Cesar Tovar	.50
406	Paul Lindblad	.50
407	Felix Millan	.50
408	Jim Colborn	.50
409	Ivan Murrell	.50
410	Willie McCovey	4.00
411	Ray Corbin	.50
412	Manny Mota	.75
413	Tom Timmerman	.50
414	Ken Rudolph	.50
415	Marty Pattin	.50
416	Paul Schaal	.50
417	Scipio Spinks	.50
418	Bobby Grich	.65
419	Casey Cox	.50
420	Tommie Agee	.50
421	Bobby Winkles (Mgr.)	.65
422	Bob Robertson	.50
423	Johnny Jeter	.50
424	Denny Doyle	.50
425	Alex Johnson	.50
426	Dave LaRoche	.50
427	Rick Auerbach	.50
428	Wayne Simpson	.50
429	Jim Fairey	.50
430	Vida Blue	.75
431	Gerry Moses	.50
432	Dan Frisella	.50
433	Willie Horton	.60
434	San F. Giants	.75
435	Rico Carty	.60
436	Jim McAndrew	.50
437	John Kennedy	.50
438	Enzo Hernandez	.50
439	Eddie Fisher	.50
440	Glenn Beckert	.50
441	Gail Hopkins	.50
442	Dick Dietz	.50
443	Danny Thompson	.50
444	Ken Brett	.50
445	Ken Berry	.50
446	Jerry Reuss	.60

NO.	PLAYER	NR. MT.
447	Joe Hague	.50
448	John Hiller	.50
449	Ken Aspromonte (Mgr.)	.65
450	Joe Torre	.75
451	John Vuckovich	.50
452	Paul Casanova	.50
453	Checklist No. 4	1.25
454	Tom Haller	.50
455	Bill Melton	.50
456	Dick Green	.50
457	John Strohmayer	.50
458	Jim Mason	.50
459	Jimmy Howarth	.50
460	Bill Freehan	.65
461	Mike Corkins	.50
462	Ron Blomberg	.50
463	Ken Tatum	.50
464	Chicago Cubs	1.00
465	Dave Giusti	.50
466	Jose Arcia	.50
467	Mike Ryan	.50
468	Tom Griffin	.50
469	Dan Monzon	.50
470	Mike Cuellar	.60
471	All-Time Hits	2.50
	Ty Cobb (4,191)	
472	All-Time Grand Slams:	2.50
	Lou Gehrig (23)	
473	All-Time Total Bases	2.50
	hank Aaron (6,172)	
474	All-Time RBI's	6.00
	Babe Ruth (2,209)	
475	All-Time Batting:	2.50
	Ty Cobb (.367)	
476	All-Time Shutouts:	1.50
	Walter Johnson (113)	
477	All-Time Victory Ldrs.	1.50
	Cy Young (511)	
478	All-Time Strikeouts:	1.50
	Walter Johnson (3,508)	
479	Hal Lanier	.60
480	Juan Marichal	4.00
481	Chicago White Sox	.75
482	Rick Reuschel (R)	5.00
483	Dal Maxvill	.50
484	Ernie McAnally	.50
485	Norm Cash	.60
486	Danny Ozark (Mgr.)	.60
487	Bruce Dal Canton	.50
488	Dave Campbell	.50
489	Jeff Burroughs	.50
490	Claude Osteen	.60
491	Bob Montgomery	.50
492	Pedro Borbon	.50
493	Duffy Dyer	.50
494	Rich Morales	.50
495	Tommy Helms	.50
496	Ray Lamb	.50
497	R. Schoendienst (Mgr.)	.60
498	Graig Nettles	2.00
499	Bob Moose	.50
500	Oakland A's	1.25
501	Larry Gura	.50
502	Bobby Valentine	.65
503	Phil Niekro	3.00
504	Earl Williams	.50
505	Bob Bailey	.50
506	Bart Johnson	.50
507	Darrel Chaney	.50
508	Gates Brown	.50
509	Jim Nash	.50
510	Amos Otis	.65
511	Sam McDowell	.60
512	Dalton Jones	.50
513	Dave Marshall	.50
514	Jerry Kenney	.50
515	Andy Messersmith	.65
516	Danny Walton	.50
517	Bill Virdon (Mgr.)	.65
518	Bob Veale	.50
519	John Edwards	.50
520	Mel Stottlemyre	.50
521	Atlanta Braves	.60
522	Leo Cardenas	.50

NO.	PLAYER	NR. MT.
523	Wayne Granger	.50
524	Gene Tenace	.65
525	Jim Fregosi	.75
526	Ollie Brown	.50
527	Dan McGinn	.50
528	Paul Blair	.50
529	Milt May	1.50
530	Jim Kaat	3.00
531	Ron Woods	1.50
532	Steve Mingori	1.50
533	Larry Stahl	1.50
534	Dave Lemonds	1.50
535	John Callison	1.50
536	Philadelphia Phillies	2.50
537	Bill Slayback	1.50
538	Jim Hart	1.50
539	Tom Murphy	1.50
540	Cleon Jones	1.75
541	Bob Bolin	1.50
542	Pat Corrales	1.75
543	Alan Foster	1.50
544	Von Joshua	1.50
545	Orlando Cepeda	3.00
546	Jim York	1.50
547	Bobby Heise	1.50
548	Don Durham	1.50
549	Whitey Herzog (Mgr.)	2.00
550	Dave Johnson	2.50
551	Mike Kilkenny	1.50
552	J.C. Martin	1.50
553	Mickey Scott	1.50
554	Dave Concepcion	2.50
555	Bill Hands	1.50
556	New York Yankees	4.00
557	Bernie Williams	1.50
558	Jerry May	1.50
559	Barry Lersch	1.50
560	Frank Howard	2.00
561	Jim Geddes	1.50
562	Wayne Garrett	1.50
563	Larry Haney	1.50
564	Mike Thompson	1.50
565	Jim Hickman	1.50
566	Lew Krausse	1.50
567	Bob Fenwick	1.50
568	Ray Newman	1.50
569	Walt Alston (Mgr.)	3.00
570	Bill Singer	1.50
571	Rusty Torres	1.50
572	Gary Sutherland	1.50
573	Fred Beene	1.50
574	Bob Didier	1.50
575	Dock Ellis	1.50
576	Montreal Expos	2.00
577	Eric Soderholm	1.50
578	Ken Wright	1.50
579	Tom Grieve	1.50
580	Joe Pepitone	2.00
581	Steve Kealey	1.50
582	Darrell Porter	1.75
583	Bill Grief	1.50
584	Chris Arnold	1.50
585	Joe Niekro	3.00
586	Bill Sudakis	1.50
587	Rich McKinney	1.50
588	Checklist No. 5	12.00
589	Ken Forsch	1.75
590	Deron Johnson	1.50
591	Mike Hedlund	1.50
592	John Boccabella	1.50
593	Jack McKeon (Mgr.)	1.50
594	Vic Harris	1.50
595	Don Gullett	1.75
596	Boston Red Sox	3.00
597	Mickey Rivers	2.00
598	Phil Roof	1.50
599	Ed Crosby	1.50
600	Dave McNally	1.50
601	Rookie Catchers:	1.75
	George Pena, Sergio Robles, R. Stelmaszek	
602	Rookie Pitchers:	1.75
	Doug Rau, Mel Behney, Ralph Garcia	

NO.	PLAYER	NR. MT.
603	Rookie 3rd Basemen:	1.75
	Billy McNulty, Ken Reitz, Terry Hughes	
604	Rookie Pitchers:	1.75
	Jesse Jefferson, Dennis O'Toole, Bob Strampe	
605	Rookie 1st Basemen:	1.75
	Pat Bourque, Enos Cabell, Gonzalo Marquez	
606	Rookie Outfielders:	3.00
	Jorge Roque, Gary Matthews, T. Paciorek	
607	Rookie Shortstops:	1.50
	Pepe Frias, Ray Busse, Mario Guerrero	
608	Rookie Pitchers:	1.50
	S. Busby, G. Medich, Dick Colpaert	
609	Rookie 2nd Basemen:	4.00
	Larvell Blanks, P. Garcia, Dave Lopes	
610	Rookie Pitchers:	3.00
	Hank Webb, J. Freeman, Charlie Hough	
611	Rookie Outfielders:	2.00
	Richie Zisk, Rich Coggins, J. Wohlford	
612	Rookie Pitchers:	1.75
	Steve Lawson, Bob Reynolds, Brent Strom	
613	Rookie Catchers:	12.00
	Bob Boone, S. Jutze, Mike Ivie	
614	Rookie Outfielders:	40.00
	A. Bumbry, Dwight Evans, Charlie Spikes	
615	Rookie 3rd Basemen:	300.00
	Ron Cey, Mike Schmidt, John Hilton	
616	Rookie Pitchers:	1.50
	S. Blateric, Norm Angelini, Mike Garman	
617	Rich Chiles	1.50
618	Andy Etchebarren	1.50
619	Billy Wilson	1.50
620	Tommy Harper	1.50
621	Joe Ferguson	1.50
622	Larry Hisle	1.50
623	Steve Renko	1.50
624	Leo Durocher (Mgr.)	2.50
625	Angel Mangual	1.50
626	Bob Barton	1.50
627	Luis Alvarado	1.50
628	Jim Slaton	1.50
629	Cleveland Indians	2.50
630	Denny McLain	2.50
631	Tom Matchick	1.50
632	Dick Selma	1.50
633	Ike Brown	1.50
634	Alan Closter	1.50
635	Gene Alley	1.50
636	Rick Clark	1.50
637	Norm Miller	1.50
638	Ken Reynolds	1.50
639	Willie Crawford	1.50
640	Dick Bosman	1.50
641	Cincinnati Reds	3.00
642	Jose LaBoy	1.50
643	Al Fitzmorris	1.50
644	Jack Heidemann	1.50
645	Bob Locker	1.50
646	Del Crandall (Mgr.)	2.00
647	George Stone	1.50
648	Tom Egan	1.50
649	Rich Folkers	1.50
650	Felipe Alou	2.00
651	Don Carrithers	1.50
652	Ted Kubiak	1.50
653	Joe Hoerner	1.50
654	Minnesota Twins	2.50
655	Clay Kirby	1.50
656	John Ellis	1.50
657	Bob Johnson	1.50
658	Elliott Maddox	1.50
659	Jose Pagan	1.50
660	F. Scherman (Exc. $.60)	3.00

1974 Topps. . . . Complete Set of 660 Cards—Value $400.00 (Mint)

Features the rookie cards of Dave Parker and Dave Winfield. This was Topps' first card set to be released all at one time. Previous card sets were released in series, several weeks or months apart. Fifteen Padres cards were printed either "San Diego" or "Washington". Because of a false rumor that the Padres were moving, Topps printed "Washington" on the cards, but it was quickly corrected.

   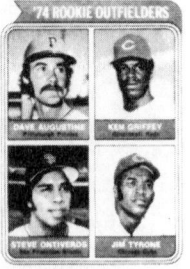 

NO. PLAYER	NR. MT.
1 Hank Aaron (Exc. $5.00). . .15.00	
Home Run King	
2 Aaron Special (1954-57).	3.00
3 Aaron Special (1958-61).	3.00
4 Aaron Special (1962-65).	3.00
5 Aaron Special (1966-69).	3.00
6 Aaron Special (1970-73).	3.00
7 Jim Hunter	3.00
8 George Theodore	.25
9 Mickey Lolich	.50
10 Johnny Bench	10.00
11 Jim Bibby	.25
12 Dave May	.25
13 Tom Hilgendorf	.25
14 Paul Popovich	.25
15 Joe Torre	.75
16 Baltimore Orioles	.50
17 Doug Bird	.25
18 Gary Thomasson	.25
19 Gerry Moses	.25
20 Nolan Ryan	12.50
21 Bob Gallagher	.25
22 Cy Acosta	.25
23 Craig Robinson	.25
24 John Hiller	.25
25 Len Singleton	.40
26 Bill Campbell (R)	.35
27 George Scott	.25
28 Manny Sanguillen	.25
29 Phil Niekro	2.50
30 Bobby Bonds	.50
31 Preston Gomez (Mgr.)	.25
32 John Grubb (SD)	.50
32 John Grubb (Wash.)	3.00
33 Don Newhauser	.25
34 Andy Kosco	.25
35 Gaylord Perry	2.50
36 St. Louis Cardinals	.45
37 Dave Sells	.25
38 Don Kessinger	.25
39 Ken Suarez	.25
40 Jim Palmer	4.00
41 Bobby Floyd	.25
42 Claude Osteen	.25
43 Jim Wynn	.25
44 Mel Stottlemyre	.35
45 Dave Johnson	.60
46 Pat Kelly	.25
47 Dick Ruthven	.25
48 Dick Sharon	.25
49 Steve Renko	.25
50 R. Carew	6.00
51 Bob Heise	.25
52 Al Oliver	1.00
53 Fred Kendall (SD)	.25
53 Fred Kendall (Wash.)	3.00
54 Elias Sosa	.25
55 Frank Robinson	3.00
56 New York Mets	1.00
57 Darold Knowles	.25
58 Charlie Spikes	.25
59 Ross Grimsley	.25
60 Lou Brock	3.00
61 Luis Aparicio	2.00
62 Bob Locker	.25
63 Bill Sudakis	.25

NO. PLAYER	NR. MT.
64 Doug Rau	.25
65 Amos Otis	.35
66 Sparky Lyle	.50
67 Tommy Helms	.25
68 Grant Jackson	.25
69 Del Unser	.25
70 Dick Allen	.50
71 Dan Frisella	.25
72 Aurelio Rodriguez	.25
73 Mike Marshall	.60
74 Minnesota Twins	.50
75 Jim Colborn	.25
76 Mickey Rivers	.25
77 Rich Troedson (SD)	.25
77 Rich Troedson (Wash)	3.00
78 Charlie Fox (Mgr.)	.25
79 Gene Tenace	.25
80 Tom Seaver	7.50
81 Frank Duffy	.25
82 Dave Giusti	.25
83 Orlando Cepeda	1.00
84 Rick Wise	.25
85 Joe Morgan	2.50
86 Joe Ferguson	.25
87 Fergie Jenkins	1.00
88 Freddie Patek	.25
89 Jackie Brown	.25
90 Bobby Murcer	.50
91 Ken Forsch	.25
92 Paul Blair	.25
93 Rod Gilbreath	.25
94 Detroit Tigers	.75
95 Steve Carlton	5.00
96 Jerry Hairston	.25
97 Bob Bailey	.25
98 Bert Blyleven	.75
99 Del Crandall (Mgr.)	.35
100 Willie Stargell	3.00
101 Bobby Valentine	.35
102 Bill Greif (SD)	.30
102 Bill Greif (Wash.)	3.00
103 Sal Bando	.50
104 Ron Bryant	.25
105 Carlton Fisk	3.00
106 Harry Parker	.25
107 Alex Johnson	.25
108 Al Hrabosky	.35
109 Bob Grich	.35
110 Billy Williams	2.50
111 Clay Carroll	.25
112 Dave Lopes	.50
113 Dick Drago	.25
114 California Angels	.50
115 Willie Horton	.40
116 Jerry Reuss	.35
117 Ron Blomberg	.25
118 Bill Lee	.30
119 Danny Ozark (Mgr.)	.30
120 Wilbur Wood	.25
121 Larry Lintz	.25
122 Jim Holt	.25
123 Nellie Briles	.25
124 Bobby Coluccio	.25
125 Nate Colbert (SD)	.30
125 Nate Colbert (Wash.)	3.00
126 Checklist No. 1	1.00

NO. PLAYER	NR. MT.
127 Tom Paciorek	.25
128 John Ellis	.25
129 Chris Speier	.25
130 Reggie Jackson	9.00
131 Bob Boone	1.00
132 Felix Milan	.25
133 David Clyde	.25
134 Denis Menke	.25
135 Roy White	.30
136 Rick Reuschel	1.50
137 Al Bumbry	.25
138 Ed Brinkman	.25
139 Aurelio Monteagudo	.25
140 Darrell Evans	.50
141 Pat Bourque	.25
142 Pedro Garcia	.25
143 Dick Woodson	.25
144 Walter Alston (Mgr.)	.75
145 Dock Ellis	.25
146 Ron Fairly	.25
147 Bart Johnson	.25
148 Dave Hilton (SD)	.30
148 Dave Hilton (Wash.)	3.00
149 Mac Scarce	.25
150 John Mayberry	.30
151 Diego Segui	.25
152 Oscar Gamble	.30
153 Jon Matlack	.25
154 Houston Astros	.40
155 Bert Campaneris	.35
156 Randy Moffitt	.25
157 Vic Harris	.25
158 Jack Billingham	.25
159 Jim Hart	.25
160 Brooks Robinson	3.00
161 Ray Burris (R)	.60
162 Bill Freehan	.40
163 Ken Berry	.25
164 Tom House	.25
165 Willie Davis	.25
166 Jack McKeon (Mgr.)	.25
167 Luis Tiant	.40
168 Danny Thompson	.25
169 Steve Rogers (R)	.75
170 Bill Melton	.25
171 Eduardo Rodriguez	.25
172 Gene Clines	.25
173 Randy Jones (SD)	.50
173 Randy Jones (Wash.)	3.50
174 Bill Robinson	.50
175 Reggie Cleveland	.25
176 John Lowenstein	.25
177 Dave Roberts	.25
178 Garry Maddox	.25
179 Yogi Berra (Mgr.)	1.00
180 Ken Holtzman	.25
181 Cesar Geronimo	.25
182 Lindy McDaniel	.25
183 Johnny Oates	.25
184 Texas Rangers	.60
185 Jose Cardenal	.25
186 Fred Scherman	.25
187 Don Baylor	1.00
188 Rudy Meoli	.25
189 Jim Brewer	.25
190 Tony Oliva	.75

NO. PLAYER	NR. MT.
191 Al Fitzmorris	.25
192 Mario Guerrero	.25
193 Tom Walker	.25
194 Darrell Porter	.25
195 Carlos May	.25
196 Jim Fregosi	.35
197 Vicente Romo (SD)	.30
197 Vicente Romo (Wash.)	3.00
198 Dave Cash	.25
199 Mike Kekich	.25
200 Cesar Cedeno	.50
201 Batting Leaders:	3.00
Rod Carew, Pete Rose	
202 Home Run Leaders:	1.25
R. Jackson, Willie Stargell	
203 RBI Leaders:	1.25
R. Jackson, Willie Stargell	
204 Stolen Base Leaders:	.75
Tommy Harper, Lou Brock	
205 Victory Leaders:	.60
Wilbur Wood, Ron Bryant	
206 ERA Leaders:	1.50
Jim Palmer, T. Seaver	
207 Strikeout Leaders:	1.50
Nolan Ryan, Tom Seaver	
208 Leading Firemen:	.50
John Hiller, M. Marshall	
209 Ted Sizemore	.25
210 Bill Singer	.25
211 Chicago Cubs	.50
212 Rollie Fingers	1.50
213 Dave Rader	.25
214 Bill Grabarkewitz	.25
215 Al Kaline	3.50
216 Ray Sadecki	.25
217 Tim Foli	.25
218 Johnny Briggs	.25
219 Doug Griffin	.25
220 Don Sutton	1.50
221 Chuck Tanner (Mgr.)	.35
222 Ramon Hernandez	.25
223 Jeff Burroughs	.50
224 Roger Metzger	.25
225 Paul Splittorff	.30
226 Padres Team (SD)	.75
226 Padres Team (Wash.)	4.00
227 Mike Lum	.25
228 Ted Kubiak	.25
229 Fritz Peterson	.25
230 Tony Perez	1.00
231 Dick Tidrow	.25
232 Steve Brye	.25
233 Jim Barr	.25
234 John Milner	.25
235 Dave McNally	.25
236 R. Schoendienst (Mgr.)	.40
237 Ken Brett	.25
238 Fran Healy	.25
239 Bill Russell	.25
240 Joe Coleman	.25
241 Glenn Beckert (SD)	.25
241 Glenn Beckert (Wash.)	3.00
242 Bill Gogolewski	.25
243 Bob Oliver	.25
244 Carl Morton	.25
245 Cleon Jones	.25

NO. PLAYER	NR. MT.
246 Oakland Athletics	.40
247 Rick Miller	.25
248 Tom Hall	.25
249 George Mitterwald	.25
250 W. McCovey (SD)	5.00
250 W. McCovey (Wash.)	20.00
251 Graig Nettles	1.25
252 Dave Parker (R)	24.00
253 John Boccabella	.25
254 Stan Bahnsen	.25
255 Larry Bowa	.60
256 Tom Griffin	.25
257 Buddy Bell	1.00
258 Jerry Morales	.25
259 Bob Reynolds	.25
260 Ted Simmons	1.00
261 Jerry Bell	.25
262 Ed Kirkpatrick	.25
263 Checklist No. 2	1.00
264 Joe Rudi	.25
265 Tug McGraw	.50
266 Jim Northrup	.25
267 Andy Messersmith	.35
268 Tom Grieve	.25
269 Bob Johnson	.25
270 Ron Santo	.40
271 Bill Hands	.25
272 Paul Casanova	.25
273 Checklist No. 3	1.00
274 Fred Beene	.25
275 Ron Hunt	.25
276 Bobby Winkles (Mgr.)	.35
277 Gary Nolan	.25
278 Cookie Rojas	.25
279 Jim Crawford	.25
280 Carl Yastrzemski	8.00
281 San F. Giants	.40
282 Doyle Alexander	.25
283 Mike Schmidt	50.00
284 Dave Duncan	.25
285 Reggie Smith	.40
286 Tony Muser	.25
287 Clay Kirby	.25
288 Gorman Thomas (R)	2.00
289 Rick Auerbach	.25
290 Vida Blue	.40
291 Don Hahn	.25
292 Chuck Seelbach	.25
293 Milt May	.25
294 Steve Foucault	.25
295 Rick Monday	.35
296 Ray Corbin	.25
297 Hal Breeden	.25
298 Roric Harrison	.25
299 Gene Michael	.30
300 Pete Rose	15.00
301 Bob Montgomery	.25
302 Rudy May	.25
303 George Hendrick	.50
304 Don Wilson	.25
305 Tito Fuentes	.25
306 Earl Weaver (Mgr.)	.60
307 Luis Melendez	.25
308 Bruce Dal Canton	.25
309 Dave Roberts (SD)	.30
309 Dave Roberts (Wash.)	4.00
310 Terry Forster	.25
311 Jerry Grote	.25
312 Deron Johnson	.25
313 Barry Lersch	.25
314 Milwaukee Brewers	.40
315 Ron Cey	1.00
316 Jim Perry	.25
317 Richie Zisk	.25
318 Jim Merritt	.25
319 Randy Hundley	.25
320 Dusty Baker	.50
321 Steve Braun	.25
322 Ernie McAnally	.25
323 Richie Scheinblum	.25
324 Steve Kline	.25
325 Tommy Harper	.25
326 Sparky Anderson (Mgr.)	.50
327 Tom Timmermann	.25
328 Skip Jutze	.25

NO. PLAYER	NR. MT.
329 Mark Belanger	.25
330 Juan Marichal	2.50
331 All-Star Catchers:	1.75
Carlton Fisk, Johnny Bench	
332 AS 1st Baseman:	1.50
Dick Allen, Hank Aaron	
333 AS 2nd Baseman:	1.75
Rod Carew, Joe Morgan	
334 AS 3rd Baseman:	1.25
B. Robinson, Ron Santo	
335 AS Shortstops:	.35
B. Campaneris, C. Speier	
336 AS Left Fielders:	2.50
Pete Rose, Bobby Mercer	
337 AS Center Fielders:	.35
Amos Otis, Cesar Cedeno	
338 AS Right Fielders:	2.00
R. Jackson, B. Williams	
339 AS Pitchers:	.75
Jim Hunter, Rick Wise	
340 Thurman Munson	5.00
341 Dan Driessen	.75
342 Jim Lonborg	.25
343 Kansas City Royals	.50
344 Mike Caldwell	.25
345 Bill North	.25
346 Ron Reed	.25
347 Sandy Alomar	.25
348 Pete Richert	.25
349 John Vukovich	.25
350 Bob Gibson	3.00
351 Dwight Evans	6.00
352 Bill Stoneman	.25
353 Rich Coggins	.25
354 Whitey Lockman (Mgr.)	.35
355 Dave Nelson	.25
356 Jerry Koosman	.50
357 Buddy Bradford	.25
358 Dal Maxvill	.25
359 Brent Strom	.25
360 Greg Luzinski	.75
361 Don Carrithers	.25
362 Hal King	.25
363 New York Yankees	1.00
364 C. Gaston (SD)	.30
364 C. Gaston (Wash.)	3.00
365 Steve Busby	.25
366 Larry Hisle	.25
367 Norm Cash	.40
368 Manny Mota	.40
369 Paul Lindblad	.25
370 Bob Watson	.35
371 Jim Slaton	.25
372 Ken Reitz	.25
373 John Curtis	.25
374 Marty Perez	.25
375 Earl Williams	.25
376 Jorge Orta	.25
377 Ron Woods	.25
378 Burt Hooton	.25
379 Billy Martin (Mgr.)	.60
380 Bud Harrelson	.60
381 Charlies Sands	.25
382 Bob Moose	.25
383 Phil. Phillies	.50
384 Chris Chambliss	.35
385 Don Gullett	.35
386 Gary Matthews	.50
387 Rich Morales (SD)	.30
387 Rich Morales (Wash.)	3.00
388 Phil Roof	.25
389 Gates Brown	.25
390 Lou Piniella	.50
391 Billy Champion	.25
392 Dick Green	.25
393 Orlando Pena	.25
394 Ken Henderson	.25
395 Doug Rader	.25
396 Tommy Davis	.35
397 George Stone	.25
398 Duke Sims	.25
399 Mike Paul	.25
400 Harmon Killebrew	3.50
401 Elliott Maddox	.25
402 Jim Rooker	.25

NO. PLAYER	NR. MT.
403 Darrell Johnson (Mgr.)	.30
404 Jim Howarth	.25
405 Ellie Rodriguez	.25
406 Steve Arlin	.25
407 Jim Wohlford	.25
408 Charlie Hough	.35
409 Ike Brown	.25
410 Pedro Borbon	.25
411 Frank Baker	.25
412 Chuck Taylor	.25
413 Don Money	.35
414 Checklist No. 4	1.00
415 Gary Gentry	.25
416 Chicago White Sox	.60
417 Rich Folkers	.25
418 Walt Williams	.25
419 Wayne Twitchell	.25
420 Ray Fosse	.25
421 Dan Fife	.25
422 Gonzalo Marquez	.25
423 Fred Stanley	.25
424 Jim Beauchamp	.25
425 Pete Broberg	.25
426 Rennie Stennett	.25
427 Bobby Bolin	.25
428 Gary Sutherland	.25
429 Dick Lange	.25
430 Matty Alou	.40
431 Gene Garber	.25
432 Chris Arnold	.25
433 Lerrin LaGrow	.25
434 Ken McMullen	.25
435 Dave Concepcion	.60
436 Don Hood	.25
437 Jim Lyttle	.25
438 Ed Herrmann	.25
439 Norm Miller	.25
440 Jim Kaat	.75
441 Tom Ragland	.25
442 Alan Foster	.25
443 Tom Hutton	.25
444 Vic Davalillo	.25
445 George Medich	.25
446 Len Randle	.25
447 Frank Quilici (Mgr.)	.30
448 Ron Hodges	.25
449 Tom McCraw	.25
450 Rich Hebner	.25
451 Tommy John	1.50
452 Gene Hiser	.25
453 Balor Moore	.25
454 Kurt Bevacqua	.25
455 Tom Bradley	.25
456 Dave Winfield (R)	45.00
457 Chuck Goggin	.25
458 Jim Ray	.25
459 Cincinnati Reds	.50
460 Boog Powell	.50
461 John Odom	.25
462 Luis Alvarado	.25
463 Pat Dobson	.25
464 Jose Cruz	.50
465 Dick Bosman	.25
466 Dick Billings	.25
467 Winston Llenas	.25
468 Pepe Frias	.25
469 Joe Decker	.25
470 A.L. Playoffs:	2.00
A's Beat Orioles	
471 N.L. Playoffs:	.50
Mets Beat Reds	
472 World Series Game 1:	.50
Oakland 2, N.Y. 1	
473 World Series Game 2:	2.00
N.Y. 10, Oakland 7	
474 World Series Game 3:	.50
Oakland 3, N.Y. 2	
475 World Series Game 4:	.50
N.Y. 6, Oakland 1	
476 World Series Game 5:	.50
N.Y. 2, Oakland 0	
477 World Series Game 6:	2.00
Oakland 3, N.Y. 1	
478 World Series Game 7:	.50
Oakland 5, N.Y. 2	

NO. PLAYER	NR. MT.
479 World Series:	.50
A's Win	
480 Willie Crawford	.25
481 Jerry Terrell	.25
482 Bob Didier	.25
483 Atlanta Braves	.50
484 Carmen Fanzone	.25
485 Felipe Alou	.40
486 Steve Stone	.30
487 Ted Martinez	.25
488 Andy Etchebarren	.25
489 Danny Murtaugh (Mgr.)	.25
490 Vada Pinson	.50
491 Roger Nelson	.25
492 Mike Rogodzinski	.25
493 Joe Hoerner	.25
494 Ed Goodson	.25
495 Dick McAuliffe	.25
496 Tom Murphy	.25
497 Bobby Mitchell	.25
498 Pat Corrales	.35
499 Rusty Torres	.25
500 Lee May	.30
501 Eddie Leon	.25
502 Dave LaRoche	.25
503 Eric Soderholm	.25
504 Joe Niekro	.50
505 Bill Buckner	.50
506 Ed Farmer	.25
507 Larry Stahl	.25
508 Montreal Expos	.40
509 Jesse Jefferson	.30
510 Wayne Garrett	.30
511 Toby Harrah	.35
512 Joe Lahoud	.25
513 Jim Campanis	.25
514 Paul Schaal	.25
515 Willie Montanez	.25
516 Horacio Pina	.25
517 Mike Hegan	.25
518 Derrel Thomas	.25
519 Bill Sharp	.25
520 Tim McCarver	.50
521 Ken Aspromonte (Mgr.)	.30
522 J.R. Richard	.40
523 Cecil Cooper	2.00
524 Bill Plummer	.25
525 Clyde Wright	.25
526 Frank Tepedino	.25
527 Bobby Darwin	.25
528 Bill Bonham	.25
529 Horace Clarke	.25
530 Mickey Stanley	.25
531 Gene Mauch (Mgr.)	.35
532 Skip Lockwood	.25
533 Mike Phillips	.25
534 Eddie Watt	.25
535 Bob Tolan	.25
536 Duffy Dyer	.25
537 Steve Mingori	.25
538 Cesar Tovar	.25
539 Lloyd Allen	.25
540 Bob Robertson	.25
541 Cleveland Indians	.60
542 Rich Gossage	2.00
543 Danny Cater	.25
544 Ron Schueler	.25
545 Billy Conigliaro	.25
546 Mike Corkins	.25
547 Glenn Borgmann	.25
548 Sonny Siebert	.25
549 Mike Jorgensen	.25
550 Sam McDowell	.35
551 Von Joshua	.25
552 Denny Doyle	.25
553 Jim Willoughby	.25
554 Tim Johnson	.25
555 Woodie Fryman	.25
556 Dave Campbell	.25
557 Jim McGlothlin	.25
558 Bill Fahey	.25
559 Darrell Chaney	.25
560 Mike Cuellar	.35
561 Ed Kranepool	.35
562 Jack Aker	.25

NO.	PLAYER	NR. MT.
563	Hal McRae	.35
564	Mike Ryan	.25
565	Milt Wilcox	.25
566	Jackie Hernandez	.25
567	Boston Red Sox	.50
568	Mike Torrez	.35
569	Rick Dempsey	.25
570	Ralph Garr	.25
571	Rich Hand	.25
572	Enzo Hernandez	.25
573	Mike Adams	.25
574	Bill Parsons	.25
575	Steve Garvey	8.00
576	Scipio Spinks	.25
577	Ralph Houk (Mgr.)	.35
578	Ralph Houk (Mgr.)	.35
579	Cecil Upshaw	.25
580	Jim Spencer	.25
581	Fred Norman	.25
582	Bucky Dent (R)	1.00
583	Marty Pattin	.25
584	Ken Rudolph	.25
585	Merv Rettenmund	.25
586	Jack Brohamer	.25
587	Larry Christenson	.25
588	Hal Lanier	.35
589	Boots Day	.25
590	Roger Moret	.25
591	Sonny Jackson	.25
592	Ed Bane	.25
593	Steve Yeager	.25
594	Leroy Stanton	.25
595	Steve Blass	.25
596	Rookie Pitchers:	.40
	Wayne Garland, Fred Holdsworth, Dick Pole, Mark Littell	

NO.	PLAYER	NR. MT.
597	Rookie Shortstops:	.75
	John Gamble, Pete MacKanin, Dave Chalk, Manny Trillo	
598	Rookie Outfielders:	4.00
	Steve Ontiveros, Dave Augustine, Ken Griffey, Jim Tyrone	
599	Rookie Pitchers	5.00
	"San Diego"—small type Ron Diorio, D. Freisleben, F. Riccelli, G. Shanahan	
599	Rookie Pitchers	2.50
	"San Diego"—large type	
599	Rookie Pitchers	1.00
	"Washington" Ron Diorio, D. Freisleben, F. Riccelli, G. Shanahan	
600	Rookie Infielders:	5.00
	Ron Cash, Jim Cox, Bill Madlock, Reggie Sanders	
601	Rookie Outfielders:	2.00
	Ed Armbrister, Rich Bladt, B. Downing, B. McBride	
602	Rookie Pitchers:	.50
	Glenn Abbott, Craig Swan R. Henninger, D. Vossler	
603	Rookie Catchers:	.50
	B. Foote, T. Lundstedt, C. Moore, S. Robles	
604	Rookie Infielders:	3.00
	Terry Hughes, John Knox, A. Thornton, F. White	

NO.	PLAYER	NR. MT.
605	Rookie Pitchers:	1.50
	Vic Albury, Ken Frailing, Kevin Kobel, Frank Tanana	
606	Rookie Outfielders:	.50
	Jim Fuller, Wilbur Howard, Tommy Smith, Otto Velez	
607	Rookie Shortstops:	.50
	Leo Foster, Dave Rosello, T. Heintzelman, F. Taveras	
608	Rookie Pitchers:	.50
	Bob Apodaca, Mike Wallace D. Baney, J. D'Acquisto	
608	"Apodaca"—error misspelled "Apodoco"	2.00
609	Rico Petrocelli	.25
610	Dave Kingman	.75
611	Rich Stelmaszek	.25
612	Luke Walker	.25
613	Dan Monzon	.25
614	Adrian Devine	.25
615	John Jeter	.25
616	Larry Gura	.35
617	Ted Ford	.25
618	Jim Mason	.25
619	Mike Anderson	.25
620	Al Downing	.35
621	Bernie Carbo	.25
622	Phil Gagliano	.25
623	Celerino Sanchez	.25
624	Bob Miller	.25
625	Ollie Brown	.25
626	Pittsburgh Pirates	.40
627	Carl Taylor	.25
628	Ivan Murrell	.25

NO.	PLAYER	NR. MT.
629	Rusty Staub	.75
630	Tommie Agee	.40
631	Steve Barber	.25
632	George Culver	.25
633	Dave Hamilton	.25
634	Eddie Mathews (Mgr.)	1.00
635	John Edwards	.25
636	Dave Goltz	.25
637	Checklist No. 5	1.00
638	Ken Sanders	.25
639	Joe Lovitto	.25
640	Milt Pappas	.40
641	Chuck Brinkman	.25
642	Terry Harmon	.25
643	Los Angeles Dodgers	.75
644	Wayne Granger	.25
645	Ken Boswell	.25
646	George Foster	1.25
647	Juan Beniquez	.60
648	Terry Crowley	.25
649	Fernando Gonzalez	.25
650	Mike Epstein	.25
651	Leron Lee	.25
652	Gail Hopkins	.25
653	Bob Stinson	.25
654	Jesus Alou	.40
654	Jesus Alou	5.00
	"outfield" deleted on front	
655	Mike Tyson	.25
656	Adrian Garrett	.25
657	Jim Shellenback	.25
658	Lee Lacy	.25
659	Joe Lis	.25
660	Larry Dierker (Exc. .15)	.50

1974 Topps Traded. . . . Complete Set of 44 Cards—Value $7.50

Topps' first Traded set. Topps issued another in 1976, and beginning in 1981 issued a Traded set every year. The traded set features players who were traded after the main set was printed. This set uses the same numbers as the regular set, followed by a "T".

NO.	PLAYER	NR. MT.
23 T	Craig Robinson	.10
42 T	Claude Osteen	.12
43 T	Jim Wynn	.15
51 T	Bobby Heise	.10
59 T	Ross Grimsley	.10
62 T	Bob Locker	.10
63 T	Bill Sudakis	.10
73 T	Mike Marshall	.15
123 T	Nelson Briles	.10
139 T	Aurelio Monteagudo	.10
151 T	Diego Segui	.10

NO.	PLAYER	NR. MT.
165 T	Willie Davis	.25
175 T	Reggie Cleveland	.10
182 T	Lindy McDaniel	.10
186 T	Fred Scherman	.10
249 T	George Mitterwald	.10
262 T	Ed Kirkpatrick	.10
269 T	Bob Johnson	.10
270 T	Ron Santo	.25
313 T	Barry Lersch	.10
319 T	Randy Hundley	.10
330 T	Juan Marichal	1.25

NO.	PLAYER	NR. MT.
348 T	Pete Richert	.10
373 T	John Curtis	.10
390 T	Lou Piniella	.60
428 T	Gary Sutherland	.10
454 T	Kurt Bevacqua	.10
458 T	Jim Ray	.10
485 T	Felipe Alou	.10
486 T	Steve Stone	.12
496 T	Tom Murphy	.10
516 T	Horacio Pina	.10
534 T	Eddie Watt	.10

NO.	PLAYER	NR. MT.
538 T	Cesar Tovar	.10
544 T	Ron Schueler	.10
579 T	Cecil Upshaw	.10
585 T	Merv Rettenmund	.10
612 T	Luke Walker	.10
616 T	Larry Gura	.20
618 T	Jim Mason	.10
630 T	Tommie Agee	.10
648 T	Terry Crowley	.10
649 T	Fernando Gonzalez	.10
—	Traded Checklist	.60

1975 Topps. . . . Complete Set of 660 Cards—Value $600.00

Features the rookie cards of Robin Yount, George Brett, Jim Rice, Gary Carter, Fred Lynn and Keith Hernandez. The set was also issued in a mini-size (2¼" x 3⅛") which was tested in a section of the country. The mini-size cards are worth 2 to 2½ times more than the regular size cards.

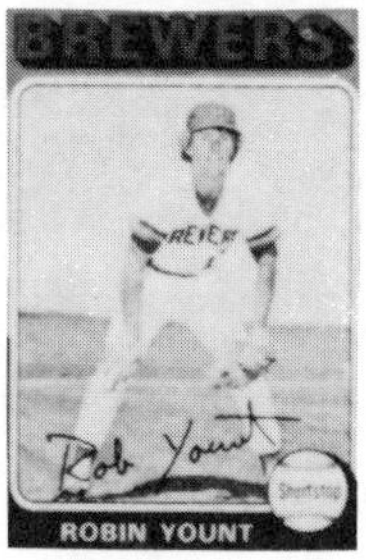

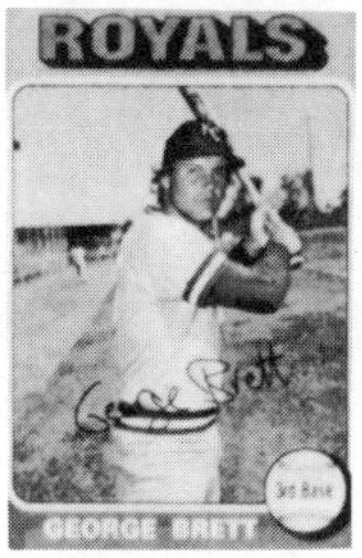

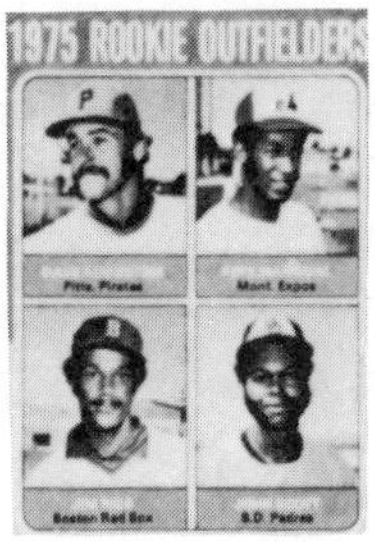

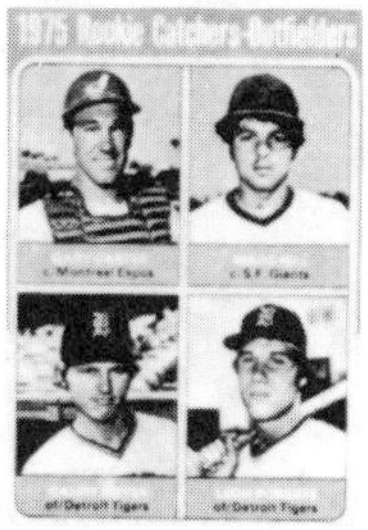
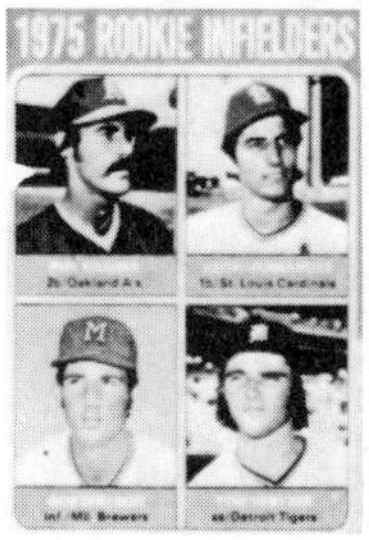

NO.	PLAYER	NR. MT.
1	Highlights: (Exc. $3.00)	12.00
	Aaron Sets Homer Mark	
2	Highlights:	2.00
	Brock Steals 118 Bases	
3	Highlights:	2.00
	Gibson's 3000th Strikeout	
4	Highlights:	2.00
	Kaline's 3000th Hit	
5	Highlights:	4.00
	Ryan Fans 300—3rd Year	
6	Highlights:	.50
	Marshall Hurls 106 Games	
7	Highlights:	.75
	No Hitters: Nolan Ryan, Dick Bosman, Steve Busby	
8	Rogelio Moret	.30
9	Frank Tepedino	.30
10	Willie Davis	.45
11	Bill Melton	.30
12	David Clyde	.30
13	Gene Locklear	.30
14	Milt Wilcox	.30
15	Jose Cardenal	.30
16	Frank Tanana	.50
17	Dave Concepcion	.65
18	Tigers/R. Houk (Mgr.)	.75
19	Jerry Koosman	.60
20	Thurman Munson	4.00
21	Rollie Fingers	1.25
22	Dave Cash	.30
23	Bill Russell	.40
24	Al Fitzmorris	.30
25	Lea May	.50
26	Dave McNally	.50
27	Ken Reitz	.30
28	Tom Murphy	.30
29	Dave Parker	6.00
30	Bert Blyleven	1.00
31	Dave Rader	.30
32	Reggie Cleveland	.30
33	Dusty Baker	.75
34	Steve Renko	.30
35	Ron Santo	.50
36	Joe Lovitto	.30
37	Dave Freisleben	.30
38	Buddy Bell	1.00
39	Andy Thornton	1.00
40	Bill Singer	.30
41	Cesar Geronimo	.30
42	Joe Coleman	.30
43	Cleon Jones	.30
44	Pat Dobson	.30
45	Joe Rudi	.50
46	Phillies/D. Ozark (Mgr.)	.75
47	Tommy John	1.25
48	Freddie Patek	.30
49	Larry Dierker	.30
50	Brook Robinson	4.00
51	Bob Forsch	1.00
52	Darrell Porter	.50
53	Dave Giusti	.30
54	Eric Soderholm	.30
55	Bobby Bonds	.60
56	Rick Wise	.30
57	Dave Johnson	.75
58	Chuck Taylor	.30

NO.	PLAYER	NR. MT.
59	Ken Henderson	.30
60	Fergie Jenkins	1.00
61	Dave Winfield	11.00
62	Fritz Peterson	.30
63	Steve Swisher	.30
64	Dave Chalk	.30
65	Don Gullett	.30
66	Willie Horton	.50
67	Tug McGraw	.60
68	Ron Blomberg	.30
69	John Odom	.30
70	Mike Schmidt	30.00
71	Charlie Hough	.40
72	Royals/J. McKeon (Mgr.	.75
73	J.R. Richard	.50
74	Mark Belanger	.50
75	Ted Simmons	1.00
76	Ed Sprague	.30
77	Richie Zisk	.50
78	Ray Corbin	.30
79	Gary Matthews	.50
80	Carlton Fisk	2.00
81	Ron Reed	.30
82	Pat Kelly	.30
83	Jim Merritt	.30
84	Enzo Hernandez	.30
85	Bill Bonham	.30
86	Joe Lis	.30
87	George Foster	1.00
88	Tom Egan	.30
89	Jim Ray	.30
90	Rusty Staub	.75
91	Dick Green	.30
92	Cecil Upshaw	.30
93	Dave Lopes	.50
94	Jim Lonborg	.30
95	John Mayberry	.50
96	Mike Cosgrove	.30
97	Earl Williams	.30
98	Rich Folkers	.30
99	Mike Hegan	.30
100	Willie Stargell	3.00
101	Expos/G. Mauch (Mgr.)	.75
102	Joe Decker	.30
103	Rick Miller	.30
104	Bill Madlock	1.50
105	Buzz Capra	.30
106	Mike Hargrove (R)	.75
107	Jim Barr	.30
108	Tom Hall	.30
109	George Hendrick	.50
110	Wilbur Wood	.40
111	Wayne Garrett	.30
112	Larry Hardy	.30
113	Elliot Maddox	.30
114	Dick Lange	.30
115	Joe Ferguson	.30
116	Lerrin LaGrow	.30
117	Orioles/E. Weaver (Mgr.)	.75
118	Mike Anderson	.30
119	Tommy Helms	.30
120	Steve Busby	.50
	(photo of Fran Healy)	
121	Bill North	.30
122	Al Hrabosky	.40
123	Johnny Briggs	.30

NO.	PLAYER	NR. MT.
124	Jerry Reuss	.45
125	Ken Singleton	.45
126	Checklist No.1	1.00
127	Glenn Borgmann	.30
128	Bill Lee	.40
129	Rick Monday	.45
130	Phil Niekro	2.00
131	Toby Harrah	.35
132	Randy Moffitt	.30
133	Dan Driessen	.45
134	Ron Hodges	.30
135	Charlie Spikes	.30
136	Jim Mason	.30
137	Terry Forster	.45
138	Del Unser	.30
139	Horacio Pina	.30
140	Steve Garvey	6.00
141	Mickey Stanley	.45
142	Bob Reynolds	.30
143	Cliff Johnson	.30
144	Jim Wohlford	.30
145	Ken Holtzman	.40
146	San Diego Padres	
	J. McNamara (Mgr.)	.75
147	Pedro Garcia	.30
148	Jim Rooker	.30
149	Tim Foli	.30
150	Bob Gibson	2.50
151	Steve Brye	.30
152	Mario Guerrero	.30
153	Rick Reuschel	.75
154	Mike Lum	.30
155	Jim Bibby	.30
156	Dave Kingman	1.00
157	Pedro Borbon	.30
158	Jerry Grote	.30
159	Steve Arlin	.30
160	Graig Nettles	1.00
161	Stan Bahnsen	.30
162	Willie Montanez	.30
163	Jim Brewer	.30
164	Mickey Rivers	.45
165	Doug Rader	.30
166	Woodie Fryman	.30
167	Rich Coggins	.30
168	Bill Greif	.30
169	Cookie Rojas	.30
170	Bert Campaneris	.50
171	Ed Kirkpatrick	.30
172	Boston Red Sox	1.00
	D. Johnson (Mgr.)	
173	Steve Rogers	.40
174	Bake McBride	.30
175	Don Money	.30
176	Burt Hooton	.40
177	Vic Correll	.30
178	Cesar Tovar	.30
179	Tom Bradley	.30
180	Joe Morgan	3.50
181	Fred Beene	.30
182	Don Hahn	.30
183	Mel Stottlemyre	.45
184	Jorge Orta	.30
185	Steve Carlton	6.00
186	Willie Crawford	.30
187	Denny Doyle	.30

NO.	PLAYER	NR. MT.
188	Tom Griffin	.30
189	1951 MVP's:	1.25
	Y. Berra, R. Campanella	
190	1952 MVP':	.50
	B. Shantz, Hank Bauer	
191	1953 MVP's:	.75
	Al Rosen, R. Campanella	
192	1954 MVP's:	1.25
	Yogi Berra, Willie Mays	
193	1955 MVP's:	1.25
	Y. Berra, R. Campanella	
194	1956 MVP's:	3.00
	M. Mantle, D. Newcombe	
195	1957 MVP's:	5.00
	Hank Aaron, M. Mantle	
196	1958 MVP's:	.75
	J. Jensen, Ernie Banks	
197	1959 MVP's:	1.00
	Nellie Fox, Ernie Banks	
198	1960 MVP's:	.75
	Roger Maris, Dick Groat	
199	1961 MVP's:	1.25
	F. Robinson, Roger Maris	
200	1962 MVP's:	3.50
	M. Mantle, Maury Wills	
201	1963 MVP's:	.75
	Elston Howard, S. Koufax	
202	1964 MVP's:	.75
	Ken Boyer, B. Robinson	
203	1965 MVP's:	1.00
	Zoilo Versalles, W. Mays	
204	1966 MVP's:	1.00
	F. Robinson, Bob Clemente	
205	1967 MVP's:	1.00
	C. Yastrzemski, O. Cepeda	
206	1968 MVP's:	1.00
	D. McLain, Bob Gibson	
207	1969 MVP's:	1.00
	W. McCovey, H. Killebrew	
208	1970 MVP's:	.75
	Boog Powell, J. Bench	
209	1971 MVP's;	.60
	Vida Blue, Joe Torre	
210	1972 MVP's:	.60
	Richie Allen, J. Bench	
211	1973 MVP's:	3.00
	Pete Rose, R. Jackson	
212	1974 MVP's:	.75
	J. Burroughs, S. Garvey	
213	Oscar Gamble	.35
214	Harry Parker	.30
215	Bobby Valentine	.45
216	San Francisco Giants	
	Wes Westrum (Mgr.)	.45
217	Lou Piniella	.60
218	Jerry Johnson	.30
219	Ed Herrmann	.30
220	Don Sutton	1.50
221	Aurelio Rodriguez	.30
222	Dan Spillner	.30
223	Robin Yount (R)	60.00
224	Ramon Hernandez	.30
225	Bob Grich	.45
226	Bill Campbell	.30
227	Bob Watson	.40
228	George Brett (R)	65.00

NO.	PLAYER	NR. MT.
229	Barry Foote	.30
230	Jim Hunter	2.00
231	Mike Tyson	.30
232	Diego Segui	.30
233	Billy Grabarkewitz	.30
234	Tom Grieve	.30
235	Jack Billingham	.30
236	Angels/D. Williams (Mgr.)	.75
237	Carl Morton	.30
238	Dave Duncan	.30
239	George Stone	.30
240	Garry Maddox	.45
241	Dick Tidrow	.30
242	Jay Johnstone	.30
243	Jim Kaat	1.00
244	Bill Buckner	.65
245	Mickey Lolich	.50
246	St. Louis Cardinals Red Schoendienst (Mgr.)	.75
247	Enos Cabell	.30
248	Randy Jones	.30
249	Danny Thompson	.30
250	Ken Brett	.30
251	Fran Healy	.30
252	Fred Scherman	.30
253	Jesus Alou	.30
254	Mike Torrez	.45
255	Dwight Evans	2.50
256	Billy Champion	.30
257	Checklist No. 2	1.00
258	Dave LaRoche	.30
259	Len Randle	.30
260	Johnny Bench	9.00
261	Andy Hassler	.30
262	Rowland Office	.30
263	Jim Perry	.30
264	John Milner	.30
265	Ron Bryant	.30
266	Sandy Alomar	.30
267	Dick Ruthven	.30
268	Hal McRae	.45
269	Doug Rau	.30
270	Ron Fairly	.30
271	Jerry Moses	.30
272	Lynn McGlothen	.30
273	Steve Braun	.30
274	Vincente Romo	.30
275	Paul Blair	.30
276	Chicago White Sox Chuck Tanner (Mgr.)	.75
277	Frank Taveras	.50
278	Paul Lindblad	.30
279	Milt May	.30
280	Carl Yastrzemski	9.00
281	Jim Slaton	.30
282	Jerry Morales	.30
283	Steve Foucault	.30
284	Ken Griffey	1.00
285	Ellie Rodriguez	.30
286	Mike Jorgensen	.30
287	Roric Harrison	.30
288	Bruce Ellingsen	.30
289	Ken Rudolph	.30
290	Jon Matlack	.40
291	Bill Sudakis	.30
292	Ron Schueler	.30
293	Dick Sharon	.30
294	Geoff Zahn	.30
295	Vada Pinson	.50
296	Alan Foster	.30
297	Craig Kusick	.30
298	Johnny Grubb	.30
299	Bucky Dent	.50
300	Reggie Jackson	9.00
301	Dave Roberts	.30
302	Rick Burleson (R)	.60
303	Grant Jackson	.30
304	Pittsburgh Pirates Danny Murtaugh (Mgr.)	.75
305	Jim Colborn	.30
306	Batting Leaders: Rod Carew, Ralph Garr	.75
307	Home Run Leaders: Dick Allen, Mike Schmidt	1.00
308	RBI Leaders: J. Burroughs, J. Bench	.75
309	Stolen Base Leaders: Bill North, Lou Brock	.60
310	Victory Leaders: Andy Messersmith, Jim Hunter, Fergie Jenkins, Phil Niekro	.60
311	ERA Leaders: Jim Hunter, Buzz Capra	.50
312	Strikeout Leaders: Nolan Ryan, Steve Carlton	3.00
313	Leading Firemen: Mike Marshall, Terry Forster	.45
314	Buck Martinez	.30
315	Don Kessinger	.40
316	Jackie Brown	.30
317	Joe LaHoud	.30
318	Ernie McAnally	.30
319	Johnny Oates	.30
320	Pete Rose	17.50
321	Rudy May	.30
322	Ed Goodson	.30
323	Fred Holdsworth	.30
324	Ed Kranepool	.45
325	Tony Oliva	1.00
326	Wayne Twitchell	.30
327	Jerry Hairston	.30
328	Sonny Siebert	.30
329	Ted Kubiak	.30
330	Mike Marshall	.40
331	Cleveland Indians Frank Robinson (Mgr.)	.75
332	Fred Kendall	.30
333	Dick Drago	.30
334	Greg Gross	.30
335	Jim Palmer	4.00
336	Rennie Stennett	.30
337	Kevin Kobel	.30
338	Rick Stelmaszek	.30
339	Jim Fregosi	.40
340	Paul Splittorff	.30
341	Hal Breeden	.30
342	Leroy Stanton	.30
343	Danny Frisella	.30
344	Ben Oglivie	.40
345	Clay Carroll	.30
346	Bobby Darwin	.30
347	Mike Caldwell	.30
348	Tony Muser	.30
349	Ray Sadecki	.30
350	Bobby Murcer	.65
351	Bob Boone	.50
352	Darold Knowles	.30
353	Luis Melendez	.30
354	Dick Bosman	.30
355	Chris Cannizzaro	.30
356	Rico Petrocelli	.40
357	Ken Frosch	.30
358	Al Bumbry	.30
359	Paul Popovich	.30
360	George Scott	.30
361	Los Angeles Dodgers Walter Alston (Mgr.)	.75
362	Steve Hargan	.30
363	Carmen Fanzone	.30
364	Doug Bird	.30
365	Bob Bailey	.30
366	Ken Sanders	.30
367	Craig Robinson	.30
368	Vic Albury	.30
369	Merv Rettenmund	.30
370	Tom Seaver	7.50
371	Gates Brown	.30
372	John D'Acquisto	.30
373	Bill Sharp	.30
374	Eddie Watt	.30
375	Roy White	.45
376	Steve Yeager	.30
377	Tom Hilgendorf	.30
378	Derrel Thomas	.30
379	Bernie Carbo	.30
380	Sal Bando	.45
381	John Curtis	.30
382	Don Baylor	1.00
383	Jim York	.30
384	Milwaukee Brewers Del Crandall (Mgr.)	.60
385	Dock Ellis	.30
386	Checklist: No. 3	1.00
387	Jim Spencer	.30
388	Steve Stone	.30
389	Tony Solaita	.30
390	Ron Cey	1.00
391	Don DeMola	.30
392	Bruce Bochte (R)	.60
393	Gary Gentry	.30
394	Larvell Blanks	.30
395	Bud Harrelson	.50
396	Fred Norman	.30
397	Bill Freehan	.40
398	Elias Sosa	.30
399	Terry Harmon	.30
400	Dick Allen	.45
401	Mike Wallace	.30
402	Bob Tolan	.30
403	Tom Buskey	.30
404	Ted Sizemore	.30
405	John Montague	.30
406	Bob Gallagher	.30
407	Herb Washington	.30
408	Clyde Wright	.30
409	Bob Robertson	.30
410	Mike Cueller	.40
411	George Mitterwald	.30
412	Bill Hands	.30
413	Marty Pattin	.30
414	Manny Mota	.45
415	John Hiller	.30
416	Larry Lintz	.30
417	Skip Lockwood	.30
418	Leo Foster	.30
419	Dave Goltz	.30
420	Larry Bowa	.60
421	Mets/Y. Berra (Mgr.)	.75
422	Brian Downing	.50
423	Clay Kirby	.30
424	John Lowenstein	.30
425	Tito Fuentes	.30
426	Geroge Medich	.30
427	Clarence Gaston	.30
428	Dave Hamilton	.30
429	Jim Dwyer	.30
430	Luis Tiant	.45
431	Rod Gilbreath	.30
432	Ken Berry	.30
433	Larry Demery	.30
434	Bob Locker	.30
435	Dave Nelson	.30
436	Ken Frailing	.30
437	Al Cowens (R)	.65
438	Don Carrithers	.30
439	Ed Brinkman	.30
440	Andy Messersmith	.40
441	Bobby Heise	.30
442	Maximino Leon	.30
443	Twins/F. Quilici (Mgr.)	.60
444	Gene Garber	.30
445	Felix Millan	.30
446	Bart Johnson	.30
447	Terry Crowley	.30
448	Frank Duffy	.30
449	Charlie Williams	.30
450	Willie McCovey	3.00
451	Rick Dempsey	.40
452	Angel Mangual	.30
453	Claude Osteen	.30
454	Doug Griffin	.30
455	Don Wilson	.30
456	Bob Coluccio	.30
457	Mario Mendoza	.30
458	Ross Grimsley	.30
459	1974 AL Champs: A's over Orioles	.50
460	1974 NL Champs: Dodgers over Pirates	.75
461	World Series Game 1: Oakland 3, Los Angeles 2	2.00
462	World Series Game 2: Los Angeles 3, Oakland 2	.60
463	World Series Game 3: Oakland 3, Los Angeles 2	.75
464	World Series Game 4: Oakland 5, Los Angeles 2	.50
465	World Series Game 5: Oakland 3, Los Angeles 2	.50
466	A's Win 3rd World Series	.60
467	Ed Halicki	.30
468	Bobby Mitchell	.30
469	Tom Dettore	.30
470	Jeff Burroughs	.40
471	Bob Stinson	.30
472	Bruce Dal Canton	.30
473	Ken McMullen	.30
474	Luke Walker	.30
475	Darrell Evans	.65
476	Eduardo Figueroa	.30
477	Tom Hutton	.30
478	Tom Burgmeier	.30
479	Ken Boswell	.30
480	Carlos May	.30
481	Will McEnaney	.30
482	Tom McCraw	.30
483	Steve Ontiveros	.30
484	Glenn Beckert	.30
485	Sparky Lyle	.45
486	Ray Fosse	.30
487	Astros/P. Gomez (Mgr.)	.75
488	Bill Travers	.30
489	Cecil Cooper	1.50
490	Reggie Smith	.40
491	Doyle Alexander	.30
492	Rich Hebner	.30
493	Don Stanhouse	.30
494	Pete LaCock	.30
495	Nelson Briles	.30
496	Pepe Frias	.30
497	Jim Nettles	.30
498	Al Downing	.30
499	Marty Perez	.30
500	Nolan Ryan	12.50
501	Bill Robinson	.30
502	Pat Bourque	.30
503	Fred Stanley	.30
504	Buddy Bradford	.30
505	Chris Speier	.30
506	Leron Lee	.30
507	Tom Carroll	.30
508	Bob Hansen	.30
509	Dave Hilton	.30
510	Vida Blue	.45
511	Rangers/B. Martin (Mgr.)	.75
512	Larry Milbourne	.30
513	Dick Pole	.30
514	Jose Cruz	.60
515	Manny Sanguillen	.30
516	Don Hood	.30
517	Checklist: No. 4	1.00
518	Leo Cardenas	.30
519	Jim Todd	.30
520	Amos Otis	.50
521	Dennis Blair	.30
522	Gary Sutherland	.30
523	Tom Paciorek	.30
524	John Doherty	.30
525	Tom House	.30
526	Larry Hisle	.30
527	Mac Scarce	.30
528	Eddie Leon	.30
529	Gary Thomasson	.30
530	Gaylord Perry	2.00
531	Cincinnati Reds Sparky Anderson (Mgr.)	.75
532	Gorman Thomas	1.00
533	Rudy Meoli	.30
534	Alex Johnson	.30
535	Gene Tenace	.30
536	Bob Moose	.30
537	Tommy Harper	.30
538	Duffy Dyer	.30
539	Jesse Jefferson	.30
540	Lou Brock	3.00

1975 Topps (Continued)

NO. PLAYER	NR. MT.
541 Roger Metzger	.30
542 Pete Broberg	.30
543 Larry Biittner	.30
544 Steve Mingori	.30
545 Billy Williams	2.00
546 John Knox	.30
547 Von Joshua	.30
548 Charlie Sands	.30
549 Bill Butler	.30
550 Ralph Garr	.30
551 Larry Christenson	.30
552 Jack Brohamer	.30
553 John Boccabella	.30
554 Rich Gossage	1.25
555 Al Oliver	.75
556 Tim Johnson	.30
557 Larry Gura	.30
558 Dave Roberts	.30
559 Bob Montgomery	.30
560 Tony Perez	1.00
561 A's/Alvin Dark (Mgr.)	.60
562 Gary Nolan	.30
563 Wilbur Howard	.30
564 Tommy Davis	.40
565 Joe Torre	.60
566 Ray Burris	.30
567 Jim Sundberg (R)	.75
568 Dale Murray	.30
569 Frank White	.75
570 Jim Wynn	.40
571 Dave Lemanczyk	.30
572 Roger Nelson	.30
573 Orlando Pena	.30
574 Tony Taylor	.30
575 Gene Clines	.30
576 Phil Roof	.30
577 John Morris	.30
578 Dave Tomlin	.30

NO. PLAYER	NR. MT.
579 Skip Pitlock	.30
580 Frank Robinson	3.00
581 Darrel Chaney	.30
582 Eduardo Rodriguez	.30
583 Andy Etchebarren	.30
584 Mike Garman	.30
585 Chris Chambliss	.50
586 Tim McCarver	.75
587 Chris Ward	.30
588 Rick Auerbach	.30
589 Braves/C. King (Mgr.)	.75
590 Cesar Cedeno	.65
591 Glenn Abbott	.30
592 Balor Moore	.30
593 Gene Lamont	.30
594 Jim Fuller	.30
595 Joe Niekro	.75
596 Ollie Brown	.30
597 Winston Llenas	.30
598 Bruce Kison	.30
599 Nate Colbert	.30
600 Rod Carew	5.00
601 Juan Beniquez	.30
602 John Vukovich	.30
603 Lew Krausse	.30
604 Oscar Zamora	.30
605 John Ellis	.30
606 Bruce Miller	.30
607 Jim Holt	.30
608 Gene Michael	.30
609 Ellie Hendricks	.30
610 Ron Hunt	.30
611 Yankees/B. Virdon (Mgr.)	.75
612 Terry Hughes	.30
613 Bill Parsons	.30
614 Rookie Pitchers:	.45
Jack Kucek, Dyar Miller,	
Paul Siebert, Vern Ruhle	

NO. PLAYER	NR. MT.
615 Rookie Pitchers:	1.00
Dennis Leonard, Tom	
Underwood, Hank Webb,	
Pat Darcy	
616 Rookie Outfielders	35.00
Jim Rice, D. Augustine,	
Pepe Mangual, J. Scott	
617 Rookie Infielders:	2.00
Mike Cubbage, Reggie	
Sanders, Manny Trillo,	
Doug DeCinces	
618 Rookie Pitchers:	3.00
Tom Johnson, Jamie	
Easterly, Scott McGregor,	
Rick Rhoden	
619 Rookie Outfielders:	.40
Benny Ayala, Nyls Nyman,	
Tommy Smith, Jerry Turner	
620 Rookie Catchers/OF's	35.00
Gary Carter, Marc Hill,	
Danny Meyer, Leon Roberts	
621 Rookie Pitchers:	.75
John Denny, Rawly	
Eastwick, Jim Kern,	
Juan Veintidos	
622 Rookie Outfielders:	12.00
Ed Armbrister, Fred Lynn,	
T. Whitfield, Tom Poquette	
623 Rookie Infielders:	24.00
Phil Garner, Bob Sheldon,	
K. Hernandez, T. Veryzer	
624 Rookie Pitchers:	.40
Doug Konieczny, Gary	
Lavelle, Jim Otten,	
Eddie Solomon	
625 Boog Powell	.50
626 Larry Haney	.30
(Photo of Dave Duncan)	

NO. PLAYER	NR. MT.
627 Tom Walker	.30
628 Ron LeFlore (R)	.60
629 Joe Hoerner	.30
630 Greg Luzinski	.75
631 Lee Lacy	.30
632 Morris Nettles	.30
633 Paul Casanova	.30
634 Cy Acosta	.30
635 Chuck Dobson	.30
636 Charlie Moore	.30
637 Ted Martinez	.30
638 Cubs/J. Marshall (Mgr.)	.75
639 Steve Kline	.30
640 Harmon Killebrew	2.50
641 Jim Northrup	.30
642 Mike Phillips	.30
643 Brent Strom	.30
644 Bill Fahey	.30
645 Danny Cater	.30
646 Checklist No. 5	1.00
647 Claudell Washington	2.00
648 Dave Pagan	.30
649 Jack Heidemann	.30
650 Dave May	.30
651 John Morlan	.30
652 Lindy McDaniel	.30
653 Lee Richards	.30
654 Jerry Terrell	.30
655 Rico Carty	.50
656 Bill Plummer	.30
657 Bob Oliver	.30
658 Vic Harris	.30
659 Bob Apodaca	.30
660 Hank Aaron	13.00

1976 Topps. . . . Complete Set of 660 Cards—Value $300.00

Features the rookie card of Ron Guidry. This set includes the only card ever issued for the Joe Garagiola and Bazooka "Bubble Gum Blowing Champ". Topps added a 44-card Traded set later in the season.

NO. PLAYER	NR. MT.
1 Record—Aaron (Exc. $2.50)	10.00
Most RBI's—2,262	
2 Record—Bonds	.30
Most Lead-Off Homers—32;	
Most Seasons of 30 HR's;	
and 30 Stolen Bases	
3 Record—Lolich	.30
Most Strikeouts	
Lefthander—2,679	
4 Record—Lopes	.30
Most Consecutive Steal	
Attempts—38	
5 Record—Seaver	1.75
Most Consecutive Seasons	
of 200 Strikeouts—8	
6 Record—Stennett	.30
Most Hits in a Nine	
Inning Game—7	
7 Jim Umbarger	.20
8 Tito Fuentes	.20

NO. PLAYER	NR. MT.
9 Paul Lindblad	.20
10 Lou Brock	2.50
11 Jim Hughes	.20
12 Richie Zisk	.30
13 Johnny Wockenfuss	.20
14 Gene Garber	.20
15 George Scott	.25
16 Bob Apodaca	.20
17 New York Yankees	1.00
18 Dale Murray	.20
19 George Brett	18.00
20 Bob Watson	.20
21 Dave LaRoche	.20
22 Bill Russell	.20
23 Brian Downing	.30
24 Cesar Geronimo	.20
25 Mick Torrez	.20
26 Andy Thornton	.30
27 Ed Figueroa	.20
28 Dusty Baker	.35

NO. PLAYER	NR. MT.
29 Rick Burleson	.30
30 John Montefusco (R)	.35
31 Len Randle	.20
32 Danny Frisella	.20
33 Bill North	.20
34 Mike Garman	.20
35 Tony Oliva	.75
36 Frank Taveras	.20
37 John Hiller	.20
38 Garry Maddox	.20
39 Pete Broberg	.20
40 Dave Kingman	.75
41 Tippy Martinez (R)	.35
42 Barry Foote	.20
43 Paul Splittorff	.30
44 Doug Rader	.20
45 Boog Powell	.40
46 Los Angeles Dodgers	.65
47 Jesse Jefferson	.20
48 Dave Concepcion	.50

NO. PLAYER	NR. MT.
49 Dave Duncan	.20
50 F. Lynn	2.00
51 Ray Buris	.20
52 Dave Chalk	.20
53 Mike Beard	.20
54 Dave Rader	.20
55 Gaylord Perry	1.50
56 Bob Toaln	.20
57 Phil Garner	.25
58 Ron Reed	.20
59 Larry Hisle	.20
60 Jerry Reuss	.25
61 Ron LeFlore	.25
62 Johnny Oates	.20
63 Bobby Darwin	.20
64 Jerry Koosman	.30
65 Chris Chambliss	.30
66 Father & Son:	.40
Gus Bell,	
Buddy Bell	

NO. PLAYER	NR. MT.
67 Father & Son:	.25
Ray Boone,	
Bob Boone	
68 Father & Son:	.25
Joe Coleman,	
Joe Coleman, Jr.	
69 Father & Son:	.25
Jim Hegan,	
Mike Hegan	
70 Father & Son:	.25
Roy Smalley,	
Roy Smalley Jr.	
71 Steve Rogers	.35
72 Hal McRae	.30
73 Baltimore Orioles	.50
74 Oscar Gamble	.25
75 Larry Dierker	.20
76 Willie Crawford	.20
77 Pedro Borbon	.20
78 Cecil Cooper	1.00
79 Jerry Morales	.20
80 Jim Kaat	.75
81 Darrell Evans	.50
82 Von Joshua	.20
83 Jim Spencer	.20
84 Brent Strom	.20
85 Mickey Rivers	.30
86 Mike Tyson	.20
87 Tom Burgmeier	.20
88 Duffy Dyer	.20
89 Vern Ruhle	.20
90 Sal Bando	.30
91 Tom Hutton	.20
92 Eduardo Rodriguez	.20
93 Mike Phillips	.20
94 Jim Dwyer	.20
95 Brooks Robinson	2.50
96 Doug Bird	.20
97 Wilbur Howard	.20
98 Dennis Eckersley (R)	5.00
99 Lee Lacy	.25
100 Jim Hunter	1.50
101 Pete LaCock	.20
102 Jim Willoughby	.20
103 Biff Pocoroba	.20
104 Cincinnati Reds	.60
105 Gary Lavelle	.20
106 Tom Grieve	.20
107 Dave Roberts	.20
108 Don Kirkwood	.20
109 Larry Lintz	.20
110 Carlos May	.20
111 Danny Thompson	.20
112 Kent Tekulve (R)	.75
113 Gary Sutherland	.20
114 Jay Johnstone	.20
115 Ken Holtzman	.20
116 Charlie Moore	.20
117 Mike Jorgensen	.20
118 Boston Red Sox	.65
119 Checklist No. 1	.75
120 Rusty Staub	.35
121 Tony Solaita	.20
122 Mike Cosgrove	.20
123 Walt Williams	.20
124 Doug Rau	.20
125 Don Baylor	.75
126 Tom Dettore	.20
127 Larvell Blanks	.20
128 Ken Griffey	.40
129 Andy Etchebarren	.20
130 Luis Tiant	.35
131 Bill Stein	.20
132 Don Hood	.20
133 Gary Matthews	.30
134 Mike Ivie	.20
135 Bake McBride	.20
136 Dave Goltz	.20
137 Bill Robinson	.20
138 Lerrin LaGrow	.20
139 Gorman Thomas	.50
140 Vida Blue	.30
141 Larry Parrish (R)	1.50
142 Dick Drago	.20
143 Jerry Grote	.20

NO. PLAYER	NR. MT.
144 Al Fitzmorris	.20
145 Larry Bowa	.50
146 George Medich	.20
147 Houston Astros	.40
148 Stan Thomas	.20
149 Tommy Davis	.30
150 Steve Garvey	4.00
151 Bill Bonham	.20
152 Leroy Stanton	.20
153 Buzz Capra	.20
154 Bucky Dent	.30
155 Jack Billingham	.20
156 Rico Carty	.30
157 Mike Caldwell	.20
158 Ken Reitz	.20
159 Jerry Terrell	.20
160 Dave Winfield	7.50
161 Bruce Kison	.20
162 Jack Pierce	.20
163 Jim Staton	.20
164 Pepe Mangual	.20
165 Gene Tenace	.20
166 Skip Lockwood	.20
167 Freddie Patek	.20
168 Tom Hilgendorf	.20
169 Graig Nettles	1.00
170 Rick Wise	.30
171 Greg Gross	.20
172 Texas Rangers	.50
173 Steve Swisher	.20
174 Charlie Hough	.30
175 Ken Singleton	.30
176 Dick Lange	.20
177 Marty Perez	.20
178 Tom Buskey	.20
179 George Foster	1.00
180 Rich Gossage	1.00
181 Willie Montanez	.20
182 Harry Rasmussen	.20
183 Steve Braun	.20
184 Bill Greif	.20
185 Dave Parker	4.00
186 Tom Walker	.20
187 Pedro Garcia	.20
188 Fred Scherman	.20
189 Claudell Washington	.50
190 Jon Matlack	.25
191 NL Batting Leaders:	.50
Ted Simmons, Bill Madlock,	
Manny Sanguillen	
192 AL Batting Leaders:	1.50
Fred Lynn, Rod Carew,	
Thurman Munson	
193 NL Home Run Leaders:	.60
Mike Schmidt, Greg	
Luzinski, Dave Kingman	
194 AL Home Run Leaders:	.60
John Mayberry, Reggie	
Jackson, George Scott	
195 NL RBI Leaders:	.50
Greg Luzinski, Johnny	
Bench, Tony Perez	
196 AL RBI Leaders:	.40
John Mayberry, George	
Scott, Fred Lynn	
197 NL Stolen Base Leaders:	.60
Dave Lopes, Lou Brock,	
Joe Morgan	
198 AL Stolen Base Leaders:	.30
Mickey Rivers, Claudell	
Washington, Amos Otis	
199 NL Victory Leaders:	.50
Tom Seaver, Randy Jones,	
Andy Messersmith	
200 AL Victory Leaders:	.60
Jim Palmer, Jim Hunter,	
Vida Blue	
201 NL ERA Leaders:	.50
Randy Jones, Andy	
Messersmith, Tom Seaver	
202 AL ERA Leaders:	.50
Jim Hunter, Dennis	
Eckersley, Jim Palmer	
203 NL Strikeout Leaders:	.50
John Montefusco, Andy	
Messersmith, Tom Seaver	

NO. PLAYER	NR. MT.
204 AL Strikeout Leaders:	.50
Frank Tanana, Gaylord	
Perry, Bert Blyleven	
205 Leading Firemen:	.35
Al Hrabosky, Rich Gossage	
206 Manny Trillo	.30
207 Andy Hassler	.20
208 Mike Lum	.20
209 Alan Ashby	.30
210 Lee May	.30
211 Clay Carroll	.20
212 Pat Kelly	.20
213 Dave Heaverlo	.20
214 Eric Soderholm	.20
215 Reggie Smith	.35
216 Montreal Expos	.60
217 Dave Freisleben	.20
218 John Knox	.20
219 Tom Murphy	.20
220 Manny Sanguillen	.30
221 Jim Todd	.20
222 Wayne Garrett	.20
223 Ollie Brown	.20
224 Jim York	.20
225 Roy White	.30
226 Jim Sundberg	.25
227 Oscar Zamora	.20
228 John Hale	.20
229 Jerry Remy (R)	.30
230 Carl Yastrzemski	6.00
231 Tom House	.20
232 Frank Duffy	.20
233 Grant Jackson	.20
234 Mike Sadek	.20
235 Bert Blyleven	.65
236 Kansas City Royals	.40
237 Dave Hamilton	.20
238 Larry Biittner	.20
239 John Curtis	.20
240 Pete Rose	15.00
241 Hector Torres	.20
242 Dan Meyer	.20
243 Jim Rooker	.20
244 Bill Sharp	.20
245 Felix Millan	.20
246 Cesar Tovar	.20
247 Terry Harmon	.20
248 Dick Tidrow	.20
249 Cliff Johnson	.20
250 Fergie Jenkins	.60
251 Rick Monday	.30
252 Tim Nordbrook	.20
253 Bill Buckner	.40
254 Rudy Meoli	.20
255 Fritz Peterson	.20
256 Rowland Office	.20
257 Ross Grimsley	.20
258 Nyls Nyman	.20
259 Darrel Chaney	.20
260 Steve Busby	.30
261 Gary Thomasson	.20
262 Checklist No. 2	.75
263 Lyman Bostock (R)	.50
264 Steve Renko	.20
265 Willie Davis	.30
266 Alan Foster	.20
267 Aurelio Rodriguez	.20
268 Del Unser	.20
269 Rick Austin	.20
270 Willie Stargell	2.50
271 Jim Lonborg	.20
272 Rick Dempsey	.25
273 Joe Niekro	.30
274 Tommy Harper	.20
275 Rick Manning (R)	.30
276 Mickey Scott	.20
277 Chicago Cubs	.50
278 Bernie Carbo	.20
279 Roy Howell	.20
280 Burt Hooton	.30
281 Dave May	.20
282 Dan Osborn	.20
283 Merv Rettenmund	.20
284 Steve Ontiveros	.20
285 Mike Cuellar	.25

NO. PLAYER	NR. MT.
286 Jim Wohlford	.20
287 Pete Mackanin	.20
288 Bill Campbell	.20
289 Enzo Hernandez	.20
290 Ted Simmons	.50
291 Ken Sanders	.20
292 Leon Roberts	.20
293 Bill Castro	.20
294 Ed Kirkpatrick	.20
295 Dave Cash	.20
296 Pat Dobson	.20
297 Roger Metzger	.20
298 Dick Bosman	.20
299 Champ Summers	.20
300 Johnny Bench	7.00
301 Jackie Brown	.20
302 Rick Miller	.20
303 Steve Foucault	.20
304 California Angels	.50
305 Andy Messersmith	.30
306 Rod Gilbreath	.20
307 Al Bumbry	.20
308 Jim Barr	.20
309 Bill Melton	.20
310 Randy Jones	.30
311 Cookie Rojas	.20
312 Don Carrithers	.20
313 Dan Ford (R)	.35
314 Ed Kranepool	.30
315 Al Hrabosky	.20
316 Robin Yount	15.00
317 John Candelaria (R)	2.00
318 Bob Boone	.50
319 Larry Gura	.20
320 Willie Horton	.30
321 Jose Cruz	.40
322 Glenn Abbott	.20
323 Rob Sperring	.20
324 Jim Bibby	.20
325 Tony Perez	.75
326 Dick Pole	.20
327 Dave Moates	.20
328 Carl Morton	.20
329 Joe Ferguson	.20
330 Nolan Ryan	9.00
331 San Diego Padres	.40
332 Charlie Williams	.20
333 Bob Coluccio	.20
334 Dennis Leonard	.25
335 Bob Grich	.25
336 Vic Albury	.20
337 Bud Harrelson	.20
338 Bob Bailey	.20
339 John Denny	.35
340 Jim Rice	8.00
341 All-Time 1B:	2.50
Lou Gehrig	
342 All-Time 2B:	1.00
Rogers Hornsby	
343 All-Time 3B:	.75
Pie Traynor	
344 All-Time SS:	1.00
Honus Wagner	
345 All-Time OF:	5.00
Babe Ruth	
346 All-Time OF:	3.00
Ty Cobb	
347 All-Time OF:	3.00
Ted Williams	
348 All-Time Catcher:	.75
Mickey Cochrane	
349 All-Time Pitcher (Right)	1.00
Walter Johnson	
350 All-Time Pitcher (Left)	.75
Lefty Grove	
351 Randy Hundley	.20
352 Dave Giusti	.20
353 Sixto Lezcano (R)	.40
354 Ron Blomberg	.20
355 Steve Carlton	4.00
356 Ted Martinez	.20
357 Ken Forsch	.20
358 Buddy Bell	.50
359 Rick Reuschel	.50
360 Jeff Burroughs	.20

NO. PLAYER	NR. MT.
361 Detroit Tigers	.60
362 Will McEnaney	.20
363 Dave Collins (R)	.75
364 Elias Sosa	.20
365 Carlton Fisk	1.50
366 Bobby Valentine	.30
367 Bruce Miller	.20
368 Wilbur Wood	.20
369 Frank White	.35
370 Ron Cey	.50
371 Ellie Hendricks	.20
372 Rick Baldwin	.20
373 Johnny Briggs	.20
374 Dan Warthen	.20
375 Ron Fairly	.20
376 Rich Hebner	.20
377 Mike Hegan	.20
378 Steve Stone	.20
379 Ken Boswell	.20
380 Bobby Bonds	.30
381 Denny Doyle	.20
382 Matt Alexander	.20
383 John Ellis	.20
384 Philadelphia Phillies	.60
385 Mickey Lolich	.35
386 Ed Goodson	.20
387 Mike Miley	.20
388 Stan Perzanowski	.20
389 Glenn Adams	.20
390 Don Gullett	.20
391 Jerry Hariston	.20
392 Checklist No. 3	.75
393 Paul Mitchell	.20
394 Fran Healy	.20
395 Jim Wynn	.25
396 Bill Lee	.20
397 Tim Foli	.20
398 Dave Tomlin	.20
399 Luis Melendez	.20
400 Rod Carew	3.50
401 Ken Brett	.20
402 Don Money	.20
403 Geoff Zahn	.20
404 Enos Cabell	.20
405 Rollie Fingers	1.00
406 Ed Herrmann	.20
407 Tom Underwood	.20
408 Charlie Spikes	.20
409 Dave Lemanczyk	.20
410 Ralph Garr	.20
411 Bill Singer	.20
412 Toby Harrah	.30
413 Pete Varney	.20
414 Wayne Garland	.20
415 Vada Pinson	.30
416 Tommy John	.75
417 Gene Clines	.20
418 Jose Morales	.20
419 Reggie Cleveland	.20
420 Joe Morgan	3.00
421 Oakland A's	.40
422 Johnny Grubb	.20
423 Ed Halicki	.20
424 Phil Roof	.20
425 Rennie Stennett	.20
426 Bob Forsch	.30
427 Kurt Bevacqua	.20
428 Jim Crawford	.20
429 Fred Stanley	.20
430 Jose Cardenal	.20
431 Dick Ruthven	.20
432 Tom Veryzer	.20
433 Rick Waits	.20
434 Morris Nettles	.20
435 Phil Niekro	1.50
436 Bill Fahey	.20
437 Terry Forster	.20
438 Doug DeCinces	.60
439 Rick Rhoden	.50
440 John Mayberry	.30
441 Gary Carter	11.00
442 Hank Webb	.20

NO. PLAYER	NR. MT.
443 S.F. Giants	.40
444 Gary Nolan	.20
445 Rico Petrocelli	.20
446 Larry Haney	.20
447 Gene Locklear	.20
448 Tom Johnson	.20
449 Bob Robertson	.20
450 Jim Palmer	3.00
451 Buddy Bradford	.20
452 Tom Hausman	.20
453 Lou Piniella	.35
454 Tom Griffin	.20
455 Dick Allen	.30
456 Joe Coleman	.20
457 Ed Crosby	.20
458 Earl Williams	.20
459 Jim Brewer	.20
460 Cesar Cedeno	.30
461 Championships:	.50
Reds Sweep Bucs,	
Bosox Surprise A's	
462 World Series:	.50
Reds Champs!	
463 Steve Hargan	.20
464 Ken Henderson	.20
465 Mike Marshall	.30
466 Bob Stinson	.20
467 Woodie Fryman	.20
468 Jesus Alou	.20
469 Rawly Eastwick	.20
470 Bobby Murcer	.40
471 Jim Burton	.20
472 Bob Davis	.20
473 Paul Blair	.20
474 Ray Corbin	.20
475 Joe Rudi	.30
476 Bob Moose	.20
477 Cleveland Indians	.40
478 Lynn McGlothen	.20
479 Bobby Mitchell	.20
480 Mike Schmidt	17.50
481 Rudy May	.20
482 Tim Hosley	.20
483 Mickey Stanley	.20
484 Eric Raich	.20
485 Mike Hargrove	.20
486 Bruce Dal Canton	.20
487 Leron Lee	.20
488 Claude Osteen	.20
489 Skip Jutze	.20
490 Frank Tanana	.30
491 Terry Crowley	.20
492 Marty Pattin	.20
493 Derrel Thomas	.20
494 Craig Swan	.20
495 Nate Colbert	.20
496 Juan Beniquez	.20
497 Joe McIntosh	.20
498 Glenn Borgmann	.20
499 Mario Guerrero	.20
500 Reggie Jackson	8.00
501 Billy Champion	.20
502 Tim McCarver	.40
503 Elliott Maddox	.20
504 Pittsburgh Pirates	.40
505 Mark Belanger	.30
506 George Mitterwald	.20
507 Ray Bare	.20
508 Duane Kuiper	.20
509 Bill Hands	.20
510 Amos Otis	.30
511 Jamie Easterley	.20
512 Ellie Rodriguez	.20
513 Bart Johnson	.20
514 Dan Driessen	.25
515 Steve Yeager	.20
516 Wayne Granger	.20
517 John Milner	.20
518 Doug Flynn	.20
519 Steve Brye	.20
520 Willie McCovey	2.50

NO. PLAYER	NR. MT.
521 Jim Colborn	.20
522 Ted Sizemore	.20
523 Bob Montgomery	.20
524 Pete Falcone	.20
525 Billy Williams	1.50
526 Checklist No. 4	.75
527 Mike Anderson	.20
528 Dock Ellis	.20
529 Deron Johnson	.20
530 Don Sutton	1.50
531 New York Mets	.75
532 Milt May	.20
533 Lee Richard	.20
534 Stan Bahnsen	.20
535 Dave Nelson	.20
536 Mike Thompson	.20
537 Tony Muser	.20
538 Pat Darcy	.20
539 John Balaz	.20
540 Bill Freehan	.30
541 Steve Mingori	.20
542 Keith Hernandez	6.00
543 Wayne Twitchell	.20
544 Pepe Frias	.20
545 Sparky Lyle	.30
546 Dave Rosello	.20
547 Roric Harrison	.20
548 Manny Mota	.30
549 Randy Tate	.20
550 Hank Aaron	9.00
551 Jerry DaVanon	.20
552 Terry Humphrey	.20
553 Randy Moffitt	.20
554 Ray Fosse	.20
555 Dyar Miller	.20
556 Minnesota Twins	.50
557 Dan Spillner	.20
558 Clarence Gaston	.20
559 Clyde Wright	.20
560 Jorge Orta	.20
561 Tom Carroll	.20
562 Adrian Garrett	.20
563 Larry Demery	.20
564 Gum Blowing Champ:	.30
Kurt Bevacqua	
565 Tug McGraw	.40
566 Ken McMullen	.20
567 George Stone	.20
568 Rob Andrews	.20
569 Nelson Briles	.20
570 George Hendrick	.30
571 Don DeMola	.20
572 Rich Coggins	.20
573 Bill Travers	.20
574 Don Kessinger	.20
575 Dwight Evans	1.75
576 Maximino Leon	.20
577 Marc Hill	.20
578 Ted Kubiak	.20
579 Clay Kirby	.20
580 Bert Campaneris	.30
581 St. Louis Cardinals	.60
582 Mike Kekich	.20
583 Tommy Helms	.20
584 Stan Wall	.20
585 Joe Torre	.35
586 Ron Schueler	.20
587 Leo Cardenas	.20
588 Kevin Kobel	.20
589 Rookie Pitchers:	2.00
Joe Pactwa, Santo Alcala,	
Mike Flanagan, P. Torrealba	
590 Rookie Outfielders:	1.25
Henry Cruz, Ellis Valentine,	
Chet Lemon, T. Whitfield	
591 Rookie Pitchers:	.30
Steve Grilli, C. Mitchell,	
Jose Sosa, George Throop	
592 Rookie Infielders:	4.50
W. Randolph, D. McKay,	
J. Royster, R. Staiger	

NO. PLAYER	NR. MT.
593 Rookie Pitchers:	.40
Larry Anderson, M. Littell,	
Butch Metzger, Ken Crosby	
594 Rookie Catchers & OF's	.40
Andy Merchant, Ed Ott,	
R. Stillman, Jerry White	
595 Rookie Pitchers:	.40
Art DeFillipis, R. Lerch,	
Sid Monge, Steve Barr	
596 Rookie Infielders:	.50
C. Reynolds, L. Johnson,	
J. LeMaster, J. Manuel	
597 RooKie Pitchers:	.60
D. Aase, Jack Kucek,	
Frank LaCorte, Mike Pazik	
598 Rookie Outfielders:	.40
Hector Cruz, J. Quirk,	
Jerry Turner, Joe Wallis	
599 Rookie Pitchers:	12.00
Rob Dressler, Ron Guidry,	
Bob McClure, Pat Zachry	
600 Tom Seaver	5.00
601 Ken Rudolph	.20
602 Doug Konieczny	.20
603 Jim Holt	.20
604 Joe Lovitto	.20
605 Al Downing	.30
606 Milwaukee Brewers	.40
607 Rich Hinton	.20
608 Vic Correll	.20
609 Fred Norman	.20
610 Greg Luzinski	.50
611 Rich Folkers	.20
612 Joe Lahoud	.20
613 Tim Johnson	.20
614 Fernando Arroyo	.20
615 Mike Cubbage	.20
616 Buck Martinez	.20
617 Darold Knowles	.20
618 Jack Brohamer	.20
619 Bill Butler	.20
620 Al Oliver	.50
621 Tom Hall	.20
622 Rick Auerbach	.20
623 Bob Allietta	.20
624 Tony Taylor	.20
625 J.R. Richard	.25
626 Bob Sheldon	.20
627 Bill Plummer	.20
628 John D'Acquisto	.20
629 Sandy Alomar	.20
630 Chris Speier	.20
631 Atlanta Braves	.40
632 Rogelio Moret	.20
633 John Stearns (R)	.25
634 Larry Christenson	.20
635 Jim Fregosi	.25
636 Joe Decker	.20
637 Bruce Bochte	.20
638 Doyle Alexander	.20
639 Fred Kendall	.20
640 Bill Madlock	1.00
641 Tom Paciorek	.20
642 Dennis Blair	.20
643 Checklist No. 5	.75
644 Tom Bradley	.20
645 Darrell Porter	.20
646 John Lowenstein	.20
647 Ramon Hernandez	.20
648 Al Cowens	.20
649 Dave Roberts	.20
650 Thurman Munson	4.00
651 John Odom	.20
652 Ed Armbrister	.20
653 Mike Norris (R)	.25
654 Doug Griffin	.20
655 Mike Vail	.20
656 Chicago White Sox	.40
657 Roy Smalley (R)	.40
658 Jerry Johnson	.20
659 Ben Oglivie	.30
660 D. Lopes (Exc. .15)	.75

1976 Topps Traded.... Complete Set of 44 Cards—Value $7.50

This set features players who were traded after the regular 1976 set was printed. The card numbers are the same as the main set, with the addition of "T" after the number.

NO. PLAYER	NR. MT.	NO. PLAYER	NR. MT.	NO. PLAYER	NR. MT.	NO. PLAYER	NR. MT.
27 T Ed Figueroa	.15	146 T George Medich	.15	380 T Bobby Bonds	.25	527 T Mike Anderson	.15
28 T Dusty Baker	.35	158 T Ken Reitz	.15	383 T John Ellis	.15	528 T Dock Ellis	.15
44 T Doug Rader	.20	208 T Mike Lum	.15	385 T Mickey Lolich	.35	532 T Milt May	.15
58 T Ron Reed	.20	211 T Clay Carroll	.15	401 T Ken Brett	.20	554 T Ray Fosse	.15
74 T Oscar Gamble	.25	231 T Tom House	.15	410 T Ken Brett	.20	579 T Clay Kirby	.15
80 T Jim Kaat	.50	250 T Fergie Jenkins	.60	411 T Bill Singer	.15	583 T Tommy Helms	.15
83 T Jim Spencer	.15	259 T Darrel Chaney	.15	428 T Jim Crawford	.15	592 T Willie Randolph	.75
85 T Mickey Rivers	.25	292 T Leon Roberts	.15	434 T Morris Nettles	.15	618 T Jack Brohamer	.15
99 T Lee Lacy	.25	296 T Pat Dobson	.15	464 T Ken Henderson	.15	632 T Rogelio Moret	.15
120 T Rusty Staub	.75	309 T Bill Melton	.15	497 T Joe McIntosh	.15	649 T Dave Roberts	.15
127 T Larvell Blanks	.15	338 T Bob Bailey	.15	524 T Pete Falcone	.15	— Checklist	.60

1977 Topps.... Complete Set of 660 Cards—Value $300.00

Dale Murphy, Tony Armas, and Andre Dawson's rookie cards are in this set. There is an error on card 634—the photos are switched.

    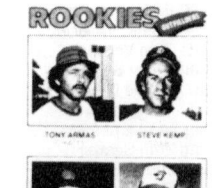

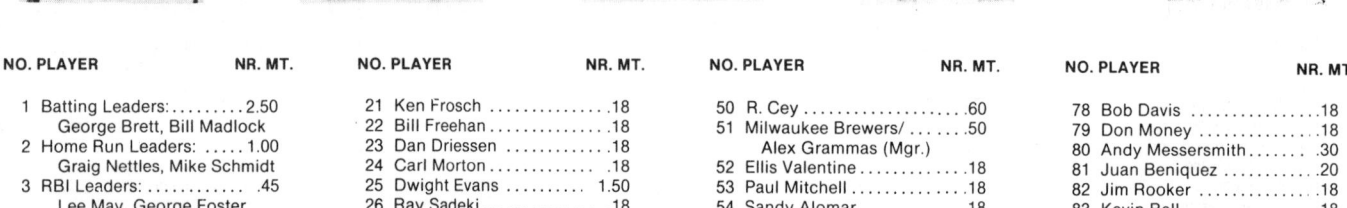

NO. PLAYER	NR. MT.	NO. PLAYER	NR. MT.	NO. PLAYER	NR. MT.	NO. PLAYER	NR. MT.
1 Batting Leaders:	2.50	21 Ken Frosch	.18	50 R. Cey	.60	78 Bob Davis	.18
George Brett, Bill Madlock		22 Bill Freehan	.18	51 Milwaukee Brewers/	.50	79 Don Money	.18
2 Home Run Leaders:	1.00	23 Dan Driessen	.18	Alex Grammas (Mgr.)		80 Andy Messersmith	.30
Graig Nettles, Mike Schmidt		24 Carl Morton	.18	52 Ellis Valentine	.18	81 Juan Beniquez	.20
3 RBI Leaders:	.45	25 Dwight Evans	1.50	53 Paul Mitchell	.18	82 Jim Rooker	.18
Lee May, George Foster		26 Ray Sadeki	.18	54 Sandy Alomar	.18	83 Kevin Bell	.18
4 Stolen Base Leaders:	.35	27 Bill Buckner	.40	55 Jeff Burroughs	.25	84 Ollie Brown	.18
B. North, Dave Lopes		28 Woodie Fryman	.18	56 Rudy May	.18	85 Duane Kuiper	.18
5 Victory Leaders:	.60	29 Bucky Dent	.25	57 Marc Hill	.18	86 Pat Zachry	.18
Jim Palmer, Randy Jones		30 Greg Luzinski	.35	58 Chet Lemon	.40	87 Glenn Borgmann	.18
6 Strikeout Leaders:	2.00	31 Jim Todd	.18	59 Larry Christenson	.18	88 Stan Wall	.18
Nolan Ryan, Tom Seaver		32 Checklist No. 1	.75	60 Jim Rice	6.00	89 Butch Hobson	.18
7 ERA Leaders:	.35	33 Wayne Garland	.18	61 Manny Sanguillen	.18	90 Cesar Cedeno	.35
Mark Fidrych, J. Denny		34 Angels/Norm Sherry (Mgr.)	.50	62 Eric Raich	.18	91 John Verhoeven	.18
8 Leading Firemen:	.30	35 Rennie Stennett	.18	63 Tito Fuentes	.18	92 Dave Rosello	.18
B. Campbell, R. Eastwick		36 John Ellis	.18	64 Larry Biittner	.18	93 Tom Poquette	.18
9 Doug Rader	.18	37 Steve Hargan	.18	65 Skip Lockwood	.18	94 Craig Swan	.18
10 Reggie Jackson	8.00	38 Craig Kusick	.18	66 Roy Smalley	.18	95 Keith Hernandez	3.00
11 Rob Dressler	.18	39 Tom Griffin	.18	67 Joaquin Andujar (R)	1.00	96 Lou Piniella	.45
12 Larry Haney	.18	40 Bobby Murcer	.50	68 Bruce Bochte	.18	97 Dave Heaverlo	.18
13 Luis Gomez	.18	41 Jim Kern	.18	69 Jim Crawford	.18	98 Milt May	.18
14 Tommy Smith	.18	42 Jose Cruz	.40	70 Johnny Bench	5.00	99 Tom Hausman	.18
15 Don Gullett	.18	43 Ray Bare	.18	71 Dock Ellis	.18	100 Joe Morgan	1.50
16 Bob Jones	.18	44 Bud Harrelson	.18	72 Mike Anderson	.18	101 Dick Bosman	.18
17 Steve Stone	.18	45 Rawly Eastwick	.18	73 Charlie Williams	.18	102 Jose Morales	.18
18 Cleveland Indians/	.60	46 Buck Martinez	.18	74 A's/J. McKeon (Mgr.)	.50	103 Mike Bacsik	.18
Frank Robinson (Mgr.)		47 Lynn McGlothen	.18	75 Dennis Leonard	.18	104 Omar Moreno (R)	.40
19 John D'Acquisto	.18	48 Tom Paciorek	.18	76 Tim Foli	.18	105 Steve Yeager	.18
20 Graig Nettles	.75	49 Grant Jackson	.18	77 Dyar Miller	.18	106 Mike Flanagan	.40

NO. PLAYER	NR. MT.
107 Bill Melton	.18
108 Alan Foster	.18
109 Jorge Orta	.18
110 Steve Carlton	4.00
111 Rico Petrocelli	.25
112 Bill Greif	.18
113 Toronto Blue Jays/ Roy Hartsfield (Mgr.)	.50
114 Bruce Dal Canton	.18
115 Rick Manning	.18
116 Joe Niekro	.40
117 Frank White	.40
118 Rick Jone	.18
119 John Stearns	.18
120 Rod Carew	3.50
121 Gary Nolan	.18
122 Ben Oglivie	.25
123 Fred Stanley	.18
124 George Mitterwald	.18
125 Bill Travers	.18
126 Rod Gilbreath	.18
127 Ron Fairly	.18
128 Tommy John	1.00
129 Mike Sadek	.18
130 Al Oliver	.50
131 Orlando Ramirez	.18
132 Chip Lang	.18
133 Ralph Garr	.18
134 San Diego Padres/ John McNamara (Mgr.)	.50
135 Mark Belanger	.30
136 Jerry Mumphrey (R)	.50
137 Jeff Terpko	.18
138 Bob Stinson	.18
139 Fred Norman	.18
140 Mike Schmidt	12.50
141 Mark Littell	.18
142 Steve Dillard	.18
143 Ed Herrmann	.18
144 Bruce Sutter (R)	3.00
145 Tom Veryzer	.18
146 Dusty Baker	.40
147 Jackie Brown	.18
148 Fran Healy	.18
149 Mike Cubbage	.18
150 Tom Seaver	4.00
151 Johnnie LeMaster	.18
152 Gaylord Perry	1.50
153 Ron Jackson	.18
154 Dave Guisti	.18
155 Joe Rudi	.25
156 Pete Mackanin	.18
157 Ken Brett	.18
158 Ted Kubiak	.18
159 Bernie Carbo	.18
160 Will McEnaney	.18
161 Garry Templeton (R)	1.25
162 Mike Cuellar	.25
163 Dave Hilton	.18
164 Tug McGraw	.35
165 Jim Wynn	.18
166 Bill Campbell	.18
167 Rich Hebner	.18
168 Charlie Spikes	.18
169 Darold Knowles	.18
170 Thurman Munson	3.00
171 Ken Sanders	.18
172 John Milner	.18
173 Chuck Scrivener	.18
174 Nelson Briles	.18
175 Butch Wynegar (R)	.75
176 Bob Robertson	.18
177 Bart Johnson	.18
178 Bombo Rivera	.18
179 Paul Hartzell	.18
180 Dave Lopes	.35
181 Ken McMullen	.18
182 Dan Spillner	.18
183 Cardinals/V. Rapp (Mgr.)	.50
184 Bo McLaughlin	.18
185 Sixto Lezcano	.18
186 Doug Flynn	.18
187 Dick Pole	.18
188 Bob Tolan	.18
189 Rick Dempsey	.20

NO. PLAYER	NR. MT.
190 Ray Burris	.18
191 Doug Griffin	.18
192 Clarence Gaston	.18
193 Larry Gura	.18
194 Gary Matthews	.35
195 Ed Figueroa	.18
196 Len Randle	.18
197 Ed Ott	.18
198 Wilbur Wood	.18
199 Pepe Frias	.18
200 Frank Tanana	.25
201 Ed Kranepool	.30
202 Tom Johnson	.18
203 Ed Armbrister	.18
204 Jeff Newman	.18
205 Pete Falcone	.18
206 Boog Powell	.40
207 Glenn Abbott	.18
208 Checklist No. 2	.75
209 Rob Andrews	.18
210 Fred Lynn	1.50
211 San Francisco Giants/ Joe Altobelli (Mgr.)	.50
212 Jim Mason	.18
213 Maximino Leon	.18
214 Darrell Porter	.30
215 Butch Metzger	.30
216 Doug DeCinces	.50
217 Tom Underwood	.18
218 John Wathan	1.25
219 Joe Coleman	.18
220 Chris Chambliss	.25
221 Bob Bailey	.18
222 Francisco Barrios	.18
223 Earl Williams	.18
224 Rusty Torres	.18
225 Bob Apodaca	.18
226 Leroy Stanton	.18
227 Joe Sambito	.40
228 Minnesota Twins/ Gene Mauch (Mgr.)	.50
229 Don Kessinger	.18
230 Vida Blue	.35
231 Record—Brett Most Consecutive Games with 3 or More Hits	1.75
232 Record—Minoso Oldest Player to Hit Safely	.35
233 Record—Morales Most Pinch-Hits for Season	.30
234 Record—Ryan Most Seasons 300 SO's	2.00
235 Cecil Cooper	.60
236 Tim Buskey	.18
237 Gene Clines	.18
238 Tippy Martinez	.18
239 Bill Plummer	.18
240 Ron LeFlore	.20
241 Dave Tomlin	.18
242 Ken Henderson	.18
243 Ron Reed	.18
244 John Mayberry	.35
245 Rick Rhoden	.30
246 Mike Vail	.18
247 Chris Knapp	.18
248 Wilbur Howard	.18
249 Pete Redfern	.18
250 Bill Madlock	.50
251 Tony Muser	.18
252 Dale Murray	.18
253 John Hale	.18
254 Doyle Alexander	.18
255 George Scott	.18
256 Joe Hoerner	.18
257 Mike Miley	.18
258 Luis Tiant	.20
259 Mets/J. Frazier (Mgr.)	.60
260 J.R. Richard	.25
261 Phil Garner	.25
262 Al Cowens	.25
263 Mike Marshall	.25
264 Tom Hutton	.18
265 Mark Fidrych (R)	.50
266 Derrel Thomas	.18
267 Ray Fosse	.18

NO. PLAYER	NR. MT.
268 Rick Sawyer	.18
269 Joe Lis	.18
270 Dave Parker	2.50
271 Terry Forster	.25
272 Lee Lacy	.20
273 Eric Soderholm	.18
274 Don Stanhouse	.18
275 Mike Hargorve	.18
276 A.L. Championship: Chambliss' Homer	.50
277 N.L. Championship: Reds Sweep Phillies in 3	.60
278 Danny Frisella	.18
279 Joe Wallis	.18
280 Jim Hunter	2.00
281 Roy Staiger	.18
282 Sid Monge	.18
283 Jerry DaVanon	.18
284 Mike Norris	.18
285 Brooks Robinson	3.00
286 Johnny Grubb	.18
287 Cincinnati Reds/ Sparky Anderson (Mgr.)	.50
288 Bob Montgomery	.18
289 Gene Garber	.18
290 Amos Otis	.35
291 Jason Thompson (R)	.60
292 Rogelio Moret	.18
293 Jack Brohamer	.18
294 George Medich	.18
295 Gary Carter	6.00
296 Don Hood	.18
297 Ken Reitz	.18
298 Charlie Hough	.18
299 Otto Velez	.18
300 Jerry Koosman	.40
301 Toby Harrah	.20
302 Mike Garman	.18
303 Gene Tenace	.18
304 Jim Hughes	.18
305 Mickey Rivers	.30
306 Rick Waits	.18
307 Gary Sutherland	.18
308 Gene Pentz	.18
309 Boston Red Sox/ Don Zimmer (Mgr.)	.50
310 Larry Bowa	.30
311 Vern Ruhle	.18
312 Rob Belloir	.18
313 Paul Blair	.18
314 Steve Mingori	.18
315 Dave Chalk	.18
316 Steve Rogers	.25
317 Kurt Bevacqua	.18
318 Duffy Dyer	.18
319 Rich Gossage	.75
320 Ken Griffey	.30
321 Dave Goltz	.18
322 Bill Russell	.18
323 Larry Lintz	.18
324 John Curtis	.18
325 Mike Ivie	.18
326 Jesse Jefferson	.18
327 Astros/B. Virdon (Mgr.)	.50
328 Tommy Boggs	.18
329 Ron Hodges	.18
330 George Hendrick	.35
331 Jim Colborn	.18
332 Elliott Maddox	.18
333 Paul Reuschel	.18
334 Bill Stein	.18
335 Bill Robinson	.18
336 Denny Doyle	.18
337 Ron Schueler	.18
338 Dave Duncan	.18
339 Adrian Devine	.18
340 Hal McRae	.25
341 Joe Kerrigan	.18
342 Jerry Remy	.18
343 Ed Halicki	.18
344 Brian Downing	.18
345 Reggie Smith	.30
346 Bill Singer	.18
347 George Foster	1.25
348 Brent Strom	.18

NO. PLAYER	NR. MT.
349 Jim Holt	.18
350 Larry Dierker	.18
351 Jim Sundberg	.18
352 Mike Phillips	.18
353 Stan Thomas	.18
354 Pirates/C. Tanner (Mgr.)	.50
355 Lou Brock	1.75
356 Checklist No. 3	.75
357 Tim McCarver	.45
358 Tom House	.18
359 Willie Randolph	.75
360 Rick Monday	.25
361 Eduardo Rodriguez	.18
362 Tommy Davis	.18
363 Dave Roberts	.18
364 Vic Correll	.18
365 Mike Torrez	.18
366 Ted Sizemore	.18
367 Dave Hamilton	.18
368 Mike Jorgensen	.18
369 Terry Humphrey	.18
370 John Montefusco	.18
371 Royals/W. Herzog (Mgr.)	.50
372 Rich Folkers	.18
373 Bert Campaneris	.25
374 Kent Tekulve	.20
375 Larry Hisle	.20
376 Nino Espinosa	.18
377 Dave McKay	.18
378 Jim Umbarger	.18
379 Larry Cox	.18
380 Lee May	.25
381 Bob Forsch	.25
382 Charlie Moore	.18
383 Stan Bahnsen	.18
384 Darrel Chaney	.18
385 Dave LaRoche	.18
386 Manny Mota	.30
387 New York Yankees/ Billy Martin (Mgr.)	.75
388 Terry Harmon	.30
389 Ken Kravec	.30
390 Dave Winfield	4.00
391 Dan Warthen	.18
392 Phil Roof	.18
393 John Lowenstein	.18
394 Bill Laxton	.18
395 Manny Trillo	.25
396 Tom Murphy	.18
397 Larry Herndon (R)	.50
398 Tom Burgmeier	.18
399 Bruce Boisclair	.18
400 Steve Garvey	3.00
401 Mickey Scott	.18
402 Tommy Helms	.18
403 Tom Grieve	.18
404 Eric Rasmussen	.18
405 Claudell Washington	.25
406 Tim Johnson	.18
407 Dave Freisleben	.18
408 Cesar Tovar	.18
409 Pete Broberg	.18
410 Willie Montanez	.18
411 World Series Morgan Homers, Bench Stars for Reds	.60
412 World Series # 1 & 2 Reds' Defense, Bench's Two Homers	.60
413 World Series # 3 & 4 Cincy Wins	.60
414 Tommy Harper	.18
415 Jay Johnstone	.18
416 Chuck Hartenstein	.18
417 Wayne Garrett	.18
418 Chicago White Sox/ Bob Lemon (Mgr.)	.50
419 Steve Swisher	.18
420 Rusty Staub	.35
421 Doug Rau	.18
422 Freddie Patek	.18
423 Gary Lavelle	.18
424 Steve Brye	.18
425 Joe Torre	.35
426 Dick Drago	.18

NO.	PLAYER	NR. MT.
427	Dave Rader	.18
428	Texas Rangers/	.50
	Frank Lucchesi (Mgr.)	
429	Ken Boswell	.18
430	Fergie Jenkins	.65
431	Dave Collins	.30
	(photo of Bobby Jones)	
432	Buzz Capra	.18
433	Turn Back Clock (1972)	.30
	Colbert Hits 5 Homers	
434	Turn Back Clock (1967)	2.00
	Yaz Wins Triple Crown	
435	Turn Back Clock (1962)	.60
	Wills 104 Steals	
436	Turn Back Clock (1957)	.30
	Keegan No-Hitter	
437	Turn Back Clock (1952)	.60
	Kiner Leads NL	
438	Marty Perez	.18
439	Gorman Thomas	.50
440	Jon Matlack	.18
441	Larvell Blanks	.18
442	Atlanta Braves/	.50
	Dave Bristol (Mgr.)	
443	Lamar Johnson	.18
444	Wayne Twitchell	.18
445	Ken Singleton	.40
446	Bill Bonham	.18
447	Jerry Turner	.18
448	Ellie Rodriguez	.18
449	Al Fitzmorris	.18
450	Pete Rose	7.50
451	Checklist No. 4	.75
452	Mike Caldwell	.18
453	Pedro Garcia	.18
454	Andy Etchebarren	.18
455	Rick Wise	.18
456	Leon Roberts	.18
457	Steve Luebber	.18
458	Leo Foster	.18
459	Steve Foucault	.18
460	Willie Stargell	2.50
461	Dick Tidrow	.18
462	Don Baylor	.60
463	Jamie Quirk	.18
464	Randy Moffitt	.18
465	Rico Carty	.35
466	Fred Holdsworth	.18
467	Philadelphia Phillies/	.50
	Danny Ozark (Mgr.)	
468	Ramon Hernandez	.18
469	Pat Kelly	.18
470	Ted Simmons	.60
471	Del Unser	.18
472	Rookie Pitchers:	.50
	Bob McClure, Don Aase,	
	Gil Patterson, Dave	
	Wehrmeister	
473	Rookie Outfielders:	30.00
	Gene Richards, John Scott,	
	D. Walling, A. Dawson	
474	Rookie Shortstops:	.40
	Bob Bailor, Kiko Garcia,	
	C. Reynolds, A. Taveras	
475	Rookie Pitchers:	.50
	Chris Batton, Rick Camp	
	S. McGregor, M. Sarmiento	
476	Rookie Catchers:	55.00
	Dale Murphy, Rick Cerone,	
	G. Alexander, K. Pasley	
477	Rookie Infielders:	.40
	R. Dauer, O. Gonzalez,	
	D. Ault, P. Mankowski	

NO.	PLAYER	NR. MT.
478	Rookie Pitchers:	.40
	Leon Hooten, Jim Gideon,	
	Mark Lemongello,	
	Dave Johnson,	
479	Rookie Outfielders:	.40
	A. Woods, Wayne Gross,	
	B. Asselstine, S. Mejias	
480	Carl Yastrzemski	4.00
481	Roger Metzger	.18
482	Tony Solaita	.18
483	Richie Zisk	.30
484	Burt Hooton	.30
485	Roy White	.30
486	Ed Bane	.18
487	Rookie Pitchers:	.35
	Joe Henderson, Ed Glynn,	
	L. Anderson, G. Terlecky	
488	Rookie Outfielders:	20.00
	Lee Mazzilli, Jack Clark,	
	R. Jones, D. Thomas	
489	Rookie Pitchers:	.50
	Len Barker, Randy Lerch,	
	Greg Minton, Mike Overy	
490	Rookie Shortstops:	.40
	T. McMillan, B. Almon,	
	M. Klutts, M. Wagner	
491	Rookie Pitchers:	1.50
	Mike Dupree, Bob Sykes,	
	D. Martinez, C. Mitchell	
492	Rookie Outfielders:	1.25
	Tony Armas, Steve Kemp,	
	C. Lopez, Gary Woods	
493	Rookie Pitchers:	1.00
	G. Wheelock, M. Krukow,	
	Jim Otten, Mike Willis	
494	Rookie Infielders:	.60
	Juan Bernhardt, J. Gantner,	
	M. Champion, B. Wills	
495	Al Hrabosky	.18
496	Gary Thomasson	.18
497	Clay Carroll	.18
498	Sal Bando	.30
499	Pablo Torealba	.18
500	Dave Kingman	.50
501	Jim Bibby	.18
502	Randy Hundley	.18
503	Bill Lee	.18
504	Los Angeles Dodgers/	.60
	Tom Lasorda (Mgr.)	
505	Oscar Gamble	.25
506	Steve Grilli	.18
507	Mike Hegan	.18
508	Dave Pagan	.18
509	Cookie Rojas	.18
510	John Candelaria	.50
511	Bill Fahey	.18
512	Jack Billingham	.18
513	Jerry Terrell	.18
514	Cliff Johnson	.18
515	Chris Speier	.18
516	Bake McBride	.20
517	Pete Vuckovich (R)	.50
518	Chicago Cubs/	.50
	Herman Franks (Mgr.)	
519	Don Kirkwood	.18
520	Garry Maddox	.20
521	Bob Grich	.25
522	Enzo Hernandez	.18
523	Rollie Fingers	.75
524	Rowland Office	.12
525	Dennis Eckersley	.75
526	Larry Parrish	.30

NO.	PLAYER	NR. MT.
527	Dan Meyer	.18
528	Bill Castro	.18
529	Jim Essian	.18
530	Rick Reuschel	.50
531	Lyman Bostock	.30
532	Jim Willoughby	.18
533	Mickey Stanley	.18
534	Paul Splittorff	.18
535	Cesar Geronimo	.18
536	Vic Albury	.18
537	Dave Roberts	.18
538	Frank Taveras	.18
539	Mike Wallace	.18
540	Bob Watson	.25
541	John Denny	.30
542	Frank Duffy	.18
543	Ron Blomberg	.18
544	Gary Ross	.18
545	Bob Boone	.35
546	Baltimore Orioles/	.50
	Earl Weaver (Mgr.)	
547	Willie McCovey	2.50
548	Joel Youngblood	.18
549	Jerry Royster	.18
550	Randy Jones	.18
551	Bill North	.18
552	Pepe Mangual	.18
553	Jack Heidemann	.18
554	Bruce Kimm	.18
555	Dan Ford	.18
556	Doug Bird	.18
557	Jerry White	.18
558	Elias Sosa	.18
559	Alan Bannister	.18
560	Dave Concepcion	.50
561	Pete LaCock	.18
562	Checklist No. 5	.75
563	Bruce Kison	.18
564	Alan Ashby	.20
565	Mickey Lolich	.25
566	Rick Miller	.18
567	Enos Cabell	.18
568	Carlos May	.18
569	Jim Lonborg	.18
570	Bobby Bonds	.30
571	Darrell Evans	.35
572	Ross Grimsley	.18
573	Joe Ferguson	.18
574	Aurelio Rodriguez	.18
575	Dick Ruthven	.18
576	Fred Kendall	.18
577	Jerry Augustine	.18
578	Bob Randall	.18
579	Don Carrithers	.18
580	George Brett	7.50
581	Pedro Borbon	.18
582	Ed Kirkpatrick	.18
583	Paul Lindblad	.18
584	Ed Goodson	.18
585	Rick Burleson	.18
586	Steve Renko	.18
587	Rick Baldwin	.18
588	Dave Moates	.18
589	Mike Cosgrove	.18
590	Buddy Bell	.40
591	Chris Arnold	.18
592	Dan Briggs	.18
593	Dennis Blair	.18
594	Biff Pocoroba	.18
595	John Hiller	.18
596	Jerry Martin	.18

NO.	PLAYER	NR. MT.
597	Seattle Mariners/	.35
	Darrell Johnson (Mgr.)	
598	Sparky Lyle	.40
599	Mike Tyson	.18
600	Jim Palmer	2.00
601	Mike Lum	.18
602	Andy Hassler	.18
603	Willie Davis	.18
604	Jim Slaton	.18
605	Felix Millan	.18
606	Steve Braun	.18
607	Larry Demery	.18
608	Roy Howell	.18
609	Jim Barr	.18
610	Jose Cardenal	.18
611	Dave Lemanczyk	.18
612	Barry Foote	.18
613	Reggie Cleveland	.18
614	Greg Gross	.18
615	Phil Niekro	1.50
616	Tommy Sandt	.18
617	Bobby Darwin	.18
618	Pat Dobson	.18
619	Johnny Oates	.18
620	Don Sutton	1.25
621	Detroit Tigers/	.50
	Ralph Houk (Mgr.)	
622	Jim Wohlford	.18
623	Jack Kucek	.18
624	Hector Cruz	.18
625	Ken Holtzman	.18
626	Al Bumbry	.18
627	Bob Myrick	.18
628	Mario Guerrero	.18
629	Bobby Valentine	.30
630	Bert Blyleven	.60
631	Big League Brothers:	1.25
	George Brett, Ken Brett	
632	Big League Brothers:	.30
	Ken Forsch, Bob Forsch	
633	Big League Brothers:	.30
	Lee May, Carlos May	
634	Big League Brothers:	.30
	Paul Reuschel, Rick	
	Reuschel (photos switched)	
635	Robin Yount	7.00
636	Santo Alcala	.18
637	Alex Johnson	.18
638	Jim Kaat	.50
639	Jerry Morales	.18
640	Carlton Fisk	1.25
641	Dan Larson	.18
642	Willie Crawford	.18
643	Mike Pazik	.18
644	Matt Alexander	.18
645	Jerry Reuss	.20
646	Andres Mora	.18
647	Montreal Expos/	.40
	Dick Williams (Mgr.)	
648	Jim Spencer	.18
649	Dave Cash	.18
650	Nolan Ryan	7.50
651	Von Joshua	.18
652	Tom Walker	.18
653	Diego Segui	.18
654	Ron Pruitt	.18
655	Tony Perez	.75
656	Ron Guidry	2.50
657	Mick Kelleher	.18
658	Marty Pattin	.18
659	Merv Rettenmund	.18
660	W. Horton (Exc. .12)	.50

1978 Topps.... Complete Set of 726 Cards—Value $225.00

After five consecutive years of issuing sets of 660 cards, Topps increased the size of its main set to 726 cards. 66 cards were double printed. Eddie Murray, Paul Molitor, and Lou Whitaker's rookie cards are in this set.

NO.	PLAYER	NR. MT.
1	Record — L. Brock	2.00
	Most Career Steals	
2	Record — S. Lyle	.25
	Most Career Relief	
3	Record — W. McCovey	.75
	Most 2 HR's in Inning	
4	Record — B. Robinson	.75
	Most Seasons — Same Club	
5	Record — P. Rose	1.75
	Most Hits — Switch Hitter	
6	Record — N. Ryan	2.50
	Games 10 or More SO's	
7	Record — R. Jackson	2.00
	Most Homers — W. Series	
8	Mike Sadek	.15
9	Doug DeCinces	.30
10	Phil Niekro	1.25
11	Rick Manning	.15
12	Don Aase	.25
13	Art Howe	.15
14	Lerrin LaGrow	.15
15	Tony Perez	.25
16	Roy White	.25
17	Mike Krukow	.30
18	Bob Grich	.25
19	Darrell Porter	.25
20	Pete Rose	3.50
21	Steve Kemp	.30
22	Charlie Hough	.15
23	Bump Wills	.15
24	Don Money	.15
25	Jon Motlack	.15
26	Rich Hebner	.15
27	Geoff Zahn	.15
28	Ed Ott	.15
29	Bob Lacey	.15
30	George Hendrick	.25
31	Glenn Abbott	.15
32	Garry Templeton	.30
33	Dave Lemanczyk	.15
34	Willie McCovey	2.00
35	Sparky Lyle	.25
36	Eddie Murray (R)	32.00
37	Rick Waits	.15
38	Willie Montanez	.15
39	Floyd Bannister (R)	1.00
40	Carl Yastrzemski	3.00
41	Burt Hooton	.15
42	Jorge Orta	.15
43	Bill Atkinson	.15
44	Toby Harrah	.15
45	Mark Fidrych	.25
46	Al Cowens	.20
47	Jack Billingham	.15
48	Don Baylor	.40
49	Ed Kranepool	.25
50	Rick Reuschel	.40
51	Charlie Moore	.15
52	Jim Lonborg	.15
53	Phil Garner	.15
54	Tom Johnson	.15
55	Mitchell Page	.15
56	Randy Jones	.15
57	Dan Meyer	.15
58	Bob Forsch	.20
59	Otto Velez	.15

NO.	PLAYER	NR. MT.
60	Thurman Munson	2.00
61	Larvell Blanks	.15
62	Jim Barr	.15
63	Don Zimmer (Mgr.)	.15
64	Gene Pentz	.15
65	Ken Singleton	.25
66	Chicago White Sox	.35
67	Claudell Washington	.20
68	Steve Foucault	.15
69	Mike Vail	.15
70	Rich Gossage	.65
71	Terry Humphrey	.15
72	Andre Dawson	6.00
73	Andy Hassler	.15
74	Checklist No. 1	.50
75	Dick Ruthven	.15
76	Steve Ontiveros	.15
77	Ed Kirpatrick	.15
78	Pablo Torrealba	.15
79	Darrell Johnson (Mgr.)	.15
80	Ken Griffey	.30
81	Pete Redfern	.15
82	San Fran. Giants	.35
83	Bob Montgomery	.15
84	Kent Tekulve	.20
85	Ron Fairly	.15
86	Dave Tomlin	.15
87	John Lowenstein	.15
88	Mike Phillips	.15
89	Ken Clay	.15
90	Larry Bowa	.20
91	Oscar Zamora	.15
92	Adrian Devine	.15
93	Bobby Cox (Mgr.)	.15
94	Chuck Scrivener	.15
95	Jamie Quirk	.15
96	Baltimore Orioles	.40
97	Stan Bahnsen	.15
98	Jim Essian	.15
99	Willie Hernandez (R)	1.25
100	George Brett	5.00
101	Sid Monge	.15
102	Matt Alexander	.15
103	Tom Murphy	.15
104	Lee Lacy	.15
105	Reggie Cleveland	.15
106	Bill Plummer	.15
107	Ed Halicki	.15
108	Von Joshua	.15
109	Joe Torre (Mgr.)	.25
110	Richie Zisk	.25
111	Mike Tyson	.15
112	Houston Astros	.30
113	Don Carrithers	.15
114	Paul Blair	.15
115	Gary Nolan	.15
116	Tucker Ashford	.15
117	John Montague	.15
118	Terry Harmon	.15
119	Denny Martinez	.15
120	Gary Carter	3.00
121	Alvis Woods	.15
122	Dennis Eckersley	.60
123	Manny Trillo	.20
124	Dave Rozema	.15
125	George Scott	.15

NO.	PLAYER	NR. MT.
126	Paul Moskau	.15
127	Chet Lemon	.20
128	Bill Russell	.15
129	Jim Colborn	.15
130	Jeff Burroughs	.20
131	Bert Blyleven	.45
132	Enos Cabell	.15
133	Jerry Augustine	.15
134	Steve Henderson	.15
135	Ron Guidry	.60
136	Ted Sizemore	.15
137	Craig Kusick	.15
138	Larry Demery	.15
139	Wayne Gross	.15
140	Rollie Fingers	.65
141	Ruppert Jones	.15
142	John Montefusco	.15
143	Keith Hernandez	2.00
144	Jesse Jefferson	.15
145	Rick Monday	.15
146	Doyle Alexander	.15
147	Lee Mazzilli	.20
148	Andre Thornton	.25
149	Dale Murray	.15
150	Bobby Bonds	.25
151	Milt Wilcox	.15
152	Ivan DeJesus	.15
153	Steve Stone	.15
154	Cecil Cooper	.30
155	Butch Hobson	.15
156	Andy Messersmith	.15
157	Pete LaCock	.15
158	Joaquin Andujar	.25
159	Lou Piniella	.40
160	Jim Palmer	1.50
161	Bob Boone	.25
162	Paul Thormodsgard	.15
163	Bill North	.15
164	Bob Owchinko	.15
165	Rennie Stennett	.15
166	Carlos Lopez	.15
167	Tim Foli	.15
168	Reggie Smith	.25
169	Jerry Johnson	.15
170	Lou Brock	1.50
171	Pat Zachry	.15
172	Mike Hargrove	.15
173	Robin Yount	4.00
174	Wayne Garland	.15
175	Jerry Morales	.15
176	Milt May	.15
177	Gene Garber	.15
178	Dave Chalk	.15
179	Dick Tidrow	.15
180	Dave Concepcion	.25
181	Ken Forsch	.15
182	Jim Spencer	.15
183	Doug Bird	.15
184	Checklist No. 2	.50
185	Ellis Valentine	.15
186	Bob Stanley (R)	.35
187	Jerry Royster	.15
188	Al Bumbry	.15
189	Tom Lasorda (Mgr.)	.20
190	John Candelaria	.20
191	Rodney Scott	.15

NO.	PLAYER	NR. MT.
192	San Diego Padres	.30
193	Rich Chiles	.15
194	Derrel Thomas	.15
195	Larry Dierker	.15
196	Bob Bailor	.15
197	Nino Espinosa	.15
198	Ron Pruitt	.15
199	Craig Reynolds	.15
200	Reggie Jackson	4.00
201	Batting Leaders:	.75
	Dave Parker, Rod Carew	
202	Home Run Leaders:	.25
	George Foster, Jim Rice	
203	RBI Leaders:	.25
	George Foster, Larry Hisle	
204	Stolen Base Leaders:	.20
	F. Taveras, Freddie Patek	
205	Victory Leaders:	.60
	Steve Carlton, D. Goltz,	
	D. Leonard, J. Palmer	
206	Strikeout Leaders:	.25
	Phil Niekro, Nolan Ryan	
207	ERA Leaders:	.20
	J. Candelaria, F. Tanana	
208	Leading Firemen:	.30
	R. Fingers, B. Campbell	
209	Dock Ellis	.15
210	Jose Cardenal	.15
211	Earl Weaver (Mgr.)	.15
212	Mike Caldwell	.15
213	Alan Bannister	.15
214	California Angels	.35
215	Darrell Evans	.35
216	Mike Paxton	.15
217	Rod Gilbreath	.15
218	Marty Pattin	.15
219	Mike Cubbage	.15
220	Pedro Borbon	.15
221	Chris Speier	.15
222	Jerry Martin	.15
223	Bruce Kison	.15
224	Jerry Tabb	.15
225	Don Gullett	.15
226	Joe Ferguson	.15
227	Al Fitzmorris	.15
228	Manny Mota	.15
229	Leo Foster	.15
230	Al Hrabosky	.15
231	Wayne Nordhagen	.15
232	Mickey Stanley	.15
233	Dick Pole	.15
234	Herman Franks (Mgr.)	.15
235	Tim McCarver	.35
236	Terry Whitfield	.15
237	Rich Dauer	.15
238	Juan Beniquez	.15
239	Dyar Miller	.15
240	Gene Tenance	.15
241	Pete Vuckovich	.20
242	Barry Bonnell	.15
243	Bob McClure	.15
244	Montreal Expos	.25
245	Rick Burleson	.15
246	Dan Driessen	.15
247	Larry Christenson	.15
248	Frank White	.15

1978 Topps (Continued)

NO. PLAYER	NR. MT.
249 Dave Goltz	.15
250 Graig Nettles	.25
251 Don Kirkwood	.15
252 Steve Swisher	.15
253 Jim Kern	.15
254 Dave Collins	.20
255 Jerry Reuss	.20
256 Joe Altobelli (Mgr.)	.15
257 Hector Cruz	.15
258 John Hiller	.15
259 Los Angeles Dodgers	.50
260 Bert Campaneris	.20
261 Tim Hosely	.15
262 Rudy May	.15
263 Danny Walton	.15
264 Jamie Easterly	.15
265 Sal Bando	.15
266 Bob Shirley	.15
267 Doug Ault	.15
268 Gil Flores	.15
269 Wayne Twitchell	.15
270 Carlton Fisk	1.00
271 Randy Lerch	.15
272 Royle Stillman	.15
273 Fred Norman	.15
274 Freddie Patek	.15
275 Dan Ford	.15
276 Bill Bonham	.15
277 Bruce Boisclair	.15
278 Enrique Romo	.15
279 Bill Virdon (Mgr.)	.20
280 Buddy Bell	.30
281 Eric Rasmussen	.15
282 New York Yankees	.60
283 Omar Moreno	.20
284 Randy Moffitt	.15
285 Steve Yeager	.15
286 Ben Oglivie	.20
287 Kiko Garcia	.15
288 Dave Hamilton	.15
289 Checklist No. 3	.50
290 Willie Horton	.20
291 Gary Ross	.15
292 Gene Richards	.15
293 Mike Willis	.15
294 Larry Parrish	.20
295 Bill Lee	.15
296 Biff Pocoroba	.15
297 Warren Brusstar	.15
298 Tony Armas	.40
299 Whitey Herzog (Mgr.)	.20
300 Joe Morgan	1.50
301 Buddy Schultz	.15
302 Chicago Cubs	.45
303 Sam Hinds	.15
304 John Milner	.15
305 Rico Carty	.25
306 Joe Niekro	.25
307 Glenn Borgmann	.15
308 Jim Rooker	.15
309 Cliff Johnson	.15
310 Don Sutton	1.00
311 Jose Baez	.15
312 Greg Minton	.15
313 Andy Etchebarren	.15
314 Paul Lindblad	.15
315 Mark Belanger	.15
316 Henry Cruz	.15
317 Dave Johnson	.30
318 Tom Griffin	.15
319 Alan Ashby	.15
320 Fred Lynn	1.00
321 Santo Alcala	.15
322 Tom Paciorek	.15
323 Jim Fregosi	.15
324 Vern Rapp (Mgr.)	.15
325 Bruce Sutter	.75
326 Mike Lum	.15
327 Rick Langford	.15
328 Milwaukee Brewers	.40
329 John Verhoeven	.15
330 Bob Watson	.15
331 Mark Littell	.15
332 Duane Kuiper	.15
333 Jim Todd	.15
334 John Stearns	.15
335 Bucky Dent	.20
336 Steve Busby	.15
337 Tom Grieve	.15
338 Dave Heaverlo	.15
339 Mario Guerrero	.15
340 Bake McBride	.15
341 Mike Flanagan	.25
342 Aurelio Rodriguez	.15
343 John Wathan	.15
344 Sam Ewing	.15
345 Luis Tiant	.25
346 Larry Biittner	.15
347 Terry Forster	.20
348 Del Unser	.15
349 Rick Camp	.15
350 Steve Garvey	2.50
351 Jeff Torborg (Mgr.)	.15
352 Tony Scott	.15
353 Doug Bair	.15
354 Cesar Geronimo	.15
355 Bill Travers	.15
356 New York Mets	.50
357 Tom Poquette	.15
358 Mark Lemongello	.15
359 Marc Hill	.15
360 Mike Schmidt	7.00
361 Chris Knapp	.15
362 Dave May	.15
363 Bob Randall	.15
364 Jerry Turner	.15
365 Ed Figueroa	.15
366 Larry Milbourne	.15
367 Rick Dempsey	.20
368 Balor Moore	.15
369 Tim Nordbrook	.15
370 Rusty Staub	.25
371 Ray Burris	.15
372 Brian Asselstine	.15
373 Jim Willoughby	.15
374 Jose Morales	.15
375 Tommy John	.60
376 Jim Wohlford	.15
377 Manny Sarmiento	.15
378 Bobby Winkles (Mgr.)	.15
379 Skip Lockwood	.15
380 Ted Simmons	.40
381 Philadelphia Phillies	.35
382 Joe Lahoud	.15
383 Mario Mendoza	.15
384 Jack Clark	3.00
385 Tito Fuentes	.15
386 Bob Gorinski	.15
387 Ken Holtzman	.15
388 Bill Fahey	.15
389 Julio Gonzalez	.15
390 Oscar Gamble	.15
391 Larry Haney	.15
392 Billy Almon	.15
393 Tippy Martinez	.15
394 Roy Howell	.15
395 Jim Hughes	.15
396 Bob Stinson	.15
397 Greg Gross	.15
398 Don Hood	.15
399 Pete Mackanin	.15
400 Nolan Ryan	6.00
401 Sparky Anderson (Mgr.)	.20
402 Dave Campbell	.15
403 Bud Harrelson	.15
404 Detroit Tigers	.60
405 Rawly Eastwick	.15
406 Mike Jorgensen	.15
407 Odell Jones	.15
408 Joe Zdeb	.15
409 Ron Schueler	.15
410 Bill Madlock	.50
411 AL Championships: Yankees Defeat Royals	.75
412 NL Championships: Dodgers Defeat Phillies	.75
413 World Series: Yankees Reign Supreme	1.50
414 Darold Knowles	.15
415 Ray Fosse	.15
416 Jack Brohamer	.15
417 Mike Garman	.15
418 Tony Muser	.15
419 Jerry Garvin	.15
420 Greg Luzinski	.30
421 Junior Moore	.15
422 Steve Braun	.15
423 Dave Rosello	.15
424 Boston Red Sox	.40
425 Steve Rogers	.15
426 Fred Kendall	.15
427 Mario Soto (R)	.60
428 Joel Youngblood	.15
429 Mike Barlow	.15
430 Al Oliver	.40
431 Butch Metzger	.15
432 Terry Bulling	.15
433 Fernando Gonzalez	.15
434 Mike Norris	.15
435 Checklist No. 4	.50
436 Vic Harris	.15
437 Bo McLaughlin	.15
438 John Ellis	.15
439 Ken Kravec	.15
440 Dave Lopes	.25
441 Larry Gura	.20
442 Elliott Maddox	.15
443 Darrell Chaney	.15
444 Roy Hartsfield (Mgr.)	.15
445 Mike Ivie	.15
446 Tug McGraw	.25
447 Leroy Stanton	.15
448 Bill Castro	.15
449 Tim Blackwell	.15
450 Tom Seaver	3.00
451 Minnesota Twins	.35
452 Jerry Mumphrey	.15
453 Doug Flynn	.15
454 Dave LaRoche	.15
455 Bill Robinson	.15
456 Vern Ruhle	.15
457 Bob Bailey	.15
458 Jeff Newman	.15
459 Charlie Spikes	.15
460 Jim Hunter	1.25
461 Rob Andrews	.15
462 Rogelio Moret	.15
463 Kevin Bell	.15
464 Jerry Grote	.15
465 Hal McRae	.20
466 Dennis Blair	.15
467 Alvin Dark (Mgr.)	.15
468 Warren Cromartie	.15
469 Rick Cerone	.15
470 J.R. Richard	.20
471 Roy Smalley	.15
472 Ron Reed	.15
473 Bill Buckner	.25
474 Jim Slaton	.15
475 Gary Matthews	.25
476 Bill Stein	.15
477 Doug Capilla	.15
478 Jerry Remy	.15
479 St. Louis Cardinals	.40
480 Ron LeFlore	.20
481 Jackson Todd	.15
482 Rick Miller	.15
483 Ken Macha	.15
484 Jim Norris	.15
485 Chris Chambliss	.20
486 John Curtis	.15
487 Jim Tyrone	.15
488 Dan Spillner	.15
489 Rudy Meoli	.15
490 Amos Otis	.20
491 Scott McGregor	.20
492 Jim Sundberg	.15
493 Steve Renko	.15
494 Chuck Tanner (Mgr.)	.15
495 Dave Cash	.15
496 Jim Clancy	.20
497 Glenn Adams	.15
498 Joe Sambito	.15
499 Seattle Mariners	.40
500 George Foster	.75
501 Dave Roberts	.15
502 Pat Rockett	.15
503 Ike Hampton	.15
504 Roger Freed	.15
505 Felix Millan	.15
506 Ron Blomberg	.15
507 Willie Crawford	.15
508 Johnny Oates	.15
509 Brent Strom	.15
510 Willie Stargell	2.50
511 Frank Duffy	.15
512 Larry Herndon	.20
513 Barry Foote	.15
514 Rob Sperring	.15
515 Tim Corcoran	.15
516 Gary Beare	.15
517 Andres Mora	.15
518 Tommy Boggs	.15
519 Brian Downing	.15
520 Larry Hisle	.15
521 Steve Staggs	.15
522 Dick Williams (Mgr.)	.20
523 Donnie Moore (R)	.40
524 Bernie Carbo	.15
525 Jerry Terrell	.15
526 Cincinnati Reds	.45
527 Vic Correll	.15
528 Rob Picciolo	.15
529 Paul Hartzell	.15
530 Dave Winfield	2.00
531 Tom Underwood	.15
532 Skip Jutze	.15
533 Sandy Alomar	.15
534 Wilbur Howard	.15
535 Checklist No. 5	.50
536 Roric Harrison	.15
537 Bruce Bochte	.15
538 Johnnie LeMaster	.15
539 Vic Davalillo	.15
540 Steve Carlton	2.00
541 Larry Cox	.15
542 Tim Johnson	.15
543 Larry Harlow	.15
544 Len Randle	.15
545 Bill Campbell	.15
546 Ted Martinez	.15
547 John Scott	.15
548 Billy Hunter (Mgr.)	.15
549 Joe Kerrigan	.15
550 John Mayberry	.20
551 Atlanta Braves	.35
552 Francisco Barrios	.15
553 Terry Puhl (R)	.45
554 Joe Coleman	.15
555 Butch Wynegar	.20
556 Ed Armbrister	.15
557 Tony Solaita	.15
558 Paul Mitchell	.15
559 Phil Mankowski	.15
560 Dave Parker	2.00
561 Charlie Williams	.15
562 Glenn Burke	.15
563 Dave Rader	.15
564 Mick Kelleher	.15
565 Jerry Koosman	.25
566 Merv Rettenmund	.15
567 Dick Drago	.15
568 Tom Hutton	.15
569 Lary Sorensen	.15
570 Dave Kingman	.50
571 Buck Martinez	.15
572 Rick Wise	.15
573 Luis Gomez	.15
574 Bob Lemon (Mgr.)	.25
575 Pat Dobson	.15
576 Sam Mejias	.15
577 Oakland A's	.30
578 Buzz Capra	.15
579 Rance Mulliniks	.15
580 Rod Carew	2.00
581 Lynn McGlothen	.15
582 Fran Healy	.15
583 George Medich	.15
584 John Hale	.15
585 Woodie Fryman	.15

NO. PLAYER	NR. MT.	NO. PLAYER	NR. MT.	NO. PLAYER	NR. MT.	NO. PLAYER	NR. MT.
586 Ed Goodson	.15	628 Ralph Garr	.15	669 Pete Falcone	.15	704 Rookie 2nd Basemen:	9.00
587 John Urrea	.15	629 Don Stanhouse	.15	670 Jim Rice	3.50	Garth Iorg, Sam Perlozzo,	
588 Jim Mason	.15	630 Ron Cey	.40	671 Gary Lavelle	.15	Dave Oliver, Lou Whitaker	
589 Bob Knepper (R)	1.50	631 Danny Ozark (Mgr.)	.20	672 Don Kessinger	.15	705 Rookie Outfielders:	.50
590 Bobby Murcer	.30	632 Rowland Office	.15	673 Steve Brye	.15	D. Bergman, W. Norwood,	
591 George Zeber	.15	633 Tom Veryzer	.15	674 Ray Knight (R)	1.00	M. Dilone, C. Hurdle	
592 Bob Apodaca	.15	634 Len Barker	.15	675 Jay Johnstone	.15	706 Rookie 1st Basemen:	.40
593 Dave Skaggs	.15	635 Joe Rudi	.15	676 Bob Myrick	.15	Wayne Cage, Ted Cox,	
594 Dave Freisleben	.15	636 Jim Bibby	.15	677 Ed Herrmann	.15	P. Putnam, D. Revering	
595 Sixto Lezcano	.15	637 Duffy Dyer	.15	678 Tom Burgmeier	.15	707 Rookie Shortstops:	30.00
596 Gary Wheelock	.15	638 Paul Splittorff	.15	679 Wayne Garrett	.15	Mickey Klutts, Paul Molitor,	
597 Steve Dillard	.15	639 Gene Clines	.15	680 Vida Blue	.20	Alan Trammell,	
598 Eddie Solomon	.15	640 Lee May	.15	681 Rob Belloir	.15	U.L. Washington	
599 Gary Woods	.15	641 Doug Rau	.15	682 Ken Brett	.15	708 Rookie Catchers:	24.00
600 Frank Tanana	.25	642 Denny Doyle	.15	683 Mike Champion	.15	Bo Diaz, Dale Murphy,	
601 Gene Mauch (Mgr.)	.20	643 Tom House	.15	684 Ralph Houk (Mgr.)	.20	Ernie Whitt, Lance Parrish	
602 Eric Soderholm	.15	644 Jim Dwyer	.15	685 Frank Taveras	.15	709 Rookie Pitchers:	.40
603 Will McEnaney	.15	645 Mike Torrez	.15	686 Gaylord Perry	1.50	Steve Burke, Lance	
604 Earl Williams	.15	646 Rick Auerbach	.15	687 Julio Cruz (R)	.30	Rautzhan, Matt Keough,	
605 Rick Rhoden	.25	647 Steve Dunning	.15	688 George Mitterwald	.15	Dan Schatzeder	
606 Pittsburgh Pirates	.35	648 Gary Thomasson	.15	689 Cleveland Indians	.35	710 Rookie Outfielders:	.75
607 Fernando Arroyo	.15	649 Moose Haas (R)	.30	690 Mickey Rivers	.20	Dell Alston, Rick Bosetti,	
608 Johnny Grubb	.15	650 Cesar Cedeno	.25	691 Ross Grimsley	.15	Mike Easler, Keith Smith	
609 John Denny	.25	651 Doug Rader	.15	692 Ken Reitz	.15	711 Rookie Pitchers:	.35
610 Garry Maddox	.20	652 Checklist No. 6	.50	693 Lamar Johnson	.15	C. Camper, D. Lamp,	
611 Pat Scanlon	.15	653 Ron Hodges	.15	694 Elias Sosa	.15	R. Thomas, C. Mitchell	
612 Ken Henderson	.15	654 Pepe Frias	.15	695 Dwight Evans	1.25	712 Bobby Valentine	.25
613 Marty Perez	.15	655 Lyman Bostock	.20	696 Steve Mingori	.15	713 Bob Davis	.15
614 Joe Wallis	.15	656 Dave Garcia (Mgr.)	.15	697 Roger Metzger	.15	714 Mike Anderson	.15
615 Clay Carroll	.15	657 Bombo Rivera	.15	698 Juan Bernhardt	.15	715 Jim Kaat	.40
616 Pat Kelly	.15	658 Manny Sanguillen	.15	699 Jackie Brown	.15	716 Clarence Gaston	.15
617 Joe Nolan	.15	659 Texas Rangers	.35	700 Johnny Bench	3.50	717 Nelson Briles	.15
618 Tommy Helms	.15	660 Jason Thompson	.25	701 Rookie Pitchers:	.40	718 Ron Jackson	.15
619 Thad Bosley	.15	661 Grant Jackson	.15	Larry Landreth, Tom Hume,		719 Randy Elliott	.15
620 Willie Randolph	.30	662 Paul Dade	.15	Steve McCatty, B. Taylor		720 Fergie Jenkins	.50
621 Craig Swan	.15	663 Paul Reuschel	.15	702 Rookie Catchers:	.25	721 Billy Martin (Mgr.)	.35
622 Champ Summers	.15	664 Fred Stanley	.15	Rick Sweet, Bill Nahordony		722 Pete Broberg	.15
623 Eduardo Rodriquez	.15	665 Dennis Leonard	.20	Kevin Pasley, Don Werner		723 John Wockenfuss	.15
624 Gary Alexander	.15	666 Billy Smith	.15	703 Rookie Pitchers:	6.00	724 K.C. Royals	.40
625 Jose Cruz	.35	667 Jeff Byrd	.15	Jack Morris, L. Andersen,		725 Kurt Bevacqua	.15
626 Toronto Blue Jays	.25	668 Dusty Baker	.25	Tim Jones, M. Mahler		726 W. Wood (Exc. .10)	.40
627 Dave Johnson	.15						

1979 Topps. . . . Complete Set of 726 Cards—Value $150.00

Features the rookie cards of Pedro Guerrero and Bob Horner. 66 cards were double printed. Card 369 (Bump Wills) was originally issued in error as a "Blue Jay". A corrected card was issued showing Wills as a "Ranger".

NO. PLAYER	MINT	NO. PLAYER	MINT	NO. PLAYER	MINT	NO. PLAYER	MINT
1 Batting Leaders:	1.50	9 Dave Campbell	.10	25 Steve Carlton	1.75	41 Minnesota Twins/	.40
Rod Carew, Dave Parker		10 Lee May	.10	26 Jamie Quirk	.10	Gene Mauch (Mgr.)	
2 Home Run Leaders:	.50	11 Marc Hill	.10	27 Dave Goltz	.10	42 Ron Blomberg	.10
Jim Rice, George Foster		12 Dick Drago	.10	28 Steve Brye	.10	43 Wayne Twitchell	.10
3 RBI Leaders:	.50	13 Paul Dade	.10	29 Rick Langford	.10	44 Kurt Bevacqua	.10
Jim Rice, George Foster		14 Rafael Landestoy	.10	30 Dave Winfield	2.50	45 Al Hrabosky	.10
4 Stolen Base Leaders:	.25	15 Ross Grimsley	.10	31 Tom House	.10	46 Ron Hodges	.10
Ron LeFlore, Omar Moreno		16 Fred Stanley	.10	32 Jerry Mumphrey	.15	47 Fred Norman	.10
5 Victory Leaders:	.40	17 Donnie Moore	.15	33 Dave Rozema	.10	48 Merv Rettenmund	.10
Ron Guidry, Gaylord Perry		18 Tony Solaita	.10	34 Rob Andrews	.10	49 Vern Ruhle	.10
6 Stikeout Leaders:	.40	19 Larry Gura	.10	35 Ed Figueroa	.10	50 Steve Garvay	1.25
Nolan Ryan, J.R. Richard		20 Joe Morgan	.40	36 Alan Ashby	.10	51 Ray Fosse	.10
7 ERA Leaders:	.25	21 Kevin Kobel	.10	37 Joe Kerrigan	.10	52 Randy Lerch	.10
Ron Guidry, Craig Swan		22 Mike Jorgensen	.10	38 Bernie Carbo	.10	53 Mick Kelleher	.10
8 Leading Firemen:	.35	23 Terry Forster	.15	39 Dale Murphy	8.00	54 Del Alston	.10
R. Gossage, R. Fingers		24 Paul Molitor	3.50	40 Dennis Eckersley	.60	55 Wlie Stargell	2.50

NO. PLAYER	MINT	NO. PLAYER	MINT	NO. PLAYER	MINT	NO. PLAYER	MINT
56 John Hale	.10	139 Luis Pujols	.10	211 Denny Martinez	.10	292 Don Reynolds	.10
57 Eric Rasmussen	.10	140 Don Gullett	.10	212 Carney Lansford (R)	4.00	293 Jerry Garvin	.10
58 Bob Randall	.10	141 Tom Paciorek	.10	213 Bill Travers	.10	294 Pepe Frias	.10
59 John Denny	.10	142 Charlie Williams	.10	214 Boston Red Sox/	.45	295 Mitchell Page	.10
60 Mickey Rivers	.15	143 Tony Scott	.10	Don Zimmer (Mgr.)		296 Preston Hanna	.10
61 Bo Diaz	.25	144 Sandy Alomar	.10	215 Willie McCovey	1.50	297 Ted Sizemore	.10
62 Randy Moffitt	.10	145 Rick Rhoden	.20	216 Wilbur Wood	.10	298 Rich Gale	.10
63 Jack Brohamer	.10	146 Duane Kuiper	.10	217 Steve Dillard	.10	299 Steve Ontiveros	.10
64 Tom Underwood	.10	147 Dave Hamilton	.10	218 Dennis Leonard	.15	300 Rod Carew	2.00
65 Mark Belanger	.10	148 Bruce Boisclair	.10	219 Roy Smalley	.10	301 Tom Hume	.10
66 Tigers/L. Moss (Mgr.)	.50	149 Manny Sarmiento	.10	220 Cesar Geronimo	.10	302 Atlanta Braves/	.35
67 Jim Mason	.10	150 Wayne Cage	.10	221 Jesse Jefferson	.10	Bobby Cox (Mgr.)	
68 Joe Niekro	.10	151 John Hiller	.10	222 Bob Beall	.10	303 Lary Sorensen	.10
69 Elliott Maddox	.10	152 Rick Cerone	.10	223 Kent Tekulve	.15	304 Steve Swisher	.10
70 John Candelaria	.15	153 Dennis Lamp	.10	224 Dave Revering	.10	305 Willie Montanez	.10
71 Brian Downing	.15	154 Jim Gantner	.10	225 Rich Gossage	.50	306 Floyd Bannister	.15
72 Steve Mingori	.10	155 Dwight Evans	1.00	226 Ron Pruitt	.10	307 Larvell Blanks	.10
73 Ken Henderson	.10	156 Buddy Solomon	.10	227 Steve Stone	.10	308 Bert Blyleven	.40
74 Shane Rawley (R)	1.00	157 U.L. Washington	.10	228 Vic Davalillo	.10	309 Ralph Garr	.10
75 Steve Yeager	.10	158 Joe Sambito	.10	229 Doug Flynn	.10	310 Thurman Munson	1.50
76 Warren Cromartie	.10	159 Roy White	.10	230 Bob Forsch	.10	311 Gary Lavelle	.10
77 Dan Briggs	.10	160 Mike Flanagan	.35	231 Johnny Wockenfuss	.10	312 Bob Robertson	.10
78 Elias Sosa	.10	161 Barry Foote	.10	232 Jimmy Sexton	.10	313 Dyar Miller	.10
79 Ted Cox	.10	162 Tom Johnson	.10	233 Paul Mitchell	.10	314 Larry Harlow	.10
80 Jason Thompson	.15	163 Glenn Burke	.10	234 Toby Harrah	.10	315 John Matlack	.10
81 Roger Erickson	.10	164 Mickey Lolich	.15	235 Steve Rogers	.15	316 Milt May	.10
82 Mets/J. Torre (Mgr.)	.40	165 Frank Taveras	.10	236 Jim Dwyer	.10	317 Jose Cardenal	.10
83 Fred Kendall	.10	166 Leon Roberts	.10	237 Billy Smith	.10	318 Bob Welch (R)	3.00
84 Greg Minton	.10	167 Roger Metzger	.10	238 Balor Moore	.10	319 Wayne Garrett	.10
85 Gary Matthews	.20	168 Dave Freisleben	.10	239 Willie Horton	.10	320 Carl Yastrzemski	2.50
86 Rodney Scott	.10	169 Bill Nahorodny	.10	240 Rick Reuschel	.20	321 Gaylord Perry	1.25
87 Pete Falcone	.10	170 Don Sutton	1.00	241 Checklist No. 2	.20	322 Danny Goodwin	.10
88 Bob Molinaro	.10	171 Gene Clines	.10	242 Pablo Torrealba	.10	323 Lynn McGlothen	.10
89 Dick Tidrow	.10	172 Mike Bruhert	.10	243 Buck Martinez	.10	324 Mike Tyson	.10
90 Bob Boone	.10	173 John Lowenstein	.10	244 Pittsburgh Pirates/	.35	325 Cecil Cooper	.60
91 Terry Crowley	.10	174 Rick Auerbach	.10	Chuck Tanner (Mgr.)		326 Pedro Borbon	.10
92 Jim Bibby	.10	175 George Hendrick	.15	245 Jeff Burroughs	.10	327 Art Howe	.10
93 Phil Mankowski	.10	176 Aurelio Rodriguez	.10	246 Darrell Jackson	.10	328 Oakland A's/	.20
94 Len Barker	.15	177 Ron Reed	.10	247 Tucker Ashford	.10	Jack McKeon (Mgr.)	
95 Robin Yount	4.00	178 Alvis Woods	.10	248 Pete LaCock	.10	329 Joe Coleman	.10
96 Cleveland Indians/	.25	179 Jim Beattie	.10	249 Paul Thormodsgard	.10	330 George Brett	3.00
Jeff Torborg (Mgr.)		180 Larry Hisle	.10	250 Willie Randolph	.25	331 Mickey Mahler	.10
97 Sam Mejias	.10	181 Mike Garman	.10	251 Jack Morris	2.50	332 Gary Alexander	.10
98 Ray Burris	.10	182 Tim Johnson	.10	252 Bob Stinson	.10	333 Chet Lemon	.35
99 John Wathan	.10	183 Paul Splittorff	.10	253 Rick Wise	.10	334 Craig Swan	.10
100 Tom Seaver	1.50	184 Darrel Chaney	.10	254 Luis Gomez	.10	335 Chris Chambliss	.15
101 Roy Howell	.10	185 Mike Torrez	.10	255 Tommy John	.60	336 Bobby Thompson	.10
102 Mike Anderson	.10	186 Eric Soderholm	.10	256 Mike Sadek	.10	337 John Montague	.10
103 Jim Todd	.10	187 Mark Lemongello	.10	257 Adrian Devine	.10	338 Vic Harris	.10
104 Johnny Oates	.10	188 Pat Kelly	.10	258 Mike Phillips	.10	339 Ron Jackson	.10
105 Rick Camp	.10	189 Eddie Whitson (R)	.75	259 Cincinnati Reds/	.40	340 Jim Palmer	1.50
106 Frank Duffy	.10	190 Ron Cey	.40	Sparky Anderson (Mgr.)		341 Willie Upshaw (R)	.75
107 Jesus Alou	.10	191 Mike Norris	.10	260 Richie Zisk	.10	342 Dave Roberts	.10
108 Eduardo Rodriguez	.10	192 St. Louis Cardinals/	.35	261 Mario Guerrero	.10	343 Ed Glynn	.10
109 Joel Youngblood	.10	Ken Boyer (Mgr.)		262 Nelson Briles	.10	344 Jerry Royster	.10
110 Vida Blue	.15	193 Glenn Adams	.10	263 Oscar Gamble	.10	345 Tug McGraw	.20
111 Roger Freed	.10	194 Randy Jones	.10	264 Don Robinson (R)	.75	346 Bill Buckner	.20
112 Philadelphia Phillies/	.35	195 Bill Madlock	.40	265 Don Money	.10	347 Doug Rau	.10
Danny Ozark (Mgr.)		196 Steve Kemp	.10	266 Jim Willoughby	.10	348 Andre Dawson	4.00
113 Pete Redfern	.10	197 Bob Apodaca	.10	267 Joe Rudi	.10	349 Jim Wright	.10
114 Cliff Johnson	.10	198 Johnny Grubb	.10	268 Julio Gonzalez	.10	350 Garry Templeton	.30
115 Nolan Ryan	5.00	199 Larry Milbourne	.10	269 Woodie Fryman	.10	351 Wayne Nordhagen	.10
116 Ozzie Smith (R)	24.00	200 Johnny Bench	1.00	270 Butch Hobson	.10	352 Steve Renko	.10
117 Grant Jackson	.10	201 Record — M. Edwards	.15	271 Rawly Eastwick	.10	353 Checklist No. 3	.20
118 Bud Harrelson	.10	Most Unassisted DP's		272 Tim Corcoran	.10	354 Bill Bonham	.10
119 Don Stanhouse	.10	by 2nd Baseman		273 Jerry Terrell	.10	355 Lee Mazzilli	.15
120 Jim Sundberg	.10	202 Record — R. Guidry	.25	274 Willie Norwood	.10	356 San Francisco Giants/	.40
121 Checklist No. 1	.20	Most Strikeouts,		275 Junior Moore	.10	Joe Altobelli (Mgr.)	
122 Mike Paxton	.10	Lefthander, 9 Inning Game		276 Jim Colborn	.10	357 Jerry Augustine	.10
123 Lou Whitaker	2.00	203 Record — J.R. Richard	.25	277 Tom Grieve	.10	358 Alan Trammell	5.00
124 Dan Schatzeder	.10	Most Season Stikeouts,		278 Andy Messersmith	.20	359 Dan Spillner	.15
125 Rick Burleson	.10	Righthander		279 Jerry Grote	.10	360 Amos Otis	.15
126 Doug Bair	.10	204 Record — P. Rose	1.25	280 Andre Thornton	.10	361 Tom Dixon	.10
127 Thad Bosley	.10	Most Consecutive Games		281 Vic Correll	.10	362 Mike Cubbage	.10
128 Ted Martinez	.10	Batting Safely		282 Toronto Blue Jays/	.20	363 Craig Skok	.10
129 Marty Pattin	.10	205 Record — J. Stearns	.20	Roy Hartsfield (Mgr.)		364 Gene Richards	.10
130 Bob Watson	.10	Most Steals by Catcher,		283 Ken Kravec	.10	365 Sparky Lyle	.15
131 Jim Clancy	.10	Season		284 Johnnie LeMaster	.10	366 Juan Bernhardt	.10
132 Rowland Office	.10	206 Record — S. Stewart	.20	285 Bobby Bonds	.20	367 Dave Skaggs	.10
133 Bill Castro	.10	7 Straight Stikeouts,		286 Duffy Dyer	.10	368 Don Aase	.10
134 Alan Bannister	.10	First Major League Game		287 Andres Mora	.10	369 Bump Wills (error)	3.00
135 Bobby Murcer	.25	207 Dave Lemanczyk	.10	288 Milt Wilcox	.10	(Blue Jays)	
136 Jim Kaat	.45	208 Clarence Gaston	.10	289 Jose Cruz	.25	369 Bump Wills (correct)	4.00
137 Larry Wolfe	.10	209 Reggie Cleveland	.10	290 Dave Lopes	.20	(Rangers)	
138 Mark Lee	.10	210 Larry Bowa	.20	291 Tom Griffin	.10	370 Dave Kingman	.40

NO. PLAYER	MINT
371 Jeff Holly	.10
372 Lamar Johnson	.10
373 Lance Rautzhan	.10
374 Ed Herrmann	.10
375 Bill Campbell	.10
376 Gorman Thomas	.35
377 Paul Moskau	.10
378 Rob Picciolo	.10
379 Dale Murray	.10
380 John Mayberry	.15
381 Houston Astros/	.25
Bill Virdon (Mgr.)	
382 Jerry Martin	.10
383 Phil Garner	.10
384 Tommy Boggs	.10
385 Dan Ford	.10
386 Francisco Barrios	.10
387 Gary Thomasson	.10
388 Jack Billingham	.10
389 Joe Zdeb	.10
390 Rollie Fingers	.60
391 Al Oliver	.35
392 Doug Ault	.10
393 Scott McGregor	.15
394 Randy Stein	.10
395 Dave Cash	.10
396 Bill Plummer	.10
397 Sergio Ferrer	.10
398 Ivan DeJesus	.10
399 David Clyde	.10
400 Jim Rice	2.50
401 Ray Knight	.15
402 Paul Hartzell	.10
403 Tim Foli	.10
404 Chicago White Sox/	.25
Don Kessinger (Mgr.)	
405 Butch Wynegar	.10
406 Joe Wallis	.10
407 Pete Vuckovich	.10
408 Charlie Moore	.10
409 Willie Wilson (R)	1.75
410 Darrell Evans	.30
411 All-Time Hits:	.50
Season — George Sisler,	
Career — Ty Cobb	
412 All-Time RBI's:	.50
Season — Hack Wilson	
Career — Hank Aaron	
413 All-Time Home Runs:	.50
Season — Roger Maris	
Career — Hank Aaron	
414 All-Time Batting Avg.:	.50
Career — Ty Cobb	
Season — R. Hornsby	
415 All-Time Stolen Bases:	.50
Career — Lou Brock	
Season — Lou Brock	
416 All-Time Wins:	.25
Career: Cy Young	
Season: J. Chesbro	
417 All-Time Strikeouts:	.25
Career: Walter Johnson	
Season: Nolan Ryan	
418 All-Time ERA:	.25
Career: W. Johnson	
Season: Dutch Leonard	
419 Dick Ruthven	.10
420 Ken Griffey	.15
421 Doug DeCinces	.20
422 Ruppert Jones	.15
423 Bob Montgomery	.10
424 California Angels/	.30
Jim Fregosi (Mgr.)	
425 Rick Manning	.10
426 Chris Speier	.10
427 Andy Replogle	.10
428 Bobby Valentine	.10
429 John Urrea	.10
430 Dave Parker	1.00
431 Glenn Borgmann	.10
432 Dave Heaverlo	.10
433 Larry Biittner	.10
434 Ken Clay	.10
435 Gene Tenace	.10
436 Hector Cruz	.10

NO. PLAYER	MINT
437 Rick Williams	.10
438 Horace Speed	.10
439 Frank White	.15
440 Rusty Staub	.20
441 Lee Lacy	.15
442 Doyle Alexander	.10
443 Bruce Bochte	.10
444 Aurelio Lopez (R)	.35
445 Steve Henderson	.10
446 Jim Lonborg	.10
447 Manny Sanguillen	.10
448 Moose Haas	.10
449 Bombo Rivera	.10
450 Dave Concepcion	.25
451 Kansas City Royals/	.25
Whitey Herzog (Mgr.)	
452 Jerry Morales	.10
453 Chris Knapp	.10
454 Len Randle	.10
455 Bill Lee	.10
456 Chuck Baker	.10
457 Bruce Sutter	.75
458 Jim Essian	.10
459 Sid Monge	.10
460 Graig Nettles	.40
461 Jim Barr	.10
462 Otto Velez	.10
463 Steve Comer	.10
464 Joe Nolan	.10
465 Reggie Smith	.20
466 Mark Littell	.10
467 Don Kessinger	.10
468 Stan Bahnsen	.10
469 Lance Parrish	3.00
470 Garry Maddox	.10
471 Joaquin Andujar	.30
472 Craig Kusick	.10
473 Dave Roberts	.10
474 Dick Davis	.10
475 Dan Driessen	.10
476 Tom Poquette	.10
477 Bob Grich	.15
478 Juan Beniquez	.10
479 San Diego Padres/	.25
Roger Craig (Mgr.)	
480 Fred Lynn	.75
481 Skip Lockwood	.10
482 Craig Reynolds	.10
483 Checklist No. 4	.20
484 Rick Waits	.10
485 Bucky Dent	.15
486 Bob Knepper	.25
487 Miguel Dilone	.10
488 Bob Owchinko	.10
489 Larry Cox	.10
(photo of Dave Rader)	
490 Al Cowens	.10
491 Tippy Martinez	.10
492 Bob Bailor	.10
493 Larry Christenson	.10
494 Jerry White	.10
495 Tony Perez	.50
496 Barry Bonnell	.10
497 Glenn Abbott	.10
498 Rich Chiles	.10
499 Texas Rangers/	.25
Pat Corrales (Mgr.)	
500 Ron Guidry	.75
501 Junior Kennedy	.10
502 Steve Braun	.10
503 Terry Humphrey	.10
504 Larry McWilliams (R)	.40
505 Ed Kranepool	.10
506 John D'Acquisto	.10
507 Tony Armas	.35
508 Charlie Hough	.10
509 Mario Mendoza	.10
510 Ted Simmons	.35
511 Paul Reuschel	.10
512 Jack Clark	2.00
513 Dave Johnson	.25
514 Mike Proly	.10
515 Enos Cabell	.10
516 Champ Summers	.10
517 Al Bumbry	.10
518 Jim Umbarger	.10

NO. PLAYER	MINT
519 Ben Oglivie	.15
520 Gary Carter	2.50
521 Sam Ewing	.10
522 Ken Holtzman	.10
523 John Milner	.10
524 Tom Burgmeier	.10
525 Freddie Patek	.10
526 Los Angeles Dodgers/	.50
Tom Lasorda (Mgr.)	
527 Lerrin LaGrow	.10
528 Wayne Gross	.10
529 Brian Asselstine	.10
530 Frank Tanana	.15
531 Fernando Gonazalez	.10
532 Buddy Schultz	.10
533 Leroy Stanton	.10
534 Ken Forsch	.10
535 Ellis Valentine	.10
536 Jerry Reuss	.15
537 Tom Veryzer	.10
538 Mike Ivie	.10
539 John Ellis	.10
540 Greg Luzinski	.25
541 Jim Slaton	.10
542 Rick Bosetti	.10
543 Kiko Garcia	.10
544 Fergie Jenkins	.40
545 John Stearns	.10
546 Bill Russell	.10
547 Clint Hurdle	.10
548 Enrique Romo	.10
549 Bob Bailey	.10
550 Sal Bando	.10
551 Chicago Cubs/	.35
Herman Franks (Mgr.)	
552 Jose Morales	.10
553 Denny Walling	.10
554 Matt Keough	.10
555 Biff Pocoroba	.10
556 Mike Lum	.10
557 Ken Brett	.10
558 Jay Johnstone	.10
559 Greg Pryor	.10
560 John Montefusco	.10
561 Ed Ott	.10
562 Dusty Baker	.20
563 Roy Thomas	.10
564 Jerry Turner	.10
565 Rico Carty	.10
566 Nino Espinosa	.10
567 Rich Hebner	.10
568 Carlos Lopez	.10
569 Bob Sykes	.10
570 Cesar Cedeno	.20
571 Darrell Porter	.15
572 Rod Gilbreath	.10
573 Jim Kern	.10
574 Claudell Washington	.15
575 Luis Tiant	.20
576 Mike Parrott	.10
577 Milwaukee Brewers/	.30
George Bamberger (Mgr.)	
578 Pete Broberg	.10
579 Greg Gross	.10
580 Ron Fairly	.10
581 Darold Knowles	.10
582 Paul Blair	.10
583 Julio Cruz	.10
584 Jim Rooker	.10
585 Hal McRae	.15
586 Bob Horner (R)	2.00
587 Ken Reitz	.10
588 Tom Murphy	.10
589 Terry Whitfield	.10
590 J.R. Richard	.15
591 Mike Hargrove	.10
592 Mike Krukow	.10
593 Rick Dempsey	.10
594 Bob Shirley	.10
595 Phil Niekro	1.00
596 Jim Wohlford	.10
597 Bob Stanley	.15
598 Mark Wagner	.10
599 Jim Spencer	.10
600 George Foster	.50

NO. PLAYER	MINT
601 Dave LaRoche	.10
602 Checklist No. 5	.20
603 Rudy May	.10
604 Jeff Newman	.10
605 Rick Monday	.10
606 Montreal Expos/	.25
Dick Williams (Mgr.)	
607 Omar Moreno	.10
608 Dave McKay	.10
609 Silvio Martinez	.10
610 Mike Schmidt	4.50
611 Jim Norris	.10
612 Rick Honeycutt (R)	.60
613 Mike Edwards	.10
614 Willie Hernandez	.50
615 Ken Singleton	.15
616 Billy Almon	.10
617 Terry Puhl	.10
618 Jerry Remy	.10
619 Ken Landreaux	.30
620 Bert Campaneris	.15
621 Pat Zachry	.10
622 Dave Collins	.15
623 Bob McClure	.10
624 Larry Herndon	.10
625 Mark Fidrych	.15
626 New York Yankees/	.40
Bob Lemon (Mgr.)	
627 Gary Serum	.10
628 Del Unser	.10
629 Gene Garber	.10
630 Bake McBride	.10
631 Jorge Orta	.10
632 Don Kirkwood	.10
633 Rob Wilfong	.10
634 Paul Lindblad	.10
635 Don Baylor	.75
636 Wayne Garland	.10
637 Bill Robinson	.10
638 Al Fitzmorris	.10
639 Manny Trillo	.10
640 Eddie Murray	5.00
641 Bobby Castillo	.10
642 Wilbur Howard	.10
643 Tom Hausman	.10
644 Manny Mota	.10
645 George Scott	.10
646 Rick Sweet	.10
647 Bob Lacey	.10
648 Lou Piniella	.30
649 John Curtis	.10
650 Pete Rose	4.00
651 Mike Caldwell	.10
652 Stan Papi	.10
653 Warren Brusstar	.10
654 Rick Miller	.10
655 Jerry Koosman	.20
656 Hosken Powell	.10
657 George Medich	.10
658 Taylor Duncan	.10
659 Seattle Mariners/	.20
Darrell Johnson (Mgr.)	
660 Ron LeFlore	.10
661 Bruce Kison	.10
662 Kevin Bell	.10
663 Mike Vail	.10
664 Doug Bird	.10
665 Lou Brock	1.25
666 Rich Dauer	.10
667 Don Hood	.10
668 Bill North	.10
669 Checklist No. 6	.20
670 Jim Hunter	.50
671 Joe Ferguson	.10
672 Ed Halicki	.10
673 Tom Hutton	.10
674 Dave Tomlin	.10
675 Tim McCarver	.25
676 Johnny Sutton	.10
677 Larry Parrish	.10
678 Geoff Zahn	.10
679 Derrel Thomas	.10
680 Carlton Fisk	.75
681 John Johnson	.10
682 Dave Chalk	.10

NO. PLAYER	MINT
683 Dan Meyer	.10
684 Jamie Easterly	.10
685 Sixto Lezcano	.10
686 Ron Schueler	.10
687 Rennie Stennett	.10
688 Mike Willis	.10
689 Baltimore Orioles/	.35
Earl Weaver (Mgr.)	
690 Buddy Bell	.10
691 Dock Ellis	.10
692 Mickey Stanley	.10
693 Dave Rader	.10
694 Burt Hooton	.10
695 Keith Hernandez	2.00
696 Andy Hassler	.10
697 Dave Bergman	.10
698 Bill Stein	.10
699 Hal Dues	.10
700 Reggie Jackson	1.50
701 Orioles Prospects:	.35
Mark Corey, John Flinn,	
Sammy Stewart	
702 Red Sox Prospects:	.20
Garry Hancock, Joel Finch,	
Allen Ripley	

NO. PLAYER	MINT
703 Angels Prospects:	.15
Bob Slater, J. Anderson,	
Dave Frost	
704 White Sox Prospects:	.15
Ross Baumgarten, Mike	
Colbern, Mike Squires	
705 Indians Prospects:	.75
Tim Norrid, D. Oliver,	
Alfredo Griffin	
706 Tigers Prospects:	.20
Dave Stegman, Dave Tobik,	
Kip Young	
707 Royals Prospects:	.15
Randy Bass, Jim Gaudet,	
R. McGilberry	
708 Brewers Prospects:	1.50
Kevin Bass, Ned Yost,	
Eddie Romero	
709 Twins Prospects:	.20
R. Sofield, Kevin Stanfield,	
Sam Perlozzo	
710 Yankees Prospects:	.40
Mike Heath, D. Rajsich,	
Brian Doyle	

NO. PLAYER	MINT
711 A's Prospects:	.45
Dwayne Murphy, Bruce	
Robinson, Alan Wirth	
712 Mariners Prospects:	.15
Greg Biercevicz,	
B. McLaughlin, B. Anderson	
713 Rangers Prospects:	.40
Danny Darwin, Pat Putnam,	
Billy Sample	
714 Blue Jays Prospects:	.15
Victor Cruz, Pat Kelly,	
Ernie Whitt	
715 Braves Prospects:	.40
Larry Whisenton, Bruce	
Benedict, Glenn Hubbard	
716 Cubs Prospects:	.20
S. Thompson, Dave Geisel,	
Karl Pagel	
717 Reds Prospects:	.45
M. LaCoss, Ron Oester,	
Harry Spilman	
718 Astros Prospects:	.15
Mike Fischlin, Bruce Bochy,	
Don Pisker	

NO. PLAYER	MINT
719 Dodgers Prospects:	8.00
Pedro Guerrero, Rudy Law,	
Joe Simpson	
720 Expos Prospects:	.30
Jerry Fry, Jerry Pirtle,	
Scott Sanderson	
721 Mets Prospects:	.25
Dwight Bernard, Juan	
Berenguer, Dan Norman	
722 Phillies Prospects:	2.00
Jim Morrison, Lonnie	
Smith, Jim Wright	
723 Pirates Prospects:	.35
Eugenio Cotes,	
B. Wiltbank, Dale Berra	
724 Cardinals Prospects:	.50
Tom Bruno, George	
Frazier, Terry Kennedy	
725 Padres Prospects:	.15
Jim Beswick, Broderick	
Perkins, Steve Mura	
726 Giants Prospects:	.20
J. Tamargo, Greg	
Johnston, Joe Strain	

1980 Topps. . . . Complete Set of 726 Cards—Value $160.00

Features the rookie cards of Rickey Henderson, Dan Quisenberry, Mike Scott and Dave Stieb. 66 cards were double printed.

NO. PLAYER	MINT
1 Highlights: Brock and	1.50
Yaz Get 3000 Hits (Exc. .30)	
2 Highlights: McCovey	.60
512 Home Runs	
3 Highlights: Manny Mota	.15
145 Pinch Hits	
4 Highlights: Pete Rose	1.50
10th 200 Hit Season	
5 Highlights: G. Templeton	.25
100 Lefty and Righty Hits	
6 Highlights: Del Unser	.15
3rd Consec. Pinch Homer	
7 Mike Lum	.08
8 Craig Swan	.08
9 Steve Braun	.08
10 Denny Martinez	.12
11 Jimmy Sexton	.08
12 John Curtis	.08
13 Ron Pruitt	.08
14 Dave Cash	.08
15 Bill Campbell	.08
16 Jerry Narron	.08
17 Bruce Sutter	.50
18 Ron Jackson	.08
19 Balor Moore	.08
20 Dan Ford	.08
21 Manny Sarmiento	.08
22 Pat Putnam	.08
23 Derrel Thomas	.08
24 Jim Slaton	.08
25 Lee Mazzili	.12
26 Marty Pattin	.08
27 Del Unser	.08
28 Bruce Kison	.08
29 Mark Wagner	.08

NO. PLAYER	MINT
30 Vida Blue	.15
31 Jay Johnstone	.08
32 Julio Cruz	.08
33 Tony Scott	.08
34 Jeff Newman	.08
35 Luis Tiant	.12
36 Rusty Torres	.08
37 Kiko Garcia	.08
38 Dan Spillner	.08
39 Rowland Office	.08
40 Carlton Fisk	.75
41 Texas Rangers/	.30
Pat Corrales (Mgr.)	
42 Dave Palmer (R)	.40
43 Bombo Rivera	.08
44 Bill Fahey	.08
45 Frank White	.15
46 Rico Carty	.15
47 Bill Bonham	.08
48 Rick Miller	.08
49 Mario Guerrero	.08
50 J. Richard	.12
51 Joe Ferguson	.08
52 Warren Brusstar	.08
53 Ben Oglivie	.12
54 Dennis Lamp	.08
55 Bill Madlock	.40
56 Bobby Valentine	.12
57 Pete Vuckovich	.12
58 Doug Flynn	.08
59 Eddy Putman	.08
60 Bucky Dent	.12
61 Gary Serum	.08
62 Mike Ivie	.08
63 Bob Stanley	.12

NO. PLAYER	MINT
64 Joe Nolan	.08
65 Al Bumbry	.08
66 Kansas City Royals/	.35
Jim Frey (Mgr.)	
67 Doyle Alexander	.08
68 Larry Harlow	.08
69 Rick Williams	.08
70 Gary Carter	2.00
71 John Milner	.08
72 Fred Howard	.08
73 Dave Collins	.08
74 Sid Monge	.08
75 Bill Russell	.08
76 John Stearns	.08
77 Dave Stieb (R)	4.00
78 Ruppert Jones	.08
79 Bob Owchinko	.08
80 Ron LeFlore	.12
81 Ted Sizemore	.08
82 Houston Astros/	.35
Bill Virdon (Mgr.)	
83 Steve Trout (R)	.30
84 Gary Lavelle	.08
85 Ted Simmons	.30
86 Dave Hamilton	.08
87 Pepe Frias	.08
88 Ken Landreaux	.12
89 Don Hood	.08
90 Manny Trillo	.08
91 Rick Dempsey	.08
92 Rick Rhoden	.12
93 Dave Roberts	.08
94 Neil Allen (R)	.40
95 Cecil Cooper	.40

NO. PLAYER	MINT
96 Oakland A's/	.35
Jim Marshall (Mgr.)	
97 Bill Lee	.15
98 Jerry Terrell	.08
99 Victor Cruz	.08
100 Johnny Bench	2.50
101 Aurelio Lopez	.08
102 Rich Dauer	.08
103 Bill Caudill (R)	.40
104 Manny Mota	.15
105 Frank Tanana	.15
106 Jeff Leonard (R)	1.50
107 Francisco Barrios	.08
108 Bob Horner	.65
109 Bill Travers	.08
110 Fred Lynn	.35
111 Bob Knepper	.20
112 Chicago White Sox/	.35
Tony LaRussa (Mgr.)	
113 Geoff Zahn	.08
114 Juan Beniquez	.12
115 Sparky Lyle	.15
116 Larry Cox	.08
117 Dock Ellis	.08
118 Phil Garner	.08
119 Sammy Stewart	.08
120 Greg Luzinski	.25
121 Checklist No. 1	.25
122 Dave Rosello	.08
123 Lynn Jones	.08
124 Dave Lemanczyk	.08
125 Tony Perez	.40
126 Dave Tomlin	.08
127 Gary Thomasson	.08
128 Tom Burgmeier	.08

NO.	PLAYER	MINT
129	Craig Reynolds	.08
130	Amos Otis	.15
131	Paul Mitchell	.08
132	Biff Pocoroba	.08
133	Jerry Turner	.08
134	Matt Keough	.08
135	Bill Buckner	.20
136	Dick Ruthven	.08
137	John Castino	.20
138	Ross Baumgarten	.08
139	Dane Iorg	.20
140	Rich Gossage	.50
141	Gary Alexander	.08
142	Phil Huffman	.08
143	Bruce Bochte	.08
144	Steve Comer	.08
145	Darrell Evans	.30
146	Bob Welch	.50
147	Terry Puhl	.08
148	Manny Sanguillen	.15
149	Tom Hume	.08
150	Jason Thompson	.15
151	Tom Hausman	.12
152	John Fulgham	.08
153	Tim Blackwell	.08
154	Lary Sorensen	.08
155	Jerry Remy	.08
156	Tony Brizzolara	.08
157	Willie Wilson	.25
158	Rob Picciolo	.08
159	Ken Clay	.08
160	Eddie Murray	3.00
161	Larry Christenson	.08
162	Bob Randall	.08
163	Steve Swisher	.08
164	Greg Pryor	.08
165	Omar Moreno	.08
166	Glenn Abbott	.08
167	Jack Clark	1.50
168	Rick Waits	.08
169	Luis Gomez	.08
170	Burt Hooton	.08
171	Fernando Gonzalez	.08
172	Ron Hodges	.08
173	John Henry Johnson	.08
174	Ray Knight	.20
175	Rick Reuschel	.12
176	Champ Summers	.08
177	Dave Heaverlo	.08
178	Tim McCarver	.20
179	Ron Davis (R)	.25
180	Warren Cromartie	.08
181	Moose Haas	.08
182	Ken Reitz	.08
183	Jim Anderson	.08
184	Steve Renko	.08
185	Hal McRae	.12
186	Junior Moore	.08
187	Alan Ashby	.08
188	Terry Crowley	.08
189	Kevin Kobel	.08
190	Buddy Bell	.25
191	Ted Martinez	.08
192	Atlanta Braves/ Bobby Cox (Mgr.)	.35
193	Dave Goltz	.08
194	Mike Easler	.25
195	John Montefusco	.15
196	Lance Parrish	1.00
197	Byron McLaughlin	.08
198	Dell Alston	.08
199	Mike LaCoss	.15
200	Jim Rice	1.50
201	Batting Leaders: K. Hernandez, Fred Lynn	.30
202	Home Run Leaders: Dave Kingman, G. Thomas	.30
203	RBI Leaders: Don Baylor, Dave Winfield	.30
204	Stolen Base Leaders: Omar Moreno, Willie Wilson	.15
205	Victory Leaders: Phil Niekro, Joe Niekro, Mike Flanagan	.25
206	Strikeout Leaders: J.R. Richard, Nolan Ryan	.25
207	ERA Leaders: J.R. Richard, Ron Guidry	.20
208	Wayne Cage	.08
209	Von Joshua	.08
210	Steve Carlton	1.50
211	Dave Skaggs	.08
212	Dave Roberts	.08
213	Mike Jorgensen	.08
214	California Angels/ Jim Fregosi (Mgr.)	.35
215	Sixto Lezcano	.08
216	Phil Mankowski	.08
217	Ed Halicki	.08
218	Jose Morales	.08
219	Steve Mingori	.08
220	Dave Concepcion	.25
221	Joe Cannon	.08
222	Ron Hassey	.25
223	Bob Sykes	.08
224	Willie Montanez	.08
225	Lou Piniella	.25
226	Bill Stein	.08
227	Len Barker	.08
228	Johnny Oates	.08
229	Jim Bibby	.08
230	Dave Winfield	1.50
231	Steve McCatty	.08
232	Alan Trammell	2.00
233	LaRue Washington	.08
234	Vern Ruhle	.08
235	Andre Dawson	2.00
236	Marc Hill	.08
237	Scott McGregor	.12
238	Rob Wilfong	.08
239	Don Aase	.08
240	Dave Kingman	.35
241	Checklist No. 2	.25
242	Lamar Johnson	.08
243	Jerry Augustine	.08
244	St. Louis Cardinals/ Ken Boyer (Mgr.)	.40
245	Phil Niekro	.75
246	Tim Foli	.08
247	Frank Riccelli	.08
248	Jamie Quirk	.08
249	Jim Clancy	.08
250	Jim Kaat	.40
251	Kip Young	.08
252	Ted Cox	.08
253	John Montague	.08
254	Paul Dade	.08
255	Dusty Baker	.08
256	Roger Erickson	.08
257	Larry Herndon	.08
258	Paul Moskau	.08
259	New York Mets/ Joe Torre (Mgr.)	.50
260	Al Oliver	.35
261	Dave Chalk	.08
262	Benny Ayala	.08
263	Dave LaRoche	.08
264	Bill Robinson	.08
265	Robin Yount	2.50
266	Bernie Carbo	.08
267	Dan Schatzeder	.08
268	Rafael Landestoy	.08
269	Dave Tobik	.08
270	Mike Schmidt	1.50
271	Dick Drago	.08
272	Ralph Garr	.08
273	Eduardo Rodriguez	.08
274	Dale Murphy	5.00
275	Jerry Koosman	.20
276	Tom Veryzer	.08
277	Rick Bosetti	.08
278	Jim Spencer	.08
279	Rob Andrews	.08
280	Gaylord Perry	.75
281	Paul Blair	.08
282	Seattle Mariners/ Darrell Johnson (Mgr.)	.35
283	John Ellis	.08
284	Larry Murray	.08
285	Don Baylor	.35
286	Darold Knowles	.08
287	John Lowenstein	.08
288	Dave Rozema	.08
289	Bruce Bochy	.08
290	Steve Garvey	1.50
291	Randy Scarberry	.08
292	Dale Berra	.08
293	Elias Sosa	.08
294	Charlie Spikes	.08
295	Larry Gura	.08
296	Dave Rader	.08
297	Tim Johnson	.08
298	Ken Holtzman	.08
299	Steve Henderson	.08
300	Ron Guidry	.60
301	Mike Edwards	.08
302	Los Angeles Dodgers/ Tom Lasorda (Mgr.)	.50
303	Bill Castro	.08
304	Butch Wynegar	.08
305	Randy Jones	.08
306	Denny Walling	.08
307	Rick Honeycutt	.12
308	Mike Hargrove	.08
309	Larry McWilliams	.12
310	Dave Parker	1.00
311	Roger Metzger	.08
312	Mike Barlow	.08
313	Johnny Grubb	.08
314	Tim Stoddard	.20
315	Steve Kemp	.15
316	Bob Lacey	.08
317	Mike Anderson	.08
318	Jerry Reuss	.12
319	Chris Speier	.08
320	Dennis Eckersley	.50
321	Keith Hernandez	1.25
322	Claudell Washington	.15
323	Mick Kelleher	.08
324	Tom Underwood	.08
325	Dan Driessen	.08
326	Bo McLaughlin	.08
327	Ray Fosse	.08
328	Minnesota Twins/ Gene Mauch (Mgr.)	.35
329	Bert Roberge	.08
330	Al Cowens	.08
331	Rich Hebner	.08
332	Enrique Romo	.08
333	Jim Norris	.08
334	Jim Beattie	.08
335	Willie McCovey	1.50
336	George Medich	.08
337	Carney Lansford	1.00
338	Johnny Wockenfuss	.08
339	John D'Acquisto	.08
340	Ken Singleton	.15
341	Jim Essian	.08
342	Odell Jones	.08
343	Mike Vail	.08
344	Randy Lerch	.08
345	Larry Parrish	.12
346	Buddy Solomon	.08
347	Harry Chappas	.08
348	Checklist No. 3	.25
349	Jack Brohamer	.08
350	George Hendrick	.15
351	Bob Davis	.08
352	Dan Briggs	.08
353	Andy Hassler	.08
354	Rick Auerbach	.08
355	Gary Matthews	.15
356	San Diego Padres/ Jerry Coleman (Mgr.)	.35
357	Bob McClure	.08
358	Lou Whitaker	1.00
359	Randy Moffitt	.08
360	Darrell Porter	.08
361	Wayne Garland	.08
362	Danny Goodwin	.08
363	Wayne Gross	.08
364	Ray Burris	.08
365	Bobby Murcer	.20
366	Rob Dressler	.08
367	Billy Smith	.08
368	Willie Aikens (R)	.25
369	Jim Kern	.08
370	Cesar Cedeno	.15
371	Jack Morris	1.25
372	Joel Youngblood	.08
373	Dan Petry (R)	.50
374	Jim Gantner	.08
375	Ross Grimsley	.08
376	Gary Allenson	.15
377	Junior Kennedy	.08
378	Jerry Mumphrey	.08
379	Kevin Bell	.08
380	Garry Maddox	.09
381	Chicago Cubs/ Preston Gomez (Mgr.)	.35
382	Dave Freisleben	.08
383	Ed Ott	.08
384	Joey McLaughlin	.08
385	Enos Cabell	.08
386	Darrell Jackson	.08
387	Fred Stanley	.08
388	Mike Paxton	.08
389	Pete LaCock	.08
390	Fergie Jenkins	.40
391	Tony Armas	.12
392	Milt Wilcox	.08
393	Ozzie Smith	3.50
394	Reggie Cleveland	.08
395	Ellis Valentine	.08
396	Dan Meyer	.08
397	Roy Thomas	.08
398	Barry Foote	.08
399	Mike Proly	.08
400	George Foster	.50
401	Pete Falcone	.08
402	Merv Rettenmund	.08
403	Pete Redfern	.08
404	Baltimore Orioles/ Earl Weaver (Mgr.)	.45
405	Dwight Evans	.75
406	Paul Molitor	1.25
407	Tony Solaita	.08
408	Bill North	.08
409	Paul Splittorff	.08
410	Bobby Bonds	.12
411	Frank LaCorte	.08
412	Thad Bosley	.08
413	Allen Ripley	.08
414	George Scott	.12
415	Bill Atkinson	.08
416	Tom Brookens	.08
417	Carig Chamberlain	.08
418	Roger Freed	.08
419	Vic Correll	.08
420	Butch Hobson	.08
421	Doug Bird	.08
422	Larry Milbourne	.08
423	Dave Frost	.08
424	New York Yankees/ Dick Howser (Mgr.)	.60
425	Mark Belanger	.15
426	Grant Jackson	.08
427	Tom Hutton	.08
428	Pat Zachry	.08
429	Duane Kuiper	.08
430	Larry Hisle	.08
431	Mike Krukow	.12
432	Willie Norwood	.08
433	Rich Gale	.08
434	Johnnie LeMaster	.08
435	Don Gullett	.08
436	Billy Almon	.08
437	Joe Niekro	.15
438	Dave Revering	.08
439	Mike Phillips	.08
440	Don Sutton	.60
441	Eric Soderholm	.08
442	Jorge Orta	.08
443	Mike Parrott	.08
444	Alvis Woods	.08
445	Mark Fidrych	.15

NO.	PLAYER	MINT
446	Duffy Dyer	.08
447	Nino Espinosa	.08
448	Jim Wohlford	.08
449	Doug Bair	.08
450	George Brett	3.50
451	Cleveland Indians/ Dave Garcia (Mgr.)	.35
452	Steve Dillard	.08
453	Mike Bacsik	.08
454	Tom Donohue	.08
455	Mike Torrez	.08
456	Frank Taveras	.08
457	Bert Blyleven	.35
458	Billy Sample	.08
459	Mickey Lolich	.08
460	Willie Randolph	.20
461	Dwayne Murphy	.15
462	Mike Sadek	.08
463	Jerry Royster	.08
464	John Denny	.15
465	Rick Monday	.15
466	Mike Squires	.08
467	Jesse Jefferson	.08
468	Aurelio Rodriquez	.08
469	Randy Niemann	.08
470	Bob Boone	.12
471	Hosken Powell	.08
472	Willie Hernandez	.25
473	Bump Wills	.08
474	Steve Busby	.08
475	Cesar Geronimo	.08
476	Bob Shirley	.08
477	Buck Martinez	.08
478	Gil Flores	.08
479	Montreal Expos/ Dick Williams (Mgr.)	.35
480	Bob Watson	.08
481	Tom Paciorek	.08
482	R. Henderson (R)	30.00
483	Bo Diaz	.08
484	Checklist No. 4	.25
485	Mickey Rivers	.15
486	Mike Tyson	.08
487	Wayne Nordhagen	.08
488	Roy Howell	.08
489	Preston Hanna	.08
490	Lee May	.15
491	Steve Mura	.08
492	Todd Cruz	.08
493	Jerry Martin	.08
494	Craig Minetto	.08
495	Bake McBride	.08
496	Silvio Martinez	.08
497	Jim Mason	.08
498	Danny Darwin	.08
499	San Francisco Giants/ Dave Bristol (Mgr.)	.35
500	Tom Seaver	1.50
501	Rennie Stennett	.08
502	Rich Wortham	.08
503	Mike Cubbage	.08
504	Gener Garber	.08
505	Bert Campaneris	.15
506	Tom Buskey	.08
507	Leon Roberts	.08
508	U.L. Washington	.08
509	Ed Glynn	.08
510	Ron Cey	.40
511	Eric Wilkins	.08
512	Jose Cardenal	.08
513	Tom Dixon	.08
514	Steve Ontiveros	.08
515	Mike Caldwell	.08
516	Hector Cruz	.08
517	Don Stanhouse	.08
518	Nelson Norman	.08
519	Steve Nicosia	.08
520	Steve Rogers	.15
521	Ken Brett	.08
522	Jim Morrison	.08
523	Ken Henderson	.08
524	Jim Wright	.08
525	Clint Hurdle	.08
526	Philadelphia Phillies/ Dallas Green (Mgr.)	.35
527	Doug Rau	.08

NO.	PLAYER	MINT
528	Adrian Devine	.08
529	Jim Barr	.08
530	Jim Sundberg	.08
531	Eric Rasmussen	.08
532	Willie Horton	.12
533	Checklist No. 5	.25
534	Andre Thornton	.15
535	Bob Forsch	.12
536	Lee Lacy	.12
537	Alex Trevino	.12
538	Joe Strain	.08
539	Rudy May	.08
540	Pete Rose	3.00
541	Miguel Dilone	.08
542	Joe Coleman	.08
543	Pat Kelly	.08
544	Rick Sutcliffe (R)	3.50
545	Jeff Burroughs	.08
546	Rick Langford	.08
547	John Wathan	.08
548	Dave Rajsich	.08
549	Larry Wolfe	.08
550	Ken Griffey	.12
551	Pittsburgh Pirates/ Chuck Tanner (Mgr.)	.35
552	Bill Nahorodny	.08
553	Dick Davis	.08
554	Art Howe	.08
555	Ed Figueroa	.08
556	Joe Rudi	.15
557	Mark Lee	.08
558	Alfredo Griffin	.15
559	Dale Murray	.08
560	Dave Lopes	.15
561	Eddie Whitson	.12
562	Joe Wallis	.08
563	Will McEnaney	.08
564	Rick Manning	.08
565	Dennis Leonard	.12
566	Bud Harrelson	.08
567	Skip Lockwood	.08
568	Gary Roenicke (R)	.30
569	Terry Kennedy	.30
570	Roy Smalley	.08
571	Joe Sambito	.08
572	Jerry Morales	.08
573	Kent Tekulve	.12
574	Scot Thompson	.08
575	Ken Kravec	.08
576	Jim Dwyer	.08
577	Toronto Blue Jays/ Bobby Mattick (Mgr.)	.30
578	Scott Sanderson	.08
579	Charlie Moore	.08
580	Nolan Ryan	3.50
581	Bob Bailor	.08
582	Brian Doyle	.08
583	Bob Stinson	.08
584	Kurt Bevacqua	.08
585	Al Hrabosky	.08
586	Mitchell Page	.08
587	Garry Templeton	.25
588	Greg Minton	.08
589	Chet Lemon	.15
590	Jim Palmer	1.25
591	Rick Cerone	.08
592	Jon Matlack	.08
593	Jesus Alou	.08
594	Dick Tidrow	.08
595	Don Money	.08
596	Rick Matula	.08
597	Tom Poquette	.08
598	Fred Kendall	.08
599	Mike Norris	.08
600	Reggie Jackson	2.00
601	Buddy Schultz	.08
602	Brian Downing	.08
603	Jack Billingham	.08
604	Glenn Adams	.08
605	Terry Forster	.12
606	Cincinnati Reds/ John McNamara (Mgr.)	.30
607	Woodie Fryman	.08
608	Alan Bannister	.08
609	Ron Reed	.08
610	Willie Stargell	1.50

NO.	PLAYER	MINT
611	Jerry Garvin	.08
612	Cliff Johnson	.08
613	Randy Stein	.08
614	John Hiller	.08
615	Doug DeCinces	.20
616	Gene Richards	.08
617	Joaquin Andujar	.30
618	Bob Montgomery	.08
619	Sergio Ferrer	.08
620	Richie Zisk	.15
621	Bob Grich	.12
622	Mario Soto	.20
623	Gorman Thomas	.25
624	Lerrin LaGrow	.08
625	Chris Chambliss	.12
626	Detroit Tigers/ S. Anderson (Mgr.)	.50
627	Pedro Borbon	.08
628	Doug Capilla	.08
629	Jim Todd	.08
630	Larry Bowa	.15
631	Mark Littell	.08
632	Barry Bonnell	.08
633	Bob Apodaca	.08
634	Glenn Borgmann	.08
635	John Candelaria	.12
636	Toby Harrah	.08
637	Joe Simpson	.08
638	Mark Clear (R)	.30
639	Larry Biittner	.08
640	Mike Flanagan	.12
641	Ed Kranepool	.15
642	Ken Forsch	.08
643	John Mayberry	.15
644	Charlie Hough	.12
645	Rick Burleson	.12
646	Checklist No. 6	.25
647	Milt May	.08
648	Roy White	.12
649	Tom Griffin	.08
650	Joe Morgan	.75
651	Rollie Fingers	.60
652	Mario Mendoza	.08
653	Stan Bahnsen	.08
654	Bruce Boisclair	.08
655	Tug McGraw	.15
656	Larvell Blanks	.08
657	Dave Edwards	.08
658	Chris Knapp	.08
659	Milwaukee Brewers/ George Bamberger (Mgr.)	.25
660	Rusty Staub	.25
661	Orioles Rookies: Wayne Krenchicki, Mark Corey, D. Ford	.15
662	Red Sox Rookies: J. Finch, Mike O'Berry, Chuck Rainey	.15
663	Angels Rookies: Ralph Botting, Bob Clark, Dickey Thon	.50
664	White Sox Rookies: Guy Hoffman, M. Colbern, Dewey Robinson	.15
665	Indians Rookies: Larry Anderson, Bobby Cuellar, Randy Wihtol	.15
666	Tigers Rookies: M. Chris, Bruce Robbins, Al Greene	.25
667	Royals Rookies: R. Martin, Bill Paschall, Dan Quisenberry	2.00
668	Brewers Rookies: Danny Boitano, W. Mueller, Lenn Sakata	.15
669	Twin Rookies: Rick Sofield, Dan Graham, Gary Ward	.50
670	Yankee Rookies: B. Brown, Brad Gulden, Darryl Jones	.25
671	A's Rookies: Derek Bryant, B. Kingman, Mike Morgan	.75

NO.	PLAYER	MINT
672	Mariners Rookies: Rodney Craig, Charlie Beamon, Rafael Vasquez	.15
673	Rangers Rookies: Brian Allard, Jerry Don Gleaton, Greg Mahlberg	.15
674	Blue Jays Rookies: Butch Edge, Pat Kelly, Ted Wilborn	.15
675	Braves Rookies: Bruce Benedict, Eddie Miller, Larry Bradford	.20
676	Cubs Rookies: Steve Macko, Dave Geisel, Karl Pagel	.20
677	Reds Rookies: Art DeFreites, Harry Spilman, Frank Pastore	.15
678	Astros Rookies: Reggie Baldwin, A. Knicely, Pete Ladd	.20
679	Dodgers Rookies: Joe Beckwith, Mickey Hatcher, Dave Patterson	.50
680	Expos Rookies: Randy Miller, Tony Bernazard, John Tamarqo	.40
681	Mets Rookies: Dan Norman, J. Orosco, Mike Scott	8.00
682	Phillies Rookies: Kevin Saucier, Ramon Aviles, Dickie Noles	.25
683	Pirates Rookies: D. Boyland, Alberto Lois, Harry Saferight	.15
684	Cardinals Rookies: George Frazier, Tom Herr, Dan O'Brien	.60
685	Padres Rookies: Brian Greer, Tim Flannery, Jim Wilhelm	.15
686	Giants Rookies: Greg Johnston, D. Littlejohn, Phil Nastu	.15
687	Mike Heath	.08
688	Steve Stone	.15
689	Boston Red Sox/ Don Zimmer (Mgr.)	.40
690	Tommy John	.50
691	Ivan DeJesus	.08
692	Rawly Eastwick	.08
693	Craig Kusick	.08
694	Jim Rooker	.08
695	Reggie Smith	.15
696	Julio Gonzalez	.08
697	David Clyde	.08
698	Oscar Gamble	.15
699	Floyd Bannister	.15
700	Rod Carew	.75
701	Ken Oberkfell	.30
702	Ed Farmer	.08
703	Otto Velez	.08
704	Gene Tenace	.08
705	Freddie Patek	.08
706	Tippy Martinez	.08
707	Elliott Maddox	.08
708	Bob Tolan	.08
709	Pat Underwood	.08
710	Graig Nettles	.25
711	Bob Galasso	.08
712	Rodney Scott	.08
713	Terry Whitfield	.08
714	Fred Norman	.08
715	Sal Bando	.15
716	Lynn McGlothen	.08
717	Mickey Klutts	.08
718	Greg Gross	.08
719	Don Robinson	.12
720	Carl Yastrzemski	1.25
721	Paul Hartzell	.08
722	Jose Cruz	.25
723	Shane Rawley	.12
724	Jerry White	.08
725	Rick Wise	.08
726	Steve Yeager	.12

1981 Topps....Complete Set of 726 Cards—Value $85.00

Features the rookie cards of Fernando Valenzuela, Kirk Gibson, Harold Baines and Tim Raines. 66 cards were double printed. In 1981 Topps began getting competition from two other card manufacturers—Donruss and Fleer.

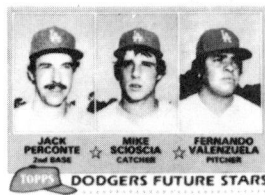

NO.	PLAYER	MINT
1	Batting Leaders: Bill Buckner, George Brett	.60
2	Home Run Leaders: Reggie Jackson, Ben Oglivie, M. Schmidt	.30
3	RBI Leaders: Cecil Cooper, Mike Schmidt	.25
4	Stolen Base Leaders: Rickey Henderson, Ron LeFlore	.20
5	Victory Leaders: Steve Carlton, Steve Stone	.15
6	Strikeout Leaders: Len Barker, Steve Carlton	.15
7	ERA Leaders: Don Sutton, Rudy May	.10
8	Leading Firemen: Dan Quisenberry, Tom Hume, Rollie Fingers	.15
9	Pete LaCock	.07
10	Mike Flanagan	.12
11	Jim Wohlford	.07
12	Mark Clear	.07
13	Joe Charboneau	.12
14	John Tudor (R)	1.50
15	Larry Parrish	.10
16	Ron Davis	.10
17	Cliff Johnson	.07
18	Glenn Adams	.07
19	Jim Clancy	.07
20	Jeff Burroughs	.07
21	Ron Oester	.07
22	Danny Darwin	.07
23	Alex Trevino	.07
24	Don Stanhouse	.07
25	Sicto Lezcano	.07
26	U.L. Washington	.07
27	Champ Summers	.07
28	Enrique Romo	.07
29	Gene Tenace	.07
30	Jack Clark	.60
31	Checklist No. 1	.15
32	Ken Oberkfell	.07
33	Rick Honeycutt	.07
34	Aurelio Rodriquez	.07
35	Mitchell Page	.07
36	Ed Farmer	.07
37	Gary Roenicke	.07
38	Win Remmerswaal	.07
39	Tom Veryzer	.07
40	Tug McGraw	.12
41	Ranger Rookies: Bob Babcock, J. Butcher, Jerry Don Gleaton	.20
42	Jerry White	.07
43	Jose Morales	.07
44	Larry McWilliams	.07
45	Enos Cabell	.07
46	Rick Bosetti	.07
47	Ken Brett	.07
48	Dave Skaggs	.07
49	Bob Shirley	.07
50	Dave Lope	.12
51	Bill Robinson	.07
52	Hector Cruz	.07

NO.	PLAYER	MINT
53	Kevin Saucler	.07
54	Ivan DeJesus	.07
55	Mike Norris	.07
56	Buck Martinez	.07
57	Dave Roberts	.07
58	Joel Youngblood	.07
59	Dan Petry	.25
60	Willie Randolph	.12
61	Butch Wynegar	.10
62	Joe Pettini	.07
63	Steve Renko	.07
64	Brian Asselstine	.07
65	Scott McGregor	.10
66	Royals Rookies: Tim Ireland, Manny Castillo, Mike Jones	.15
67	Ken Kravec	.07
68	Matt Alexander	.07
69	Ed Halicki	.07
70	Al Oliver	.12
71	Hal Dues	.07
72	Barry Evans	.07
73	Doug Bair	.07
74	Mike Hargrove	.07
75	Reggie Smith	.12
76	Mario Mendoza	.07
77	Mike Barlow	.07
78	Steve Dillard	.07
79	Bruce Robbins	.07
80	Rusty Staub	.15
81	Dave Stapleton	.15
82	Astros Rookies: Bobby Sprowl, Danny Heep, Alan Knicely	.10
83	Mike Proly	.07
84	Johnnie LeMaster	.07
85	Mike Caldwell	.07
86	Wayne Gross	.07
87	Rick Camp	.07
88	Joe LeFebvre	.15
89	Darrell Jackson	.07
90	Bake McBride	.07
91	Tim Stoddard	.07
92	Mike Easler	.12
93	Ed Glynn	.07
94	Harry Spilman	.07
95	Jim Sundberg	.07
96	A's Rookies: Dave Beard, Pat Dempsey, E. Camacho	.12
97	Chris Speier	.07
98	Clint Hurdle	.07
99	Eric Wilkins	.07
100	Rod Carew	1.00
101	Benny Ayala	.07
102	Dave Tobik	.07
103	Jerry Martin	.07
104	Terry Forster	.12
105	Jose Cruz	.20
106	Don Money	.07
107	Rich Wortham	.07
108	Bruce Benedict	.07
109	Mike Scott	1.25
110	Carl Yastrzemski	1.50
111	Greg Minton	.07

NO.	PLAYER	MINT
112	White Sox Rookies: Rusty Kuntz, F. Mullin, Leo Sutherland	.15
113	Mike Phillips	.07
114	Tom Underwood	.07
115	Roy Smalley	.07
116	Joe Simpson	.07
117	Pete Falcone	.07
118	Kurt Bevacqua	.07
119	Tippy Martinez	.07
120	Larry Bowa	.12
121	Larry Harlow	.07
122	John Denny	.15
123	Al Cowens	.07
124	Jerry Garvin	.07
125	Andre Dawson	1.00
126	Charlie Leibrandt (R)	.50
127	Rudy Law	.07
128	Garry Allenson	.07
129	Art Howe	.07
130	Larry Gura	.07
131	Keith Moreland (R)	.50
132	Tommy Boggs	.07
133	Jeff Cox	.07
134	Steve Mura	.07
135	Gorman Thomas	.20
136	Doug Capilla	.07
137	Hosken Powell	.07
138	Rich Dotson (R)	.35
139	Oscar Gamble	.07
140	Bob Forsch	.07
141	Miguel Dilone	.07
142	Jackson Todd	.07
143	Dan Meyer	.07
144	Allen Ripley	.07
145	Mickey Rivers	.10
146	Bobby Castillo	.07
147	Dale Berra	.07
148	Randy Niemann	.07
149	Joe Nolan	.07
150	Mark Fidrych	.10
151	Claudell Washington	.10
152	John Urrea	.07
153	Tom Poquette	.07
154	Rick Langford	.07
155	Chris Chambliss	.10
156	Bob McClure	.07
157	John Wathan	.07
158	Fergie Jenkins	.30
159	Brian Doyle	.07
160	Garry Maddox	.07
161	Dan Graham	.07
162	Doug Corbett	.12
163	Billy Almon	.07
164	LaMarr Hoyt (R)	.20
165	Tony Scott	.07
166	Floyd Bannister	.07
167	Terry Whitfield	.07
168	Don Robinson	.07
169	John Mayberry	.07
170	Ross Grimsley	.07
171	Gene Richards	.07
172	Gary Woods	.07
173	Bump Wills	.07
174	Doug Rau	.07
175	Dave Collins	.07

NO.	PLAYER	MINT
176	Mike Krukow	.07
177	Rick Peters	.12
178	Jim Essian	.07
179	Rudy May	.07
180	Pete Rose	3.00
181	Elias Sosa	.07
182	Bob Grich	.12
183	Dick Davis	.07
184	Jim Dwyer	.07
185	Dennis Leonard	.07
186	Wayne Nordhagen	.07
187	Mike Parrott	.07
188	Doug DeCinces	.15
189	Craig Swan	.07
190	Cesar Cedeno	.15
191	Rick Sutcliffe	.50
192	Braves Rookies: Terry Harper, Rafael Ramirez, Ed Miller	.35
193	Pete Vuckovich	.12
194	Rod Scurry	.10
195	Rich Murray	.07
196	Duffy Dyer	.07
197	Jim Kern	.07
198	Jerry Dybzinski	.07
199	Chuck Rainey	.07
200	George Foster	.30
201	Record—J. Bench Most HR's, Catcher, Career	.45
202	Record—S. Carlton Strikeouts, Lefty, Career	.35
203	Record—B. Gullickson Strikeouts, Game, Rookie	.12
204	Rec.—LeFlore, Scott SB's, Teammates, Season	.12
205	Record—P. Rose Most Consecutive Seasons, 600 or More At-Bats	.75
206	Record—M. Schmidt Homers, 3B, Season	.45
207	Record—O. Smith Assists, SS, Season	.15
208	Record—W. Wilson Most At-Bats, Season	.15
209	Dickie Thon	.07
210	Jim Palmer	.75
211	Derrel Thomas	.07
212	Steve Nicosia	.07
213	Al Holland (R)	.25
214	Angels Rookies: John Harris, Ralph Botting, Jim Dorsey	.15
215	Larry Hisle	.07
216	John Henry Johnson	.07
217	Rich Hebner	.07
218	Paul Splittorff	.07
219	Ken Landreaux	.07
220	Tom Seaver	1.00
221	Bob Davis	.07
222	Jorge Orta	.07
223	Roy Lee Jackson	.10
224	Pat Zachry	.07
225	Ruppert Jones	.07
226	Manny Sanguillen	.07
227	Fred Martinez	.07
228	Tom Paciorek	.07

NO. PLAYER	MINT
229 Rollie Fingers	.50
230 George Hendrick	.12
231 Joe Beckwith	.07
232 Mickey Klutts	.07
233 Skip Lockwood	.07
234 Lou Whitaker	.40
235 Scott Sanderson	.07
236 Mike Ivie	.07
237 Charlie Moore	.07
238 Willie Hernandez	.20
239 Rick Miller	.07
240 Nolan Ryan	2.25
241 Checklist No. 2	.15
242 Chet Lemon	.12
243 Sal Butera	.07
244 Cardinals Rookies:	.20
Andy Rincon, T. Landrum,	
Al Olmsted	
245 Ed Figueroa	.07
246 Ed Ott	.07
247 Glenn Hubbard	.07
248 Joey McLaughlin	.07
249 Larry Cox	.07
250 Ron Guidry	.40
251 Tom Brookens	.07
252 Victor Cruz	.07
253 Dave Bergman	.07
254 Ozzie Smith	1.50
255 Mark Littell	.07
256 Bombo Rivera	.07
257 Rennie Stennett	.07
258 Joe Price	.07
259 Mets Rookies:	2.00
Juan Berenguer, H. Brooks,	
Mookie Wilson	
260 Ron Cey	.30
261 Ricky Henderson	5.00
262 Sammy Stewart	.07
263 Brian Downing	.07
264 Jim Norris	.07
265 John Candelaria	.10
266 Tom Herr	.20
267 Stan Bahnsen	.07
268 Jerry Royster	.07
269 Ken Forsch	.07
270 Greg Luzinski	.15
271 Bill Castro	.07
272 Bruce Kimm	.07
273 Stan Papi	.07
274 Craig Chamberlain	.07
275 Dwight Evans	.35
276 Dan Spillner	.07
277 Alfredo Griffin	.10
278 Rick Sofield	.07
279 Bob Knepper	.12
280 Ken Griffey	.12
281 Fred Stanley	.07
282 Mariners Rookies:	.15
Rick Anderson, Rodney	
Craig, Greg Biercevicz	
283 Billy Sample	.07
284 Brian Kingman	.07
285 Jerry Turner	.07
286 Dave Frost	.07
287 Lenn Sakata	.07
288 Bob Clark	.07
289 Mickey Hatcher	.07
290 Bob Boone	.07
291 Aurelio Lopez	.07
292 Mike Squires	.07
293 Charlie Lea (R)	.20
294 Mike Tyson	.07
295 Hal McRae	.10
296 Bill Nahorodny	.07
297 Bob Bailor	.07
298 Buddy Solomon	.07
299 Elliott Maddox	.07
300 Paul Molitor	.40
301 Matt Keough	.07
302 Dodgers Rookies:	6.00
Mike Scioscia, Jack	
Perconte, F. Valenzuela	
303 Johnny Oates	.07
304 John Castino	.07
305 Ken Clay	.07

NO. PLAYER	MINT
306 Juan Beniquez	.07
307 Gene Garber	.07
308 Rick Manning	.07
309 Luis Salazar	.15
310 Vida Blue	.07
311 Freddie Patek	.07
312 Rick Rhoden	.12
313 Luis Pujols	.07
314 Rich Dauer	.07
315 Kirk Gibson (R)	7.50
316 Craig Minetto	.07
317 Lonnie Smith	.15
318 Steve Yeager	.07
319 Rowland Office	.07
320 Tom Burgmeier	.07
321 Leon Durham (R)	.50
322 Neil Allen	.07
323 Jim Morrison	.07
324 Mike Willis	.07
325 Ray Knight	.15
326 Biff Pocoroba	.07
327 Moose Haas	.07
328 Twins Rookies:	.35
Dave Engle, G. Johnston,	
Gary Ward	
329 Joaquin Andujar	.15
330 Frank White	.12
331 Dennis Lamp	.07
332 Lee Lacy	.07
333 Sid Monge	.07
334 Dane Iorg	.07
335 Rick Cerone	.07
336 Eddie Whitson	.10
337 Lynn Jones	.05
338 Checklist No.3	.15
339 John Ellis	.07
340 Bruce Kison	.07
341 Dwayne Murphy	.12
342 Eric Rasmussen	.07
343 Frank Taveras	.07
344 Byron McLaughlin	.07
345 Warren Cromartie	.07
346 Larry Christenson	.07
347 Harold Baines (R)	4.00
348 Bob Sykes	.12
349 Glenn Hoffman	.15
350 J.R. Richard	.12
351 Otto Velez	.07
352 Dick Tidrow	.07
353 Terry Kennedy	.15
354 Mario Soto	.15
355 Bob Horner	.30
356 Padres Rookies:	.15
George Stablein, C. Stimac,	
Tom Tellmann	
357 Jim Slaton	.07
358 Mark Wagner	.07
359 Tom Hausman	.07
360 Willie Wilson	.25
361 Joe Strain	.07
362 Bo Diaz	.07
363 Geoff Zahn	.07
364 Mike Davis (R)	.30
365 Graig Nettles	.07
366 Mike Ramsey	.07
367 Denny Martinez	.07
368 Leon Roberts	.07
369 Frank Tanana	.15
370 Dave Winfield	1.25
371 Charlie Hough	.07
372 Jay Johnstone	.07
373 Pat Underwood	.07
374 Tom Hutton	.07
375 Dave Concepcion	.15
376 Ron Reed	.07
377 Jerry Morales	.07
378 Dave Rader	.07
379 Lary Sorensen	.07
380 Willie Stargell	1.00
381 Cubs Rookies:	.20
Carlos Lezcano, Steve	
Macko, Randy Martz	
382 Paul Mirabella	.07
383 Eric Soderholm	.07
384 Mike Sadek	.07

NO. PLAYER	MINT
385 Joe Sambito	.07
386 Dave Edwards	.07
387 Phil Niekro	.65
388 Andre Thornton	.15
389 Marty Pattin	.07
390 Cesar Geronimo	.07
391 Dave Lemanczyk	.07
392 Lance Parrish	.60
393 Broderick Perkins	.07
394 Woodie Fryman	.07
395 Scot Thompson	.07
396 Bill Campbell	.07
397 Julio Cruz	.07
398 Ross Baumgarten	.07
399 Orioles Rookies:	1.50
Mike Boddicker, Mark	
Corey, Floyd Rayford	
400 Reggie Jackson	1.50
401 A.L. Championships:	.40
Royals Sweep Yanks	
402 N.L. Championships:	.25
Phillies Beat Astros	
403 1980 World Series:	.25
Phillies Beat Royals	
404 1980 World Series:	.25
Phillies Win	
405 Nino Espinosa	.07
406 Dickie Noles	.07
407 Ernie Whitt	.07
408 Fernando Arroyo	.07
409 Larry Herndon	.07
410 Bert Campaneris	.07
411 Terry Puhl	.07
412 Britt Burns (R)	.20
413 Tony Bernazard	.07
414 John Pacella	.07
415 Ben Oglivie	.12
416 Gary Alexander	.07
417 Dan Schatzeder	.07
418 Bobby Brown	.07
419 Tom Hume	.07
420 Keith Hernandez	.75
421 Bob Stanley	.07
422 Dan Ford	.07
423 Shane Rawley	.12
424 Yankees Rookies:	.20
Tim Lollar, Bruce	
Robinson, Dennis Werth	
425 Al Bumbry	.07
426 Warren Brusstar	.07
427 Jonn D'Acquisto	.07
428 John Stearns	.07
429 Mick Kelleher	.07
430 Jim Bibby	.07
431 Dave Roberts	.07
432 Len Barker	.12
433 Rance Mulliniks	.07
434 Roger Erickson	.07
435 Jim Spencer	.07
436 Gary Lucas	.12
437 Mike Heath	.07
438 John Montefusco	.07
439 Denny Walling	.07
440 Jerry Reuss	.12
441 Ken Reitz	.07
442 Ron Pruitt	.07
443 Jim Beattie	.07
444 Garth Iorg	.07
445 Ellis Valentine	.07
446 Checklist No. 4	.15
447 Junior Kennedy	.07
448 Tim Corcoran	.07
449 Paul Mitchell	.07
450 Dave Kingman	.15
451 Indians Rookies:	.20
Chris Bando, Tom Brennan,	
Sandy Wihtol	
452 Renie Martin	.07
453 Rob Wilfong	.07
454 Andy Hassler	.07
455 Rick Burleson	.12
456 Jeff Reardon (R)	.75
457 Mike Lum	.07
458 Randy Jones	.07
459 Greg Gross	.07

NO. PLAYER	MINT
460 Rich Gossage	.35
461 Dave McKay	.07
462 Jack Brohamer	.07
463 Milt May	.07
464 Adrian Devine	.07
465 Bill Russell	.07
466 Bob Molinaro	.07
467 Dave Stieb	.50
468 Johnny Wockenfuss	.07
469 Jeff Leonard	.30
470 Manny Trillo	.07
471 Mike Vail	.07
472 Dyar Miller	.07
473 Jose Cardenal	.07
474 Mike LaCoss	.07
475 Buddy Bell	.20
476 Jerry Koosman	.15
477 Luis Gomez	.07
478 Juan Eichelberger	.07
479 Expos Rookies:	9.00
B. Pate, Tim Raines,	
Roberto Ramos	
480 Carlton Fisk	.50
481 Bob Lacey	.07
482 Jim Gantner	.07
483 Mike Griffin	.07
484 Max Venable	.07
485 Garry Templeton	.20
486 Marc Hill	.07
487 Dewey Robinson	.07
488 Damaso Garcia (R)	.30
489 John Littlefield	.07
490 Eddie Murray	1.25
491 Gordy Pladson	.07
492 Barry Foote	.07
493 Dan Quisenberry	.30
494 Bob Walk	.25
495 Dusty Baker	.12
496 Paul Dade	.07
497 Fred Norman	.07
498 Pat Putnam	.07
499 Frank Pastore	.07
500 Jim Rice	.75
501 Tim Foli	.07
502 Giants Rookies:	.15
Chris Bourjos, Mike	
Rowland, A. Hargesheimer	
503 Steve McCatty	.07
504 Dale Murphy	2.50
505 Jason Thompson	.12
506 Phil Huffman	.07
507 Jamie Quirk	.07
508 Rob Dressler	.07
509 Pete Mackanin	.07
510 Lee Mazzilli	.07
511 Wayne Garland	.07
512 Gary Thomasson	.07
513 Frank LaCorte	.07
514 George Riley	.07
515 Robin Yount	1.25
516 Doug Bird	.07
517 Richie Zisk	.07
518 Grant Jackson	.07
519 John Tamargo	.07
520 Steve Stone	.07
521 Sam Mejias	.07
522 Mike Colbern	.07
523 John Fulgham	.07
524 Willie Aikens	.10
525 Mike Torrez	.07
526 Phillies Rookies:	.25
Marty Bystrom, Jay	
Loviglio, J. Wright	
527 Danny Goodwin	.07
528 Gary Matthews	.12
529 Dave LaRoche	.07
530 Steve Garvey	1.00
531 John Curtis	.07
532 Bill Stein	.07
533 Jesus Figueroa	.07
534 Dave Smith	.35
535 Omar Moreno	.12
536 Bob Owchinko	.07
537 Ron Hodges	.07
538 Tom Griffin	.07

NO. PLAYER	MINT
539 Rodney Scott	.07
540 Mike Schmidt	1.00
541 Steve Swisher	.07
542 Larry Bradford	.07
543 Terry Crowley	.07
544 Rich Gale	.07
545 Johnny Grubb	.07
546 Paul Moskau	.07
547 Mario Guerrero	.07
548 Dave Goltz	.07
549 Jerry Remy	.07
550 Tommy John	.30
551 Pirates Rookies:	2.00
Vance Law, Pascual Perez	
Tony Pena	
552 Steve Trout	.07
553 Tim Blackwell	.07
554 Bert Blyleven	.25
555 Cecil Cooper	.30
556 Jerry Mumphrey	.07
557 Chris Knapp	.07
558 Barry Bonnell	.07
559 Willie Montanez	.07
560 Joe Morgan	.75
561 Dennis Littlejohn	.07
562 Checklist No. 5	.15
563 Jim Kaat	.25
564 Ron Hassey	.07
565 Burt Hooton	.07
566 Del Unser	.07
567 Mark Bomback	.07
568 Dave Revering	.07
569 Al Williams	.07
570 Ken Singleton	.12
571 Todd Cruz	.07
572 Jack Morris	.50
573 Phil Garner	.07
574 Bill Caudill	.15
575 Tony Perez	.25
576 Reggie Cleveland	.07
577 Blue Jays Rookies:	.25
Luis Leal, Brian Miller,	
Ken Schrom	
578 Bill Gullickson (R)	.30
579 Tim Flannery	.07
580 Don Baylor	.30
581 Roy Howell	.07
582 Gaylord Perry	.50
583 Larry Milbourne	.07
584 Randy Lerch	.07

NO. PLAYER	MINT
585 Amos Otis	.12
586 Silvio Martinez	.07
587 Jeff Newman	.07
588 Gary Lavelle	.07
589 Lamar Johnson	.07
590 Bruce Sutter	.30
591 John Lowenstèin	.07
592 Steve Comer	.07
593 Steve Kemp	.15
594 Preston Hanna	.07
595 Butch Hobson	.07
596 Jerry Augustine	.07
597 Rafael Landestoy	.07
598 George Vukovich	.07
599 Dennis Kinney	.07
600 Johnny Bench	1.25
601 Don Aase	.07
602 Bobby Murcer	.15
603 John Verhoeven	.07
604 Rob Picciolo	.07
605 Don Sutton	.40
606 Reds Rookies:	.15
Bruce Berenyi, Geoff	
Combe, P. Householder	
607 Dave Palmer	.07
608 Greg Pryor	.07
609 Lynn McGlothen	.07
610 Darrell Porter	.07
611 Rick Matula	.07
612 Duane Kuiper	.07
613 Jim Anderson	.07
614 Dave Rozema	.07
615 Rick Dempsey	.07
616 Rick Wise	.07
617 Craig Reynolds	.07
618 John Milner	.07
619 Steve Henderson	.07
620 Dennis Eckersley	.07
621 Tom Donohue	.07
622 Randy Moffitt	.07
623 Sal Bando	.07
624 Bob Welch	.07
625 Bill Buckner	.15
626 Tigers Rookies:	.20
D. Steffen, Jerry Ujdur,	
Roger Weaver	
627 Luis Tiant	.12
628 Vic Correll	.07
629 Tony Armas	.20
630 Steve Carlton	.75

NO. PLAYER	MINT
631 Ron Jackson	.07
632 Alan Bannister	.07
633 Bill Lee	.07
634 Doug Flynn	.07
635 Bobby Bonds	.12
636 Al Hrabosky	.07
637 Jerry Narron	.07
638 Checklist No. 6	.15
639 Carney Lansford	.30
640 Dave Parker	.50
641 Mark Belanger	.07
642 Vern Ruhle	.07
643 Lloyd Moseby (R)	1.25
644 Ramon Aviles	.07
645 Rick Reuschel	.15
646 Marvis Foley	.07
647 Dick Drago	.07
648 Darrell Evans	.20
649 Manny Sarmiento	.07
650 Bucky Dent	.12
651 Pedro Guerrero	1.00
652 John Montague	.07
653 Bill Fahey	.07
654 Ray Burris	.07
655 Dan Driessen	.07
656 Jon Matlack	.07
657 Mike Cubbage	.07
658 Milt Wilcox	.07
659 Brewers Rookies:	.07
Ned Yost, J. Flinn,	
Ed Romero	
660 Gary Carter	1.25
661 Orioles Team	.20
662 Red Sox Team	.20
663 Angels Team	.20
664 White Sox Team	.20
665 Indians Team	.20
666 Tigers Team	.25
667 Royals Team	.20
668 Brewers Team	.20
669 Twins Team	.20
670 Yankees Team	.25
671 A's Team	.20
672 Mariners Team	.15
673 Rangers Team	.20
674 Blue Jays Team	.20
675 Braves Team	.20
676 Cubs Team	.20
677 Reds Team	.20
678 Astros Team	.20

NO. PLAYER	MINT
679 Dodgers Team	.25
680 Expos Team	.15
681 Mets Team	.20
682 Phillies Team	.20
683 Pirates Team	.20
684 Cardinals Team	.20
685 Padres Team	.20
686 Giants Team	.20
687 Jeff Jones	.10
688 Kiko Garcia	.07
689 Red Sox Rookies:	2.00
Bruce Hurst, Reid Nichols,	
Keith MacWhorter	
690 Bob Watson	.07
691 Dick Ruthven	.07
692 Lenny Randle	.07
693 Steve Howe (R)	.20
694 Bud Harrelson	.07
695 Kent Tekulve	.07
696 Alan Ashby	.07
697 Rick Waits	.07
698 Mike Jorgensen	.07
699 Glenn Abbott	.07
700 George Brett	2.00
701 Joe Rudi	.07
702 George Medich	.07
703 Alvis Woods	.07
704 Bill Travers	.07
705 Ted Simmons	.25
706 Dave Ford	.07
707 Dave Cash	.07
708 Doyle Alexander	.07
709 Alan Trammell	.25
710 Ron LeFlore	.07
711 Joe Ferguson	.07
712 Bill Bonham	.07
713 Bill North	.07
714 Pete Redfern	.07
715 Bill Madlock	.25
716 Glenn Borgmann	.07
717 Jim Barr	.07
718 Larry Biittner	.07
719 Sparky Lyle	.12
720 Fred Lynn	.35
721 Toby Harrah	.07
722 Joe Niekro	.12
723 Bruce Bochte	.07
724 Lou Piniella	.15
725 Steve Rogers	.12
726 Rick Monday	.15

1981 Topps Traded....Complete Set of 132 Cards—Value $25.00

This was the first Topps "traded" set issued since 1976. It updates the main 1981 card set with players who had changed teams during the season and rookies who joined their teams early in the season. The first card in the traded set is numbered 727. It begins where the main set ends. The complete set was packaged in a printed box and only distributed through card hobby dealers.

NO. PLAYER	MINT
727 Danny Ainge (RR)	.50
728 Doyle Alexander	.15
729 Gary Alexander	.08
730 Billy Almon	.08
731 Joaquin Andujar	.20
732 Bob Bailor	.08
733 Juan Beniquez	.12

NO. PLAYER	MINT
734 Dave Bergman	.08
735 Tony Bernazard	.08
736 Larry Biittner	.08
737 Doug Bird	.08
738 Bert Blyleven	.60
739 Mark Bomback	.08
740 Bobby Bonds	.12

NO. PLAYER	MINT
741 Rick Bosetti	.08
742 Hubie Brooks	1.25
743 Rick Burleson	.10
744 Ray Burris	.08
745 Jeff Burroughs	.10
746 Enos Cabell	.08
747 Ken Clay	.08

NO. PLAYER	MINT
748 Mark Clear	.08
749 Larry Cox	.08
750 Hector Cruz	.08
751 Victor Cruz	.08
752 Mike Cubbage	.08
753 Dick Davis	.08
754 Brian Doyle	.08

1981 Topps Traded (Continued)

NO. PLAYER	MINT	NO. PLAYER	MINT	NO. PLAYER	MINT	NO. PLAYER	MINT
755 Dick Drago	.08	781 Dave Kingman	.30	807 Joe Morgan	1.25	833 Harry Spilman	.08
756 Leon Durham	.50	782 Bob Knepper	.12	808 Jerry Mumphrey	.12	834 Fred Stanley	.08
757 Jim Dwyer	.08	783 Ken Kravec	.08	809 Gene Nelson (RR)	.35	835 Rusty Staub	.25
758 Dave Edwards	.08	784 Bob Lacey	.08	810 Ed Ott	.08	836 Bill Stein	.08
759 Jim Essian	.08	785 Dennis Lamp	.08	811 Bob Owchinko	.08	837 Joe Strain	.08
760 Bill Fahey	.08	786 Rafael Landestoy	.08	812 Gaylord Perry	1.00	838 Bruce Sutter	.50
761 Rollie Ringers	.75	787 Ken Landreaux	.12	813 Mike Phillips	.08	839 Don Sutton	1.00
762 Carlton Fisk	1.00	788 Carney Lansford	.60	814 Darrell Porter	.12	840 Steve Swisher	.08
763 Barry Foote	.08	789 Dave LaRoche	.08	815 Mike Proly	.08	841 Frank Tanana	.08
764 Ken Forsch	.12	790 Joe LeFebvre	.08	816 Tim Raines	8.00	842 Gene Tenace	.08
765 Kiko Garcia	.08	791 Ron LeFlore	.12	817 Lenny Randle	.08	843 Jason Thompson	.15
766 Cesar Geronimo	.08	792 Randy Lerch	.08	818 Doug Rau	.08	844 Dickie Thon	.25
767 Gary Gray	.08	793 Sixto Lezcano	.12	819 Jeff Reardon	.50	845 Bill Travers	.08
768 Mickey Hatcher	.08	794 John Littlefield	.08	820 Ken Reitz	.08	846 Tom Underwood	.08
769 Steve Henderson	.12	795 Mike Lum	.08	821 Steve Renko	.08	847 John Urrea	.08
770 Marc Hill	.08	796 Greg Luzinski	.30	822 Rick Reuschel	.20	848 Mike Vail	.08
771 Butch Hobson	.08	797 Fred Lynn	.65	823 Dave Revering	.08	849 Ellis Valentine	.12
772 Rick Honeycutt	.12	798 Jerry Martin	.08	824 Dave Roberts	.08	850 Fernando Valenzuela	5.00
773 Roy Howell	.08	799 Buck Martinez	.08	825 Leon Roberts	.08	851 Pete Vuckovich	.12
774 Mike Ivie	.08	800 Gary Matthews	.12	826 Joe Rudi	.12	852 Mark Wagner	.08
775 Roy Lee Jackson	.08	801 Mario Mendoza	.08	827 Kevin Saucier	.08	853 Bob Walk	.08
776 Cliff Johnson	.08	802 Larry Milbourne	.08	828 Tony Scott	.08	854 Claudell Washington	.12
777 Randy Jones	.10	803 Rick Miller	.08	829 Bob Shirley	.08	855 Dave Winfield	2.00
778 Ruppert Jones	.08	804 John Montefusco	.12	830 Ted Simmons	.40	856 Geoff Zahn	.08
779 Mick Kelleher	.08	805 Jerry Morales	.08	831 Lary Sorensen	.08	857 Richie Zisk	.12
780 Terry Kennedy	.30	806 Jose Morales	.08	832 Jim Spencer	.08	858 Traded Checklist	.20

1982 Topps. . . . Complete Set of 792 Cards—Value $100.00

The complete set was increased to 792 cards. Double printed cards were eliminated (66 double prints were in each set from 1978 to 1981). Includes the rookie cards of Cal Ripken, Jesse Barfield, Kent Hrbek and Steve Sax. Card 342 exists with the *autograph* deleted.

NO. PLAYER	MINT	NO. PLAYER	MINT	NO. PLAYER	MINT	NO. PLAYER	MINT
1 Highlights—Carlton	.50	27 Tom Herr	.15	58 John D'Acquisto	.07	89 Steve Henderson	.07
Sets NL Strikeout Record		28 John Urrea	.07	59 Rich Gedman (R)	.50	90 Nolan Ryan	1.50
2 Highlights—Davis	.10	29 Dwayne Murphy	.07	60 Tony Armas	.20	91 Carney Lansford	.15
Fans 8 Straight		30 Tom Seaver	.75	61 Tommy Boggs	.07	92 Brad Havens	.10
3 Highlights—Raines	.25	31 Seaver (Action)	.25	62 Mike Tyson	.07	93 Larry Hisle	.07
Swipes 71 Bases, Rookie		32 Gene Garber	.07	63 Mario Soto	.15	94 Andy Hassler	.75
4 Highlights—Rose	.60	33 Jerry Morales	.07	64 Lynn Jones	.07	95 Ozzie Smith	.20
Sets NL Career Hit Mark		34 Joe Sambito	.07	65 Terry Kennedy	.15	96 Royals Leaders:	.20
5 Highlights—Ryan	.40	35 Willie Aikens	.10	66 Astros Leaders:	.15	G. Brett, L. Gura	
5th Career No-Hitter		36 Rangers Leaders:	.15	Art Howe, Nolan Ryan		97 Paul Moskau	.07
6 Highlights—Valenzuela	.25	Al Oliver, George Medich		67 Rich Gale	.07	98 Terry Bulling	.07
8 Rookie Shutouts		37 Dan Graham	.07	68 Roy Howell	.07	99 Barry Bonnell	.07
7 Scott Sanderson	.07	38 Charlie Lea	.07	69 Al Williams	.07	100 Mike Schmidt	1.25
8 Rich Dauer	.07	39 Lou Whitaker	.35	70 Tim Raines	2.00	101 Schmidt (Action)	.60
9 Ron Guidry	.30	40 Dave Parker	.40	71 Roy Lee Jackson	.07	102 Dan Briggs	.07
10 Guidry (Action)	.15	41 Parker (Action)	.20	72 Rick Auerbach	.07	103 Bob Lacey	.07
11 Gary Alexander	.07	42 Rick Sofield	.07	73 Buddy Solomon	.07	104 Rance Mulliniks	.07
12 Moose Haas	.07	43 Mike Cubbage	.07	74 Bob Clark	.07	105 Kirk Gibson	1.25
13 Lamar Johnson	.07	44 Britt Burns	.10	75 Tommy John	.25	106 Enrique Romo	.07
14 Steve Howe	.07	45 Rick Cerone	.07	76 Greg Pryor	.07	107 Wayne Krenchicki	.07
15 Ellis Valentine	.07	46 Jerry Augustine	.07	77 Miguel Dilone	.07	108 Bob Sykes	.07
16 Steve Comer	.07	47 Jeff Leonard	.15	78 George Medich	.07	109 Dave Revering	.07
17 Darrell Evans	.15	48 Bobby Castillo	.07	79 Bob Bailor	.07	110 Carlton Fisk	.45
18 Fernando Arroyo	.07	49 Alvis Woods	.07	80 Jim Palmer	.50	111 Fisk (Action)	.15
19 Ernie Whitt	.07	50 Buddy Bell	.15	81 Palmer (Action)	.15	112 Billy Sample	.07
20 Garry Maddox	.07	51 Cubs Rookies:	.40	82 Bob Welch	.10	113 Steve McCatty	.07
21 Orioles Rookies:	13.00	Jay Howell, C. Lezcano,		83 Yankees Rookies:	.50	114 Ken Landreaux	.07
Bob Bonner, Cal Ripken,		Ty Waler		S. Balboni, A. Robertson,		115 Gaylord Perry	.40
Jeff Schneider		52 Larry Andersen	.07	A. McGaffigan		116 Jim Wohlford	.07
22 Jim Beattie	.07	53 Greg Gross	.07	84 Rennie Stennett	.07	117 Rawly Eastwick	.07
23 Willie Hernandez	.20	54 Ron Hassey	.07	85 Lynn McGlothen	.07	118 Expos Rookies:	.50
24 Dave Frost	.07	55 Rick Burleson	.07	86 Dane Iorg	.07	Brad Mills, Terry Francona,	
25 Jerry Remy	.07	56 Mark Littell	.07	87 Matt Keough	.07	Bryn Smith	
26 George Orta	.07	57 Craig Reynolds	.07	88 Biff Pocoroba	.07	119 Joe Pittman	.07

NO.	PLAYER	MINT
120	Gary Lucas	.07
121	Ed Lynch	.12
122	Jamie Easterly	.07
123	Danny Goodwin	.07
124	Reid Nichols	.07
125	Danny Ainge	.07
126	Braves Leaders:	.15
	C. Washington, Rick Mahler	
127	Lonnie Smith	.12
128	Frank Pastore	.07
129	Checklist No. 1	.15
130	Julio Cruz	.07
131	Stan Bahnsen	.07
132	Lee May	.07
133	Pat Underwood	.07
134	Dan Ford	.07
135	Adny Rincon	.07
136	Lenn Sakata	.07
137	George Cappuzzello	.07
138	Tony Pena	.25
139	Jeff Jones	.07
140	Ron Leflore	.07
141	Indians Rookies:	1.50
	Chris Bando, Von Hayes, Tom Brennan	
142	Dave LaRoche	.07
143	Mookie Wilson	.15
144	Fred Breining	.12
145	Bob Horner	.25
146	Mike Griffin	.07
147	Denny Walling	.07
148	Mickey Klutts	.07
149	Pat Putnam	.07
150	Ted Simmons	.15
151	Dave Edwards	.07
152	Ramon Aviles	.07
153	Roger Erickson	.07
154	Dennis Werth	.07
155	Otto Velez	.07
156	A's Leaders:	.15
	Rickey Henderson, Steve McCatty	
157	Steve Crawford	.10
158	Brian Downing	.07
159	Larry Biittner	.07
160	Luis Tiant	.10
161	Batting Leaders:	.15
	B. Madlock, C. Lansford	
162	Home Run Leaders:	.25
	Bobby Grich, Mike Schmidt, Dwight Evans, Eddie Murray	
163	RBI Leaders:	.25
	M. Schmidt, E. Murray	
164	Stolen Base Leaders:	.25
	R. Henderson, T. Raines	
165	Victory Leaders:	.25
	Tom Seaver, D. Martinez, Steve McCatty, Pete Vuckovich, Jack Morris	
166	Strikeout Leaders:	.20
	F. Valenzuela, L. Barker	
167	ERA Leaders:	.20
	Steve McCatty, Nolan Ryan	
168	Leading Relievers:	.25
	Bruce Sutter, Rollie Fingers	
169	Charlie Leibrandt	.10
170	Jim Bibby	.07
171	Giants Rookies:	1.00
	Bob Tufts, Bob Brenly, Chili Davis	
172	Bill Gullickson	.07
173	Jamie Quirk	.07
174	Dave Ford	.07
175	Jerry Mumphrey	.07
176	Dewey Robinson	.07
177	John Ellis	.07
178	Dyar Miller	.07
179	Steve Garvey	.75
180	Garvey (Action)	.35
181	Silvio Martinez	.07
182	Larry Herndon	.07
183	Mike Proly	.07
184	Mick Kelleher	.07
185	Phil Niekro	.50

NO.	PLAYER	MINT
186	Cardinals Leaders:	.15
	K. Hernandez, B. Forsch	
187	Jeff Newman	.07
188	Randy Martz	.07
189	Glenn Hoffman	.07
190	J.R. Richard	.10
191	Tim Wallach (R)	1.50
192	Broderick Perkins	.07
193	Darrell Jackson	.07
194	Mike Vail	.07
195	Paul Molitor	.35
196	Willie Upshaw	.25
197	Shane Rawley	.07
198	Chris Speier	.07
199	Don Aase	.07
200	George Brett	1.50
201	Brett (Action)	.60
202	Rick Manning	.07
203	Blue Jays Rookies:	5.00
	Jesse Barfield, Brian Milner, Boomer Wells	
204	Gray Roenicke	.07
205	Neil Allen	.07
206	Tony Bernazard	.07
207	Rod Scurry	.07
208	Bobby Murcer	.15
209	Gary Lavelle	.07
210	Keith Hernandez	.50
211	Dan Petry	.25
212	Mario Mendoza	.07
213	Dave Stewart	3.00
214	Brian Asselstine	.07
215	Mike Krukow	.07
216	White Sox Leaders:	.15
	Chet Lemon, Dennis Lamp	
217	Bo McLaughlin	.07
218	Dave Roberts	.07
219	John Curtis	.07
220	Manny Trillo	.07
221	Jim Slaton	.07
222	Butch Wynegar	.07
223	Lloyd Moseby	.25
224	Bruce Bochte	.07
225	Mike Torrez	.07
226	Checklist No. 2	.15
227	Ray Burris	.07
228	Sam Mejias	.07
229	Geoff Zahn	.07
230	Willie Wilson	.25
231	Phillies Rookies:	.75
	Ozzie Virgil, Bob Dernier, Mark Davis	
232	Terry Crowley	.07
233	Duane Kuiper	.07
234	Ron Hodges	.07
235	Mike Easler	.10
236	John Martin	.07
237	Rusty Kuntz	.07
238	Kevin Saucier	.07
239	Jon Matlack	.07
240	Bucky Dent	.10
241	Dent (Action)	.07
242	Milt May	.07
243	Bob Owchinko	.07
244	Rufino Linares	.07
245	Ken Reitz	.07
246	Mets Leaders	.20
	Hubie Brooks, Mike Scott	
247	Pedro Guerrero	.75
248	Frank LaCorte	.07
249	Tim Flannery	.07
250	Tug McGraw	.10
251	Fred Lynn	.35
252	Lynn (Action)	.20
253	Chuck Baker	.07
254	Jorge Bell (R)	9.00
255	Tony Perez	.20
256	Perez (Action)	.12
257	Larry Harlow	.07
258	Bo Diaz	.10
259	Rodney Scott	.07
260	Bruce Sutter	.25
261	Tigers Rookies:	.20
	Howard Bailey, M. Castillo, Dave Rucker	

NO.	PLAYER	MINT
262	Doug Bair	.07
263	Victor Cruz	.07
264	Dan Quisenberry	.20
265	Al Bumbry	.07
266	Rick Leach	.12
267	Kurt Bevacqua	.07
268	Rickey Keeton	.07
269	Jim Essian	.07
270	Rusty Staub	.20
271	Larry Bradford	.07
272	Bump Wills	.07
273	Doug Bird	.07
274	Bob Ojeda (R)	.75
275	Bob Watson	.07
276	Angels Leaders:	.20
	Ken Forsch, Rod Carew	
277	Terry Puhl	.07
278	John Littlefield	.07
279	Bill Russell	.07
280	Ben Oglivie	.10
281	John Verhoeven	.07
282	Ken Macha	.07
283	Brian Allard	.07
284	Bob Grich	.10
285	Sparky Lyle	.10
286	Bill Fahey	.07
287	Alan Bannister	.07
288	Garry Templeton	.15
289	Bob Stanley	.07
290	Ken Singleton	.15
291	Pirates Rookies:	.85
	Vance Law, Bob Long, Johnny Ray	
292	David Palmer	.07
293	Rob Picciolo	.07
294	Mike LaCoss	.07
295	Jason Thompson	.10
296	Bob Walk	.07
297	Clint Hurdle	.07
298	Danny Darwin	.07
299	Steve Trout	.07
300	Reggie Jackson	1.00
301	Jackson (Action)	.40
302	Doug Flynn	.07
303	Bill Caudill	.10
304	Johnnie LeMaster	.07
305	Don Sutton	.40
306	Sutton (Action)	.10
307	Randy Bass	.07
308	Charlie Moore	.07
309	Pete Redfern	.07
310	Mike Hargrove	.10
311	Dodgers Leaders:	.20
	Dusty Baker, Burt Hooton	
312	Lenny Randle	.07
313	John Harris	.07
314	Buck Martinez	.07
315	Burt Hooton	.07
316	Steve Braun	.07
317	Dick Ruthven	.07
318	Mike Heath	.07
319	Dave Rozema	.07
320	Chris Chambliss	.10
321	Chambliss (Action)	.07
322	Garry Hancock	.07
323	Bill Lee	.07
324	Steve Dillard	.07
325	Jose Cruz	.15
326	Pete Falcone	.07
327	Joe Nolan	.07
328	Ed Farmer	.07
329	U.L. Washington	.07
330	Rick Wise	.07
331	Benny Ayala	.07
332	Don Robinson	.07
333	Brewers Rookies:	.20
	Frank DiPino, M. Edwards, Chuck Porter	
334	Aurelio Rodriguez	.07
335	Jim Sundberg	.07
336	Mariners Leaders:	.15
	G. Abbott, T. Paciorek	
337	Pete Rose (AS)	.75
338	Dave Lopes (AS)	.10
339	Mike Schmidt (AS)	.45

NO.	PLAYER	MINT
340	Dave Concepcion (AS)	.15
341	Andre Dawson (AS)	.20
342	George Foster (AS)	.25
342	George Foster	2.50
	(autograph deleted)	
343	Dave Parker (AS)	.25
344	Gary Carter (AS)	.25
345	F. Valenzuela (AS)	.25
346	Tom Seaver (AS)	.25
347	Bruce Sutter (AS)	.15
348	Derrel Thomas	.07
349	George Frazier	.07
350	Thad Bosley	.07
351	Reds Rookies:	.15
	Geoff Coumbe, Scott Brown, P. Householder	
352	Dick Davis	.07
353	Jack O'Connor	.07
354	Roberto Ramos	.07
355	Dwight Evans	.15
356	Denny Lewallyn	.07
357	Butch Hobson	.07
358	Mike Parrott	.07
359	Jim Dwyer	.07
360	Len Barker	.07
361	Rafael Landestoy	.07
362	Jim Wright	.07
	(wrong autograph)	
363	Bob Molinaro	.07
364	Doyle Alexander	.07
365	Bill Madlock	.25
366	Padres Leaders:	.15
	L. Salazar, J. Eichelberger	
367	Jim Kaat	.15
368	Alex Trevino	.07
369	Champ Summers	.07
370	Mike Norris	.07
371	Jerry Don Gleaton	.07
372	Luis Gomez	.07
373	Gene Nelson	.10
374	Tim Blackwell	.07
375	Dusty Baker	.12
376	Chris Welsh	.10
377	Kiko Garcia	.07
378	Mike Caldwell	.07
379	Rob Wilfong	.07
380	Dave Stieb	.20
381	Red Sox Rookies:	.75
	D. Schmidt, Julio Valdez, Bruce Hurst	
382	Joe Simpson	.07
383	Pascual Perez	.20
383	P. Perez (error)	30.00
	No position on front	
384	Keith Moreland	.07
385	Ken Forsch	.07
386	Jerry White	.07
387	Tom Veryzer	.07
388	Joe Rudi	.07
389	George Vukovich	.07
390	Eddie Murray	1.00
391	Dave Tobik	.07
392	Rick Bosetti	.07
393	Al Hrabosky	.07
394	Checklist No. 3	.12
395	Omar Moreno	.10
396	Twins Leaders:	.15
	John Castino, F. Arroyo	
397	Ken Brett	.07
398	Mike Squires	.07
399	Pat Zachry	.07
400	Johnny Bench	1.00
401	Bench (Action)	.50
402	Bill Stein	.07
403	Jim Tracy	.07
404	Dickie Thon	.10
405	Rick Reuschel	.07
406	Al Holland	.07
407	Danny Boone	.07
408	Ed Romero	.07
409	Don Cooper	.07
410	Ron Cey	.15
411	Cey (Action)	.10
412	Luis Leal	.07
413	Dan Meyer	.07
414	Elias Sosa	.07
415	Don Baylor	.15

NO. PLAYER	MINT
416 Marty Bystrom	.07
417 Pat Kelly	.07
418 Rangers Rookies:	.25
John Butcher, B. Johnson, Dave Schmidt	
419 Steve Stone	.10
420 George Hendrick	.10
421 Mark Clear	.07
422 Cliff Johnson	.07
423 Stan Papi	.07
424 Bruce Benedict	.07
425 John Candelaria	.10
426 Orioles Leaders:	.15
Eddie Murray, S. Stewart	
427 Ron Oester	.07
428 LaMarr Hoyt	.15
429 John Wathan	.07
430 Vida Blue	.10
431 Blue (Action)	.07
432 Mike Scott	.75
433 Alan Ashby	.07
434 Joe LeFebvre	.07
435 Robin Yount	1.00
436 Joe Strain	.07
437 Juan Berenguer	.07
438 Pete Mackanin	.07
439 Dave Righetti (R)	2.00
440 Jeff Burroughs	.07
441 Astros Rookies:	.15
Danny Heep, Billy Smith, Bobby Sprowl	
442 Bruce Kison	.07
443 Mark Wagner	.07
444 Terry Forster	.10
445 Larry Parrish	.10
446 Wayne Garland	.07
447 Darrell Porter	.12
448 Porter (Action)	.07
449 Luis Aguayo	.07
450 Jack Morris	.50
451 Ed Miller	.07
452 Lee Smith (R)	1.00
453 Art Howe	.07
454 Rick Langford	.07
455 Tom Burgmeier	.07
456 Cubs Leaders:	.15
R. Martz, Bill Buckner	
457 Tim Stoddard	.07
458 Willie Montanez	.07
459 Bruce Berenyi	.07
460 Jack Clark	.50
461 Rich Dotson	.10
462 Dave Chalk	.07
463 Jim Kern	.07
464 Juan Bonilla	.10
465 Lee Mazzilli	.07
466 Randy Lerch	.07
467 Mickey Hatcher	.07
468 Floyd Bannister	.10
469 Ed Ott	.07
470 John Mayberry	.07
471 Royals Rookies:	.25
Mike Jones, Atlee Hammaker, Darryl Motley	
472 Oscar Gamble	.07
473 Mike Stanton	.07
474 Ken Oberkfell	.07
475 Alan Trammell	.50
476 Brian Kingman	.07
477 Steve Yeager	.10
478 Ray Searage	.10
479 Rowland Office	.07
480 Steve Carlton	.75
481 Carlton (Action)	.30
482 Glenn Hubbard	.07
483 Gary Woods	.07
484 Ivan DeJesus	.07
485 Kent Tekulve	.10
486 Yankees Leaders:	.20
J. Mumphrey, Tommy John	
487 Bob McClure	.07
488 Ron Jackson	.07
489 Rick Dempsey	.07
490 Dennis Eckersley	.07
491 Checklist No. 4	.15

NO. PLAYER	MINT
492 Joe Price	.07
493 Chet Lemon	.10
494 Hubie Brooks	.25
495 Dennis Leonard	.07
496 Johnny Grubb	.07
497 Jim Anderson	.07
498 Dave Bergman	.07
499 Paul Mirabella	.07
500 Rod Carew	.75
501 Carew (Action)	.30
502 Braves Rookies:	1.50
Steve Bedrosian, B. Butler, Larry Owen	
503 Julio Gonzalez	.07
504 Rick Peters	.07
505 Graig Nettles	.20
506 Nettles (Action)	.15
507 Terry Harper	.07
508 Jody Davis (R)	.50
509 Harry Spilman	.07
510 Fernando Valenzuela	1.00
511 Ruppert Jones	.07
512 Jerry Dybzinski	.07
513 Rick Rhoden	.07
514 Joe Ferguson	.07
515 Larry Bowa	.10
516 Bowa (Action)	.07
517 Mark Brouhard	.10
518 Garth Iorg	.07
519 Glenn Adams	.07
520 Mike Flanagan	.10
521 Billy Almon	.07
522 Chuck Rainey	.07
523 Gary Gray	.07
524 Tom Hausman	.07
525 Ray Knight	.07
526 Expos Leaders:	.15
W. Cromartie, Bill Gullickson	
527 John Henry Johnson	.07
528 Matt Alexander	.07
529 Allen Ripley	.07
530 Dickie Noles	.07
531 A's Rookies:	.12
Rich Bordi, M. Budaska, Kelvin Moore	
532 Toby Harrah	.07
533 Joaquin Andujar	.15
534 Dave McKay	.07
535 Lance Parrish	.30
536 Rafael Ramirez	.07
537 Doug Capilla	.07
538 Lou Piniella	.15
539 Vern Ruhle	.07
540 Andre Dawson	.50
541 Barry Evans	.07
542 Ned Yost	.07
543 Bill Robinson	.07
544 Larry Christenson	.07
545 Reggie Smith	.10
546 Smith (Action)	.07
547 Rod Carew (AS)	.25
548 Willie Randolph (AS)	.12
549 George Brett (AS)	.40
550 Bucky Dent (AS)	.12
551 Reggie Jackson (AS)	.40
552 Ken Singleton (AS)	.12
553 Dave Winfield (AS)	.35
554 Carlton Fisk (AS)	.20
555 Scott McGregor (AS)	.12
556 Jack Morris (AS)	.15
557 Rich Gossage (AS)	.20
558 John Tudor	.25
559 Indians Leaders:	.15
M. Hargrove, B. Blyleven	
560 Doug Corbett	.07
561 Cardinals Rookies:	.20
Glenn Brummer, Luis DeLeon, Gene Roof	
562 Mike O'Berry	.07
563 Ross Baumgarten	.07
564 Doug DeCinces	.15
565 Jackson Todd	.07
566 Mike Jorgensen	.07
567 Bob Babcock	.07

NO. PLAYER	MINT
568 Joe Pettini	.07
569 Willie Randolph	.10
570 Randolph (Action)	.07
571 Glenn Abbott	.07
572 Juan Beniquez	.07
573 Rick Waits	.07
574 Mike Ramsey	.07
575 Al Cowens	.07
576 Giants Leaders:	.12
Milt May, Vida Blue	
577 Rick Monday	.07
578 Shooty Babitt	.07
579 Rick Mahler (R)	.35
580 Bobby Bonds	.10
581 Ron Reed	.07
582 Lou Pujols	.07
583 Tippy Martinez	.07
584 Hosken Powell	.07
585 Rollie Fingers	.35
586 Fingers (Action)	.15
587 Tim Lollar	.07
588 Dale Berra	.07
589 Dave Stapleton	.07
590 Al Oliver	.25
591 Oliver (Action)	.15
592 Craig Swan	.07
593 Billy Smith	.07
594 Renie Martin	.07
595 Dave Collins	.07
596 Damaso Garcia	.12
597 Wayne Nordhagen	.07
598 Bob Galasso	.07
599 White Sox Rookies:	.12
Jay Loviglio, R. Patterson, Leo Sutherland	
600 Dave Winfield	.75
601 Sid Monge	.07
602 Freddie Patek	.07
603 Rich Hebner	.07
604 Orlando Sanchez	.10
605 Steve Rogers	.10
606 Blue Jays Leaders:	.10
John Mayberry, Dave Stieb	
607 Leon Durham	.30
608 Jerry Royster	.07
609 Rick Sutcliffe	.20
610 Rickey Henderson	2.00
611 Joe Niekro	.12
612 Gary Ward	.07
613 Jim Gantner	.07
614 Juan Eichelberger	.07
615 Bob Boone	.07
616 Boone (Action)	.07
617 Scott McGregor	.10
618 Tim Foli	.07
619 Bill Campbell	.07
620 Ken Griffey	.12
621 Griffey (Action)	.07
622 Dennis Lamp	.07
623 Mets Rookies:	.75
Ron Gardenhire, T. Leach, Tim Leary	
624 Fergie Jenkins	.15
625 Hal McRae	.10
626 Randy Jones	.07
627 Enos Cabell	.07
628 Bill Travers	.07
629 Johnny Wockenfuss	.07
630 Joe Charboneau	.07
631 Gene Tenace	.07
632 Bryan Clark	.10
633 Mitchell Page	.07
634 Checklist No. 5	.15
635 Ron Davis	.07
636 Phillies Leaders:	.25
Pete Rose, Steve Carlton	
637 Rick Camp	.07
638 John Milner	.07
639 Ken Kravec	.07
640 Cesar Cedeno	.10
641 Steve Mura	.07
642 Mike Scioscia	.07
643 Pete Vuckovich	.12
644 John Castino	.07
645 Frank White	.10

NO. PLAYER	MINT
646 White (Action)	.07
647 Warren Brusstar	.07
648 Jose Morales	.07
649 Ken Clay	.07
650 Carl Yastrzemski	1.25
651 Yastrzemski (Action)	.50
652 Steve Nicosia	.07
653 Angels Rookies:	1.75
Luis Sanchez, Tom Brunansky, Daryl Sconiers	
654 Jim Morrison	.07
655 Joel Youngblood	.07
656 Eddie Whitson	.10
657 Tom Poquette	.07
658 Tito Landrum	.07
659 Fred Martinez	.07
660 Dave Concepcion	.12
661 Concepcion (Action)	.07
662 Luis Salazar	.07
663 Hector Cruz	.07
664 Dan Spillner	.07
665 Jim Clancy	.07
666 Tigers Leaders:	.20
Steve Kemp, Dan Petry	
667 Jeff Reardon	.10
668 Dale Murphy	2.00
669 Larry Milbourne	.07
670 Steve Kemp	.10
671 Mike Davis	.15
672 Bob Knepper	.07
673 Keith Drumright	.07
674 Dave Goltz	.07
675 Cecil Cooper	.25
676 Sal Butera	.07
677 Alfredo Griffin	.10
678 Tom Paciorek	.07
679 Sammy Stewart	.07
680 Gary Matthews	.10
681 Dodgers Rookies:	4.50
Steve Sax, Mike Marshall, Ron Roenicke	
682 Jesse Jefferson	.07
683 Phil Garner	.07
684 Harold Baines	.75
685 Bert Blyleven	.25
686 Gary Allenson	.07
687 Greg Minton	.07
688 Leon Roberts	.07
689 Lary Sorensen	.07
690 Dave Kingman	.20
691 Dan Schatzeder	.07
692 Wayne Gross	.07
693 Cesar Geronimo	.07
694 Dave Wehrmeister	.07
695 Warren Cromartie	.07
696 Pirates Leaders:	.15
Bill Madlock, B. Solomon	
697 John Montefusco	.07
698 Tony Scott	.07
699 Dick Tidrow	.07
700 George Foster	.25
701 Foster (Action)	.15
702 Steve Renko	.07
703 Brewers Leaders:	.15
Cecil Cooper, P. Vuckovich	
704 Mickey Rivers	.07
705 Rivers (Action)	.07
706 Barry Foote	.07
707 Mark Bomback	.07
708 Gene Richards	.07
709 Don Money	.07
710 Jerry Reuss	.07
711 Mariners Rookies:	1.00
Dave Edler, Reggie Walton, Dave Henderson	
712 Denny Martinez	.07
713 Del Unser	.07
714 Jerry Koosman	.10
715 Willie Stargell	.50
716 Stargell (Action)	.20
717 Rick Miller	.07
718 Charlie Hough	.07
719 Jerry Narron	.07
720 Greg Luzinski	.15
721 Luzinski (Action)	.10

NO. PLAYER	MINT
722 Jerry Martin	.07
723 Junior Kennedy	.07
724 Dave Rosello	.07
725 Amos Otis	.10
726 Otis (Action)	.07
727 Sixto Lezcano	.07
728 Aurelio Lopez	.07
729 Jim Spencer	.07
730 Gary Carter	.75
731 Padres Rookies:	.15
Doug Gwosdz, Mike	
Armstrong, Fred Kuhaulua	
732 Mike Lum	.07
733 Larry McWilliams	.10
734 Mike Ivie	.07
735 Rudy May	.07
736 Jerry Turner	.07
737 Reggie Cleveland	.07
738 Dave Engle	.07
739 Joey McLaughlin	.07

NO. PLAYER	MINT
740 Dave Lopes	.10
741 Lopes (Action)	.07
742 Dick Drago	.07
743 John Stearns	.07
744 Mike Witt (R)	1.00
745 Bake McBride	.07
746 Andre Thornton	.12
747 John Lowenstein	.07
748 Marc Hill	.07
749 Bob Shirley	.07
750 Jim Rice	.75
751 Rick Honeycutt	.07
752 Lee Lacy	.07
753 Tom Brookens	.07
754 Joe Morgan	.50
755 Morgan (Action)	.20
756 Reds Leaders:	.20
Ken Griffey, Tom Seaver	
757 Tom Underwood	.07

NO. PLAYER	MINT
758 Claudell Washington	.12
759 Paul Splittorff	.07
760 Bill Buckner	.15
761 Dave Smith	.07
762 Mike Phillips	.07
763 Tom Hume	.07
764 Steve Swisher	.07
765 Gorman Thomas	.12
766 Twins Rookies:	4.00
Lenny Faedo, Kent Hrbek,	
Tim Laudner	
767 Roy Smalley	.07
768 Jerry Garvin	.07
769 Richie Zisk	.07
770 Rich Gossage	.25
771 Gossage (Action)	.15
772 Bert Campaneris	.07
773 John Denny	.10
774 Jay Johnstone	.07

NO. PLAYER	MINT
775 Bob Forsch	.07
776 Mark Belanger	.07
777 Tom Griffin	.07
778 Kevin Hickey	.07
779 Grant Jackson	.07
780 Pete Rose	2.50
781 Rose (Action)	.85
782 Frank Taveras	.07
783 Greg Harris	.20
784 Milt Wilcox	.07
785 Dan Driessen	.07
786 Red Sox Leaders:	.20
C. Lansford, M. Torrez	
787 Fred Stanley	.07
788 Woodie Fryman	.07
789 Checklist No. 6	.15
790 Larry Gura	.07
791 Bobby Brown	.07
792 Frank Tanana	.15

1982 Topps Traded.... Complete Set of 132 Cards—Value $30.00

Updates the main 1982 card set with players who changed teams during the season and rookies. Unlike the 1981 Traded set, the cards are numbered from 1T to 132T. The complete set was packaged in a printed box and only distributed through card hobby dealers.

NO. PLAYER	MINT
1 T Doyle Alexander	.15
2 T Jesse Barfield	2.50
3 T Ross Baumgarten	.10
4 T Steve Bedrosian	.75
5 T Mark Belanger	.10
6 T Kurt Bevacqua	.10
7 T Tim Blackwell	.10
8 T Vida Blue	.15
9 T Bob Boone	.10
10 T Larry Bowa	.20
11 T Dan Briggs	.10
12 T Bobby Brown	.10
13 T Tom Brunansky	1.50
14 T Jeff Burroughs	.12
15 T Enos Cabell	.10
16 T Bill Campbell	.10
17 T Bobby Castillo	.10
18 T Bill Caudill	.15
19 T Cesar Cedeno	.15
20 T Dave Collins	.12
21 T Doug Corbett	.10
22 T Al Cowens	.15
23 T Chili Davis	1.25
24 T Dick Davis	.10
25 T Ron Davis	.10
26 T Doug DeCince	.25
27 T Ivan DeJesus	.12
28 T Bob Dernier	.20
29 T Bo Diaz	.10
30 T Roger Erickson	.10
31 T Jim Essian	.10
32 T Ed Farmer	.10
33 T Doug Flynn	.10

NO. PLAYER	MINT
34 T Tim Foli	.10
35 T Dan Ford	.10
36 T George Foster	.35
37 T Dave Frost	.10
38 T Rich Gale	.10
39 T Ron Gardenhire	.10
40 T Ken Griffey	.15
41 T Greg Harris	.10
42 T Von Hayes	1.25
43 T Larry Herndon	.10
44 T Kent Hrbek	4.00
45 T Mike Ivie	.10
46 T Grant Jackson	.10
47 T Reggie Jackson	2.50
48 T Ron Jackson	.10
49 T Fergie Jenkins	.40
50 T Lamar Johnson	.10
51 T Ray Johnson	.10
52 T Jay Johnstone	.10
53 T Mick Kelleher	.10
54 T Steve Kemp	.12
55 T Junior Kennedy	.10
56 T Jim Kern	.10
57 T Ray Knight	.20
58 T Wayne Krenchicki	.10
59 T Mike Krukow	.10
60 T Duane Kuiper	.10
61 T Mike LaCoss	.10
62 T Chet Lemon	.15
63 T Sixto Lezcano	.10
64 T Dave Lopes	.15
65 T Jerry Martin	.10
66 T Renie Martin	.10

NO. PLAYER	MINT
67 T John Mayberry	.10
68 T Lee Mazzilli	.10
69 T Bake McBride	.15
70 T Dan Meyer	.10
71 T Larry Milbourne	.10
72 T Eddie Milner	.25
73 T Sid Monge	.10
74 T John Montefusco	.10
75 T Jose Morales	.10
76 T Keith Moreland	.15
77 T Jim Morrison	.10
78 T Rance Mulliniks	.10
79 T Steve Mura	.10
80 T Gene Nelson	.10
81 T Joe Nolan	.10
82 T Dickie Noles	.10
83 T Al Oliver	.35
84 T Jorge Orta	.10
85 T Tom Paciorek	.10
86 T Larry Parrish	.20
87 T Jack Perconte	.10
88 T Gaylord Perry	1.00
89 T Rob Picciolo	.10
90 T Joe Pittman	.10
91 T Hosken Powell	.10
92 T Mike Proly	.10
93 T Greg Pryor	.10
94 T Charlie Puleo	.10
95 T Shane Rawley	.12
96 T Johnny Ray	.75
97 T Dave Revering	.10
98 T Cal Ripken	10.00
99 T Allen Ripley	.10

NO. PLAYER	MINT
100 T Bill Robinson	.10
101 T Aurelio Rodriquez	.10
102 T Joe Rudi	.10
103 T Steve Sax	3.50
104 T Dan Schatzeder	.10
105 T Bob Shirley	.10
106 T Eric Show (RR)	.75
107 T Roy Smalley	.10
108 T Lonnie Smith	.15
109 T Ozzie Smith	3.50
110 T Reggie Smith	.20
111 T Lary Sorensen	.10
112 T Elias Sosa	.10
113 T Mike Stanton	.10
114 T Steve Stroughter	.10
115 T Champ Summers	.10
116 T Rick Sutcliffe	.50
117 T Frank Tanana	.10
118 T Frank Taveras	.10
119 T Garry Templeton	.20
120 T Alex Trevino	.10
121 T Jerry Turner	.10
122 T Ed VandeBerg (RR)	.25
123 T Tom Veryzer	.10
124 T Ron Washington	.10
125 T Bob Watson	.10
126 T Dennis Werth	.10
127 T Eddie Whitson	.10
128 T Rob Wilfong	.10
129 T Bump Wills	.10
130 T Gary Woods	.10
131 T Butch Wynegar	.10
132 T Traded Checklist	.25

1983 Topps.... Complete Set of 792 Cards—Value $115.00

Features the rookie cards of Willie McGee, Ryne Sandberg, Wade Boggs, Tony Gwynn, Frank Viola and Gary Gaetti.

NO. PLAYER	MINT	NO. PLAYER	MINT	NO. PLAYER	MINT	NO. PLAYER	MINT
1 Record—T. Armas	.20	59 Benny Ayala	.06	123 George Frazier	.06	187 Terry Leach	.06
11 Rightfield Putouts		60 Johnny Bench	.75	124 Marc Hill	.06	188 Rick Miller	.06
2 Record—R. Henderson	.30	61 Bench (Veteran)	.30	125 Leon Durham	.25	189 Dan Schatzeder	.06
Stolen Base Record		62 Bob McClure	.06	126 Joe Torre (Mgr.)	.08	190 Cecil Cooper	.20
3 Record—G. Minton	.08	63 Rick Monday	.06	127 Preston Hanna	.06	191 Joe Price	.06
No HR's in 269⅓ Innings		64 Bill Stein	.06	128 Mike Ramsey	.06	192 Floyd Rayford	.06
4 Record—L. Parrish	.15	65 Jack Morris	.35	129 Checklist No. 1	.12	193 Harry Spilman	.06
Threw Out 3 in AS Game		66 Bob Lillis (Mgr.)	.06	130 Dave Stieb	.25	194 Cesar Geronimo	.06
5 Record—Trillo	.08	67 Sal Butera	.06	131 Ed Ott	.06	195 Bob Stoddard	.10
479 Errorless Chances		68 Eric Show (R)	.30	132 Todd Cruz	.06	196 Bill Fahey	.06
6 Record—J. Wathan	.08	69 Lee Lacy	.08	133 Jim Barr	.06	197 Jim Eisenreich	.50
31st Stolen Base, Catcher		70 Steve Carlton	.50	134 Hubie Brooks	.10	198 Kiko Garcia	.06
7 Gene Richards	.06	71 Carlton (Veteran)	.25	135 Dwight Evans	.15	199 Marty Bystrom	.06
8 Steve Balboni	.10	72 Tom Paciorek	.06	136 Willie Aikens	.06	200 Rod Carew	.50
9 Joey McLaughlin	.06	73 Allen Ripley	.06	137 Woodie Fryman	.06	201 Rod Carew (Veteran)	.25
10 Gorman Thomas	.15	74 Julio Gonzalez	.06	138 Rick Dempsey	.08	202 Blue Jays Leaders:	.12
11 Billy Gardner (Mgr.)	.06	75 Amos Otis	.06	139 Bruce Berenyi	.06	Damaso Garcia, Dave Stieb	
12 Paul Mirabella	.06	76 Rick Mahler	.06	140 Willie Randolph	.10	203 Mike Morgan	.06
13 Larry Herndon	.08	77 Hosken Powell	.06	141 Indians Leaders:	.12	204 Junior Kennedy	.06
14 Frank LaCorte	.06	78 Bill Caudill	.08	Toby Harrah, Rick Sutcliffe		205 Dave Parker	.35
15 Ron Cey	.15	79 Mick Kelleher	.06	142 Mike Caldwell	.06	206 Ken Oberkfell	.06
16 George Vukovich	.06	80 George Foster	.25	143 Joe Pettini	.06	207 Rick Camp	.06
17 Kent Tekulve	.06	81 Yankees Leaders:	.20	144 Mark Wagner	.06	208 Dan Meyer	.06
18 Tekulve (Veteran)	.06	J. Mumphrey, D. Righetti		145 Don Sutton	.35	209 Mike Moore (R)	1.25
19 Oscar Gamble	.08	82 Bruce Hurst	.06	146 Don Sutton (Veteran)	.15	210 Jack Clark	.40
20 Carlton Fisk	.20	83 Ryne Sandberg (R)	7.00	147 Rick Leach	.06	211 John Denny	.15
21 Orioles Leaders:	.20	84 Milt May	.06	148 Dave Roberts	.06	212 John Stearns	.06
Eddie Murray, Jim Palmer		85 Ken Singleton	.08	149 Johnny Ray	.15	213 Tom Burgmeier	.06
22 Randy Martz	.06	86 Tom Hume	.06	150 Bruce Sutter	.20	214 Jerry White	.06
23 Mike Heath	.06	87 Joe Rudi	.06	151 B. Sutter (Veteran)	.15	215 Mario Soto	.10
24 Steve Mura	.06	88 Jim Gantner	.06	152 Jay Johnstone	.06	216 Tony LaRussa (Mgr.)	.08
25 Hal McRae	.06	89 Leon Roberts	.06	153 Jerry Koosman	.06	217 Tim Stoddard	.06
26 Jerry Roystar	.06	90 Jerry Reuss	.08	154 Johnnie LeMaster	.06	218 Roy Howell	.06
27 Doug Corbett	.06	91 Larry Milbourne	.06	155 Dan Quisenberry	.25	219 Mike Armstrong	.06
28 Bruce Bochte	.06	92 Mike LaCoss	.06	156 Billy Martin (Mgr.)	.15	220 Dusty Baker	.12
29 Randy Jones	.06	93 John Castino	.06	157 Steve Bedrosian	.12	221 Joe Niekro	.08
30 Jim Rice	.50	94 Dave Edwards	.06	158 Rob Wilfong	.06	222 Damaso Garcia	.15
31 Bill Gullickson	.08	95 Alan Trammell	.35	159 Mike Stanton	.06	223 John Montefusco	.06
32 Dave Bergman	.06	96 Dick Howser (Mgr.)	.06	160 Dave Kingman	.15	224 Mickey Rivers	.06
33 Jack O'Connor	.06	97 Ross Baumgarten	.06	161 D. Kingman (Veteran)	.10	225 Enos Cabell	.06
34 Paul Householder	.06	98 Vance Law	.06	162 Mark Clear	.06	226 Enrique Romo	.06
35 Rollie Fingers	.25	99 Dickie Noles	.06	163 Cal Ripken	2.00	227 Chris Bando	.06
36 Fingers (Veteran)	.15	100 Pete Rose	2.00	164 David Palmer	.06	228 Joaquin Andujar	.12
37 Darrell Johnson (Mgr.)	.06	101 Rose (Veteran)	.60	165 Dan Driessen	.06	229 Phillies Leaders:	.12
38 Tim Flannery	.06	102 Dave Beard	.06	166 John Pacella	.06	Bo Diaz, Steve Carlton	
39 Terry Puhl	.06	103 Darrell Porter	.08	167 Mark Brouhard	.06	230 Fergie Jenkins	.12
40 Fernando Valenzuela	.40	104 Bob Walk	.06	168 Juan Eichelberger	.06	231 F. Jenkins (Veteran)	.08
41 Jerry Turner	.06	105 Don Baylor	.20	169 Doug Flynn	.06	232 Tom Brunansky	.30
42 Dale Murray	.06	106 Gene Nelson	.06	170 Steve Howe	.06	233 Wayne Gross	.06
43 Bob Dernier	.08	107 Mike Jorgensen	.06	171 Giants Leaders:	.12	234 Larry Andersen	.06
44 Don Robinson	.06	108 Glenn Hoffman	.06	Bill Laskey, Joe Morgan		235 Claudell Washington	.15
45 John Mayberry	.06	109 Luis Leal	.06	172 Vern Ruhle	.06	236 Steve Renko	.06
46 Richard Dotson	.08	110 Ken Griffey	.15	173 Jim Morrison	.06	237 Dan Norman	.06
47 Dave McKay	.06	111 Expos Leaders:	.15	174 Jerry Ujdur	.06	238 Bud Black (R)	.30
48 Lary Sorensen	.06	Al Oliver, Steve Rogers		175 Bo Diaz	.06	239 Dave Stapleton	.06
49 Willie McGee (R)	2.50	112 Bob Shirley	.06	176 Dave Righetti	.35	240 Rich Gossage	.25
50 Bob Horner	.15	113 Ron Roenicke	.06	177 Harold Baines	.30	241 Gossage (Veteran)	.15
51 Cubs Leaders:	.20	114 Jim Slaton	.06	178 Luis Tiant	.08	242 Joe Nolan	.06
Leon Durham, F. Jenkins		115 Chili Davis	.15	179 Luis Tiant (Veteran)	.06	243 Duane Walker	.12
52 Onix Concepcion	.15	116 Dave Schmidt	.06	180 Rickey Henderson	1.00	244 Dwight Bernard	.06
53 Mike Witt	.20	117 Alan Knicely	.06	181 Terry Felton	.12	245 Steve Sax	.50
54 Jim Maler	.10	118 Chris Welsh	.06	182 Mike Fischlin	.06	246 G. Bamberger (Mgr.)	.06
55 Mookie Wilson	.08	119 Tom Brookens	.06	183 Ed VandeBerg (R)	.25	247 Dave Smith	.06
56 Chuck Rainey	.06	120 Len Barker	.06	184 Bob Clark	.06	248 Bake McBride	.06
57 Tim Blackwell	.06	121 Mickey Hatcher	.06	185 Tim Lollar	.06	249 Checklist No. 2	.12
58 Al Holland	.06	122 Jimmy Smith	.10	186 Whitey Herzog (Mgr.)	.06	250 Bill Buckner	.15

NO.	PLAYER	MINT
251	Alan Wiggins (R)	.25
252	Luis Aguayo	.06
253	Larry McWilliams	.06
254	Rick Cerone	.06
255	Gene Garber	.06
256	G. Garber (Veteran)	.06
257	Jesse Barfield	.70
258	Manny Castillo	.06
259	Jeff Jones	.06
260	Steve Kemp	.08
261	Tigers Leaders:	.12
	L. Herndon, Dan Petry	
262	Ron Jackson	.06
263	Renie Martin	.06
264	Jamie Quirk	.06
265	Joel Youngblood	.06
266	Paul Boris	.08
267	Terry Francona	.06
268	Storm Davis (R)	1.00
269	Ron Oester	.06
270	Dennis Eckersley	.06
271	Ed Romero	.06
272	Frank Tanana	.06
273	Mark Belanger	.06
274	Terry Kennedy	.10
275	Ray Knight	.06
276	Gene Mauch (Mgr.)	.06
277	Rance Mulliniks	.06
278	Kevin Hickey	.06
279	Greg Gross	.06
280	Bert Blyleven	.15
281	Andre Robertson	.06
282	Reggie Smith	.10
283	R. Smith (Veteran)	.08
284	Jeff Lahti	.15
285	Lance Parrish	.35
286	Rick Langford	.06
287	Bobby Brown	.06
288	Joe Cowley (R)	.30
289	Jerry Dybzinski	.06
290	Jeff Reardon	.08
291	Pirates Leaders:	.12
	B. Madlock, J. Candelaria	
292	Craig Swan	.06
293	Glen Gulliver	.08
294	Dave Engle	.06
295	Jerry Remy	.06
296	Greg Harris	.06
297	Ned Yost	.06
298	Floyd Chiffer	.10
299	George Wright	.20
300	Mike Schmidt	1.00
301	M. Schmidt (Veteran)	.25
302	Ernie Whitt	.06
303	Miguel Dilone	.06
304	Dave Rucker	.06
305	Larry Bowa	.10
306	Tom Lasorda (Mgr.)	.10
307	Lou Piniella	.12
308	Jesus Vega	.08
309	Jeff Leonard	.15
310	Greg Luzinski	.15
311	Glenn Brummer	.06
312	Brian Kingman	.06
313	Gary Gray	.06
314	Ken Dayley	.06
315	Rick Burleson	.06
316	Paul Splittorff	.06
317	Gary Rajsich	.10
318	John Tudor	.30
319	Lenn Sakata	.06
320	Steve Rogers	.08
321	Brewers Leaders:	.15
	P. Vuckovich, R. Yount	
322	Dave Van Gorder	.10
323	Luis DeLeon	.06
324	Mike Marshall	.25
325	Von Hayes	.20
326	Garth Iorg	.06
327	Bobby Castillo	.06
328	Craig Reynolds	.06
329	Randy Niemann	.06
330	Buddy Bell	.15
331	Mike Krukow	.06
332	Glenn Wilson (R)	.50
333	Dave LaRoche	.06
334	D. LaRoche (Veteran)	.06
335	Steve Henderson	.06
336	R. Lachemann (Mgr.)	.06
337	Tito Landrum	.06
338	Bob Owchinko	.06
339	Terry Harper	.06
340	Larry Gura	.06
341	Doug DeCinces	.15
342	Atlee Hammaker	.08
343	Bob Bailor	.06
344	Roger LaFrancois	.08
345	Jim Clancy	.06
346	Joe Pittman	.06
347	Sammy Stewart	.06
348	Alan Bannister	.06
349	Checklist No. 3	.12
350	Robin Yount	.50
351	Reds Leaders:	.12
	Cesar Cedeno, Mario Soto	
352	Mike Scioscia	.06
353	Steve Comer	.06
354	Randy Johnson	.06
355	Jim Bibby	.06
356	Gary Woods	.06
357	Len Matuszek	.15
358	Jerry Garvin	.06
359	Dave Collins	.08
360	Nolan Ryan	1.00
361	N. Ryan (Veteran)	.20
362	Bill Almon	.06
363	John Stuper	.15
364	Bret Butler	.15
365	Dave Lopes	.07
366	Dick Williams (Mgr.)	.06
367	Bud Anderson	.06
368	Richie Zisk	.06
369	Jesse Orosco	.10
370	Gary Carter	.50
371	Mike Richardt	.08
372	Terry Crowley	.06
373	Kevin Saucier	.06
374	Wayne Krenchicki	.06
375	Pete Vuckovich	.06
376	Ken Landreaux	.06
377	Lee May	.06
378	Lee May (Veteran)	.06
379	Guy Sularz	.10
380	Ron Davis	.06
381	Red Sox Leaders:	.15
	Bob Stanley, Jim Rice	
382	Bob Knepper	.06
383	Ozzie Virgil	.06
384	Dave Dravecky (R)	.75
385	Mike Easler	.06
386	Rod Carew (AS)	.25
387	Bob Grich (AS)	.08
388	George Brett (AS)	.40
389	Robin Yount (AS)	.35
390	Reggie Jackson (AS)	.30
391	Rickey Henderson (AS)	.35
392	Fred Lynn (AS)	.15
393	Carlton Fisk (AS)	.15
394	Pete Vuckovich (AS)	.08
395	Larry Gura (AS)	.08
396	Dan Quisenberry (AS)	.12
397	Pete Rose (AS)	.60
398	Manny Trillo (AS)	.08
399	Mike Schmidt (AS)	.35
400	Dave Concepcion (AS)	.10
401	Dale Murphy (AS)	.50
402	Andre Dawson (AS)	.20
403	Tim Raines (AS)	.18
404	Gary Carter (AS)	.25
405	Steve Rogers (AS)	.08
406	Steve Carlton (AS)	.25
407	Bruce Sutter (AS)	.20
408	Rudy May	.06
409	Marvis Foley	.06
410	Phil Niekro	.25
411	P. Niekro (Veteran)	.12
412	Rangers Leaders:	.10
	Buddy Bell, Charlie Hough	
413	Matt Keough	.06
414	Julio Cruz	.06
415	Bob Forsch	.06
416	Joe Ferguson	.06
417	Tom Hausman	.06
418	Greg Pryor	.06
419	Steve Crawford	.06
420	Al Oliver	.15
421	Al Oliver (Veteran)	.08
422	George Cappuzzello	.06
423	Tom Lawless	.08
424	Jerry Augustine	.06
425	Pedro Guerrero	.50
426	Earl Weaver (Mgr.)	.12
427	Roy Lee Jackson	.06
428	Champ Summers	.06
429	Eddie Whitson	.08
430	Kirk Gibson	.40
431	Gary Gaetti (R)	4.00
432	Porfirio Altamirano	.10
433	Dale Berra	.06
434	Dennis Lamp	.06
435	Tony Armas	.15
436	Bill Campbell	.06
437	Rick Sweet	.06
438	Dave LaPoint (R)	.35
439	Rafael Ramirez	.06
440	Ron Guidry	.25
441	Astros Leaders:	.12
	Joe Niekro, Ray Knight	
442	Brian Downing	.06
443	Don Hood	.06
444	Wally Backman	.20
445	Mike Flanagan	.08
446	Reid Nichols	.06
447	Bryn Smith	.06
448	Darrell Evans	.12
449	Eddie Milner	.12
450	Ted Simmons	.15
451	Ted Simmons (Veteran)	.10
452	Lloyd Moseby	.15
453	Lamar Johnson	.06
454	Bob Welch	.06
455	Sixto Lezcano	.06
456	Lee Elia (Mgr.)	.06
457	Milt Wilcox	.06
458	Ron Washington	.08
459	Ed Farmer	.06
460	Roy Smalley	.06
461	Steve Trout	.06
462	Steve Nicosia	.06
463	Gaylord Perry	.25
464	G. Perry (Veteran)	.12
465	Lonnie Smith	.12
466	Tom Underwood	.06
467	Rufino Linares	.06
468	Dave Goltz	.06
469	Ron Gardenhire	.06
470	Greg Minton	.06
471	Royals Leaders:	.12
	Willie Wilson, Vida Blue	
472	Gary Allenson	.06
473	John Lowenstein	.06
474	Ray Burris	.06
475	Cesar Cedeno	.12
476	Rob Picciolo	.06
477	Tom Niedenfuer	.12
478	Phil Garner	.06
479	Charlie Hough	.06
480	Toby Harrah	.06
481	Scot Thompson	.06
482	Tony Gwynn (R)	17.50
483	Lynn Jones	.06
484	Dick Ruthven	.06
485	Omar Moreno	.06
486	Clyde King (Mgr.)	.06
487	Jerry Hariston	.06
488	Alfredo Griffin	.06
489	Tom Herr	.20
490	Jim Palmer	.35
491	Jim Palmer (Veteran)	.15
492	Paul Serna	.06
493	Steve McCatty	.06
494	Bob Brenly	.08
495	Warren Cromartie	.06
496	Tom Veryzer	.06
497	Rick Sutcliffe	.20
498	Wade Boggs (R)	32.00
499	Jeff Little	.10
500	Reggie Jackson	.75
501	R. Jackson (Veteran)	.25
502	Braves Leaders:	.15
	Dale Murphy, Phil Niekro	
503	Moose Haas	.06
504	Don Werner	.06
505	Garry Templeton	.15
506	Jim Gott	.25
507	Tony Scott	.06
508	Tom Filer (R)	.20
509	Lou Whitaker	.25
510	Tug McGraw	.08
511	Tug McGraw (Veteran)	.06
512	Doyle Alexander	.06
513	Fred Stanley	.06
514	Rudy Law	.06
515	Gene Tenace	.06
516	Bill Virdon (Mgr.)	.06
517	Gary Ward	.06
518	Bill Laskey (R)	.25
519	Terry Bulling	.06
520	Fred Lynn	.25
521	Bruce Benedict	.06
522	Pat Zachry	.06
523	Carney Lansford	.15
524	Tom Brennan	.06
525	Frank White	.06
526	Checklist No. 4	.12
527	Larry Biittner	.06
528	Jamie Easterly	.06
529	Tim Laudner	.06
530	Eddie Murray	.60
531	A's Leaders:	.15
	R. Henderson, R. Langford	
532	Dave Stewart	.25
533	Luis Salazar	.06
534	John Butcher	.06
535	Manny Trillo	.08
536	Johnny Wockenfuss	.06
537	Rod Scurry	.06
538	Danny Heep	.06
539	Roger Erickson	.06
540	Ozzie Smith	.50
541	Britt Burns	.08
542	Jody Davis	.10
543	Alan Fowlkes	.10
544	Larry Whisenton	.06
545	Floyd Bannister	.06
546	Dave Garcia (Mgr.)	.06
547	Geoff Zahn	.06
548	Brian Giles	.08
549	Charlie Puleo	.09
550	Carl Yastrzemski	.75
551	Yastrzemski (Veteran)	.30
552	Tim Wallach	.30
553	Denny Martinez	.06
554	Mike Vail	.06
555	Steve Yeager	.06
556	Willie Upshaw	.15
557	Rick Honeycutt	.06
558	Dickie Thon	.08
559	Peter Redfern	.06
560	Ron LeFlore	.08
561	Cardinals Leaders:	.12
	L. Smith, J. Andujar	
562	Dave Rozema	.06
563	Juan Bonilla	.06
564	Sid Monge	.06
565	Bucky Dent	.06
566	Manny Sarmiento	.06
567	Joe Simpson	.06
568	Willie Hernandez	.20
569	Jack Perconte	.06
570	Vida Blue	.08
571	Mickey Klutts	.06
572	Bob Watson	.06
573	Andy Hassler	.06
574	Glenn Adams	.06
575	Neil Allen	.06
576	Frank Robinson (Mgr.)	.15
577	Luis Aponte	.08
578	David Green	.15
579	Rich Dauer	.06

1983 Topps (Continued)

NO. PLAYER	MINT
580 Tom Seaver	.75
581 T. Seaver (Veteran)	.25
582 Marshall Edwards	.06
583 Terry Forster	.08
584 Dave Hostetler	.12
585 Jose Cruz	.12
586 Frank Viola (R)	5.00
587 Ivan DeJesus	.06
588 Pat Underwood	.06
589 Alvis Woods	.06
590 Tony Pena	.15
591 White Sox Leaders: Greg Luzinski, LaMarr Hoyt	.12
592 Shane Rawley	.06
593 Broderick Perkins	.06
594 Eric Rasmussen	.06
595 Tim Raines	.75
596 Randy Johnson	.10
597 Mike Proly	.06
598 Dwayne Murphy	.06
599 Don Aase	.06
600 George Brett	.85
601 Ed Lynch	.06
602 Rich Gedman	.15
603 Joe Morgan	.35
604 Joe Morgan (Veteran)	.15
605 Gary Roenicke	.06
606 Bobby Cox (Mgr.)	.06
607 Charlie Leibrandt	.08
608 Don Money	.06
609 Danny Darwin	.06
610 Steve Garvey	.60
611 Bert Roberge	.06
612 Steve Swisher	.06
613 Mike Ivie	.06
614 Ed Glynn	.08
615 Garry Maddox	.06
616 Bill Nahorodny	.06
617 Butch Wynegar	.06
618 LaMarr Hoyt	.15
619 Keith Moreland	.08
620 Mike Norris	.06
621 Mets Leaders: Mookie Wilson, Craig Swan	.12
622 Dave Edler	.06
623 Luis Sanchez	.06
624 Glenn Hubbard	.06
625 Ken Forsch	.06
626 Jerry Martin	.06
627 Doug Bair	.06
628 Julio Valdez	.06
629 Charlie Lea	.06
630 Paul Molitor	.30
631 Tippy Martinez	.06
632 Alex Trevino	.06
633 Vicente Romo	.06
634 Max Venable	.06
635 Graig Nettles	.15
636 G. Nettles (Veteran)	.10
637 Pat Corrales (Mgr.)	.06
638 Dan Petry	.15
639 Art Howe	.06
640 Andre Thornton	.10
641 Billy Sample	.06
642 Checklist: No. 5	.12
643 Bump Wills	.06
644 Joe LeFebvre	.06
645 Bill Madlock	.15
646 Jim Essian	.06
647 Bobby Mitchell	.06
648 Jeff Burroughs	.06
649 Tommy Boggs	.06
650 George Hendrick	.10
651 Angels Leaders: Rod Carew, Mike Witt	.20
652 Butch Hobson	.06
653 Ellis Valentine	.06
654 Bob Ojeda	.12
655 Al Bumbry	.06
656 Dave Frost	.06
657 Mike Gates	.08
658 Frank Pastore	.06
659 Charlie Moore	.06
660 Mike Hargrove	.06
661 Bill Russell	.06
662 Joe Sambito	.06
663 Tom O'Malley (R)	.12
664 Bob Molinaro	.06
665 Jim Sundberg	.06
666 Sparky Anderson (Mgr.)	.06
667 Dick Davis	.06
668 Larry Christenson	.06
669 Mike Squires	.06
670 Jerry Mumphrey	.06
671 Lenny Faedo	.06
672 Jim Kaat	.10
673 Jim Kaat (Veteran)	.06
674 Kurt Bevacqua	.06
675 Jim Beattie	.06
676 Biff Pocoroba	.06
677 Dave Revering	.06
678 Juan Beniquez	.06
679 Mike Scott	.40
680 Andre Dawson	.30
681 Dodgers Leaders: Fernando Valenzuela, Pedro Guerrero	.15
682 Bob Stanley	.06
683 Dan Ford	.06
684 Rafael Landestoy	.06
685 Lee Mazzilli	.06
686 Randy Lerch	.06
687 U.L. Washington	.06
688 Jim Wohlford	.06
689 Ron Hassey	.06
690 Kent Hrbek	.60
691 Dave Tobik	.06
692 Denny Walling	.06
693 Sparky Lyle	.08
694 S. Lyle (Veteran)	.06
695 Ruppert Jones	.06
696 Chuck Tanner (Mgr.)	.06
697 Barry Foote	.06
698 Tony Bernazard	.06
699 Lee Smith	.10
700 Keith Hernandez	.40
701 Batting Leaders: Willie Wilson, Al Oliver	.15
702 Home Run Leaders: Gorman Thomas, Reggie Jackson, Dave Kingman	.15
703 RBI Leaders: Hal McRae, Al Oliver, Dale Murphy	.15
704 Stolen Base Leaders: R. Henderson, T. Raines	.25
705 Victory Leaders: LaMarr Hoyt, Steve Carlton	.15
706 Strikeout Leaders: F. Bannister, Steve Carlton	.15
707 ERA Leaders: Rick Sutcliffe, Steve Rogers	.12
708 Leading Firemen: D. Quisenberry, B. Sutter	.12
709 Jimmy Sexton	.06
710 Willie Wilson	.20
711 Mariners Leaders: Bruce Bochte, Jim Beattie	.10
712 Bruce Kison	.06
713 Ron Hodges	.06
714 Wayne Nordhagen	.06
715 Tony Perez	.15
716 T. Perez (Veteran)	.10
717 Scott Sanderson	.06
718 Jim Dwyer	.06
719 Rich Gale	.06
720 Dave Concepcion	.12
721 John Martin	.06
722 Jorge Orta	.06
723 Randy Moffitt	.06
724 Johnny Grubb	.06
725 Dan Spillner	.06
726 Harvey Kuenn (Mgr.)	.06
727 Chet Lemon	.10
728 Ron Reed	.06
729 Jerry Morales	.06
730 Jason Thompson	.12
731 Al Williams	.06
732 Dave Henderson	.06
733 Buck Martinez	.06
734 Steve Braun	.06
735 Tommy John	.15
736 T. John (Veteran)	.08
737 Mitchell Page	.06
738 Tim Foli	.06
739 Rick Ownbey	.08
740 Rusty Staub	.12
741 R. Staub (Veteran)	.08
742 Padres Leaders: Terry Kennedy, Tim Lollar	.10
743 Mike Torrez	.06
744 Brad Mills	.06
745 Scott McGregor	.18
746 John Wathan	.06
747 Fred Breining	.06
748 Derrel Thomas	.06
749 Jon Matlack	.06
750 Ben Oglivie	.10
751 Brad Havens	.06
752 Luis Pujols	.06
753 Elias Sosa	.06
754 Bill Robinson	.06
755 John Candelaria	.06
756 Russ Nixon (Mgr.)	.06
757 Rick Manning	.06
758 Aurelio Rodriguez	.06
759 Doug Bird	.06
760 Dale Murphy	1.50
761 Gary Lucas	.06
762 Cliff Johnson	.06
763 Al Cowens	.06
764 Pete Falcone	.06
765 Bob Boone	.06
766 Barry Bonnell	.06
767 Duane Kuiper	.06
768 Chris Speier	.06
769 Checklist No. 6	.12
770 Dave Winfield	.50
771 Twins Leaders: Kent Hrbek, Bobby Castillo	.10
772 Jim Kern	.06
773 Larry Hisle	.06
774 Alan Ashby	.06
775 Burt Hooton	.06
776 Larry Parrish	.06
777 John Curtis	.06
778 Rich Hebner	.06
779 Rick Waits	.06
780 Gary Matthews	.10
781 Rick Rhoden	.06
782 Bobby Murcer	.08
783 B. Murcer (Veteran)	.06
784 Jeff Newman	.06
785 Dennis Leonard	.06
786 Ralph Houk (Mgr.)	.06
787 Dick Tidrow	.06
788 Dane Iorg	.06
789 Bryan Clark	.06
790 Bob Grich	.06
791 Gary Lavelle	.06
792 Chris Chambliss	.15

1983 Topps Traded. . . . Complete Set of 132 Cards—Value $90.00

Updates the main 1983 card set with players who changed teams during the season, and rookies. Features the first Topps card of Darryl Strawberry. The complete set was packaged in a printed box and only distributed through card hobby dealers.

1983 Topps Traded (Continued)

NO.	PLAYER	MINT
1 T	Neil Allen	.12
2 T	Bill Almon	.09
3 T	Joe Altobelli (Mgr.)	.09
4 T	Tony Armas	.25
5 T	Doug Bair	.09
6 T	Steve Baker	.09
7 T	Floyd Bannister	.12
8 T	Don Baylor	.25
9 T	Tony Bernazard	.09
10 T	Larry Biittner	.09
11 T	Dann Bilardello	.09
12 T	Doug Bird	.09
13 T	Steve Boros (Mgr.)	.09
14 T	Greg Brock (RR)	.40
15 T	Mike Brown	.12
16 T	Tom Burgmeier	.09
17 T	Randy Bush	.20
18 T	Bert Campaneris	.20
19 T	Ron Cey	.25
20 T	Chris Codiroli	.12
21 T	Dave Collins	.15
22 T	Terry Crowley	.09
23 T	Julio Cruz	.09
24 T	Mike Davis	.15
25 T	Frank DiPino	.12
26 T	Bill Doran (RR)	1.25
27 T	Jerry Dybzinski	.09
28 T	Jamie Easterly	.09
29 T	Juan Eichelberger	.09
30 T	Jim Essian	.09
31 T	Pete Falcone	.09
32 T	Mike Ferraro (Mgr.)	.09
33 T	Terry Forster	.12
34 T	Julio Franco (RR)	2.50
35 T	Rich Gale	.09
36 T	Kiko Garcia	.09
37 T	Steve Garvey	1.25
38 T	Johnny Grubb	.09
39 T	Mel Hall	.75
40 T	Von Hayes	.75
41 T	Danny Heep	.09
42 T	Steve Henderson	.09
43 T	Keith Hernandez	.75
44 T	Leo Hernandez	.20
45 T	Willie Hernandez	.40
46 T	Al Holland	.12
47 T	F. Howard (Mgr.)	.09
48 T	Bobby Johnson	.09
49 T	Cliff Johnson	.09
50 T	Odell Jones	.09
51 T	Mike Jorgenson	.09
52 T	Bob Kearney	.09
53 T	Steve Kemp	.12
54 T	Matt Keough	.09
55 T	Ron Kittle (RR)	.75
56 T	Mickey Klutts	.09
57 T	Alan Knicely	.09
58 T	Mike Krukow	.09
59 T	Rafael Landestoy	.09
60 T	Carney Lansford	.20
61 T	Joe Lefebvre	.09
62 T	Bryan Little	.12
63 T	Aurelio Lopez	.15
64 T	Mike Madden	.25
65 T	Rick Manning	.09
66 T	Billy Martin (Mgr.)	.15
67 T	Lee Mazzilli	.12
68 T	Andy McGaffigan	.09
69 T	Craig McMurtry	.25
70 T	J. McNamara (Mgr.)	.09
71 T	Orlando Mercado	.09
72 T	Larry Milbourne	.09
73 T	Randy Moffitt	.09
74 T	Sid Monge	.09
75 T	Jose Morales	.09
76 T	Omar Moreno	.12
77 T	Joe Morgan	.75
78 T	Mike Morgan	.09
79 T	Dale Murray	.09
80 T	Jeff Newman	.09
81 T	Pete O'Brien (RR)	1.50
82 T	Jorge Orta	.09
83 T	Alejandro Pena (RR)	.50
84 T	Pascual Perez	.12
85 T	Tony Perez	.50
86 T	Broderick Perkins	.09
87 T	Tony Phillips	.09
88 T	Charlie Puleo	.09
89 T	Pat Putnam	.09
90 T	Jamie Quirk	.09
91 T	Doug Rader (Mgr.)	.12
92 T	Chuck Rainey	.09
93 T	Bobby Ramos	.09
94 T	Gary Redus (RR)	.50
95 T	Steve Renko	.09
96 T	Leon Roberts	.09
97 T	Aurelio Rodriquez	.09
98 T	Dick Ruthven	.09
99 T	Daryl Sconiers	.09
100 T	Mike Scott	1.00
101 T	Tom Seaver	1.50
102 T	John Shelby (RR)	.40
103 T	Bob Shirley	.08
104 T	Joe Simpson	.08
105 T	Doug Sisk	.15
106 T	Mike Smithson (RR)	.25
107 T	Elias Sosa	.06
108 T	D. Strawberry (RR)	60.00
109 T	Tom Tellmann	.08
110 T	Gene Tenace	.08
111 T	Gorman Thomas	.25
112 T	Dick Tidrow	.08
113 T	Dave Tobik	.08
114 T	Wayne Tolleson	.12
115 T	Mike Torrez	.10
116 T	Manny Trillo	.12
117 T	Steve Trout	.10
118 T	Lee Tunnell	.12
119 T	Mike Vail	.08
120 T	Ellis Valentine	.15
121 T	Tom Veryzer	.08
122 T	George Vukovich	.08
123 T	Rick Waits	.08
124 T	Greg Walker (RR)	1.25
125 T	Chris Welsh	.08
126 T	Len Whitehouse	.08
127 T	Eddie Whitson	.10
128 T	Jim Wohlford	.08
129 T	Matt Young (RR)	.20
130 T	Joel Youngblood	.08
131 T	Pat Zachry	.08
132 T	Traded Checklist	.25

1984 Topps.... Complete Set of 792 Cards—Value $110.00

Features the rookie cards of Don Mattingly and Darryl Strawberry. Topps also introduced a "Tiffany" version of the set—printed on white stock, high gloss finish, and production limited to 10,000 sets.

NO.	PLAYER	MINT
1	Highlight—S. Carlton 300th Win and SO King	.25
2	Highlight—Henderson 100 SB's, 3 Seasons	.30
3	Highlight—Quisenberry Save Record	.15
4	Highlight—N. Ryan, G. Perry, S. Carlton— Surpass Walter Johnson	.25
5	Highlight—D. Righetti, B. Forsch, B. Warren— No Hitters	.15
6	Highlight—Bench, Yaz, Perry,—All Retire	.35
7	Gary Lucas	.06
8	Don Mattingly (R)	25.00
9	Jim Gott	.06
10	Robin Yount	.50
11	Twins Leaders: Kent Hrbek, Ken Schrom	.10
12	Billy Sample	.06
13	Scott Holman	.06
14	Tom Brookens	.06
15	Burt Hooton	.06
16	Omar Moreno	.08
17	John Denny	.08
18	Dale Berra	.06
19	Ray Fontenot	.15
20	Greg Luzinski	.12
21	Joe Altobelli (Mgr.)	.06
22	Bryan Clark	.06
23	Keith Moreland	.08
24	John Martin	.06
25	Glenn Hubbard	.08
26	Bill Black	.06
27	Daryl Sconiers	.06
28	Frank Viola	.75
29	Danny Heep	.06
30	Wade Boggs	7.50
31	Andy McGaffigan	.06
32	Bobby Ramos	.06
33	Tom Burgmeier	.06
34	Eddie Milner	.06
35	Don Sutton	.25
36	Denny Walling	.06
37	Rangers Leaders: Buddy Bell, Rick Honeycutt	.10
38	Luis DeLeon	.06
39	Garth Iorg	.06
40	Dusty Baker	.10
41	Tony Bernazard	.06
42	Johnny Grubb	.06
43	Ron Reed	.06
44	Jim Morrison	.06
45	Jerry Mumphrey	.06
46	Ray Smith	.08
47	Rudy Law	.06
48	Julio Franco	1.00
49	Jim Stuper	.06
50	Chris Chambliss	.08
51	Jim Fray (Mgr.)	.06
52	Paul Splittorff	.06
53	Juan Beniquez	.08
54	Jesse Orosco	.10
55	Dave Concepcion	.15
56	Gary Allenson	.06
57	Dan Schatzeder	.06
58	Max Venable	.06
59	Sammy Stewart	.06
60	Paul Molitor	.15
61	Chris Codiroli (R)	.15
62	Dave Hostetler	.06
63	Ed VandeBerg	.08
64	Mike Scioscia	.06
65	Kirk Gibson	.40
66	Astros Leaders: Nolan Ryan, Jose Cruz	.10
67	Gary Ward	.06
68	Luis Salazar	.06
69	Rod Scurry	.06
70	Gary Matthews	.08
71	Leo Hernandez	.15
72	Mike Squires	.06
73	Jody Davis	.10
74	Jerry Martin	.06
75	Bob Forsch	.06
76	Alfredo Griffin	.06
77	Brett Butler	.08
78	Mike Torrez	.06
79	Rob Wilfong	.06
80	Steve Rogers	.08
81	Billy Martin (Mgr.)	.15
82	Doug Bird	.06
83	Richie Zisk	.08
84	Lenny Faedo	.06
85	Atlee Hammaker	.06
86	John Shelby	.30
87	Frank Pastore	.06
88	Rob Picciolo	.06
89	Mike Smithson	.15
90	Pedro Guerrero	.40
91	Dan Spillner	.06
92	Lloyd Moseby	.20
93	Bob Knepper	.06

NO.	PLAYER	MINT
94	Mario Ramirez	.08
95	Aurelio Lopez	.06
96	Royals Leaders: Hal McRae, Larry Gura	.10
97	LaMarr Hoyt	.15
98	Steve Nicosia	.06
99	Criag Lefferts (R)	.15
100	Reggie Jackson	.50
101	Porfirio Altamirano	.06
102	Ken Oberkfell	.06
103	Dwayne Murphy	.08
104	Ken Dayley	.06
105	Tony Armas	.15
106	Tim Stoddard	.06
107	Ned Yost	.06
108	Randy Moffitt	.06
109	Brad Wellman	.08
110	Ron Guidry	.20
111	Bill Virdon (Mgr.)	.06
112	Tom Niedenfuer	.08
113	Kelly Paris	.12
114	Checklist No. 1	.08
115	Andre Thornton	.08
116	George Bjorkman	.08
117	Tom Veryzer	.06
118	Charlie Hough	.06
119	Johnny Wockenfuss	.06
120	Keith Hernandez	.35
121	Pat Sheridan	.15
122	Cecilio Guante	.06
123	Butch Wynegar	.06
124	Damaso Garcia	.10
125	Britt Burns	.08
126	Braves Leaders: Dale Murphy, C. McMurtry	.10
127	Mike Madden	.15
128	Rick Manning	.06
129	Bill Laskey	.06
130	Ozzie Smith	.40
131	Batting Leaders: Bill Madlock, Wade Boggs	.35
132	Home Run Leaders: Mike Schmidt, Jim Rice	.30
133	RBI Leaders: Dale Murphy, C. Cooper, Jim Rice	.25
134	Stolen Base Leaders: T. Raines, R. Henderson	.25
135	Victory Leaders: John Denny, LaMarr Hoyt	.15
136	Stikeout Leaders: Steve Carlton, Jack Morris	.10
137	ERA Leaders: A. Hammaker, R. Honeycutt	.08
138	Leading Firemen: A. Holland, D. Quisenberry	.10
139	Bert Campaneris	.06
140	Storm Davis	.12
141	Pat Corrales (Mgr.)	.06
142	Rich Gale	.06
143	Jose Morales	.06
144	Brian Harper	.15
145	Gary Lavelle	.06
146	Ed Romero	.06
147	Dan Petry	.15
148	Joe Lefebvre	.06
149	Jon Matlack	.06
150	Dale Murphy	1.00
151	Steve Trout	.06
152	Glenn Brummer	.06
153	Dick Tidrow	.06
154	Dave Henderson	.06
155	Frank White	.06
156	A's Leaders: R. Henderson, T. Conroy	.10
157	Gary Gaetti	.60
158	John Curtis	.06
159	Darryl Cias	.08
160	Mario Soto	.08
161	Junior Ortiz	.10
162	Bob Ojeda	.06
163	Lorenzo Gray	.08
164	Scott Sanderson	.06
165	Ken Singleton	.08
166	Jamie Nelson	.12

NO.	PLAYER	MINT
167	Marshall Edwards	.06
168	Juan Bonilla	.06
169	Larry Parrish	.06
170	Jerry Reuss	.08
171	Frank Robinson (Mgr.)	.12
172	Frank DiPino	.06
173	Marvell Wynne	.15
174	Juan Berenguer	.06
175	Graig Nettles	.15
176	Lee Smith	.10
177	Jerry Hairston	.06
178	Bill Krueger	.12
179	Buck Martinez	.06
180	Manny Trillo	.08
181	Roy Thomas	.06
182	Darryl Strawberry (R)	13.00
183	Al Williams	.06
184	Mike O'Berry	.06
185	Sixto Lezcano	.06
186	Cardinal Leaders: Lonnie Smith, John Stuper	.10
187	Luis Aponte	.06
188	Bryan Little	.08
189	Tim Conroy	.12
190	Ben Oglivie	.08
191	Mike Boddicker	.15
192	Nick Esasky (R)	1.50
193	Darrell Brown	.08
194	Domingo Ramos	.08
195	Jack Morris	.20
196	Don Slaught	.06
197	Garry Hancock	.06
198	Bill Doran (R)	.75
199	Willie Hernandez	.30
200	Andre Dawson	.25
201	Bruce Kison	.06
202	Bobby Cox (Mgr.)	.06
203	Matt Keough	.06
204	Bobby Meacham (R)	.25
205	Greg Minton	.06
206	Andy Van Slyke (R)	2.50
207	Donnie Moore	.08
208	Jose Oquendo (R)	.40
209	Manny Sarmiento	.06
210	Joe Morgan	.20
211	Rick Sweet	.06
212	Broderick Perkins	.06
213	Bruce Hurst	.06
214	Paul Householder	.06
215	Tippy Martinez	.06
216	White Sox Leaders: C. Fisk, R. Dotson	.10
217	Alan Ashby	.06
218	Rick Waits	.06
219	Joe Simpson	.06
220	Fernando Valenzuela	.40
221	Cliff Johnson	.06
222	Rick Honeycutt	.08
223	Wayne Krenchicki	.06
224	Sid Monge	.06
225	Lee Mazzilli	.06
226	Juan Eichelberger	.06
227	Steve Braun	.06
228	John Rabb	.15
229	Paul Owens (Mgr.)	.06
230	Rickey Henderson	.75
231	Gary Woods	.06
232	Tim Wallach	.10
233	Checklist No. 2	.08
234	Rafael Ramirez	.06
235	Matt Young	.20
236	Ellis Valentine	.06
237	John Castino	.06
238	Reid Nichols	.06
239	Jay Howell	.06
240	Eddie Murray	.50
241	Billy Almon	.06
242	Alex Trevino	.06
243	Pete Ladd	.06
244	Candy Maldonado	.30
245	Rick Sutcliffe	.25
246	Mets Leaders: M. Wilson, Tom Seaver	.12
247	Onix Concepcion	.06
248	Bill Dawley (R)	.20

NO.	PLAYER	MINT
249	Jay Johnstone	.06
250	Bill Madlock	.15
251	Tony Gwynn	3.50
252	Larry Christenson	.06
253	Jim Wohlford	.06
254	Shane Rawley	.06
255	Bruce Benedict	.06
256	Dave Geisel	.06
257	Julio Cruz	.06
258	Luis Sanchez	.06
259	Sparky Anderson (Mgr.)	.08
260	Scott McGregor	.08
261	Bobby Brown	.06
262	Tom Candiotti	.25
263	Jack Fimple	.08
264	Doug Frobel	.12
265	Donnie Hill (R)	.15
266	Steve Lubratich	.08
267	Carmelo Martinez (R)	.25
268	Jack O'Connor	.06
269	Aurelio Rodriquez	.06
270	Jeff Russell	.30
271	Moose Haas	.06
272	Rick Dempsey	.06
273	Charlie Puleo	.06
274	Rick Monday	.06
275	Len Matuszek	.06
276	Angels Leaders: Rod Carew, Geoff Zahn	.10
277	Eddie Whitson	.06
278	Jorge Bell	1.00
279	Ivan DeJesus	.06
280	Floyd Bannister	.10
281	Larry Milbourne	.06
282	Jim Barr	.06
283	Larry Biittner	.06
284	Howard Bailey	.06
285	Darrell Porter	.06
286	Lary Sorensen	.06
287	Warren Cromartie	.06
288	Jim Beattie	.06
289	Randy Johnson	.06
290	Dave Dravecky	.08
291	Chuck Tanner (Mgr.)	.06
292	Tony Scott	.06
293	Ed Lynch	.06
294	U.L. Washington	.06
295	Mike Flanagan	.08
296	Jeff Newman	.06
297	Bruce Berenyi	.06
298	Jim Gantner	.06
299	John Butcher	.06
300	Pete Rose	1.25
301	Frank LaCorte	.06
302	Barry Bonnell	.06
303	Marty Castillo	.06
304	Warren Brusstar	.06
305	Roy Smalley	.06
306	Dodgers Leaders: Pedro Guerrero, Bob Welch	.12
307	Bobby Mitchell	.06
308	Ron Hassey	.06
309	Tony Phillips	.08
310	Willie McGee	.40
311	Jerry Koosman	.06
312	Jorge Orta	.06
313	Mike Jorgensen	.06
314	Orlando Mercado	.08
315	Bob Grich	.06
316	Mark Bradley	.08
317	Greg Pryor	.06
318	Bill Gullickson	.08
319	Al Bumbry	.06
320	Bob Stanley	.06
321	Harvey Kuenn (Mgr.)	.06
322	Ken Schrom	.06
323	Alan Knicely	.06
324	Alejandro Pena (R)	.30
325	Darrell Evans	.12
326	Bob Kearney	.06
327	Ruppert Jones	.06
328	Vern Ruhle	.06
329	Pat Tabler	.20
330	John Candelaria	.06
331	Bucky Dent	.06

NO.	PLAYER	MINT
332	Kevin Gross (R)	.30
333	Larry Herndon	.06
334	Chuck Rainey	.06
335	Don Baylor	.12
336	Mariners Leaders: Pat Putnam, M. Young	.10
337	Kevin Hagen	.08
338	Mike Warren	.12
339	Roy Lee Jackson	.06
340	Hal McRae	.06
341	Dave Tobik	.06
342	Tim Foli	.06
343	Mark Davis	.06
344	Rick Miller	.06
345	Kent Hrbek	.30
346	Kurt Bevacqua	.06
347	Allan Ramirez	.08
348	Toby Harrah	.06
349	Bob Gibson	.12
350	George Foster	.20
351	Russ Nixon (Mgr.)	.06
352	Dave Stewart	.30
353	Jim Anderson	.06
354	Jeff Burroughs	.06
355	Jason Thompson	.08
356	Glenn Abbott	.06
357	Ron Cey	.15
358	Bob Dernier	.08
359	Jim Acker (R)	.15
360	Willie Randolph	.08
361	Dave Smith	.06
362	David Green	.06
363	Tim Laudner	.06
364	Scott Fletcher	.12
365	Steve Bedrosian	.08
366	Padres Leaders: T. Kennedy, D. Dravecky	.10
367	Jamie Easterly	.06
368	Hubie Brooks	.10
369	Steve McCatty	.06
370	Tim Raines	.50
371	Dave Gumpert	.08
372	Gary Roenicke	.06
373	Bill Scherrer	.08
374	Don Money	.06
375	Dennis Leonard	.06
376	Dave Anderson	.15
377	Danny Darwin	.06
378	Bob Brenly	.06
379	Checklist No.3	.08
380	Steve Garvey	.40
381	Ralph Houk (Mgr.)	.06
382	Chris Nyman	.08
383	Terry Puhl	.06
384	Lee Tunnell	.12
385	Tony Perez	.15
386	George Hendrick (AS)	.10
387	Johnny Ray (AS)	.10
388	Mike Schmidt (AS)	.30
389	Ozzie Smith (AS)	.12
390	Tim Raines (AS)	.20
391	Dale Murphy (AS)	.40
392	Andre Dawson (AS)	.25
393	Gary Carter (AS)	.30
394	Steve Rogers (AS)	.12
395	Steve Carlton (AS)	.30
396	Jesse Orosco (AS)	.08
397	Eddie Murray (AS)	.35
398	Lou Whitaker (AS)	.12
399	George Brett (AS)	.40
400	Cal Ripken (AS)	.30
401	Jim Rice (AS)	.25
402	Dave Winfield (AS)	.25
403	Lloyd Moseby (AS)	.12
404	Ted Simmons (AS)	.12
405	LaMarr Hoyt (AS)	.12
406	Ron Guidry (AS)	.15
407	Dan Quisenberry (AS)	.15
408	Lou Piniella	.10
409	Juan Agosto	.15
410	Claudell Washington	.08
411	Houston Jimenez	.08
412	Doug Rader (Mgr.)	.06
413	Spike Owen (R)	.20
414	Mitchell Page	.06

NO.	PLAYER	MINT
415	Tommy John	.15
416	Dane Iorg	.06
417	Mike Armstrong	.06
418	Ron Hodges	.06
419	John Johnson	.06
420	Cecil Cooper	.15
421	Charlie Lea	.06
422	Jose Cruz	.12
423	Mike Morgan	.06
424	Dann Bilardello	.08
425	Steve Howe	.06
426	Orioles Leaders:	.12
	M. Boddicker, C. Ripken	
427	Rick Leach	.06
428	Fred Breining	.06
429	Randy Bush	.20
430	Rusty Staub	.10
431	Chris Bando	.06
432	Charlie Hudson (R)	.20
433	Rich Hebner	.06
434	Harold Baines	.20
435	Neil Allen	.06
436	Rick Peters	.06
437	Mike Proly	.06
438	Biff Pocoroba	.06
439	Bob Stoddard	.06
440	Steve Kemp	.06
441	Bob Lillis (Mgr.)	.06
442	Byron McLaughlin	.06
443	Benny Ayala	.06
444	Steve Renko	.06
445	Jerry Remy	.06
446	Luis Pujols	.06
447	Tom Brunansky	.20
448	Ben Hayes	.06
449	Joe Pettini	.06
450	Gary Carter	.45
451	Bob Jones	.06
452	Chuck Porter	.06
453	Willie Upshaw	.15
454	Joe Beckwith	.06
455	Terry Kennedy	.10
456	Cubs Leaders:	.12
	F. Jenkins, K. Moreland	
457	Dave Rozema	.06
458	Kiko Garcia	.06
459	Kevin Hickey	.06
460	Dave Winfield	.40
461	Jim Maler	.06
462	Lee Lacy	.06
463	Dave Engle	.06
464	Jeff Jones	.06
465	Mookie Wilson	.08
466	Gene Garber	.06
467	Mike Ramsey	.06
468	Geoff Zahn	.06
469	Tom O'Malley	.06
470	Nolan Ryan	1.00
471	Dick Howser (Mgr.)	.06
472	Mike Brown	.08
473	Jim Dwyer	.06
474	Greg Bargar	.09
475	Gary Redus (R)	.30
476	Tom Tellmann	.06
477	Rafael Landestoy	.06
478	Alan Bannister	.06
479	Frank Tanana	.06
480	Ron Kittle	.25
481	Mark Thurmond (R)	.20
482	Enos Cabell	.06
483	Fergie Jenkins	.15
484	Ozzie Virgil	.06
485	Rick Rhoden	.06
486	Yankees Leaders:	.12
	Don Baylor, Ron Guidry	
487	Ricky Adams	.08
488	Jesse Barfield	.30
489	Dave Von Ohlen	.09
490	Cal Ripken	.75
491	Bobby Castillo	.06
492	Tucker Ashford	.06
493	Mike Norris	.06
494	Chili Davis	.15
495	Rollie Fingers	.15
496	Terry Francona	.06

NO.	PLAYER	MINT
497	Bud Anderson	.06
498	Rich Gedman	.06
499	Mike Witt	.20
500	George Brett	.80
501	Steve Henderson	.06
502	Joe Torre (Mgr.)	.08
503	Elias Sosa	.06
504	Mickey Rivers	.08
505	Pete Vuckovich	.08
506	Ernie Whitt	.06
507	Mike LaCoss	.06
508	Mel Hall	.40
509	Brad Havens	.06
510	Alan Trammell	.30
511	Marty Bystrom	.06
512	Oscar Gamble	.06
513	Dave Beard	.06
514	Floyd Rayford	.06
515	Gorman Thomas	.15
516	Expos Leaders:	.10
	Al Oliver, Charlie Lea	
517	John Moses	.08
518	Greg Walker (R)	.75
519	Ron Davis	.06
520	Bob Boone	.06
521	Pete Falcone	.06
522	Dave Bergman	.06
523	Glenn Hoffman	.06
524	Carlos Diaz	.06
525	Willie Wilson	.20
526	Ron Oester	.06
527	Checklist No. 4	.08
528	Mark Brouhard	.06
529	Keith Atherton	.08
530	Dan Ford	.06
531	Steve Boros (Mgr.)	.06
532	Eric Show	.06
533	Ken Landreaux	.06
534	Pete O'Brien (R)	1.00
535	Bo Diaz	.06
536	Doug Bair	.06
537	Johnny Ray	.12
538	Kevin Bass	.06
539	George Frazier	.06
540	George Hendrick	.08
541	Dennis Lamp	.06
542	Duane Kuiper	.06
543	Craig McMurtry (R)	.15
544	Cesar Geronimo	.06
545	Bill Buckner	.10
546	Indians Leaders:	.08
	Mike Hargrove, L. Sorensen	
547	Mike Moore	.06
548	Ron Jackson	.06
549	Walt Terrell (R)	.35
550	Jim Rice	.40
551	Scott Ullger	.08
552	Ray Burris	.06
553	Joe Nolan	.06
554	Ted Power	.06
555	Greg Brock	.10
556	Joey McLaughlin	.06
557	Wayne Tolleson	.10
558	Mike Davis	.08
559	Mike Scott	.35
560	Carlton Fisk	.25
561	Whitey Herzog (Mgr.)	.08
562	Manny Castillo	.06
563	Glenn Wilson	.12
564	Al Holland	.06
565	Leon Durham	.20
566	Jim Bibby	.06
567	Mike Heath	.06
568	Pete Filson	.10
569	Bake McBride	.06
570	Dan Quisenberry	.20
571	Bruce Bochy	.06
572	Jerry Royster	.06
573	Dave Kingman	.10
574	Brian Downing	.06
575	Jim Clancy	.06
576	Giants Leaders:	.07
	J. Leonard, A. Hammaker	
577	Mark Clear	.06
578	Lenn Sakata	.06

NO.	PLAYER	MINT
579	Bob James (R)	.25
580	Lonnie Smith	.08
581	Jose DeLeon (R)	.35
582	Bob McClure	.06
583	Derrel Thomas	.06
584	Dave Schmidt	.06
585	Dan Driessen	.06
586	Joe Niekro	.08
587	Von Hayes	.20
588	Milt Wilcox	.06
589	Mike Easler	.08
590	Dave Stieb	.20
591	Tony LaRussa (Mgr.)	.06
592	Andre Robertson	.06
593	Jeff Lahti	.06
594	Gene Richards	.06
595	Jeff Reardon	.08
596	Ryne Sandberg	1.00
597	Rick Camp	.06
598	Rusty Kuntz	.06
599	Doug Sisk (R)	.15
600	Rod Carew	.50
601	John Tudor	.15
602	John Wathan	.06
603	Renie Martin	.06
604	John Lowenstein	.06
605	Mike Caldwell	.06
606	Blue Jays Leaders:	.10
	Lloyd Moseby, Dave Stieb	
607	Tom Hume	.06
608	Bobby Johnson	.06
609	Dan Meyer	.06
610	Steve Sax	.25
611	Chet Lemon	.08
612	Harry Spilman	.06
613	Greg Gross	.06
614	Len Barker	.06
615	Garry Templeton	.12
616	Don Robinson	.06
617	Rick Cerone	.06
618	Dickie Noles	.06
619	Jerry Dybzinski	.06
620	Al Oliver	.15
621	Frank Howard (Mgr.)	.06
622	Al Cowens	.06
623	Ron Washington	.06
624	Terry Harper	.06
625	Larry Gura	.06
626	Bob Clark	.06
627	Dave LaPoint	.06
628	Ed Jurak	.08
629	Rick Langford	.06
630	Ted Simmons	.12
631	Denny Martinez	.06
632	Tom Foley	.12
633	Mike Krukow	.06
634	Mike Marshall	.15
635	Dave Righetti	.20
636	Pat Putnam	.06
637	Phillies Leaders:	.10
	G. Matthews, J. Denny	
638	George Vuckovich	.06
639	Rick Lysander	.08
640	Lance Parrish	.25
641	Mike Richardt	.06
642	Tom Underwood	.06
643	Mike Brown (R)	.15
644	Tim Lollar	.06
645	Tony Pena	.12
646	Checklist No.5	.08
647	Ron Roenicke	.06
648	Len Whitehouse	.08
649	Tom Herr	.12
650	Phil Niekro	.25
651	J. McNamara (Mgr.)	.06
652	Rudy May	.06
653	Dave Stapleton	.06
654	Bob Bailor	.06
655	Amos Otis	.06
656	Bryn Smith	.06
657	Thad Bosley	.06
658	Jerry Augustine	.06
659	Duane Walker	.06
660	Ray Knight	.06
661	Steve Yeager	.06

NO.	PLAYER	MINT
662	Tom Brennan	.06
663	Johnnie LeMaster	.06
664	Dave Stegman	.06
665	Buddy Bell	.15
666	Tigers Leaders:	.12
	Lou Whitaker, J. Morris	
667	Vance Law	.06
668	Larry McWilliams	.06
669	Dave Lopes	.08
670	Rich Gossage	.20
671	Jamie Quirk	.06
672	Ricky Nelson	.12
673	Mike Walters	.12
674	Tim Flannery	.06
675	Pascual Perez	.08
676	Brian Giles	.06
677	Doyle Alexander	.06
678	Chris Speier	.06
679	Art Howe	.06
680	Fred Lynn	.20
681	Tom Lasorda (Mgr.)	.08
682	Dan Morogiello	.08
683	Marty Barrett (R)	1.50
684	Bob Shirley	.06
685	Willie Aikens	.06
686	Joe Price	.06
687	Roy Howell	.06
688	George Wright	.06
689	Mike Fischlin	.06
690	Jack Clark	.30
691	Steve Lake	.08
692	Dickie Thon	.06
693	Alan Wiggins	.08
694	Mike Stanton	.06
695	Lou Whitaker	.20
696	Pirates Leaders:	.08
	Bill Madlock, Rick Rhoden	
697	Dale Murray	.06
698	Marc Hill	.06
699	Dave Rucker	.06
700	Mike Schmidt	.75
701	Batting Leaders:	.30
	Bill Madlock, Dave Parker, Pete Rose	
702	Hit Leaders:	.30
	Pete Rose, Rusty Staub, Tony Perez	
703	Home Run Leaders:	.25
	Mike Schmidt, Tony Perez, D. Kingman	
704	RBI Leaders:	.15
	Rusty Staub, Tony Perez, Al Oliver	
705	Stolen Bases Leaders:	.12
	Larry Bowa, Joe Morgan, Cesar Cedeno	
706	Victory Leaders:	.15
	Steve Carlton, F. Jenkins, Tom Seaver	
707	Strikeout Leaders:	.20
	Tom Seaver, Steve Carlton, Nolan Ryan	
708	ERA Leaders:	.15
	Tom Seaver, Steve Rogers, Steve Carlton	
709	Save Leaders:	.12
	Bruce Sutter, Tug McGraw, G. Garber	
710	Batting Leaders:	.25
	Rod Carew, Cecil Cooper, George Brett	
711	Hit Leaders:	.20
	Reggie Jackson, Rod Carew, Bert Campaneris	
712	Home Run Leaders:	.20
	Graig Nettles, Reggie Jackson, Greg Luzinski	
713	RBI Leaders:	.20
	Reggie Jackson, Ted Simmons, Graig Nettles	
714	Stolen Bases Leaders:	.12
	Bert Campaneris, D. Lopes, Omar Moreno	
715	Victory Leaders:	.15
	Jim Palmer, Don Sutton, Tommy John	

NO.	PLAYER	MINT	NO.	PLAYER	MINT	NO.	PLAYER	MINT	NO.	PLAYER	MINT
716	Strikeouts Leaders: Don Sutton, Jerry Koosman, Bert Blyleven	.12	731	Lynn Jones	.06	752	Phil Garner	.06	772	Jim Slaton	.06
717	ERA Leaders: Jim Palmer, R. Fingers, Ron Guidry	.15	732	Terry Crowley	.06	753	Doug Gwosdz	.06	773	Todd Cruz	.06
			733	Dave Collins	.06	754	Kent Tekulve	.06	774	Tom Gorman	.12
			734	Odell Jones	.06	755	Garry Maddox	.06	775	Dave Parker	.25
718	Save Leaders: Rollie Fingers, R. Gossage, Dan Quisenberry	.15	735	Rick Burleson	.06	756	Reds Leaders: Ron Oester, Mario Soto	.08	776	Craig Reynolds	.06
			736	Dick Ruthven	.06				777	Tom Paciorek	.06
719	Andy Hassler	.06	737	Jim Essian	.06	757	Larry Bowa	.08	778	Andy Hawkins (R)	.50
720	Dwight Evans	.15	738	Bill Schroeder (R)	.20	758	Bill Stein	.06	779	Jim Sundberg	.06
721	Del Crandall (Mgr.)	.06	739	Bob Watson	.06	759	Richard Dotson	.08	780	Steve Carlton	.35
722	Bob Welch	.06	740	Tom Seaver	.35	760	Bob Horner	.25	781	Checklist No. 6	.08
723	Rich Dauer	.06	741	Wayne Gross	.06	761	John Montefusco	.06	782	Steve Balboni	.06
724	Eric Rasmussen	.06	742	Dick Williams (Mgr.)	.06	762	Rance Mulliniks	.06	783	Luis Leal	.06
725	Cesar Cedeno	.08	743	Don Hood	.06	763	Craig Swan	.06	784	Leon Roberts	.06
726	Brewers Leaders: Ted Simmons, Moose Haas	.10	744	Jamie Allen	.12	764	Mike Hargrove	.06	785	Joaquin Andujar	.12
			745	Dennis Eckersley	.06	765	Ken Forsch	.06	786	Red Sox Leaders: Bob Ojeda, Wade Boggs	.20
727	Joel Youngblood	.06	746	Mickey Hatcher	.06	766	Mike Vail	.06			
728	Tug McGraw	.08	747	Pat Zachry	.06	767	Carney Lansford	.08	787	Bill Campbell	.06
729	Gene Tenace	.06	748	Jeff Leonard	.06	768	Champ Summers	.06	788	Milt May	.06
730	Bruce Sutter	.20	749	Doug Flynn	.06	769	Bill Caudill	.08	789	Bert Blyleven	.08
			750	Jim Palmer	.40	770	Ken Griffey	.08	790	Doug DeCinces	.08
			751	Charlie Moore	.06	771	Billy Gardner (Mgr.)	.06	791	Terry Forster	.06
									792	Bill Russell	.12

1984 Topps Traded. . . . Complete Set of 132 Cards—Value $100.00

Updates the main 1984 card set with players who changed teams during the season and rookies. Features the first Topps card for Dwight Gooden and Bret Saberhagen. The complete set was packaged in a printed box and only distributed through card hobby dealers.

NO.	PLAYER	MINT	NO.	PLAYER	MINT	NO.	PLAYER	MINT	NO.	PLAYER	MINT
1 T	Willie Aikens	.15	34 T	Dennis Eckersley	.12	67 T	R. Lachemann (Mgr.)	.10	100 T	Jose Rijo (RR)	.75
2 T	Luis Aponte	.10	35 T	Jim Essian	.08	68 T	Frank LaCorte	.10	101 T	Jeff Robinson	.25
3 T	Mike Armstrong	.10	36 T	Darrell Evans	.25	69 T	Dennis Lamp	.10	102 T	Ron Romanick (RR)	.25
4 T	Bob Bailor	.10	37 T	Mike Fitzgerald	.15	70 T	Mark Langston (RR)	9.00	103 T	Pete Rose	7.00
5 T	Dusty Baker	.12	38 T	Tim Foli	.10	71 T	Rich Leach	.10	104 T	B. Saberhagen (RR)	13.00
6 T	Steve Balboni	.15	39 T	George Frazier	.10	72 T	Craig Lefferts	.10	105 T	Juan Samuel (RR)	3.00
7 T	Alan Bannister	.10	40 T	Rich Gale	.10	73 T	Gary Lucas	.10	106 T	Scott Sanderson	.12
8 T	Dave Beard	.10	41 T	Barbaro Garbey	.20	74 T	Jerry Martin	.10	107 T	Dick Schofield	.50
9 T	Joe Beckwith	.10	42 T	D. Gooden (RR)	40.00	75 T	Carmelo Martinez	.25	108 T	Tom Seaver	3.00
10 T	Bruce Berenyi	.10	43 T	Rich Gossage	.30	76 T	Mike Mason	.20	109 T	Jim Slaton	.08
11 T	Dave Bergman	.10	44 T	Wayne Gross	.10	77 T	Gary Matthews	.15	110 T	Mike Smithson	.08
12 T	Tony Bernazard	.10	45 T	Mark Gublcza (RR)	2.00	78 T	Andy McGaffigan	.10	111 T	Lary Sorensen	.08
13 T	Yogi Berra (Mgr.)	.50	46 T	Jackie Gutierrez	.15	79 T	Larry Milbourne	.10	112 T	Tim Stoddard	.08
14 T	Barry Bonnell	.10	47 T	Mel Hall	.20	80 T	Sid Monge	.10	113 T	Champ Summers	.08
15 T	Phil Bradley (RR)	2.50	48 T	Toby Harrah	.12	81 T	Jackie Moore (Mgr.)	.10	114 T	Jim Sundberg	.08
16 T	Fred Breining	.10	49 T	Ron Hassey	.10	82 T	Joe Morgan	1.25	115 T	Rick Sutcliffe	.50
17 T	Bill Buckner	.25	50 T	Rich Hebner	.10	83 T	Graig Nettles	.50	116 T	Craig Swan	.10
18 T	Ray Burris	.10	51 T	Willie Hernandaz	.40	84 T	Phil Niekro	1.25	117 T	Tim Teufel (RR)	.40
19 T	John Butcher	.10	52 T	Ricky Horton (RR)	.35	85 T	Ken Oberkfell	.12	118 T	Derrel Thomas	.10
20 T	Brett Butler	.35	53 T	Art Howe	.10	86 T	Mike O'Berry	.10	119 T	Gorman Thomas	.15
21 T	Enos Cabell	.10	54 T	Dane Iorg	.10	87 T	Al Oliver	.20	120 T	Alex Trevino	.08
22 T	Bill Campbell	.10	55 T	Brook Jacoby (RR)	1.50	88 T	Jorge Orta	.10	121 T	Manny Trillo	.12
23 T	Bill Caudill	.15	56 T	Mike Jeffcoat	.15	89 T	Amos Otis	.15	122 T	John Tudor	.30
24 T	Bob Clark	.10	57 T	D. Johnson (Mgr.)	.25	90 T	Dave Parker	.75	123 T	Tom Underwood	.10
25 T	Bryan Clark	.10	58 T	Lynn Jones	.10	91 T	Tony Perez	.50	124 T	Mike Vail	.10
26 T	Jaimes Cocanower	.20	59 T	Ruppert Jones	.10	92 T	Gerald Perry	1.25	125 T	Tom Waddell	.20
27 T	Ron Darling (RR)	5.00	60 T	Mike Jorgensen	.10	93 T	Gary Pettis (RR)	.35	126 T	Gary Ward	.20
28 T	Alvin Davis (RR)	4.50	61 T	Bob Kearney	.10	94 T	Rob Picciolo	.08	127 T	Curt Wilkerson	.25
29 T	Ken Dayley	.12	62 T	Jimmy Key (RR)	3.00	95 T	Vern Rapp (Mgr.)	.08	128 T	Frank Williams	.20
30 T	Jeff Dedmon	.20	63 T	Dave Kingman	.25	96 T	Floyd Rayford	.08	129 T	Glenn Wilson	.25
31 T	Bob Dernier	.10	64 T	Jerry Koosman	.40	97 T	Randy Ready (RR)	.35	130 T	Johnny Wockenfuss	.10
32 T	Carlos Diaz	.10	65 T	Wayne Krenchicki	.10	98 T	Ron Reed	.10	131 T	Ned Yost	.10
33 T	Mike Easler	.12	66 T	Rusty Kuntz	.10	99 T	Gene Richards	.10	132 T	Traded Checklist	.15

1985 Topps.... Complete Set of 792 Cards—Value $120.00

Features the rookie cards of Dwight Gooden, Roger Clemens, Eric Davis, Bret Saberhagen, Mark McGwire, Orel Hershiser, and Kirby Puckett.
Includes players and coaches of the 1984 USA Olympic Baseball Team, "#1 Draft Picks" and a revival of "Father & Son" cards.

NO. PLAYER	MINT	NO. PLAYER	MINT	NO. PLAYER	MINT	NO. PLAYER	MINT
1 Record—C. Fisk	.15	57 Pat Zachry	.05	123 Dave Smith	.05	176 Bill Schroeder	.05
Longest Game, Catcher		58 Orlando Mercado	.05	124 Rich Hebner	.05	177 Dave Von Ohlen	.05
2 Record—S. Garvey	.20	59 Rick Waits	.05	125 Ken Tekulve	.05	178 Miguel Dilone	.05
Errorless Games, 18		60 George Hendrick	.08	126 Ruppert Jones	.05	179 Tommy John	.15
3 Record—D. Gooden	.75	61 Curt Kaufman (R)	.15	127 Mark Gubicza (R)	1.25	180 Dave Winfield	.40
Most Strikeouts, Rookie		62 Mike Ramsey	.05	128 Ernie Whitt	.05	181 Roger Clemens (R)	10.00
4 Record—C. Johnson	.08	63 Steve McCatty	.05	129 Gene Garber	.05	182 Tim Flannery	.05
Most Pinch Homers		64 Mark Bailey (R)	.15	130 Al Oliver	.10	183 Larry McWilliams	.05
5 Record—J. Morgan	.15	65 Bill Buckner	.10	131 Father & Son:	.07	184 Carmen Castillo	.05
Most Homers, 2B		66 Dick Williams (Mgr.)	.05	Gus and Buddy Bell		185 Al Holland	.05
6 Record—P. Rose	.50	67 Rafael Santana (R)	.20	132 Father & Son:	.07	186 Bob Lillis (Mgr.)	.05
Most Singles, Career		68 Von Hayes	.15	Yogi and Dale Berra		187 Mike Walters	.05
7 Record—N. Ryan	.35	69 Jim Winn	.12	133 Father & Son:	.07	188 Greg Pryor	.05
Most Strikeouts, Career		70 Don Baylor	.10	Ray and Bob Boone		189 Warren Brusstar	.05
8 Record—J. Samuel	.15	71 Tim Laudner	.05	134 Father & Son:	.07	190 Rusty Staub	.12
Stolen Bases, Rookie		72 Rick Sutcliffe	.15	Tito and Terry Francona		191 Steve Nicosia	.05
9 Record—B. Sutter	.12	73 Rusty Kuntz	.05	135 Father & Son:	.07	192 Howard Johnson	4.00
Most Saves, Season		74 Mike Krukow	.05	Bob and Terry Kennedy		193 Jimmy Key (R)	1.00
10 Record—D. Sutton	.12	75 Willie Upshaw	.10	136 Father & Son:	.07	194 Dave Stegman	.05
100 Strikeout Seasons		76 Alan Bannister	.05	Jim and Jeff Kunkel		195 Glenn Hubbard	.05
11 Ralph Houk (Mgr.)	.05	77 Joe Beckwith	.05	137 Father & Son:	.07	196 Pete O'Brien	.10
12 Dave Lopes	.08	78 Scott Fletcher	.05	Vern and Vance Law		197 Mike Warren	.05
13 Tim Lollar	.05	79 Rick Mahler	.05	138 Father & Son:	.07	198 Eddie Milner	.05
14 Chris Bando	.05	80 Keith Hernandez	.30	Dick and Dick Schofield		199 Denny Martinez	.05
15 Jerry Koosman	.15	81 Lenn Sakata	.05	139 Father & Son:	.07	200 Reggie Jackson	.40
16 Bobby Meacham	.05	82 Joe Price	.05	Bob and Joel Skinner		201 Burt Hooton	.05
17 Mike Scott	.30	83 Charlie Moore	.05	140 Father & Son:	.07	202 Gorman Thomas	.08
18 Mickey Hatcher	.05	84 Spike Owen	.05	Roy and Roy Smalley		203 Bob McClure	.05
19 George Frazier	.05	85 Mike Marshall	.12	141 Father & Son:	.07	204 Art Howe	.05
20 Chet Lemon	.08	86 Don Aase	.05	Dave and Mike Stenhouse		205 Steve Rogers	.05
21 Lee Tunnell	.05	87 David Green	.05	142 Father & Son:	.07	206 Phil Garner	.05
22 Duane Kuiper	.05	88 Bryn Smith	.05	Dizzy and Steve Trout		207 Mark Clear	.05
23 Bret Saberhagen (R)	5.00	89 Jackie Gutierrez	.12	143 Father & Son:	.07	208 Champ Summers	.05
24 Jesse Barfield	.35	90 Rich Gossage	.15	Ossie and Ozzie Virgil		209 Bill Campbell	.05
25 Steve Bedrosian	.15	91 Jeff Burroughs	.05	144 Ron Gardenhire	.05	210 Gary Matthews	.08
26 Ray Smalley	.05	92 Paul Owens (Mgr.)	.05	145 Alvin Davis (R)	1.50	211 Clay Christiansen	.15
27 Bruce Berenyi	.05	93 Don Schulze	.10	146 Gary Redus	.08	212 George Vukovich	.05
28 Dann Bilardello	.05	94 Toby Harrah	.05	147 Bill Swaggerty	.12	213 Billy Gardner (Mgr.)	.05
29 Odell Jones	.05	95 Jose Cruz	.08	148 Steve Yeager	.05	214 John Tudor	.15
30 Cal Ripken	.50	96 Johnny Ray	.12	149 Dickie Noles	.05	215 Bob Brenly	.08
31 Terry Whitfield	.05	97 Pete Filson	.05	150 Jim Rice	.25	216 Jerry Don Gleaton	.05
32 Chuck Porter	.05	98 Steve Lake	.05	151 Moose Haas	.05	217 Leon Roberts	.05
33 Tito Landrum	.05	99 Milt Wilcox	.05	152 Steve Braun	.05	218 Doyle Alexander	.05
34 Ed Nunez	.10	100 George Brett	.50	153 Frank LaCorte	.05	219 Gerald Perry	.30
35 Graig Nettles	.12	101 Jim Acker	.05	154 Argenis Salazar	.12	220 Fred Lynn	.15
36 Fred Breining	.05	102 Tommy Dunbar	.08	155 Yogi Berra (Mgr.)	.12	221 Ron Reed	.05
37 Reid Nichols	.05	103 Randy Lerch	.05	156 Craig Reynolds	.05	222 Hubie Brooks	.08
38 Jackie Moore (Mgr.)	.05	104 Mike Fitzgerald	.07	157 Tug McGraw	.08	223 Tom Hume	.05
39 Johnny Wockenfuss	.05	105 Ron Kittle	.15	158 Pat Tabler	.05	224 Al Cowens	.05
40 Phil Niekro	.20	106 Pascual Perez	.05	159 Carlos Diaz	.05	225 Mike Boddicker	.10
41 Mike Fischlin	.05	107 Tom Foley	.05	160 Lance Parrish	.20	226 Juan Beniquez	.05
42 Luis Sanchez	.05	108 Darnell Coles	.15	161 Ken Schrom	.05	227 Danny Darwin	.05
43 Andre David	.12	109 Gary Roenicke	.05	162 Benny Distefano	.15	228 Dion James	.20
44 Dickie Thon	.07	110 Alejandro Pena	.05	163 Dennis Eckersley	.05	229 Dave LaPoint	.05
45 Greg Minton	.05	111 Doug DeCinces	.10	164 Jorge Orta	.05	230 Gary Carter	.35
46 Gary Woods	.05	112 Tom Tellmann	.05	165 Dusty Baker	.08	231 Dwayne Murphy	.08
47 Dave Rozema	.05	113 Tom Herr	.15	166 Keith Atherton	.05	232 Dave Beard	.05
48 Tony Fernandez	1.25	114 Bob James	.05	167 Rufino Linares	.05	233 Ed Jurak	.05
49 Butch Davis	.08	115 Rickey Henderson	.50	168 Garth Iorg	.05	234 Jerry Narron	.05
50 John Candelaria	.08	116 Dennis Boyd	.25	169 Dan Spillner	.05	235 Garry Maddox	.05
51 Rob Watson	.05	117 Greg Gross	.05	170 George Foster	.15	236 Mark Thurmond	.08
52 Jerry Dybzinski	.05	118 Eric Show	.08	171 Bill Stein	.05	237 Julio Franco	.35
53 Tom Gorman	.07	119 Pat Corrales (Mgr.)	.05	172 Jack Perconte	.05	238 Jose Rijo (R)	.40
54 Cesar Cedeno	.08	120 Steve Kemp	.05	173 Mike Young	.10	239 Tim Teufel	.20
55 Frank Tanana	.05	121 Checklist No. 1	.08	174 Rick Honeycutt	.05	240 Dave Stieb	.15
56 Jim Dwyer	.05	122 Tom Brunansky	.25	175 Dave Parker	.25	241 Jim Frey (Mgr.)	.05

NO.	PLAYER	MINT
242	Greg Harris	.05
243	Barbaro Garbey	.12
244	Mike Jones	.05
245	Chili Davis	.08
246	Mike Norris	.05
247	Wayne Tolleson	.05
248	Terry Forster	.05
249	Harold Baines	.20
250	Jesse Orosco	.05
251	Brad Gulden	.05
252	Dan Ford	.05
253	Sid Bream (R)	.35
254	Pete Vuckovich	.08
255	Lonnie Smith	.08
256	Mike Stanton	.05
257	Bryan Little	.05
258	Mike Brown	.05
259	Gary Allenson	.05
260	Dave Righetti	.12
261	Checklist No. 2	.08
262	Greg Booker	.12
263	Mel Hall	.10
264	Joe Sambito	.05
265	Juan Samuel	.60
266	Frank Viola	.30
267	Henry Cotto	.20
268	Chuck Tanner (Mgr.)	.05
269	Doug Baker	.12
270	Dan Quisenberry	.15

No. 271 to 282 (# 1 Draft Picks)

NO.	PLAYER	MINT
271	Tim Foli (1968)	.12
272	Jeff Burroughs (1969)	.12
273	Bill Almon (1974)	.12
274	Floyd Bannister (1976)	.12
275	Harold Baines (1977)	.18
276	Bob Horner (1978)	.18
277	Al Chambers (1979)	.12
278	D. Strawberry (1980)	1.00
279	Mike Moore (1981)	.12
280	S. Dunston (R) (1982)	1.25
281	Tim Belcher (R) (1983)	1.25
282	S. Abner (R) (1984)	.45
283	Fran Mullins	.05
284	Marty Bystrom	.05
285	Dan Driessen	.05
286	Rudy Law	.05
287	Walt Terrell	.05
288	Jeff Kunkel	.12
289	Tom Underwood	.05
290	Cecil Cooper	.15
291	Bob Welch	.05
292	Brad Komminsk	.10
293	Curt Young (R)	.40
294	Tom Nieto	.12
295	Joe Niekro	.12
296	Ricky Nelson	.05
297	Gary Lucas	.05
298	Marty Barrett	.12
299	Andy Hawkins	.08
300	Rod Carew	.35
301	John Montefusco	.05
302	Tim Corcoran	.05
303	Mike Jeffcoat	.08
304	Gary Gaetti	.40
305	Dale Berra	.05
306	Rick Reuschel	.10
307	Sparky Anderson (Mgr.)	.05
308	John Wathan	.05
309	Mike Witt	.10
310	Manny Trillo	.05
311	Jim Gott	.05
312	Marc Hill	.05
313	Dave Schmidt	.05
314	Ron Oester	.05
315	Doug Sisk	.05
316	John Lowenstein	.05
317	Jack Lazorko	.12
318	Ted Simmons	.10
319	Jeff Jones	.05
320	Dale Murphy	.60
321	Ricky Horton (R)	.25
322	Dave Stapleton	.05
323	Andy McGaffigan	.05
324	Bruce Bochy	.05
325	John Denny	.05

NO.	PLAYER	MINT
326	Kevin Bass	.15
327	Brook Jacoby	.35
328	Bob Shirley	.05
329	Ron Washington	.05
330	Leon Durham	.15
331	Bill Laskey	.05
332	Brian Harper	.05
333	Willie Hernandez	.15
334	Dick Howser (Mgr.)	.05
335	Bruce Benedict	.05
336	Rance Mulliniks	.05
337	Billy Sample	.05
338	Britt Burns	.05
339	Danny Heep	.05
340	Robin Yount	.50
341	Floyd Rayford	.05
342	Ted Power	.05
343	Bill Russell	.05
344	Dave Henderson	.05
345	Charlie Lea	.05
346	Terry Pendleton (R)	.50
347	Rick Langford	.05
348	Bob Boone	.05
349	Domingo Ramos	.05
350	Wade Boggs	4.00
351	Juan Agosto	.05
352	Joe Morgan	.25
353	Julio Solano	.12
354	Andre Robertson	.05
355	Bert Blyleven	.10
356	Dave Meier	.12
357	Rich Bordi	.05
358	Tony Pena	.12
359	Pat Sheridan	.05
360	Steve Carlton	.30
361	Alfredo Griffin	.05
362	Craig McMurtry	.05
363	Ron Hodges	.05
364	Richard Dotson	.05
365	Danny Ozark (Mgr.)	.05
366	Todd Cruz	.05
367	Keefe Cato	.12
368	Dave Bergman	.05
369	R.J. Reynolds (R)	.25
370	Bruce Sutter	.15
371	Mickey Rivers	.05
372	Roy Howell	.05
373	Mike Moore	.07
374	Brian Downing	.05
375	Jeff Reardon	.15
376	Jeff Newman	.05
377	Checklist No.3	.08
378	Alan Wiggins	.08
379	Charles Hudson	.05
380	Ken Griffey	.08
381	Roy Smith	.12
382	Denny Walling	.05
383	Rick Lysander	.05
384	Jody Davis	.10
385	Jose DeLeon	.05
386	Dan Gladden (R)	.30
387	Buddy Biancalana	.12
388	Bert Roberge	.05

No. 389 to 404 (U.S. Olympic Team)

NO.	PLAYER	MINT
389	Rod Dedeaux (Coach)	.10
390	Sid Akins	.10
391	Flavio Alfaro	.10
392	Don August	.50
393	Scott Bankhead	.75
394	Bob Caffrey	.10
395	Mike Dunne (R)	.60
396	Gary Green	.10
397	John Hoover	.10
398	Shane Mack (R)	.40
399	John Marzano (R)	.35
400	Oddibe McDowell (R)	.75
401	Mark McGwire (R)	17.50
402	Pat Pacillo (R)	.25
403	Cory Snyder (R)	5.00
404	Billy Swift	.20
405	Tom Veryzer	.05
406	Len Whitehouse	.05
407	Bobby Ramos	.05
408	Sid Monge	.05
409	Brad Wellman	.05

NO.	PLAYER	MINT
410	Bob Horner	.20
411	Bobby Cox (Mgr.)	.05
412	Bud Black	.05
413	Vance Law	.05
414	Gary Ward	.05
415	Ron Darling	1.25
416	Wayne Gross	.05
417	John Franco (R)	1.00
418	Ken Landreaux	.05
419	Mike Caldwell	.05
420	Andre Dawson	.35
421	Dave Rucker	.05
422	Carney Lansford	.10
423	Barry Bonnell	.05
424	Al Nipper (R)	.25
425	Mike Hargrove	.05
426	Vern Ruhle	.05
427	Mario Ramirez	.05
428	Larry Andersen	.05
429	Rick Cerone	.05
430	Ron Davis	.05
431	U.L. Washington	.05
432	Thad Bosley	.05
433	Jim Morrison	.05
434	Gene Richards	.05
435	Dan Petry	.12
436	Willie Aikens	.05
437	Al Jones	.12
438	Joe Torre (Mgr.)	.07
439	Junior Ortiz	.05
440	Fernando Valenzuela	.30
441	Duane Walker	.05
442	Ken Forsch	.05
443	George Wright	.05
444	Tony Phillips	.05
445	Tippy Martinez	.05
446	Jim Sundberg	.05
447	Jeff Lahti	.05
448	Derrel Thomas	.05
449	Phil Bradley (R)	.75
450	Steve Garvey	.40
451	Bruce Hurst	.05
452	John Castino	.05
453	Tom Waddell	.12
454	Glenn Wilson	.10
455	Bob Knepper	.05
456	Tim Foli	.05
457	Cecilio Guante	.05
458	Randy Johnson	.05
459	Charlie Leibrandt	.05
460	Ryne Sandberg	.40
461	Marty Castillo	.05
462	Gary Lavelle	.05
463	Dave Collins	.05
464	Mike Mason	.12
465	Bob Grich	.07
466	Tony LaRussa (Mgr.)	.05
467	Ed Lynch	.05
468	Wayne Krenchicki	.05
469	Sammy Stewart	.05
470	Steve Sax	.30
471	Pete Ladd	.05
472	Jim Essian	.05
473	Tim Wallach	.12
474	Kurt Kepshire	.12
475	Andre Thornton	.08
476	Jeff Stone (R)	.20
477	Bob Ojeda	.05
478	Kurt Bevacqua	.05
479	Mike Madden	.05
480	Lou Whitaker	.15
481	Dale Murray	.05
482	Harry Spilman	.05
483	Mike Smithson	.05
484	Larry Bowa	.05
485	Matt Young	.06
486	Steve Balboni	.06
487	Frank Williams	.12
488	Joel Skinner	.10
489	Bryan Clark	.05
490	Jason Thompson	.08
491	Rick Camp	.05
492	Dave Johnson (Mgr.)	.20
493	Orel Hershiser (R)	7.50
494	Rich Dauer	.05

NO.	PLAYER	MINT
495	Mario Soto	.08
496	Donnie Scott	.12
497	Gary Pettis (wrong photo—It's his brother—Lynn)	.30
498	Ed Romero	.05
499	Danny Cox	.25
500	Mike Schmidt	.50
501	Dan Schatzeder	.05
502	Rick Miller	.05
503	Tim Conroy	.05
504	Jerry Willard	.08
505	Jim Beattie	.05
506	Franklin Stubbs (R)	.40
507	Ray Fontenot	.05
508	John Shelby	.05
509	Milt May	.05
510	Kent Hrbek	.30
511	Lee Smith	.08
512	Tom Brookens	.05
513	Lynn Jones	.05
514	Jeff Cornell	.12
515	Dave Concepcion	.08
516	Roy Lee Jackson	.05
517	Jerry Martin	.05
518	Chris Chambliss	.05
519	Doug Rader (Mgr.)	.05
520	LaMarr Hoyt	.08
521	Rick Dempsey	.05
522	Paul Molitor	.20
523	Candy Maldonado	.15
524	Rob Wilfong	.05
525	Darrell Porter	.05
526	Dave Palmer	.05
527	Checklist No. 4	.08
528	Bill Krueger	.05
529	Rich Gedman	.05
530	Dave Dravecky	.08
531	Joe Lefebvre	.25
532	Frank DiPino	.05
533	Tony Bernazard	.05
534	Brian Dayett	.08
535	Pat Putnam	.05
536	Kirby Puckett (R)	12.00
537	Don Robinson	.05
538	Keith Moreland	.05
539	Aurelio Lopez	.05
540	Claudell Washington	.08
541	Mark Davis	.05
542	Don Slaught	.05
543	Mike Squires	.05
544	Bruce Kison	.05
545	Lloyd Moseby	.15
546	Brent Gaff	.08
547	Pete Rose (Mgr.)	.50
548	Larry Parrish	.07
549	Mike Scioscia	.05
550	Scott McGregor	.07
551	Andy Van Slyke	.35
552	Chris Codiroli	.05
553	Bob Clark	.05
554	Doug Flynn	.05
555	Bob Stanley	.05
556	Sixto Lezcano	.05
557	Len Barker	.05
558	Carmelo Martinez	.05
559	Jay Howell	.05
560	Bill Madlock	.15
561	Darryl Motley	.05
562	Houston Jimenez	.05
563	Dick Ruthven	.05
564	Alan Ashby	.05
565	Kirk Gibson	.35
566	Ed Vande Berg	.05
567	Joel Youngblood	.05
568	Cliff Johnson	.05
569	Ken Oberkfell	.05
570	Darryl Strawberry	3.00
571	Charlie Hough	.05
572	Tom Paciorek	.05
573	Jay Tibbs (R)	.20
574	Joe Altobelli (Mgr.)	.05
575	Pedro Guerrero	.25
576	Jaime Cocanower	.12
577	Chris Speier	.05

NO. PLAYER	MINT	NO. PLAYER	MINT	NO. PLAYER	MINT	NO. PLAYER	MINT
578 Terry Francona	.05	632 Bruce Bochte	.05	686 Mike Easler	.05	740 Jack Clark	.30
579 Ron Romanick (R)	.15	633 Glenn Hoffman	.05	687 Bill Gullickson	.05	741 John Butcher	.05
580 Dwight Evans	.12	634 Bill Dawley	.05	688 Len Matuszek	.05	742 Ron Hassey	.05
581 Mark Wagner	.05	635 Terry Kennedy	.08	689 Luis DeLeon	.05	743 Frank White	.05
582 Ken Phelps	.30	636 Shane Rawley	.05	690 Alan Trammell	.35	744 Doug Bair	.05
583 Bobby Brown	.05	637 Brett Butler	.08	691 Dennis Rasmussen	.25	745 Buddy Bell	.10
584 Kevin Gross	.05	638 Mike Pagliarulo (R)	.65	692 Randy Bush	.05	746 Jim Clancy	.05
585 Butch Wynegar	.05	639 Ed Hodge	.10	693 Tim Stoddard	.05	747 Alex Trevino	.05
586 Bill Scherrer	.05	640 Steve Henderson	.05	694 Joe Carter	2.00	748 Lee Mazzilli	.05
587 Doug Frobel	.05	641 Rod Scurry	.05	695 Rick Rhoden	.05	749 Julio Cruz	.05
588 Bobby Castillo	.05	642 Dave Owen	.10	696 John Rabb	.05	750 Rollie Fingers	.15
589 Bob Dernier	.05	643 Johnny Grubb	.05	697 Onix Concepcion	.05	751 Kelvin Chapman	.12
590 Ray Knight	.05	644 Mark Huismann	.10	698 Jorge Bell	.60	752 Bob Owchinko	.05
591 Larry Herndon	.05	645 Damaso Garcia	.08	699 Donnie Moore	.08	753 Greg Brock	.08
592 Jeff Robinson	.30	646 Scot Thompson	.05	700 Eddie Murray	.45	754 Larry Milbourne	.05
593 Rick Leach	.05	647 Rafael Ramierz	.05	701 Eddie Murray (AS)	.25	755 Ken Singleton	.08
594 Curt Wilkerson	.08	648 Bob Jones	.05	702 Damaso Garcia (AS)	.10	756 Rob Picciolo	.05
595 Larry Gura	.05	649 Sid Fernandez	1.00	703 George Brett (AS)	.30	757 Willie McGee	.35
596 Jerry Hairston	.05	650 Greg Luzinski	.08	704 Cal Ripken (AS)	.25	758 Ray Burris	.05
597 Brad Lesley	.05	651 Jeff Russell	.05	705 Dave Winfield (AS)	.20	759 Jim Fanning (Mgr.)	.05
598 Jose Oquendo	.05	652 Joe Nolan	.05	706 Rickey Henderson (AS)	.30	760 Nolan Ryan	.75
599 Storm Davis	.08	653 Mark Brouhard	.05	707 Tony Armas (AS)	.10	761 Jerry Remy	.05
600 Pete Rose	1.00	654 Dave Anderson	.05	708 Lance Parrish (AS)	.15	762 Eddie Whitson	.05
601 Tom Lasorda (Mgr.)	.08	655 Joaquin Andujar	.08	709 Mike Boddicker (AS)	.10	763 Kiko Garcia	.05
602 Jeff Dedmon	.12	656 Chuck Cottier (Mgr.)	.05	710 Frank Viola (AS)	.10	764 Jamie Easterly	.05
603 Rick Manning	.05	657 Jim Slaton	.05	711 Dan Quisenberry (AS)	.15	765 Willie Randolph	.05
604 Daryl Sconiers	.05	658 Mike Stenhouse	.08	712 Keith Hernandez (AS)	.20	766 Paul Mirabella	.05
605 Ozzie Smith	.30	659 Checklist No. 5	.08	713 Ryne Sandberg (AS)	.25	767 Darrell Brown	.05
606 Rich Gale	.05	660 Tony Gwynn	1.00	714 Mike Schmidt (AS)	.25	768 Ron Cey	.10
607 Bill Almon	.05	661 Steve Crawford	.05	715 Ozzie Smith (AS)	.10	769 Joe Cowley	.05
608 Craig Lefferts	.05	662 Mike Heath	.05	716 Dale Murphy (AS)	.30	770 Carlton Fisk	.25
609 Broderick Perkins	.05	663 Luis Aguayo	.05	717 Tony Gwynn (AS)	.25	771 Geoff Zahn	.05
610 Jack Morris	.25	664 Steve Farr	.20	718 Jeff Leonard (AS)	.10	772 Johnnie LeMaster	.05
611 Ozzie Virgil	.05	665 Don Mattingly	8.00	719 Gary Carter (AS)	.20	773 Hal McRae	.05
612 Mike Armstrong	.05	666 Mike LaCoss	.05	720 Rick Sutcliffe (AS)	.15	774 Dennis Lamp	.05
613 Terry Puhl	.05	667 Dave Engle	.05	721 Bob Knepper (AS)	.10	775 Mookie Wilson	.08
614 Al Williams	.05	668 Steve Trout	.05	722 Bruce Sutter (AS)	.15	776 Jerry Royster	.05
615 Marvell Wynne	.05	669 Lee Lacy	.05	723 Dave Stewart	.25	777 Ned Yost	.05
616 Scott Sanderson	.05	670 Tom Seaver	.35	724 Oscar Gamble	.05	778 Mike Davis	.08
617 Willie Wilson	.15	671 Dane Iorg	.05	725 Floyd Bannister	.05	779 Nick Esasky	.05
618 Pete Falcone	.05	672 Juan Berenguer	.05	726 Al Bumbry	.05	780 Mike Flanagan	.05
619 Jeff Leonard	.05	673 Buck Martinez	.05	727 Frank Pastore	.05	781 Jim Gantner	.05
620 Dwight Gooden (R)	9.00	674 Atlee Hammaker	.05	728 Bob Bailor	.05	782 Tom Niedenfuer	.05
621 Marvis Foley	.05	675 Tony Perez	.15	729 Don Sutton	.20	783 Mike Jorgensen	.05
622 Luis Leal	.05	676 Albert Hall	.12	730 Dave Kingman	.10	784 Checklist No. 6	.08
623 Greg Walker	.12	677 Wally Backman	.05	731 Neil Allen	.05	785 Tony Armas	.12
624 Benny Ayala	.05	678 Joey McLaughlin	.05	732 John McNamara (Mgr.)	.05	786 Enos Cabell	.05
625 Mark Langston (R)	2.00	679 Bob Kearney	.05	733 Tony Scott	.05	787 Jim Wohlford	.05
626 German Rivera	.15	680 Jerry Reuss	.05	734 John Henry Johnson	.05	788 Steve Comer	.05
627 Eric Davis (R)	13.00	681 Ben Oglivie	.05	735 Garry Templeton	.10	789 Luis Salazar	.05
628 R. Lachemann (Mgr.)	.05	682 Doug Corbett	.05	736 Jerry Mumphrey	.05	790 Ron Guidry	.20
629 Dick Schofield	.12	683 Whitey Herzog (Mgr.)	.05	737 Bo Diaz	.05	791 Ivan DeJesus	.05
630 Tim Raines	.40	684 Bill Doran	.10	738 Omar Moreno	.05	792 Darrell Evans	.12
631 Bob Forsch	.05	685 Bill Caudill	.08	739 Ernie Camacho	.05		

1985 Topps Traded.... Complete Set of 132 Cards—Value $16.00

Updates the main 1985 card set with players who changed teams during the season and rookies who joined their teams early in the season. Features the first Topps card of Vince Coleman, Tom Browning and Teddy Higuera. The complete set was packaged in a printed box and only distributed through card hobby dealers. Topps also tested a small quantity of wax packs. A "Tiffany" version of the set was also issued.

NO. PLAYER	MINT	NO. PLAYER	MINT	NO. PLAYER	MINT	NO. PLAYER	MINT
1 T Don Aase	.08	5 T G. Bamberger (Mgr.)	.06	9 T Hubie Brooks	.12	13 T Ray Burris	.06
2 T Bill Almon	.06	6 T Dale Berra	.10	10 T Chris Brown (RR)	.30	14 T Jeff Burroughs	.06
3 T Benny Ayala	.06	7 T Rich Bordi	.06	11 T T. Browning (RR)	1.00	15 T Bill Campbell	.06
4 T Dusty Baker	.12	8 T Daryl Boston (RR)	.20	12 T Al Bumbry	.06	16 T Don Carman	.25

1985 Topps Traded (Continued)

NO. PLAYER	MINT	NO. PLAYER	MINT	NO. PLAYER	MINT	NO. PLAYER	MINT
17 T Gary Carter	.75	46 T Toby Harrah	.08	75 T Sixto Lezcano	.06	104 T Rick Schu	.15
18 T Bobby Castillo	.06	47 T Greg Harris	.06	76 T Tim Lollar	.06	105 T Donnie Scott	.06
19 T Bill Caudill	.10	48 T Ron Hassey	.06	77 T Fred Lynn	.20	106 T Larry Sheets	.50
20 T Rick Cerone	.08	49 T Rickey Henderson	1.00	78 T Billy Martin (Mgr.)	.15	107 T Don Slaught	.06
21 T Bryan Clark	.06	50 T Steve Henderson	.06	79 T Ron Mathis	.15	108 T Roy Smalley	.08
22 T Jack Clark	.40	51 T George Hendrick	.12	80 T Len Matuszek	.06	109 T Lonnie Smith	.12
23 T Pat Clements	.25	52 T Joe Hesketh (RR)	.25	81 T Gene Mauch (Mgr.)	.06	110 T Nate Snell	.20
24 T V. Coleman (RR)	5.00	53 T T. Higuera (RR)	2.00	82 T Oddibe McDowell	.50	111 T Chris Speier	.06
25 T Dave Collins	.08	54 T Donnie Hill	.06	83 T R. McDowell (RR)	1.00	112 T Mike Stenhouse	.06
26 T Dave Darwin	.06	55 T Al Holland	.08	84 T J. McNamara (Mgr.)	.06	113 T Tim Stoddard	.06
27 T J. Davenport (Mgr.)	.06	56 T Burt Hooton	.06	85 T Donnie Moore	.08	114 T Jim Sundberg	.08
28 T Jerry Davis	.12	57 T Jay Howell	.08	86 T Gene Nelson	.06	115 T Bruce Sutter	.25
29 T Brian Dayett	.06	58 T Ken Howell	.20	87 T Steve Nicosia	.06	116 T Don Sutton	.50
30 T Ivan DeJesus	.06	59 T LaMarr Hoyt	.12	88 T Al Oliver	.12	117 T Kent Tekulve	.08
31 T Ken Dixon	.25	60 T Tim Hulett	.12	89 T Joe Orsulak	.15	118 T Tom Tellmann	.06
32 T M. Duncan (RR)	.30	61 T Bob James	.06	90 T Rob Picciolo	.06	119 T Walt Terrell	.06
33 T John Felske (Mgr.)	.06	62 T Steve Jeltz (RR)	.25	91 T Chris Pittaro	.15	120 T Mickey Tettleton (RR)	.75
34 T Mike Fitzgerald	.06	63 T Cliff Johnson	.06	92 T Jim Presley (RR)	.80	121 T Derrel Thomas	.06
35 T Ray Fontenot	.06	64 T Howard Johnson	2.00	93 T Rick Reuschel	.15	122 T Rich Thompson	.15
36 T Greg Gagne	.35	65 T Ruppert Jones	.08	94 T Bert Roberge	.06	123 T Alex Trevino	.06
37 T Oscar Gamble	.10	66 T Steve Kemp	.06	95 T Bob Rodgers (Mgr.)	.06	124 T John Tudor	.20
38 T Scott Garrelts (RR)	.75	67 T Bruce Kison	.06	96 T Jerry Royster	.06	125 T Jose Uribe	.30
39 T Bob Gibson	.06	68 T Alan Knicely	.06	97 T Dave Rozema	.06	126 T B. Valentine (Mgr.)	.10
40 T Jim Gott	.06	69 T Mike LaCoss	.06	98 T Dave Rucker	.06	127 T Dave Von Ohlen	.06
41 T David Green	.12	70 T Lee Lacy	.08	99 T Vern Ruhle	.06	128 T U.L. Washington	.06
42 T Alfredo Griffin	.12	71 T Dave LaPoint	.06	100 T Paul Runge	.15	129 T Earl Weaver (Mgr.)	.12
43 T Ozzie Guillen (RR)	.75	72 T Gary Lavelle	.06	101 T Mark Salas (R)	.15	130 T Eddie Whitson	.08
44 T Eddie Haas (Mgr.)	.06	73 T Vance Law	.06	102 T Luis Salazar	.06	131 T Herm Winningham	.15
45 T Terry Harper	.06	74 T Johnnie LeMaster	.06	103 T Joe Sambito	.08	132 T Traded Checklist	.10

1986 Topps. . . . Complete Set of 792 Cards—Value $40.00

Features the rookie cards of Vince Coleman and Teddy Higuera. There are no card numbers 51 or 171. They were given wrong numbers in error. A "Tiffany" version of the set was also issued.

VINCE COLEMAN

TEDDY HIGUERA

ROGER McDOWELL

LEN DYKSTRA

HAROLD REYNOLDS

NO. PLAYER	MINT	NO. PLAYER	MINT	NO. PLAYER	MINT	NO. PLAYER	MINT
1 Pete Rose	1.00	28 Eric Davis	2.50	53 Len Dykstra (R)	.75	80 Darryl Strawberry	.75
2 Rose (Years 1963-66)	.35	29 Tony Phillips	.04	54 John Franco	.08	81 Gene Mauch (Mgr.)	.08
3 Rose (Years 1967-70)	.35	30 Eddie Murray	.40	55 Fred Lynn	.20	Angels Checklist	
4 Rose (Years 1971-74)	.35	31 Jamie Easterly	.04	56 Tom Niedenfuer	.08	82 Tippy Martinez	.04
5 Rose (Years 1975-78)	.35	32 Steve Yeager	.06	57 Bill Doran	.08	83 Phil Garner	.04
6 Rose (Years 1979-82)	.35	33 Jeff Lahti	.04	58 Bill Krueger	.04	84 Curt Young	.04
7 Rose (Years 1983-85)	.35	34 Ken Phelps	.04	59 Andre Thornton	.08	85 Tony Perez	.30
8 Dwayne Murphy	.08	35 Jeff Reardon	.12	60 Dwight Evans	.12	86 Tom Waddell	.04
9 Roy Smith	.04	36 Tigers Leaders:	.15	61 Karl Best	.12	87 Candy Maldonado	.04
10 Tony Gwynn	.50	Lance Parrish		62 Bob Boone	.04	88 Tom Nieto	.04
11 Bob Ojeda	.05	37 Mark Thurmond	.04	63 Ron Roenicke	.04	89 Randy St. Claire	.08
12 Jose Uribe (R)	.30	38 Glenn Hoffman	.04	64 Floyd Bannister	.04	90 Garry Templeton	.15
13 Bob Kearney	.04	39 Dave Rucker	.04	65 Dan Driessen	.04	91 Steve Crawford	.04
14 Julio Cruz	.04	40 Ken Griffey	.10	66 Cardinals Leaders:	.08	92 Al Cowens	.04
15 Eddie Whitson	.06	41 Brad Wellman	.04	Bob Forsch		93 Scot Thompson	.04
16 Rick Schu	.10	42 Geoff Zahn	.04	67 Carmelo Martinez	.04	94 Rich Bordi	.04
17 Mike Stenhouse	.04	43 Dave Engle	.04	68 Ed Lynch	.04	95 Ozzie Virgil	.04
18 Brent Gaff	.04	44 Lance McCullers (R)	.30	69 Luis Aguayo	.04	96 Blue Jays Leaders:	.06
19 Rich Hebner	.04	45 Damaso Garcia	.12	70 Dave Winfield	.30	Jim Clancy	
20 Lou Whitaker	.15	46 Billy Hatcher	.20	71 Ken Schrom	.04	97 Gary Gaetti	.20
21 G. Bamberger (Mgr.)	.04	47 Juan Berenguer	.04	72 Shawon Dunston	.25	98 Dick Ruthven	.04
Brewers Checklist		48 Bill Almon	.04	73 Randy O'Neal	.08	99 Buddy Biancalana	.04
22 Duane Walker	.08	49 Rick Manning	.04	74 Rance Mulliniks	.04	100 Nolan Ryan	.50
23 Manny Lee	.15	50 Dan Quisenberry	.15	75 Jose DeLeon	.04	101 Dave Bergman	.04
24 Len Barker	.06	51 Rob Wine (Mgr.)	.08	76 Dion James	.04	102 Joe Orsulak (R)	.20
25 Willie Wilson	.20	Braves Checklist		77 Charlie Leibrandt	.06	103 Luis Salazar	.04
26 Frank DePino	.04	Error-reads card no. 57		78 Bruce Benedict	.04	104 Sid Fernandez	.15
27 Ray Knight	.06	52 Chris Welsh	.04	79 Dave Schmidt	.04	105 Gary Ward	.04

NO.	PLAYER	MINT
106	Ray Burris	.04
107	Rafael Ramirez	.04
108	Ted Power	.04
109	Len Matuszek	.04
110	Scott McGregor	.06
111	Roger Craig (Mgr.) Giants Checklist	.08
112	Bill Campbell	.04
113	U.L. Washington	.04
114	Mike Brown	.04
115	Jay Howell	.04
116	Brook Jacoby	.10
117	Bruce Kison	.04
118	Jerry Royster	.04
119	Barry Bonnell	.04
120	Steve Carlton	.30
121	Nelson Simmons	.20
122	Pete Filson	.04
123	Greg Walker	.10
124	Luis Sanchez	.04
125	Dave Lopes	.06
126	Mets Leaders: Mookie Wilson	.08
127	Jack Howell (R)	.30
128	John Wathan	.04
129	Jeff Dedmon	.04
130	Alan Trammell	.20
131	Checklist No. 1	.08
132	Razor Shines	.08
133	Andy McGaffigan	.04
134	Carney Lansford	.08
135	Joe Niekro	.08
136	Mike Hargrove	.04
137	Charlie Moore	.04
138	Mark Davis	.04
139	Daryl Boston	.10
140	John Candelaria	.08
141	Chuck Cottier (Mgr.) Mariners Checklist see card 171	.08
142	Bob Jones	.04
143	Dave Van Gorder	.04
144	Doug Sisk	.04
145	Pedro Guerrero	.25
146	Jack Perconte	.04
147	Larry Sheets	.20
148	Mike Heath	.04
149	Brett Butler	.10
150	Joaquin Andujar	.08
151	Dave Stapleton	.04
152	Mike Morgan	.04
153	Ricky Adams	.04
154	Bert Roberge	.04
155	Bob Grich	.06
156	White Sox Leaders: Richard Dotson	.08
157	Ron Hassey	.04
158	Derrel Thomas	.04
159	Orel Hershiser	1.00
160	Chet Lemon	.06
161	Lee Tunnell	.04
162	Greg Gagne	.12
163	Pete Ladd	.04
164	Steve Balboni	.08
165	Mike Davis	.06
166	Dickie Thon	.04
167	Zane Smith	.15
168	Jeff Burroughs	.04
169	George Wright	.04
170	Gary Carter	.30
171	Bob Rodgers (Mgr.) Expo Checklist error—reads #141	.08
172	Jerry Reed	.15
173	Wayne Gross	.04
174	Brian Snyder	.15
175	Steve Sax	.15
176	Jay Tibbs	.04
177	Joel Youngblood	.04
178	Ivan DeJesus	.04
179	Stu Cliburn	.20
180	Don Mattingly	3.00
181	Al Nipper	.04
182	Bobby Brown	.04
183	Larry Andersen	.04

NO.	PLAYER	MINT
184	Tim Laudner	.04
185	Rollie Fingers	.15
186	Astros Leaders: Jose Cruz	.08
187	Scott Fletcher	.04
188	Bob Dernier	.04
189	Mike Mason	.04
190	George Hendrick	.08
191	Wally Backman	.04
192	Milt Wilcox	.04
193	Daryl Sconiers	.04
194	Craig McMurtry	.04
195	Dave Concepcion	.08
196	Doyle Alexander	.04
197	Enos Cabell	.04
198	Ken Dixon	.08
199	Dick Howser (Mgr.) (Royals Checklist)	.08
200	Mike Schmidt	.40
201	Record—V. Coleman Most Stolen Bases— Season, Rookie	.30
202	Record—D. Gooden Youngest 20-Game Winner	.40
203	Rec.—K. Hernandez Most Game Winning RBI, Season	.20
204	Record—Phil Niekro Oldest Shutout Pitcher	.15
205	Record—Tony Perez Oldest to Hit Grand Slam	.12
206	Record—Pete Rose Most Hits, Career	.40
207	Record—F. Valenzuela Most Consecutive Innings, No Earned Runs	.15
208	Ramon Romero	.15
209	Randy Ready	.10
210	Calvin Schiraldi	.10
211	Ed Wojna	.15
212	Chris Speier	.04
213	Bob Shirley	.04
214	Randy Bush	.04
215	Frank White	.04
216	A's Leaders: Dwayne Murphy	.08
217	Bill Scherrer	.04
218	Randy Hunt	.12
219	Dennis Lamp	.04
220	Bob Horner	.15
221	Dave Henderson	.04
222	Craig Gerber	.15
223	Atlee Hammaker	.06
224	Cesar Cedeno	.08
225	Ron Darling	.20
226	Lee Lacy	.04
227	Al Jones	.04
228	Tom Lawless	.04
229	Bill Gullickson	.04
230	Terry Kennedy	.06
231	Jim Frey (Mgr.) Cubs Checklist	.08
232	Rick Rhoden	.04
233	Steve Lyons	.10
234	Doug Corbett	.04
235	Butch Wynegar	.06
236	Frank Eufemia	.15
237	Ted Simmons	.15
238	Larry Parrish	.06
239	Joel Skinner	.04
240	Tommy John	.15
241	Tony Fernandez	.20
242	Rich Thompson	.12
243	Johnny Grubb	.04
244	Craig Lefferts	.04
245	Jim Sundberg	.04
246	Phillies Leaders: Steve Carlton	.15
247	Terry Harper	.04
248	Spike Owen	.04
249	Rob Deer	.40
250	Dwight Gooden	1.50
251	Rich Dauer	.04
252	Bobby Castillo	.04
253	Dann Bilardello	.04

NO.	PLAYER	MINT
254	Ozzie Guillen (R)	.40
255	Tony Armas	.10
256	Kurt Kepshire	.04
257	Doug DeCinces	.08
258	Tim Burke (R)	.25
259	Dan Pasqua	.25
260	Tony Pena	.10
261	Bobby Valentine (Mgr.) Rangers Checklist	.08
262	Mario Ramirez	.04
263	Checklist No. 2	.08
264	Darren Daulton (R)	.20
265	Ron Davis	.04
266	Keith Moreland	.04
267	Paul Molitor	.20
268	Mike Scott	.30
269	Dane Iorg	.04
270	Jack Morris	.15
271	Dave Collins	.04
272	Tim Tolman	.15
273	Jerry Willard	.04
274	Ron Gardenhire	.04
275	Charlie Hough	.04
276	Yankees Leaders: Willie Randolph	.10
277	Jaime Cocanower	.04
278	Sixto Lezcano	.04
279	Al Pardo	.15
280	Tim Raines	.25
281	Steve Mura	.04
282	Jerry Mumphrey	.04
283	Mike Fischlin	.04
284	Brian Dayett	.04
285	Buddy Bell	.10
286	Luis DeLeon	.04
287	John Christensen	.15
288	Don Aase	.04
289	Johnnie LeMaster	.04
290	Carlton Fisk	.15
291	Tom Lasorda (Mgr.) Dodgers Checklist	.12
292	Chuck Porter	.04
293	Chris Chambliss	.06
294	Danny Cox	.10
295	Kirk Gibson	.30
296	Geno Petralli	.04
297	Tim Lollar	.04
298	Craig Reynolds	.04
299	Bryn Smith	.04
300	George Brett	.50
301	Dennis Rasmussen	.04
302	Greg Gross	.04
303	Curt Wardle	.15
304	Mike Gallego	.15
305	Phil Bradley	.20
306	Padres Leaders: Terry Kennedy	.08
307	Dave Sax	.04
308	Ray Fontenot	.04
309	John Shelby	.04
310	Greg Minton	.04
311	Dick Schofield	.04
312	Tom Filer	.04
313	Joe De Sa	.15
314	Frank Pastore	.04
315	Mookie Wilson	.06
316	Sammy Khalifa	.15
317	Ed Romero	.04
318	Terry Whitfield	.04
319	Rick Camp	.04
320	Jim Rice	.25
321	Earl Weaver (Mgr.) Orioles Checklist	.12
322	Bob Forsch	.04
323	Jerry Davis	.08
324	Dan Schatzeder	.04
325	Juan Beniquez	.04
326	Kent Tekulve	.04
327	Mike Pagliarulo	.12
328	Pete O'Brien	.12
329	Kirby Puckett	2.00
330	Rick Sutcliffe	.12
331	Alan Ashby	.04
332	Darryl Motley	.04
333	Tom Henke	.25

NO.	PLAYER	MINT
334	Ken Oberkfell	.04
335	Don Sutton	.20
336	Indians Leaders: Andre Thornton	.08
337	Darnell Coles	.04
338	Jorge Bell	.35
339	Bruce Berenyi	.04
340	Cal Ripken	.40
341	Frank Williams	.04
342	Gary Redus	.04
343	Carlos Diaz	.04
344	Jim Wohlford	.04
345	Donnie Moore	.04
346	Bryan Little	.04
347	Teddy Higuera (R)	1.00
348	Cliff Johnson	.04
349	Mark Clear	.04
350	Jack Clark	.30
351	Chuck Tanner (Mgr.) Pirates Checklist	.08
352	Harry Spilman	.04
353	Keith Atherton	.04
354	Tony Bernazard	.04
355	Lee Smith	.06
356	Mickey Hatcher	.04
357	Ed VandeBerg	.04
358	Rick Dempsey	.04
359	Mike LaCoss	.04
360	Lloyd Moseby	.15
361	Shane Rawley	.04
362	Tom Paciorek	.04
363	Terry Forster	.06
364	Reid Nichols	.04
365	Mike Flanagan	.06
366	Reds Leaders: Dave Concepcion	.10
367	Aurelio Lopez	.04
368	Greg Brock	.06
369	Al Holland	.04
370	Vince Coleman (R)	1.50
371	Bill Stein	.04
372	Ben Ogilvie	.06
373	Urbano Lugo	.15
374	Terry Francona	.06
375	Rich Gedman	.06
376	Bill Dawley	.04
377	Joe Carter	.20
378	Bruce Bochte	.04
379	Bobby Meacham	.04
380	LaMarr Hoyt	.10
381	Ray Miller (Mgr.) Twins Checklist	.08
382	Ivan Calderon (R)	.50
383	Chris Brown (R)	.30
384	Steve Trout	.04
385	Cecil Cooper	.15
386	Cecil Fielder (R)	.25
387	Steve Kemp	.06
388	Dickie Noles	.04
389	Glenn Davis	1.50
390	Tom Seaver	.25
391	Julio Franco	.15
392	John Russell	.08
393	Chris Pittaro	.15
394	Checklist No. 3	.08
395	Scott Garrelts	.25
396	Red Sox Leaders: Dwight Evans	.08
397	Steve Buechele (R)	.20
398	Earnie Riles (R)	.25
399	Bill Swift	.04
400	Rod Carew	.30
401	Turn Back the Clock: F. Valenzuela (1981)	.15
402	Turn Back the Clock: Tom Seaver (1976)	.15
403	Turn Back the Clock: Willie Mays (1971)	.15
404	Turn Back the Clock: Frank Robinson (1966)	.15
405	Turn Back the Clock: Roger Maris (1961)	.15
406	Scott Sanderson	.04
407	Sal Butera	.04
408	Dave Smith	.04

NO. PLAYER	MINT
409 Paul Runge (R)	.15
410 Dave Kingman	.10
411 Sparky Anderson (Mgr.)	.10
Tigers Checklist	
412 Jim Clancy	.04
413 Tim Flannery	.04
414 Tom Gorman	.04
415 Hal McRae	.04
416 Denny Martinez	.04
417 R.J. Reynolds	.04
418 Alan Knicely	.04
419 Frank Wills	.15
420 Von Hayes	.15
421 Dave Palmer	.04
422 Mike Jorgensen	.04
423 Dan Spillner	.04
424 Rick Miller	.04
425 Larry McWilliams	.04
426 Brewers Leaders:	.04
Charlie Moore	
427 Joe Cowley	.04
428 Max Venable	.04
429 Greg Booker	.04
430 Kent Hrbek	.25
431 George Frazier	.04
432 Mark Bailey	.04
433 Chirs Codiroli	.04
434 Curt Wilkerson	.04
435 Bill Caudill	.04
436 Doug Flynn	.04
437 Rick Mahler	.04
438 Clint Hurdle	.04
439 Rick Honeycutt	.04
440 Alvin Davis	.20
441 Whitey Herzog (Mgr.)	.10
Cardinals Checklist	
442 Ron Robinson	.08
443 Bill Buckner	.08
444 Alex Trevino	.04
445 Bert Blyleven	.10
446 Lenn Sakata	.04
447 Jerry Don Gleaton	.04
448 Herm Winningham	.15
449 Rod Scurry	.04
450 Graig Nettles	.15
451 Mark Brown	.15
452 Bob Clark	.04
453 Steve Jeltz	.10
454 Burt Hooton	.04
455 Willie Randolph	.08
456 Braves Leaders:	.20
Dale Murphy	
457 Mickey Tettleton	.35
458 Kevin Bass	.04
459 Luis Leal	.04
460 Leon Durham	.15
461 Walt Terrell	.04
462 Domingo Ramos	.04
463 Jim Gott	.04
464 Ruppert Jones	.04
465 Jesse Orosco	.04
466 Tom Foley	.04
467 Bob James	.04
468 Mike Scioscia	.04
469 Storm Davis	.08
470 Bill Madlock	.15
471 Bobby Cox (Mgr.)	.08
Blue Jays Checklist	
472 Joe Hesketh	.15
473 Mark Brouhard	.04
474 John Tudor	.15
475 Juan Samuel	.15
476 Ron Mathis	.12
477 Mike Easler	.04
478 Andy Hawkins	.08
479 Bob Melvin	.12
480 Oddibe McDowell	.20
481 Scott Bradley	.10
482 Rick Lysander	.04
483 George Vukovich	.04
484 Donnie Hill	.04
485 Gary Matthews	.06
486 Angels Leaders:	.08
Bob Grich	
487 Bret Saberhagen	.50

NO. PLAYER	MINT
488 Lou Thornton	.12
489 Jim Winn	.04
490 Jeff Leonard	.04
491 Pascual Perez	.04
492 Kelvin Chapman	.04
493 Gene Nelson	.04
494 Garry Roenicke	.04
495 Mark Langston	.25
496 Jay Johnstone	.04
497 John Stuper	.04
498 Tito Landrum	.04
499 Bob Gibson	.04
500 Rickey Henderson	.45
501 Dave Johnson (Mgr.)	.12
Mets Checklist	
502 Glen Cook	.12
503 Mike Fitzgerald	.04
504 Denny Walling	.04
505 Jerry Koosman	.08
506 Bill Russell	.04
507 Steve Ontiveros (R)	.20
508 Alan Wiggins	.08
509 Ernie Camacho	.04
510 Wade Boggs	2.00
511 Ed Nunez	.04
512 Thad Bosley	.04
513 Ron Washington	.04
514 Mike Jones	.04
515 Darrell Evans	.08
516 Giants Leaders:	.08
Greg Minton	
517 Milt Thompson (R)	.40
518 Buck Martinez	.04
519 Danny Darwin	.04
520 Keith Hernandez	.25
521 Nate Snell	.12
522 Bob Bailor	.04
523 Joe Price	.04
524 Darrell Miller	.08
525 Marvel Wynne	.04
526 Charlie Lea	.04
527 Checklist No. 4	.08
528 Terry Pendleton	.08
529 Marc Sullivan	.12
530 Rich Gossage	.15
531 Tony LaRussa (Mgr.)	.08
White Sox Checklist	
532 Don Carman (R)	.25
533 Billy Sample	.04
534 Jeff Calhoun	.12
535 Toby Harrah	.04
536 Jose Rijo	.04
537 Mark Salas	.15
538 Dennis Eckersley	.08
539 Glenn Hubbard	.04
540 Dan Petry	.15
541 Jorge Orta	.04
542 Don Schulze	.04
543 Jerry Narron	.04
544 Eddie Milner	.04
545 Jimmy Key	.12
546 Mariners Leaders:	.06
Dave Henderson	
547 Roger McDowell (R)	.45
548 Mike Young	.20
549 Bob Welch	.06
550 Tom Herr	.10
551 Dave LaPoint	.04
552 Marc Hill	.04
553 Jim Morrison	.04
554 Paul Householder	.04
555 Hubie Brooks	.08
556 John Denny	.06
557 Gerald Perry	.20
558 Tim Stoddard	.04
559 Tommy Dunbar	.04
560 Dave Righetti	.10
561 Bob Lillis (Mgr.)	.06
Astros Checklist	
562 Joe Beckwith	.04
563 Alejandro Sanchez	.08
564 Warren Brusstar	.04
565 Tom Brunansky	.12
566 Alfredo Griffin	.04
567 Jeff Barkley	.12

NO. PLAYER	MINT
568 Donnie Scott	.04
569 Jim Acker	.04
570 Rusty Staub	.08
571 Mike Jeffcoat	.04
572 Paul Zuvella	.08
573 Tom Hume	.04
574 Ron Kittle	.10
575 Mike Boddicker	.10
576 Expos Leaders:	.12
Andre Dawson	
577 Jerry Reuss	.06
578 Lee Mazzilli	.04
579 Jim Slaton	.04
580 Willie McGee	.25
581 Bruce Hurst	.04
582 Jim Gantner	.04
583 Al Bumbry	.04
584 Brian Fisher (R)	.30
585 Garry Maddox	.04
586 Greg Harris	.04
587 Rafael Santana	.04
588 Steve Lake	.04
589 Sid Bream	.04
590 Bob Knepper	.04
591 Jackie Moore (Mgr.)	.08
A's Checklist	
592 Frank Tanana	.06
593 Jesse Barfield	.25
594 Chris Bando	.04
595 Dave Parker	.25
596 Onix Concepcion	.04
597 Sammy Stewart	.04
598 Jim Presley	.30
599 Rick Aguilera (R)	.35
600 Dale Murphy	.40
601 Gary Lucas	.04
602 Mariano Duncan (R)	.25
603 Bill Laskey	.04
604 Gary Pettis	.08
605 Dennis Boyd	.06
606 Royals Leaders:	.10
Hal McRae	
607 Ken Dayley	.04
608 Bruce Bochy	.04
609 Barbaro Garbey	.04
610 Ron Guidry	.15
611 Gary Woods	.04
612 Richard Dotson	.06
613 Roy Smalley	.04
614 Rick Waits	.04
615 Johnny Ray	.08
616 Glenn Brummer	.04
617 Lonnie Smith	.08
618 Jim Pankovits	.06
619 Danny Heep	.04
620 Bruce Sutter	.15
621 John Felske (Mgr.)	.08
Phillies Checklist	
622 Gary Lavelle	.04
623 Floyd Rayford	.04
624 Steve McCatty	.04
625 Bob Brenly	.04
626 Roy Thomas	.04
627 Ron Oester	.04
628 Kirk McCaskill (R)	.40
629 Mitch Webster (R)	.30
630 Fernando Valenzuela	.25
631 Steve Braun	.04
632 Dave Von Ohlen	.04
633 Jackie Gutierrez	.04
634 Roy Lee Jackson	.04
635 Jason Thompson	.06
636 Cubs Leaders:	.10
Lee Smith	
637 Rudy Law	.04
638 John Butcher	.04
639 Bo Diaz	.04
640 Jose Cruz	.08
641 Wayne Tolleson	.04
642 Ray Searage	.04
643 Tom Brookens	.04
644 Mark Gubicza	.06
645 Dusty Baker	.04
646 Mike Moore	.04
647 Mel Hall	.06

NO. PLAYER	MINT
648 Steve Bedrosian	.10
649 Ronn Reynolds	.10
650 Dave Stieb	.15
651 Billy Martin (Mgr.)	.10
Yankees Checklist	
652 Tom Browning	.20
653 Jim Dwyer	.04
654 Ken Howell	.10
655 Manny Trillo	.04
656 Brian Harper	.04
657 Juan Agosto	.04
658 Rob Wilfong	.04
659 Checklist No. 5	.08
660 Steve Garvey	.30
661 Roger Clemens	.50
662 Bill Schroeder	.04
663 Neil Allen	.04
664 Tim Corcoran	.04
665 Alejandro Pena	.06
666 Rangers Leaders:	.06
Charlie Hough	
667 Tim Tuefel	.08
668 Cecilio Guante	.04
669 Ron Cey	.10
670 Willie Hernandez	.12
671 Lynn Jones	.04
672 Rob Picciolo	.04
673 Ernie Whitt	.04
674 Pat Tabler	.04
675 Claudell Washington	.06
676 Matt Young	.04
677 Nick Esasky	.06
678 Dan Gladden	.06
679 Britt Burns	.06
680 George Foster	.15
681 Dick Williams (Mgr.)	.08
Padres Checklist	
682 Junior Ortiz	.04
683 Andy Van Slyke	.15
684 Bob McClure	.04
685 Tim Wallach	.08
686 Jeff Stone	.06
687 Mike Trujillo	.12
688 Larry Herndon	.04
689 Dave Stewart	.15
690 Ryne Sandberg	.30
691 Mike Madden	.04
692 Dale Berra	.04
693 Tom Tellmann	.04
694 Garth Iorg	.04
695 Mike Smithson	.04
696 Dodgers Leaders:	.10
Bill Russell	
697 Bud Black	.04
698 Brad Komminsk	.06
699 Pat Corrales (Mgr.)	.08
Indians Checklist	
700 Reggie Jackson	.40
701 Keith Hernandez (AS)	.15
702 Tom Herr (AS)	.08
703 Tim Wallach (AS)	.08
704 Ozzie Smith (AS)	.08
705 Dale Murphy (AS)	.30
706 Pedro Guerrero (AS)	.20
707 Willie McGee (AS)	.20
708 Gary Carter (AS)	.20
709 Dwight Gooden (AS)	.45
710 John Tudor (AS)	.08
711 Jeff Reardon (AS)	.08
712 Don Mattingly (AS)	.70
713 Damaso Garcia (AS)	.08
714 George Brett (AS)	.35
715 Cal Ripken (AS)	.30
716 Rickey Henderson (AS)	.30
717 Dave Winfield (AS)	.25
718 Jorge Bell (AS)	.08
719 Carlton Fisk (AS)	.10
720 Bret Saberhagen (AS)	.25
721 Ron Guidry (AS)	.10
722 Dan Quisenberry (AS)	.10
723 Marty Bystrom	.04
724 Tim Hulett	.08
725 Mario Soto	.08
726 Orioles Leaders:	.08
Rick Dempsey	

1986 Topps (Continued)

NO.	PLAYER	MINT
727	David Green	.04
728	Mike Marshall	.15
729	Jim Beattie	.04
730	Ozzie Smith	.20
731	Don Robinson	.04
732	Floyd Youmans (R)	.35
733	Ron Romanick	.06
734	Marty Barrett	.15
735	Dave Dravecky	.04
736	Glenn Wilson	.08
737	Pete Vuckovich	.04
738	Andre Robertson	.04
739	Dave Rozema	.04
740	Lance Parrish	.20
741	Pete Rose (Mgr.)	.40
	Reds Checklist	
742	Frank Viola	.25
743	Pat Sheridan	.04
744	Lary Sorensen	.04
745	Willie Upshaw	.08
746	Denny Gonzalez	.08
747	Rick Cerone	.04

NO.	PLAYER	MINT
748	Steve Henderson	.04
749	Ed Jurak	.04
750	Gorman Thomas	.08
751	Howard Johnson	.30
752	Mike Krukow	.04
753	Dan Ford	.04
754	Pat Clements (R)	.12
755	Harold Baines	.20
756	Pirates Leaders:	.06
	Rick Rhoden	
757	Darrell Porter	.04
758	Dave Anderson	.04
759	Moose Haas	.04
760	Andre Dawson	.25
761	Don Slaught	.04
762	Eric Show	.04
763	Terry Puhl	.04
764	Kevin Gross	.04
765	Don Baylor	.15
766	Rick Langford	.04
767	Jody Davis	.08
768	Vern Ruhle	.04

NO.	PLAYER	MINT
769	Harold Reynolds (R)	.50
770	Vida Blue	.08
771	John McNamara (Mgr.)	.08
	Red Sox Checklist	
772	Brian Downing	.04
773	Greg Pryor	.04
774	Terry Leach	.04
775	Al Oliver	.10
776	Gene Garber	.04
777	Wayne Krenchicki	.04
778	Jerry Hairston	.04
779	Rick Reuschel	.04
780	Robin Yount	.30
781	Joe Nolan	.04
782	Ken Landreaux	.04
783	Ricky Horton	.04
784	Alan Bannister	.04
785	Bob Stanley	.04
786	Twins Leaders:	.06
	Mickey Hatcher	
787	Vance Law	.04
788	Marty Castillo	.04

NO.	PLAYER	MINT
789	Kurt Bevacqua	.04
790	Phil Niekro	.15
791	Checklist No. 6	.08
792	Charles Hudson	.06

1986 Topps Traded. . . . Complete Set of 132 Cards—Value $27.00

Updates the main 1986 card set with players who changed teams during the season, and rookies. Features the first Topps card of Jose Canseco, Will Clark, Kevin Mitchell and Bo Jackson. The set was packaged in a printed box and distributed exclusively through card hobby dealers. A "Tiffany" version of the set was also issued.

JOSE CANSECO

WILL CLARK

KEVIN MITCHELL

BO JACKSON

WALLY JOYNER

NO.	PLAYER	MINT
1T	Andy Allanson	.15
2T	Neil Allen	.06
3T	Joaquin Andujar	.06
4T	Paul Assenmacher	.15
5T	Scott Bailes	.15
6T	Don Baylor	.10
7T	Steve Bedrosian	.10
8T	Juan Beniquez	.06
9T	Juan Berenguer	.06
10T	Mike Bielecki	.25
11T	Barry Bonds (RR)	1.00
12T	Bobby Bonilla (RR)	1.00
13T	Juan Bonilla	.06
14T	Rich Bordi	.06
15T	Steve Boros	.06
16T	Rick Burleson	.06
17T	Bill Campbell	.06
18T	Tom Candiotti	.06
19T	John Cangelosi	.15
20T	Jose Canseco (RR)	8.00
21T	Carmen Castillo	.10
22T	Rick Cerone	.06
23T	John Cerutti	.30
24T	Will Clark (RR)	9.00
25T	Mark Clear	.06
26T	Darrell Coles	.08
27T	Dave Collins	.06
28T	Tim Conroy	.06
29T	Joe Cowley	.10
30T	Joel Davis	.08
31T	Rob Deer	.30
32T	John Denny	.06
33T	Mike Easler	.06

NO.	PLAYER	MINT
34T	Mark Eichhorn (RR)	.15
35T	Steve Farr	.06
36T	Scott Fletcher	.06
37T	Terry Forster	.06
38T	Terry Francona	.06
39T	Jim Fregosi	.06
40T	Andres Galarraga (RR)	1.50
41T	Ken Griffey	.06
42T	Bill Gullickson	.06
43T	Jose Guzman	.25
44T	Moose Haas	.06
45T	Billy Hatcher	.20
46T	Mike Heath	.06
47T	Tom Hume	.06
48T	Pete Incaviglia (RR)	.75
49T	Dane Iorg	.06
50T	Bo Jackson (RR)	7.00
51T	Wa. Joyner (RR)	2.00
52T	Charlie Kerfeld	.15
53T	Eric King	.20
54T	Bob Kipper	.06
55T	Wayne Krenchicki	.06
56T	John Kruk (RR)	.40
57T	Mike LaCoss	.06
58T	Pete Ladd	.06
59T	Mike Laga	.06
60T	Hal Lanier	.06
61T	Dave LaPoint	.06
62T	Rudy Law	.06
63T	Rick Leach	.06
64T	Tim Leary	.06
65T	Dennis Leonard	.06
66T	Jim Leyland	.06

NO.	PLAYER	MINT
67T	Steve Lyons	.06
68T	Mickey Mahler	.06
69T	Candy Maldonado	.15
70T	Roger Mason	.10
71T	Bob McClure	.06
72T	Andy McGaffigan	.06
73T	Gene Michael	.06
74T	Kevin Mitchell (RR)	6.00
75T	Omar Moreno	.06
76T	Jerry Mumphrey	.06
77T	Phil Niekro	.30
78T	Randy Nieman	.06
79T	Juan Nieves	.25
80T	Otis Nixon	.15
81T	Bob Ojeda	.08
82T	Jose Oquendo	.10
83T	Tom Paciorek	.06
84T	Dave Palmer	.06
85T	Frank Pastore	.06
86T	Lou Piniella	.08
87T	Dan Plesac	.30
88T	Darrell Porter	.06
89T	Rey Quinones	.20
90T	Gary Redus	.06
91T	Bip Roberts	.20
92T	Billy Jo Robidoux	.15
93T	Jeff Robinson	.06
94T	Gary Roenicke	.06
95T	Ed Romero	.06
96T	Argenis Salazar	.06
97T	Joe Sambito	.06
98T	Billy Sample	.06
99T	Dave Schmidt	.06

NO.	PLAYER	MINT
100T	Ken Schrom	.06
101T	Tom Seaver	.45
102T	Ted Simmons	.06
103T	Sammy Stewart	.06
104T	Kurt Stillwell	.30
105T	Franklin Stubbs	.30
106T	Dale Sveum	.30
107T	Chuck Tanner	.06
108T	Danny Tartabull	.90
109T	Tim Teufel	.06
110T	Bob Tewksbury	.15
111T	Andres Thomas	.25
112T	Milt Thomson	.06
113T	Robby Thompson	.35
114T	Jay Tibbs	.06
115T	Wayne Tolleson	.06
116T	Alex Trevino	.06
117T	Manny Trillo	.06
118T	Ed VandeBerg	.06
119T	Ozzie Virgil	.06
120T	Bob Walk	.06
121T	Gene Walter	.10
122T	C. Washington	.06
123T	Bill Wegman	.15
124T	Dick Williams	.06
125T	Mitch Williams	.35
126T	Bobby Witt (RR)	.35
127T	Todd Worrell (RR)	.45
128T	George Wright	.06
129T	Ricky Wright	.12
130T	Steve Yeager	.06
131T	Paul Zuvella	.06
132T	Checklist	.06

1987 Topps. . . . Complete Set of 792 Cards—Value $35.00

Features the rookie cards of Will Clark, Bo Jackson, Ruben Sierra and Mike Greenwell. A "Tiffany" version of the set was also issued.

NO. PLAYER	MINT
1 '86 Record: Clemens	.45
2 '86 Record: Deshaies	.08
3 '86 Record: Evans	.10
4 '86 Record: Lopes	.10
5 '86 Record: Righetti	.08
6 '86 Record: Sierra	.20
7 '86 Record: Worrell	.10
8 Terry Pendleton	.04
9 Jay Tibbs	.04
10 Cecil Cooper	.08
11 Indians Leaders	.06
12 Jeff Sellers (R)	.15
13 Nick Esasky	.04
14 Dave Stewart	.04
15 Claudell Washington	.04
16 Pat Clements	.04
17 Pete O'Brien	.10
18 Dick Howser (Mgr.)	.04
19 Matt Young	.04
20 Gary Carter	.25
21 Mark Davis	.04
22 Doug DeCinces	.06
23 Lee Smith	.04
24 Tony Walker (R)	.15
25 Bert Blyleven	.08
26 C. Brock	.04
27 Joe Cowley	.04
28 Rick Dempsey	.04
29 Jimmy Key	.15
30 Tim Raines	.25
31 Braves Leaders	.06
32 Tim Leary	.04
33 Andy Van Slyke	.12
34 Jose Rijo	.04
35 Sid Bream	.04
36 Eric King (R)	.20
37 Marvell Wynne	.04
38 Dennis Leonard	.04
39 Marty Barrett	.06
40 Dave Righetti	.10
41 Bo Diaz	.04
42 Gary Redus	.04
43 Gene Michael (Mgr.)	.04
44 Greg Harris	.04
45 Jim Presley	.15
46 Danny Gladden	.04
47 Dennis Powell	.12
48 Wally Backman	.04
49 Terry Harper	.04
50 Dave Smith	.04
51 M. Hall	.04
52 Keith Atherton	.04
53 Ruppert Jones	.04
54 Bill Dawley	.04
55 Tim Wallach	.08
56 Brewers Leaders	.06
57 Scott Nielsen (R)	.20
58 Thad Bosley	.04
59 Ken Dayley	.04
60 Tony Pena	.10
61 Bobby Thigpen (R)	.25
62 Bobby Meacham	.04
63 Fred Toliver	.12
64 Harry Spilman	.04
65 Tom Browning	.10
66 Marc Sullivan	.04

NO. PLAYER	MINT
67 Bill Swift	.04
68 Tony LaRussa (Mgr.)	.04
69 Lonnie Smith	.04
70 Charlie Hough	.04
71 Mike Aldrete (R)	.25
72 Walt Terrell	.04
73 Dave Anderson	.04
74 Dan Pasqua	.15
75 Ron Darling	.20
76 Rafael Ramirez	.04
77 Bryan Oelkers	.04
78 Tom Foley	.04
79 Juan Nieves	.15
80 Wally Joyner (R)	1.25
81 Padres Leaders	.06
82 Rob Murphy (R)	.20
83 Mike Davis	.04
84 Steve Lake	.04
85 Kevin Bass	.04
86 Nate Snell	.04
87 Mark Salas	.04
88 Ed Wojna	.04
89 Ozzie Guillen	.08
90 Dave Stieb	.10
91 Harold Reynolds	.08
92 U. Lugo	.05
92 U. Lugo (no t.m.)	.30
93 Jim Leyland (Mgr.)	.04
94 Calvin Schiraldi	.08
95 Oddibe McDowell	.10
96 Frank Williams	.04
97 Glenn Wilson	.08
98 Bill Scherrer	.04
99 Darryl Motley	.04
100 Steve Garvey	.25
101 Carl Willis (R)	.15
102 Paul Zuvella	.04
103 Rick Aguilera	.04
104 Billy Sample	.04
105 Floyd Youmans	.15
106 Blue Jays Leaders	.06
107 John Butcher	.04
108 Jim Gantner	.04
109 R. J. Reynolds	.04
110 John Tudor	.12
111 Alfredo Griffin	.04
112 Alan Ashby	.04
113 Neil Allen	.04
114 Billy Beane	.08
115 Donnie Moore	.04
116 Bill Russell	.04
117 Jim Beattie	.04
118 Bobby Valentine (Mgr.)	.04
119 Ron Robinson	.04
120 Eddie Murray	.30
121 Kevin Romine (R)	.15
122 Jim Clancy	.04
123 John Kruk (R)	.30
124 Ray Fontenot	.04
125 Bob Brenly	.04
126 Mike Loynd (R)	.15
127 Vance Law	.04
128 Checklist: 1-132	.06
129 Rick Cerone	.04
130 Dwight Gooden	.75
131 Pirates Leaders	.06
132 P. Assenmacher (R)	.15

NO. PLAYER	MINT
133 Jose Oquendo	.04
134 Rich Yett (R)	.15
135 Mike Easler	.04
136 Ron Romanick	.04
137 Jerry Willard	.04
138 Roy Lee Jackson	.04
139 Devon White (R)	.75
140 Bret Saberhagen	.25
141 Herm Winningham	.04
142 Rick Sutcliffe	.12
143 Steve Boros (Mgr.)	.04
144 Mike Scioscia	.04
145 Charlie Kerfeld	.15
146 Tracy Jones (R)	.40
147 Randy Niemann	.04
148 Dave Collins	.04
149 Ray Searage	.04
150 Wade Boggs	1.25
151 Mike LaCoss	.04
152 Toby Harrah	.04
153 Duane Ward (R)	.20
154 Tom O'Malley	.04
155 Eddie Whitson	.04
156 Mariners Leaders	.06
157 Danny Darwin	.04
158 Tim Teufel	.04
159 Ed Olwine (R)	.15
160 Julio Franco	.10
161 Steve Ontiveros	.04
162 Mike LaValliere (R)	.20
163 Kevin Gross	.04
164 Sammy Khalifa	.04
165 Jeff Reardon	.08
166 Bob Boone	.04
167 Jim Deshaies (R)	.25
168 Lou Piniella (Mgr.)	.06
169 Ron Washington	.04
170 Bo Jackson (R)	3.50
171 Chuck Cary (R)	.15
172 Ron Oester	.04
173 Alex Trevino	.04
174 Henry Cotto	.04
175 Bob Stanley	.04
176 Steve Buechele	.04
177 Keith Moreland	.04
178 Cecil Fielder	.08
179 Bill Wegman	.04
180 Chris Brown	.10
181 Cardinals Leaders	.06
182 Lee Lacy	.04
183 Andy Hawkins	.04
184 Bobby Bonilla (R)	.80
185 Roger McDowell	.10
186 Bruce Benedict	.04
187 Mark Huismann	.04
188 Tony Phillips	.04
189 Joe Hesketh	.04
190 Jim Sundberg	.04
191 Charles Hudson	.04
192 Cory Snyder	.50
193 Roger Craig (Mgr.)	.04
194 Kirk McCaskill	.10
195 Mike Pagliarulo	.20
196 Randy O'Neal	.04
197 Mark Bailey	.04
198 Lee Mazzilli	.08

NO. PLAYER	MINT
199 Mariano Duncan	.10
200 Pete Rose	.60
201 John Cangelosi (R)	.25
202 Ricky Wright	.04
203 Mike Kingery (R)	.25
204 Sammy Stewart	.04
205 Graig Nettles	.08
206 Twins Leaders	.06
207 George Frazier	.04
208 John Shelby	.04
209 Rick Schu	.04
210 Lloyd Moseby	.12
211 John Morris	.04
212 Mike Fitzgerald	.04
213 Randy Myers (R)	.50
214 Omar Moreno	.04
215 Mark Langston	.15
216 B.J. Surhoff (R)	.40
217 Chris Codiroli	.04
218 S. Anderson (Mgr.)	.04
219 Cecilio Guante	.04
220 Joe Carter	.25
221 Vern Ruhle	.04
222 Denny Walling	.04
223 Charlie Leibrandt	.04
224 Wayne Tolleson	.04
225 Mike Smithson	.04
226 Max Venable	.04
227 Jamie Moyer (R)	.20
228 Curt Wilkerson	.04
229 Mike Birkbeck (R)	.15
230 Don Baylor	.12
231 Giants Leaders	.06
232 Reggie Williams (R)	.12
233 Russ Morman (R)	.12
234 Pat Sheridan	.04
235 Alvin Davis	.12
236 Tommy John	.12
237 Jim Morrison	.04
238 Bill Krueger	.04
239 Juan Espino	.04
240 Steve Balboni	.08
241 Danny Heep	.04
242 Rick Mahler	.04
243 Whitey Herzog (Mgr.)	.04
244 Dickie Noles	.04
245 Willie Upshaw	.04
246 Jim Dwyer	.04
247 Jeff Reed	.04
248 Gene Walter	.10
249 Jim Pankovits	.04
250 Teddy Higuera	.20
251 Rob Wilfong	.04
252 Denny Martinez	.04
253 Eddie Milner	.04
254 Bob Tewksbury (R)	.15
255 Juan Samuel	.15
256 Royals Leaders	.06
257 Bob Forsch	.04
258 Steve Yeager	.04
259 Mike Greenwell (R)	4.00
260 Vida Blue	.06
261 Ruben Sierra (R)	2.00
262 Jim Winn	.04
263 Stan Javier	.08
264 Checklist: 133-264	.06

NO.	PLAYER	MINT
265	Darrell Evans	.10
266	Jeff Hamilton (R)	.15
267	Howard Johnson	.15
268	Pat Corrales (Mgr.)	.04
269	Cliff Speck (R)	.15
270	Jody Davis	.04
271	Mike Brown	.04
272	Andres Galarraga	1.00
273	Gene Nelson	.04
274	Jeff Hearron (R)	.15
275	LaMarr Hoyt	.04
276	Jackie Gutierrez	.04
277	Juan Agosto	.04
278	Gary Pettis	.04
279	Dan Plesac (R)	.30
280	Jeffrey Leonard	.04
281	Reds Leaders	.12
282	Jeff Calhoun	.04
283	Doug Drabek (R)	.25
284	John Moses	.10
285	Dennis Boyd	.12
286	Mike Woodard	.10
287	Dave Von Ohlen	.04
288	Tito Landrum	.04
289	Bob Kipper	.04
290	Leon Durham	.10
291	Mitch Williams (R)	.30
292	Franklin Stubbs	.12
293	Bob Rodgers (Mgr.)	.04
294	Steve Jeltz	.04
295	Len Dykstra	.15
296	Andres Thomas (R)	.20
297	Don Schulze	.04
298	Larry Herndon	.04
299	Joel Davis	.10
300	Reggie Jackson	.30
301	Luis Aquino	.15
302	Bill Schroeder	.04
303	Juan Berenguer	.04
304	Phil Garner	.04
305	John Franco	.10
306	Red Sox Leaders	.10
307	Lee Guetterman (R)	.15
308	Don Slaught	.04
309	Mike Young	.04
310	Frank Viola	.20
311	Turn Back—1982	.15
312	Turn Back-1977	.15
313	Turn Back—1972	.15
314	Turn Back—1967	.15
315	Turn Back—1962	.15
316	Brian Fisher	.04
317	Clint Hurdle	.04
318	Jim Fregosi (Mgr.)	.04
319	Greg Swindell (R)	.75
320	Barry Bonds (R)	.75
321	Mike Laga	.04
322	Chris Bando	.04
323	Al Newman (R)	.15
324	Dave Palmer	.04
325	Garry Templeton	.04
326	Mark Gubicza	.04
327	Dale Sveum (R)	.25
328	Bob Welch	.04
329	Ron Roenicke	.04
330	Mike Scott	.25
331	Mets Leaders	.25
332	Joe Price	.04
333	Ken Phelps	.04
334	Ed Correa (R)	.20
335	Candy Maldonado	.06
336	Allan Anderson (R)	.30
337	Darrell Miller	.04
338	Tim Conroy	.04
339	Donnie Hill	.04
340	Roger Clemens	1.00
341	Mike Brown	.04
342	Bob James	.04
343	Hal Lanier (Mgr.)	.04
344	Joe Niekro	.06
345	Andre Dawson	.25
346	Shawon Dunston	.15
347	Mickey Brantley	.15
348	Carmelo Martinez	.04
349	Storm Davis	.06

NO.	PLAYER	MINT
350	Keith Hernandez	.25
351	Gene Garber	.04
352	Mike Felder	.12
353	Ernie Camacho	.04
354	Jamie Quick	.04
355	Don Carman	.04
356	White Sox Leaders	.06
357	Steve Fireovid (R)	.15
358	Sal Butera	.04
359	Doug Corbett	.04
360	Pedro Guerrero	.20
361	Mark Thurmond	.04
362	Luis Quinones (R)	.15
363	Jose Guzman	.15
364	Randy Bush	.04
365	Rick Rhoden	.04
366	Mark McGwire	2.50
367	Jeff Lahti	.04
368	J. McNamara (Mgr.)	.04
369	Brian Dayett	.04
370	Fred Lynn	.15
371	Mark Eichhorn (R)	.12
372	Jerry Mumphrey	.04
373	Jeff Dedmon	.04
374	Glenn Hoffman	.04
375	Ron Guidry	.15
376	Scott Bradley	.04
377	John Henry Johnson	.04
378	Rafael Santana	.04
379	John Russell	.04
380	Rich Gossage	.12
381	Expos Leaders	.06
382	Rudy Law	.04
383	Ron Davis	.04
384	Johnny Grubb	.04
385	Orel Hershiser	.30
386	Dickie Thon	.04
387	T. R. Bryden (R)	.20
388	Geno Petralli	.04
389	Jeff Robinson	.04
390	Gary Matthews	.04
391	Jay Howell	.04
392	Checklist: 265-396	.06
393	Pete Rose (Mgr.)	.40
394	Mike Bielecki	.12
395	Damaso Garcia	.04
396	Tim Lollar	.04
397	Greg Walker	.08
398	Brad Havens	.04
399	Curt Ford	.12
400	George Brett	.35
401	Billy Jo Robidoux	.15
402	Mike Trujillo	.04
403	Jerry Royster	.04
404	Doug Sisk	.04
405	Brook Jacoby	.10
406	Yankees Leaders	.25
407	Jim Acker	.04
408	John Mizerock	.04
409	Milt Thompson	.04
410	Fernando Valenzuela	.20
411	Darnell Coles	.04
412	Eric Davis	.75
413	Moose Haas	.04
414	Joe Orsulak	.04
415	Bobby Witt (R)	.35
416	Tom Nieto	.04
417	Pat Perry	.08
418	Dick Williams (Mgr.)	.04
419	Mark Portugal (R)	.15
420	Will Clark (R)	5.00
421	Jose DeLeon	.04
422	Jack Howell	.04
423	Jaime Cocanower	.04
424	Chris Speier	.04
425	Tom Seaver	.30
426	Floyd Rayford	.04
427	Ed Nunez	.04
428	Bruce Bochy	.04
429	Tim Pyznarski (R)	.15
430	Mike Schmidt	.30
431	Dodgers Leaders	.15
432	Jim Slaton	.04
433	Ed Hearn (R)	.12

NO.	PLAYER	MINT
434	Mike Fischlin	.04
435	Bruce Sutter	.10
436	Andy Allanson (R)	.15
437	Ted Power	.04
438	Kelly Downs (R)	.25
439	Karl Best	.04
440	Willie McGee	.15
441	Dave Leiper	.15
442	Mitch Webster	.04
443	John Felske (Mgr.)	.04
444	Jeff Russell	.04
445	Dave Lopes	.08
446	Chuck Finley (R)	.30
447	Bill Almon	.04
448	Chris Bosio (R)	.20
449	Pat Dodson (R)	.20
450	Kirby Puckett	.60
451	Joe Sambito	.04
452	Dave Henderson	.04
453	Scott Terry (R)	.20
454	Luis Salazar	.04
455	Mike Boddicker	.04
456	A's Leaders	.06
457	Len Matuszek	.04
458	Kelly Gruber	.08
459	Dennis Eckersley	.06
460	Darryl Strawberry	.50
461	Craig McMurtry	.04
462	Scott Fletcher	.04
463	Tom Candiotti	.04
464	Butch Wynegar	.04
465	Todd Worrell	.25
466	Kal Daniels	.75
467	Randy St. Claire	.04
468	G. Bamberger (Mgr.)	.04
469	Mike Diaz (R)	.20
470	Dave Dravecky	.04
471	Ronn Reynolds	.04
472	Bill Doran	.08
473	Steve Farr	.04
474	Jerry Narron	.04
475	Scott Garrelts	.04
476	Danny Tartabull	.75
477	Ken Howell	.04
478	Tim Laudner	.04
479	Bob Sebra (R)	.15
480	Jim Rice	.20
481	Phillies Leaders	.06
482	Daryl Boston	.04
483	Dwight Lowry (R)	.15
484	Jim Traber	.10
485	Tony Fernandez	.12
486	Otis Nixon	.08
487	Dave Gumpert	.04
488	Ray Knight	.04
489	Bill Gullickson	.04
490	Dale Murphy	.40
491	Ron Karkovice (R)	.15
492	Mike Heath	.04
493	Tom Lasorda	.04
494	Barry Jones (R)	.15
495	Gorman Thomas	.10
496	Bruce Bochte	.04
497	Dale Mohorcic (R)	.15
498	Bob Kearney	.04
499	Bruce Ruffin (R)	.25
500	Don Mattingly	1.25
501	Craig Lefferts	.04
502	Dick Schofield	.04
503	Larry Andersen	.04
504	Mickey Hatcher	.04
505	Bryn Smith	.04
506	Orioles Leaders	.08
507	Dave Stapleton	.04
508	Scott Bankhead	.15
509	Enos Cabell	.04
510	Tom Henke	.10
511	Steve Lyons	.04
512	Dave Magadan (R)	.40
513	Carmen Castillo	.04
514	Orlando Mercado	.04
515	Willie Hernandez	.10
516	Ted Simmons	.10
517	Mario Soto	.04
518	Gene Mauch (Mgr.)	.04

NO.	PLAYER	MINT
519	Curt Young	.04
520	Jack Clark	.25
521	Rick Reuschel	.04
522	Checklist: 397-528	.06
523	Earnie Riles	.04
524	Bob Shirley	.04
525	Phil Bradley	.12
526	Roger Mason	.08
527	Jim Wohlford	.04
528	Ken Dixon	.04
529	Alvaro Espinoza (R)	.10
530	Tony Gwynn	.45
531	Astros Leaders	.06
532	Jeff Stone	.04
533	Argenis Salazar	.04
534	Scott Sanderson	.04
535	Tony Armas	.06
536	Terry Mulholland (R)	.15
537	Rance Mulliniks	.04
538	Tom Niedenfuer	.04
539	Reid Nichols	.04
540	Terry Kennedy	.04
541	Rafael Belliard (R)	.12
542	Ricky Horton	.04
543	Dave Johnson (Mgr.)	.04
544	Zane Smith	.06
545	Buddy Bell	.10
546	Mike Morgan	.04
547	Rob Deer	.20
548	Bill Mooneyham (R)	.15
549	Bob Melvin	.04
550	Pete Incaviglia (R)	.75
551	Frank Wills	.04
552	Larry Sheets	.15
553	Mike Maddux (R)	.15
554	Buddy Biancalana	.04
555	Dennis Rasmussen	.10
556	Angels Leaders	.06
557	John Cerutti (R)	.20
558	Greg Gagne	.04
559	Lance McCullers	.04
560	Glenn Davis	.30
561	Rey Quinones (R)	.20
562	B. Clutterbuck (R)	.15
563	John Stefero	.04
564	Larry McWilliams	.04
565	Dusty Baker	.10
566	Tim Hulett	.04
567	Greg Mathews (R)	.25
568	Earl Weaver (Mgr.)	.04
569	Wade Rowdon	.15
570	Sid Fernandez	.20
571	Ozzie Virgil	.04
572	Pete Ladd	.04
573	Hal McRae	.04
574	Manny Lee	.04
575	Pat Tabler	.04
576	Frank Pastore	.04
577	Dann Bilardello	.04
578	Billy Hatcher	.08
579	Rick Burleson	.04
580	Mike Krukow	.04
581	Cubs Leaders	.08
582	Bruce Berenyi	.04
583	Junior Ortiz	.04
584	Ron Kittle	.08
585	Scott Bailes (R)	.15
586	Ben Oglivie	.04
587	Eric Plunk	.10
588	Wallace Johnson	.04
589	Steve Crawford	.04
590	Vince Coleman	.30
591	Spike Owen	.04
592	Chris Welsh	.04
593	Chuck Tanner (Mgr.)	.08
594	Rick Anderson (R)	.15
595	Keith Hernandez (AS)	.15
596	Steve Sax (AS)	.10
597	Mike Schmidt (AS)	.25
598	Ozzie Smith (AS)	.10
599	Tony Gwynn (AS)	.25
600	Dave Parker (AS)	.15
601	Darryl Strawberry (AS)	.25
602	Gary Carter (AS)	.20
603	Dwight Gooden (AS)	.35
603	D. Gooden (no t.m.)	1.00

NO.	PLAYER	MINT
604	F. Valenzuela (AS)	.15
605	Todd Worrell (AS)	.15
606	Don Mattingly (AS)	.65
606	D. Matt (no t.m.)	2.00
607	Tony Bernazard (AS)	.08
608	Wade Boggs (AS)	.40
609	Cal Ripken (AS)	.15
610	Jim Rice (AS)	.15
611	Kirby Puckett (AS)	.25
612	George Bell (AS)	.15
613	Lance Parrish (AS)	.10
614	Roger Clemens (AS)	.35
615	Teddy Higuera (AS)	.10
616	Dave Righetti (AS)	.10
617	Al Nipper	.04
618	Tom Kelly (Mgr.)	.04
619	Jerry Reed	.04
620	Jose Canseco	4.00
621	Danny Cox	.08
622	Glenn Braggs (R)	.50
623	Kurt Stillwell (R)	.30
624	Tim Burke	.04
625	Mookie Wilson	.04
626	Joel Skinner	.04
627	Ken Oberkfell	.04
628	Bob Walk	.04
629	Larry Parrish	.04
630	John Candelaria	.04
631	Tigers Leaders	.15
632	Rob Woodward	.08
633	Jose Uribe	.04
634	Rafael Palmeiro (R)	1.00
635	Ken Schrom	.04
636	Darren Daulton	.04
637	Bip Roberts (R)	.15
638	Rich Bordi	.04
639	Gerald Perry	.20
640	Mark Clear	.04
641	Domino Ramos	.04
642	Al Pulido	.04
643	Ron Shepherd	.15
644	John Denny	.04
645	Dwight Evans	.12
646	Mike Mason	.04
647	Tom Lawless	.04
648	Barry Larkin (R)	1.25
649	Mickey Tettleton	.04
650	Hubie Brooks	.10
651	Benny Distefano	.04
652	Terry Forster	.04
653	Kevin Mitchell (R)	3.50

NO.	PLAYER	MINT
654	Checklist: 529-660	.06
655	Jesse Barfield	.25
656	Rangers Leaders	.06
657	Tom Waddell	.04
658	Robby Thompson (R)	.30
659	Aurelio Lopez	.04
660	Bob Horner	.10
661	Lou Whitaker	.10
662	Frank DiPino	.04
663	Cliff Johnson	.04
664	Mike Marshall	.12
665	Rod Scurry	.04
666	Von Hayes	.10
667	Ron Hassey	.04
668	Juan Bonilla	.04
669	Bud Black	.04
670	Jose Cruz	.08
671	Ray Soff (R)	.12
672	Chili Davis	.10
673	Don Sutton	.10
674	Bill Campbell	.04
675	Ed Romero	.04
676	Charlie Moore	.04
677	Bob Grich	.04
678	Carney Lansford	.10
679	Kent Hrbek	.15
680	Ryne Sandberg	.20
681	George Bell	.30
682	Jerry Reuss	.04
683	Gary Roenicke	.04
684	Kent Tekulve	.04
685	Jerry Hairston	.04
686	Doyle Alexander	.04
687	Alan Trammell	.15
688	Juan Beniquez	.04
689	Darrell Porter	.04
690	Dane Iorg	.04
691	Dave Parker	.20
692	Frank White	.04
693	Terry Puhl	.04
694	Phil Niekro	.15
695	Chico Walker (R)	.20
696	Gary Lucas	.04
697	Ed Lynch	.04
698	Ernie Whitt	.04
699	Ken Landreaux	.04
700	Dave Bergman	.04
701	Willie Randolph	.08
702	Greg Gross	.04
703	Dave Schmidt	.04

NO.	PLAYER	MINT
704	Jesse Orosco	.06
705	Bruce Hurst	.12
706	Rick Manning	.04
707	Bob McClure	.04
708	Scott McGregor	.04
709	Dave Kingman	.10
710	Gary Gaetti	.10
711	Ken Griffey	.08
712	Don Robinson	.04
713	Tom Brookens	.04
714	Don Quisenberry	.12
715	Bob Dernier	.04
716	Rick Leach	.04
717	Ed Vande Berg	.04
718	Steve Carlton	.25
719	Tom Hume	.04
720	Richard Dotson	.04
721	Tom Herr	.04
722	Bob Knepper	.08
723	Brett Butler	.04
724	Greg Minton	.04
725	George Hendrick	.04
726	Frank Tanana	.04
727	Mike Moore	.04
728	Tippy Martinez	.04
729	Tom Paciorek	.04
730	Eric Show	.06
731	Dave Concepcion	.08
732	Manny Trillo	.04
733	Bill Caudill	.04
734	Bill Madlock	.12
735	Rickey Henderson	.35
736	Steve Bedrosian	.10
737	Floyd Bannister	.04
738	Jorge Orta	.04
739	Chet Lemon	.06
740	Rich Gedman	.04
741	Paul Molitor	.15
742	Andy McGaffigan	.04
743	Dwayne Murphy	.04
744	Roy Smalley	.04
745	Glenn Hubbard	.04
746	Bob Ojeda	.12
747	Johnny Ray	.04
748	Mike Flanagan	.06
749	Ozzie Smith	.15
750	Steve Trout	.04
751	Garth Iorg	.04
752	Dan Petry	.04
753	Rick Honeycutt	.04

NO.	PLAYER	MINT
754	Dave LaPoint	.04
755	Luis Aguayo	.04
756	Carlton Fisk	.15
757	Nolan Ryan	.35
758	Tony Bernazard	.04
759	Joel Youngblood	.04
760	Mike Witt	.10
761	Greg Pryor	.04
762	Gary Ward	.04
763	Tim Flannery	.04
764	Bill Buckner	.04
765	Kirk Gibson	.20
766	Don Aase	.04
767	Ron Cey	.04
768	Dennis Lamp	.04
769	Steve Sax	.15
770	Dave Winfield	.25
771	Shane Rawley	.04
772	Harold Baines	.15
773	Robin Yount	.25
774	Wayne Krenchicki	.04
775	Joaquin Andujar	.04
776	Tom Brunansky	.12
777	Chris Chambliss	.04
778	Jack Morris	.15
779	Craig Reynolds	.04
780	Andre Thornton	.04
781	Atlee Hammaker	.04
782	Brian Downing	.04
783	Willie Wilson	.10
784	Cal Ripken	.25
785	Terry Francona	.04
786	Jimy Williams (Mgr.)	.04
787	Alejandro Pena	.04
788	Tim Stoddard	.04
789	Dan Schatzeder	.04
790	Julio Cruz	.04
791	Lance Parrish	.15
792	Checklist: 661-792	.06

1987 Topps Traded.... Complete Set of 132 Cards—Value $15.00

Updates the main 1987 card set with players who changed teams during the season and rookies who joined their teams early in the season. Features the first Topps card of Ellis Burks, David Cone, Fred McGriff and Matt Williams. The complete set was packaged in a printed box and primarily distributed through card hobby dealers. A "Tiffany" version of the set was also issued.

NO.	PLAYER	MINT
1T	Bill Almon	.06
2T	Scott Bankhead	.10
3T	Eric Bell	.15
4T	Juan Beniquez	.06
5T	Juan Berenguer	.06
6T	Greg Booker	.06
7T	Thad Bosley	.06

NO.	PLAYER	MINT
8T	Larry Bowa	.08
9T	Greg Brock	.10
10T	Bob Brower	.15
11T	Jerry Browne	.25
12T	Ralph Bryant	.15
13T	DeWayne Buice	.12
14T	Ellis Burks (RR)	1.50

NO.	PLAYER	MINT
15T	Ivan Calderon	.25
16T	Jeff Calhoun	.06
17T	Casey Candaele	.15
18T	John Cangelosi	.10
19T	Steve Carlton	.25
20T	Juan Castillo	.10
21T	Rick Cerone	.06

NO.	PLAYER	MINT
22T	Ron Cey	.12
23T	John Christensen	.06
24T	Dave Cone	1.75
25T	Chuck Grim	.20
26T	Storm Daviss	.06
27T	Andre Dawson	.45
28T	Rick Dempsey	.10

NO. PLAYER	MINT	NO. PLAYER	MINT	NO. PLAYER	MINT	NO. PLAYER	MINT
29T Doug Drabek	.12	55T Stan Jefferson	.25	81T Kevin Mitchell	1.00	107T Mark Salas	.06
30T Mike Dunne	.15	56T Joe Johnson	.06	82T Charlie Moore	.06	108T Luis Salazar	.06
31T Dennis Eckersley	.15	57T Terry Kennedy	.08	83T Jeff Musselman	.20	109T Benny Santiago (RR)	.75
32T Lee Ella	.06	58T Mike Kingery	.10	84T Gene Nelson	.06	110T Dave Schmidt	.06
33T Brian Fisher	.10	59T Ray Knight	.08	85T Graig Nettles	.15	111T Kevin Seitzer (RR)	1.00
34T Terry Francona	.06	60T Gene Larkin	.25	86T Al Newman	.06	112T John Shelby	.06
35T Willie Fraser	.12	61T Mike LaValliere	.10	87T Reid Nichols	.06	113T Steve Shields	.25
36T Billy Gardner	.06	62T Jack Lazorko	.06	88T Tom Niedenfuer	.06	114T John Smiley	.45
37T Ken Gerhart	.15	63T Terry Leach	.15	89T Joe Niekro	.15	115T Chris Speier	.06
38T Danny Gladden	.10	64T Tim Leary	.06	90T Tom Nieto	.06	116T Mike Stanley (RR)	.25
39T Jim Gott	.12	65T Jim Lindeman (RR)	.15	91T Matt Nokes (RR)	.75	117T Terry Steinbach (RR)	.40
40T Cecilio Guante	.06	66T Steve Lombardozzi	.15	92T Dickie Noles	.06	118T Les Straker	.20
41T Albert Hall	.08	67T Bill Long	.20	93T Pat Pacillo	.15	119T Jim Sundberg	.06
42T Terry Harper	.06	68T Barry Lyons	.25	94T Lance Parrish	.15	120T Danny Tartabull	.40
43T Mickey Hatcher	.06	69T Shane Mack	.25	95T Tony Pena	.15	121T Tom Trebelhorn	.06
44T Brad Havens	.06	70T Greg Maddux	.60	96T Luis Polonia	.30	122T Dave Valle	.06
45T Neal Heaton	.10	71T Bill Madlock	.15	97T Randy Ready	.08	123T Ed VandeBerg	.06
46T Mike Henneman	.40	72T Joe Magrane (RR)	1.50	98T Jeff Reardon	.12	124T Andy Van Slyke	.35
47T Donnie Hill	.06	73T Dave Martinez	.25	99T Gary Redus	.08	125T Gary Ward	.06
48T Guy Hoffman	.06	74T Fred McGriff (RR)	2.50	100T Jeff Reed	.06	126T Alan Wiggins	.06
49T Brian Holton	.25	75T Mark McLemore	.12	101T Rick Rhoden	.10	127T Bill Wilkinson	.10
50T Charles Hudson	.06	76T Kevin McReynolds	.30	102T Cal Ripken, Sr.	.06	128T Frank Williams	.06
51T Dany Jackson	.35	77T Dave Meads	.12	103T Wally Ritchie	.15	129T Matt Williams (RR)	1.25
52T Reggie Jackson	.60	78T Eddie Milner	.06	104T Jeff Robinson (RR)	.50	130T Jim Winn	.06
53T Chris James (RR)	.45	79T Greg Minton	.06	105T Gary Roenicke	.06	131T Matt Young	.06
54T Dion James	.12	80T John Mitchell	.15	106T Jerry Royster	.06	132T Checklist	.06

1988 Topps. . . . Complete Set of 792 Cards—Value $25.00

Features the rookie cards of Ellis Burks, Matt Williams, Sam Horn, and Al Leiter. A new feature of this year's set was "This Way to the Clubhouse" which explained how a player joined his current team. A "Tiffany" version of the set was also issued.

NO. PLAYER	MINT	NO. PLAYER	MINT	NO. PLAYER	MINT	NO. PLAYER	MINT
1 '87 Record: Coleman	.20	29 Argenis Salazar	.04	57 Tim Crews (R)	.15	85 Howard Johnson	.15
2 '87 Record: Mattingly	.40	30 Sid Fernandez	.10	58 Dave Magadan	.08	86 Ron Karkovice	.04
3 '87 Record: McGwire	.40	31 Bruce Bochy	.04	59 Danny Cox	.04	87 Mike Mason	.04
3 McGwire (error)	1.00	32 Mike Morgan	.04	60 Rickey Henderson	.30	88 Earnie Riles	.04
4 '87 Record: Murray	.25	33 Rob Deer	.15	61 Mark Knudson (R)	.15	89 Gary Thurman (R)	.25
4 Murray (error)	1.00	34 Rickey Horton	.04	62 Jeff Hamilton	.04	90 Dale Murphy	.25
5 '87 Record: Niekro Bros	.10	35 Harold Baines	.10	63 Jimmy Jones	.10	91 Joey Cora (R)	.15
6 '87 Record: Ryan	.20	36 Jamie Moyer	.04	64 Ken Caminiti (R)	.20	92 Len Matuszek	.04
7 '87 Record: Santiago	.15	37 Ed Romero	.04	65 Leon Durham	.06	93 Bob Sebra	.04
8 Kevin Elster	.30	38 Jeff Calhoun	.04	66 Shane Rawley	.04	94 Chuck Johnson (R)	.15
9 Andy Hawkins	.04	39 Gerald Perry	.08	67 Ken Oberkfell	.04	95 Lance Parrish	.08
10 Ryne Sandberg	.12	40 Orel Hershiser	.20	68 Dave Dravecky	.06	96 Todd Benzinger (R)	.35
11 Mike Young	.04	41 Bob Melvin	.04	69 Mike Hart (R)	.12	97 Scott Garrelts	.04
12 Bill Schroeder	.04	42 Bill Landrum (R)	.15	70 Roger Clemens	.40	98 Rene Gonzales (R)	.15
13 Andres Thomas	.04	43 Dick Schofield	.04	71 Gary Pettis	.04	99 Chuck Finley	.04
14 Sparky Anderson	.04	44 Lou Piniella	.06	72 Dennis Eckersley	.06	100 Jack Clark	.15
15 Chili Davis	.08	45 Kent Hrbek	.10	73 Randy Bush	.04	101 Allan Anderson	.04
16 Kirk McCaskill	.06	46 Darnell Coles	.04	74 Tom Lasorda (Mgr.)	.04	102 Barry Larkin	.15
17 Ron Oester	.04	47 Joaquin Andujar	.04	75 Joe Carter	.12	103 Curt Young	.04
18 Al Leiter (error-R)	1.25	48 Alan Ashby	.04	76 Denny Martinez	.04	104 Dick Williams	.04
18 Al Leiter (correct-R)	.75	49 Dave Clark	.12	77 Tom O'Malley	.04	105 Jesse Orosco	.06
19 Mark Davidson (R)	.15	50 Hubie Brooks	.04	78 Dan Petry	.06	106 Jim Walewander (R)	.15
20 Kevin Gross	.04	51 Oriole Team	.10	79 Ernie Whitt	.04	107 Scott Bailes	.04
21 Red Sox Team	.08	52 Don Robinson	.04	80 Mark Langston	.10	108 Steve Lyons	.04
22 Greg Swindell	.12	53 Curt Wilkerson	.04	81 Reds Team	.06	109 Joel Skinner	.04
23 Ken Landreaux	.04	54 Jim Clancy	.04	82 Darrel Akerfelds (R)	.15	110 Teddy Higuera	.12
24 Jim Deshaies	.04	55 Phil Bradley	.10	83 Jose Oquendo	.06	111 Expos Team	.06
25 Andres Galarraga	.20	56 Ed Hearn	.04	84 Cecilio Guante	.04	112 Les Lancaster (R)	.15
26 Mitch William	.04						
27 R.J. Reynolds	.04						
28 Jose Nunez (R)	.15						

NO. PLAYER	MINT
113 Kelly Gruber	.04
114 Jeff Russell	.04
115 Johnny Ray	.04
116 J.D. Gleaton	.04
117 James Steels (R)	.10
118 Bob Welch	.04
119 Robbie Wine (R)	.15
120 Kirby Puckett	.40
121 Checklist: 1-132	.06
122 Tony Bernazard	.04
123 Tom Candiotti	.06
124 Ray Knight	.04
125 Bruce Hurst	.08
126 Steve Jeltz	.04
127 Jim Gott	.04
128 Johnny Grubb	.04
129 Greg Minton	.04
130 Buddy Bell	.15
131 Don Schulze	.04
132 Donnie Hill	.04
133 Greg Mathews	.04
134 Chuck Tanner (mgr.)	.04
135 Dennis Rasmussen	.06
136 Brian Dayett	.04
137 Chris Bosio	.04
138 Mitch Webster	.06
139 Jerry Browne	.12
140 Jesse Barfield	.15
141 Royals Team	.10
142 Andy Van Slyke	.12
143 Mickey Tettleton	.04
144 Don Gordon (R)	.10
145 Bill Madlock	.08
146 Donnell Nixon (R)	.12
147 Bill Buckner	.04
148 Carmelo Martinez	.04
149 Ken Howell	.04
150 Eric Davis	.40
151 Bob Knepper	.04
152 Jody Reed (R)	.30
153 John Habyan	.08
154 Jeff Stone	.04
155 Bruce Sutter	.08
156 Gary Mathews	.04
157 Atlee Hammaker	.04
158 Tim Hulett	.04
159 Brad Arnsberg (R)	.20
160 Willie McGee	.10
161 Bryn Smith	.04
162 Mark McLemore	.08
163 Dale Mahorcic	.04
164 Dave Johnson	.04
165 Robin Yount	.25
166 Rick Rodriguez (R)	.12
167 Rance Mulliniks	.04
168 Barry Jones	.04
169 Ross Jones (R)	.15
170 Rich Gossage	.08
171 Cubs Team	.06
172 Lloyd McClendon (R)	.15
173 Eric Plunk	.04
174 Phil Garner	.04
175 Kevin Bass	.10
176 Jeff Reed	.04
177 Frank Tanana	.08
178 Dwayne Henry	.08
179 Charlie Puleo	.04
180 Terry Kennedy	.04
181 Dave Cone	1.00
182 Ken Phelps	.04
183 Tom Lawless	.04
184 Ivan Calderon	.15
185 Rick Rhoden	.04
186 Rafael Palmeiro	.25
187 Steve Kiefer	.12
188 John Russell	.04
189 Wes Gardner (R)	.15
190 Candy Maldonado	.10
191 John Cerutti	.04
192 Devon White	.20
193 Brian Fisher	.06
194 Tom Kelly	.04
195 Dan Quisenberry	.08
196 Dave Engle	.04
197 Lance McCullers	.04

NO. PLAYER	MINT
198 Franklin Stubbs	.06
199 Dave Meads (R)	.12
200 Wade Boggs	.75
201 Rangers Team	.06
202 Glenn Hoffman	.04
203 Fred Toliver	.04
204 Paul O'Neill	.10
205 Nelson Liriano (R)	.20
206 Domingo Ramos	.04
207 John Mitchell (R)	.15
208 Steve Lake	.04
209 Richard Dotson	.04
210 Willie Randolph	.10
211 Frank Dipino	.04
212 Greg Brock	.04
213 Albert Hall	.04
214 Dave Schmidt	.04
215 Von Hayes	.08
216 Jerry Reuss	.04
217 Harry Spillman	.04
218 Dan Schatzeder	.04
219 Mike Stanley	.12
220 Tom Henke	.04
221 Rafael Belliard	.04
222 Steve Farr	.04
223 Stan Jefferson	.12
224 Tom Trebelhorn (R)	.12
225 Mike Scioscia	.04
226 Dave Lopes	.06
227 Ed Correa	.04
228 Wallace Johnson	.04
229 Jeff Musselman	.12
230 Pat Tabler	.04
231 Pirates Team	.06
232 Bob James	.04
233 Rafael Santana	.04
234 Ken Dayley	.04
235 Gary Ward	.04
236 Ted Power	.04
237 Mike Heath	.04
238 Luis Polonia (R)	.20
239 Roy Smalley	.04
240 Lee Smith	.08
241 Damaso Garcia	.06
242 Tom Niedenfuer	.04
243 Mark Ryal	.12
244 Jeff D. Robinson	.04
245 Rich Gedman	.04
246 Mike Campbell (R)	.20
247 Thad Bosley	.04
248 Storm Davis	.04
249 Mike Marshall	.08
250 Nolan Ryan	.25
251 Tom Foley	.04
252 Bob Brower	.08
253 Checklist: 133-264	.06
254 Lee Elia	.04
255 Mookie Wilson	.06
256 Ken Schrom	.04
257 Jerry Royster	.04
258 Ed Nunez	.04
259 Ron Kittle	.06
260 Vince Coleman	.20
261 Giants Team	.06
262 Drew Hall	.12
263 Glenn Braggs	.12
264 Les Straker (R)	.15
265 Bo Diaz	.04
266 Paul Assenmacher	.04
267 Billy Bean (R)	.15
268 Bruce Ruffin	.04
269 Ellis Burks (R)	1.00
270 Mike Witt	.06
271 Ken Gerhart	.10
272 Steve Ontiveros	.04
273 Garth Iorg	.04
274 Junior Ortiz	.04
275 Kevin Seitzer	.65
276 Luis Salazar	.04
277 Alejandro Pena	.04
278 Jose Cruz	.04
279 Randy St. Claire	.04
280 Pete Incaviglia	.20
281 Jerry Hairston	.04
282 Pat Perry	.04

NO. PLAYER	MINT
283 Phil Lombardi	.08
284 Larry Bowa	.04
285 Jim Presley	.08
286 Chuck Grim (R)	.12
287 Manny Trillo	.04
288 Pat Pacillo	.12
289 Dave Bergman	.04
290 Tony Fernandez	.12
291 Astros Team	.06
292 Carney Lansford	.04
293 Doug Jones (R)	.25
294 Al Pedrique (R)	.12
295 Bert Blyleven	.06
296 Floyd Rayford	.04
297 Zane Smith	.04
298 Milt Thompson	.04
299 Steve Crawford	.04
300 Don Mattingly	1.25
301 Bud Black	.06
302 Jose Uribe	.04
303 Eric Show	.06
304 George Hendrick	.06
305 Steve Sax	.10
306 Billy Hatcher	.10
307 Mike Trujillo	.04
308 Lee Mazzilli	.06
309 Bill Long (R)	.15
310 Tom Herr	.04
311 Scott Sanderson	.04
312 Joey Meyer	.25
313 Bob McClure	.04
314 Jimy Williams	.12
315 Dave Parker	.15
316 Jose Rijo	.04
317 Tom Nieto	.04
318 Mel Hall	.04
319 Mike Loynd	.04
320 Alan Trammell	.15
321 White Sox Team	.06
322 Vincente Palacios (R)	.15
323 Rick Leach	.04
324 Danny Jackson	.15
325 Glenn Hubbard	.04
326 Al Nipper	.04
327 Larry Sheets	.12
328 Greg Cadaret (R)	.15
329 Chris Speier	.04
330 Eddie Whitson	.04
331 Brian Downing	.04
332 Jerry Reed	.04
333 Wally Backman	.04
334 Dave LaPoint	.04
335 C. Washington	.04
336 Ed Lynch	.04
337 Jim Gantner	.04
338 Brian Holton	.08
339 Kurt Stillwell	.08
340 Jack Morris	.12
341 Carmen Castillo	.04
342 Larry Andersen	.04
343 Greg Gagne	.04
344 Tony LaRussa	.04
345 Scott Fletcher	.04
346 Vance Law	.04
347 Joe Johnson	.06
348 Jim Eisenreich	.04
349 Bob Walk	.04
350 Will Clark	1.00
351 Cardinals Team	.06
352 Billy Ripken (R)	.25
353 Ed Olwine	.04
354 Marc Sullivan	.04
355 Roger McDowell	.04
356 Luis Aguayo	.04
357 Floyd Bannister	.04
358 Rey Quinones	.04
359 Tim Stoddard	.04
360 Tony Gwynn	.35
361 Greg Maddux	.30
362 Juan Castillo	.10
363 Willie Fraser	.10
364 Nick Esasky	.04
365 Floyd Youmans	.04
366 Chet Lemon	.04
367 Tim Leary	.04

NO. PLAYER	MINT
368 Gerald Young (R)	.25
369 Greg Harris	.04
370 Jose Canseco	1.25
371 Joe Hesketh	.04
372 Matt Williams (R)	.75
373 Checklist: 265-396	.06
374 Doc Edwards	.04
375 Tom Brunansky	.08
376 Bill Wilkinson (R)	.12
377 Sam Horn (R)	.30
378 Todd Frohwirth (R)	.15
379 Rafael Ramirez	.04
380 Joe Magrane (R)	.40
381 Angels Team	.06
382 Keith Miller (R)	.20
383 Eric Bell (R)	.12
384 Neil Allen	.04
385 Carlton Fisk	.10
386 Don Mattingly (AS)	.50
387 Willie Randolph (AS)	.08
388 Wade Boggs (AS)	.40
389 Alan Trammell (AS)	.08
390 George Bell (AS)	.15
391 Kirby Puckett (AS)	.20
392 Dave Winfield (AS)	.12
393 Matt Nokes (AS)	.25
394 Roger Clemens (AS)	.30
395 Jimmy Key (AS)	.04
396 Tom Henke (AS)	.04
397 Jack Clark (AS)	.15
398 Juan Samuel (AS)	.08
399 Tim Wallach (AS)	.06
400 Ozzie Smith (AS)	.08
401 Andre Dawson (AS)	.12
402 Tony Gwynn (AS)	.15
403 Tim Raines (AS)	.10
404 Benny Santiago (AS)	.15
405 Dwight Gooden (AS)	.20
406 Shane Rawley (AS)	.06
407 Steve Bedrosian (AS)	.08
408 Dion James	.04
409 Joel McKeon	.04
410 Tony Pena	.04
411 Wayne Tolleson	.04
412 Randy Myers	.12
413 John Christensen	.04
414 John McNamara	.04
415 Don Carman	.04
416 Keith Moreland	.04
417 Mark Ciardi (R)	.12
418 Joel Youngblood	.04
419 Scott McGregor	.04
420 Wally Joyner	.30
421 Ed VandeBerg	.04
422 Dave Concepcion	.04
423 John Smiley (R)	.30
424 Dwayne Murphy	.04
425 Jeff Reardon	.04
426 Randy Ready	.04
427 Paul Kilgus (R)	.12
428 John Shelby	.04
429 Tigers Team	.08
430 Glenn Davis	.12
431 Casey Candaele	.08
432 Mike Moore	.04
433 Bill Pecota (R)	.15
434 Rick Aguilera	.04
435 Mike Pagliarulo	.06
436 Mike Bielecki	.04
437 Fred Manrique (R)	.15
438 Rob Ducey (R)	.20
439 Dave Martinez	.15
440 Steve Bedrosian	.10
441 Rick Manning	.04
442 Tom Bolton (R)	.12
443 Ken Griffey	.04
444 Cal Ripken, Sr.	.04
445 Mike Krukow	.04
446 Doug DeCinces	.04
447 Jeff Montgomery (R)	.25
448 Mike Davis	.04
449 Jeff M. Robinson (R)	.25
450 Barry Bonds	.15
451 Keith Atherton	.04
452 Willie Wilson	.08

NO.	PLAYER	MINT
453	Dennis Powell	.04
454	Marvell Wynne	.04
455	Shawn Hillegas (R)	.25
456	Dave Anderson	.04
457	Terry Leach	.04
458	Ron Hassey	.04
459	Yankees Team	.08
460	Ozzie Smith	.12
461	Danny Darwin	.04
462	Don Slaught	.04
463	Fred McGriff	1.00
464	Jay Tibbs	.04
465	Paul Molitor	.08
466	Jerry Mumphrey	.04
467	Don Aase	.04
468	Darren Daulton	.04
469	Jeff Dedmon	.04
470	Dwight Evans	.08
471	Donnie Moore	.04
472	Robby Thompson	.04
473	Joe Niekro	.06
474	Tom Brookens	.04
475	Pete Rose (mgr.)	.30
476	Dave Stewart	.04
477	Jamie Quirk	.04
478	Sid Bream	.04
479	Brett Butler	.04
480	Dwight Gooden	.40
481	Mariano Duncan	.06
482	Mark Davis	.04
483	Rod Booker (R)	.15
484	Pat Clements	.04
485	Harold Reynolds	.04
486	Pat Keedy (R)	.12
487	Jim Pankovits	.04
488	Andy McGaffigan	.04
489	Dodgers Team	.10
490	Larry Parrish	.04
491	B.J. Surhoff	.15
492	Doyle Alexander	.04
493	Mike Greenwell	1.00
494	Wally Ritchie (R)	.12
495	Eddie Murray	.25
496	Guy Hoffman	.04
497	Kevin Mitchell	.30
498	Bob Boone	.04
499	Eric King	.04
500	Andre Dawson	.20
501	Tim Birtsas	.04
502	Danny Gladden	.04
503	Junior Noboa (R)	.12
504	Bob Rodgers	.04
505	Willie Upshaw	.06
506	John Cangelosi	.04
507	Mark Gubicza	.04
508	Tim Teufel	.04
509	Bill Dawley	.04
510	Dave Winfield	.25
511	Joel Davis	.04
512	Alex Trevino	.04
513	Tim Flannery	.04
514	Pat Sheridan	.04
515	Juan Nieves	.04
516	Jim Sundberg	.04
517	Ron Robinson	.04
518	Greg Gross	.04
519	Mariners Team	.04
520	Dave Smith	.04
521	Jim Dwyer	.04
522	Bob Patterson (R)	.12
523	Gary Roenicke	.04
524	Gary Lucas	.04
525	Marty Barrett	.06
526	Juan Berenguer	.04
527	Steve Henderson	.04
528	Checklist: 397-528	.12
529	Tim Burke	.04
530	Gary Carter	.20
531	Rich Yett	.04
532	Mike Kingery	.04
533	John Farrell (R)	.20
534	John Wathan	.04
535	Ron Guidry	.10
536	John Morris	.04
537	Steve Buechele	.04
538	Bill Wegman	.04
539	Mike LaValliere	.04
540	Bret Saberhagen	.12
541	Juan Beniquez	.04
542	Paul Noce (R)	.12
543	Kent Tekulve	.04
544	Jim Traber	.04
545	Don Baylor	.08
546	John Candelaria	.06
547	Felix Fermin (R)	.10
548	Shane Mack	.15
549	Braves Team	.06
550	Pedro Guerrero	.20
551	Terry Steinbach	.15
552	Mark Thurmond	.04
553	Tracy Jones	.10
554	Mike Smithson	.04
555	Brook Jacoby	.08
556	Stan Clarke (R)	.10
557	Craig Reynolds	.04
558	Bob Ojeda	.04
559	Ken Williams (R)	.25
560	Tim Wallach	.08
561	Rick Cerone	.04
562	Jim Lindeman	.15
563	Jose Guzman	.04
564	Frank Lucchesi	.04
565	Lloyd Moseby	.15
566	Charlie O'Brien (R)	.10
567	Mike Diaz	.04
568	Chris Brown	.10
569	C. Liebrandt	.06
570	Jeffrey Leonard	.04
571	Mark Williamson (R)	.15
572	Chris James	.20
573	Bob Stanley	.04
574	Graig Nettles	.10
575	Don Sutton	.15
576	Tommy Hinzo (R)	.12
577	Tom Browning	.06
578	Gary Gaetti	.12
579	Mets Team	.15
580	Mark McGwire	1.00
581	Tito Landrum	.04
582	Mike Henneman (R)	.15
583	Dave Valle	.08
584	Steve Trout	.04
585	Ozzie Guillen	.04
586	Bob Forsch	.04
587	Terry Puhl	.04
588	Jeff Parrett (R)	.15
589	Geno Petralli	.04
590	George Bell	.20
591	Doug Drabek	.04
592	Dale Sveum	.06
593	Bob Tewksbury	.04
594	Bobby Valentine	.04
595	Frank White	.04
596	John Kruk	.20
597	Gene Garber	.04
598	Lee Lacy	.04
599	Calvin Schiraldi	.04
600	Mike Schmidt	.35
601	Jack Lazorko	.04
602	Mike Aldrete	.04
603	Rob Murphy	.04
604	Chris Bando	.04
605	Kirk Gibson	.15
606	Moose Haas	.04
607	Mickey Hatcher	.04
608	Charlie Kerfeld	.06
609	Twins Team	.08
610	Keith Hernandez	.15
611	Tommy John	.08
612	Curt Ford	.04
613	Bobby Thigpen	.04
614	Herm Winningham	.04
615	Jody Davis	.04
616	Jay Aldrich (R)	.12
617	Oddibe McDowell	.10
618	Cecil Fielder	.04
619	Mike Dunne	.20
620	Cory Snyder	.15
621	Gene Nelson	.04
622	Kal Daniels	.20
623	Mike Flanagan	.04
624	Jim Leyland	.04
625	Frank Viola	.15
626	Glenn Wilson	.04
627	Joe Boever (R)	.12
628	Dave Henderson	.04
629	Kelly Downs	.04
630	Darrell Evans	.12
631	Jack Howell	.04
632	Steve Shields	.10
633	Barry Lyons (R)	.20
634	Jose DeLeon	.06
635	Terry Pendleton	.06
636	Charles Hudson	.04
637	Jay Bell (R)	.20
638	Steve Balboni	.04
639	Brewers Team	.06
640	Garry Templeton	.06
641	Rick Honeycutt	.06
642	Bob Dernier	.04
643	Rocky Childress (R)	.12
644	Terry McGriff (R)	.15
645	Matt Nokes (R)	.40
646	Checklist: 529-660	.06
647	Pascual Perez	.04
648	Al Newman	.04
649	DeWayne Buice (R)	.15
650	Cal Ripken	.20
651	Mike Jackson	.20
652	Bruce Benedict	.04
653	Jeff Sellers	.04
654	Roger Craig	.04
655	Len Dykstra	.15
656	Lee Guetterman	.04
657	Gary Redus	.04
658	Tim Conroy	.04
659	Bobby Meacham	.04
660	Rick Reuschel	.04
661	Turn Back—1983	.08
662	Turn Back—1978	.08
663	Turn Back—1973	.08
664	Turn Back—1968	.08
665	Turn Back—1963	.10
666	Mario Soto	.04
667	Luis Quinones	.04
668	Walt Terrell	.04
669	Phillies Team	.06
670	Dan Plesac	.04
671	Tim Laudner	.04
672	John Davis (R)	.20
673	Tony Phillips	.04
674	Mike Fitzgerald	.04
675	Jim Rice	.15
676	Ken Dixon	.04
677	Eddie Milner	.04
678	Jim Acker	.04
679	Darrell Miller	.04
680	Charlie Hough	.06
681	Bobby Bonilla	.15
682	Jimmy Key	.12
683	Julio Franco	.04
684	Hal Lanier	.04
685	Ron Darling	.15
686	Terry Francona	.04
687	Mickey Brantley	.08
688	Jim Winn	.04
689	Tom Pagnozzi (R)	.15
690	Jay Howell	.04
691	Dan Pasqua	.10
692	Mike Birkbeck	.04
693	Benny Santiago	.45
694	Eric Nolte (R)	.12
695	Shawon Dunston	.04
696	Duane Ward	.04
697	S. Lombardozzi	.10
698	Brad Havens	.04
699	Padres Team	.15
700	George Brett	.25
701	Sammy Stewart	.04
702	Mike Gallego	.04
703	Bob Brenly	.04
704	Dennis Boyd	.04
705	Juan Samuel	.15
706	Rick Mahler	.04
707	Fred Lynn	.10
708	Gus Polidor	.08
709	George Frazier	.04
710	D. Strawberry	.40
711	Bill Gullickson	.04
712	John Moses	.04
713	Willie Hernandez	.08
714	Jim Fregosi	.04
715	Todd Worrell	.10
716	Lenn Sakata	.04
717	Jay Baller	.08
718	Mike Felder	.04
719	Denny Walling	.04
720	Tim Raines	.20
721	Pete O'Brien	.10
722	Manny Lee	.04
723	Bob Kipper	.04
724	Danny Tartabull	.25
725	Mike Boddicker	.04
726	Alfredo Griffin	.04
727	Greg Booker	.04
728	Andy Allanson	.04
729	Blue Jays Team	.06
730	John Franco	.06
731	Rick Schu	.04
732	Dave Palmer	.04
733	Spike Owen	.04
734	Craig Lefferts	.04
735	Kevin McReynolds	.15
736	Matt Young	.04
737	Butch Wynegar	.04
738	Scott Bankhead	.04
739	Daryl Boston	.04
740	Rick Sutcliffe	.15
741	Mike Easler	.04
742	Mark Clear	.04
743	Larry Herndon	.04
744	Whitey Herzog (mgr.)	.04
745	Bill Doran	.10
746	Gene Larkin (R)	.25
747	Bobby Witt	.04
748	Reid Nichols	.04
749	Mark Eichhorn	.04
750	Bo Jackson	.50
751	Jim Morrison	.04
752	Mark Grant	.08
753	Danny Heep	.04
754	Mike LaCoss	.04
755	Ozzie Virgil	.06
756	Mike Maddux	.04
757	John Marzano	.15
758	Eddie Williams (R)	.25
759	A's Team	.30
760	Mike Scott	.15
761	Tony Armas	.06
762	Scott Bradley	.04
763	Doug Sisk	.04
764	Greg Walker	.08
765	Neal Heaton	.10
766	Henry Cotto	.04
767	Jose Lind (R)	.25
768	Dickie Noles	.04
769	Cecil Cooper	.06
770	Lou Whitaker	.15
771	Ruben Sierra	.30
772	Sal Butera	.04
773	Frank Williams	.04
774	Gene Mauch	.04
775	Dave Stieb	.06
776	Checklist: 661-792	.06
777	Lonnie Smith	.04
778	K. Comstock (R)(error)	7.00
778	K. Comstock (R)(correct)	.35
779	Tom Glavine (R)	.25
780	F. Valenzuela	.15
781	Keith Hughes (R)	.20
782	Jeff Ballard (R)	.30
783	Ron Roenicke	.04
784	Joe Sambito	.04
785	Alvin Davis	.08
786	Joe Price	.04
787	Bill Almon	.04
788	Ray Searage	.04
789	Indians Team	.08
790	Dave Righetti	.10
791	Ted Simmons	.08
792	John Tudor	.08

1988 Topps Traded.... Complete Set of 132 Cards—Value $25.00

Updates the main 1988 card set with players who changed teams during the season and rookies. Features the first Topps card for Mark Grace, Jim Abbott, Andy Benes and the USA Olympic Team. The complete set was packaged in a printed box and distributed primarily through card hobby dealers. A "Tiffany" version of the set was also issued.

NO. PLAYER	MINT	NO. PLAYER	MINT	NO. PLAYER	MINT	NO. PLAYER	MINT
1 T Jim Abbott (OLY)	7.50	34 T Jose DeLeon	.06	67 T Billy Masse (OLY)	.25	100 T Luis Salazar	.06
2 T Juan Agosto	.06	35 T Richard Dotson	.06	68 T Jack McDowell	.15	101 T Rafael Santana	.06
3 T Luis Alicea	.15	36 T Cecil Espy	.10	69 T Jack McKeon	.06	102 T Nelson Santovenia	.15
4 T Roberto Alomar	.50	37 T Tom Filer	.06	70 T Larry McWilliams	.06	103 T Mackey Sasser	.20
5 T Brady Anderson	.35	38 T Mike Fiore (OLY)	.25	71 T M. Morandini (OLY)	.30	104 T Calvin Schiraldi	.06
6 T Jack Armstrong	.25	39 T Ron Gant	.45	72 T Keith Moreland	.06	105 T Mike Schooler	.15
7 T Don August	.12	40 T Kirk Gibson	.20	73 T Mike Morgan	.06	106 T Scott Servais (OLY)	.20
8 T Floyd Bannister	.06	41 T Rich Gossage	.06	74 T Charles Nagy (OLY)	.25	107 T Dave Silvestri (OLY)	.20
9 T Bret Barberie (OLY)	.20	42 T Mark Grace (RR)	2.00	75 T Al Nipper	.06	108 T Don Slaught	.06
10 T Jose Bautista	.15	43 T Alfredo Griffin	.06	76 T Russ Nixon	.06	109 T Joe Slusarski (OLY)	.20
11 T Don Baylor	.06	44 T Ty Griffin (OLY)	.90	77 T Jesse Orosco	.06	110 T Lee Smith	.06
12 T Tim Belcher	.06	45 T Bryan Harvey	.30	78 T Joe Orsulak	.06	111 T Pete Smith	.20
13 T Buddy Bell	.06	46 T Ron Hassey	.06	79 T Dave Palmer	.06	112 T Jim Snyder	.06
14 T Andy Benes (OLY)	2.00	47 T Ray Hayward	.15	80 T Mark Parent	.20	113 T Ed Sprague (OLY)	.25
15 T Damon Berryhill	.35	48 T Dave Henderson	.06	81 T Dave Parker	.15	114 T Pete Stanicek	.15
16 T Bud Black	.06	49 T Tom Herr	.06	82 T Dan Pasqua	.06	115 T Kurt Stillwell	.06
17 T Pat Borders	.25	50 T Bob Horner	.06	83 T Melido Perez	.20	116 T Todd Stottlemyre	.25
18 T Phil Bradley	.06	51 T Rickey Horton	.06	84 T Steve Peters	.20	117 T Bill Swift	.06
19 T Jeff Branson (OLY)	.20	52 T Jay Howell	.06	85 T Dan Petry	.06	118 T Pat Tabler	.06
20 T Tom Brunansky	.15	53 T Glenn Hubbard	.06	86 T Gary Pettis	.06	119 T Scott Terry	.06
21 T Jay Buhner	.30	54 T Jeff Innis	.20	87 T Jeff Pico	.15	120 T Mickey Tettleton	.06
22 T Brett Butler	.06	55 T Danny Jackson	.20	88 T Jim Poole (OLY)	.20	121 T Dickie Thon	.06
23 T Jim Campanis (OLY)	.25	56 T Darrin Jackson	.20	89 T Ted Power	.06	122 T Jeff Treadway	.25
24 T Sil Campusano	.25	57 T Roberto Kelly (RR)	.50	90 T Rafael Ramirez	.06	123 T Willie Upshaw	.06
25 T John Candelaria	.06	58 T Ron Kittle	.06	91 T Dennis Rasmussen	.06	124 T Robin Ventura (OLY)	1.50
26 T Jose Cecana	.20	59 T Ray Knight	.06	92 T Jose Rijo	.06	125 T Ron Washington	.06
27 T Rick Cerone	.06	60 T Vance Law	.06	93 T Ernie Riles	.06	126 T Walt Weiss (RR)	1.00
28 T Jack Clark	.15	61 T Jeffrey Leonard	.06	94 T Luis Rivera	.15	127 T Bob Welch	.06
29 T Kevin Coffman	.15	62 T Mike Macfarlane	.15	95 T Doug Robbins	.20	128 T David Wells	.15
30 T Pat Combs (OLY)	.75	63 T Scott Madison	.15	96 T Frank Robinson	.15	129 T Glenn Wilson	.06
31 T Henry Cotto	.06	64 T Kirt Manwaring	.15	97 T Cookie Rojas	.06	130 T Ted Wood (OLY)	.40
32 T Chill Davis	.06	65 T Mark Marquess	.06	98 T Chris Sabo (RR)	1.50	131 T Don Zimmer	.06
33 T Mike Davis	.06	66 T Tino Martinez (OLY)	.75	99 T Mark Salas	.06	132 T Checklist	.06

1989 Topps.... Complete Set of 792 Cards—Value $25.00

Features the rookie cards of Sandy Alomar, Jr., Ricky Jordan, Robin Ventura and Gary Sheffield. New features this year are "#1 Draft Picks" and 1988 "Monthly Scoreboard." A "Tiffany" version of the set was also issued.

NO. PLAYER	MINT	NO. PLAYER	MINT	NO. PLAYER	MINT	NO. PLAYER	MINT
1 '88 Record: G. Bell	.15	4 '88 Record: Dawson	.10	7 '88 Rec.: McReynolds	.10	10 Andre Dawson	.15
2 '88 Record: Boggs	.20	5 '88 Rec.: Hershiser	.10	8 Dave Eiland (R)	.15	11 Bruce Sutter	.08
3 '88 Record: G. Carter	.10	6 '88 Record: D. Jones	.05	9 Tim Teufel	.05	12 Dale Sveum	.08

NO.	PLAYER	MINT	NO.	PLAYER	MINT	NO.	PLAYER	MINT	NO.	PLAYER	MINT
13	Doug Sisk	.05	98	Larry Sheets	.05	183	Oddibe McDowell	.08	268	Keith Miller	.15
14	Tom Kelly	.05	99	Sherman Corbett (R)	.15	184	John Costello (R)	.15	269	Tom Bolton	.05
15	Robby Thompson	.05	100	Mike Schmidt	.25	185	Claudell Washington	.05	270	Wally Joyner	.15
16	Ron Robinson	.08	101	Les Straker	.05	186	Pat Perry	.05	271	Jay Tibbs	.05
17	Brian Downing	.08	102	Mike Gallego	.05	187	Darren Daulton	.05	272	Ron Hassey	.05
18	Rick Rhoden	.05	103	Tim Birtsas	.05	188	Dennis Lamp	.05	273	Jose Lind	.05
19	Greg Gagne	.05	104	Dallas Green	.05	189	Kevin Mitchell	.30	274	Mark Eichhorn	.05
20	Steve Bedrosian	.08	105	Ron Darling	.10	190	Mike Witt	.08	275	Danny Tartabull	.15
21	Walker: *Bonus*	.05	106	Willie Upshaw	.05	191	Sil Campusano (R)	.20	276	Paul Kilgus	.05
22	Tim Crews	.05	107	Jose DeLeon	.05	192	Paul Mirabella	.05	277	Mike Davis	.05
23	Mike Fitzgerald	.05	108	Fred Manrique	.05	193	Sparky Anderson	.05	278	Andy McGaffigan	.05
24	Larry Andersen	.05	109	Hipolito Pena (R)	.15	194	Greg Harris (R)	.20	279	Scott Bradley	.05
25	Frank White	.05	110	Paul Molitor	.08	195	Ozzie Guillen	.08	280	Bob Knepper	.05
26	Dale Mohorcac	.05	111	Davis: *Bonus*	.15	196	Denny Walling	.05	281	Gary Redus	.05
27	Orestes Destrade (R)	.25	112	Jim Presley	.05	197	Neal Heaton	.05	282	Cris Carpenter (R)	.20
28	Mike Moore	.05	113	Lloyd Moseby	.12	198	Danny Heep	.05	283	Andy Allanson	.05
29	Kelly Gruber	.05	114	Bob Kipper	.05	199	Mike Schooler (R)	.20	284	Jim Leyland	.05
30	Doc Gooden	.35	115	Jody Davis	.05	200	George Brett	.25	285	John Candelaria	.08
31	Terry Francona	.10	116	Jeff Montgomery	.05	201	Gruber: *Bonus*	.05	286	Darrin Jackson	.12
32	Dennis Rasmussen	.05	117	Dave Anderson	.05	202	Brad Moore (R)	.15	287	Juan Nieves	.05
33	B.J. Surhoff	.08	118	Checklist: 1-132	.08	203	Rob Ducey	.05	288	Pat Sheridan	.05
34	Ken Williams	.05	119	Terry Puhl	.05	204	Brad Havens	.05	289	Ernie Whitt	.05
35	John Tudor	.05	120	Frank Viola	.15	205	Dwight Evans	.15	290	John Franco	.08
36	Mitch Webster	.05	121	Garry Templeton	.05	206	Roberto Alomar	.35	291	Strawberry: *Bonus*	.20
37	Bob Stanley	.05	122	Lance Johnson	.10	207	Terry Leach	.05	292	Jim Corsi (R)	.20
38	Paul Runge	.05	123	Spike Owen	.05	208	Tom Pagnozzi	.05	293	Glenn Wilson	.05
39	Mike Maddux	.05	124	Jim Traber	.05	209	Jeff Bittiger (R)	.15	294	Juan Berenguer	.05
40	Steve Sax	.12	125	Mike Krukow	.08	210	Dale Murphy	.25	295	Scott Fletcher	.05
41	Terry Mulholland	.05	126	Sid Bream	.05	211	Mike Pagliarulo	.10	296	Ron Gant	.25
42	Jim Eppard	.10	127	Walt Terrell	.05	212	Scott Sanderson	.05	297	Oswald Peraza (R)	.15
43	Guillermo Hernandez	.05	128	Milt Thompson	.05	213	Rene Gonzales	.05	298	Chris James	.08
44	Jim Snyder	.10	129	Terry Clark (R)	.20	214	Charlie O'Brien	.05	299	Steve Ellsworth (R)	.15
45	Kal Daniels	.15	130	Gerald Perry	.10	215	Kevin Gross	.05	300	Darryl Strawberry	.35
46	Mark Portugal	.05	131	Dave Otto	.15	216	Jack Howell	.08	301	Charlie Leibrandt	.08
47	Carney Lansford	.08	132	Curt Ford	.05	217	Joe Price	.05	302	Gary Ward	.05
48	Tim Burke	.05	133	Bill Long	.05	218	Mike LaValliere	.05	303	Felix Fermin	.05
49	Craig Biggio (R)	.35	134	Don Zimmer	.05	219	Jim Clancy	.05	304	Joel Youngblood	.05
50	George Bell	.15	135	Jose Rijo	.08	220	Gary Gaetti	.10	305	Dave Smith	.05
51	McLemore: *Bonus*	.05	136	Joey Meyer	.05	221	Cecil Espy	.10	306	Tracy Woodson	.10
52	Bob Brenly	.05	137	Geno Petralli	.05	222	Mark Lewis	.40	307	Lance McCullers	.08
53	Ruben Sierra	.15	138	Wallace Johnson	.05	223	Jay Buhner	.25	308	Ron Karkovice	.05
54	Steve Trout	.05	139	Mike Flanagan	.05	224	Tony LaRussa	.05	309	Mario Diaz	.10
55	Julio Franco	.08	140	Shawon Dunston	.10	225	Ramon Martinez (R)	.40	310	Rafael Palmeiro	.15
56	Pat Tabler	.08	141	Jacoby: *Bonus*	.05	226	Bill Doran	.08	311	Chris Bosio	.05
57	Alejandro Pena	.08	142	Mike Diaz	.05	227	John Farrell	.05	312	Tom Lawless	.05
58	Lee Mazzilli	.05	143	Mike Campbell	.05	228	Nelson Santovenia (R)	.15	313	Denny Martinez	.05
59	Mark Davis	.05	144	Jay Bell	.05	229	Jimmy Key	.12	314	Bobby Valentine	.05
60	Tom Brunansky	.08	145	Dave Stewart	.10	230	Ozzie Smith	.08	315	Greg Swindell	.10
61	Neil Allen	.05	146	Gary Pettis	.05	231	R. Alomar: *Bonus*	.10	316	Walt Weiss	.35
62	Alfredo Griffin	.05	147	DeWayne Buice	.05	232	Ricky Horton	.05	317	Jack Armstrong (R)	.20
63	Mark Clear	.05	148	Bill Pecota	.05	233	Gregg Jefferies	2.50	318	Gene Larkin	.05
64	Alex Trevino	.05	149	Doug Dascenzo (R)	.20	234	Tom Browning	.08	319	Greg Booker	.05
65	Rick Reuschel	.05	150	Fernando Valenzuela	.10	235	John Kruk	.15	320	Lou Whitaker	.08
66	Manny Trillo	.05	151	Terry McGriff	.05	236	Charles Hudson	.08	321	Reed: *Bonus*	.10
67	Dave Palmer	.05	152	Mark Thurmond	.05	237	Glenn Hubbard	.05	322	John Smiley	.08
68	Darrell Miller	.05	153	Jim Pankovits	.05	238	Eric King	.05	323	Gary Thurman	.05
69	Jeff Ballard	.05	154	Don Carman	.05	239	Tim Laudner	.05	324	Bob Milacki (R)	.20
70	Mark McGwire	.50	155	Marty Barrett	.05	240	Greg Maddux	.15	325	Jesse Barfield	.12
71	Mike Boddicker	.08	156	Dave Gallagher (R)	.25	241	Brett Butler	.08	326	Dennis Boyd	.08
72	John Moses	.05	157	Tom Glavine	.05	242	Ed VandeBerg	.05	327	Mark Lemke (R)	.25
73	Pascual Perez	.05	158	Mike Aldrete	.05	243	Bob Boone	.05	328	Rick Honeycutt	.05
74	Nick Leyva	.05	159	Pat Clements	.05	244	Jim Acker	.05	329	Bob Melvin	.05
75	Tom Henke	.05	160	Jeffrey Leonard	.05	245	Jim Rice	.12	330	Eric Davis	.30
76	Terry Blocker (R)	.15	161	Gregg Olson (R)	.75	246	Rey Quinones	.05	331	Curt Wilkerson	.05
77	Doyle Alexander	.05	162	John Davis	.05	247	Shawn Hillegas	.05	332	Tony Armas	.05
78	Jim Sundberg	.05	163	Bob Forsch	.05	248	Tony Phillips	.05	333	Bob Ojeda	.08
79	Scott Bankhead	.05	164	Hal Lanier	.05	249	Tim Leary	.10	334	Steve Lyons	.05
80	Cory Snyder	.15	165	Mike Dunne	.05	250	Cal Ripken	.20	335	Dave Righetti	.10
81	Raines: *Bonus*	.08	166	Doug Jennings (R)	.25	251	John Dopson (R)	.25	336	Steve Balboni	.05
82	Dave Leiper	.05	167	Steve Searcy (R)	.20	252	Billy Hatcher	.05	337	Calvin Schiraldi	.05
83	Jeff Blauser	.10	168	Willie Wilson	.08	253	Jose Alvarez (R)	.15	338	Jim Adduci	.08
84	Bill Bene (R)	.20	169	Mike Jackson	.05	254	Tom Lasorda	.05	339	Scott Bailes	.05
85	Kevin McReynolds	.15	170	Tony Fernandez	.10	255	Ron Guidry	.08	340	Kirk Gibson	.20
86	Al Nipper	.05	171	Thomas: *Bonus*	.05	256	Benny Santiago	.10	341	Jim Deshaies	.05
87	Larry Owen	.05	172	Frank Williams	.05	257	Rick Aguilera	.05	342	Tom Brookens	.05
88	Darryl Hamilton (R)	.20	173	Mel Hall	.05	258	Checklist: 133-264	.08	343	Gary Sheffield (R)	1.50
89	Dave LaPoint	.05	174	Todd Burns (R)	.25	259	Larry McWilliams	.05	344	Tom Trebelhorn	.05
90	Vince Coleman	.15	175	John Shelby	.05	260	Dave Winfield	.15	345	Charlie Hough	.08
91	Floyd Youmans	.05	176	Jeff Parrett	.08	261	Brunansky *Bonus*	.08	346	Rex Hudler	.10
92	Jeff Kunkel	.05	177	Monty Fariss (R)	.25	262	Jeff Pico (R)	.15	347	John Cerutti	.05
93	Ken Howell	.05	178	Mark Grant	.05	263	Mike Felder	.05	348	Ed Hearn	.05
94	Chris Speier	.05	179	Ozzie Virgil	.05	264	Rob Dibble (R)	.20	349	Ron Jones (R)	.25
95	Gerald Young	.08	180	Mike Scott	.15	265	Kent Hrbek	.10	350	Andy Van Slyke	.15
96	Rick Cerone	.05	181	Craig Worthington (R)	.25	266	Luis Aquino	.05	351	Melvin: *Bonus*	.05
97	Greg Mathews	.05	182	Bob McClure	.05	267	Jeff Robinson	.05	352	Rick Schu	.05

NO.	PLAYER	MINT
353	Marvell Wynne	.05
354	Larry Parrish	.05
355	Mark Langston	.10
356	Kevin Elster	.08
357	Jerry Reuss	.05
358	Ricky Jordan (R)	1.50
359	Tommy John	.10
360	Ryne Sandberg	.12
361	Kelly Downs	.05
362	Jack Lazorko	.05
363	Rich Yett	.05
364	Rob Deer	.08
365	Mike Henneman	.05
366	Herm Winningham	.05
367	Johnny Paredes (R)	.15
368	Brian Holton	.05
369	Ken Caminiti	.05
370	Dennis Eckersley	.10
371	Manny Lee	.05
372	Craig Lefferts	.05
373	Tracy Jones	.05
374	John Wathan	.05
375	Terry Pendleton	.08
376	Steve Lombardozzi	.05
377	Mike Smithson	.05
378	Checklist: 265-396	.08
379	Tim Flannery	.05
380	Rickey Henderson	.25
381	Sheets: Bonus	.05
382	John Smoltz (R)	.30
383	Howard Johnson	.15
384	Mark Salas	.05
385	Von Hayes	.05
386	Andres Galarraga (AS)	.10
387	Ryne Sandberg (AS)	.10
388	Bobby Bonilla (AS)	.10
389	Ozzie Smith (AS)	.08
390	Darryl Strawberry (AS)	.20
391	Andre Dawson (AS)	.10
392	Andy Van Slyke (AS)	.10
393	Gary Carter (AS)	.10
394	Orel Hershiser (AS)	.10
395	Danny Jackson (AS)	.08
396	Kirk Gibson (AS)	.10
397	Don Mattingly (AS)	.35
398	Julio Franco (AS)	.08
399	Wade Boggs (AS)	.25
400	Alan Trammell (AS)	.08
401	Jose Canseco (AS)	.40
402	Mike Greenwell (AS)	.25
403	Kirby Puckett (AS)	.15
404	Bob Boone (AS)	.05
405	Roger Clemens (AS)	.20
406	Frank Viola (AS)	.10
407	Dave Winfield (AS)	.08
408	Greg Walker	.05
409	Ken Dayley	.05
410	Jack Clark	.10
411	Mitch Williams	.05
412	Barry Lyons	.05
413	Mike Kingery	.05
414	Jim Fregosi	.05
415	Rich Gossage	.08
416	Fred Lynn	.08
417	Mike LaCoss	.05
418	Bob Dernier	.05
419	Tom Filer	.05
420	Joe Carter	.15
421	Kirk McCaskill	.05
422	Bo Diaz	.05
423	Brian Fisher	.05
424	Luis Polonia	.05
425	Jay Howell	.08
426	Danny Gladden	.05
427	Eric Show	.05
428	Craig Reynolds	.05
429	Gagne: Bonus	.05
430	Mark Gubicza	.10
431	Luis Rivera	.15
432	Chad Kreuter (R)	.20
433	Albert Hall	.05
434	Ken Patterson (R)	.15
435	Len Dykstra	.15
436	Bobby Meacham	.05
437	Andy Benes (R)	.65

NO.	PLAYER	MINT
438	Greg Gross	.05
439	Frank Dipino	.05
440	Bobby Bonilla	.15
441	Jerry Reed	.05
442	Jose Oquendo	.05
443	Rod Nichols (R)	.20
444	Moose Stubing	.05
445	Matt Nokes	.10
446	Rob Murphy	.05
447	Donell Nixon	.05
448	Eric Plunk	.05
449	Carmelo Martinez	.05
450	Roger Clemens	.25
451	Mark Davidson	.05
452	Israel Sanchez (R)	.15
453	Tom Prince	.10
454	Paul Assenmacher	.05
455	Johnny Ray	.10
456	Tim Belcher	.15
457	Mackey Sasser	.15
458	Donn Pall (R)	.15
459	Valle: Bonus	.05
460	Dave Stieb	.08
461	Buddy Bell	.08
462	Jose Guzman	.05
463	Steve Lake	.05
464	Bryn Smith	.05
465	Mark Grace	1.50
466	Chuck Crim	.05
467	Jim Walewander	.05
468	Henry Cotto	.05
469	Jose Bautista (R)	.15
470	Lance Parrish	.10
471	Steve Curry (R)	.15
472	Brian Harper	.05
473	Don Robinson	.05
474	Bob Rodgers	.05
475	Dave Parker	.10
476	Jon Perlman	.05
477	Dick Schofield	.05
478	Doug Drabek	.10
479	Mike Macfarlane (R)	.20
480	Keith Hernandez	.15
481	Chris Brown	.08
482	Steve Peters (R)	.15
483	Mickey Hatcher	.05
484	Steve Shields	.05
485	Hubie Brooks	.05
486	Jack McDowell	.12
487	Scott Lusader	.10
488	Kevin Coffman	.10
489	Schmidt: Bonus	.15
490	Chris Sabo (R)	.60
491	Mike Birkbeck	.05
492	Alan Ashby	.05
493	Todd Benzinger	.15
494	Shane Rawley	.05
495	Candy Maldonado	.10
496	Dwayne Henry	.05
497	Pete Stanicek	.08
498	Dave Valle	.05
499	Don Heinkel (R)	.15
500	Jose Canseco	1.00
501	Vance Law	.05
502	Duane Ward	.05
503	Al Newman	.05
504	Bob Walk	.05
505	Pete Rose	.20
506	Kirt Manwaring	.15
507	Steve Farr	.05
508	Wally Backman	.05
509	Bud Black	.05
510	Bob Horner	.05
511	Richard Dotson	.08
512	Donnie Hill	.05
513	Jesse Orosco	.05
514	Chet Lemon	.05
515	Barry Larkin	.10
516	Eddie Whitson	.05
517	Greg Brock	.05
518	Bruce Ruffin	.05
519	Randolph: Bonus	.08
520	Rick Sutcliffe	.10
521	Mickey Tettleton	.05
522	Randy Kramer (R)	.15

NO.	PLAYER	MINT
523	Andres Thomas	.05
524	Checklist: 397-528	.08
525	Chili Davis	.08
526	Wes Gardner	.05
527	Dave Henderson	.05
528	Luis Medina (R)	.35
529	Tom Foley	.05
530	Nolan Ryan	.25
531	Dave Hengel	.10
532	Jerry Browne	.05
533	Andy Hawkins	.05
534	Doc Edwards	.05
535	Todd Worrell	.08
536	Joel Skinner	.05
537	Pete Smith	.12
538	Juan Castillo	.05
539	Barry Jones	.05
540	Bo Jackson	.40
541	Cecil Fielder	.05
542	Todd Frohwirth	.05
543	Damon Berryhill	.25
544	Jeff Sellers	.05
545	Mookie Wilson	.08
546	Mark Williamson	.05
547	Mark McLemore	.05
548	Bobby Witt	.05
549	Moyer: Bonus	.05
550	Orel Hershiser	.25
551	Randy Ready	.05
552	Greg Cadaret	.05
553	Luis Salazar	.05
554	Nick Esasky	.10
555	Bert Blyleven	.15
556	Bruce Fields	.10
557	Keith Miller	.05
558	Dan Pasqua	.08
559	Juan Agosto	.05
560	Tim Raines	.15
561	Luis Aguayo	.05
562	Danny Cox	.05
563	Bill Schroeder	.05
564	Russ Nixon	.05
565	Jeff Russell	.05
566	Al Pedrique	.05
567	David Wells	.10
568	Mickey Brantley	.08
569	German Jimenez (R)	.15
570	Tony Gwynn	.25
571	Billy Ripken	.05
572	Atlee Hammaker	.05
573	Jim Abbott (R)	2.00
574	Dave Clark	.05
575	Juan Samuel	.10
576	Greg Minton	.05
577	Randy Bush	.05
578	John Morris	.05
579	G. Davis: Bonus	.08
580	Harold Reynolds	.08
581	Gene Nelson	.05
582	Mike Marshall	.08
583	Paul Gibson (R)	.15
584	Randy Velarde	.15
585	Harold Baines	.10
586	Joe Boever	.05
587	Mike Stanley	.05
588	Luis Alicea (R)	.15
589	Dave Meads	.05
590	Andres Galarraga	.15
591	Jeff Musselman	.05
592	John Cangelosi	.05
593	Drew Hall	.05
594	Jimy Williams	.05
595	Teddy Higuera	.10
596	Kurt Stillwell	.05
597	Terry Taylor (R)	.20
598	Ken Gerhart	.05
599	Tom Candiotti	.08
600	Wade Boggs	.50
601	Dave Dravecky	.05
602	Devon White	.08
603	Frank Tanana	.08
604	Paul O'Neill	.15
605	Bob Welch (Correct)	.20
605	Bob Welch (error)	3.00
606	Rick Dempsey	.05
607	Willie Ansley (R)	.40

NO.	PLAYER	MINT
608	Phil Bradley	.08
609	Tanana: Bonus	.08
610	Randy Myers	.08
611	Don Slaught	.05
612	Dan Quisenberry	.08
613	Gary Varsho (R)	.15
614	Joe Hesketh	.05
615	Robin Yount	.15
616	Steve Rosenberg (R)	.15
617	Mark Parent (R)	.15
618	Rance Mulliniks	.05
619	Checklist: 529-660	.08
620	Barry Bonds	.15
621	Rick Mahler	.05
622	Stan Javier	.05
623	Fred Toliver	.05
624	Jack McKeon	.05
625	Eddie Murray	.20
626	Jeff Reed	.05
627	Greg Harris	.20
628	Matt Williams	.08
629	Pete O'Brien	.10
630	Mike Greenwell	.50
631	Dave Bergman	.05
632	Bryan Harvey (R)	.25
633	Daryl Boston	.05
634	Marvin Freeman	.10
635	Willie Randolph	.08
636	Bill Wilkinson	.05
637	Carmen Castillo	.05
638	Floyd Bannister	.05
639	Weiss: Bonus	.15
640	Willie McGee	.08
641	Curt Young	.05
642	Argenis Salazar	.05
643	Louie Meadows (R)	.15
644	Lloyd McClendon	.05
645	Jack Morris	.10
646	Kevin Bass	.08
647	Randy Johnson (R)	.25
648	Sandy Alomar (R)	1.50
649	Stewart Cliburn	.05
650	Kirby Puckett	.25
651	Tom Niedenfuer	.05
652	Rich Gedman	.05
653	Tommy Barrett (R)	.15
654	Whitey Herzog	.05
655	Dave Magadan	.10
656	Ivan Calderon	.10
657	Joe Magrane	.10
658	R.J. Reynolds	.05
659	Al Leiter	.10
660	Will Clark	.50
661	Turn Back—1984	.15
662	Turn Back—1979	.15
663	Turn Back—1974	.15
664	Turn Back—1969	.15
665	Turn Back—1964	.15
666	Randy St. Claire	.15
667	Dwayne Murphy	.05
668	Mike Bielecki	.05
669	Hershiser: Bonus	.15
670	Kevin Seitzer	.15
671	Jim Gantner	.05
672	Allan Anderson	.08
673	Don Baylor	.08
674	Otis Nixon	.05
675	Bruce Hurst	.15
676	Ernie Riles	.05
677	Dave Schmidt	.05
678	Dion James	.05
679	Willie Fraser	.05
680	Gary Carter	.15
681	Jeff Robinson	.15
682	Rick Leach	.05
683	Jose Cecena (R)	.15
684	Dave Johnson	.05
685	Jeff Treadway	.15
686	Scott Terry	.08
687	Alvin Davis	.08
688	Zane Smith	.05
689	Stan Jefferson	.08
690	Doug Jones	.05
691	Roberto Kelly	.25
692	Steve Ontiveros	.05

NO.	PLAYER	MINT
693	Pat Borders (R)	.15
694	Les Lancaster	.05
695	Carlton Fisk	.10
696	Don August	.10
697	Franklin Stubbs	.05
698	Keith Atherton	.05
699	Pedrique: Bonus	.05
700	Don Mattingly	.75
701	Storm Davis	.05
702	Jamie Quirk	.05
703	Scott Garrelts	.05
704	Carlos Quintana (R)	.35
705	Terry Kennedy	.05
706	Pete Incaviglia	.10
707	Steve Jeltz	.05
708	Chuck Finley	.05
709	Tom Herr	.05
710	Dave Cone	.25
711	Candy Sierra (R)	.15
712	Bill Swift	.05
713	Ty Griffin (R)	.75
714	Joe Morgan	.05
715	Tony Pena	.08
716	Wayne Tolleson	.05
717	Jamie Moyer	.05

NO.	PLAYER	MINT
718	Glenn Braggs	.05
719	Danny Darwin	.05
720	Tim Wallach	.08
721	Ron Tingley	.10
722	Todd Stottlemyre	.12
723	Rafael Belliard	.05
724	Jerry Don Gleaton	.05
725	Terry Steinbach	.12
726	Dickie Thon	.05
727	Joe Orsulak	.05
728	Charlie Puleo	.05
729	Buechele: Bonus	.05
730	Danny Jackson	.10
731	Mike Young	.05
732	Steve Buechele	.05
733	Randy Bockus (R)	.15
734	Jody Reed	.15
735	Roger McDowell	.05
736	Jeff Hamilton	.05
737	Norm Charlton (R)	.20
738	Darnell Coles	.05
739	Brook Jacoby	.05
740	Dan Plesac	.05
741	Ken Phelps	.05
742	Mike Harkey (R)	.35

NO.	PLAYER	MINT
743	Mike Heath	.05
744	Roger Craig	.05
745	Fred McGriff	.25
746	German Gonzalez (R)	.15
747	Wil Tejada	.10
748	Jimmy Jones	.05
749	Rafael Ramirez	.05
750	Bret Saberhagen	.10
751	Ken Oberkfell	.05
752	Jim Gott	.05
753	Jose Uribe	.05
754	Bob Brower	.05
755	Mike Scioscia	.05
756	Scott Medvin (R)	.15
757	Brady Anderson (R)	.25
758	Gene Walter	.05
759	Deer: Bonus	.05
760	Lee Smith	.08
761	Dante Bichette (R)	.20
762	Bobby Thigpen	.05
763	Dave Martinez	.05
764	Robin Ventura (R)	1.25
765	Glenn Davis	.10
766	Cecilio Guante	.05
767	Mike Capel (R)	.15

NO.	PLAYER	MINT
768	Bill Wegman	.05
769	Junior Ortiz	.05
770	Alan Trammell	.10
771	Ron Kittle	.08
772	Ron Oester	.05
773	Keith Moreland	.05
774	Frank Robinson	.08
775	Jeff Reardon	.08
776	Nelson Liriano	.05
777	Ted Power	.05
778	Bruce Benedict	.05
779	Craig McMurtry	.05
780	Pedro Guerrero	.15
781	Greg Briley (R)	.40
782	Checklist: 681-792	.08
783	Trevor Wilson (R)	.20
784	Steve Avery (R)	.40
785	Ellis Burks	.30
786	Melido Perez	.25
787	Dave West (R)	.40
788	Mike Morgan	.05
789	Jackson: Bonus	.08
790	Sid Fernandez	.10
791	Jim Lindeman	.05
792	Rafael Santana	.05

1989 Topps Traded.... Complete Set of 132 Cards—Value $15.00

Updates the main 1989 card set with players who changed teams during the season and rookies who joined their teams early in the season. Features the first Topps Card of Ken Griffey, Jr., Jerome Walton, Tom Gordon, Junior Felix and Dwight Smith. The complete set was packaged in a printed box and distributed primarily through card hobby dealers.

NO.	PLAYER	MINT
1	Don Aase	.05
2	Jim Abbott	1.25
3	Kent Anderson	.15
4	Keith Atherton	.05
5	Wally Backman	.05
6	Steve Balboni	.05
7	Jesse Barfield	.05
8	Steve Bedrosian	.05
9	Todd Benzinger	.05
10	Geronimo Berroa	.10
11	Bert Blyleven	.05
12	Bob Boone	.05
13	Phil Bradley	.05
14	Jeff Brantley	.25
15	Kevin Brown	.20
16	Jerry Browne	.05
17	Chuck Cary	.10
18	Carmen Castillo	.05
19	Jim Clancy	.05
20	Jack Clark	.10
21	Bryan Clutterbuck	.05
22	Jody Davis	.05
23	Mike Devereaux	.15
24	Frank DiPino	.05
25	Benny DiStefano	.05
26	John Dopson	.10
27	Len Dykstra	.05
28	Jim Eisenreich	.05
29	Nick Esasky	.10
30	Alvaro Espinoza	.10
31	Darrell Evans	.05
32	Junior Felix (RR)	1.00
33	Felix Fermin	.05

NO.	PLAYER	MINT
34	Julio Franco	.15
35	Terry Francona	.05
36	Cito Gaston	.05
37	Bob Geren	.50
38	Tom Gordon (RR)	1.25
39	Tommy Gregg	.15
40	Ken Griffey	.15
41	Ken Griffey, Jr. (RR)	3.50
42	Kevin Gross	.05
43	Lee Guetterman	.05
44	Mel Hall	.05
45	Erik Hanson	.20
46	Gene Harris	.25
47	Andy Hawkins	.05
48	Rickey Henderson	.30
49	Tom Herr	.05
50	Ken Hill	.20
51	Brian Holman	.25
52	Brian Holton	.05
53	Art Howe	.05
54	Ken Howell	.05
55	Bruce Hurst	.05
56	Chris James	.05
57	Randy Johnson	.10
58	Jimmy Jones	.05
59	Terry Kennedy	.05
60	Paul Kilgus	.05
61	Eric King	.05
62	Ron Kittle	.05
63	John Kruk	.05
64	Randy Kutcher	.05
65	Steve Lake	.05
66	Mark Langston	.25

NO.	PLAYER	MINT
67	Dave LaPoint	.05
68	Rick Leach	.05
69	Terry Leach	.05
70	Jim Levebvre	.05
71	Al Leiter	.05
72	Jeffrey Leonard	.05
73	Derek Lilliquist	.25
74	Rick Mahler	.05
75	Tom McCarthy	.20
76	Lloyd McClendon	.10
77	Lance McCullers	.05
78	Oddibe McDowell	.05
79	Roger McDowell	.05
80	Larry McWilliams	.05
81	Randy Milligan	.10
82	Mike Moore	.10
83	Keith Moreland	.05
84	Mike Morgan	.05
85	Jamie Moyer	.05
86	Rob Murphy	.05
87	Eddie Murray	.20
88	Pete O'Brien	.05
89	Gregg Olson	.60
90	Steve Ontiveros	.05
91	Jesse Orosco	.05
92	Spike Owen	.05
93	Rafael Palmeiro	.15
94	Clay Parker	.20
95	Jeff Parrtt	.05
96	Lance Parrish	.05
97	Dennis Powell	.05
98	Rey Quinones	.05
99	Doug Rader	.05

NO.	PLAYER	MINT
100	Willie Randolph	.05
101	Shane Rawley	.05
102	Randy Ready	.05
103	Bip Roberts	.05
104	Kenny Rogers	.15
105	Ed Romero	.05
106	Nolan Ryan	1.00
107	Luis Salazar	.05
108	Juan Samuel	.05
109	Alex Sanchez	.20
110	Deion Sanders (RR)	1.00
111	Steve Sax	.10
112	Rick Schu	.05
113	Dwight Smith (RR)	1.50
114	Lonnie Smith	.05
115	Billy Spiers	.40
116	Kent Tekulve	.05
117	Walt Terrell	.05
118	Milt Thompson	.05
119	Dickie Thon	.05
120	Jeff Torborg	.05
121	Jeff Treadway	.05
122	Omar Vizquel	.25
123	Jerome Walton (RR)	4.00
124	Gary Ward	.05
125	Claudell Washington	.05
126	Curt Wilkerson	.05
127	Eddie Williams	.05
128	Frank Williams	.05
129	Ken Williams	.05
130	Mitch Williams	.15
131	Steve Wilson	.15
132	Checklist	.05

1990 Topps.... Complete Set of 792 Cards—Value $25.00

The front of the cards feature six different color schemes. A card was issued to honor deceased Commissioner Giamatti. Four special cards were issued to honor Nolan Ryan—each card showed him with a different team. In a revised checklist format, the cards were listed by team.

NO. PLAYER	MINT	NO. PLAYER	MINT	NO. PLAYER	MINT	NO. PLAYER	MINT
1 Nolan Ryan	30	64 Danny Darwin	05	131 Matt Nokes	08	198 Mike Marshall	08
2 Nolan Ryan	20	65 Devon White	10	132 Lance Blankenship	08	199 Sergio Valdez (R)	15
Mets (1965 to 1971)		66 Greg Litton (R)	15	133 Ricky Horton	05	200 Don Mattingly	50
3 Nolan Ryan	20	67 Scott Sanderson	05	134 Earl Cunningham (R)	35	201 Cito Gaston (Mgr.)	05
Angels (1972 to 1979)		68 Dave Henderson	05	135 Dave Magadan	08	202 Mike MacFarlane	05
4 Nolan Ryan	20	69 Todd Frohwirth	05	136 Kevin Brown	08	203 Mike Roesler (R)	15
Astros (1980 to 1988)		70 Mike Greenwell	25	137 Marty Pevey (R)	15	204 Bob Dernier	05
5 Nolan Ryan	20	71 Allan Anderson	08	138 Al Leiter	05	205 Mark Davis	10
Rangers (1989)		72 Jeff Huson (R)	20	139 Greg Brock	05	206 Nick Esasky	05
6 '89 Record: V. Coleman	08	73 Bob Milacki	08	140 Andre Dawson	12	207 Bob Ojeda	05
7 '89 Record: R. Henderson	10	74 Jeff Jackson (R)	30	141 John Hart (Mgr.)	05	208 Brook Jacoby	05
8 '89 Record: C. Ripken	08	75 Doug Jones	05	142 Jeff Wetherby (R)	15	209 Greg Mathews	05
9 Eric Plunk	05	76 Dave Valle	05	143 Rafael Belliard	05	210 Ryne Sandberg	10
10 Barry Larking	08	77 Dave Bergman	05	144 Bud Black	05	211 John Cerutti	05
11 Paul Gibson	05	78 Mike Flanagan	05	145 Terry Steinbach	10	212 Joe Orsulak	05
12 Joe Girardi (R)	15	79 Ron Kittle	05	146 Rob Richie (R)	15	213 Scott Bankhead	05
13 Mark Williamson	05	80 Jeff Russell	05	147 Chuck Finley	08	214 Terry Francona	05
14 Mike Fetters (R)	15	81 Bob Rodgers	05	148 Edgar Martinez	05	215 Kirk McCaskill	08
15 Teddy Higuera	05	82 Scott Terry	05	149 Steve Farr	05	216 Ricky Jordan	25
16 Kent Anderson (R)	15	83 Hensley Meulens	20	150 Kirk Gibson	08	217 Don Robinson	05
17 Kelly Downs	08	84 Ray Searage	05	151 Rick Mahler	05	218 Wally Backman	05
18 Carlos Quintana	08	85 Jaun Samuel	08	152 Lonnie Smith	05	219 Donn Pall	05
19 Al Newman	05	86 Paul Kilgus	05	153 Randy Milligan	05	220 Barry Bonds	10
20 Mark Gubicza	05	87 Rick Luecken (R)	15	154 Mike Maddux	05	221 Gary Mielke (R)	15
21 Jeff Torborg	05	88 Glenn Braggs	05	155 Ellis Burks	20	222 Kurt Stillwell	05
22 Bruce Ruffin	05	89 Clint Zavaras (R)	12	156 Ken Patterson	05	223 Tommy Gregg	05
23 Randy Velarde	05	90 Jack Clark	08	157 Craig Biggio	10	224 Delino DeShields (R)	35
24 Joe Hesketh	05	91 Steve Frey (R)	15	158 Craig Lefferts	05	225 Jim Deshaies	05
25 Willie Randolph	08	92 Mike Stanley	05	159 Mike Felder	05	226 Mickey Hatcher	05
26 Don Slaught	05	93 Shawn Hillegas	05	160 Dave Righetti	10	227 Kevin Tapani (R)	20
27 Rick Leach	05	94 Herm Winningham	05	161 Harold Reynolds	05	228 Dave Martinez	05
28 Duane Ward	05	95 Todd Worrell	08	162 Todd Zeile (R)	1.25	229 David Wells	05
29 John Cangelosi	05	96 Jody Reed	05	163 Phil Bradley	08	230 Keith Hernandez	08
30 David Cone	12	97 Curt Schilling	10	164 Jeff Juden (R)	30	231 Jack McKeon (Mgr.)	05
31 Henry Cotto	05	98 Jose Gonzalez	05	165 Walt Weiss	10	232 Darnell Coles	05
32 John Farrell	08	99 Rich Monteleone	10	166 Bobby Witt	05	233 Ken Hill	08
33 Greg Walker	05	100 Will Clark	50	167 Kevin Appier (R)	15	234 Mariano Duncan	05
34 Tony Fossas (R)	15	101 Shane Rawley	05	168 Jose Lind	05	235 Jeff Reardon	08
35 Benny Santiago	10	102 Stan Javier	05	169 Richard Dotson	05	236 Hal Morris	05
36 John Costello	05	103 Marvin Freeman	05	170 George Bell	10	237 Kevin Ritz (R)	15
37 Domingo Ramos	05	104 Bob Knepper	05	171 Russ Nixon (Mgr.)	05	238 Felix Jose	05
38 Wes Gardner	05	105 Randy Myers	08	172 Tom Lampkin	05	239 Eric Show	05
39 Curt Ford	05	106 Charlie O'Brien	05	173 Tim Belcher	08	240 Mark Grace	25
40 Jay Howell	08	107 Fred Lynn	08	174 Jeff Kunkel	05	241 Mike Krukow	08
41 Matt Williams	12	108 Rod Nichols	05	175 Mike Moore	08	242 Fred Manrique	05
42 Jeff Robinson	08	109 Roberto Kelly	08	176 Luis Quinones	05	243 Barry Jones	05
43 Dante Bichette	05	110 Tommy Helms (Mgr.)	05	177 Mike Henneman	05	244 Bill Schroeder	05
44 Roger Salkeld (R)	25	111 Ed Whited (R)	15	178 Chris James	05	245 Roger Clemens	25
45 Dave Parker	10	112 Glenn Wilson	05	179 Brian Holton	05	246 Jim Eisenreich	05
46 Rob Dibble	10	113 Manny Lee	05	180 Rock Raines	12	247 Jerry Reed	05
47 Brian Harper	08	114 Mike Bielecki	05	181 Juan Agosto	05	248 Dave Anderson	05
48 Zane Smith	05	115 Tony Pena	08	182 Mookie Wilson	08	249 Mike Smith (R)	15
49 Tom Lawless	05	116 Floyd Bannister	05	183 Steve Lake	05	250 Jose Canseco	60
50 Glenn Davis	10	117 Mike Sharperson	05	184 Danny Cox	05	251 Jeff Blauser	05
51 Doug Rader	05	118 Eric Hanson	08	185 Ruben Sierra	20	252 Otis Nixon	05
52 Jack Daugherty (R)	15	119 Billy Hatcher	05	186 Dave LaPoint	05	253 Mark Portugal	05
53 Mike LaCoss	05	120 John Franco	08	187 Rick Wrona (R)	10	254 Francisco Cabrera (R)	15
54 Joel Skinner	05	121 Robin Ventura	30	188 Mike Smithson	05	255 Bobby Thigpen	05
55 Darrell Evans	05	122 Shawn Abner	05	189 Dick Schofield	05	256 Marvell Wynne	05
56 Franklin Stubbs	05	123 Rich Gedman	05	190 Rick Reuschel	08	257 Jose DeLeon	05
57 Greg Vaughn (R)	1.35	124 Dave Dravecky	05	191 Pat Borders	05	258 Barry Lyons	05
58 Keith Miller	05	125 Kent Hrbek	08	192 Don August	08	259 Lance McCullers	05
59 Ted Power	05	126 Randy Kramer	05	193 Andy Benes	25	260 Eric Davis	25
60 George Brett	15	127 Mike Deveraux	08	194 Glenallen Hill	15	261 Whitey Herzog (Mgr.)	05
61 Deion Sanders (R)	50	128 Checklist No. 1	05	195 Tim Burke	05	262 Checklist No. 2	05
62 Ramon Martinez	12	129 Ron Jones	05	196 Gerard Young	05	263 Mel Stottlemyre, Jr.	15
63 Mike Pagliarulo	08	130 Bert Blyleven	08	197 Doug Drabek	05	264 Bryan Clutterbuck	05

NO.	PLAYER	MINT
265	Pete O'Brien	.08
266	German Gonzalez	.05
267	Mark Davidson	.05
268	Rob Murphy	.05
269	Dickie Thon	.05
270	Dave Stewart	.10
271	Chet Lemon	.05
272	Bryan Harvey	.05
273	Bobby Bonilla	.10
274	Goose Gozzo (R)	.15
275	Mickey Tettleton	.05
276	Gary Thurman	.05
277	Lenny Harris	.05
278	Pascual Perez	.05
279	Steve Buechele	.05
280	Lou Whitaker	.08
281	Kevin Bass	.05
282	Derek Lilliquist	.08
283	Joey Belle (R)	.45
284	Mark Gardner (R)	.15
285	Willie McGee	.08
286	Lee Guetterman	.05
287	Vance Law	.05
288	Greg Briley	.05
289	Norm Charlton	.05
290	Robin Yount	.20
291	Dave Johnson (Mgr.)	.05
292	Jim Gott	.05
293	Mike Gallego	.05
294	Craig McMurtry	.05
295	Fred McGriff	.15
296	Jeff Ballard	.08
297	Tom Herr	.08
298	Danny Gladden	.05
299	Adam Petterson	.08
300	Bo Jackson	.50
301	Don Aase	.05
302	Marcus Lawton (R)	.20
303	Rick Cerone	.05
304	Marty Clary	.05
305	Eddie Murray	.10
306	Tom Niedenfuer	.05
307	Bip Roberts	.05
308	Jose Guzman	.05
309	Eric Yelding (R)	.10
310	Steve Bedrosian	.05
311	Dwight Smith	.65
312	Dan Quisenberry	.05
313	Gus Polidor	.05
314	Donald Harris (R)	.25
315	Bruce Hurst	.05
316	Carney Lansford	.08
317	Mark Guthrie (R)	.15
318	Wallace Johnson	.05
319	Dion James	.05
320	Dave Stieb	.05
321	Joe Morgan (Mgr.)	.05
322	Junior Ortiz	.05
323	Willie Wilson	.08
324	Pete Harnisch	.08
325	Robby Thompson	.10
326	Tom McCarthy (R)	.15
327	Ken Williams	.05
328	Curt Young	.05
329	Oddibe McDowell	.05
330	Ron Darling	.10
331	Juan Gonzalez (R)	.50
332	Paul O'Neill (R)	.15
333	Bill Wegman	.05
334	Johnny Ray	.08
335	Andy Hawkins	.05
336	Ken Griffey, Jr.	1.25
337	Lloyd McClendon	.05
338	Dannis Lamp	.05
339	Dave Clark	.05
340	Fernando Valenzuela	.10
341	Tom Foley	.05
342	Alex Trevino	.05
343	Frank Tanana	.05
344	George Canale (R)	.15
345	Harold Baines	.08
346	Jim Presley	.05
347	Junior Felix (R)	.30
348	Gary Wayne (R)	.10
349	Steve Finley (R)	.12
350	Bret Saberhagen	.10

NO.	PLAYER	MINT
351	Craig Roger (Mgr.)	.05
352	Bryn Smith	.05
353	Sandy Alomar	.30
354	Stan Belinda (R)	.15
355	Marty Barrett	.05
356	Randy Ready	.05
357	Dave West	.10
358	Andres Thomas	.05
359	Jimmy Jones	.05
360	Paul Molitor	.10
361	Randy McCament (R)	.15
362	Damon Berryhill	.08
363	Dan Petry	.05
364	Rolando Roomes	.08
365	Ozzie Guillen	.08
366	Mike Heath	.05
367	Mike Morgan	.05
368	Bill Doran	.05
369	Todd Burns	.05
370	Tim Wallach	.05
371	Jimmy Key	.08
372	Terry Kennedy	.05
373	Alvin Davis	.08
374	Steve Cummings (R)	.15
375	Dwight Evans	.08
376	Checklist No. 3	.05
377	Mickey Weston (R)	.15
378	Luis Salazar	.05
379	Steve Rosenburg	.05
380	Dave Winfield	.15
381	Frank Robinson (Mgr.)	.10
382	Jeff Mussleman	.05
383	John Morris	.05
384	Pat Combs (R)	.40
385	Fred McGriff (AS)	.12
386	Franco Julio (AS)	.08
387	Wade Boggs (AS)	.15
388	Cal Ripken (AS)	.12
389	Robin Yount (AS)	.15
390	Ruben Sierra (AS)	.15
391	Kirby Puckett (AS)	.20
392	Carlton Fisk (AS)	.10
393	Bret Saberhagen (AS)	.05
394	Jeff Ballard (AS)	.08
395	Jeff Russell (AS)	.05
396	A. Bartlett Giamatti Baseball Commissioner (deceased)	.50
397	Will Clark (AS)	.25
398	Ryne Sandberg (AS)	.10
399	Howard Johnson (AS)	.10
400	Ozzie Smith (AS)	.08
401	Kevin Mitchell (AS)	.15
402	Eric Davis (AS)	.15
403	Tony Gwynn (AS)	.15
404	Craig Biggio (AS)	.10
405	Mike Scott (AS)	.10
406	Joe Magrane (AS)	.10
407	Mark Davis (AS)	.10
408	Trevor Wilson (R)	.05
409	Tom Brunansky	.05
410	Jose Boever	.05
411	Ken Phelps	.05
412	Jamie Moyer	.05
413	Brian Dubois (R)	.15
414	Frank Thomas (R)	.35
415	Shawon Dunston	.08
416	Dave Johnson (R)	.12
417	Jim Gantner	.05
418	Tom Browning	.05
419	Beau Allred (R)	.20
420	Carlton Fisk	.10
421	Greg Minton	.05
422	Pat Sheridan	.05
423	Fred Toliver	.05
424	Jerry Reuss	.05
425	Bill Landrum	.05
426	Jeff Hamilton	.05
427	Carmen Castillo	.05
428	Steve Davis (R)	.15
429	Tom Kelly (Mgr.)	.05
430	Pete Incaviglia	.10
431	Randy Johnson	.08
432	Damaso Garcia	.05
433	Steve Olin (R)	.15
434	Mark Carreon	.05

NO.	PLAYER	MINT
435	Kevin Seitzer	.10
436	Mel Hall	.05
437	Les Lancaster	.05
438	Greg Myers	.05
439	Jeff Parrett	.05
440	Alan Trammell	.08
441	Bob Kipper	.05
442	Jerry Browne	.08
443	Cris Carpenter	.05
444	Kyle Abbott (R)	.20
445	Danny Jackson	.08
446	Dan Pasqua	.05
447	Atlee Hammaker	.05
448	Greg Gagne	.05
449	Dennis Rasmussen	.05
450	Rickey Henderson	.20
451	Mark Lemke	.05
452	Luis de los Santos	.10
453	Jody Davis	.05
454	Jeff King	.10
455	Jeffrey Leonard	.05
456	Chris Gwynn	.08
457	Gregg Jefferies	.35
458	Bob McClure	.05
459	Jim Lefebvre (Mgr.)	.05
460	Mike Scott	.08
461	Carlos Martinez (R)	.15
462	Denny Walling	.05
463	Drew Hall	.05
464	Jerome Walton	1.25
465	Kevin Gross	.05
466	Rance Mullniks	.05
467	Juan Nieves	.05
468	Billy Ripken	.08
469	John Kruk	.05
470	Frank Viola	.10
471	Mike Brumley	.05
472	Jose Uribe	.05
473	Joe Price	.05
474	Rich Thompson	.08
475	Bob Welch	.05
476	Brad Komminsk	.05
477	Willie Fraser	.05
478	Mike LaValliere	.05
479	Frank White	.05
480	Sid Fernandez	.08
481	Garry Templeton	.05
482	Steve Carter (R)	.15
483	Alejandro Pena	.05
484	Mike Fitzgerald	.05
485	John Candelaria	.05
486	Jeff Treadway	.05
487	Steve Searcy	.10
488	Ken Oberfell	.05
489	Nick Leyva (Mgr.)	.05
490	Dan Plesac	.05
491	Dave Cochrane (R)	.12
492	Ron Oester	.05
493	Jason Grimsley (R)	.15
494	Terry Puhl	.05
495	Lee Smith	.08
496	Cecil Espy	.05
497	Dave Schmidt	.08
498	Rick Schu	.05
499	Bill Long	.05
500	Kevin Mitchell	.25
501	Matt Young	.05
502	Mitch Webster	.05
503	Randy St. Claire	.05
504	Tom O'Malley	.05
505	Kelly Gruber	.08
506	Tom Glavine	.08
507	Gary Redus	.05
508	Terry Leach	.08
509	Tom Pagnozzi	.05
510	Doc Gooden	.20
511	Clay Parker	.05
512	Gary Pettis	.05
513	Mark Eichhorn	.05
514	Andy Allanson	.05
515	Lenny Dykstra	.05
516	Tim Leary	.05
517	Roberto Alomar	.10
518	Bill Krueger	.05
519	Bucky Dent (Mgr.)	.05
520	Mitch Williams	.08

NO.	PLAYER	MINT
521	Craig Worthington	.08
522	Mike Dunne	.05
523	Jay Bell	.05
524	Daryl Boston	.05
525	Wally Joyner	.10
526	Checklist No. 4	.05
527	Ron Hassey	.05
528	Kevin Wickander	.10
529	Greg Harris	.05
530	Mark Langston	.10
531	Ken Caminiti	.05
532	Cecilio Guante	.10
533	Tim Jones	.05
534	Louie Meadows	.05
535	John Smoltz	.08
536	Bob Geren (R)	.15
537	Mark Grant	.05
538	Billy Spiers (R)	.15
539	Neal Heaton	.05
540	Danny Tartabull	.10
541	Pat Perry	.05
542	Darren Daulton	.05
543	Nelson Liriano	.05
544	Dennis Boyd	.05
545	Kevin McReynolds	.10
546	Kevin Hickey (R)	.15
547	Jack Howell	.05
548	Pat Clements	.05
549	Don Zimmer (Mgr.)	.05
550	Julio Franco	.10
551	Tim Crews	.05
552	Mike Smith (R)	.15
553	Scott Scudder (R)	.10
554	Jay Buhner	.08
555	Jack Morris	.10
556	Gene Larkin	.05
557	Jeff Innis	.10
558	Rafael Ramirez	.05
559	Andy McGaffigan	.05
560	Steve Sax	.08
561	Ken Dayley	.05
562	Chad Kreuter	.05
563	Alex Sanchez	.10
564	Tyler Houston (R)	.45
565	Scott Fletcher	.05
566	Mark Knudson	.05
567	Ron Gant	.05
568	John Smiley	.08
569	Ivan Calderon	.05
570	Cal Ripken	.12
571	Brett Butler	.05
572	Greg Harris	.05
573	Danny Heep	.05
574	Bill Swift	.05
575	Lance Parrish	.08
576	Mike Dyer (R)	.15
577	Charlie Hayes	.05
578	Joe Magrane	.10
579	Art Howe (Mgr.)	.05
580	Joe Carter	.10
581	Ken Griffey	.05
582	Rick Honeycutt	.05
583	Bruce Benedict	.05
584	Phil Stephenson (R)	.10
585	Kal Daniels	.10
586	Ed Nunez	.05
587	Lance Johnson	.05
588	Rick Rhoden	.05
589	Mike Aldrete	.05
590	Ozzie Smith	.08
591	Todd Stottlemyre	.10
592	R.J. Reynolds	.05
593	Scott Bradley	.05
594	Luis Sojo (R)	.20
595	Greg Swindell	.10
596	Jose DeJesus	.05
597	Chris Bosio	.05
598	Brady Anderson	.05
599	Frank Williams	.05
600	Darryl Strawberry	.30
601	Luis Rivera	.05
602	Scott Garrelts	.08
603	Tony Armas	.05
604	Ron Robinson	.05
605	Mike Scioscia	.08
606	Storm Davis	.05

NO.	PLAYER	MINT
607	Steve Jeltz	.05
608	Eric Anthony (R)	1.50
609	Sparky Anderson (Mgr.)	.05
610	Pedro Guerrero	.10
611	Walt Terrell	.05
612	Dave Gallagher	.05
613	Jeff Pico	.05
614	Nelson Santovenia	.05
615	Rob Deer	.05
616	Brian Holman	.05
617	Geronimo Berroa	.05
618	Eddie Whitson	.05
619	Rob Ducey	.07
620	Tony Castillo	.10
621	Melido Perez	.05
622	Sid Bream	.05
623	Jim Corsi	.05
624	Darrin Jackson	.05
625	Roger McDowell	.05
626	Bob Melvin	.05
627	Jose Rojo	.05
628	Candy Maldonado	.05
629	Eric Hetzel	.05
630	Gary Gaetti	.10
631	John Wetteland (R)	.05
632	Scott Lusader	.05
633	Dennis Cook	.10
634	Luis Polonia	.05
635	Brian Downing	.05
636	Jesse Orosco	.05
637	Craig Reynolds	.05
638	Jeff Montgomery	.08
639	Tony LaRussa (Mgr.)	.05
640	Rick Sutcliffe	.05
641	Doug Strange (R)	.15
642	Jack Armstrong	.05
643	Alfredo Griffin	.08
644	Paul Assenmacher	.05
645	Jose Oquendo	.05
646	Checklist No. 5	.05
647	Rex Hudler	.05
648	Jim Clancy	.05
649	Dan Murphy (R)	.12
650	Mike Witt	.08
651	Rafael Santana	.05
652	Mike Boddicker	.08
653	John Moses	.05
654	Paul Coleman (R)	.30

NO.	PLAYER	MINT
655	Gregg Olson	.20
656	Mackey Sasser	.05
657	Terry Mulholland	.05
658	Donell Nixon	.05
659	Greg Cadaret	.05
660	Vince Coleman	.08
661	Turn Back Clock—1985 Dick Howser	.08
662	Turn Back Clock—1980 Mike Schmidt	.12
663	Turn Back Clock—1975 Fred Lynn	.08
664	Turn Back Clock—1970 Johnny Bench	.08
665	Turn Back Clock—1965 Sandy Koufax	.08
666	Brian Fisher	.05
667	Curt Wilkerson	.05
668	Joe Oliver (R)	.15
669	Tom Lasorda (Mgr.)	.05
670	Dennis Eckersley	.08
671	Bob Boone	.05
672	Roy Smith	.05
673	Joey Meyer	.05
674	Spike Owen	.05
675	Jim Abbott	.40
676	Randy Kutcher	.05
677	Jay Tibbs	.05
678	Kirt Manwaring	.05
679	Gary Ward	.05
680	Howard Johnson	.10
681	Mike Schooler	.10
682	Dann Bilardello	.05
683	Kenny Rogers (R)	.15
684	Julio Machado (R)	.15
685	Tony Fernandez	.10
686	Carmelo Martinez	.05
687	Tim Birtsas	.05
688	Milt Thompson	.05
689	Rich Yett	.05
690	Mark McGwire	.30
691	Chuck Cary	.05
692	Sammy Sosa (R)	.40
693	Calvin Schiraldi	.05
694	Mike Stanton (R)	.15
695	Tom Henke	.05
696	B.J. Surhoff	.05
697	Mike Davis	.05

NO.	PLAYER	MINT
698	Omar Vizquel (R)	.20
699	Jim Leyland (Mgr.)	.05
700	Kirby Puckett	.20
701	Bernie Williams (R)	.40
702	Tony Phillips	.05
703	Jeff Brantley (R)	.15
704	Chip Hale (R)	.15
705	Claudell Washington	.05
706	Geno Petralli	.05
707	Luis Aquino	.05
708	Larry Sheets	.05
709	Juan Berenguer	.05
710	Von Hayes	.08
711	Rick Aguilera	.05
712	Todd Benzinger	.05
713	Tim Drummond (R)	.15
714	Marquis Grissom (R)	.40
715	Greg Maddux	.12
716	Steve Balboni	.05
717	Ron Karkovice	.05
718	Gary Sheffield	.25
719	Wally Whitehurst (R)	.15
720	Andres Galarraga	.10
721	Lee Mazzilli	.05
722	Felix Fermin	.05
723	Jeff Robinson	.08
724	Jaun Bell	.15
725	Terry Pendleton	.05
726	Gene Nelson	.05
727	Pat Tabler	.05
728	Jim Acker	.05
729	Bobby Valentine (Mgr.)	.05
730	Tony Gwynn	.15
731	Don Carman	.05
732	Ernie Riles	.05
733	John Dobson	.08
734	Kevin Elster	.08
735	Charlie Hough	.05
736	Rick Dempsey	.05
737	Chris Sabo	.10
738	Gene Harris (R)	.15
739	Dale Sveum	.05
740	Jesse Barfield	.05
741	Steve Wilson	.10
742	Ernie Whitt	.05
743	Tom Candiotti	.05
744	Kelly Mann (R)	.15
745	Hubie Brooks	.05

NO.	PLAYER	MINT
746	Dave Smith	.08
747	Randy Bush	.05
748	Doyle Alexander	.08
749	Mark Parent	.05
750	Dale Murphy	.12
751	Steve Lyons	.05
752	Tom Gordon	.50
753	Chris Speier	.05
754	Bob Walk	.05
755	Rafael Palmeiro	.10
756	Ken Howell	.05
757	Larry Walker (R)	.25
758	Mark Thurmond	.05
759	Tom Trebelhorn (Mgr.)	.05
760	Wade Boggs	.30
761	Mike Jackson	.05
762	Doug Dascenzo	.05
763	Denny Martinez	.05
764	Tim Teufel	.05
765	Chili Davis	.05
766	Brian Meyer	.10
767	Tracy Jones	.05
768	Chuck Crim	.05
769	Greg Hibbard (R)	.15
770	Cory Snyder (R)	.10
771	Pete Smith	.05
772	Jeff Reed	.05
773	Dave Leiper	.05
774	Ben McDonald (R)	1.50
775	Andy Van Slyke	.10
776	Charlie Leibrandt	.08
777	Tim Laudner	.05
778	Mike Jeffcoat	.05
779	Lloyd Moseby	.08
780	Orel Hershiser	.12
781	Mario Diaz	.05
782	Jose Alvarez	.05
783	Checklist No. 6	.05
784	Scott Bailes	.05
785	Jim Rice	.10
786	Eric King	.05
787	Rene Gonzales	.05
788	Frank DiPino	.05
789	John Wathan (Mgr.)	.05
790	Gary Carter	.08
791	Alvaro Espinoza	.05
792	Gerald Perry	.05

1981 Donruss.... Complete Set of 605 Cards (1st printing)— Value $30.00; Complete Set of 605 Cards (2nd printing)—Value $25.00

This was Donruss' *first* baseball card set. Over 35 cards contained *errors*; they were corrected in the 2nd printing run. There is very little interest by collectors in the *variety* (error) cards; none are scarce or worth much more than ordinary cards. If a *variety* (error) is significant, it is listed and explained; if it is *minor*, it is noted by an *asterisk*. This set features the rookie cards of Tim Raines and Leon Durham. The 2½"x3½" cards were printed on thinner than usual paper stock. The checklist *cards* are *not* numbered.

MOOKIE WILSON SHORTSTOP

JEFF REARDON PITCHER

LEON DURHAM INFIELD-O.F.

JOHN TUDOR PITCHER

TIM RAINES SECOND BASE

NO. PLAYER	MINT
1 Ozzie Smith	.60
2 Rollie Fingers	.30
3 Rick Wise	.05
4 Gene Richards	.05
5 Alan Trammell	.40
6 Tom Brookens	.05
7 Duffy Dyer*	.05
8 Mark Fidrych	.08
9 Dave Rozema	.05
10 Ricky Peters	.05
11 Mike Schmidt	1.00
12 Willie Stargell	.40
13 Tim Foli	.05
14 Manny Sanguillen	.05
15 Grant Jackson	.05
16 Eddie Solomon	.05
17 Omar Moreno	.05
18 Joe Morgan	.35
19 Rafael Landestoy	.05
20 Bruce Bochy	.05
21 Joe Sambito	.05
22 Manny Trillo	.05
23 Dave Smith* (R)	.25
24 Terry Puhl	.05
25 Bump Wills	.05
26 John Ellis (error)	.50
(photo of Danny Walten)	
26 John Ellis (correct)	.10
27 Jim Kern	.05
28 Richie Zisk	.05
29 John Mayberry	.05
30 Bob Davis	.05
31 Jackson Todd	.05
32 Al Woods	.05
33 Steve Carlton	.60
34 Lee Mazzilli	.05
35 John Stearns	.05
36 Roy Jackson	.08
37 Mike Scott	.75
38 Lamar Johnson	.05
39 Kevin Bell	.05
40 Ed Farmer	.05
41 Ross Baumgarten	.05
42 Leo Sutherland	.05
43 Danny Meyer	.05
44 Ron Reed	.05
45 Mario Mendoza	.05
46 Rick Honeycutt	.05
47 Glenn Abbott	.05
48 Leon Roberts	.05
49 Rod Carew	.50
50 Bert Campaneris	.05
51 Tom Donahue	.10
52 Dave Frost	.05
53 Ed Halicki	.05
54 Dan Ford	.05
55 Garry Maddox	.05
56 Steve Garvey*	.65
57 Bill Russell	.05
58 Don Sutton	.25
59 Reggie Smith	.10
60 Rick Monday	.05
61 Ray Knight	.05
62 Johnny Bench	.75
63 Mario Soto	.15
64 Doug Bair	.05

NO. PLAYER	MINT
65 George Foster	.25
66 Jeff Burroughs	.05
67 Keith Hernandez	.40
68 Tommy Herr	.15
69 Bob Forsch	.05
70 John Fulgham	.05
71 Bobby Bonds*	.12
72 Rennie Stennett*	.10
73 Joe Strain	.05
74 Ed Whitson	.10
75 Tom Griffin	.05
76 Bill North	.05
77 Gene Garber	.05
78 Mike Hargrove	.05
79 Dave Rosello	.05
80 Ron Hassey	.05
81 Sid Monge	.05
82 Joe Charboneau*	.10
83 Cecil Cooper	.25
84 Sal Bando	.05
85 Moose Haas	.05
86 Mike Caldwell	.05
87 Larry Hisle*	.10
88 Luis Gomez	.05
89 Larry Parrish	.10
90 Gary Carter	.50
91 Bill Gullickson (R)	.30
92 Fred Norman	.05
93 Tom Hutton	.05
94 Carl Yastrzemski	.75
95 Glenn Hoffman	.08
96 Dennis Eckersley	.05
97 Tom Burgmeier*	.10
98 Win Remmerswaal	.05
99 Bob Horner	.25
100 George Brett	.75
101 Dave Chalk	.05
102 Dennis Leonard	.05
103 Renie Martin	.05
104 Amos Otis	.05
105 Graig Nettles	.15
106 Eric Soderholm	.05
107 Tommy John	.20
108 Tom Underwood	.05
109 Lou Piniella	.15
110 Mickey Klutts	.05
111 Bobby Murcer	.10
112 Eddie Murray	.75
113 Rick Dempsey	.05
114 Scott McGregor	.05
115 Ken Singleton	.05
116 Gary Roenicke	.05
117 Dave Revering	.05
118 Mike Norris	.05
119 Rickey Henderson	1.25
120 Mike Heath	.05
121 Dave Cash	.05
122 Randy Jones	.05
123 Eric Rasmussen	.05
124 Jerry Mumphrey	.05
125 Richie Hebner	.05
126 Mark Wagner	.05
127 Jack Morris	.30
128 Dan Petry	.25
129 Bruce Robbins	.05
130 Champ Summers	.05

NO. PLAYER	MINT
131 Pete Rose*	1.50
132 Willie Stargell	.30
133 Ed Ott	.05
134 Jim Bibby	.05
135 Bert Blyleven	.10
136 Dave Parker	.40
137 Bill Robinson	.05
138 Enos Cabell	.05
139 Dave Bergman	.05
140 J.R. Richard	.05
141 Ken Forsch	.05
142 Larry Bowa	.05
143 Frank LaCorte	.05
144 Dennis Walling	.05
145 Buddy Bell	.10
146 Ferguson Jenkins	.10
147 Danny Darwin	.05
148 Johnny Grubb	.05
149 Alfredo Griffin	.05
150 Jerry Garvin	.05
151 Paul Mirabella	.05
152 Rick Bosetti	.05
153 Dick Ruthven	.05
154 Frank Taveras	.05
155 Craig Swan	.05
156 Jeff Reardon (R)	.60
157 Steve Henderson	.05
158 Jim Morrison	.05
159 Glenn Borgmann	.05
160 LaMarr Hoyt	.20
161 Rich Wortham	.05
162 Thad Bosley	.05
163 Julio Cruz	.05
164 Del Unser*	.05
165 Jim Anderson	.05
166 Jim Beattie	.05
167 Shane Rawley	.05
168 Joe Simpson	.05
169 Rod Carew	.50
170 Freddie Patek	.05
171 Frank Tanana	.05
172 Alfredo Martinez	.05
173 Chris Knapp	.05
174 Joe Rudi	.05
175 Greg Luzinski	.10
176 Steve Garvey	.50
177 Joe Ferguson	.05
178 Bob Welch	.05
179 Dusty Baker	.10
180 Rudy Law	.05
181 Dave Concepcion	.15
182 Johnny Bench	.75
183 Mike LaCoss	.05
184 Ken Griffey	.10
185 Dave Collins	.05
186 Brian Asselstine	.05
187 Garry Templeton	.10
188 Mike Phillips	.05
189 Pete Vuckovich	.08
190 John Urrea	.05
191 Tony Scott	.05
192 Darrell Evans	.10
193 Milt May	.05
194 Bob Knepper	.05
195 Randy Moffitt	.05
196 Larry Herndon	.05

NO. PLAYER	MINT
197 Rick Camp	.05
198 Andre Thornton	.10
199 Tom Veryzer	.05
200 Gary Alexander	.05
201 Rick Waits	.05
202 Rick Manning	.05
203 Paul Molitor	.25
204 Jim Gantner	.05
205 Paul Mitchell	.05
206 Reggie Cleveland	.05
207 Sixto Lezcano	.05
208 Bruce Benedict	.05
209 Rodney Scott	.05
210 John Tamargo	.05
211 Bill Lee	.05
212 Andre Dawson	.40
213 Rowland Office	.05
214 Carl Yastrzemski	.75
215 Jerry Remy	.05
216 Mike Torrez	.05
217 Skip Lockwood	.05
218 Fred Lynn	.25
219 Chris Chambliss	.08
220 Willie Aikens	.05
221 John Wathan	.05
222 Dan Quisenberry	.30
223 Willie Wilson	.15
224 Clint Hurdle	.05
225 Bob Watson	.05
226 Jim Spencer	.05
227 Ron Guidry	.25
228 Reggie Jackson	.75
229 Oscar Gamble	.05
230 Jeff Cox	.05
231 Luis Tiant	.05
232 Rich Dauer	.05
233 Dan Graham	.05
234 Mike Flanagan	.05
235 John Lowenstein	.05
236 Benny Ayala	.05
237 Wayne Gross	.05
238 Rick Langford	.05
239 Tony Armas	.20
240 Bob Lacey*	.10
241 Gene Tenace	.05
242 Bob Shirley	.05
243 Gary Lucas	.05
244 Jerry Turner	.05
245 John Wockenfuss	.05
246 Stan Papi	.05
247 Milt Wilcox	.05
248 Dan Schatzeder	.05
249 Steve Kemp	.08
250 Jim Lentine	.05
251 Pete Rose	1.25
252 Bill Madlock	.25
253 Dale Berra	.05
254 Kent Tekulve	.05
255 Enrique Romo	.05
256 Mike Easler	.05
257 Chuck Tanner (Mgr.)	.05
258 Art Howe	.05
259 Alan Ashby	.05
260 Nolan Ryan	1.00
261 Vern Ruhle (error)	.50
(Photo of Ken Forsch)	

NO.	PLAYER	MINT
261	Vern Ruhle (correct)	.10
262	Bob Boone	.08
263	Cesar Cedeno	.08
264	Jeff Leonard	.15
265	Pat Putnam	.05
266	John Matlack	.05
267	Dave Rajsich	.05
268	Billy Sample	.05
269	Damaso Garcia (R)	.30
270	Tom Buskey	.05
271	Joey McLaughlin	.05
272	Barry Bonnell	.05
273	Tug McGraw	.08
274	Mike Jorgensen	.05
275	Pat Zachry	.05
276	Neil Allen	.05
277	Joel Youngblood	.05
278	Greg Pryor	.05
279	Britt Burns (R)	.25
280	Rich Dotson (R)	.40
281	Chet Lemon	.10
282	Rusty Kuntz	.05
283	Ted Cox	.05
284	Sparky Lyle	.08
285	Larry Cox	.05
286	Floyd Bannister	.05
287	Byron McLaughlin	.05
288	Rodney Craig	.05
289	Bob Grich	.08
290	Dickie Thon	.10
291	Mark Clear	.05
292	Dave Lemanczyk	.05
293	Jason Thompson	.05
294	Rick Miller	.05
295	Lonnie Smith	.08
296	Ron Cey	.15
297	Steve Yeager	.05
298	Bobby Castillo	.05
299	Manny Mota	.05
300	Jay Johnstone	.05
301	Dan Driessen	.05
302	Joe Nolan	.05
303	Paul Householder	.08
304	Harry Spilman	.05
305	Cesar Geronimo	.05
306	Gary Matthews*	.10
307	Ken Reitz	.05
308	Ted Simmons	.10
309	John Littlefield	.05
310	George Frazier	.05
311	Dane Iorg	.05
312	Mike Ivie	.05
313	Dennis Littlejohn	.05
314	Gary LaVelle	.05
315	Jack Clark	.35
316	Jim Wohlford	.05
317	Rick Matula	.05
318	Toby Harrah	.05
319	Duane Kuiper*	.10
320	Len Barker	.05
321	Victor Cruz	.05
322	Dell Alston	.05
323	Robin Yount	.50
324	Charlie Moore	.05
325	Lary Sorensen	.05
326	Gorman Thomas*	.15
327	Bob Rodgers	.05
328	Phil Niekro	.30
329	Chris Speier	.05
330	Steve Rogers*	.10
331	Woodie Fryman	.05
332	Warren Cromartie	.05
333	Jerry White	.05
334	Tony Perez	.20
335	Carlton Fisk	.30
336	Dick Drago	.05
337	Steve Renko	.05
338	Jim Rice	.40
339	Jerry Royster	.05
340	Frank White	.05
341	Jamie Quirk	.05
342	Paul Splittorff*	.05
343	Marty Pattin	.05
344	Pete LaCock	.05
345	Willie Randolph	.10
346	Rick Cerone	.05
347	Rich Gossage	.25
348	Reggie Jackson	.75
349	Ruppert Jones	.05
350	Dave McKay	.05
351	Yogi Berra	.20
352	Doug DeCinces	.15
353	Jim Palmer	.30
354	Tippy Martinez	.05
355	Al Bumbry	.05
356	Earl Weaver (Mgr.)	.10
357	Rob Picciolo*	.10
358	Matt Keough	.05
359	Dwayne Murphy	.05
360	Brian Kingman	.05
361	Bill Fahey	.05
362	Steve Mura	.05
363	Dennis Kinney	.05
364	Dave Winfield	.50
365	Lou Whitaker	.30
366	Lance Parrish	.25
367	Tim Corcoran	.05
368	Pat Underwood	.05
369	Al Cowens	.05
370	Sparky Anderson (Mgr.)	.05
371	Pete Rose	1.25
372	Phil Garner	.05
373	Steve Nicosia	.05
374	John Candelaria	.05
375	Don Robinson	.05
376	Lee Lacy	.05
377	John Milner	.05
378	Craig Reynolds	.05
379	Luis Pujols*	.10
380	Joe Niekro	.10
381	Joaquin Andujar	.15
382	Keith Moreland (R)	.40
383	Jose Cruz	.15
384	Bill Virdon (Mgr.)	.05
385	Jim Sundberg	.05
386	Doc Medich	.05
387	Al Oliver	.15
388	Jim Norris	.05
389	Bob Bailor	.05
390	Ernie Whitt	.05
391	Otto Velez	.05
392	Roy Howell	.05
393	Bob Walk	.20
394	Doug Flynn	.05
395	Pete Falcone	.05
396	Tom Hausman	.05
397	Elliott Maddox	.05
398	Mike Squires	.05
399	Marvis Foley	.05
400	Steve Trout	.05
401	Wayne Nordhagen	.05
402	Tony LaRussa (Mgr.)	.05
403	Bruce Bochte	.05
404	Bake McBride	.05
405	Jerry Narron	.05
406	Rob Dressler	.05
407	Dave Heaverlo	.05
408	Tom Paciorek	.05
409	Carney Lansford	.15
410	Brian Downing	.05
411	Don Aase	.05
412	Jim Barr	.05
413	Don Baylor	.25
414	Jim Fregosi (Mgr.)	.05
415	Dallas Green (Mgr.)	.05
416	Dave Lopes	.10
417	Jerry Reuss	.05
418	Rick Sutcliffe	.35
419	Derrel Thomas	.05
420	Tommy Lasorda (Mgr.)	.15
421	Charlie Leibrandt (R)	.35
422	Tom Seaver	.40
423	Ron Oester	.05
424	Junior Kennedy	.05
425	Tom Seaver	.40
426	Bobby Cox (Mgr.)	.05
427	Leon Durham (R)	.40
428	Terry Kennedy	.10
429	Silvio Martinez	.05
430	George Hendrick	.05
431	R. Schoendienst (Mgr.)	.05
432	John LeMaster	.05
433	Vida Blue	.05
434	John Montefusco	.05
435	Terry Whitfield	.05
436	Dave Bristol (Mgr.)	.05
437	Dale Murphy	1.25
438	Jerry Dybzinski	.05
439	Jorge Orta	.05
440	Wayne Garland	.05
441	Miguel Dilone	.05
442	Dave Garcia (Mgr.)	.05
443	Don Money	.05
444	Buck Martinez*	.10
445	Jerry Augustine	.05
446	Ben Oglivie	.10
447	Jim Slaton	.05
448	Doyle Alexander	.05
449	Tony Bernazard	.05
450	Scott Sanderson	.05
451	Dave Palmer	.05
452	Stan Bahnsen	.05
453	Dick Williams (Mgr.)	.05
454	Rick Burleson	.05
455	Gary Allenson	.05
456	Bob Stanley	.05
457	John Tudor (R)	.75
458	Dwight Evans	.15
459	Glenn Hubbard	.05
460	U.L. Washington	.05
461	Larry Gura	.05
462	Rich Gale	.05
463	Hal McRae	.05
464	Jim Frey (Mgr.)	.05
465	Bucky Dent	.05
466	Dennis Werth	.05
467	Ron Davis	.05
468	Reggie Jackson	.75
469	Bobby Brown	.05
470	Mike Davis (R)	.30
471	Gaylord Perry	.30
472	Mark Belanger	.05
473	Jim Palmer	.30
474	Sammy Stewart	.05
475	Tim Stoddard	.05
476	Steve Stone	.05
477	Jeff Newman	.05
478	Steve McCatty	.05
479	Billy Martin (Mgr.)	.15
480	Mitchell Page	.05
481	S. Carlton (Cy Young)	.35
482	Bill Buckner	.15
483	Ivan DeJesus*	.10
484	Cliff Johnson	.05
485	Lenny Randle	.05
486	Larry Milbourne	.05
487	Roy Smalley	.05
488	John Castino	.05
489	Ron Jackson	.05
490	Dave Roberts*	.05
491	George Brett (MVP)	.60
492	Mike Cubbage	.05
493	Rob Wilfong	.05
494	Danny Goodwin	.05
495	Jose Morales	.05
496	Mickey Rivers	.05
497	Mike Edwards	.05
498	Mike Sadek	.05
499	Lenn Sakata	.05
500	Gene Michael (Mgr.)	.05
501	Dave Roberts	.05
502	Steve Dillard	.05
503	Jim Essian	.05
504	Rance Mulliniks	.05
505	Darrell Porter	.10
506	Joe Torre (Mgr.)	.05
507	Terry Crowley	.05
508	Bill Travers	.05
509	Nelson Norman	.05
510	Bob McClure	.05
511	Steve Howe (R)	.15
512	Dave Rader	.05
513	Mick Kelleher	.05
514	Kiko Garcia	.05
515	Larry Biittner	.05
516	Willie Norwood*	.05
517	Bo Diaz	.10
518	Juan Beniqez	.05
519	Scot Thompson	.05
520	Jim Tracy	.05
521	Carlos Lezcano	.05
522	Joe Amalfitano	.05
523	Preston Hanna	.05
524	Ray Burris*	.10
525	Broderick Perkins	.05
526	Mickey Hatcher	.05
527	John Goryl (Mgr.)	.05
528	Dick Davis	.05
529	Butch Wynegar	.05
530	Sal Butera	.05
531	Jerry Koosman	.05
532	Jeff Zahn*	.10
533	Dennis Martinez	.05
534	Gary Thomasson	.05
535	Steve Macko	.05
536	Jim Kaat	.15
537	Best Hitters: George Brett, Rod Carew	1.00
538	Tim Raines (R)	5.00
539	Keith Smith	.05
540	Ken Macha	.05
541	Burt Hooton	.05
542	Butch Hobson	.05
543	Bill Stein	.05
544	Dave Stapleton (R)	.15
545	Bob Pate	.05
546	Doug Corbett	.08
547	Darrell Jackson	.05
548	Pete Redfern	.05
549	Roger Erickson	.05
550	Al Hrabosky	.05
551	Dick Tidrow	.05
552	Dave Ford	.05
553	Dave Kingman	.15
554	Mike Vail*	.10
555	Jerry Martin*	.10
556	Jesus Figueroa*	.10
557	Don Stanhouse	.05
558	Barry Foote	.05
559	Tim Blackwell	.05
560	Bruce Sutter	.25
561	Rick Reuschel	.05
562	Lynn McGlothen	.05
563	Bob Owchinko*	.10
564	John Verhoeven	.05
565	Ken Landreaux	.05
566	Glenn Adams*	.10
567	Hosken Powell	.05
568	Dick Noles	.05
569	Danny Ainge (R)	.30
570	Bobby Mattick (Mgr.)	.05
571	Joe LeFebvre (R)	.15
572	Bobby Clark	.05
573	Dennis Lamp	.05
574	Randy Lerch	.05
575	Mookie Wilson (R)	.60
576	Ron LeFlore	.05
577	Jim Dwyer	.05
578	Bill Castro	.05
579	Greg Minton	.05
580	Mark Littell	.05
581	Andy Hassler	.05
582	Dave Stieb	.25
583	Ken Oberkfell	.05
584	Larry Bradford	.05
585	Fred Stanley	.05
586	Bill Caudill	.10
587	Doug Capilla	.05
588	George Riley	.05
589	Willie Hernandez	.20
590	Mike Schmidt (MVP)	.50
591	Steve Stone (Cy Young)	.10
592	Rick Sofield	.05
593	Bombo Rivera	.05
594	Gary Ward	.05
595	Dave Edwards*	.10
596	Mike Proly	.05
597	Tommy Boggs	.05
598	Greg Gross	.05
599	Elias Sosa	.05
600	Pat Kelly	.05
—	Checklist No. 1*	.10
—	Checklist No. 2	.10
—	Checklist No. 3*	.10
—	Checklist No. 4*	.10
—	Checklist No. 5*	.10

1982 Donruss.... Complete Set of 660 Cards—Value $35.00

Features the rookie cards of Cal Ripken, George Bell and Dave Stewart. Several errors were corrected; none are scarce or worth much more than ordinary cards. If a *variety* (error) is significant, it is listed and explained; if it is minor, it is noted by an *asterisk*. The *checklist* cards are *not* numbered.

NO. PLAYER	MINT	NO. PLAYER	MINT	NO. PLAYER	MINT	NO. PLAYER	MINT
No. 1 to 26—Diamond Kings		66 Bruce Kison	.05	132 Gorman Thomas	.15	198 Duane Kuiper	.05
1 Pete Rose (DK)	1.25	67 Wayne Nordhagen	.05	133 Dan Petry	.15	199 Rick Cerone	.05
2 Gary Carter (DK)	.50	68 Woodie Fryman	.05	134 Bob Stanley	.05	200 Jim Rice	.30
3 Steve Garvey (DK)	.50	69 Billy Sample	.05	135 Lou Piniella	.10	201 Steve Yeager	.05
4 Vida Blue (DK)	.10	70 Amos Otis	.10	136 Pedro Guerrero	.35	202 Tom Brookens	.05
5 Alan Trammell* (DK)	.30	71 Matt Keough	.05	137 Len Barker	.05	203 Jose Morales	.05
6 Len Barker (DK)	.10	72 Toby Harrah	.05	138 Richard Gale	.05	204 Roy Howell	.05
7 Dwight Evans (DK)	.15	73 Dave Righetti (R)	1.50	139 Wayne Gross	.05	205 Tippy Martinez	.05
8 Rod Carew (DK)	.40	74 Carl Yastrzemski	.75	140 Tim Wallach (R)	1.00	206 Moose Haas	.05
9 George Hendrick (DK)	.10	75 Bob Welch	.10	141 Gene Mauch	.05	207 Al Cowens	.05
10 Phil Niekro (DK)	.25	76 Alan Trammell*	.35	142 Doc Medich	.05	208 Dave Stapleton	.05
11 Richie Zisk (DK)	.10	77 Rick Dempsey	.05	143 Tony Bernazard	.05	209 Bucky Dent	.05
12 Dave Parker (DK)	.30	78 Paul Molitor	.30	144 Bill Virdon (Mgr.)	.05	210 Ron Cey	.15
13 Nolan Ryan (DK)	.75	79 Dennis Martinez	.05	145 John Littlefield	.05	211 Jorge Orta	.05
14 Ivan DeJesus (DK)	.10	80 Jim Slaton	.05	146 Dave Bergman	.05	212 Jamie Quirk	.05
15 George Brett (DK)	.75	81 Champ Summers	.05	147 Dick Davis	.05	213 Jeff Jones	.05
16 Tom Seaver (DK)	.50	82 Carney Lansford	.10	148 Tom Seaver	.50	214 Tim Raines	.75
17 Dave Kingman (DK)	.10	83 Barry Foote	.05	149 Matt Sinatro	.07	215 Jon Matlack	.05
18 Dave Winfield (DK)	.50	84 Steve Garvey	.50	150 Chuck Tanner (Mgr.)	.05	216 Rod Carew	.45
19 Mike Norris (DK)	.10	85 Rick Manning	.05	151 Leon Durham	.25	217 Jim Kaat	.10
20 Carlton Fisk (DK)	.25	86 John Wathan	.05	152 Gene Tenace	.05	218 Joe Pittman	.05
21 Ozzie Smith (DK)	.15	87 Brian Kingman	.05	153 Al Bumbry	.05	219 Larry Christenson	.05
22 Roy Smalley (DK)	.10	88 Andre Dawson	.40	154 Mark Brouhard	.05	220 Juan Bonilla	.07
23 Buddy Bell (DK)	.10	89 Jim Kern	.05	155 Rick Peters	.05	221 Mike Easler	.05
24 Ken Singleton (DK)	.10	90 Bobby Grich	.05	156 Jerry Remy	.05	222 Vida Blue	.05
25 John Mayberry (DK)	.10	91 Bob Forsch	.05	157 Rick Reuschel	.10	223 Rick Camp	.05
26 Garmon Thomas (DK)	.10	92 Art Howe	.05	158 Steve Howe	.05	224 Mike Jorgensen	.05
27 Earl Weaver (Mgr.)	.10	93 Marty Bystrom	.05	159 Alan Bannister	.05	225 Jody Davis (R)	.40
28 Rollie Fingers	.20	94 Ozzie Smith	.35	160 U.L. Wasington	.05	226 Mike Parrott	.05
29 Sparky Anderson (Mgr.)	.10	95 Dave Parker	.30	161 Rick Langford	.05	227 Jim Clancy	.05
30 Dennis Eckersley	.05	96 Doyle Alexander	.05	162 Bill Gullickson	.05	228 Hosken Powell	.05
31 Dave Winfield	.50	97 Al Hrabosky	.05	163 Mark Wagner	.05	229 Tom Hume	.05
32 Burt Hooton	.05	98 Frank Taveras	.05	164 Geoff Zahn	.05	230 Britt Burns	.05
33 Rick Waits	.05	99 Tim Blackwell	.05	165 Ron LeFlore	.05	231 Jim Palmer	.30
34 George Brett	.60	100 Floyd Bannister	.05	166 Dane Iorg	.05	232 Bob Rodgers (Mgr.)	.05
35 Steve McCatty	.05	101 Alfredo Griffin	.05	167 Joe Niekro	.10	233 Milt Wilcox	.05
36 Steve Rogers	.05	102 Dave Engle	.05	168 Pete Rose	1.00	234 Dave Revering	.05
37 Bill Stein	.05	103 Mario Soto	.15	169 Dave Collins	.05	235 Mike Torrez	.05
38 Steve Renko	.05	104 Ross Baumgarten	.05	170 Rick Wise	.05	236 Bobby Castillo	.05
39 Mike Squires	.05	105 Ken Singleton	.10	171 Jim Bibby	.05	237 Von Hayes (R)	.75
40 George Hendrick	.08	106 Ted Simmons	.15	172 Larry Herndon	.05	238 Renie Martin	.05
41 Bob Knepper	.12	107 Jack Morris	.25	173 Bob Horner	.15	239 Dwayne Murphy	.05
42 Steve Carlton	.50	108 Bob Watson	.05	174 Steve Dillard	.05	240 Rodney Scott	.05
43 Larry Biittner	.05	109 Dwight Evans	.15	175 Mookie Wilson	.10	241 Freddie Patek	.05
44 Chris Welsh	.07	110 Tommy LaSorda (Mgr.)	.10	176 Danny Meyer	.05	242 Mickey Rivers	.05
45 Steve Nicosia	.05	111 Bert Blyleven	.15	177 Fernando Arroyo	.05	243 Steve Trout	.05
46 Jack Clark	.30	112 Dan Quisenberry	.25	178 Jackson Todd	.05	244 Jose Cruz	.10
47 Chris Chambliss	.05	113 Rickey Henderson	.75	179 Darrell Jackson	.05	245 Manny Trillo	.05
48 Ivan DeJesus	.05	114 Gary Carter	.50	180 Al Woods	.05	246 Lary Sorensen	.05
49 Lee Mazzilli	.05	115 Brian Downing	.05	181 Jim Anderson	.05	247 Dave Edwards	.05
50 Julio Cruz	.05	116 Al Oliver	.15	182 Dave Kingman	.15	248 Dan Driessen	.05
51 Pete Redfern	.05	117 LaMarr Hoyt	.15	183 Steve Henderson	.05	249 Tommy Boggs	.05
52 Dave Stieb	.25	118 Cesar Cedeno	.10	184 Brian Asselstine	.05	250 Dale Berra	.05
53 Doug Corbett	.05	119 Keith Moreland	.05	185 Rod Scurry	.05	251 Ed Whitson	.05
54 Jorge Bell (R)	6.00	120 Bob Shirley	.05	186 Fred Breining	.08	252 Lee Smith (R)	.50
55 Joe Simpson	.05	121 Terry Kennedy	.10	187 Danny Boone	.05	253 Tom Paciorek	.05
56 Rusty Staub	.10	122 Frank Pastore	.05	188 Junior Kennedy	.05	254 Pat Zachry	.05
57 Hector Cruz	.05	123 Gene Garber	.05	189 Sparky Lyle	.05	255 Luis Leal	.05
58 Claudell Washington	.10	124 Tony Pena	.25	190 Whitey Herzog (Mgr.)	.05	256 John Castino	.05
59 Enrique Romo	.05	125 Allen Ripley	.05	191 Dave Smith	.05	257 Rich Dauer	.05
60 Gary Lavelle	.05	126 Randy Martz	.05	192 Ed Ott	.05	258 Cecil Cooper	.20
61 Tim Flannery	.05	127 Richie Zisk	.05	193 Greg Luzinski	.10	259 Dave Rozema	.05
62 Joe Nolan	.05	128 Mike Scott	.35	194 Bill Lee	.05	260 John Tudor	.10
63 Larry Bowa	.05	129 Lloyd Moseby	.25	195 Don Zimmer (Mgr.)	.05	261 Jerry Mumphrey	.05
64 Sixto Lezcano	.05	130 Rob Wilfong	.05	196 Hal McRae	.05	262 Jay Johnstone	.05
65 Joe Sambito	.05	131 Tim Stoddard	.05	197 Mike Norris	.05	263 Bo Diaz	.05

NO.	PLAYER	MINT
264	Dennis Leonard	.05
265	Jim Spencer	.05
266	John Milner	.05
267	Don Aase	.05
268	Jim Sundberg	.05
269	Lamar Johnson	.05
270	Frank LaCorte	.05
271	Barry Evans	.05
272	Enos Cabell	.05
273	Del Unser	.05
274	George Foster	.20
275	Brett Butler (R)	.75
276	Lee Lacy	.05
277	Ken Reitz	.05
278	Keith Hernandez	.40
279	Doug DeCinces	.10
280	Charlie Moore	.05
281	Lance Parrish	.25
282	Ralph Houk (Mgr.)	.05
283	Rich Gossage	.20
284	Jerry Reuss	.05
285	Mike Stanton	.05
286	Frank White	.05
287	Bob Owchinko	.05
288	Scott Sanderson	.05
289	Bump Wills	.05
290	Dave Frost	.05
291	Chet Lemon	.05
292	Tito Landrum	.05
293	Vern Ruhle	.05
294	Mike Schmidt	.75
295	San Mejias	.05
296	Gary Lucas	.05
297	John Candelaria	.05
298	Jerry Martin	.05
299	Dale Murphy	.75
300	Mike Lum	.05
301	Tom Hausman	.05
302	Glenn Abbott	.05
303	Roger Erickson	.05
304	Otto Velez	.05
305	Danny Goodwin	.05
306	John Mayberry	.05
307	Lenny Randle	.05
308	Bob Bailor	.05
309	Jerry Morales	.05
310	Rufino Linares	.05
311	Kent Tekulve	.05
312	Joe Morgan	.30
313	John Urrea	.05
314	Paul Householder	.05
315	Garry Maddox	.05
316	Mike Ramsey	.05
317	Alan Ashby	.05
318	Bob Clark	.05
319	Tony LaRussa (Mgr.)	.05
320	Charlie Lea	.05
321	Danny Darwin	.05
322	Cesar Geronimo	.05
323	Tom Underwood	.05
324	Andre Thornton	.10
325	Rudy May	.05
326	Frank Tanana	.05
327	Davey Lopes	.05
328	Richie Hebner	.05
329	Mike Flanagan	.08
330	Mike Caldwell	.05
331	Scott McGregor	.05
332	Jerry Augustine	.05
333	Stan Papi	.05
334	Rick Miller	.05
335	Graig Nettles	.15
336	Dusty Baker	.10
337	Dave Garcia (Mgr.)	.05
338	Larry Gura	.05
339	Cliff Johnson	.05
340	Warren Cromartie	.05
341	Steve Comer	.05
342	Rick Burleson	.05
343	John Martin	.05
344	Craig Reynolds	.05
345	Mike Proly	.05
346	Ruppert Jones	.05
347	Omar Moreno	.05
348	Greg Minton	.05
349	Rick Mahler (R)	.25
350	Alex Trevino	.05
351	Mike Krukow	.05
352	Shane Rawley	.50
	(photo of Jim Anderson)	
352	Shane Rawley (correct)	.10
353	Garth Iorg	.05
354	Pete Mackanin	.05
355	Paul Moskau	.05
356	Rich Dotson	.05
357	Steve Stone	.05
358	Larry Hisle	.05
359	Aurelio Lopez	.05
360	Oscar Gamble	.05
361	Tom Burgmeier	.05
362	Terry Forster	.08
363	Joe Charboneau	.05
364	Ken Brett	.05
365	Tony Armas	.15
366	Chris Speier	.05
367	Fred Lynn	.20
368	Buddy Bell	.10
369	Jim Essian	.05
370	Terry Puhl	.05
371	Greg Gross	.05
372	Bruce Sutter	.25
373	Joe LeFebvre	.05
374	Ray Knight	.05
375	Bruce Benedict	.05
376	Tim Foli	.05
377	Al Holland	.05
378	Ken Kravec	.05
379	Jeff Burroughs	.05
380	Pete Falcone	.05
381	Ernie Whitt	.05
382	Brad Havens	.05
383	Terry Crowley	.05
384	Don Money	.05
385	Dan Schatzeder	.05
386	Gary Allenson	.05
387	Yogi Berra	.15
388	Ken Landreaux	.05
389	Mike Hargrove	.05
390	Darryl Motley	.20
391	Dave McKay	.05
392	Stan Bahnsen	.05
393	Ken Forsch	.05
394	Mario Mendoza	.05
395	Jim Morrison	.05
396	Mike Ivie	.05
397	Broderick Perkins	.05
398	Darrell Evans	.10
399	Ron Reed	.05
400	Johnny Bench	.60
401	Steve Bedrosian (R)	.75
402	Bill Robinson	.05
403	Bill Buckner	.15
404	Ken Oberkfell	.05
405	Cal Ripken Jr. (R)	8.00
406	Jim Gantner	.05
407	Kirk Gibson	1.50
408	Tony Perez	.15
409	Tommy John	.15
410	Dave Stewart (R)	3.00
411	Dan Spillner	.05
412	Willie Aikens	.05
413	Mike Heath	.05
414	Ray Burris	.05
415	Leon Roberts	.05
416	Mike Witt (R)	.75
417	Bobby Molinaro	.05
418	Steve Braun	.05
419	Nolan Ryan	1.00
420	Tug McGraw	.05
421	Dave Concepcion	.10
422	Juan Eichelberger	.45
	(photo of Gary Lucas)	
422	J. Eichelberger (correct)	.05
423	Rick Rhoden	.05
424	Frank Robinson (Mgr.)	.15
425	Eddie Miller	.05
426	Bill Caudill	.05
427	Doug Flynn	.05
428	Larry Andersen	.05
429	Al Williams	.05
430	Jerry Garvin	.05
431	Glenn Adams	.05
432	Barry Bonnell	.05
433	Jerry Narron	.05
434	John Stearns	.05
435	Mike Tyson	.05
436	Glenn Hubbard	.05
437	Eddie Solomon	.05
438	Jeff Leonard	.05
439	Randy Bass	.05
440	Mike LaCoss	.05
441	Gary Matthews	.10
442	Mark Littell	.05
443	Don Sutton	.35
444	John Harris	.05
445	Vada Pinson	.05
446	Elias Sosa	.05
447	Charlie Hough	.05
448	Willie Wilson	.20
449	Fred Stanley	.05
450	Tommy Veryzer	.05
451	Ron Davis	.05
452	Mark Clear	.05
453	Bill Russell	.05
454	Lou Whitaker	.20
455	Dan Graham	.05
456	Reggie Cleveland	.05
457	Sammy Stewart	.05
458	Pete Vuckovich	.10
459	John Wockenfuss	.05
460	Glenn Hoffman	.05
461	Willie Randolph	.05
462	Fernando Valenzuela	.60
463	Ron Hassey	.05
464	Paul Splittorff	.05
465	Rob Picciolo	.05
466	Larry Parrish	.05
467	John Grubb	.05
468	Dan Ford	.05
469	Silvio Martinez	.05
470	Kiko Garcia	.05
471	Bob Boone	.05
472	Luis Salazar	.15
473	Randy Niemann	.05
474	Tom Griffin	.05
475	Phil Niekro	.20
476	Hubie Brooks	.35
477	Dick Tidrow	.05
478	Jim Beattie	.05
479	Damaso Garcia	.10
480	Mickey Hatcher	.05
481	Joe Price	.05
482	Ed Farmer	.05
483	Eddie Murray	.60
484	Ben Oglivie	.10
485	Kevin Saucier	.05
486	Bobby Murcer	.10
487	Bill Campbell	.05
488	Reggie Smith	.10
489	Wayne Garland	.05
490	Jim Wright	.05
491	Billy Martin (Mgr.)	.20
492	Jim Fanning (Mgr.)	.05
493	Don Baylor	.15
494	Rick Honeycutt	.05
495	Carlton Fisk	.20
496	Denny Walling	.05
497	Bake McBride	.05
498	Darrell Porter	.05
499	Gene Richards	.05
500	Ron Oester	.05
501	Ken Dayley (R)	.25
502	Jason Thompson	.10
503	Milt May	.05
504	Doug Bird	.05
505	Bruce Bochte	.05
506	Neil Allen	.05
507	Joey McLaughlin	.05
508	Butch Wynegar	.06
509	Gary Roenicke	.05
510	Robin Yount	.75
511	Dave Tobik	.05
512	Rich Gedman (R)	.35
513	Gene Nelson	.08
514	Rick Monday	.05
515	Miguel Dilone	.05
516	Clint Hurdle	.05
517	Jeff Newman	.05
518	Grant Jackson	.05
519	Andy Hassler	.05
520	Pat Putnam	.05
521	Greg Pryor	.05
522	Tony Scott	.05
523	Steve Mura	.05
524	John LeMaster	.05
525	Dick Ruthven	.05
526	John McNamara (Mgr.)	.05
527	Larry McWilliams	.05
528	Johnny Ray (R)	.50
529	Pat Tabler (R)	.60
530	Tom Herr	.10
531	San Diego Chicken*	1.00
532	Sal Butera	.05
533	Mike Griffin	.05
534	Kelvin Moore	.05
535	Reggie Jackson	.50
536	Ed Romero	.05
537	Derrel Thomas	.05
538	Mike O'Berry	.05
539	Jack O'Connor	.05
540	Bob Ojeda (R)	.50
541	Roy Lee Jackson	.05
542	Lynn Jones	.05
543	Gaylord Perry	.25
544	Phil Garner*	.10
545	Garry Templeton	.10
546	Rafael Ramirez	.05
547	Jeff Reardon	.05
548	Ron Guidry	.20
549	Tim Laudner	.15
550	John Henry Johnson	.05
551	Chris Bando	.05
552	Bobby Brown	.05
553	Larry Bradford	.05
554	Scott Fletcher (R)	.35
555	Jerry Royster	.05
556	Shooty Babbitt	.05
557	Kent Hrbek (R)	3.50
558	Yankee Winners:	.15
	Ron Guidry, Tommy John	
559	Mark Bomback	.05
560	Julio Valdez	.08
561	Buck Martinez	.05
562	Mike Marshall (R)	1.00
563	Rennie Stennett	.05
564	Steve Crawford	.07
565	Bob Babcock	.05
566	Johnny Podres	.05
567	Paul Serna	.07
568	Harold Baines	.60
569	Dave LaRoche	.05
570	Lee May	.05
571	Gary Ward	.05
572	John Denny	.05
573	Roy Smalley	.05
574	Don Brenly	.25
575	Bronx Bombers:	.45
	R. Jackson, D. Winfield	
576	Luis Pujols	.05
577	Butch Hobson	.05
578	Harvey Kuenn (Mgr.)	.05
579	Cal Ripken, Sr.	.05
580	Juan Berenguer	.05
581	Benny Ayala	.05
582	Vance Law	.15
583	Rick Leach	.08
584	George Frazier	.05
585	Phillies Finest:	.60
	Pete Rose, Mike Schmidt	
586	Joe Rudi	.05
587	Juan Beniquez	.05
588	Luis DeLeon (R)	.15
589	Craig Swan	.05
590	Dave Chalk	.05
591	Billy Gardner (Mgr.)	.05
592	Sal Bando	.05
593	Bert Campaneris	.05
594	Steve Kemp	.05
595	Randy Lerch' (Braves)	.35
595	Randy Lerch (Brewers)	.08

NO.	PLAYER	MINT
596	Bryan Clark	.08
597	Dave Ford	.05
598	Mike Scioscia	.15
599	John Lowenstein	.05
600	Rene Lachmann (Mgr.)	.05
601	Mick Kelleher	.05
602	Ron Jackson	.05
603	Jerry Koosman	.15
604	Dave Goltz	.05
605	Ellis Valentine	.05
606	Lonnie Smith	.10
607	Joaquin Andujar	.15
608	Garry Hancock	.05
609	Jerry Turner	.05
610	Bob Bonner	.05
611	Jim Dwyer	.05
612	Terry Bulling	.05

NO.	PLAYER	MINT
613	Joel Youngblood	.05
614	Larry Milbourne	.05
615	Phil Roof	.07
616	Keith Drumright	.05
617	Dave Rosello	.05
618	Rickey Keeton	.05
619	Dennis Lamp	.05
620	Sid Monge	.05
621	Jerry White	.05
622	Luis Aguayo	.05
623	Jamie Easterly	.05
624	Steve Sax (R)	2.50
625	Dave Roberts	.05
626	Rick Bosetti	.05
627	Terry Francona (R)	.20
628	Pride of Reds:	.35
	Tom Seaver, Johnny Bench	

NO.	PLAYER	MINT
629	Paul Mirabella	.05
630	Rance Mulliniks	.05
631	Kevin Hickey	.05
632	Reid Nichols	.05
633	Dave Geisel	.05
634	Ken Griffey	.10
635	Bob Lemon (Mgr.)	.10
636	Orlando Sanchez	.08
637	Bill Almon	.05
638	Danny Ainge	.05
639	Willie Stargell	.40
640	Bob Sykes	.05
641	Ed Lynch (R)	.10
642	John Ellis	.05
643	Fergie Jenkins	.10
644	Lenn Sakata	.05
645	Julio Gonzalez	.05

NO.	PLAYER	MINT
646	Jesse Orosco	.10
647	Jerry Dybzinski	.05
648	Tommy Davis	.05
649	Ron Gardenhire	.10
650	Felipe Alou	.05
651	Harvey Haddix	.05
652	Willie Upshaw	.10
653	Bill Madlock	.15
	DK Checklist*	.10
—	Checklist No. 1	.08
—	Checklist No. 2	.08
—	Checklist No. 3	.08
—	Checklist No. 4	.08
—	Checklist No. 5	.08
—	Checklist No. 6	.08

1983 Donruss.... Complete Set of 660 Cards—Value $65.00 (Factory-Sealed set—Value $80.00)

Features the rookie cards of Wade Boggs, Howard Johnson, Ryne Sandberg and Tony Gwynn. The *checklist* cards are *not* numbered.

NO.	PLAYER	MINT
No. 1 to 26—Diamond Kings		
1	F. Valenzuela (DK)	.50
2	Rollie Fingers (DK)	.25
3	Reggie Jackson (DK)	.50
4	Jim Palmer (DK)	.30
5	Jack Morris (DK)	.30
6	George Foster (DK)	.20
7	Jim Sundberg (DK)	.10
8	Willie Stargell (DK)	.35
9	Dave Stieb (DK)	.30
10	Joe Niekro (DK)	.10
11	Rickey Henderson (DK)	.60
12	Dale Murphy (DK)	.75
13	Toby Harrah (DK)	.10
14	Bill Buckner (DK)	.15
15	Willie Wilson (DK)	.25
16	Steve Carlton (DK)	.40
17	Ron Guidry (DK)	.30
18	Steve Rogers (DK)	.10
19	Kent Hrbek (DK)	.35
20	Keith Hernandez (DK)	.35
21	Floyd Bannister (DK)	.10
22	Johnny Bench (DK)	.60
23	Britt Burns (DK)	.10
24	Joe Morgan (DK)	.25
25	Carl Yastrzemski (DK)	.60
26	Jerry Kennedy (DK)	.10
27	Gary Roenicke	.05
28	Dwight Bernard	.05
29	Pat Underwood	.05
30	Gary Allenson	.05
31	Ron Guidry	.20
32	Burt Hooton	.05
33	Chris Bando	.05
34	Vida Blue	.05
35	Rickey Henderson	.50
36	Ray Burris	.05
37	John Butcher	.05
38	Don Aase	.05
39	Jerry Koosman	.05
40	Bruce Sutter	.20

NO.	PLAYER	MINT
41	Jose Cruz	.10
42	Pete Rose	1.00
43	Cesar Cedeno	.10
44	Floyd Chiffer	.07
45	Larry McWilliams	.05
46	Alan Fowlkes	.07
47	Dale Murphy	.75
48	Doug Bird	.05
49	Hubie Brooks	.08
50	Floyd Bannister	.05
51	Joe O'Connor	.05
52	Steve Senteney	.07
53	Gary Gaetti (R)	3.00
54	Damaso Garcia	.10
55	Gene Nelson	.05
56	Mookie Wilson	.08
57	Allen Ripley	.05
58	Bob Horner	.20
59	Tony Pena	.15
60	Gary Lavelle	.05
61	Tim Lollar	.05
62	Frank Pastore	.05
63	Garry Maddox	.05
64	Bob Forsch	.05
65	Harry Spilman	.05
66	Geoff Zahn	.05
67	Salome Barojas	.07
68	David Palmer	.05
69	Charlie Hough	.05
70	Dan Quisenberry	.20
71	Tony Armas	.15
72	Rick Sutcliffe	.20
73	Steve Balboni	.10
74	Jerry Remy	.05
75	Mike Scioscia	.05
76	John Wockenfuss	.05
77	Jim Palmer	.30
78	Rollie Fingers	.25
79	Joe Nolan	.05
80	Pete Vuckovich	.05
81	Rick Leach	.05

NO.	PLAYER	MINT
82	Rick Miller	.05
83	Graig Nettles	.10
84	Ron Cey	.15
85	Miguel Dilone	.05
86	John Wathan	.05
87	Kelvin Moore	.05
88	Bryn Smith	.35
89	Dave Hostetler	.08
90	Rod Carew	.40
91	Lonnie Smith	.07
92	Bob Knepper	.05
93	Marty Bystrom	.05
94	Chris Welsh	.05
95	Jason Thompson	.07
96	Tom O'Malley	.08
97	Phil Niekro	.20
98	Neil Allen	.05
99	Bill Buckner	.10
100	Ed VandeBerg	.10
101	Jim Clancy	.05
102	Robert Castillo	.05
103	Bruce Berenyi	.05
104	Carlton Fisk	.20
105	Mike Flanagan	.10
106	Cecil Cooper	.15
107	Jack Morris	.20
108	Mike Morgan	.05
109	Luis Aponte	.05
110	Pedro Guerrero	.30
111	Len Barker	.05
112	Willie Wilson	.20
113	Dave Beard	.05
114	Mike Gates	.07
115	Reggie Jackson	.45
116	George Wright	.15
117	Vance Law	.05
118	Nolan Ryan	.75
119	Mike Krukow	.05
120	Ozzie Smith	.25
121	Broderick Perkins	.05
122	Tom Seaver	.35

NO.	PLAYER	MINT
123	Chris Chambliss	.05
124	Chuck Tanner (Mgr.)	.05
125	Johnnie LeMaster	.05
126	Mel Hall (R)	.60
127	Bruce Bochte	.05
128	Charlie Puleo	.07
129	Luis Leal	.05
130	John Pacella	.05
131	Glenn Gulliver	.07
132	Don Money	.05
133	Dave Rozema	.05
134	Bruce Hurst	.30
135	Rudy May	.05
136	Tom LaSorda (Mgr.)	.10
137	Dan Spillner	.10
	(photo of Ed Whitson)	
138	Jerry Martin	.05
139	Mike Norris	.05
140	Al Oliver	.10
141	Daryl Sconiers	.05
142	Lamar Johnson	.05
143	Harold Baines	.20
144	Alan Ashby	.05
145	Garry Templeton	.10
146	Al Holland	.05
147	Bo Diaz	.05
148	Dave Concepcion	.10
149	Rick Camp	.05
150	Jim Morrison	.05
151	Randy Martz	.05
152	Keith Hernandez	.30
153	John Lowenstein	.05
154	Mike Caldwell	.05
155	Milt Wilcox	.05
156	Rich Gedman	.05
157	Rich Gossage	.20
158	Jerry Reuss	.05
159	Ron Hassey	.05
160	Larry Gura	.05
161	Dwayne Murphy	.05
162	Woodie Fryman	.05

NO.	PLAYER	MINT	NO.	PLAYER	MINT	NO.	PLAYER	MINT	NO.	PLAYER	MINT
163	Steve Comer	.05	247	Joe Pittman	.10	330	Jim Slaton	.05	414	Charlie Lea	.05
164	Ken Forsch	.05		(photo of Juan Eichelberger)		331	Benny Ayala	.05	415	Rick Honeycutt	.05
165	Dennis Lamp	.05	248	Mario Soto	.10	332	Ted Simmons	.10	416	Mike Witt	.25
166	David Green (R)	.15	249	Claudell Washington	.10	333	Lou Whitaker	.20	417	Steve Trout	.05
167	Terry Puhl	.05	250	Rick Rhoden	.05	334	Chuck Rainey	.05	418	Glenn Brummer	.05
168	Mike Schmidt	.60	251	Darrell Evans	.10	335	Lou Piniella	.10	419	Denny Walling	.05
169	Eddie Milner (R)	.15	252	Steve Henderson	.05	336	Steve Sax	.30	420	Gary Matthews	.10
170	John Curtis	.05	253	Manny Castillo	.05	337	Toby Harrah	.05	421	Charlie Leibrandt	.05
171	Don Robinson	.05	254	Craig Swan	.05	338	George Brett	.50	422	Juan Eichelberger	.05
172	Richard Gale	.05	255	Joey McLaughlin	.05	339	Davey Lopes	.05	423	Matt Guante	.07
173	Steve Bedrosian	.20	256	Pete Redfern	.05	340	Gary Carter	.40	424	Bill Laskey (R)	.15
174	Willie Hernandez	.20	257	Ken Singleton	.08	341	John Grubb	.05	425	Jerry Royster	.05
175	Ron Gardenhire	.05	258	Robin Yount	.40	342	Tim Foli	.05	426	Dickie Noles	.05
176	Jim Beattie	.05	259	Elias Sosa	.05	343	Jim Kaat	.05	427	George Foster	.20
177	Tim Laudner	.05	260	Bob Ojeda	.08	344	Mike LaCoss	.05	428	Mike Moore (R)	1.25
178	Buck Martinez	.05	261	Bobby Murcer	.10	345	Larry Christenson	.05	429	Gary Ward	.05
179	Kent Hrbek	.40	262	Candy Maldonado (R)	.50	346	Juan Bonilla	.05	430	Barry Bonnell	.05
180	Alfredo Griffin	.05	263	Rick Waits	.05	347	Omar Moreno	.05	431	Ron Washington	.08
181	Larry Andersen	.05	264	Greg Pryor	.05	348	Chili Davis	.30	432	Rance Mulliniks	.05
182	Pete Falcone	.05	265	Bob Owchinko	.05	349	Tommy Boggs	.05	433	Mike Stanton	.05
183	Jody Davis	.10	266	Chris Speier	.05	350	Rusty Staub	.10	434	Jesse Orosco	.10
184	Glenn Hubbard	.05	267	Bruce Kison	.05	351	Bump Wills	.05	435	Larry Bowa	.08
185	Dale Berra	.05	268	Mark Wagner	.05	352	Rick Sweet	.05	436	Biff Pocoroba	.05
186	Greg Minton	.05	269	Steve Kemp	.05	353	Jim Gott	.25	437	Johnny Ray	.12
187	Gary Lucas	.05	270	Phil Garner	.05	354	Terry Felton	.05	438	Joe Morgan	.30
188	Dave Van Gorder	.08	271	Gene Richards	.05	355	Jim Kern	.05	439	Eric Show (R)	.30
189	Bob Dernier	.05	272	Renie Martin	.05	356	Bill Almon	.05	440	Larry Biittner	.05
190	Willie McGee (R)	2.00	273	Dave Roberts	.05	357	Tippy Martinez	.05	441	Greg Gross	.05
191	Dickie Thon	.07	274	Dan Driessen	.05	358	Roy Howell	.05	442	Gene Tenace	.05
192	Bob Boone	.05	275	Rufino Linares	.05	359	Dan Petry	.20	443	Danny Heep	.05
193	Britt Burns	.05	276	Lee Lacy	.05	360	Jerry Mumphrey	.05	444	Bobby Clark	.05
194	Jeff Reardon	.10	277	Ryne Sandberg (R)	6.00	361	Mark Clear	.05	445	Kevin Hickey	.05
195	Jon Matlack	.05	278	Darrell Porter	.05	362	Mike Marshall	.20	446	Scott Sanderson	.05
196	Don Slaught (R)	.25	279	Cal Ripken	1.00	363	Lary Sorensen	.05	447	Frank Tanana	.10
197	Fred Stanley	.05	280	Jamie Easterly	.05	364	Amos Otis	.08	448	Cesar Geronimo	.05
198	Rick Manning	.05	281	Bill Fahey	.05	365	Rick Langford	.05	449	Jimmy Sexton	.05
199	Dave Righetti	.25	282	Glenn Hoffman	.05	366	Brad Mills	.05	450	Mike Hargrove	.05
200	Dave Stapleton	.05	283	Willie Randolph	.10	367	Brian Downing	.05	451	Doyle Alexander	.05
201	Steve Yeager	.05	284	Fernando Valenzuela	.30	368	Mike Richardt	.07	452	Dwight Evans	.20
202	Enos Cabell	.05	285	Alan Bannister	.05	369	Aurelio Rodriguez	.05	453	Terry Forster	.05
203	Sammy Stewart	.05	286	Paul Splittorff	.05	370	Dave Smith	.05	454	Tom Brookens	.05
204	Moose Haas	.05	287	Joe Rudi	.05	371	Tug McGraw	.08	455	Rich Dauer	.05
205	Lenn Sakata	.05	288	Bill Gullickson	.05	372	Doug Bair	.10	456	Rob Picciolo	.05
206	Charlie Moore	.05	289	Danny Darwin	.05	373	Ruppert Jones	.05	457	Terry Crowley	.05
207	Alan Trammell	.25	290	Andy Hassler	.05	374	Alex Trevino	.05	458	Ned Yost	.05
208	Jim Rice	.30	291	Ernesto Escarrega	.07	375	Ken Dayley	.05	459	Kirk Gibson	.40
209	Roy Smalley	.05	292	Steve Mura	.05	376	Rod Scurry	.05	460	Reid Nichols	.05
210	Bill Russell	.05	293	Tony Scott	.05	377	Bob Brenly	.05	461	Oscar Gamble	.05
211	Andre Thornton	.07	294	Manny Trillo	.05	378	Scot Thompson	.05	462	Dusty Baker	.10
212	Willie Aikens	.05	295	Greg Harris	.05	379	Julio Cruz	.05	463	Jack Perconte	.05
213	Dave McKay	.05	296	Luis DeLeon	.05	380	John Stearns	.05	464	Frank White	.05
214	Tim Blackwell	.05	297	Kent Tekulve	.05	381	Dale Murray	.05	465	Mickey Klutts	.05
215	Buddy Bell	.10	298	Atlee Hammaker	.05	382	Frank Viola (R)	4.00	466	Warren Cromartie	.05
216	Doug DeCinces	.15	299	Bruce Benedict	.05	383	Al Bumbry	.05	467	Larry Parrish	.05
217	Tom Herr	.10	300	Fergie Jenkins	.10	384	Ben Oglivie	.10	468	Bobby Grich	.08
218	Frank LaCorte	.05	301	Dave Kingman	.10	385	Dave Tobik	.05	469	Dane Iorg	.05
219	Steve Carlton	.30	302	Bill Caudill	.05	386	Bob Stanley	.05	470	Joe Niekro	.10
220	Terry Kennedy	.10	303	John Castino	.05	387	Andre Robertson	.05	471	Ed Farmer	.05
221	Mike Easler	.05	304	Ernie Whitt	.05	388	Jorge Orta	.05	472	Tim Flannery	.05
222	Jack Clark	.25	305	Randy Johnson	.05	389	Ed Whitson	.05	473	Dave Parker	.30
223	Gene Garber	.05	306	Garth Iorg	.05	390	Don Hood	.05	474	Jeff Leonard	.05
224	Scott Holman	.07	307	Gaylord Perry	.20	391	Tom Underwood	.05	475	Al Hrabosky	.05
225	Mike Proly	.05	308	Ed Lynch	.05	392	Tim Wallach	.15	476	Ron Hodges	.05
226	Terry Bulling	.05	309	Keith Moreland	.10	393	Steve Renko	.05	477	Leon Durham	.20
227	Jerry Garvin	.05	310	Rafael Ramirez	.05	394	Mickey Rivers	.05	478	Jim Essian	.05
228	Ron Davis	.05	311	Bill Madlock	.15	395	Greg Luzinski	.10	479	Roy Lee Jackson	.05
229	Tom Hume	.05	312	Milt May	.05	396	Art Howe	.05	480	Brad Havens	.05
230	Marc Hill	.05	313	John Montefusco	.05	397	Alan Wiggins (R)	.20	481	Joe Price	.05
231	Dennis Martinez	.05	314	Wayne Krenchicki	.05	398	Jim Barr	.05	482	Tony Bernazard	.05
232	Jim Gantner	.05	315	George Vukovich	.05	399	Ivan DeJesus	.05	483	Scott McGregor	.08
233	Larry Pashnick	.07	316	Joaquin Andujar	.10	400	Tom Lawless	.08	484	Paul Molitor	.20
234	Dave Collins	.05	317	Craig Reynolds	.05	401	Bob Walk	.05	485	Mike Ivie	.05
235	Tom Burgmeier	.05	318	Rick Burleson	.05	402	Jimmy Smith	.07	486	Ken Griffey	.10
236	Ken Landreaux	.05	319	Richard Dotson	.05	403	Lee Smith	.10	487	Dennis Eckersley	.08
237	John Denny	.10	320	Steve Rogers	.05	404	George Hendrick	.10	488	Steve Garvey	.40
238	Hal McRae	.05	321	Dave Schmidt	.10	405	Eddie Murray	.50	489	Mike Fischlin	.05
239	Matt Keough	.05	322	Bud Black (R)	.25	406	Marshall Edwards	.05	490	U.L. Washington	.05
240	Doug Flynn	.05	323	Jeff Burroughs	.05	407	Lance Parrish	.20	491	Steve McCatty	.05
241	Fred Lynn	.20	324	Von Hayes	.25	408	Carney Lansford	.10	492	Roy Johnson	.07
242	Billy Sample	.05	325	Butch Wynegar	.05	409	Dave Winfield	.40	493	Don Baylor	.10
243	Tom Paciorek	.05	326	Carl Yastrzemski	.75	410	Bob Welch	.05	494	Bobby Johnson	.05
244	Joe Sambito	.05	327	Ron Roenicke	.05	411	Larry Milbourne	.05	495	Mike Squires	.05
245	Sid Monge	.05	328	Howard Johnson (R)	7.50	412	Dennis Leonard	.05	496	Bert Roberge	.05
246	Ken Oberkfell	.05	329	Rick Dempsey	.05	413	Dan Meyer	.05	497	Dick Ruthven	.05

NO. PLAYER	MINT	NO. PLAYER	MINT	NO. PLAYER	MINT	NO. PLAYER	MINT
498 Tito Landrum	.05	540 Tim Raines	.40	582 Bob McClure	.05	623 Gene Petralli	.07
499 Sixto Lezcano	.05	541 Paul Mirabella	.05	583 Jim Dwyer	.05	624 Duane Walker (R)	.15
500 Johnny Bench	.45	542 Luis Tiant	.10	584 Ed Romero	.05	625 Dick Williams (R)	.05
501 Larry Whisenton	.05	543 Ron LeFlore	.05	585 Larry Herndon	.05	626 Pat Corrales (Mgr.)	.05
502 Manny Sarmiento	.05	544 Dave LaPoint (R)	.35	586 Wade Boggs (R)	15.00	627 Vern Ruhle	.05
503 Fred Breining	.05	545 Randy Moffitt	.05	587 Jay Howell	.05	628 Joe Torre (Mgr.)	.05
504 Bill Campbell	.05	546 Luis Aguayo	.05	588 Dave Stewart	.40	629 Anthony Johnson	.08
505 Todd Cruz	.05	547 Brad Lesley	.10	589 Bert Blyleven	.12	630 Steve Howe	.05
506 Bob Bailor	.05	548 Luis Salazar	.05	590 Dick Howser (Mgr.)	.08	631 Gary Woods	.05
507 Dave Stieb	.20	549 John Candelaria	.05	591 Wayne Gross	.05	632 LaMarr Hoyt	.15
508 Al Williams	.05	550 Dave Bergman	.05	592 Terry Francona	.08	633 Steve Swisher	.05
509 Dan Ford	.05	551 Bob Watson	.05	593 Don Werner	.05	634 Terry Leach	.20
510 Gorman Thomas	.10	552 Pat Tabler	.05	594 Bill Stein	.05	635 Jeff Newman	.05
511 Chet Lemon	.10	553 Brent Gaff	.08	595 Jesse Barfield	.75	636 Brett Butler	.10
512 Mike Torrez	.05	554 Al Cowens	.05	596 Bobby Molinaro	.05	637 Gary Gray	.05
513 Shane Rawley	.05	555 Tom Brunansky	.50	597 Mike Vail	.05	638 Lee Mazzilli	.05
514 Mark Belanger	.05	556 Lloyd Moseby	.15	598 Tony Gwynn (R)	12.00	639 R. Jackson	.10
515 Rodney Craig	.05	557 Pascual Perez	.05	599 Gary Rajsich	.08	639 R. Jackson (error)	10.00
516 Onix Concepcion (R)	.10	558 Willie Upshaw	.10	600 Jerry Ujdur	.05	640 Juan Beniquez	.05
517 Mike Heath	.05	559 Richie Zisk	.05	601 Cliff Johnson	.05	641 Dave Rucker	.05
518 Andre Dawson	.35	560 Pat Zachry	.05	602 Jerry White	.05	642 Luis Pujols	.05
519 Luis Sanchez	.05	561 Jay Johnstone	.05	603 Bryan Clark	.05	643 Rick Monday	.05
520 Terry Bogener	.07	562 Carlos Diaz	.10	604 Joe Ferguson	.05	644 Hosken Powell	.05
521 Rudy Law	.05	563 John Tudor	.10	605 Guy Sularz	.07	645 The Chicken	.20
522 Ray Knight	.05	564 Frank Robinson (Mgr.)	.15	606 Ozzie Virgil	.10	646 Dave Engle	.05
523 Joe LeFebvre	.05	565 Dave Edwards	.05	607 Terry Harper	.05	647 Dick Davis	.05
524 Jim Wohlford	.05	566 Paul Householder	.05	608 Harvey Kuenn (Mgr.)	.05	648 MVP's: Frank Robinson,	.15
525 Julio Franco (R)	3.50	567 Ron Reed	.05	609 Jim Sundberg	.05	Vida Blue, Joe Morgan	
526 Ron Oester	.05	568 Mike Ramsey	.05	610 Willie Stargell	.30	649 Al Chambers	.10
527 Rick Mahler	.05	569 Kiko Garcia	.05	611 Reggie Smith	.10	650 Jesus Vega	.07
528 Steve Nicosia	.05	570 Tommy John	.20	612 Rob Wilfong	.05	651 Jeff Jones	.05
529 Junior Kennedy	.05	571 Tony LaRussa (Mgr.)	.05	613 Niekro Brothers	.15	652 Marvis Foley	.05
530 Whitey Herzog (Mgr.)	.05	572 Joel Youngblood	.05	Joe and Phil		653 Ty Cobb Puzzle	.20
531 Don Sutton	.35	573 Wayne Tolleson	.20	614 Lee Elia (Mgr.)	.05	— Checklist (DK)	.08
532 Mark Brouhard	.05	574 Keith Creel	.07	615 Mickey Hatcher	.05	— Checklist No. 1	.08
533 Sparky Anderson (Mgr.)	.05	575 Billy Martin (Mgr.)	.15	616 Jerry Hairston	.05	— Checklist No. 2	.08
534 Roger LaFrancois	.05	576 Jerry Dybzinski	.05	617 John Martin	.05	— Checklist No. 3	.08
535 George Frazier	.05	577 Rick Cerone	.05	618 Wally Backman	.20	— Checklist No. 4	.08
536 Tom Niedenfuer	.07	578 Tony Perez	.15	619 Storm Davis (R)	.75	— Checklist No. 5	.08
537 Ed Glynn	.05	579 Greg Brock (R)	.35	620 Alan Knicely	.05	— Checklist No. 6	.08
538 Lee May	.05	580 Glen Wilson (R)	.45	621 John Stuper	.10		
539 Bob Kearney	.10	581 Tim Stoddard	.05	622 Matt Sinatro	.05		

1984 Donruss. . . . Complete Set of 658 Cards—Value $225.00

(Factory-Sealed set which includes corrected cards no. 29 and 30—Value $275.00)

Features the rookie cards of Don Mattingly, Darryl Strawberry, Ron Darling, Kevin McReynolds and Joe Carter. For the first time Donruss limited production of its main card set causing the price to rise substantially. *Living Legends* cards "A" and "B" were only issued in wax packs and were not part of the factory sealed set. The *checklist* cards are *not* numbered. Cards 29 and 30 exist with the card numbers deleted. Values for card no's. 1 to 26 are for the error cards (Perez "Steel") on the back. The corrected cards (Perez "Steele") are worth double the value.

NO. PLAYER	MINT	NO. PLAYER	MINT	NO. PLAYER	MINT	NO. PLAYER	MINT
No. 1 to 26—Diamond Kings		18 Ron Kittle (DK)	.25	31 Dion James (R)	.50	49 Lance Parrish	.30
1 Robin Yount (DK)	.75	19 Jim Clancy (DK)	.15	32 Tony Fernandez (R)	7.50	50 Jim Rice	.50
2 Dave Concepcion (DK)	.20	20 Bill Madlock (DK)	.20	33 Angel Salazar (R)	.15	51 Dav Winfeld	.50
3 Dwayne Murphy (DK)	.15	21 Larry Parrish (DK)	.20	34 Kevin McReynolds (R)	10.00	52 Fernando Valenzuela	.50
4 John Castino (DK)	.15	22 Eddie Murray (DK)	.75	35 Dick Schofield (R)	.50	53 George Brett	1.00
5 Leon Durham (DK)	.30	23 Mike Schmidt (DK)	1.00	36 Brad Komminsk (R)	.30	54 Rickey Henderson	1.00
6 Rusty Staub (DK)	.15	24 Pedro Guerrero (DK)	.40	37 Tim Teufel (R)	.45	55 Gary Carter	.60
7 Jack Clark (DK)	.30	25 Andre Thornton (DK)	.15	38 Doug Frobel (R)	.15	56 Buddy Bell	.15
8 Dave Dravecky (DK)	.15	26 Wade Bogg (DK)	3.50	39 Greg Gagne (R)	.50	57 Reggie Jackson	1.25
9 Al Oliver (DK)	.20	**No. 27 to 46—(Rated Rookies)**		40 Mike Fuentes (R)	.15	58 Harold Baines	.30
10 Dave Righetti (DK)	.25	27 Joel Skinner (R)	.30	41 Joe Carter (R)	12.00	59 Ozzie Smith	.75
11 Hal McRae (DK)	.15	28 Tommy Dunbar (R)	.15	42 Mike Brown (R)	.25	60 Nolan Ryan	2.00
12 Ray Knight (DK)	.15	29 Mike Stenhouse (R)	.25	43 Mike Jeffcoat (R)	.15	61 Pete Rose	2.00
13 Bruce Sutter (DK)	.25	(no number on back)		44 Sid Fernandez (R)	6.00	62 Ron Oester	.10
14 Bob Horner (DK)	.25	29 Mike Stenhouse (R)	2.50	45 Brian Dayett (R)	.20	63 Steve Garvey	.75
15 Lance Parrish (DK)	.30	30 Ron Darling (R)	5.00	46 Chris Smith (R)	.15	64 Jason Thompson	.15
16 Matt Young (DK)	.15	(no number on back)		47 Eddie Murray	.75	65 Jack Clark	.35
17 Fred Lynn (DK)	.25	30 Ron Darling (R)	15.00	48 Robin Yount	1.00	66 Dale Murphy	1.35

NO. PLAYER	MINT
67 Leon Durham	.30
68 Darryl Strawberry (R)	35.00
69 Richie Zisk	.10
70 Kent Hrbek	.50
71 Dave Stieb	.25
72 Ken Schrom	.10
73 George Bell	1.75
74 Jon Moses	.15
75 Ed Lynch	.10
76 Chuck Rainey	.10
77 Biff Pocoroba	.10
78 Cecilio Guante	.10
79 Jim Barr	.10
80 Kurt Bevacqua	.10
81 Tom Foley	.15
82 Joe LeFebvre	.10
83 Andy Van Slyke (R)	3.00
84 Bob Lillis (Mgr.)	.10
85 Rick Adams	.15
86 Jerry Hairston	.10
87 Bob James	.25
88 Joe Altobelli (Mgr.)	.10
89 Ed Romero	.10
90 John Grubb	.10
91 John H. Johnson	.10
92 Juan Espino	.12
93 Candy Maldonado	.20
94 Andre Thornton	.15
95 Onix Concepcion	.10
96 Don Hill	.12
97 Andre Dawson	.50
98 Frank Tanana	.15
99 Curt Wilkerson	.15
100 Larry Gura	.10
101 Dwayne Murphy	.15
102 Tom Brennan	.10
103 Dave Righetti	.30
104 Steve Sax	.50
105 Dan Petry	.20
106 Cal Ripken	1.00
107 Paul Molitor	.30
108 Fred Lynn	.25
109 Neil Allen	.15
110 Joe Niekro	.15
111 Steve Carlton	.50
112 Terry Kennedy	.15
113 Bill Madlock	.20
114 Chili Davis	.15
115 Jim Gantner	.10
116 Tom Seaver	.75
117 Bill Buckner	.15
118 Bill Caudill	.10
119 Jim Clancy	.10
120 John Castino	.10
121 Dave Concepcion	.15
122 Greg Luzinski	.15
123 Mike Boddicker	.15
124 Pete Ladd	.10
125 Juan Berenguer	.10
126 John Montefusco	.10
127 Ed Jurak	.12
128 Tom Niedenfuer	.10
129 Bert Blyleven	.15
130 Bud Black	.10
131 Gorman Heimueller	.15
132 Dan Schatzeder	.10
133 Ron Jackson	.10
134 Tom Henke (R)	.75
135 Kevin Hickey	.10
136 Mike Scott	.40
137 Bo Diaz	.10
138 Glenn Brummer	.10
139 Sid Monge	.10
140 Rich Gale	.10
141 Brett Butler	.15
142 Brian Harper	.12
143 John Rabb	.12
144 Gary Woods	.10
145 Pat Putnam	.10
146 Jim Acker	.15
147 Mickey Hatcher	.10
148 Todd Cruz	.10
149 Tom Tellmann	.10
150 John Wockenfuss	.10
151 Wade Boggs	10.00
152 Don Baylor	.20
153 Bob Welch	.15
154 Alan Bannister	.10
155 Willie Aikens	.10
156 Jeff Burroughs	.10
157 Bryan Little	.15
158 Bob Boone	.15
159 Dave Hostetler	.10
160 Jerry Dybzinski	.10
161 Mike Madden	.15
162 Luis DeLeon	.10
163 Willie Hernandez	.25
164 Frank Pastore	.10
165 Rick Camp	.10
166 Lee Mazzilli	.12
167 Scot Thompson	.10
168 Bob Forsch	.12
169 Mike Flanagan	.10
170 Rick Manning	.10
171 Chet Lemon	.15
172 Jerry Remy	.10
173 Ron Guidry	.30
174 Pedro Guerrero	.40
175 Willie Wilson	.25
176 Carney Lansford	.15
177 Al Oliver	.15
178 Jim Sundberg	.10
179 Bobby Grich	.15
180 Richard Dotson	.10
181 Joaquin Andujar	.15
182 Jose Cruz	.10
183 Mike Schmidt	2.00
184 Gary Redus (R)	.40
185 Garry Templeton	.15
186 Tony Pena	.15
187 Greg Minton	.10
188 Phil Niekro	.35
189 Ferguson Jenkins	.25
190 Mookie Wilson	.15
191 Jim Beattie	.10
192 Gary Ward	.10
193 Jesse Barfield	.35
194 Pete Filson	.15
195 Roy Lee Jackson	.10
196 Rick Sweet	.10
197 Jesse Orosco	.15
198 Steve Lake	.12
199 Ken Dayley	.10
200 Manny Sarmiento	.10
201 Mark Davis	.60
202 Tim Flannery	.10
203 Bill Scherrer	.12
204 Al Holland	.10
205 Dave Von Ohlen	.15
206 Mike LaCoss	.10
207 Juan Beniquez	.10
208 Juan Agosto	.25
209 Bobby Ramos	.10
210 Al Bumbry	.10
211 Mark Brouhard	.10
212 Howard Bailey	.10
213 Bruce Hurst	.15
214 Bob Shirley	.10
215 Pat Zachry	.10
216 Julio Franco	.75
217 Mike Armstrong	.10
218 Dave Beard	.10
219 Steve Rogers	.10
220 John Butcher	.10
221 Mike Smithson	.15
222 Frank White	.12
223 Mike Heath	.10
224 Chris Bando	.10
225 Roy Smalley	.10
226 Dusty Baker	.10
227 Lou Whitaker	.30
228 John Lowenstein	.10
229 Ben Ogilvie	.10
230 Doug DeCinces	.15
231 Lonnie Smith	.15
232 Ray Knight	.15
233 Gary Matthews	.15
234 Juan Bonilla	.10
235 Rod Scurry	.10
236 Atlee Hammaker	.10
237 Mike Caldwell	.10
238 Keith Hernandez	.60
239 Larry Bowa	.10
240 Tony Bernazard	.10
241 Damaso Garcia	.15
242 Tom Brunansky	.40
243 Dan Driessen	.15
244 Ron Kittle	.25
245 Tim Stoddard	.10
246 Bob Gibson	.10
247 Marty Castillo	.10
248 Don Mattingly (R)	55.00
249 Jeff Newman	.10
250 Alejandro Pena	.35
251 Toby Harrah	.12
252 Cesar Geronimo	.10
253 Tom Underwood	.10
254 Doug Flynn	.10
255 Andy Hassler	.10
256 Odell Jones	.10
257 Rudy Law	.10
258 Harry Spilman	.10
259 Marty Bystrom	.10
260 Dave Rucker	.10
261 Ruppert Jones	.10
262 Jeff Jones	.15
263 Gerald Perry	1.25
264 Gene Tenace	.10
265 Brad Wellman	.12
266 Dickie Noles	.10
267 Jamie Allen	.12
268 Jim Gott	.12
269 Ron Davis	.10
270 Benny Ayala	.10
271 Ned Yost	.10
272 Dave Rozema	.10
273 Dave Stapleton	.10
274 Lou Piniella	.10
275 Jose Morales	.10
276 Brod Perkins	.10
277 Butch Davis	.15
278 Tony Phillips	.12
279 Jeff Reardon	.15
280 Ken Forsch	.10
281 Pete O'Brien (R)	1.50
282 Tom Paciorek	.10
283 Frank LaCorte	.10
284 Tim Lollar	.10
285 Greg Gross	.10
286 Alex Trevino	.10
287 Gene Garber	.10
288 Dave Parker	.40
289 Lee Smith	.15
290 Dave LaPoint	.10
291 John Shelby	.60
292 Charlie Moore	.10
293 Alan Trammell	.40
294 Tony Armas	.15
295 Shane Rawley	.12
296 Greg Brock	.15
297 Hal McRae	.12
298 Mike Davis	.10
299 Tim Raines	.60
300 Bucky Dent	.12
301 Tommy John	.30
302 Carlton Fisk	.30
303 Darrell Porter	.10
304 Dickie Thon	.10
305 Garry Maddox	.10
306 Cesar Cedeno	.15
307 Gary Lucas	.10
308 Johnny Ray	.20
309 Andy McGaffigan	.10
310 Claudell Washington	.15
311 Ryne Sandberg	2.00
312 George Foster	.20
313 Spike Owen (R)	.35
314 Gary Gaetti	.75
315 Willie Upshaw	.15
316 Al Williams	.10
317 Jorge Orta	.10
318 Orlando Mercado	.12
319 Junior Ortiz	.12
320 Mike Proly	.10
321 Randy Johnson	.10
322 Jim Morrison	.10
323 Max Venable	.10
324 Tony Gwynn	5.00
325 Duane Walker	.10
326 Ozzie Virgil	.10
327 Jeff Lahti	.10
328 Bill Dawley	.20
329 Rob Wilfong	.10
330 Marc Hill	.10
331 Ray Burris	.10
332 Allan Ramirez	.12
333 Chuck Porter	.10
334 Wayne Krenchicki	.10
335 Gary Allenson	.10
336 Bob Meacham	.25
337 Joe Beckwith	.10
338 Rick Sutcliffe	.30
339 Mark Huismann	.15
340 Tim Conroy	.15
341 Scott Sanderson	.10
342 Larry Biittner	.10
343 Dave Stewart	.50
344 Darryl Motley	.10
345 Chris Codiroli	.12
346 Rich Behenna	.12
347 Andre Robertson	.10
348 Mike Marshall	.20
349 Larry Herndon	.10
350 Rich Dauer	.10
351 Cecil Cooper	.15
352 Rod Carew	.50
353 Willie McGee	.50
354 Phil Garner	.10
355 Joe Morgan	.40
356 Luis Salazar	.10
357 John Candelaria	.15
358 Bill Laskey	.10
359 Bob McClure	.10
360 Dave Kingman	.15
361 Ron Cey	.15
362 Matt Young (R)	.20
363 Lloyd Moseby	.20
364 Frank Viola	1.00
365 Eddie Milner	.10
366 Floyd Bannister	.12
367 Dan Ford	.12
368 Moose Haas	.10
369 Doug Bair	.10
370 Ray Fontenot (R)	.15
371 Luis Aponte	.10
372 Jack Fimple	.10
373 Neal Heaton	.20
374 Greg Pryor	.10
375 Wayne Gross	.10
376 Charlie Lea	.10
377 Steve Lubratich	.12
378 Jon Matlack	.12
379 Julio Cruz	.10
380 John Mizerock	.12
381 Kevin Gross (R)	.40
382 Mike Ramsey	.10
383 Doug Gwosdz	.10
384 Kelly Paris	.15
385 Pete Falcone	.10
386 Milt May	.10
387 Fred Breining	.10
388 Craig Lefferts (R)	.20
389 Steve Henderson	.10
390 Randy Moffitt	.10
391 Ron Washington	.10
392 Gary Roenicke	.10
393 Tom Candiotti (R)	.30
394 Larry Pashnick	.10
395 Dwight Evans	.25
396 Goose Gossage	.20
397 Derrel Thomas	.10
398 Juan Eichelberger	.10
399 Leon Roberts	.10
400 Davey Lopes	.15
401 Bill Gullickson	.12
402 Geoff Zahn	.10
403 Billy Sample	.10
404 Mike Squires	.10
405 Craig Reynolds	.10
406 Eric Show	.10

NO.	PLAYER	MINT
407	John Denny	.20
408	Dann Bilardello	.12
409	Bruce Benedict	.10
410	Kent Tekulve	.12
411	Mel Hall	.15
412	John Stuper	.10
413	Rick Dempsey	.12
414	Don Sutton	.40
415	Jack Morris	.30
416	John Tudor	.30
417	Willie Randolph	.15
418	Jerry Reuss	.12
419	Don Slaught	.12
420	Steve McCatty	.10
421	Tim Wallach	.20
422	Larry Parrish	.15
423	Brian Downing	.15
424	Britt Burns	.15
425	David Green	.15
426	Jerry Mumphrey	.10
427	Ivn DeJesus	.10
428	Mario Soto	.12
429	Gene Richards	.10
430	Dale Berra	.10
431	Darrell Evans	.15
432	Glenn Hubbard	.10
433	Jody Davis	.12
434	Danny Heep	.10
435	Ed Nunez	.25
436	Bobby Castillo	.10
437	Ernie Whitt	.10
438	Scott Ullger	.15
439	Doyle Alexander	.15
440	Domingo Ramos	.12
441	Craig Swan	.10
442	Warren Brusstar	.10
443	Len Barker	.10
444	Mike Easler	.10
445	Renie Martin	.10
446	Dennis Rasmussen (R)	.60
447	Ted Power	.15
448	Charlie Hudson (R)	.25
449	Danny Cox (R)	.75
450	Kevin Bass	.25
451	Daryl Sconiers	.10
452	Scott Fletcher	.12
453	Bryn Smith	.12
454	Jim Dwyer	.10
455	Rob Picciolo	.10
456	Enos Cabell	.10
457	"Oil Can" Boyd (R)	.75
458	Butch Wynegar	.10
459	Burt Hooton	.10
460	Ron Hassey	.10
461	Danny Jackson (R)	3.50
462	Bob Kearney	.10
463	Terry Francona	.10
464	Wayne Tolleson	.10
465	Mickey Rivers	.15
466	John Wathan	.10
467	Bill Almon	.10
468	George Vukovich	.10
469	Steve Kemp	.12
470	Ken Landreaux	.10
471	Milt Wilcox	.10
472	Tippy Martinez	.10
473	Ted Simmons	.15
474	Tim Foli	.10
475	George Hendrick	.10
476	Terry Puhl	.15
477	Von Hayes	.20
478	Bobby Brown	.10
479	Lee Lacy	.10
480	Joel Youngblood	.10
481	Jim Slaton	.10
482	Mike Fitzgerald	.10
483	Keith Moreland	.10
484	Ron Roenicke	.10
485	Luis Leal	.10
486	Bryan Oelkers	.12
487	Bruce Berenyi	.10
488	LaMarr Hoyt	.15
489	Joe Nolan	.10
490	Marshall Edwards	.10
491	Mike Laga	.12
492	Rick Cerone	.10
493	Rick Miller	.10
494	Rick Honeycutt	.12
495	Mike Hargrove	.12
496	Joe Simpson	.10
497	Keith Atherton	.12
498	Chris Welsh	.10
499	Bruce Kison	.10
500	Bobby Johnson	.10
501	Jerry Koosman	.20
502	Frank DiPino	.10
503	Tony Perez	.20
504	Ken Oberkfell	.10
505	Mark Thurmond (R)	.20
506	Joe Price	.10
507	Pascual Perez	.35
508	Marvell Wynne	.20
509	Mike Krukow	.15
510	Dick Ruthven	.10
511	Al Cowens	.10
512	Cliff Johnson	.10
513	Randy Bush	.25
514	Sammy Stewart	.10
515	Bill Schroeder (R)	.20
516	Aurelio Lopez	.10
517	Mike Brown	.15
518	Graig Nettles	.20
519	Dave Sax	.12
520	Gerry Willard	.15
521	Paul Splittorff	.12
522	Tom Burgmeier	.10
523	Chris Speier	.10
524	Bobby Clark	.10
525	George Wright	.10
526	Dennis Lamp	.10
527	Tony Scott	.10
528	Ed Whitson	.12
529	Ron Reed	.10
530	Charlie Puleo	.10
531	Jerry Royster	.10
532	Don Robinson	.10
533	Steve Trout	.10
534	Bruce Sutter	.20
535	Bob Horner	.20
536	Pat Tabler	.15
537	Chris Chambliss	.15
538	Bob Ojeda	.20
539	Alan Ashby	.10
540	Jay Johnstone	.12
541	Bob Dernier	.10
542	Brook Jacoby (R)	1.50
543	U.L. Washington	.10
544	Danny Darwin	.10
545	Kiko Garcia	.10
546	Vance Law	.10
547	Tug McGraw	.15
548	Dave Smith	.10
549	Len Matuszek	.10
550	Tom Hume	.10
551	Dave Dravecky	.40
552	Rick Rhoden	.15
553	Duane Kuiper	.10
554	Rusty Staub	.15
555	Bill Campbell	.10
556	Mike Torrez	.10
557	Dave Henderson	.25
558	Len Whitehouse	.12
559	Barry Bonnell	.10
560	Rick Lysander	.12
561	Garth Iorg	.10
562	Bryan Clark	.10
563	Brian Giles	.10
564	Vern Ruhle	.10
565	Steve Bedrosian	.25
566	Larry McWilliams	.10
567	Jeff Leonard	.15
568	Alan Wiggins	.12
569	Jeff Russell	.45
570	Salome Barojas	.10
571	Dane Iorg	.10
572	Bob Knepper	.15
573	Gary Lavelle	.10
574	Gorman Thomas	.15
575	Manny Trillo	.10
576	Jim Palmer	.50
577	Dale Murray	.10
578	Tom Brookens	.10
579	Rich Gedman	.12
580	Bill Doran (R)	1.00
581	Steve Yeager	.10
582	Dan Spillner	.10
583	Dan Quisenberry	.25
584	Rance Mulliniks	.10
585	Storm Davis	.15
586	Dave Schmidt	.10
587	Bill Russell	.10
588	Pat Sheridan	.30
589	Rafael Ramirez	.12
590	Bud Anderson	.10
591	George Frazier	.10
592	Lee Tunnell	.15
593	Kirk Gibson	.50
594	Scott McGregor	.10
595	Bob Bailor	.10
596	Tom Herr	.15
597	Luis Sanchez	.10
598	Dave Engle	.10
599	Craig McMurtry (R)	.15
600	Carlos Diaz	.10
601	Tom O'Malley	.10
602	Nick Esasky (R)	3.50
603	Ron Hodges	.10
604	Ed Vande Berg	.10
605	Alfredo Griffin	.15
606	Glenn Hoffman	.10
607	Hubie Brooks	.25
608	Richard Barnes	.12
609	Greg Walker (R)	.50
610	Ken Singleton	.15
611	Mark Clear	.10
612	Buck Martinez	.10
613	Ken Griffey	.15
614	Reid Nichols	.10
615	Doug Sisk (R)	.15
616	Bob Brenly	.10
617	Joey McLaughlin	.10
618	Glenn Wilson	.15
619	Bob Stoddard	.10
620	Len Sakata	.08
621	Mike Young (R)	.35
622	John Stefero	.12
623	Carmelo Martinez (R)	.30
624	Dave Bergman	.10
625	Runnin' Redbirds:	.25
	David Green, Willie McGee,	
	Lonnie Smith, Ozzie Smith	
626	Rudy May	.10
627	Matt Keough	.10
628	Jose DeLeon (R)	.75
629	Jim Essian	.10
630	Darnell Coles (R)	.35
631	Mike Warren	.15
632	Del Crandall (Mgr.)	.10
633	Dennis Martinez	.12
634	Mike Moore	.10
635	Lary Sorensen	.10
636	Ricky Nelson	.15
637	Omar Moreno	.10
638	Charlie Hough	.10
639	Dennis Eckersley	.25
640	Walt Terrell (R)	.35
641	Denny Walling	.10
642	Dave Anderson	.25
643	Jose Oquendo (R)	.75
644	Bob Stanley	.10
645	Dave Geisel	.10
646	Scott Garrelts (R)	1.50
647	Gary Pettis (R)	.40
648	Duke Snider Puzzle	.15
649	Johnnie LeMaster	.10
650	Dave Collins	.12
651	The Chicken	.25
—	Checklist (DK)	.18
—	Checklist No. 1	.15
—	Checklist No. 2	.15
—	Checklist No. 3	.15
—	Checklist No. 4	.15
—	Checklist No. 5	.15
—	Checklist No. 6	.15

Cards From Wax Packs

A	Living Legends:	2.00
	G. Perry, R. Fingers	
B	Living Legends:	5.00
	C. Yastrzemski, J. Bench	

1985 Donruss. . . . Complete Set of 660 Cards—Value $160.00

(Factory-Sealed set which includes corrected cards no. 424 and 534—Value $190.00)

Features the rookie cards of Dwight Gooden, Roger Clemens, Eric Davis, Orel Hershiser, Bret Saberhagen and Kirby Puckett. As in 1984, Donruss limited the quantity of cards printed. The *checklist* cards are *not* numbered.

NO. PLAYER	MINT
No. 1 to 26 (Diamond Kings)	
1 Ryne Sandberg (DK)	.60
2 Doug DeCinces (DK)	.12
3 Rich Dotson (DK)	.12
4 Bert Blyleven (DK)	.12
5 Lou Whitaker (DK)	.20
6 Dan Quisenberry (DK)	.20
7 Don Mattingly (DK)	6.00
8 Carney Lansford (DK)	.12
9 Frank Tanana (DK)	.12
10 Willie Upshaw (DK)	.12
11 C. Washington (DK)	.12
12 Mike Marshall (DK)	.15
13 Joaquin Andujar (DK)	.12
14 Cal Ripken (DK)	.50
15 Jim Rice (DK)	.35
16 Don Sutton (DK)	.25
17 Frank Viola (DK)	.45
18 Alvin Davis (DK)	.40
19 Mario Soto (DK)	.12
20 Jose Cruz (DK)	.12
21 Charlie Lea (DK)	.12
22 Jesse Orosco (DK)	.12
23 Juan Samuel (DK)	.30
24 Tony Pena (DK)	.12
25 Tony Gwynn (DK)	.75
26 Bob Brenly (DK)	.12
No. 27 to 46 (Rated Rookies)	
27 Danny Tartabull (R)	7.00
28 Mike Bielecki (R)	1.00
29 Steve Lyons (R)	.15
30 Jeff Reed (R)	.15
31 Tony Brewer (R)	.15
32 John Morris (R)	.15
33 Daryl Boston (R)	.25
34 Alfonso Pulido (R)	.15
35 Steve Kiefer (R)	.15
36 Larry Sheets (R)	.40
37 Scott Bradley (R)	.35
38 Calvin Schiraldi (R)	.30
39 Shawon Dunston (R)	2.50
40 Charlie Mitchell (R)	.15
41 Billy Hatcher (R)	.45
42 Russ Stephans (R)	.15
43 Alejandro Sanchez (R)	.15
44 Steve Jeltz (R)	.20
45 Jim Traber (R)	.30
46 Doug Loman (R)	.20
47 Eddie Murray	.50
48 Robin Yount	.60
49 Lance Parrish	.20
50 Jim Rice	.35
51 Dave Winfield	.35
52 Fernando Valenzuela	.25
53 George Brett	.60
54 Dave Kingman	.10
55 Gary Carter	.30
56 Buddy Bell	.10
57 Reggie Jackson	.40
58 Harold Baines	.20
59 Ozzie Smith	.30
60 Nolan Ryan	.75
61 Mike Schmidt	.75
62 Dave Parker	.20
63 Tony Gwynn	1.00
64 Tony Pena	.15
65 Jack Clark	.30
66 Dale Murphy	.75
67 Ryne Sandberg	.50
68 Keith Hernandez	.30
69 Alvin Davis (R)	2.50
70 Kent Hrbek	.40
71 Willie Upshaw	.10
72 Dave Engle	.08
73 Alfredo Griffin	.08
74 Jack Perconte	.08
75 Jesse Orosco	.10
76 Jody Davis	.10
77 Bob Horner	.15
78 Larry McWilliams	.08
79 Joel Youngblood	.08
80 Alan Wiggins	.10
81 Ron Oester	.08
82 Ozzie Virgil	.08
83 Ricky Horton (R)	.25

NO. PLAYER	MINT
84 Bill Doran	.15
85 Rod Carew	.50
86 LaMarr Hoyt	.10
87 Tim Wallach	.12
88 Mike Flanagan	.08
89 Jim Sundberg	.08
90 Chet Lemon	.08
91 Bob Stanley	.08
92 Willie Randolph	.08
93 Bill Russell	.08
94 Julio Franco	.30
95 Dan Quisenberry	.20
96 Bill Claudill	.08
97 Bill Gullickson	.08
98 Danny Darwin	.08
99 Curt Wilkerson	.08
100 Bud Black	.08
101 Tony Phillips	.08
102 Tony Bernazard	.08
103 Jay Howell	.08
104 Burt Hooton	.08
105 Milt Wilcox	.08
106 Rich Dauer	.08
107 Don Sutton	.20
108 Mike Witt	.12
109 Bruce Sutter	.15
110 Enos Cabell	.08
111 John Denny	.12
112 Dave Dravecky	.25
113 Marvell Wynne	.08
114 John LeMaster	.08
115 Chuck Porter	.08
116 John Gibbons	.15
117 Keith Moreland	.08
118 Darnell Coles	.08
119 Dennis Lamp	.08
120 Ron Davis	.08
121 Nick Esasky	.08
122 Vance Law	.08
123 Gary Roenicke	.08
124 Bill Schroeder	.08
125 Dave Rozema	.08
126 Bobby Meacham	.08
127 Marty Barrett	.25
128 R.J. Reynolds (R)	.35
129 Ernie Camacho	.08
130 Jorge Orta	.08
131 Lary Sorensen	.08
132 Terry Francona	.08
133 Fred Lynn	.20
134 Bobby Jones	.08
135 Jerry Hairston	.08
136 Kevin Bass	.15
137 Garry Maddox	.08
138 Dave LaPoint	.08
139 Kevin McReynolds	.75
140 Wayne Krenchicki	.08
141 Rafael Ramirez	.08
142 Rod Scurry	.08
143 Greg Minton	.08
144 Tim Stoddard	.08
145 Steve Henderson	.08
146 George Bell	.60
147 Dave Meier	.15
148 Sammy Stewart	.08
149 Mark Brouhard	.08
150 Larry Herndon	.08
151 Oil Can Boyd	.15
152 Brian Dayett	.08
153 Tom Niedenfuer	.08
154 Brook Jacoby	.15
155 Onix Concepcion	.08
156 Tim Conroy	.08
157 Joe Hesketh (R)	.20
158 Brian Downing	.15
159 Tom Dunbar	.08
160 Marc Hill	.08
161 Phil Garner	.08
162 Jerry Davis	.12
163 Bill Campbell	.08
164 John Franco (R)	2.00
165 Len Barker	.08
166 Benny Distefano	.12
167 George Frazier	.08
168 Tito Landrum	.08

NO. PLAYER	MINT
169 Cal Ripken, Jr.	.45
170 Cecil Cooper	.15
171 Alan Trammell	.25
172 Wade Boggs	5.00
173 Don Baylor	.15
174 Pedro Guerrero	.25
175 Frank White	.08
176 Rickey Henderson	.50
177 Charlie Lea	.08
178 Pete O'Brien	.12
179 Doug DeCinces	.12
180 Ron Kittle	.15
181 George Hendrick	.08
182 Joe Niekro	.12
183 Juan Samuel	1.00
184 Mario Soto	.12
185 Goose Gossage	.15
186 Johnny Ray	.12
187 Bob Brenly	.08
188 Craig McMurtey	.08
189 Leon Durham	.15
190 Dwight Gooden (R)	12.00
191 Barry Bonnell	.08
192 Tim Teufel	.08
193 Dave Stieb	.25
194 Mickey Hatcher	.08
195 Jesse Barfield	.30
196 Al Cowens	.08
197 Hubie Brooks	.15
198 Steve Trout	.08
199 Glenn Hubbard	.08
200 Bill Madlock	.12
201 Jeff Robinson (R)	.35
202 Eric Show	.15
203 Dave Concepcion	.12
204 Ivan DeJesus	.08
205 Neil Allen	.10
206 Jerry Mumphrey	.08
207 Mike Brown	.08
208 Carlton Fisk	.20
209 Bryn Smith	.08
210 Tippy Martinez	.08
211 Dion James	.08
212 Willie Hernandez	.15
213 Mike Easler	.08
214 Ron Guidry	.20
215 Rick Honeycutt	.08
216 Brett Butler	.10
217 Larry Gura	.08
218 Ray Burris	.08
219 Steve Rogers	.08
220 Frank Tanana	.08
221 Ned Yost	.08
222 Bret Saberhagen (R)	7.00
223 Mike Davis	.08
224 Bert Blyleven	.15
225 Steve Kemp	.08
226 Jerry Reuss	.08
227 Darrell Evans	.15
228 Wayne Gross	.08
229 Jim Gantner	.08
230 Bob Boone	.08
231 Lonnie Smith	.08
232 Frank DiPino	.08
233 Jerry Koosman	.08
234 Graig Nettles	.15
235 John Tudor	.15
236 John Rabb	.08
237 Rick Manning	.08
238 Mike Fitzgerald	.08
239 Gary Matthews	.08
240 Jim Presley (R)	1.00
241 Dave Collins	.08
242 Gary Gaetti	.35
243 Dann Bilardello	.08
244 Rudy Law	.08
245 John Lowenstein	.08
246 Tom Tellman	.08
247 Howard Johnson	1.25
248 Ray Fontenot	.08
249 Tony Armas	.12
250 Candy Maldonado	.15
251 Mike Jeffcoat	.08
252 Dane Iorg	.08
253 Bruce Bochte	.08

NO. PLAYER	MINT
254 Pete Rose	1.25
255 Don Aase	.10
256 George Wright	.08
257 Britt Burns	.08
258 Mike Scott	.35
259 Len Matuszek	.08
260 Dave Rucker	.08
261 Craig Lefferts	.08
262 Jay Tibbs	.20
263 Bruce Benedict	.08
264 Don Robinson	.08
265 Gary Lavelle	.08
266 Scott Sanderson	.08
267 Matt Young	.08
268 Ernie Whitt	.08
269 Houston Jimenez	.08
270 Ken Dixon	.20
271 Peter Ladd	.08
272 Juan Berenguer	.08
273 Roger Clemens (R)	13.50
274 Rick Cerone	.08
275 Dave Anderson	.08
276 George Vukovich	.08
277 Greg Pryor	.08
278 Mike Warren	.08
279 Bob James	.08
280 Bobby Grich	.10
281 Mike Mason	.15
282 Ron Reed	.08
283 Alan Ashby	.08
284 Mark Thurmond	.08
285 Joe Lefebvre	.08
286 Ted Power	.08
287 Chris Chambliss	.08
288 Lee Tunnell	.08
289 Rich Bordi	.08
290 Glenn Brummer	.08
291 Mike Boddicker	.10
292 Rollie Fingers	.15
293 Lou Whitaker	.20
294 Dwight Evans	.15
295 Don Mattingly	15.00
296 Mike Marshall	.15
297 Willie Wilson	.12
298 Mike Heath	.08
299 Tim Raines	.40
300 Larry Parrish	.08
301 Geoff Zahn	.08
302 Rich Dotson	.08
303 David Green	.08
304 Jose Cruz	.10
305 Steve Carlton	.35
306 Gary Redus	.08
307 Steve Garvey	.35
308 Jose DeLeon	.08
309 Randy Lerch	.08
310 Claudell Washington	.10
311 Lee Smith	.10
312 Darryl Strawberry	5.00
313 Jim Beattie	.08
314 John Butcher	.08
315 Damaso Garcia	.10
316 Mike Smithson	.08
317 Luis Leal	.08
318 Ken Phelps	.50
319 Wally Backman	.08
320 Ron Cey	.12
321 Brad Komminsk	.12
322 Jason Thompson	.10
323 Frank Williams	.12
324 Tim Lollar	.08
325 Eric Davis (R)	16.00
326 Von Hayes	.20
327 Andy Van Slyke	.50
328 Craig Reynolds	.08
329 Dick Schofield	.10
330 Scott Fletcher	.10
331 Jeff Reardon	.10
332 Rick Dempsey	.10
333 Ben Oglivie	.15
334 Dan Petry	.15
335 Jackie Gutierrez	.15
336 Dave Righetti	.15
337 Alejandro Pena	.08
338 Mel Hall	.08

NO.	PLAYER	MINT
339	Pat Sheridan	.08
340	Keith Atherton	.08
341	David Palmer	.08
342	Gary Ward	.08
343	Dave Stewart	.25
344	Mark Gubicza (R)	1.25
345	Carney Lansford	.12
346	Jerry Willard	.08
347	Ken Griffey	.08
348	Franklin Stubbs (R)	.40
349	Aurelio Lopez	.08
350	Al Bumbry	.08
351	Charlie Moore	.08
352	Luis Sanchez	.08
353	Darrell Porter	.08
354	Bill Dawley	.08
355	Charlie Hudson	.08
356	Garry Templeton	.12
357	Cecilio Guante	.08
358	Jeff Leonard	.12
359	Paul Molitor	.25
360	Ron Gardenhire	.08
361	Larry Bowa	.08
362	Bob Kearney	.08
363	Garth Iorg	.08
364	Tom Brunansky	.30
365	Brad Gulden	.08
366	Greg Walker	.12
367	Mike Young	.15
368	Rick Waits	.08
369	Doug Bair	.08
370	Bob Shirley	.08
371	Bob Ojeda	.08
372	Bob Welch	.08
373	Neal Heaton	.08
374	Dan Jackson	.50
375	Donnie Hill	.08
376	Mike Stenhouse	.08
377	Bruce Kison	.08
378	Wayne Tolleson	.08
379	Floyd Bannister	.08
380	Vern Ruhle	.08
381	Tim Corcoran	.08
382	Kurt Kepshire (R)	.15
383	Bobby Brown	.08
384	Dave Van Gorder	.08
385	Rick Mahler	.08
386	Lee Mazzilli	.08
387	Bill Laskey	.08
388	Thad Bosley	.08
389	Al Chambers	.08
390	Tony Fernandez	.50
391	Ron Washington	.08
392	Bill Swaggerty (R)	.15
393	Bob L. Gibson	.08
394	Marty Castillo	.08
395	Steve Crawford	.08
396	Clay Christiansen (R)	.15
397	Bob Bailor	.08
398	Mike Hargrove	.08
399	Charlie Leibrandt	.08
400	Tom Burgmeier	.08
401	Razor Shines (R)	.15
402	Rob Wilfong	.08
403	Tom Henke	.15
404	Al Jones (R)	.15
405	Mike LaCoss	.08
406	Luis DeLeon	.08
407	Greg Gross	.08
408	Tom Hume	.08
409	Rick Camp	.08
410	Milt May	.08
411	Henry Cotto (R)	.20
412	David Von Ohlen	.08
413	Scott McGregor	.10
414	Ted Simmons	.10
415	Jack Morris	.20
416	Bill Buckner	.10
417	Butch Wynegar	.08
418	Steve Sax	.25
419	Steve Balboni	.08
420	Dwayne Murphy	.08
421	Andre Dawson	.25
422	Charlie Hough	.08
423	Tommy John	.15
424	Tom Seaver (photo of Floyd Bannister)	1.00
424	Tom Seaver	7.00
425	Tom Herr	.10
426	Terry Puhl	.08
427	Al Holland	.08
428	Eddie Milner	.08
429	Terry Kennedy	.08
430	John Candelaria	.08
431	Manny Trillo	.08
432	Ken Oberkfell	.08
433	Rick Sutcliffe	.15
434	Ron Darling	1.00
435	Spike Owen	.08
436	Frank Viola	.50
437	Lloyd Moseby	.20
438	Kirby Puckett (R)	15.00
439	Jim Clancy	.08
440	Mike Moore	.08
441	Doug Sisk	.08
442	Dennis Eckersley	.08
443	Gerald Perry	.25
444	Dale Berra	.08
445	Dusty Baker	.08
446	Ed Whitson	.08
447	Cesar Cedeno	.10
448	Rick Schu (R)	.25
449	Joaquin Andujar	.10
450	Mark Bailey (R)	.15
451	Ron Romanick (R)	.20
452	Julio Cruz	.08
453	Miguel Dilone	.08
454	Storm Davis	.08
455	Jaime Cocanower (R)	.15
456	Barbaro Garbey (R)	.15
457	Rich Gedman	.08
458	Phil Niekro	.20
459	Mike Scioscia	.08
460	Pat Tabler	.12
461	Darryl Motley	.08
462	Chris Codiroli	.08
463	Doug Flynn	.08
464	Billy Sample	.08
465	Mickey Rivers	.08
466	John Wathan	.08
467	Bill Krueger	.08
468	Andre Thornton	.12
469	Rex Hudler (R)	.15
470	Sid Bream (R)	.35
471	Kirk Gibson	.30
472	John Shelby	.08
473	Moose Haas	.08
474	Doug Corbett	.08
475	Willie McGee	.30
476	Bob Knepper	.12
477	Kevin Gross	.08
478	Carmelo Martinez	.12
479	Kent Tekulve	.08
480	Chili Davis	.12
481	Bobby Clark	.08
482	Mookie Wilson	.08
483	Dave Owen (R)	.15
484	Ed Nunez	.08
485	Rance Mulliniks	.08
486	Ken Schrom	.08
487	Jeff Russell	.08
488	Tom Paciorek	.08
489	Dan Ford	.08
490	Mike Caldwell	.08
491	Scottie Earl (R)	.15
492	Jose Rijo (R)	.50
493	Bruce Hurst	.08
494	Ken Landreaux	.08
495	Mike Fischlin	.08
496	Don Slaught	.08
497	Steve McCatty	.08
498	Gary Lucas	.08
499	Gary Pettis	.10
500	Marvis Foley	.08
501	Mike Squires	.08
502	Jim Pankovitz	.12
503	Luis Aguayo	.08
504	Ralph Citarella	.12
505	Bruce Bochy	.08
506	Bob Owchinko	.08
507	Pascual Perez	.08
508	Lee Lacy	.08
509	Atlee Hammaker	.08
510	Bob Dernier	.08
511	Ed Vande Berg	.08
512	Cliff Johnson	.08
513	Len Whitehouse	.08
514	Dennis Martinez	.10
515	Ed Romero	.08
516	Rusty Kuntz	.08
517	Rick Miller	.08
518	Dennis Rasmussen	.10
519	Steve Yeager	.08
520	Chris Bando	.08
521	U.L. Washington	.08
522	Curt Young (R)	.35
523	Angel Salazar	.08
524	Curt Kaufman (R)	.15
525	Odell Jones	.08
526	Juan Agosto	.08
527	Denny Walling	.08
528	Andy Hawkins	.25
529	Sixto Lezcano	.08
530	Skeeter Barnes	.12
531	Randy Johnson	.08
532	Jim Morrison	.08
533	Warren Brusstar	.08
534	Jeff Pendleton (incorrect first name)	.75
534	Terry Pendleton	2.50
535	Vic Rodriguez (R)	.15
536	Bob McClure	.08
537	Dave Bergman	.08
538	Mark Clear	.08
539	Mike Pagliarulo (R)	1.00
540	Terry Whitfield	.08
541	Joe Beckwith	.08
542	Jeff Burroughs	.08
543	Dan Schatzeder	.08
544	Donnie Scott	.12
545	Jim Slaton	.08
546	Greg Luzinski	.10
547	Mark Salas (R)	.20
548	Dave Smith	.08
549	John Wockenfuss	.08
550	Frank Pastore	.08
551	Tim Flannery	.08
552	Rick Rhoden	.12
553	Mark Davis	.08
554	Jeff Dedmon (R)	.12
555	Gary Woods	.08
556	Danny Heep	.08
557	Mark Langston (R)	4.00
558	Darrell Brown	.08
559	Jimmy Key (R)	1.75
560	Rick Lysander	.08
561	Doyle Alexander	.08
562	Mike Stanton	.08
563	Sid Fernandez	.75
564	Richie Hebner	.08
565	Alex Trevino	.08
566	Brian Harper	.08
567	Dan Gladden (R)	.40
568	Luis Salazar	.08
569	Tom Foley	.08
570	Larry Andersen	.08
571	Danny Cox	.12
572	Joe Sambito	.08
573	Juan Beniquez	.08
574	Joel Skinner	.08
575	Randy St. Claire	.12
576	Floyd Rayford	.08
577	Roy Howell	.08
578	John Grubb	.08
579	Ed Jurak	.08
580	John Montefusco	.08
581	Orel Hershiser (R)	12.00
582	Tom Waddell (R)	.15
583	Mark Huismann	.08
584	Joe Morgan	.30
585	Jim Wohlford	.08
586	Dave Schmidt	.08
587	Jeff Kunkel	.15
588	Hal McRae	.08
589	Bill Almon	.08
590	Carmen Castillo	.08
591	Omar Moreno	.08
592	Ken Howell (R)	.20
593	Tom Brookens	.08
594	Joe Nolan	.08
595	Willie Lozado	.12
596	Tom Nieto	.15
597	Walt Terrell	.08
598	Al Oliver	.10
599	Shane Rawley	.08
600	Denny Gonzalez	.12
601	Mark Grant	.15
602	Mike Armstrong	.08
603	George Foster	.15
604	Davey Lopes	.12
605	Salome Barojas	.08
606	Roy Lee Jackson	.08
607	Pete Filson	.08
608	Duane Walker	.08
609	Glenn Wilson	.10
610	Rafael Santana (R)	.25
611	Roy Smith	.15
612	Ruppert Jones	.08
613	Joe Cowley	.08
614	Al Nipper (R)	.20
615	Gene Nelson	.08
616	Joe Carter	1.50
617	Ray Knight	.10
618	Chuck Rainey	.08
619	Dan Driessen	.08
620	Daryl Sconiers	.08
621	Bill Stein	.08
622	Roy Smalley	.08
623	Ed Lynch	.08
624	Jeff Stone (R)	.20
625	Bruce Berenyi	.08
626	Kelvin Chapman (R)	.15
627	Joe Price	.08
628	Steve Bedrosian	.12
629	Vic Mata	.15
630	Mike Krukow	.10
631	Phil Bradley (R)	1.00
632	Jim Gott	.08
633	Randy Bush	.08
634	Tom Browning (R)	1.50
635	Lou Gehrig Puzzle	.10
636	Reid Nichols	.08
637	Dan Pasqua (R)	.75
638	German Rivera	.12
639	Don Schulze	.10
640	Mike Jones	.10
641	Pete Rose (Mgr.)	1.00
642	Wade Rowdon	.10
643	Jerry Narron	.08
644	Darrell Miller	.15
645	Tim Hulett (R)	.15
646	Andy McGaffigan	.08
647	Kurt Bevacqua	.05
648	John Russell (R)	.15
649	Ron Robinson	.20
650	Donnie Moore	.08
651	Two For the Title: D. Winfield, D. Mattingly	5.00
652	Tim Laudner	.08
653	Steve Farr	.25
—	Checklist (DK)	.10
—	Checklist No. 1	.08
—	Checklist No. 2	.08
—	Checklist No. 3	.08
—	Checklist No. 4	.08
—	Checklist No. 5	.08
—	Checklist No. 6	.08

1986 Donruss. . . . Complete Set of 660 Cards—Value $135.00 (Factory-Sealed set—Value $160.00)

Features the rookie cards of Jose Canseco and Fred McGriff. Donruss limited production. The *checklist* cards are *not* numbered.

NO. PLAYER	MINT
No. 1 to 26—Diamond Kings	
1 Kirk Gibson (DK)	.35
2 Goose Gossage (DK)	.15
3 Willie McGee (DK)	.30
4 George Bell (DK)	.20
5 Tony Armas (DK)	.10
6 Chili Davis (DK)	.10
7 Cecil Cooper (DK)	.15
8 Mike Boddicker (DK)	.10
9 Davey Lopes (DK)	.10
10 Bill Doran (DK)	.10
11 Bret Saberhagen (DK)	.30
12 Brett Butler (DK)	.10
13 Harold Baines (DK)	.20
14 Mike Davis (DK)	.10
15 Tony Perez (DK)	.15
16 Willie Randolph (DK)	.10
17 Bob Boone (DK)	.10
18 Orel Hershiser (DK)	1.00
19 Johnny Ray (DK)	.10
20 Gary Ward (DK)	.10
21 Rick Mahler (DK)	.10
22 Phil Bradley (DK)	.20
23 Jerry Koosman (DK)	.10
24 Tom Brunansky (DK)	.10
25 Andre Dawson (DK)	.25
26 Dwigt Gooden (DK)	1.00
No. 27 to 46 (Rated Rookies)	
27 Kal Daniels (R)	4.00
28 Fred McGriff (R)	16.00
29 Cory Snyder (R)	3.00
30 Jose Guzman (R)	.40
31 Ty Gainey (R)	.15
32 Johnny Abrego (R)	.15
33 Andres Galarraga (R)	5.00
34 Dave Shipanoff (R)	.15
35 Mark McLemore (R)	.20
36 Marty Clary (R)	.15
37 Paul O'Neill (R)	.30
38 Danny Tartabull	1.50
39 Jose Canseco (R)	50.00
40 Juan Nieves (R)	.30
41 Lance McCullers (R)	.35
42 Rick Surhoff (R)	.15
43 Todd Worrell (R)	.75
44 Bob Kipper (R)	.20
45 John Habyan (R)	.15
46 Mike Woodard (R)	.15
47 Mike Boddicker	.10
48 Robin Yount	.30
49 Lou Whitaker	.15
50 Oil Can Boyd	.05
51 Ricky Henderson	.35
52 Mike Marshall	.10
53 George Brett	.50
54 Dave Kingman	.10
55 Hubie Brooks	.10
56 Oddibe McDowell	.30
57 Doug DeCinces	.10
58 Britt Burns	.05
59 Ozzie Smith	.35
60 Jose Cruz	.10
61 Mike Schmidt	.50
62 Pete Rose	.75
63 Steve Garvey	.35
64 Tony Pena	.10

NO. PLAYER	MINT
65 Chili Davis	.10
66 Dale Murphy	.50
67 Ryne Sandberg	.30
68 Gary Carter	.30
69 Alvin Davis	.15
70 Kent Hrbek	.15
71 George Bell	.30
72 Kirby Puckett	1.50
73 Lloyd Moseby	.10
74 Bob Kearney	.07
75 Dwight Gooden	2.00
76 Gary Matthews	.07
77 Rick Mahler	.07
78 Benny Distefano	.07
79 Jeff Leonard	.07
80 Kevin McReynolds	.40
81 Ron Oester	.07
82 John Russell	.07
83 Tommy Herr	.10
84 Jerry Mumphrey	.07
85 Ron Romanick	.07
86 Daryl Boston	.07
87 Andre Dawson	.25
88 Eddie Murray	.40
89 Dion James	.07
90 Chet Lemon	.07
91 Bob Stanley	.07
92 Willie Randolph	.07
93 Mike Scioscia	.07
94 Tom Waddell	.07
95 Danny Jackson	.30
96 Mike Davis	.07
97 Mike Fitzgerald	.07
98 Gary Ward	.07
99 Pete O'Brien	.07
100 Bret Saberhagen	.75
101 Alfredo Griffin	.07
102 Brett Butler	.07
103 Ron Guidry	.15
104 Jerry Reuss	.07
105 Jack Morris	.15
106 Rick Dempsey	.07
107 Ray Burris	.07
108 Brian Downing	.07
109 Willie McGee	.20
110 Bill Doran	.07
111 Kent Tekulve	.07
112 Tony Gwynn	.75
113 Marvell Wynne	.07
114 David Green	.07
115 Jim Gantner	.07
116 George Foster	.15
117 Steve Trout	.07
118 Mark Langston	.50
119 Tony Fernandez	.20
120 John Butcher	.07
121 Ron Robinson	.07
122 Dan Spillner	.07
123 Mike Young	.15
124 Paul Molitor	.20
125 Kirk Gibson	.30
126 Ken Griffey	.07
127 Tony Armas	.10
128 Mariano Duncan (R)	.20
129 Pat Tabler	.07
130 Frank White	.07

NO. PLAYER	MINT
131 Carney Lansford	.10
132 Vance Law	.07
133 Dick Schofield	.07
134 Wayne Tolleson	.07
135 Greg Walker	.10
136 Denny Walling	.07
137 Ozzie Virgil	.07
138 Ricky Horton	.07
139 LaMarr Hoyt	.10
140 Wayne Krenchicki	.07
141 Glenn Hubbard	.07
142 Cecilio Guante	.07
143 Mike Krukow	.07
144 Lee Smith	.07
145 Ed Nunez	.07
146 Dave Stieb	.15
147 Mike Smithson	.07
148 Ken Dixon	.07
149 Danny Darwin	.07
150 Chris Pittaro	.15
151 Bill Buckner	.10
152 Mike Pagliarulo	.15
153 Bill Russell	.07
154 Brook Jacoby	.10
155 Pat Sheridan	.07
156 Mike Gallego	.12
157 Jim Wohlford	.07
158 Gary Pettis	.10
159 Toby Harrah	.07
160 Rich Dotson	.07
161 Bob Knepper	.07
162 Dave Dravecky	.07
163 Greg Gross	.07
164 Eric Davis	3.00
165 Gerald Perry	.20
166 Rick Rhoden	.07
167 Keith Moreland	.07
168 Jack Clark	.25
169 Storm Davis	.07
170 Cecil Cooper	.15
171 Alan Trammell	.25
172 Roger Clemens	3.50
173 Don Mattingly	5.00
174 Pedro Guerrero	.25
175 Willie Wilson	.15
176 Dwayne Murphy	.07
177 Tim Raines	.30
178 Larry Parrish	.07
179 Mike Witt	.10
180 Harold Baines	.20
181 Vince Coleman (R)	2.00
182 Jeff Heathcock (R)	.15
183 Steve Carlton	.30
184 Mario Soto	.10
185 Goose Gossage	.15
186 Johnny Ray	.10
187 Dan Gladden	.07
188 Bob Horner	.15
189 Rick Sutcliffe	.15
190 Keith Hernandez	.25
191 Phil Bradley	.15
192 Tom Brunansky	.20
193 Jesse Barfield	.25
194 Frank Viola	.40
195 Willie Upshaw	.10
196 Jim Beattie	.07

NO. PLAYER	MINT
197 Darryl Strawberry	3.00
198 Ron Cey	.10
199 Steve Bedrosian	.15
200 Steve Kemp	.07
201 Manny Trillo	.07
202 Garry Templeton	.07
203 Dave Parker	.20
204 John Denny	.07
205 Terry Pendleton	.07
206 Terry Puhl	.07
207 Bobby Grich	.07
208 Ozzie Guillen (R)	.50
209 Jeff Reardon	.10
210 Cal Ripken, Jr.	.40
211 Bill Schroeder	.07
212 Dan Petry	.15
213 Jim Rice	.25
214 Dave Righetti	.10
215 Fernando Valenzuela	.25
216 Julio Franco	.20
217 Darryl Motley	.07
218 Dave Collins	.07
219 Tim Wallach	.10
220 George Wright	.07
221 Tommy Dunbar	.07
222 Steve Balboni	.07
223 Jay Howell	.07
224 Joe Carter	.35
225 Ed Whitson	.07
226 Orel Hershiser	2.00
227 Willie Hernandez	.15
228 Lee Lacy	.07
229 Rollie Fingers	.15
230 Bob Boone	.07
231 Joaquin Andujar	.10
232 Craig Reynolds	.07
233 Shane Rawley	.07
234 Eric Show	.07
235 Jose DeLeon	.07
236 Jose Uribe (R)	.25
237 Moose Haas	.07
238 Wally Backman	.07
239 Dennis Eckersley	.07
240 Mike Moore	.07
241 Damaso Garcia	.07
242 Tim Teufel	.07
243 Dave Concepcion	.07
244 Floyd Bannister	.07
245 Fred Lynn	.15
246 Charlie Moore	.07
247 Walt Terrell	.07
248 Dave Winfield	.30
249 Dwight Evans	.10
250 Dennis Powell	.12
251 Andre Thornton	.07
252 Onix Concepcion	.07
253 Mike Heath	.07
254 David Palmer	.07
255 Donnie Moore	.07
256 Curtis Wilkerson	.07
257 Julio Cruz	.07
258 Nolan Ryan	.60
259 Jeff Stone	.07
260 John Tudor	.15
261 Mark Thurmond	.07
262 Jay Tibbs	.07

NO. PLAYER	MINT	NO. PLAYER	MINT	NO. PLAYER	MINT	NO. PLAYER	MINT
263 Rafael Ramirez	.07	348 Carlos Diaz	.07	433 Billy Hatcher	.10	518 Rich Bordi	.07
264 Larry McWilliams	.07	349 Barbaro Garbey	.07	434 Clint Hurdle	.07	519 Steve Yeager	.07
265 Mark Davis	.07	350 Larry Sheets	.15	435 Ivan Calderon (R)	.75	520 Tony Bernazard	.07
266 Bob Dernier	.07	351 Teddy Higuera (R)	1.50	436 Pete Filson	.07	521 Hal McRae	.07
267 Matt Young	.07	352 Juan Beniquez	.07	437 Tom Henke	.10	522 Jose Rijo	.07
268 Jim Clancy	.07	353 Bob Forsch	.07	438 Dave Engle	.07	523 Mitch Webster (R)	.40
269 Mickey Hatcher	.07	354 Mark Bailey	.07	439 Tom Filer	.07	524 Jack Howell (R)	.50
270 Sammy Stewart	.07	355 Larry Andersen	.07	440 Gorman Thomas	.10	525 Alan Bannister	.07
271 Bob Gibson	.07	356 Terry Kennedy	.07	441 Rick Aguilera (R)	.35	526 Ron Kittle	.10
272 Nelson Simmons (R)	.15	357 Don Robinson	.07	442 Scott Sanderson	.07	527 Phil Garner	.07
273 Rich Gedman	.07	358 Jim Gott	.07	443 Jeff Dedmon	.07	528 Kurt Bevacqua	.07
274 Butch Wynegar	.07	359 Earnest Riles (R)	.30	444 Joe Orsulak (R)	.20	529 Kevin Gross	.07
275 Ken Howell	.07	360 John Christensen	.15	445 Atlee Hammaker	.07	530 Bo Diaz	.07
276 Mel Hall	.07	361 Ray Fontenot	.07	446 Jerry Royster	.07	531 Ken Oberkfell	.07
277 Jim Sundberg	.07	362 Spike Owen	.07	447 Buddy Bell	.10	532 Rick Reuschel	.07
278 Chris Codiroli	.07	363 Jim Acker	.07	448 Dave Rucker	.07	533 Ron Meridith (R)	.15
279 H. Winningham (R)	.15	364 Ron Davis	.07	449 Ivan DeJesus	.07	534 Steve Braun	.07
280 Rod Carew	.30	365 Tom Hume	.07	450 Jim Pankovits	.07	535 Wayne Gross	.07
281 Don Slaught	.07	366 Carlton Fisk	.20	451 Jerry Narron	.07	536 Ray Searage	.07
282 Scott Fletcher	.07	367 Nate Snell (R)	.15	452 Bryan Little	.07	537 Tom Brookens	.07
283 Bill Dawley	.07	368 Rick Manning	.07	453 Gary Lucas	.07	538 Al Nipper	.07
284 Andy Hawkins	.07	369 Darrell Evans	.10	454 Dennis Martinez	.07	539 Billy Sample	.07
285 Glenn Wilson	.10	370 Ron Hassey	.07	455 Ed Romero	.07	540 Steve Sax	.20
286 Nick Esasky	.07	371 Wade Boggs	2.50	456 Bob Melvin (R)	.12	541 Dan Quisenberry	.15
287 Claudell Washington	.07	372 Rick Honeycutt	.07	457 Glenn Hoffman	.07	542 Tony Phillips	.07
288 Lee Mazzilli	.07	373 Chris Bando	.07	458 Bob Shirley	.07	543 Floyd Youmans (R)	.50
289 Jody Davis	.07	374 Bud Black	.07	459 Bob Welch	.07	544 Steve Buechele (R)	.25
290 Darrell Porter	.07	375 Steve Henderson	.07	460 Carmen Castillo	.07	545 Craig Gerber (R)	.10
291 Scott McGregor	.07	376 Charlie Lea	.07	461 Dave Leeper (R)	.12	546 Joe DeSa (R)	.15
292 Ted Simmons	.10	377 Reggie Jackson	.40	462 Tim Birtsas (R)	.15	547 Brian Harper	.07
293 Aurelio Lopez	.07	378 Dave Schmidt	.07	463 Randy St. Claire	.07	548 Kevin Bass	.07
294 Marty Barrett	.07	379 Bob James	.07	464 Chris Welsh	.07	549 Tom Foley	.07
295 Dale Berra	.07	380 Glenn Davis	2.50	465 Greg Harris	.07	550 Dave Van Gorder	.07
296 Greg Brock	.07	381 Tim Corcoran	.07	466 Lynn Jones	.07	551 Bruce Bochy	.07
297 Charlie Leibrandt	.07	382 Danny Cox	.10	467 Dusty Baker	.07	552 R.J. Reynolds	.07
298 Bill Krueger	.07	383 Tim Flannery	.07	468 Roy Smith	.07	553 Chris Brown (R)	.30
299 Bryn Smith	.07	384 Tom Browning	.15	469 Andre Robertson	.07	554 Bruce Benedict	.07
300 Burt Hooton	.07	385 Rick Camp	.07	470 Ken Landreaux	.07	555 Warren Brusstar	.07
301 Stu Cliburn (R)	.15	386 Jim Morrison	.07	471 Dave Bergman	.07	556 Danny Heep	.07
302 Luis Salazar	.07	387 Dave LaPoint	.07	472 Gary Roenicke	.07	557 Darnell Coles	.07
303 Ken Dayley	.07	388 Davey Lopes	.07	473 Pete Vuckovich	.07	558 Greg Gagne	.07
304 Frank DiPino	.07	389 Al Cowens	.07	474 Kirk McCaskill (R)	.50	559 Ernie Whitt	.07
305 Von Hayes	.15	390 Doyle Alexander	.07	475 Jeff Lahti	.07	560 Ron Washington	.07
306 Gary Redus	.07	391 Tim Laudner	.07	476 Mike Scott	.35	561 Jimmy Key	.15
307 Craig Lefferts	.07	392 Don Aase	.07	477 Darren Daulton (R)	.25	562 Billy Swift	.07
308 Sam Khalifa	.15	393 Jaime Cocanower	.07	478 Graig Nettles	.10	563 Ron Darling	.25
309 Scott Garrelts	.07	394 Randy O'Neal	.07	479 Bill Almon	.07	564 Dick Ruthven	.07
310 Rick Cerone	.07	395 Mike Easler	.07	480 Greg Minton	.07	565 Zane Smith	.25
311 Shawon Dunston	.30	396 Scott Bradley	.07	481 Randy Ready	.07	566 Sid Bream	.07
312 Howard Johnson	.60	397 Tom Niedenfuer	.07	482 Len Dykstra (R)	.75	567 Joel Youngblood	.07
313 Jim Presley	.15	398 Jerry Willard	.07	483 Thad Bosley	.07	568 Mario Ramirez	.07
314 Gary Gaetti	.30	399 Lonnie Smith	.10	484 Harold Reynolds (R)	.50	569 Tom Runnells (R)	.10
315 Luis Leal	.07	400 Bruce Bochte	.07	485 Al Oliver	.10	570 Rick Schu	.07
316 Mark Salas	.07	401 Terry Francona	.07	486 Roy Smalley	.07	571 Bill Campbell	.07
317 Bill Caudill	.07	402 Jim Slaton	.07	487 John Franco	.15	572 Dickie Thon	.07
318 Dave Henderson	.07	403 Bill Stein	.07	488 Juan Agosto	.07	573 Al Holland	.07
319 Rafael Santana	.07	404 Timmy Hulett	.07	489 Al Pardo	.15	574 Reid Nichols	.07
320 Leon Durham	.15	405 Alan Ashby	.07	490 Bill Wegman (R)	.15	575 Bert Roberge	.07
321 Bruce Sutter	.15	406 Tim Stoddard	.07	491 Frank Tanana	.07	576 Mike Flanagan	.07
322 Jason Thompson	.07	407 Garry Maddox	.07	492 Brian Fisher (R)	.30	577 Tim Leary	.35
323 Bob Brenly	.07	408 Ted Power	.07	493 Mark Clear	.07	578 Mike Young	.07
324 Carmelo Martinez	.07	409 Len Barker	.07	494 Len Matuszek	.07	579 Steve Lyons	.07
325 Eddie Milner	.07	410 Denny Gonzalez	.07	495 Ramon Romero (R)	.10	580 Phil Niekro	.20
326 Juan Samuel	.15	411 George Frazier	.07	496 John Wathan	.07	581 Gilberto Reyes (R)	.15
327 Tom Nieto	.07	412 Andy Van Slyke	.30	497 Rob Picciolo	.07	582 Jamie Easterly	.07
328 Dave Smith	.07	413 Jim Dwyer	.07	498 U.L. Washington	.07	583 Mark Gubicza	.07
329 Urbano Lugo (R)	.15	414 Paul Householder	.07	499 John Candelaria	.07	584 Stan Javier (R)	.20
330 Joel Skinner	.07	415 Alejandro Sanchez	.07	500 Duane Walker	.07	585 Bill Laskey	.07
331 Bill Gullickson	.07	416 Steve Crawford	.07	501 Gene Nelson	.07	586 Jeff Russell	.07
332 Floyd Rayford	.07	417 Dan Pasqua	.15	502 John Mizerock	.07	587 Dickie Noles	.07
333 Ben Oglivie	.07	418 Enos Cabell	.07	503 Luis Aguayo	.07	588 Steve Farr	.07
334 Lance Parrish	.15	419 Mike Jones	.07	504 Kurt Kepshire	.07	589 Steve Ontiveros (R)	.15
335 Jackie Gutierrez	.07	420 Steve Kiefer	.07	505 Ed Wojna (R)	.15	590 Mike Hargrove	.07
336 Dennis Rasmussen	.07	421 Tim Burke (R)	.30	506 Joe Price	.07	591 Marty Bystrom	.07
337 Terry Whitfield	.07	422 Mike Mason	.07	507 Milt Thompson (R)	.45	592 Franklin Stubbs	.10
338 Neal Heaton	.07	423 Ruppert Jones	.07	508 Junior Ortiz	.07	593 Larry Herndon	.07
339 Jorge Orta	.07	424 Jerry Hairston	.07	509 Vida Blue	.07	594 Bill Swaggerty	.07
340 Donnie Hill	.07	425 Tito Landrum	.07	510 Steve Engel (R)	.10	595 Carlos Ponce (R)	.10
341 Joe Hesketh	.10	426 Jeff Calhoun (R)	.12	511 Karl Best (R)	.10	596 Pat Perry (R)	.10
342 Charlie Hough	.07	427 Don Carman (R)	.25	512 Cecil Fielder (R)	.25	597 Ray Knight	.07
343 Dave Rozema	.07	428 Tony Perez	.15	513 Frank Eufemia (R)	.15	598 Steve Lombardozzi (R)	.20
344 Greg Pryor	.07	429 Jerry Davis	.07	514 Tippy Martinez	.07	599 Brad Havens	.07
345 Mickey Tettleton (R)	.50	430 Bob Walk	.07	515 Billy Robidoux (R)	.20	600 Pat Clements (R)	.20
346 George Vukovich	.07	431 Brad Wellman	.07	516 Bill Scherrer	.07	601 Joe Niekro	.10
347 Don Baylor	.10	432 Terry Forster	.07	517 Bruce Hurst	.10	602 Hank Aaron Puzzle	.15

1986 Donruss (Continued)

NO.	PLAYER	MINT	NO.	PLAYER	MINT	NO.	PLAYER	MINT	NO.	PLAYER	MINT
603	Dwayne Henry (R)	.10	622	Charles Hudson	.07	640	Garth Iorg	.07	—	Checklist (DK)	.08
604	Mookie Wilson	.07	623	Joel Davis (R)	.15	641	Dan Driessen	.07	—	Checklist No. 1	.08
605	Buddy Biancalana	.07	624	Joe Johnson (R)	.15	642	Mike Brown	.07	—	Checklist No. 2	.08
606	Rance Mulliniks	.07	625	Sid Fernandez	.15	643	John Shelby	.07	—	Checklist No. 3	.08
607	Alan Wiggins	.07	626	Dennis Lamp	.07	644	Pete Rose Ty-Breaking		—	Checklist No. 4	.08
608	Joe Cowley	.07	627	Terry Harper	.07		Hit #4192	.30	—	Checklist No. 5	.08
609	Tom Seaver	.50	628	Jack Lazorko	.07	645	Knuckle Brothers:	.10	—	Checklist No. 6	.08
610	Neil Allen	.07	629	Roger McDowell (R)	.50		Phil and Joe Niekro				
611	Don Sutton	.20	630	Mark Funderburk (R)	.20	646	Jesse Orosco	.07			
612	Fred Toliver (R)	.15	631	Ed Lynch	.07	647	Billy Beane (R)	.15			
613	Jay Baller (R)	.15	632	Rudy Law	.07	648	Cesar Cedeno	.07			
614	Marc Sullivan (R)	.10	633	Roger Mason (R)	.07	649	Bert Blyleven	.10			
615	John Grubb	.07	634	Mike Felder (R)	.15	650	Max Venable	.07			
616	Bruce Kison	.07	635	Ken Schrom	.07	651	Fleet Feet:	.30			
617	Bill Madlock	.10	636	Bob Ojeda	.07		W. McGee, V. Coleman				
618	Chris Chambliss	.07	637	Ed Vande Berg	.07	652	Calvin Schiraldi	.07			
619	Dave Stewart	.30	638	Bobby Meacham	.07	653	King of Kings:	.75			
620	Tim Lollar	.07	639	Cliff Johnson	.07		Pete Rose				
621	Gary Lavelle	.07									

1986 Donruss Rookies. . . . Complete Set of 56 Cards—Value $45.00

Features the outstanding rookies of the 1986 season. The cards are coated with a glossy finish. The entire set was packaged in a printed box, and distributed exclusively through card hobby dealers.

NO.	PLAYER	MINT	NO.	PLAYER	MINT	NO.	PLAYER	MINT	NO.	PLAYER	MINT
1	Wally Joyner (RR)	3.50	15	Cory Snyder	1.25	29	Jeff Sellers	.20	43	Andy Allanson	.20
2	Tracy Jones	.50	16	Kelly Gruber	.40	30	Bobby Bonilla	1.25	44	Mark Portugal	.30
3	Allan Anderson	.50	17	Kevin Mitchell (RR)	7.50	31	Doug Drabek	.35	45	Danny Tartabull	.75
4	Ed Correa	.20	18	Steve Lombardozzi	.15	32	Will Clark (RR)	10.00	46	Bob Kpper	.20
5	Reggie Williams	.25	19	Mitch Williams	.50	33	Leon "Bip" Roberts	.30	47	Gene Walter	.25
6	Charlie Kerfeld	.20	20	John Cerutti	.35	34	Jim Deshaies	.35	48	Rey Quinonez	.25
7	Andres Galarraga	1.00	21	Todd Worrell	.45	35	Mike Lavalliere	.30	49	Bobby Witt	.40
8	Bob Tewksbury	.20	22	Jose Canseco	8.00	36	Scott Bankhead	.30	50	Bill Mooneyham	.20
9	Al Newman	.20	23	Pete Incaviglia (RR)	1.00	37	Dale Sveum	.35	51	John Cangelos	.20
10	Andres Thomas	.25	24	Jose Guzman	.20	38	Bo Jackson (RR)	9.00	52	Ruben Sierra (RR)	6.00
11	Barry Bonds (RR)	1.00	25	Scott Bailes	.20	39	Rob Thompson	.35	53	Rob Woodward	.20
12	Juan Nieves	.20	26	Greg Matthews	.30	40	Eric Plunk	.25	54	Ed Hearn	.20
13	Mark Eichhorn	.20	27	Eric King	.25	41	Bill Bathe	.20	55	Joel McKeon	.20
14	Dan Plesac	.35	28	Paul Assenmacher	.20	42	John Kruk..(RR)	.50	56	Checklist	.20

1987 Donruss.... Complete Set of 660 Cards—Value $40.00 (Factory-Sealed set—Value $50.00)

Features the rookie cards of Bo Jackson, Wally Joyner, Kevin Mitchell, Will Clark, Ruben Sierra and Mike Greenwell. Donruss limited production. Cards 14, 22 and 25 exist with the "yellow" strip missing on back—worth triple the value of the corrected cards.

NO. PLAYER	MINT
No. 1 to 26—Diamond Kings	
1 Wally Joyner (DK)	1.00
2 Roger Clemens (DK)	.75
3 Dale Murphy (DK)	.40
4 Darryl Strawberry (DK)	.60
5 Ozzie Smith (DK)	.10
6 Jose Canseco (DK)	1.50
7 Charlie Hough (DK)	.10
8 Brook Jacoby (DK)	.10
9 Fred Lynn (DK)	.15
10 Rick Rhoden (DK)	.10
11 Chris Brown (DK)	.15
12 Von Hayes (DK)	.10
13 Jack Morris (DK)	.20
14 K. McReynolds (DK)	.35
14 McReynolds (error)	1.00
15 George Brett (DK)	.35
16 Ted Higuera (DK)	.20
17 Hubie Brooks (DK)	.10
18 Mike Scott (DK)	.20
19 Kirby Puckett (DK)	.45
20 Dave Winfield (DK)	.25
21 Lloyd Moseby (DK)	.10
22 Eric Davis (DK)	1.00
22 E. Davis (error)	2.50
23 Jim Presley (DK)	.15
24 Keith Moreland (DK)	.10
25 Greg Walker (DK)	.15
26 St. Sax (DK)	.20
27 Checklist (DK)	.10
No. 28 to 47—Rated Rookies	
28 B.J. Surhoff (R)	.50
29 Randy Myers (R)	.50
30 Ken Gerhart (R)	.20
31 Benito Santiago	1.50
32 Greg Swindell (R)	1.25
33 Mike Birkbeck (R)	.20
34 Terry Steinbach (R)	.75
35 Bo Jackson (R)	5.00
36 Greg Maddux (R)	1.25
37 Jim Lindeman (R)	.20
38 Devon White (R)	1.00
39 Eric Bell (R)	.15
40 Will Fraser (R)	.20
41 Jerry Browne (R)	.40
42 Chris James (R)	.75
43 Rafael Palmeiro (R)	1.75
44 Pat Dodson (R)	.20
45 Duane Ward (R)	.30
46 Mark McGwire	8.00
47 Bruce Fields (R)	.15
48 Eddie Murray	.30
49 Ted Higuera	.20
50 Kirk Gibson	.30
51 Oil Can Boid	.10
52 Don Mattingly	2.50
53 Pedro Guerrero	.20
54 George Brett	.40
55 Jose Rijo	.05
56 Tim Raines	.25
57 Ed Correa (R)	.20
58 Mike Witt	.10
59 Greg Walker	.05
60 Ozzie Smith	.25
61 Glenn Davis	.35
62 Glenn Wilson	.10
63 Tom Browning	.05
64 Tony Gwynn	.50

NO. PLAYER	MINT
65 R.J. Reynolds	.05
66 Will Clark (R)	10.00
67 Ozzie Virgil	.05
68 Rick Sutcliffe	.10
69 Gary Carter	.30
70 Mike Moore	.05
71 Bert Blyleven	.05
72 Tony Fernandez	.15
73 Kent Hrbek	.15
74 Lloyd Moseby	.10
75 Alvin Davis	.10
76 Keith Hernandez	.25
77 Ryne Sandberg	.20
78 Dale Murphy	.40
79 Sid Bream	.05
80 Chris Brown	.15
81 Steve Garvey	.30
82 Mario Soto	.05
83 Shane Rawley	.05
84 Willie McGee	.20
85 Jose Cruz	.12
86 Brian Downing	.05
87 Ozzie Guillen	.10
88 Hubie Brooks	.12
89 Cal Ripken	.30
90 Juan Nieves	.10
91 Lance Parrish	.20
92 Jim Rice	.25
93 Ron Guidry	.15
94 Fernando Valenzuela	.25
95 Andy Allanson (R)	.15
96 Willie Wilson	.15
97 Jose Canseco	7.00
98 Jeff Reardon	.05
99 Bobby Witt (R)	.40
100 Checklist: 28 to 133	.10
101 Jose Guzman	.20
102 Steve Balboni	.10
103 Tony Phillips	.05
104 Brook Jacoby	.10
105 Dave Winfield	.25
106 Orel Hershiser	.40
107 Lou Whitaker	.15
108 Fred Lynn	.15
109 Bill Wegman	.05
110 Donnie Moore	.05
111 Jack Clark	.20
112 Bob Knepper	.05
113 Von Hayes	.10
114 "Bip" Roberts (R)	.15
115 Tony Pena	.12
116 Scott Garrelts	.05
117 Paul Molitor	.15
118 Darryl Strawberry	.75
119 Shawon Dunston	.10
120 Jim Presley	.20
121 Jesse Barfield	.25
122 Gary Gaetti	.20
123 Kurt Stillwell (R)	.30
124 Joel Davis	.05
125 Mike Boddicker	.05
126 Robin Yount	.35
127 Alan Trammell	.20
128 Dave Righetti	.15
129 Dwight Evans	.10
130 Mike Scioscia	.05

NO. PLAYER	MINT
131 Julio Franco	.12
132 Bret Saberhagen	.20
133 Mike Davis	.05
134 Joe Hesketh	.05
135 Wally Joyner (R)	2.00
136 Don Slaught	.05
137 Daryl Boston	.05
138 Nolan Ryan	.50
139 Mike Schmidt	.45
140 Tommy Herr	.05
141 Garry Templeton	.05
142 Kal Daniels	.75
143 Billy Sample	.05
144 Johnny Ray	.12
145 Rob Thompson (R)	.30
146 Bob Dernier	.05
147 Danny Tartabull	.40
148 Ernie Whitt	.05
149 Kirby Puckett	.60
150 Mike Young	.05
151 Ernest Riles	.15
152 Frank Tanana	.05
153 Rich Gedman	.05
154 Willie Randolph	.08
155 Bill Madlock	.15
156 Joe Carter	.20
157 Danny Jackson	.20
158 Carney Lansford	.05
159 Bryn Smith	.05
160 Gary Pettis	.05
161 Oddibe McDowell	.15
162 John Cangelosi (R)	.12
163 Mike Scott	.20
164 Eric Show	.05
165 Juan Samuel	.12
166 Nick Esasky	.05
167 Zane Smith	.05
168 Mike Brown	.05
169 Keith Moreland	.05
170 John Tudor	.10
171 Ken Dixon	.05
172 Jim Gantner	.05
173 Jack Morris	.15
174 Bruce Hurst	.10
175 Dennis Rasmussen	.12
176 Mike Marshall	.10
177 Dan Quisenberry	.12
178 Eric Plunk	.10
179 Tim Wallach	.05
180 Steve Buechele	.05
181 Don Sutton	.15
182 Dave Schmidt	.05
183 Terry Pendleton	.05
184 Jim Deshaies (R)	.25
185 Steve Bedrosian	.15
186 Pete Rose (Mgr.)	.50
187 Dave Dravecky	.05
188 Rick Reuschel	.05
189 Dan Gladden	.05
190 Rick Mahler	.05
191 Thad Bosley	.05
192 Ron Darling	.20
193 Matt Young	.05
194 Tom Brunansky	.20
195 Dave Stieb	.15
196 Frank Viola	.25

NO. PLAYER	MINT
197 Tom Henke	.10
198 Karl Best	.05
199 Dwight Gooden	.75
200 Checklist: 134-209	.08
201 Steve Trout	.05
202 Rafael Ramirez	.05
203 Bob Walk	.05
204 Roger Mason	.05
205 Terry Kennedy	.05
206 Ron Oester	.05
207 John Russell	.05
208 Greg Mathews (R)	.25
209 Charlie Kerfeld	.10
210 Reggie Jackson	.35
211 Floyd Bannister	.05
212 Vance Law	.05
213 Rich Bordi	.05
214 Dan Plesac (R)	.30
215 Dave Collins	.05
216 Bob Stanley	.05
217 Joe Niekro	.10
218 Tom Niedenfuer	.05
219 Brett Butler	.05
220 Charlie Leibrandt	.05
221 Steve Ontiveros	.05
222 Tim Burke	.05
223 Curtis Wilkerson	.05
224 Pete Incaviglia (R)	.75
225 Lonnie Smith	.05
226 Chris Codiroli	.05
227 Scott Bailes (R)	.15
228 Rickey Henderson	.40
229 Ken Howell	.05
230 Darnell Coles	.08
231 Don Aase	.05
232 Tim Leary	.05
233 Bob Boone	.05
234 Ricky Horton	.05
235 Mark Bailey	.05
236 Kevin Gross	.05
237 Lance McCullers	.10
238 Cecilio Guante	.05
239 Bob Melvin	.05
240 Billy Jo Robidoux	.12
241 Roger McDowell	.15
242 Leon Durham	.10
243 Ed Nunez	.05
244 Jimmy Key	.10
245 Mike Smithson	.05
246 Bo Diaz	.05
247 Carlton Fisk	.15
248 Larry Sheets	.15
249 Juan Castillo	.12
250 Eric King (R)	.15
251 Doug Drabek (R)	.30
252 Wade Boggs	1.50
253 Mariano Duncan	.10
254 Pat Tabler	.05
255 Frank White	.05
256 Alfredo Griffin	.05
257 Floyd Youmans	.15
258 Rob Wilfong	.05
259 Pete O'Brien	.08
260 Tim Hulett	.05
261 Dickie Thon	.05
262 Darren Daulton	.05

NO.	PLAYER	MINT
263	Vince Coleman	.40
264	Andy Hawkins	.05
265	Eric Davis	1.50
266	Andres Thomas (R)	.25
267	Mike Diaz (R)	.15
268	Chili Davis	.10
269	Jody Davis	.05
270	Phil Bradley	.10
271	George Bell	.25
272	Keith Atherton	.05
273	Storm Davis	.08
274	Rob Deer	.25
275	Walt Terrell	.05
276	Roger Clemens	1.25
277	Mike Easler	.05
278	Steve Sax	.15
279	Andre Thornton	.05
280	Jim Sundberg	.05
281	Bill Bathe (R)	.15
282	Jay Tibbs	.05
283	Dick Schofield	.05
284	Mike Mason	.05
285	Jerry Hairston	.05
286	Bill Doran	.05
287	Tim Flannery	.05
288	Gary Redus	.05
289	John Franco	.05
290	P. Assenmacher (R)	.15
291	Joe Orsulak	.05
292	Lee Smith	.05
293	Mike Laga	.05
294	Rick Dempsey	.05
295	Mike Felder	.05
296	Tom Brookens	.05
297	Al Nipper	.05
298	Mike Pagliarulo	.15
299	Franklin Stubbs	.15
300	Checklist: 240-345	.08
301	Steve Farr	.05
302	Bill Mooneyham (R)	.15
303	Andres Galarraga	.35
304	Scott Fletcher	.05
305	Jack Howell	.05
306	Russ Morman (R)	.15
307	Todd Worrell	.20
308	Dave Smith	.05
309	Jeff Stone	.05
310	Ron Robinson	.05
311	Bruce Bochy	.05
312	Jim Winn	.08
313	Mark Davis	.05
314	Jeff Dedmon	.05
315	Jamie Moyer (R)	.20
316	Wally Backman	.05
317	Ken Phelps	.05
318	Steve Lombardozzi	.12
319	Rance Mulliniks	.05
320	Tim Laudner	.05
321	Mark Eichhorn (R)	.20
322	Lee Guetterman (R)	.15
323	Sid Fernandez	.20
324	Jerry Mumphrey	.05
325	David Palmer	.05
326	Bill Almon	.05
327	Candy Maldonado	.10
328	John Kruk (R)	.30
329	John Denny	.05
330	Milt Thompson	.05
331	Mike LaValliere (R)	.25
332	Alan Ashby	.05
333	Doug Corbett	.05
334	Ron Karkovice (R)	.15
335	Mitch Webster	.05
336	Lee Lacy	.05
337	Glenn Braggs	.50
338	Dwight Lowry (R)	.15
339	Don Baylor	.15
340	Brian Fisher	.05
341	Reggie Williams (R)	.15
342	Tom Candiotti	.05
343	Rudy Law	.05
344	Curt Young	.05
345	Mike Fitzgerald	.05
346	Ruben Sierra (R)	4.00
347	Mitch Williams (R)	.50
348	Jorge Orta	.05
349	Mickey Tettleton	.15
350	Ernie Camacho	.05
351	Ron Kittle	.10
352	Ken Landreaux	.05
353	Chet Lemon	.08
354	John Shelby	.05
355	Mark Clear	.05
356	Doug DeCinces	.08
357	Ken Kayley	.05
358	Phil Garner	.05
359	Steve Jeltz	.05
360	Ed Whitson	.05
361	Barry Bonds (R)	1.00
362	Vida Blue	.08
363	Cecil Cooper	.10
364	Bob Ojeda	.15
365	Dennis Eckersley	.08
366	Mike Morgan	.05
367	Willie Upshaw	.05
368	Allan Anderson (R)	.40
369	Bill Gullickson	.05
370	Bobby Thigpen (R)	.25
371	Juan Beniquez	.05
372	Charlie Moore	.05
373	Dan Petry	.08
374	Rod Scurry	.05
375	Tom Seaver	.35
376	Ed Vande Berg	.05
377	Tony Bernazard	.05
378	Greg Pryor	.05
379	Dwayne Murphy	.05
380	Andy McGaffigan	.05
381	Kirk McCaskill	.10
382	Greg Harris	.05
383	Rich Dotson	.05
384	Craig Reynolds	.05
385	Greg Gross	.05
386	Tito Landrum	.05
387	Craig Lefferts	.05
388	Dave Parker	.20
389	Bob Horner	.15
390	Pat Clements	.05
391	Jeff Leonard	.10
392	Chris Speier	.05
393	John Moses	.15
394	Garth Iorg	.05
395	Greg Gagne	.05
396	Nate Snell	.05
397	Bryan Clutterbuck (R)	.15
398	Darrell Evans	.12
399	Steve Crawford	.05
400	Checklist: 346-451	.08
401	Phil Lombardi (R)	.20
402	Rick Honeycutt	.05
403	Ken Schrom	.05
404	Bud Black	.05
405	Donnie Hill	.05
406	Wayne Krenchicki	.05
407	Chuck Finley (R)	.30
408	Toby Harrah	.05
409	Steve Lyons	.05
410	Kevin Bass	.10
411	Marvell Wynne	.05
412	Ron Roenicke	.05
413	Tracy Jones (R)	.30
414	Gene Garber	.05
415	Mike Bielecki	.05
416	Frank DiPino	.05
417	Andy Van Slyke	.15
418	Jim Dwyer	.05
419	Ben Oglivie	.05
420	Dave Bergman	.05
421	Joe Sambito	.05
422	Bob Tewksbury (R)	.20
423	Len Matuszek	.05
424	Mike Kingery (R)	.15
425	Dave Kingman	.10
426	Al Newman	.15
427	Gary Ward	.05
428	Ruppert Jones	.05
429	Harold Baines	.12
430	Pat Perry	.05
431	Terry Puhl	.05
432	Don Carman	.05
433	Eddie Milner	.05
434	LaMarr Hoyt	.05
435	Rick Rhoden	.05
436	Jose Uribe	.05
437	Ken Oberkfell	.05
438	Ron Davis	.05
439	Jesse Orosco	.08
440	Scott Bradley	.05
441	Randy Bush	.05
442	John Cerutti (R)	.20
443	Roy Smalley	.05
444	Kelly Gruber	.10
445	Bob Kearney	.05
446	Ed Hearn (R)	.15
447	Scott Sanderson	.05
448	Bruce Benedict	.05
449	Junior Ortiz	.05
450	Mike Aldrete (R)	.30
451	Kevin McReynolds	.30
452	Rob Murphy (R)	.25
453	Kent Tekulve	.05
454	Curt Ford	.12
455	Davey Lopes	.08
456	Bobby Grich	.05
457	Jose DeLeon	.05
458	Andre Dawson	.25
459	Mike Flanagan	.05
460	Joey Meyer (R)	.50
461	Chuck Cary (R)	.20
462	Bill Buckner	.08
463	Bob Shirley	.05
464	Jeff Hamilton (R)	.25
465	Phil Niekro	.20
466	Mark Gubicza	.05
467	Jerry Willard	.05
468	Bob Sebra (R)	.15
469	Larry Parrish	.05
470	Charlie Hough	.05
471	Hal McRae	.05
472	Dave Leiper	.12
473	Mel Hall	.05
474	Dan Pasqua	.15
475	Bob Welch	.05
476	Johnny Grubb	.05
477	Jim Traber	.12
478	Chris Bosio (R)	.30
479	Mark McLemore	.08
480	John Morris	.05
481	Billy Hatcher	.05
482	Dan Schatzeder	.05
483	Rich Gossage	.12
484	Jim Morrison	.05
485	Bob Brenly	.05
486	Bill Schroeder	.05
487	Mookie Wilson	.05
488	Dave Martinez	.25
489	Harold Reynolds	.05
490	Jeff Hearron (R)	.15
491	Mickey Hatcher	.05
492	Barry Larkin (R)	2.00
493	Bob James	.05
494	John Habyan	.05
495	Jim Adduci (R)	.15
496	Mike Heath	.05
497	Tim Stoddard	.05
498	Tony Armas	.08
499	Dennis Powell	.05
500	Checklist: 452-557	.08
501	Chris Bando	.05
502	David Cone (R)	4.00
503	Jay Howell	.05
504	Tom Foley	.05
505	Ray Chadwick (R)	.15
506	Mike Loynd (R)	.15
507	Neil Allen	.05
508	Danny Darwin	.05
509	Rick Schu	.05
510	Jose Oquendo	.05
511	Gene Walter	.10
512	Terry McGriff (R)	.15
513	Ken Griffey	.08
514	Benny Distefano	.05
515	Terry Mulholland (R)	.15
516	Ed Lynch	.05
517	Bill Swift	.05
518	Manny Lee	.05
519	Andre David	.05
520	Scott McGregor	.05
521	Rick Manning	.05
522	Willie Hernandez	.05
523	Marty Barrett	.10
524	Wayne Tolleson	.05
525	Jose Gonzalez (R)	.20
526	Cory Snyder	.50
527	Buddy Biancalana	.05
528	Moose Haas	.05
529	Wilfredo Tejada (R)	.15
530	Stu Cliburn	.05
531	Dale Mohorcic (R)	.15
532	Ron Hassey	.05
533	Ty Gainey	.05
534	Jerry Royster	.05
535	Mike Maddux (R)	.25
536	Ted Power	.05
537	Ted Simmons	.08
538	Rafael Belliard (R)	.15
539	Chico Walker	.15
540	Bob Forsch	.05
541	John Stefero	.05
542	Dale Sveum (R)	.25
543	Mark Thurmond	.05
544	Jeff Sellers (R)	.20
545	Joel Skinner	.05
546	Alex Trevino	.05
547	Randy Kutcher (R)	.15
548	Joaquin Andujar	.05
549	Casey Candaele (R)	.15
550	Jeff Russell	.05
551	John Candelaria	.08
552	Joe Cowley	.05
553	Danny Cox	.05
554	Denny Walling	.05
555	Bruce Ruffin (R)	.25
556	Buddy Bell	.10
557	Jimmy Jones (R)	.35
558	Bobby Bonilla (R)	1.00
559	Jeff Robinson	.05
560	Ed Olwine (R)	.15
561	Glenallen Hill (R)	.25
562	Lee Mazzilli	.08
563	Mike Brown	.05
564	George Frazier	.05
565	Mike Sharperson (R)	.15
566	Mark Portugal (R)	.20
567	Rick Leach	.05
568	Mark Langston	.20
569	Rafael Santana	.05
570	Manny Trillo	.05
571	Cliff Speck (R)	.15
572	Bob Kipper	.05
573	Kelly Downs (R)	.35
574	Randy Asadoor (R)	.15
575	Dave Magadan (R)	.50
576	Marvin Freeman (R)	.15
577	Jeff Lahti	.05
578	Jeff Calhoun	.05
579	Gus Polidor	.08
580	Gene Nelson	.05
581	Tim Teufel	.05
582	Odell Jones	.05
583	Mark Ryal (R)	.15
584	Randy O'Neal	.05
585	Mike Greenwell	10.00
586	Ray Knight	.10
587	Ralph Bryant (R)	.20
588	Carmen Castillo	.05
589	Ed Wojna	.05
590	Stan Javier	.05
591	Jeff Musselman (R)	.20
592	Mike Stanley (R)	.20
593	Darrell Porter	.05
594	Drew Hall	.15
595	Rob Nelson (R)	.15
596	Bryan Oelkers	.05
597	Scott Nielsen (R)	.15
598	Brian Holton (R)	.20

1987 Donruss (Continued)

NO.	PLAYER	MINT
599	Kevin Mitchell (R)	5.00
600	Checklist: 558-660	.08
601	Jackie Gutierrez	.05
602	Barry Jones (R)	.20
603	Jerry Narron	.05
604	Steve Lake	.05
605	Jim Pankovits	.05
606	Ed Romero	.05
607	Dave LaPoint	.05
608	Don Robinson	.05
609	Mike Krukow	.05
610	Dave Valle	.12
611	Len Dykstra	.20
612	"Puzzle"—Clemente	.08
613	Mike Trujillo	.08
614	Damaso Garcia	.05
615	Neal Heaton	.05
616	Juan Berenguer	.05

NO.	PLAYER	MINT
617	Steve Carlton	.25
618	Gary Lucas	.05
619	Geno Petralli	.05
620	Rick Aguilera	.08
621	Fred McGriff	3.50
622	Dave Henderson	.05
623	Dave Clark (R)	.30
624	Angel Salazar	.05
625	Randy Hunt	.05
626	John Gibbons	.05
627	Kevin Brown (R)	.25
628	Bill Dawley	.05
629	Aurelio Lopez	.05
630	Charlie Hudson	.05
631	Ray Soff (R)	.15
632	Ray Hayward (R)	.15
633	Spike Owen	.05
634	Glenn Hubbard	.05

NO.	PLAYER	MINT
635	Kevin Elster (R)	.60
636	Mike LaCoss	.05
637	Dwayne Henry	.05
638	Rey Quinones (R)	.25
639	Jim Clancy	.05
640	Larry Anderson	.05
641	Calvin Schiraldi	.08
642	Stan Jefferson (R)	.30
643	Marc Sullivan	.05
644	Mark Grant (R)	.15
645	Cliff Johnson	.05
646	Howard Johnson	.30
647	Dave Sax	.05
648	Dave Stewart	.05
649	Danny Heep	.05
650	Joe Johnson	.05
651	Bob Brower (R)	.20
652	Rob Woodward	.08

NO.	PLAYER	MINT
653	John Mizerock	.05
654	Tim Pyznarski (R)	.15
655	Luis Aquino	.12
656	Mickey Brantley	.20
657	Doyle Alexander	.05
658	Sammy Stewart	.05
659	Jim Acker	.05
660	Pete Ladd	.05

1987 Donruss Rookies. . . . Complete Set of 56 Cards—Value $15.00

Features the outstanding rookies of the 1987 season. The cards are coated with a glossy finish. The entire set was packaged in a printed box and distributed exclusively through card hobby dealers. Features Donruss' first card of Ellis Burks, Matt Williams and Matt Nokes.

NO.	PLAYER	MINT
1	Mark McGwire	2.50
2	Eric Bell	.10
3	Mark Williamson	.20
4	Mike Greenwell	3.00
5	Ellis Burks (RR)	2.00
6	DeWayne Buice	.15
7	Mark McLemore	.10
8	Devon White	.50
9	Willie Fraser	.10
10	Les Lancaster	.20
11	Ken Williams	.25
12	Matt Nokes (RR)	.60
13	Jeff Robinson	.40
14	Bo Jackson	3.00

NO.	PLAYER	MINT
15	Kevin Seitzer (RR)	1.50
16	Billy Ripken (RR)	.25
17	B.J. Surhoff	.25
18	Chuck Crim	.20
19	Mike Birkbeck	.10
20	Chris Bosio	.10
21	Les Straker	.20
22	Mark Davidson	.15
23	Gene Larkin	.35
24	Ken Gerhart	.20
25	Luis Polonia	.40
26	Jerry Steinbach	.25
27	Mickey Brantley	.20
28	Mike Stanley	.15

NO.	PLAYER	MINT
29	Jerry Browne	.10
30	Todd Benzinger (RR)	2.00
31	Fred McGriff	.75
32	Mike Henneman	.35
33	Casey Candaele	.10
34	Dave Magadan	.25
35	David Cone	1.25
36	Mike Jackson	.25
37	John Mitchell	.20
38	Mike Dunne (RR)	.30
39	John Smiley	.50
40	Joe Magrane (RR)	1.00
41	Jim Lindeman	.20
42	Shane Mack (RR)	.30

NO.	PLAYER	MINT
43	Stanley Jefferson	.15
44	Benito Santiago	.50
45	Matt Williams (RR)	2.50
46	Dave Meads	.15
47	Rafael Palmeiro	.75
48	Bill Long	.15
49	Bob Brower	.10
50	James Steels	.15
51	Paul Noci	.15
52	Greg Maddux	.60
53	Jeff Musselman	.10
54	Brian Holton	.10
55	Chuck Jackson	.20
56	Checklist	.15

1988 Donruss. . . . Complete Set of 660 Cards—Value $30.00 (Factory-Sealed set—Value $40.00)

Features the rookie cards of Mark Grace, Matt Williams, Ellis Burks and Gregg Jefferies. Donruss limited production. 26 cards were issued in much smaller quantities than other cards in the set (see asterisk) and are worth a premium. Six checklist cards were issued two ways to indicate the inclusion of the Bonus MVP cards.

NO. PLAYER	MINT
No. 1 to 26—Diamond Kings	
1 Mark McGwire (DK)	1.00
2 Tim Raines (DK)	.25
3 Benito Santiago (DK)	.30
4 Alan Trammell (DK)	.20
5 Danny Tartabull (DK)	.20
6 Ron Darling (DK)	.15
7 Paul Molitor (DK)	.15
8 Devon White (DK)	.20
9 Andre Dawson (DK)	.15
10 Julio Franco (DK)	.10
11 Scott Fletcher (DK)	.10
12 Tony Fernandez (DK)	.15
13 Shane Rawley (DK)	.10
14 Kal Daniels (DK)	.25
15 Jack Clark (DK)	.15
16 Dwight Evans (DK)	.10
17 Tommy John (DK)	.10
18 Andy Van Slyke (DK)	.15
19 Gary Gaetti (DK)	.10
20 Mark Langston (DK)	.10
21 Will Clark (DK)	.60
22 Glenn Hubbard (DK)	.10
23 Billy Hatcher (DK)	.15
24 Bob Welch (DK)	.10
25 Ivan Calderon (DK)	.10
26 Cal Ripkin, Jr., (DK)	.25
27 Checklist	.15
No. 28 to 47—Rated Rookies	
28 Mackey Sasser (R)	.30
29 Jeff Treadway (R)	.30
30 Mike Campbell (R)	.25
31 Lance Johnson (R)	.20
32 Nelson Liriano (R)	.25
33 Shawn Abner	.30
34 Roberto Alomar (R)	.75
35 Shawn Hillegas (R)	.25
36 Joey Meyer	.25
37 Kevin Elster	.20
38 Jose Lind (R)	.30
39 Kirt Manwaring (R)	.35
40 Mark Grace (R)	4.00
41 Jody Reed (R)	.60
42 John Farrell (R)	.25
43 Al Leiter (R)	1.75
44 Gary Thurman (R)	.35
45 Vincente Palacios (R)	.15
46 Eddie Williams (R)	.25
47 Jack McDowell (R)	.30
48 Ken Dixon	.05
49 Mike Birkbeck	.05
50 Eric King	.05
51 Roger Clemen	.50
52 Pat Clements	.05
53 Fernando Valenzuela	.20
54 Mark Gubicza	.05
55 Jay Howell	.05
56 Floyd Youmans	.12
57 Ed Correa	.10
58 DeWayne Buice (R)	.15
59 Jose DeLeon	.05
60 Danny Cox	.08
61 Nolan Ryan	.35
62 Steve Bedrosian	.10
63 Tom Browning	.08
64 Mark Davis	.05
65 R.J. Reynolds	.08
66 Kevin Mitchell	.50
67 Ken Oberkfell	.05
68 Rick Sutcliffe	.12
69 Dwight Gooden	.50
70 Scott Bankhead	.12
71 Bert Blyleven	.15
72 Jimmy Key	.12
73 Les Straker (R)	.15
74 Jim Clancy	.08
75 Mike Moore	.08
76 Ron Darling	.15
77 Ed Lynch	.08
78 Dale Murphy	.35
79 Doug Drabek	.05
80 Scott Garrelts	.05
81 Ed Whitson	.05
82 Rob Murphy	.05
83 Shane Rawley	.05
84 Greg Mathews	.08

NO. PLAYER	MINT
85 Jim Deshaies	.10
86 Mike Witt	.12
87 Donnie Hill	.08
88 Jeff Reed	.08
89 Mike Boddicker	.12
90 Ted Higuera	.15
91 Walt Terrell	.08
92 Bob Stanley	.05
93 Dave Righetti	.15
94 Orel Hershiser	.20
95 Chris Bando	.05
96 Bret Saberhagen	.15
97 Curt Young	.05
98 Tim Burke	.05
99 Charlie Hough	.05
100 Checklist	.05
101 Bobby Witt	.10
102 George Brett	.35
103 Mickey Tettleton	.05
104 Scott Bailes	.05
105 Mike Pagliarulo	.10
106 Mike Scioscia	.05
107 Tom Brookens	.05
108 Ray Knight	.10
109 Dan Plesac	.12
110 Wally Joyner	.45
111 Bob Forsch	.08
112 Mike Scott	.15
113 Kevin Gross	.08
114 Benito Santiago	.30
115 Bob Kipper	.05
116 Mike Krukow	.05
117 Chris Bosio	.05
118 Sid Fernandez	.12
119 Jody Davis	.05
120 Mike Morgan	.05
121 Mark Eichhorn	.05
122 Jeff Reardon	.10
123 John Franco	.08
124 Richard Dotson	.05
125 Eric Bell	.05
126 Juan Nieves	.10
127 Jack Morris	.15
128 Rick Rhoden	.08
129 Rich Gedman	.05
130 Ken Howell	.05
131 Brook Jacoby	.08
132 Danny Jackson	.10
133 Gene Nelson	.05
134 Neal Heaton	.05
135 Willie Fraser	.05
136 Jose Guzman	.05
137 Ozzie Guillen	.10
138 Bob Knepper	.08
139 Mike Jackson (R)	.15
140 Joe Magrane (R)	.50
141 Jimmy Jones	.05
142 Ted Power	.05
143 Ozzie Virgil	.05
144 Felix Fermin (R)	.15
145 Kelly Downs	.08
146 Shawon Dunston	.08
147 Scott Bradley	.05
148 Dave Stieb	.12
149 Frank Viola	.15
150 Terry Kennedy	.05
151 Bill Wegman	.05
152 Matt Nokes (R)	.60
153 Wade Boggs	1.00
154 Wayne Tolleson	.05
155 Mariano Duncan	.05
156 Julio Franco	.12
157 Charlie Leibrandt	.08
158 Terry Steinbach	.12
159 Mike Fitzgerald	.05
160 Jack Lazorko	.05
161 Mitch Williams	.05
162 Greg Walker	.05
163 Alan Ashby	.05
164 Tony Gwynn	.30
165 Bruce Ruffin	.08
166 Ron Robinson	.05
167 Zane Smith	.08
168 Junior Ortiz	.05
169 Jamie Moyer	.05
170 Tony Pena	.08

NO. PLAYER	MINT
171 Cal Ripken	.25
172 B.J. Surhoff	.20
173 Lou Whitaker	.15
174 Ellis Burks (R)	1.50
175 Ron Guidry	.15
176 Steve Sax	.15
177 Danny Tartabull	.20
178 Carney Lansford	.05
179 Casey Candaele	.05
180 Scott Fletcher	.05
181 Mark McLemore	.05
182 Ivan Calderon	.15
183 Jack Clark	.20
184 Glenn Davis	.15
185 Luis Aguayo	.05
186 Bo Diaz	.05
187 Stan Jefferson	.08
188 Sid Bream	.05
189 Bob Brenly	.05
190 Dion James	.05
191 Leon Durham	.10
192 Jesse Orosco	.05
193 Alvin Davis	.10
194 Gary Gaetti	.12
195 Fred McGriff	.45
196 Steve Lombardozzi	.08
197 Rance Mulliniks	.05
198 Rey Quinones	.05
199 Gary Carter	.25
200 Checklist	.08
201 Keith Moreland	.05
202 Ken Griffey	.05
203 Tommy Gregg (R)	.25
204 Will Clark	.75
205 John Kruk	.35
206 Buddy Bell	.15
207 Von Hayes	.10
208 Tommy Herr	.05
209 Craig Reynolds	.05
210 Gary Pettis	.05
211 Harold Baines	.15
212 Vance Law	.05
213 Ken Gerhart	.08
214 Jim Gantner	.05
215 Chet Lemon	.08
216 Dwight Evans	.10
217 Don Mattingly	1.50
218 Franklin Stubbs	.08
219 Pat Tabler	.05
220 Bo Jackson	1.00
221 Tony Phillips	.05
222 Tim Wallach	.08
223 Ruben Sierra	.50
224 Steve Buechele	.05
225 Frank White	.05
226 Alfredo Griffin	.05
227 Greg Swindell	.20
228 Willie Randolph	.10
229 Mike Marshall	.10
230 Alan Trammell	.15
231 Eddie Murray	.25
232 Dale Sveum	.08
233 Dick Schofield	.05
234 Jose Oquendo	.05
235 Bill Doran	.05
236 Milt Thompson	.05
237 Marvell Wynne	.05
238 Bobby Bonilla	.20
239 Chris Speier	.05
240 Glenn Braggs	.10
241 Wally Backman	.05
242 Ryne Sandberg	.20
243 Phil Bradley	.12
244 Kelly Gruber	.05
245 Tom Brunansky	.10
246 Ron Oester	.05
247 Bobby Thigpen	.05
248 Fred Lynn	.15
249 Paul Molitor	.15
250 Darrell Evans	.10
251 Gary Ward	.08
252 Bruce Hurst	.08
253 Bob Welch	.05
254 Joe Carter	.12
255 Willie Wilson	.12
256 Mark McGwire	1.25

NO. PLAYER	MINT
257 Mitch Webster	.05
258 Brian Downing	.05
259 Mike Stanley	.05
260 Carlton Fisk	.15
261 Billy Hatcher	.10
262 Glenn Wilson	.05
263 Ozzie Smith	.15
264 Randy Ready	.05
265 Kurt Stillwell	.10
266 David Palmer	.05
267 Mike Diaz	.05
268 Rob Thompson	.08
269 Andre Dawson	.20
270 Lee Guetterman	.05
271 Willie Upshaw	.05
272 Randy Bush	.05
273 Larry Sheets	.12
274 Rob Deer	.10
275 Kirk Gibson	.20
276 Marty Barrett	.10
277 Rickey Henderson	.35
278 Pedro Guerrero	.20
279 Brett Butler	.05
280 Kevin Seitzer	.75
281 Mike Davis	.05
282 Andres Galarraga	.20
283 Devon White	.20
284 Pete O'Brien	.10
285 Jerry Hairston	.05
286 Kevin Bass	.08
287 Carmelo Martinez	.05
288 Juan Samuel	.10
289 Kal Daniels	.20
290 Albert Hall	.05
291 Andy Van Slyke	.12
292 Lee Smith	.10
293 Vince Coleman	.20
294 Tom Niedenfuer	.05
295 Robin Yount	.25
296 Jeff Robinson (R)	.30
297 Todd Benzinger (R)	.40
298 Dave Winfield	.25
299 Mickey Hatcher	.05
300 Checklist	.08
301 Bud Black	.05
302 Jose Canseco	1.50
303 Tom Foley	.05
304 Pete Incaviglia	.20
305 Bob Boone	.05
306 Bill Long (R)	.15
307 Willie McGee	.15
308 Ken Caminiti (R)	.25
309 Darren Daulton	.05
310 Tracy Jones	.10
311 Greg Booker	.05
312 Mike LaValliere	.05
313 Chili Davis	.10
314 Glenn Hubbard	.05
315 Paul Noce (R)	.15
316 Keith Hernandez	.20
317 Mark Langston	.10
318 Keith Atherton	.05
319 Tony Fernandez	.12
320 Kent Hrbek	.15
321 John Cerutti	.05
322 Mike Kingery	.05
323 Dave Magadan	.15
324 Rafael Palmeiro	.40
325 Jeff Dedmon	.05
326 Barry Bonds	.20
327 Jeffrey Leonard	.05
328 Tim Flannery	.05
329 Dave Concepcion	.05
330 Mike Schmidt	.30
331 Bill Dawley	.05
332 Larry Anderson	.05
333 Jack Howell	.05
334 Ken Williams (R)	.25
335 Bryn Smith	.05
336 Billy Ripken (R)	.20
337 Greg Brock	.05
338 Mike Heath	.05
339 Mike Greenwell	1.25
340 Claudell Washington	.05
341 Jose Gonzalez	.05
342 Mel Hall	.05

NO. PLAYER	MINT	NO. PLAYER	MINT	NO. PLAYER	MINT	NO. PLAYER	MINT
343 Jim Eisenreich	.08	430 Ricky Horton	.05	516 Manny Trillo	.05	602 Don August	.20
344 Tony Bernazard	.05	431 Gerald Young (R)	.40	517 Jerry Reed	.05	*603 Terry Leach	.12
345 Tim Raines	.25	432 Rick Schu	.05	518 Rick Leach	.05	604 Tom Newell (R)	.15
346 Bob Brower	.05	433 Paul O'Neill	.05	519 Mark Davidson (R)	.15	*605 Randall Byers (R)	.25
347 Larry Parrish	.05	434 Rich Gossage	.15	520 Jeff Ballard (R)	.30	606 Jim Gott	.05
348 Thad Bosley	.05	435 John Cangelosi	.05	521 Dave Stapleton	.15	607 Harry Spilman	.05
349 Dennis Eckersley	.05	436 Mike LaCoss	.05	522 Pat Sheridan	.05	608 John Candelaria	.05
350 Cory Snyder	.20	437 Gerald Perry	.10	523 Al Nipper	.05	609 Mike Brumley (R)	.20
351 Rick Cerone	.05	438 Dave Martinez	.05	524 Steve Trout	.05	610 Mickey Brantley	.15
352 John Shelby	.05	439 Darryl Strawberry	.50	525 Jeff Hamilton	.05	*611 Jose Nunez (R)	.25
353 Larry Herndon	.05	440 John Moses	.05	526 Tommy Hinzo (R)	.15	612 Tom Nieto	.05
354 John Habyan	.05	441 Greg Gagne	.05	527 Lonnie Smith	.08	613 Rick Reuschel	.05
355 Chuck Crim (R)	.15	442 Jesse Barfield	.15	528 Greg Cadaret (R)	.20	*614 Lee Mazzilli	.12
356 Gus Polidor	.05	443 George Frazier	.05	529 Rob McClure	.05	615 Scott Lusader (R)	.20
357 Ken Dayley	.05	444 Garth Iorg	.05	530 Chuck Finley	.05	616 Bobby Meacham	.05
358 Danny Darwin	.05	445 Ed Nunez	.05	531 Jeff Russell	.05	*617 Kevin McReynolds	.20
359 Lance Parrish	.15	446 Rick Aguilera	.05	532 Steve Lyons	.05	618 Gene Garber	.05
360 James Steels (R)	.15	447 Jerry Mumphrey	.05	533 Terry Puhl	.05	• 619 Barry Lyons	.25
361 Al Pedrique (R)	.15	448 Rafael Ramirez	.05	534 Eric Nolte (R)	.20	620 Randy Myers	.15
362 Mike Aldrete	.05	449 John Smiley (R)	.30	535 Kent Tekulve	.05	621 Donnie Moore	.05
363 Juan Castillo	.05	450 Atlee Hammaker	.05	536 Pat Pacillo	.15	622 Domingo Ramos	.05
364 Len Dykstra	.15	451 Lance McCullers	.08	537 Charlie Puleo	.05	623 Ed Romero	.05
365 Luis Quinones	.05	452 Guy Hoffman	.05	538 Tom Prince	.15	624 Greg Myers (R)	.15
366 Jim Presley	.10	453 Chris James	.10	539 Greg Maddux	.15	625 Ripken Family	.25
367 Lloyd Moseby	.10	454 Terry Pendleton	.05	540 Jim Lindeman	.10	626 Pat Perry	.15
368 Kirby Puckett	.40	455 Dave Meads (R)	.15	541 Pete Stanicek (R)	.25	*627 Andres Thomas	.15
369 Eric Davis	.75	456 Bill Buckner	.05	542 Steve Kiefer	.05	*628 Matt Williams (R)	1.25
370 Gary Redus	.05	457 John Pawlowski (R)	.15	543 Jim Morrison	.05	629 Dave Hengel (R)	.20
371 Dave Schmidt	.05	458 Bob Sebra	.05	544 Spike Owen	.05	*630 Jeff Musselman	.15
372 Mark Clear	.05	459 Jim Dwyer	.05	545 Jay Buhner (R)	.50	631 Tim Laudner	.05
373 Dave Bergman	.05	460 Jay Aldrich (R)	.15	546 Mike Devereaux (R)	.30	* 632 Bob Ojeda	.12
374 Charles Hudson	.05	461 Frank Tanana	.05	547 Jerry Don Gleaton	.05	633 Rafael Santana	.05
375 Calvin Schiraldi	.05	462 Oil Can Boyd	.05	548 Jose Rijo	.05	634 Wes Gardner (R)	.25
376 Alex Trevino	.05	463 Dan Pasqua	.08	549 Dennis Martinez	.05	*635 Roberto Kelly (R)	1.00
377 Tom Candiotti	.05	464 Tim Crews (R)	.20	550 Mike Loynd	.05	*636 Mike Flanagan	.15
378 Steve Farr	.05	465 Andy Allanson	.05	551 Darrell Miller	.05	637 Jay Bell (R)	.25
379 Mike Gallego	.05	466 Bill Pecota (R)	.15	552 Dave LaPoint	.05	638 Bob Melvin	.05
380 Andy McGaffigan	.05	467 Steve Ontiveros	.05	553 John Tudor	.10	639 Damon Berryhill (R)	.35
381 Kirk McCaskill	.05	468 Hubie Brooks	.05	554 Rocky Childress (R)	.15	*640 David Wells (R)	.25
382 Oddibe McDowell	.08	469 Paul Kilgus (R)	.20	555 Wally Ritchie (R)	.15	641 Puzzle Card	.05
383 Floyd Bannister	.08	470 Dale Mohorcic	.05	556 Terry McGriff	.05	642 Doug Sisk	.05
384 Denny Walling	.05	471 Dan Quisenberry	.10	557 Dave Leiper	.05	643 Keith Hughes (R)	.20
385 Don Carman	.05	472 Dave Stewart	.08	558 Jeff Robinson	.05	644 Tom Glavine (R)	.30
386 Todd Worrell	.15	473 Dave Clark	.05	559 Jose Uribe	.05	:645 Al Newman	.15
387 Eric Show	.05	474 Joel Skinner	.05	560 Ted Simmons	.05	646 Scott Sanderson	.05
388 Dave Parker	.20	475 Dave Anderson	.05	561 Lester Lancaster (R)	.20	647 Scott Terry	.15
389 Rick Mahler	.05	476 Dan Petry	.05	562 Keith Miller (R)	.25	*648 Tim Teufel	.15
390 Mike Dunne	.25	477 Carl Nichols (R)	.15	563 Harold Reynolds	.05	*649 Garry Templeton	.15
391 Candy Maldonado	.08	478 Ernest Riles	.05	564 Gene Larkin (R)	.25	*650 Manny Lee	.15
392 Bob Dernier	.05	479 George Hendrick	.05	565 Cecil Fielder	.05	*651 Roger McDowell	.15
393 Dave Valle	.05	480 John Morris	.05	566 Roy Smalley	.05	*652 Mookie Wilson	.15
394 Ernie Whitt	.08	481 Manny Hernandez (R)	.15	567 Duane Ward	.05	*653 David Cone	.60
395 Juan Berenguer	.05	482 Jeff Stone	.05	568 Bill Wilkinson (R)	.15	*654 Ron Gant	.50
396 Mike Young	.08	483 Chris Brown	.10	569 Howard Johnson	.20	*655 Joe Price	.15
397 Mike Felder	.05	484 Mike Bielecki	.05	570 Frank DiPino	.05	*656 George Bell	.25
398 Willie Hernandez	.08	485 Dave Dravecky	.05	571 Pete Smith (R)	.15	*657 Gregg Jefferies (R)	5.00
399 Jim Rice	.20	486 Rick Manning	.05	572 Darnell Coles	.05	*658 Todd Stottlemyre (R)	.40
400 Checklist	.08	487 Bill Almon	.05	573 Don Robinson	.05	*659 Geronimo Berroa (R)	.35
401 Tommy John	.12	488 Jim Sundberg	.05	574 Rob Nelson	.05	*660 Jerry Royster	.15
402 Brian Holton	.05	489 Ken Phelps	.05	575 Dennis Rasmussen	.05		
403 Carmen Castillo	.05	490 Tom Henke	.05	576 Steve Jeltz	.05		
404 Jamie Quirk	.05	491 Dan Gladden	.05	577 Tom Pagnozzi (R)	.15		
405 Dwayne Murphy	.05	492 Barry Larkin	.35	578 Ty Gainey	.05		
406 Jeff Parrett (R)	.15	493 Fred Manrique (R)	.20	579 Gary Lucas	.05		
407 Don Sutton	.15	494 Mike Griffin	.05	580 Ron Hassey	.05		
408 Jerry Browne	.05	495 Mark Knudson (R)	.12	581 Herm Winningham	.05		
409 Jim Winn	.05	496 Bill Madlock	.12	582 Rene Gonzales (R)	.15		
410 Dave Smith	.05	497 Tim Stoddard	.05	583 Brad Komminsk	.05		
411 Shane Mack	.20	498 Sam Horn (R)	.25	584 Doyle Alexander	.05		
412 Greg Gross	.05	499 Tracy Woodson (R)	.20	585 Jeff Sellers	.05		
413 Nick Esasky	.05	500 Checklist	.08	586 Bill Gullickson	.05		
414 Damaso Garcia	.05	501 Ken Schrom	.05	587 Tim Belcher	.40		
415 Brian Fisher	.05	502 Angel Salazar	.05	588 Doug Jones (R)	.35		
416 Brian Dayett	.05	503 Eric Plunk	.05	589 Melido Perez (R)	.25		
417 Curt Ford	.05	504 Joe Hesketh	.05	590 Rick Honeycutt	.05		
418 Mark Williamson (R)	.15	505 Greg Minton	.05	591 Pascual Perez	.05		
419 Bill Schroeder	.05	506 Geno Petralli	.05	592 Curt Wilkerson	.05		
420 Mike Henneman (R)	.25	507 Bob James	.05	593 Steve Howe	.05		
421 John Marzano	.20	508 Robbie Wine (R)	.15	594 John Davis (R)	.20		
422 Ron Kittle	.08	509 Jeff Calhoun	.05	595 Storm Davis	.05		
423 Matt Young	.05	510 Steve Lake	.05	596 Sammy Stewart	.05		
424 Steve Balboni	.05	511 Mark Grant	.05	597 Neil Allen	.05		
425 Luis Polonia (R)	.25	512 Frank Williams	.05	598 Alejandro Pena	.05		
426 Randy St. Claire	.05	513 Jeff Blauser (R)	.25	599 Mark Thurmond	.05		
427 Greg Harris	.05	514 Bob Walk	.05	600 Checklist	.08		
428 Johnny Ray	.05	515 Craig Lefferts	.05	601 Jose Mesa (R)	.15		
429 Ray Searage	.05						

1988 Donruss Rookies. . . . Complete Set of 56 Cards—Value $12.00

Features the outstanding rookies of the 1988 season. The cards are coated with a glossy finish. The entire set was packaged in a printed box and distributed primarily through card hobby dealers. Features Donruss' first card of Chris Sabo and Walt Weiss.

NO.	PLAYER	MINT	NO.	PLAYER	MINT	NO.	PLAYER	MINT	NO.	PLAYER	MINT
1	Mark Grace	2.50	15	Pete Stanicek	.15	29	Johnny Paredes	.15	43	John Dopson	25
2	Mike Campbell	.10	16	Roberto Kelly	.30	30	Chris Sabo (RR)	2.00	44	Jody Reed	20
3	Todd Frohwirth	10	17	Jeff Treadway	.15	31	Dannon Berryhill	.25	45	Darrin Jackson	20
4	Dave Stapleton	10	18	Walt Weiss (RR)	1.00	32	Randy Miligan	15	46	Mike Capel	10
5	Shawn Abner	15	19	Paul Gibson	.20	33	Gary Thurman	15	47	Ron Gant	.25
6	Jose Cecenazi	.10	20	Tim Crews	.10	34	Kevin Elster	.20	48	John Davis	.10
7	Dave Gallagher	.25	21	Melido Perez	.15	35	Roberto Alomar	.25	49	Kevin Coffman	.15
8	Mark Parent	15	22	Steve Peters	.15	36	Edgar Martinez	.25	50	Cris Carpenter (RR)	.35
9	Cecil Espy	.20	23	Craig Worthington	.35	37	Todd Stottlemyre	.15	51	Mick Sasser	.15
10	Pete Smith	.10	24	John Trautwein	.20	38	Joey Meyer	.20	52	Luis Alicea	.15
11	Jay Buhner	.25	25	DeWayne Vaughn	.15	39	Carl Nichols	10	53	Bryan Harvey (RR)	.35
12	Pat Borders	.25	26	David Well	.15	40	Jack McDowell	15	54	Steve Ellsworth	20
13	Doug Jennings	.20	27	Al Leiter	.20	41	Jose Bautista	20	55	Mike Macfarlane	20
14	Brady Anderson	.35	28	Tim Belcher	.25	42	Sil Campusano	25	56	Checklist	10

1989 Donruss. . . . Complete Set of 660 Cards—Value $30.00

Features the rookie cards of Sandy Alomar, Jr., Ken Griffey, Jr., Tom Gordon, Gary Sheffield and Rickey Jordan.

NO.	PLAYER	MINT	NO.	PLAYER	MINT	NO.	PLAYER	MINT	NO.	PLAYER	MINT
	No. 1 to 26—Diamond Kings		7	Carlton Fisk (DK)	.08	14	Andres Galarraga (DK)	.15	21	Harold Reynolds (DK)	.10
1	Mike Greenwell (DK)	.50	8	Cory Snyder (DK)	.10	15	Kirk Gibson (DK)	.10	22	Gerald Perry (DK)	.10
2	Bobby Bonilla (DK)	.15	9	David Cone (DK)	.25	16	Fred McGriff (DK)	.25	23	Frank Viola (DK)	.20
3	Pete Incaviglia (DK)	.10	10	Kevin Seitzer (DK)	.15	17	Mark Grace (DK)	.50	24	Steve Bedrosian (DK)	.08
4	Chris Sabo (DK)	.40	11	Rick Rueschel (DK)	.08	18	Jeff Robinson (DK)	.10	25	Glenn Davis (DK)	.10
5	Robin Yount (DK)	.10	12	Johnny Ray (DK)	.08	19	Vince Coleman (DK)	.10	26	Don Mattingly (DK)	.75
6	Tony Gwynn (DK)	.20	13	Dave Schmidt (DK)	.08	20	Dave Henderson (DK)	.10	27	Diamond King Checklist	.08

NO.	PLAYER	MINT
	No. 28 to 47—Rated Rookies	
28	Sandy Alomar, Jr. (R)	1.25
29	Steve Searcy (R)	.25
30	Cameron Drew (R)	.25
31	Gary Sheffield (R)	2.00
32	Erik Hanson (R)	.30
33	Ken Griffey, Jr. (R)	4.00
34	Greg Harris (R)	.20
35	Gregg Jefferies	1.50
36	Luis Medina (R)	.40
37	Carlos Quintana (R)	.35
38	Felix Jose (R)	.25
39	Cris Carpenter (R)	.20
40	Ron Jones (R)	.35
41	Dave West (R)	.50
42	Randy Johnson (R)	.30
43	Mike Harkey (R)	.30
44	Pete Harnisch (R)	.20
45	Tom Gordon (R)	2.50
46	Gregg Olson (R)	.60
47	Alex Sanchez (R)	.25
48	Ruben Sierra	.20
49	Rafael Palmeiro	.15
50	Ron Gant	.20
51	Cal Ripken, Jr.	.20
52	Wally Joyner	.15
53	Gary Carter	.20
54	Andy Van Slyke	.15
55	Robin Yount	.15
56	Pete Incaviglia	.10
57	Greg Brock	.05
58	Melido Perez	.10
59	Craig Lefferts	.05
60	Gary Pettis	.05
61	Danny Tartabull	.15
62	Guillermo Hernandez	.05
63	Ozzie Smith	.15
64	Gary Gaetti	.10
65	Mark Davis	.05
66	Lee Smith	.08
67	Dennis Eckersley	.10
68	Wade Boggs	.75
69	Mike Scott	.15
70	Fred McGriff	.30
71	Tom Browning	.08
72	Claudell Washington	.05
73	Mel Hall	.05
74	Don Mattingly	1.00
75	Steve Bedrosian	.08
76	Juan Samuel	.10
77	Mike Scioscia	.05
78	Dave Righetti	.10
79	Alfredo Griffin	.05
80	Eric Davis	.30
81	Juan Berenguer	.05
82	Todd Worrell	.05
83	Joe Carter	.15
84	Steve Sax	.12
85	Frank White	.05
86	John Kruk	.15
87	Rance Mulliniks	.05
88	Alan Ashby	.05
89	Charlie Leibrandt	.08
90	Frank Tanana	.08
91	Jose Canseco	1.00
92	Barry Bonds	.15
93	Harold Reynolds	.08
94	Mark McLemore	.05
95	Mark McGwire	.50
96	Eddie Murray	.20
97	Tim Raines	.15
98	Rob Thompsomn	.05
99	Kevin McReynolds	.15
100	Checklist	.08
101	Carlton Fisk	.10
102	Dave Martinez	.05
103	Glenn Braggs	.05
104	Dale Murphy	.20
105	Ryne Sandberg	.12
106	Dennis Martinez	.05
107	Pete O'Brien	.10
108	Dick Schofield	.05
109	Henry Cotto	.05
110	Mike Marshall	.08

NO.	PLAYER	MINT
111	Keith Moreland	.08
112	Tom Brunansky	.08
113	Kelly Gruber	.05
114	Brook Jacoby	.05
115	Keith Brown (R)	.20
116	Matt Nokes	.10
117	Keith Hernandez	.15
118	Bob Forsch	.05
119	Bert Blyleven	.15
120	Willie Wilson	.08
121	Tommy Gregg	.05
122	Jim Rice	.12
123	Bob Knepper	.05
124	Danny Jackson	.10
125	Eric Plunk	.05
126	Brian Fisher	.05
127	Mike Pagliarulo	.10
128	Tony Gwynn	.25
129	Lance McCullers	.08
130	Andres Galarraga	.15
131	Jose Uribe	.05
132	Kirk Gibson	.20
133	David Palmer	.05
134	R. J. Reynolds	.05
135	Greg Walker	.05
136	Kirk McCaskill	.05
137	Shawon Dunston	.10
138	Andy Allanson	.05
139	Rob Murphy	.05
140	Mike Aldrete	.05
141	Terry Kennedy	.05
142	Scott Fletcher	.05
143	Steve Balboni	.05
144	Bret Saberhagen	.10
145	Ozzie Virgil	.05
146	Dale Sveum	.08
147	Darryl Strawberry	.45
148	Harold Baines	.10
149	George Bell	.15
150	Dave Parker	.10
151	Bobby Bonilla	.15
152	Mookie Wilson	.08
153	Tod Power	.05
154	Nolan Ryan	.25
155	Jeff Reardon	.08
156	Tim Wallach	.08
157	Jamie Moyer	.05
158	Rich Gossage	.08
159	Dave Winfield	.15
160	Von Hayes	.08
161	Willie McGee	.08
162	Rich Gedman	.05
163	Tony Pena	.08
164	Mike Morgan	.05
165	Charlie Hough	.08
166	Mike Stanley	.05
167	Andre Dawson	.15
168	Joe Boever	.05
169	Pete Stanicek	.05
170	Bob Boone	.05
171	Ron Darling	.10
172	Bob Walk	.05
173	Rob Deer	.08
174	Steve Buechele	.05
175	Ted Higuera	.10
176	Ozzie Guillen	.08
177	Candy Maldonado	.10
178	Doyle Alexander	.05
179	Mark Gubicza	.10
180	Alan Trammell	.10
181	Vince Coleman	.15
182	Kirby Puckett	.25
183	Chris Brown	.08
184	Marty Barrett	.05
185	Stan Javier	.05
186	Mike Greenwell	.75
187	Billy Hatcher	.05
188	Jimmy Key	.12
189	Nick Esasky	.10
190	Don Slaught	.05
191	Cory Snyder	.15
192	John Candelaria	.08
193	Mike Schmidt	.30
194	Kevin Gross	.05

NO.	PLAYER	MINT
195	John Tudor	.05
196	Neil Allen	.05
197	Orel Hershiser	.25
198	Kal Daniels	.15
199	Kent Hrbek	.10
200	Checklist	.08
201	Joe Magrane	.10
202	Scott Bailes	.05
203	Tim Belcher	.15
204	George Brett	.25
205	Benito Santiago	.10
206	Tony Fernandez	.10
207	Gerald Young	.08
208	Bo Jackson	.60
209	Chet Lemon	.05
210	Storm Davis	.05
211	Doug Drabek	.10
212	Mickey Brantley	.08
213	Devon White	.08
214	Dave Stewart	.10
215	Dave Schmidt	.05
216	Bryn Smith	.05
217	Brett Butler	.05
218	Bob Ojeda	.08
219	Steve Rosenberg (R)	.15
220	Hubie Brooks	.05
221	B.J. Surhoff	.08
222	Rick Mahler	.05
223	Rick Sutcliffe	.10
224	Neal Heaton	.05
225	Mitch Williams	.05
226	Chuck Finley	.05
227	Mark Langston	.10
228	Jesse Orosco	.05
229	Ed Whitson	.05
230	Terry Pendleton	.08
231	Lloyd Moseby	.15
232	Greg Swindell	.10
233	John Franco	.08
234	Jack Morris	.10
235	Howard Johnson	.15
236	Glenn Davis	.10
237	Frank Viola	.15
238	Kevin Seitzer	.15
239	Gerald Perry	.10
240	Dwight Evans	.15
241	Jim Deshaies	.05
242	Bo Diaz	.05
243	Carney Lansford	.08
244	Mike Lavalliere	.05
245	Rickey Henderson	.30
246	Roberto Alomar	.15
247	Jimmy Jones	.05
248	Pascual Perez	.05
249	Will Clark	.75
250	Fernando Valenzuela	.10
251	Shane Rawley	.05
252	Sid Bream	.05
253	Steve Lyons	.05
254	Brian Downing	.08
255	Mark Grace	1.00
256	Tom Candiotti	.08
257	Barry Larkin	.10
258	Mike Krukow	.08
259	Billy Ripken	.05
260	Cecilio Guante	.05
261	Scott Bradley	.05
262	Floyd Bannister	.05
263	Pete Smith	.08
264	Jim Gantner	.05
265	Roger McDowell	.05
266	Bobby Thigpen	.05
267	Jim Clancy	.05
268	Terry Steinbach	.12
269	Mike Dunne	.05
270	Dwight Gooden	.40
271	Mike Heath	.05
272	Dave Smith	.05
273	Keith Atherton	.05
274	Tim Burke	.05
275	Damon Beryhill	.15
276	Vance Law	.05
277	Rich Dotson	.08
278	Lance Parrish	.10

NO.	PLAYER	MINT
279	Denny Walling	.05
280	Roger Clemens	.40
281	Greg Mathews	.05
282	Tom Niedenfuer	.05
283	Paul Kilgus	.05
284	Jose Guzman	.05
285	Calvin Schiraldi	.05
286	Charlie Puleo	.05
287	Joe Orsulak	.08
288	Jack Howell	.08
289	Kevin Elster	.08
290	Jose Lind	.08
291	Paul Molitor	.08
292	Cecil Espy	.10
293	Bill Wegman	.05
294	Dan Pasqua	.08
295	Scott Garrelts	.05
296	Walt Terrell	.05
297	Ed Hearn	.05
298	Lou Whitaker	.08
299	Ken Dayley	.05
300	Checklist	.08
301	Tommy Herr	.05
302	Mike Brumley	.05
303	Ellis Burks	.35
304	Curt Young	.05
305	Jody Reed	.15
306	Bill Doran	.08
307	David Wells	.05
308	Ron Robinson	.08
309	Rafael Santana	.05
310	Julio Franco	.08
311	Jack Clark	.10
312	Chris James	.08
313	Milt Thompson	.05
314	John Shelby	.05
315	Al Leiter	.10
316	Mike Davis	.05
317	Chris Sabo (R)	.75
318	Greg Gagne	.05
319	Jose Oquendo	.05
320	John Farrell	.10
321	Franklin Stubbs	.05
322	Kurt Stillwell	.05
323	Shawn Abner	.05
324	Mike Flanagan	.05
325	Kevin Bass	.08
326	Pat Tabler	.05
327	Mike Henneman	.05
328	Rick Honeycutt	.05
329	John Smiley	.08
330	Rey Quinones	.05
331	Johnny Ray	.10
332	Bob Welch	.08
333	Larry Sheets	.05
334	Jeff Parrett	.08
335	Rick Rueschel	.05
336	Randy Myers	.08
337	Ken Williams	.05
338	Andy McGaffigan	.05
339	Joey Meyer	.05
340	Dion James	.05
341	Les Lancaster	.05
342	Tom Foley	.05
343	Geno Petralli	.05
344	Dan Petry	.05
345	Alvin Davis	.08
346	Mickey Hatcher	.05
347	Marvelle Wynn	.05
348	Danny Cox	.05
349	Dave Stieb	.08
350	Jay Bell	.05
351	Jeff Treadway	.05
352	Luis Salazar	.05
353	Lenny Dykstra	.15
354	Juan Agosto	.05
355	Gene Larkin	.05
356	Steve Farr	.05
357	Paul Assenmacher	.05
358	Todd Benzinger	.15
359	Larry Andersen	.05
360	Paul O'Neill	.05
361	Ron Hassey	.05
362	Jim Gott	.05

NO.	PLAYER	MINT
363	Ken Phelps	.05
364	Tim Flannery	.05
365	Randy Ready	.05
366	Nelson Santovenia (R)	.15
367	Kelly Downs	.05
368	Danny Heep	.05
369	Phil Bradley	.08
370	Jeff Robinson	.05
371	Ivan Calderon	.10
372	Mike Witt	.08
373	Greg Maddux	.20
374	Carmen Castillo	.05
375	Jose Rijo	.08
376	Joe Price	.05
377	R.C. Gonzalez	.05
378	Oddibe McDowell	.08
379	Jim Presley	.05
380	Brad Wellman	.05
381	Tom Glavine	.05
382	Dan Plesac	.05
383	Wally Backman	.05
384	Dave Gallagher (R)	.25
385	Tom Henke	.05
386	Luis Polonia	.05
387	Junior Ortiz	.05
388	David Cone	.30
389	Dave Bergman	.05
390	Danny Darwin	.05
391	Dan Gladden	.05
392	John Dopson (R)	.25
393	Frank DiPino	.05
394	Al Nipper	.05
395	Willie Randolph	.08
396	Don Carmen	.05
397	Scott Terry	.05
398	Rick Cerone	.05
399	Tom Pagnozzi	.05
400	Checklist	.08
401	Mickey Tettleton	.05
402	Curtis Wilkerson	.05
403	Jeff Russel	.05
404	Pat Perry	.05
405	Jose Alvarez (R)	.15
406	Rick Schu	.05
407	Sherman Corbett (R)	.15
408	Dave Magadan	.10
409	Bob Kipper	.05
410	Don August	.10
411	Bob Brower	.05
412	Chris Bosio	.05
413	Jerry Reuss	.05
414	Atlee Hammaker	.05
415	Jim Walewander	.10
416	Mike Macfarlane (R)	.20
417	Pat Sheridan	.05
418	Pedro Guerrero	.15
419	Allan Anderson	.08
420	Mark Parent (R)	.15
421	Bob Stanley	.05
422	Mike Gallego	.05
423	Bruce Hurst	.15
424	Dave Meads	.05
425	Jesse Barfield	.12
426	Rob Dibble (R)	.25
427	Joel Skinner	.05
428	Ron Kittle	.08
429	Rick Rhoden	.05
430	Bob Dernier	.05
431	Steve Jeltz	.05
432	Rick Dempsey	.05
433	Roberto Kelly	.15
434	Dave Anderson	.05
435	Herm Winningham	.05
436	Al Newman	.05
437	Jose Deleon	.05
438	Doug Jones	.05
439	Brian Holton	.05
440	Jeff Montgomery	.10
441	Dickie Thon	.05
442	Cecil Fielder	.05
443	John Fishel (R)	.15

NO.	PLAYER	MINT
444	Jerry Don Gleaton	.05
445	Paul Gibson (R)	.15
446	Walt Weiss	.40
447	Glenn Wilson	.05
448	Mike Moore	.05
449	Chili Davis	.08
450	Dave Henderson	.05
451	Jose Bautista (R)	.15
452	Rex Hudler	.10
453	Bob Brenly	.05
454	Mackey Sasser	.08
455	Daryl Boston	.05
456	Mike Fitzgerald	.05
457	Jefferey Leonard	.05
458	Bruce Sutter	.08
459	Mitch Webster	.05
460	Joe Hesketh	.05
461	Bobby Witt	.05
462	Stew Cliburn	.05
463	Scott Bankhead	.05
464	Ramon Martinez (R)	.35
465	Dave Leiper	.05
466	Luis Alicea (R)	.15
467	John Cerutti	.05
468	Ron Washington	.05
469	Jeff Reed	.05
470	Jeff Robinson	.10
471	Sid Fernandez	.10
472	Terry Puhl	.05
473	Charlie Lea	.05
474	Israel Sanchez (R)	.15
475	Bruce Benedict	.05
476	Oil Can Boyd	.08
477	Craig Reynolds	.05
478	Frank Williams	.05
479	Greg Cadaret	.05
480	Randy Kramer (R)	.15
481	Dave Eiland (R)	.20
482	Eric Show	.05
483	Garry Templeton	.05
484	Wallace Johnson	.05
485	Kevin Mitchell	.35
486	Tim Crews	.05
487	Mike Maddux	.05
488	Dave LaPoint	.05
489	Fred Manrique	.05
490	Greg Minton	.05
491	Doug Dascenzo (R)	.30
492	Willie Upshaw	.05
493	Jack Armstrong (R)	.20
494	Kirt Manwaring	.05
495	Jeff Ballard	.05
496	Jeff Kunkel	.05
497	Mike Campbell	.05
498	Gary Thurman	.05
499	Zane Smith	.05
500	Checklist	.08
501	Mike Birkbeck	.05
502	Terry Leach	.05
503	Shawn Hillegas	.05
504	Manny Lee	.05
505	Doug Jennings (R)	.30
506	Ken Oberkfell	.05
507	Tim Tuefel	.05
508	Tom Brookens	.05
509	Rafael Ramirez	.05
510	Fred Toliver	.05
511	Brian Holman (R)	.20
512	Mike Bielecki	.05
513	Jeff Pico (R)	.20
514	Charles Hudson	.08
515	Bruce Ruffin	.05
516	Larry McWilliams	.05
517	Jeff Sellers	.05
518	John Costello (R)	.15
519	Brady Anderson (R)	.25
520	Craig McMurtry	.05
521	Ray Hayward	.05
522	Drew Hall	.10
523	Mark Lemke (R)	.20
524	Oswald Peraza (R)	.15

NO.	PLAYER	MINT
525	Bryan Harvey (R)	.25
526	Rick Aguilera	.05
527	Tom Prince	.05
528	Mark Clear	.05
529	Jerry Browne	.05
530	Juan Castillo	.05
531	Jack McDowell	.10
532	Chris Speier	.05
533	Darrell Evans	.05
534	Luis Aquino	.05
535	Eric King	.05
536	Ken Hill (R)	.20
537	Randy Bush	.05
538	Shane Mack	.05
539	Tom Bolton	.05
540	Gene Nelson	.05
541	Wes Gardner	.05
542	Ken Caminiti	.05
543	Duane Ward	.05
544	Norm Charlton (R)	.20
545	Hal Morris (R)	.25
546	Rich Yett	.05
547	Hensley Meulens (R)	.50
548	Greg Harris	.15
549	Darren Daulton	.05
550	Jeff Hamilton	.05
551	Luis Aguayo	.05
552	Tim Leary	.10
553	Ron Oester	.05
554	Steve Lombardozzi	.05
555	Tim Jones (R)	.15
556	Bud Black	.05
557	Alejandro Pena	.08
558	Jose DeJesus (R)	.15
559	Dennis Rasmussen	.05
560	Pat Borders (R)	.15
561	Craig Biggio (R)	.50
562	Luis de los Santos (R)	.20
563	Fred Lynn	.08
564	Todd Burns (R)	.25
565	Felix Fermin	.05
566	Darnell Coles	.05
567	Willie Fraser	.05
568	Glenn Hubbard	.05
569	Craig Worthington (R)	.30
570	Johnny Paredes (R)	.20
571	Don Robinson	.05
572	Barry Lyons	.05
573	Bill Long	.05
574	Tracy Jones	.05
575	Juan Nieves	.05
576	Andres Thomas	.05
577	Rolando Roomes (R)	.35
578	Luis Rivera	.15
579	Chad Kreuter (R)	.20
580	Tony Armas	.05
581	Jay Buhner	.15
582	Ricky Horton	.05
583	Andy Hawkins	.05
584	Sil Campusano (R)	.20
585	Dave Cark	.05
586	Van Snider (R)	.20
587	Todd Frohwirth	.05
588	Puzzle Card	.08
589	William Brennan (R)	.15
590	German Gonzalez (R)	.20
591	Ernie Whitt	.05
592	Jeff Blauser	.05
593	Spike Owen	.05
594	Matt Williams	.25
595	Lloyd McClendon	.10
596	Steve Ontiveros	.05
597	Scott Medvin (R)	.15
598	Hipolito Pena (R)	.15
599	Jerald Clark (R)	.20
600	Checklist	.08
601	Carmelo Martinez	.05
602	Mike LaCoss	.05
603	Mike Devereaux	.05
604	Alex Madrid (R)	.15
605	Gary Redus	.05

NO.	PLAYER	MINT
606	Lance Johnson	.05
607	Terry Clark (R)	.15
608	Manny Trillo	.05
609	Scott Jordan (R)	.15
610	Jay Howell	.08
611	Francisco Melendez (R)	.25
612	Mike Boddicker	.08
613	Kevin Brown (R)	.25
614	Dave Valle	.05
615	Tim Laudner	.05
616	Andy Nezelek (R)	.25
617	Chuck Crim	.05
618	Jack Savage	.15
619	Adam Peterson	.12
620	Todd Stottlemyre	.08
621	Lance Blankenship (R)	.25
622	Miquel Garcia (R)	.15
623	Keith Miller	.05
624	Ricky Jordan (R)	1.50
625	Ernest Riles	.05
626	John Moses	.05
627	Nelson Liriano	.05
628	Mike Smithson	.05
629	Scott Sanderson	.05
630	Dale Mohorcic	.05
631	Marvin Freeman	.05
632	Mike Young	.05
633	Dennis Lamp	.05
634	Dante Bichette (R)	.25
635	Curt Schilling (R)	.15
636	Scott May (R)	.15
637	Mike Schooler (R)	.35
638	Rick Leach	.05
639	Tom Lampkin (R)	.15
640	Brian Meyer (R)	.15
641	Brian Harper	.05
642	John Smoltz (R)	.60
643	Jose—40/40 Club	.60
644	Bill Schroeder	.05
645	Edgar Martinez	.15
646	Dennis Cook (R)	.25
647	Barry Jones	.05
648	Orel—59 and Counting	.20
649	Rod Nichols (R)	.15
650	Jody Davis	.05
651	Bob Milacki (R)	.25
652	Mike Jackson	.05
653	Derek Lilliquist (R)	.35
654	Paul Mirabella	.05
655	Mike Diaz	.05
656	Jeff Musselman	.05
657	Jerry Reed	.05
658	Kevin Blankenship (R)	.20
659	Wayne Tolleson	.05
660	Eric Hetzel (R)	.20

1989 Donruss Rookies. . . . Complete Set of 56 Cards—Value $30.00

Features the outstanding rookies of the 1989 Season. The cards are coated with a glossy finish. The entire set was packaged in a printed box and distributed primarily through card hobby dealers. Features Donruss' first card of Jim Abbott, Jerome Walton and Dwight Smith.

NO. PLAYER	MINT	NO. PLAYER	MINT	NO. PLAYER	MINT	NO. PLAYER	MINT
1 Gary Sheffield	.75	15 Edgar Martinez	.10	29 Dante Bichette	.10	43 Randy Johnson	.10
2 Gregg Jefferies	.75	16 Jim Abbott (RR)	2.50	30 Alexis Infante	.15	44 Kevin Brown	.10
3 Ken Griffey, Jr.	2.50	17 Torey Lovullo	.15	31 Ken Hill	.10	45 Ramon Martinez	.20
4 Tom Gordon	2.00	18 Mark Carreon	.15	32 Dwight Smith (RR)	1.50	46 Greg Harris	.15
5 Billy Spiers	.35	19 Geronimo Berroa	.10	33 Luis de los Santos	.15	47 Steve Finley	.25
6 Deion Sanders (RR)	1.25	20 Luis Medina	.15	34 Eric Yelding	.20	48 Randy Kramer	.10
7 Donn Pall	.15	21 Sandy Alomar, Jr.	.50	35 Gregg Olson	.40	49 Erik Hanson	.15
8 Steve Carter	.20	22 Bob Milacki	.12	36 Phil Stephenson	.15	50 Matt Merullo	.20
9 Francisco Oliveras	.15	23 Joe Girardi	.30	37 Ken Patterson	.15	51 Mike Devereaux	.10
10 Steve Wilson	.20	24 German Gonzalez	.10	38 Rick Wrona	.30	52 Clay Parker	.20
11 Bob Geren	.40	25 Craig Worthington	.20	39 Mike Brumley	.10	53 Omar Vizquel	.25
12 Tony Castillo	.20	26 Jerome Walton (RR)	6.00	40 Cris Carpenter	.10	54 Derek Lilliquist	.20
13 Kenny Rogers	.20	27 Gary Wayne	.20	41 Jeff Brantley	.15	55 Junior Felix (RR)	1.25
14 Carlos Martinez	.15	28 Tim Jones	.10	42 Ron Jones	.20	56 Checklist	.10

1990 Donruss. . . . Complete Set of 716 Cards—Value $30.00

The set was increased from 660 to 716 cards. Special cards honor Mike Schmidt's retirement and Nolan Ryan's strikeout record. Features the rookie cards of Todd Zeile, Eric Anthony, Andy Benes and Ben McDonald. Special Packaging is being introduced this year to help reduce tampering.

NO. PLAYER	MINT	NO. PLAYER	MINT	NO. PLAYER	MINT	NO. PLAYER	MINT
No. 1 to 26—Diamond Kings		12 Kelly Gruber (DK)	.10	24 Pete O'Brien (DK)	.10	35 Mike Fetters (R)	.20
1 Bo Jackson (DK)	.40	13 Joe Magrane (DK)	.12	25 Bryn Smith (DK)	.10	36 Marquis Grissom (R)	.50
2 Steve Sax (DK)	.10	14 John Franco (DK)	.10	26 Ed Whitson (DK)	.10	37 Greg Vaughn (R)	1.25
3 Ruben Sierra (DK)	.20	15 Ozzie Guillen (DK)	.10	27 DK Checklist	.05	38 Brian Dubois (R)	.20
4 Ken Griffey Jr. (DK)	.35	16 Lou Whitaker (DK)	.10	**No. 28 to 47—Rated Rookies**		39 Steve Avery	.30
5 Mickey Tettleton (DK)	.10	17 John Smiley (DK)	.10	28 Robin Ventura	.50	40 Mark Gardner (R)	.20
6 Dave Stewart (DK)	.10	18 Howard Johnson (DK)	.15	29 Todd Zeile (R)	1.25	41 Andy Benes	.50
7 Jim DeShaies (DK)	.10	19 Willie Randolph (DK)	.10	30 Sandy Alomar Jr.	.20	42 Delino Deshields (R)	.30
8 John Smoltz (DK)	.10	20 Chris Bosio (DK)	.10	31 Kent Mercker (R)	.35	43 Scott Coolbaugh (R)	.35
9 Mike Bielecki (DK)	.10	21 Tommy Herr (DK)	.10	32 Ben McDonald (R)	1.50	44 Pat Combs	.40
10 Brian Downing (DK)	.20	22 Dan Gladden (DK)	.10	33 Juan Gonzalez (R)	.60	45 Alex Sanchez	.15
11 Kevin Mitchell (DK)	.20	23 Ellis Burks (DK)	.15	34 Eric Anthony (R)	1.50	46 Kelly Mann (R)	.20

NO. PLAYER	MINT	NO. PLAYER	MINT	NO. PLAYER	MINT	NO. PLAYER	MINT
47 Julio Machado (R)	.20	131 Ernest Riles	.05	215 Steve Finley	.20	299 Terry Pendleton	.05
48 Pete Incaviglia	.10	132 Mike Morgan	.05	216 Tim Raines	.12	300 Checklist No. 2	.05
49 Shawon Dunston	.08	133 Steve Jeltz	.05	217 Scott Garrelts	.08	301 Juan Berenguer	.05
50 Jeff Treadway	.05	134 Jeff Robinson	.08	218 Kevin McReynolds	.12	302 Mark Davis	.10
51 Jeff Ballard	.08	135 Ozzie Guillen	.08	219 Dave Gallagher	.05	303 Nick Esasky	.05
52 Claudell Washington	.08	136 Chili Davis	.05	220 Tim Wallach	.05	304 Rickey Henderson	.25
53 Juan Samuel	.08	137 Mitch Webster	.05	221 Chuck Crim	.05	305 Rick Cerone	.05
54 John Smiley	.10	138 Jerry Browne	.08	222 Lonnie Smith	.05	306 Craig Biggio	.12
55 Rob Deer	.05	139 Bo Diaz	.05	223 Andre Dawson	.15	307 Duane Ward	.05
56 Geno Petralli	.05	140 Robby Thompson	.10	224 Nelson Santovenia	.05	308 Tom Browning	.05
57 Chris Bosio	.05	141 Craig Worthington	.10	225 Rafael Palmeiro	.10	309 Walt Terrell	.05
58 Carlton Fisk	.12	142 Julio Franco	.08	226 Devon White	.12	310 Greg Swindell	.10
59 Kirt Manwaring	.05	143 Brian Holman	.05	227 Harold Reynolds	.05	311 Dave Righetti	.10
60 Chet Lemon	.05	144 George Brett	.15	228 Ellis Burks	.20	312 Mike Maddux	.05
61 Bo Jackson	.50	145 Tom Glavine	.10	229 Mark Parent	.05	313 Lenny Dykstra	.08
62 Doyle Alexander	.08	146 Robin Yount	.20	230 Will Clark	.60	314 Jose Gonzalez	.05
63 Pedro Guerrero	.12	147 Gary Carter	.10	231 Jimmy Key	.10	315 Steve Balboni	.05
64 Allan Anderson	.08	148 Ron Kittle	.05	232 John Ferrell	.08	316 Mike Scioscia	.08
65 Greg Harris	.05	149 Tony Fernandez	.10	233 Eric Davis	.25	317 Ron Oester	.05
66 Mike Greenwell	.30	150 Dave Stewart	.10	234 Johnny Ray	.08	318 Gary Wayne (R)	.15
67 Walt Weiss	.15	151 Gary Gaetti	.10	235 Darryl Strawberry	.30	319 Todd Worrell	.08
68 Wade Boggs	.30	152 Kevin Elster	.08	236 Bill Doran	.05	320 Doug Jones	.05
69 Jim Clancy	.05	153 Gerald Perry	.05	237 Greg Gagne	.05	321 Jeff Hamilton	.05
70 Junior Felix (R)	.35	154 Jesse Orosco	.05	238 Jim Eisenreich	.05	322 Danny Tartabull	.10
71 Barry Larkin	.08	155 Wally Backman	.05	239 Tommy Gregg	.05	323 Chris James	.05
72 Dave LaPoint	.05	156 Dennis Martinez	.05	240 Marty Barrett	.05	324 Mike Flanagan	.05
73 Joel Skinner	.05	157 Rick Sutcliffe	.05	241 Rafael Ramirez	.05	325 Gerald Young	.05
74 Jesse Barfield	.05	158 Greg Maddux	.10	242 Chris Sabo	.10	326 Bob Boone	.05
75 Tommy Herr	.08	159 Andy Hawkins	.05	243 Dave Henderson	.08	327 Frank Williams	.05
76 Ricky Jordan	.25	160 John Kruk	.05	244 Andy Van Slyke	.10	328 Dave Parker	.12
77 Eddie Murray	.12	161 Jose Oquendo	.05	245 Alvaro Espinoza	.05	329 Sid Bream	.05
78 Steve Sax	.10	162 John Dopson	.08	246 Garry Templeton	.05	330 Mike Schooler	.10
79 Tim Belcher	.08	163 Joe Magrane	.10	247 Gene Harris (R)	.20	331 Bert Blyleven	.08
80 Danny Jackson	.10	164 Billy Ripken	.05	248 Kevin Gross	.05	332 Bob Welch	.05
81 Kent Hrbek	.10	165 Fred Manrique	.05	249 Brett Butler	.05	333 Bob Milacki	.08
82 Milt Thompson	.05	166 Nolan Ryan	.30	250 Willie Randolph	.10	334 Tim Burke	.05
83 Brook Jacoby	.05	167 Damon Berryhill	.08	251 Roger McDowell	.05	335 Jose Uribe	.05
84 Mike Marshall	.08	168 Dale Murphy	.15	252 Rafael Belliard	.05	336 Randy Myers	.08
85 Kevin Seitzer	.08	169 Mickey Tettleton	.05	253 Steve Rosenberg	.05	337 Eric King	.05
86 Tony Gwynn	.20	170 Kirk McCaskill	.08	254 Jack Howell	.05	338 Mark Langston	.10
87 Dave Stieb	.05	171 Dwight Gooden	.25	255 Marvell Wynne	.05	339 Ted Higuera	.05
88 Dave Smith	.08	172 Jose Lind	.05	256 Tom Candiotti	.05	340 Oddibe McDowell	.05
89 Bret Saberhagen	.12	173 B.J. Surhoff	.05	257 Todd Benzinger	.08	341 Lloyd McClendon	.05
90 Alan Trammell	.10	174 Ruben Sierra	.25	258 Don Robinson	.05	342 Pascual Perez	.05
91 Tony Phillips	.05	175 Dan Plesac	.05	259 Phil Bradley	.08	343 Kevin Brown	.05
92 Doug Drabek	.05	176 Dan Pasqua	.05	260 Cecil Espy	.05	344 Chuck Finley	.08
93 Jeffrey Leonard	.05	177 Kelly Downs	.08	261 Scott Bankhead	.05	345 Erik Hanson	.08
94 Wally Joyner	.15	178 Matt Nokes	.10	262 Frank White	.05	346 Rich Gedman	.05
95 Carney Lansford	.08	179 Luis Aquino	.05	263 Andres Thomas	.05	347 Bip Roberts	.05
96 Cal Ripken	.15	180 Frank Tanana	.05	264 Glenn Braggs	.05	348 Matt Williams	.15
97 Andres Galarraga	.10	181 Tony Pena	.08	265 David Cone	.10	349 Tom Henke	.05
98 Kevin Mitchell	.25	182 Dan Gladden	.05	266 Bobby Thigpen	.05	350 Brad Komminsk	.05
99 Howard Johnson	.10	183 Bruce Hurst	.05	267 Nelson Liriano	.05	351 Jeff Reed	.05
100 Checklist	.05	184 Roger Clemens	.30	268 Terry Steinbach	.12	352 Brian Downing	.05
101 Melido Perez	.05	185 Mark McGwire	.30	269 Kirby Puckett	.30	353 Frank Viola	.08
102 Spike Owen	.05	186 Rob Murphy	.05	270 Gregg Jefferies	.35	354 Terry Puhl	.05
103 Paul Molitor	.10	187 Jim Deshaies	.05	271 Jeff Blauser	.05	355 Brian Harper	.05
104 Geronimo Berroa	.05	188 Fred McGriff	.15	272 Cory Snyder	.10	356 Steve Farr	.05
105 Ryne Sandberg	.12	189 Rob Dibble	.12	273 Roy Smith	.05	357 Joe Boever	.05
106 Bryn Smith	.05	190 Don Mattingly	.50	274 Tom Foley	.05	358 Danny Heep	.05
107 Steve Buechele	.05	191 Felix Fermin	.05	275 Mitch Williams	.08	359 Larry Anderson	.05
108 Jim Abbott	.65	192 Roberto Kelly	.10	276 Paul Kilgus	.05	360 Rolando Roomes	.08
109 Alvin Davis	.10	193 Dennis Cook	.05	277 Don Slaught	.05	361 Mike Gallego	.05
110 Leo Smith	.25	194 Darren Daulton	.05	278 Von Hayes	.08	362 Bob Kipper	.05
111 Roberto Alomar	.10	195 Alfredo Griffen	.08	279 Vince Coleman	.10	363 Clay Parker	.08
112 Rick Reuschel	.08	196 Eric Plunk	.05	280 Mike Boddicker	.08	364 Mike Pagliarulo	.08
113 Kelly Gruber	.08	197 Orel Hershiser	.15	281 Ken Dayley	.05	365 Ken Griffey Jr.	.75
114 Joe Carter	.12	198 Paul O'Brien	.10	282 Mike Devereaux	.08	366 Rex Hudler	.05
115 Jose Rijo	.05	199 Randy Bush	.05	283 Kenny Rogers (R)	.15	367 Pat Sheridan	.05
116 Greg Minton	.05	200 Checklist	.05	284 Jeff Russell	.05	368 Kirk Gibson	.10
117 Bob Ojeda	.05	201 Ozzie Smith	.10	285 Jerome Walton	1.25	369 Jeff Parrett	.05
118 Glenn Davis	.12	202 Pete O'Brien	.10	286 Derek Lilliquist	.10	370 Bob Walk	.05
119 Jeff Reardon	.08	203 Jay Howell	.08	287 Joe Orsulak	.05	371 Ken Patterson	.08
120 Kurt Stillwell	.05	204 Mark Gubicza	.05	288 Dick Schofield	.05	372 Bryan Harvey	.05
121 John Smoltz	.10	205 Ed Whitson	.05	289 Ron Darling	.10	373 Mike Bielecki	.05
122 Dwight Evans	.08	206 George Bell	.10	290 Bobby Bonilla	.10	374 Tom Magrann (R)	.20
123 Eric Yelding (R)	.15	207 Mike Scott	.08	291 Jim Gantner	.05	375 Rick Mahler	.05
124 John Smoltz	.20	208 Charlie Leibrandt	.05	292 Bobby Witt	.08	376 Craig Lefferts	.05
125 Jose Canseco	.60	209 Mike Heath	.05	293 Greg Brock	.05	377 Gregg Olson	.20
126 Barry Bonds	.08	210 Dennis Eckersley	.10	294 Ivan Calderon	.05	378 Jamie Moyer	.05
127 Lee Guetterman	.05	211 Mike LaValliere	.05	295 Steve Bedrosian	.05	379 Randy Johnson	.08
128 Jack Clark	.08	212 Darnell Coles	.05	296 Mike Henneman	.05	380 Jeff Montgomery	.08
129 Dave Valle	.05	213 Lance Parrish	.08	297 Tim Gordon	.45	381 Marty Clary	.05
130 Hubie Brooks	.05	214 Mike Moore	.08	298 Lou Whitaker	.08	382 Bill Spiers (R)	.20

NO. PLAYER	MINT	NO. PLAYER	MINT	NO. PLAYER	MINT	NO. PLAYER	MINT
383 Dave Magadan	.08	467 Jose Nunez	.05	551 Dave Winfield	.15	635 Brian Holton	.05
384 Greg Hibbard (R)	.20	468 Scott Bailes	.05	552 Mike Davis	.05	636 Tracy Jones	.05
385 Ernie Whitt	.05	469 Ken Griffey	.05	553 Ron Robinson	.05	637 Terry Steinbach (AS)	.08
386 Rick Honeycutt	.05	470 Bob McClure	.05	554 Carmen Castillo	.05	638 Brady Anderson	.05
387 Dave West	.12	471 Mackey Sasser	.05	555 John Costello	.05	639 Jack Morns	.15
388 Keith Hernandez	.08	472 Glenn Wilson	.05	556 Bud Black	.05	640 Jaime Navarro (R)	.20
389 Jose Alvarez	.05	473 Kevin Tapani (R)	.20	557 Rick Dempsey	.05	641 Darrin Jackson	.12
390 Joey Belle (R)	.50	474 Bill Buckner	.05	558 Jim Acker	.05	642 Mike Dyer (R)	.20
391 Rick Aguilera	.05	475 Ron Gant	.05	559 Eric Show	.05	643 Mike Schmidt	.20
392 Mike Fitzgerald	.05	476 Kevin Romine	.05	560 Pat Borders	.05	644 Henry Cotto	.05
393 Dwight Smith	.75	477 Juan Agosto	.05	561 Danny Darwin	.05	645 John Cerutti	.05
394 Steve Wilson	.10	478 Herm Winningham	.05	562 Rick Luecken (R)	.20	646 Francisco Cabera (R)	.20
395 Bob Geren (R)	.20	479 Storm Davis	.05	563 Edwin Nunez	.05	647 Scott Sanderson	.05
396 Randy Ready	.05	480 Jeff King	.10	564 Felix Jose	.05	648 Brian Meyer	.10
397 Ken Hill	.08	481 Kevin Mmahat (R)	.20	565 John Cangelosi	.05	649 Ray Searage	.05
398 Jody Reed	.05	482 Carmelo Martinez	.05	566 Billy Swift	.05	650 Bo Jackson (AS)	.50
399 Tom Brunansky	.05	483 Omar Vizquel (R)	.15	567 Bill Schroeder	.05	651 Steve Lyons	.05
400 Checklist No. 3	.05	484 Jim Dwyer	.05	568 Stan Javier	.05	652 Mike LaCoss	.05
401 Rene Gonzales	.05	485 Bob Knepper	.05	569 Jim Traber	.05	653 Ted Power	.05
402 Harold Baines	.05	486 Dave Anderson	.05	570 Wallace Johnson	.05	654 Howard Johnson (AS)	.10
403 Cecilio Guante	.05	487 Ron Jones	.05	571 Donnell Nixon	.05	655 Mauro Gozzo (R)	.15
404 Joe Girardi	.20	488 Jay Bell	.05	572 Sid Fernandez	.08	656 Mike Blowers (R)	.20
405 Sergio Valdez (R)	.15	489 Sammy Sosa (R)	.40	573 Lance Johnson	.05	657 Paul Gibson	.05
406 Mark Williamson	.05	490 Kent Anderson (R)	.12	574 Andy McGaffigan	.05	658 Neal Heaton	.05
407 Glenn Hoffman	.05	491 Domingo Ramos	.05	575 Mark Knudson	.05	659 N. Ryan 5000 K	1.00
408 Jeff Innis	.10	492 Dave Clark	.05	576 Tommy Greene (R)	.35	660 Harold Baines (AS)	.08
409 Randy Kramer	.05	493 Tim Birtsas	.05	577 Mark Grace	.30	661 Steve Lyons	.05
410 Charlie O'Brien	.05	494 Ken Oberkfell	.05	578 Larry Walker (R)	.20	662 Clint Zavaras (R)	.15
411 Charlie Hough	.05	495 Larry Sheets	.05	579 Mike Stanley	.05	663 Rick Reuschel (AS)	.08
412 Gus Polidor	.05	496 Jeff Kunkel	.05	580 Mike Witt	.08	664 Alejandro Pena	.05
413 Ron Karkovice	.05	497 Jim Presley	.05	581 Scott Bradley	.05	665 Nolan Ryan	1.00
414 Trevor Wilson	.10	498 Mike Macfarlane	.05	582 Greg Harris	.05	666 Ricky Horton	.05
415 Kevin Ritz (R)	.20	499 Pete Smith	.05	583 Kevin Hickey	.10	667 Curt Schilling	.05
416 Gary Thurman	.05	500 Checklist	.05	584 Lee Mazzilli	.05	668 Bill Landrum	.05
417 Jeff Robinson	.08	501 Gary Sheffield	.40	585 Jeff Pico	.05	669 Todd Stottlemyre	.10
418 Scott Terry	.05	502 Terry Bross (R)	.20	586 Joe Oliver (R)	.15	670 Tim Leary	.08
419 Tim Laudner	.05	503 Jerry Kutzler (R)	.20	587 Willie Fraser	.05	671 John Wettleland (R)	.25
420 Dennis Rasmussen	.05	504 Lloyd Moseby	.08	588 Puzzle Card	.05	672 Calvin Schiraldi	.05
421 Luis Rivera	.05	505 Curt Young	.05	589 Kevin Bass	.05	673 Ruben Sierra (AS)	.25
422 Jim Corsi	.05	506 Al Newman	.05	590 John Moses	.05	674 Pedro Guerrero (AS)	.12
423 Dennis Lampl	.05	507 Keith Miller	.05	591 Tom Pagnozzi	.05	675 Ken Phelps	.05
424 Ken Caminiti	.05	508 Mike Stanton (R)	.20	592 Tony Castillo	.10	676 Cal Ripken (AS)	.15
425 David Wells	.05	509 Rich Yett	.05	593 Jerald Clark	.05	677 Denny Walling	.05
426 Norm Charlton	.05	510 Tim Drummond (R)	.20	594 Dan Schatzeder	.05	678 Goose Gossage	.05
427 Deion Sanders (R)	.60	511 Joe Hesketh	.05	595 Luis Quinones	.05	679 Gary Mielke (R)	.15
428 Dion James	.05	512 Rick Wrona (R)	.15	596 Pete Harnisch	.08	680 Bill Bathe	.05
429 Chuck Cary	.05	513 Luis Salazar	.05	597 Gary Redus	.05	681 Tom Lawless	.05
430 Ken Howell	.05	514 Hal Morns	.05	598 Mel Hall	.08	682 Xavier Hernandez (R)	.20
431 Steve Lake	.05	515 Terry Mulholland	.05	599 Rick Schu	.05	683 Kirby Puckett (AS)	.30
432 Kal Daniels	.10	516 John Morris	.05	600 Checklist	.05	684 Mariano Duncan	.05
433 Lance McCullers	.05	517 Carlos Quintana	.10	601 Mike Kingery	.05	685 Ramon Martinez	.10
434 Lenny Harris	.05	518 Frank DiPino	.10	602 Terry Kennedy	.05	686 Tim Jones	.05
435 Scott Scudder (R)	.15	519 Randy Milligan	.08	603 Mike Sharperson	.05	687 Tom Filer	.05
436 Gene Larkin	.05	520 Chad Kreuter	.05	604 Don Carman	.05	688 Steve Lombardozzi	.05
437 Dan Quisenberry	.05	521 Mike Jeffcoat	.05	605 Jim Gott	.05	689 Bernie Williams (R)	.50
438 Steve Olin (R)	.20	522 Mike Harkey	.10	606 Donn Pall	.05	690 Chip Hale (R)	.20
439 Mickey Hatcher	.05	523 Andy Nezalek	.05	607 Rance Mulliniks	.05	691 Beau Allerd (R)	.20
440 Willie Wilson	.08	524 Dave Schmidt	.08	608 Curt Wilkerson	.05	692 Ryne Sandberg (AS)	.15
441 Mark Grant	.05	525 Tony Armas	.05	609 Mike Felder	.05	693 Jeff Huson (R)	.20
442 Mookie Wilson	.08	526 Barry Lyons	.05	610 Guillermo Hernandez	.05	694 Curt Ford	.05
443 Alex Trevino	.05	527 Rick Reed (R)	.35	611 Candy Maldonado	.05	695 Eric Davis (AS)	.25
444 Pat Tabler	.05	528 Jerry Reuss	.05	612 Mark Thurmond	.05	696 Scott Lusader	.05
445 Dave Bergman	.05	529 Dean Palmer (R)	.20	613 Rick Leach	.05	697 Mark McGwire (AS)	.30
446 Todd Burns	.05	530 Jeff Peterek (R)	.20	614 Jerry Reed	.05	698 Steve Cummings (R)	.15
447 R.J. Reynolds	.05	531 Carlos Martinez (R)	.20	615 Franklin Stubbs	.05	699 George Canale (R)	.20
448 Jay Buhner	.08	532 Atlee Hammaker	.05	616 Billy Hatcher	.05	700 Checklist	.05
449 Les Stevens (R)	.25	533 Mike Brumley	.05	617 Don August	.08	701 Julio Franco (AS)	.12
450 Ron Hassey	.05	534 Terry Leach	.05	618 Tim Teufel	.05	702 Dave Johnson	.12
451 Bob Melvin	.05	535 Doug Strange (R)	.20	619 Shawn Hillegas	.05	703 Dave Stewart (AS)	.12
452 Dave Martinez	.05	536 Jose DeLeon	.05	620 Manny Lee	.05	704 Dave Justice (R)	.25
453 Greg Litton (R)	.20	537 Shane Rawley	.05	621 Gary Ward	.05	705 Tony Gwynn (AS)	.20
454 Mark Carreon	.05	538 Joey Cora	.05	622 Mark Guthrie (R)	.15	706 Greg Myers	.05
455 Scott Fletcher	.05	539 Eric Hetzel	.05	623 Jeff Musselman	.05	707 Will Clark (AS)	.50
456 Otis Nixon	.05	540 Gene Nelson	.05	624 Mark Lemke	.05	708 Benito Santiago (AS)	.12
457 Tony Fossas (R)	.15	541 Wes Gardner	.05	625 Fernando Valenzuela	.10	709 Larry McWilliams	.05
458 John Russel	.05	542 Mark Portugal	.05	626 Paul Sorrento (R)	.20	710 Ozzie Smith (AS)	.10
459 Paul Assenmacher	.05	543 Al Leiter	.05	627 Glenallen Hill	.10	711 John Olerud (R)	2.00
460 Zane Smith	.05	544 Jack Armstrong	.05	628 Les Lancaster	.05	712 Wade Boggs (AS)	.30
461 Jack Daugherty (R)	.20	545 Greg Cadaret	.05	629 Vance Law	.05	713 Gary Eave (R)	.20
462 Rich Monteleone (R)	.15	546 Rod Nichols	.05	630 Randy Velarde	.05	714 Bob Tewksbury	.05
463 Greg Briley	.15	547 Luis Polonia	.05	631 Todd Frohwirth	.05	715 Kevin Mitchell (AS)	.25
464 Mike Smithson	.05	548 Charles Hayes	.05	632 Willie McGee	.08	716 A. Bartlett Giamatti	.75
465 Benito Santiago	.10	549 Dickie Thon	.05	633 Oil Can Boyd	.05	BB Commissioner	
466 Jeff Brantley (R)	.15	550 Tim Crews	.05	634 Cris Carpenter	.05		

1981 Fleer....Complete Set of 660 Cards (1st printing, with corrected "Graig" Nettles)—Value $25.00; Complete Set of 660 Cards (1st printing, with error "Craig" Nettles)—Value $30.00; Complete Set of 660 Cards (2nd printing)—Value $22.00; Complete Set of 660 Cards (3rd printing)—Value $25.00

This was Fleer's first baseball-card set since 1963. Over 30 cards contained errors; they were corrected in the 2nd and 3rd printing runs. The "Craig" Nettles error was corrected during the first printing. There is very little interest by collectors in the *variety* (error) cards; none are scarce or worth much more than ordinary cards, except card 87, "Craig" Nettles. If a *variety* (error) is significant, it is listed and explained; if it is *minor*, it is noted by an *asterisk*. This set features the rookie cards of Fernando Valenzuela, Kirk Gibson and Harold Baines.

  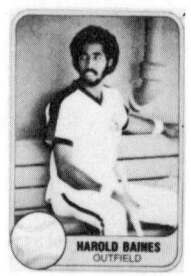  

NO. PLAYER	MINT
PHILADELPHIA PHILLIES	
1 Pete Rose	1.50
2 Larry Bowa	.12
3 Manny Trillo	.05
4 Bob Boone	.05
5 Mike Schmidt	1.00
(MVP) Third Base	
See No. 640	
6 Steve Carlton	.75
(Pitcher of Year)	
See No. 660	
Error—"1066"	
Cardinals" on Back	
6 Steve Carlton	2.00
Corrected "1966" Cardinals	
7 Tug McGraw	.07
See No. 657	
8 Larry Christenson	.05
9 Bake McBride	.05
10 Greg Luzinski	.10
11 Ron Reed	.05
12 Dickie Noles	.05
13 Keith Moreland (R)	.40
14 Bob Walk	.30
15 Lonnie Smith	.08
16 Dick Ruthven	.05
17 Sparky Lyle	.07
18 Greg Gross	.05
19 Garry Maddox	.05
20 Nino Espinosa	.05
21 George Vukovich	.05
22 John Vukovich	.05
23 Ramon Aviles	.05
24 Ken Saucier*	.08
25 Randy Lerch	.05
26 Del Uncer	.05
27 Tim McCarver	.08
KANSAS CITY ROYALS	
28 George Brett—MVP	.75
See No. 655	
29 Willie Wilson	.20
See No. 653	
30 Paul Splittorff	.05
31 Dan Quisenberry	.20
32 Amos Otis*	.10
33 Steve Busby	.05
34 U.L. Washington	.05
35 Dave Chalk	.05
36 Darrell Porter	.08
37 Marty Pattin	.05
38 Larry Gura	.05
39 Renie Martin	.05
40 Rich Gale	.05
41 Hal McRae*	.40
42 Dennis Leonard	.05
43 Willie Aikens	.05
44 Frank White	.08
45 Clint Hurdle	.05
46 John Wathan	.05
47 Pete LaCock	.05
48 Rance Mulliniks	.05

NO. PLAYER	MINT
49 Jeff Twitty	.05
50 Jamie Quirk	.05
HOUSTON ASTROS	
51 Art How	.05
52 Ken Forsch	.05
53 Vern Ruhle	.05
54 Joe Niekro	.08
55 Frank LaCorte	.05
56 J.R. Richard	.08
57 Nolan Ryan	1.00
58 Enos Cabell	.05
59 Cesar Cedeno	.08
60 Jose Cruz	.15
61 Bill Virdon (Mgr.)	.05
62 Terry Puhl	.05
63 Joaquin Andujar	.10
64 Alan Ashby	.05
65 Joe Sambito	.05
66 Denny Walling	.05
67 Jeff Leonard	.05
68 Luis Pujols	.05
69 Bruce Bochy	.05
70 Rafael Landestoy	.05
71 Dave Smith (R)	.30
72 Danny Heep	.20
73 Julio Gonzalez	.05
74 Craig Reynolds	.05
75 Gary Woods	.05
76 Dave Bergman	.05
77 Randy Niemann	.05
78 Joe Morgan	.30
NEW YORK YANKEES	
79 Reggie Jackson	.75
See No. 650	
80 Bucky Dent	.07
81 Tommy John	.15
82 Luis Tiant	.05
83 Rick Cerone	.05
84 Dick Howser (Mgr.)	.05
85 Lou Piniella	.10
86 Ron Davis	.05
87 Graig Nettles	11.00
Error—"Craig" on Back	
87 Graig Nettles	.30
Corrected—"Graig"	
88 Ron Guidry	.25
89 Rich Gossage	.20
90 Rudy May	.05
91 Gaylord Perry	.30
92 Eric Soderholm	.05
93 Bob Watson	.05
94 Bobby Murcer	.08
95 Bobby Brown	.05
96 Jim Spencer	.05
97 Tom Underwood	.05
98 Oscar Gamble	.05
99 Johnny Oates	.05
100 Fred Stanley	.05
101 Ruppert Jones	.05
102 Dennis Werth	.05
103 Joe LeFebvre	.12

NO. PLAYER	MINT
104 Brian Doyle	.05
105 Aurelio Rodriguez	.05
106 Doug Bird	.05
107 Mike Griffin	.05
108 Tim Lollar (R)	.20
109 Willie Randolph	.12
LOS ANGELES DODGERS	
110 Steve Garvey	.50
111 Reggie Smith	.08
112 Don Sutton	.25
113 Burt Hooton	.05
114 Dave Lopes*	.08
115 Dusty Baker	.10
116 Tom Lasorda (Mgr.)	.08
117 Bill Russell	.05
118 Jerry Reuss	.08
119 Terry Forster	.05
120 Robert Welch*	.15
121 Don Stanhouse	.05
122 Rick Monday	.08
123 Derrel Thomas	.05
124 Joe Ferguson	.05
125 Rick Sutcliffe	.30
126 Ron Cey*	.15
127 Dave Goltz	.05
128 Jay Johnstone	.05
129 Steve Yeager	.05
130 Gary Weiss	.05
131 Mike Scioscia (R)	.50
132 Vic Davalillo	.05
133 Doug Rau	.05
134 Pepe Frias	.05
135 Mickey Hatcher	.05
136 Steve Howe (R)	.15
137 Robert Castillo	.05
138 Gary Thomasson	.05
139 Rudy Law	.05
140 F. Valenzuela (R)	4.00
141 Manny Mota	.08
MONTREAL EXPOS	
142 Gary Carter	.40
143 Steve Rogers	.08
144 Warren Cromartie	.05
145 Andre Dawson	.30
146 Larry Parrish	.05
147 Rowland Office	.05
148 Ellis Valentine	.05
149 Dick Williams (Mgr.)	.05
150 Bill Gullickson (R)	.25
151 Elias Sosa	.05
152 John Tamargo	.05
153 Chris Speier	.05
154 Ron LeFlore	.05
155 Rodney Scott	.05
156 Stan Bahnsen	.05
157 Bill Lee	.05
158 Fred Norman	.05
159 Woodie Fryman	.05
160 Dave Palmer	.05
161 Jerry White	.05
162 Roberto Ramos	.05

NO. PLAYER	MINT
163 John D'Acquisto	.05
164 Tommy Hutton	.05
165 Charlie Lea (R)	.25
166 Scott Sanderson	.05
167 Ken Macha	.05
168 Tony Bernazard	.05
BALTIMORE ORIOLES	
169 Jim Palmer	.35
170 Steve Stone	.05
171 Mike Flanagan	.08
172 Al Bumbry	.05
173 Doug DeCinces	.12
174 Scott McGregor	.08
175 Mark Belanger	.05
176 Tim Stoddard	.05
177 Rick Dempsey*	.10
178 Earl Weaver (Mgr.)	.10
179 Tippy Martinez	.05
180 Dennis Martinez	.05
181 Sammy Stewart	.05
182 Rich Dauer	.05
183 Lee May	.05
184 Eddie Murray	.60
185 Benny Ayala	.05
186 John Lowenstein	.05
187 Gary Roenicke	.05
188 Ken Singleton	.08
189 Dan Graham	.05
190 Terry Crowley	.05
191 Kiko Garcia	.05
192 Dave Ford	.05
193 Mark Corey	.05
194 Lenn Sakata	.05
195 Doug DeCinces	.08
CINCINNATI REDS	
196 Johnny Bench	.75
197 Dave Concepcion	.15
198 Ray Knight	.08
199 Ken Griffey	.08
200 Tom Seaver	.40
201 Dave Collins	.07
202 George Foster	.20
(Slugger) Error—No. 216	
202 George Foster	.20
(Slugger) Correct No. 202	
203 Junior Kennedy	.05
204 Frank Pastore	.05
205 Dan Driessen	.05
206 Hector Cruz	.05
207 Paul Moskau	.05
208 Charlie Leibrandt (R)	.25
209 Harry Spilman	.05
210 Joe Price	.05
211 Tom Hume	.05
212 Joe Nolan	.05
213 Doug Bair	.05
214 Mario Soto	.08
215 Bill Bonham*	.08
216 George Foster	.20
See No. 202	
217 Paul Householder	.10

NO.	PLAYER	MINT
218	Ron Oester	.05
219	Sam Mejias	.05
220	Sheldon Burnside	.05
BOSTON RED SOX		
221	Carl Yastrzemski	.75
222	Jim Rice	.30
223	Fred Lynn	.25
224	Carlton Fisk	.25
225	Rick Burleson	.05
226	Dennis Eckersley	.10
227	Butch Hobson	.05
228	Tom Burgmeier	.05
229	Garry Hancock	.05
230	Don Zimmer (Mgr.)	.05
231	Steve Renko	.05
232	Dwight Evans	.20
233	Mike Torrez	.05
234	Bob Stanley	.08
235	Jim Dwyer	.05
236	Dave Stapleton	.14
237	Glenn Hoffman	.12
238	Jerry Remy	.05
239	Dick Drago	.05
240	Bill Campbell	.05
241	Tony Perez	.15
ATLANTA BRAVES		
242	Phil Niekro	.25
243	Dale Murphy	1.00
244	Bob Horner	.20
245	Jeff Burroughs	.05
246	Rick Camp	.05
247	Bob Cox (Mgr.)	.05
248	Bruce Benedict	.05
249	Gene Garber	.05
250	Jerry Royster	.05
251	Gary Matthews*	.10
252	Chris Chambliss	.08
253	Luis Gomez	.05
254	Bill Nahorodny	.05
255	Doyle Alexander	.10
256	Brian Asselstine	.05
257	Biff Pocoroba	.05
258	Mike Lum	.05
259	Charlie Spikes	.05
260	Glenn Hubbard	.05
261	Tommy Boggs	.05
262	Al Hrabosky	.05
263	Rick Matula	.05
264	Preston Hanna	.05
265	Larry Bradford	.05
266	Rafael Ramirez	.20
267	Larry McWilliams	.05
CALIFORNIA ANGELS		
268	Rod Carew	.50
269	Bobby Grich	.08
270	Carney Lansford	.10
271	Don Baylor	.20
272	Joe Rudi	.05
273	Dan Ford	.05
274	Jim Fregosi	.05
275	Dave Frost	.05
276	Frank Tanana	.10
277	Dickie Thon	.07
278	Jason Thompson	.08
279	Rick Miller	.05
280	Bert Campaneris	.10
281	Tom Donohue	.05
282	Brian Downing	.05
283	Fred Patek	.05
284	Bruce Kison	.05
285	Dave LaRoche	.05
286	Don Aase	.05
287	Jim Barr	.05
288	Alfredo Martinez	.05
289	Larry Harlow	.05
290	Andy Hassler	.05
CHICAGO CUBS		
291	Dave Kingman	.12
292	Bill Buckner	.10
293	Rick Reuschel	.10
294	Bruce Sutter	.20
295	Jerry Martin	.05
296	Scot Thompson	.05
297	Ivan DeJesus	.05
298	Steve Dillard	.05
299	Dick Tidrow	.05
300	Randy Martz	.05
301	Lenny Randle	.05
302	Lynn McGlothen	.05
303	Cliff Johnson	.05
304	Tim Blackwell	.05
305	Dennis Lamp	.05
306	Bill Caudill	.08
307	Carlos Lezcano	.05
308	Jim Tracy	.05
309	Doug Capilla	.05
310	Willie Hernandez	.20
311	Mike Vail	.05
312	Mike Krukow	.05
313	Barry Foote	.05
314	Larry Biittner	.05
315	Mike Tyson	.05
NEW YORK METS		
316	Lee Mazzilli	.05
317	John Stearns	.05
318	Alex Trevino	.05
319	Craig Swan	.05
320	Frank Taveras	.05
321	Steve Henderson	.05
322	Neil Allen	.05
323	Mark Bomback	.05
324	Mike Jorgensen	.05
325	Joe Torre	.07
326	Elliott Maddox	.05
327	Pete Falcone	.05
328	Ray Burris	.05
329	Claudell Washington	.08
330	Doug Flynn	.05
331	Joel Youngblood	.05
332	Bill Almon	.05
333	Tom Hausman	.05
334	Pat Zachry	.05
335	Jeff Reardon (R)	.75
336	Wally Backman (R)	.40
337	Dan Norman	.05
338	Jerry Morales	.05
CHICAGO WHITE SOX (Except 351)		
339	Ed Farmer	.05
340	Bob Molinaro	.05
341	Todd Cruz	.05
342	Britt Burns*	.35
343	Kevin Bell	.05
344	Tony LaRussa (Mgr.)	.05
345	Steve Trout	.05
346	Harold Baines (R)	1.50
347	Richard Wortham	.05
348	Wayne Nordhagen	.05
349	Mike Squires	.05
350	Lamar Johnson	.05
351	Rickey Henderson	1.50
	Most Stolen Bases, AL	
352	Francisco Barrios	.05
353	Thad Bosley	.05
354	Chet Lemon	.08
355	Bruce Kimm	.05
356	Richard Dotson (R)	.35
357	Jim Morrison	.05
358	Mike Proly	.05
359	Greg Pryor	.05
PITTSBURGH PIRATES		
360	Dave Parker	.30
361	Omar Moreno	.05
362	Kent Tekulve*	.10
363	Willie Stargell	.30
364	Phil Garner	.05
365	Ed Ott	.05
366	Don Robinson	.05
367	Chuck Tanner (Mgr.)	.05
368	Jim Rooker	.05
369	Dale Berra	.05
370	Jim Bibby	.05
371	Steve Nicosia	.05
372	Mike Easler	.10
373	Bill Robinson	.05
374	Lee Lacy	.05
375	John Candelaria	.10
376	Manny Sanguillen	.05
377	Rick Rhoden	.12
378	Grant Jackson	.05
379	Tim Foli	.05
380	Rod Scurry	.05
381	Bill Madlock	.15
382	Kurt Bevacqua*	.08
383	Bert Blyleven	.12
384	Eddie Solomon	.05
385	Enrique Romo	.05
386	John Milner	.05
CLEVELAND INDIANS		
387	Mike Hargrove	.05
388	Jorge Orta	.05
389	Toby Harrah	.05
390	Tom Veryzer	.05
391	Miguel Dilone	.05
392	Dan Spillner	.05
393	Jack Brohamer	.05
394	Wayne Garland	.05
395	Sid Monge	.05
396	Rick Waits	.05
397	Joe Charboneau	.12
398	Gary Alexander	.05
399	Jerry Dybzinski	.05
400	Mike Stanton	.05
401	Mike Paxton	.05
402	Gary Gray	.05
403	Rick Manning	.05
404	Bo Diaz	.08
405	Ron Hassey	.05
406	Ross Grimsley	.05
407	Victor Cruz	.05
408	Len Barker	.08
TORONTO BLUE JAYS		
409	Bob Bailor	.05
410	Otto Velez	.05
411	Ernie Whitt	.05
412	Jim Clancy	.05
413	Barry Bonnell	.05
414	Dave Stieb	.30
415	Damaso Garcia (R)	.15
416	John Mayberry	.05
417	Roy Howell	.05
418	Dan Ainge	.25
419	Jesse Jefferson*	.08
420	Joey McLaughlin	.05
421	Lloyd Moseby (R)	.60
422	Al Woods	.05
423	Garth Iorg	.05
424	Doug Ault	.05
425	Ken Schrom	.15
426	Mike Willis	.05
427	Steve Braun	.05
428	Bob Davis	.05
429	Jerry Garvin	.05
430	Alfredo Griffin	.08
431	Bob Mattick (Mgr.)	.05
SAN FRANCISCO GIANTS		
432	Vida Blue	.08
433	Jack Clark	.30
434	Willie McCovey	.35
435	Mike Ivie	.05
436	Darrell Evans*	.15
437	Terry Whitfield	.05
438	Rennie Stennett	.05
439	John Montefusco	.05
440	Jim Wohlford	.05
441	Bill North	.05
442	Milt May	.05
443	Max Venable	.05
444	Ed Whitson	.05
445	Al Holland	.15
446	Randy Moffitt	.05
447	Bob Knepper	.05
448	Gary Lavelle	.05
449	Greg Minton	.05
450	Johnnie LeMaster	.05
451	Larry Herndon	.05
452	Rich Murray	.05
453	Joe Pettini	.05
454	Allen Ripley	.05
455	Dennis Littlejohn	.05
456	Tom Griffin	.05
457	Alan Hargesheimer	.05
458	Joe Strain	.05
DETROIT TIGERS		
459	Steve Kemp	.08
460	Sparky Anderson (Mgr.)	.08
461	Alan Trammell	.30
462	Mark Fidrych	.08
463	Lou Whitaker	.25
464	Dave Rozema	.05
465	Milt Wilcox	.05
466	Champ Summers	.05
467	Lance Parrish	.30
468	Dan Petry	.15
469	Pat Underwood	.05
470	Rick Peters	.10
471	Al Cowens	.05
472	John Wockenfuss	.05
473	Tom Brookens	.05
474	Richie Hebner	.05
475	Jack Morris	.35
476	Jim Lentine	.05
477	Bruce Robbins	.05
478	Mark Wagner	.05
479	Tim Corcoran	.05
480	Stan Papi*	.08
481	Kirk Gibson (R)	4.00
482	Dan Schatzeder	.05
483	Amos Otis	.60
	See card No. 32	
SAN DIEGO PADRES		
484	Dave Winfield	.50
485	Rollie Fingers	.30
486	Gene Richards	.05
487	Randy Jones	.05
488	Ozzie Smith	.40
489	Gene Tenace	.05
490	Bill Fahey	.05
491	John Curtis	.05
492	Dave Cash	.05
493	Tim Flannery*	.12
494	Jerry Mumphrey	.05
495	Bob Shirley	.05
496	Steve Mura	.05
497	Eric Rasmussen	.05
498	Broderick Perkins	.05
499	Barry Evans	.05
500	Chuck Baker	.05
501	Luis Salazar	.15
502	Gary Lucas	.10
503	Mike Armstrong	.05
504	Jerry Turner	.05
505	Dennis Kinney	.05
506	Willie Montanez	.05
MILWAUKEE BREWERS		
507	Gorman Thomas	.15
508	Ben Oglivie	.08
509	Larry Hisle	.05
510	Sal Bando	.50
511	Robin Yount	.50
512	Mike Caldwell	.05
513	Sixto Lezcano	.05
514	Bill Travers	.15
	Error—Jerry Augustine photo and back	
514	Bill Travers	.08
515	Paul Molitor	.30
516	Moose Haas	.05
517	Bill Castro	.05
518	Jim Slaton	.05
519	Lary Sorensen	.05
520	Bob McClure	.05
521	Charlie Moore	.05
522	Jim Gantner	.05
523	Reggie Cleveland	.05
524	Don Money	.05
525	Bill Travers	.05
526	Buck Martinez	.05
527	Dick Davis	.05
ST. LOUIS CARDINALS		
528	Ted Simmons	.12
529	Garry Templeton	.12
530	Ken Reitz	.05
531	Tony Scott	.05
532	Ken Oberkfell	.05
533	Bob Sykes	.05
534	Keith Smith	.05
535	John Littlefield	.05
536	Jim Kaat	.10
537	Bob Forsch	.05
538	Mike Phillips	.05

1981 Fleer (Continued)

NO. PLAYER	MINT
539 Terry Landrum	.08
540 Leon Durham (R)	.30
541 Terry Kennedy	.08
542 George Hendrick	.08
543 Dane Iorg	.05
544 Mark Littell	.05
545 Keith Hernandez	.30
546 Silvio Martinez	.05
547 Don Hood	.25
Error—Pete Vuckovich photo and back	
547 Don Hood	.10
548 Bobby Bonds	.08
549 Mike Ramsey	.05
550 Tom Herr	.15

MINNESOTA TWINS

NO. PLAYER	MINT
551 Roy Smalley	.05
552 Jerry Koosman	.15
553 Ken Landreaux	.05
554 John Castino	.05
555 Doug Corbett	.12
556 Bombo Rivera	.05
557 Ron Jackson	.05
558 Butch Wynegar	.05
559 Hosken Powell	.05
560 Pete Redfern	.05
561 Roger Erickson	.05
562 Glenn Adams	.08
563 Rick Sofield	.05
564 Geoff Zahn	.05
565 Pete Mackanin	.05
566 Mike Cubbage	.05
567 Darrell Jackson	.05
568 Dave Edwards	.05
569 Rob Wilfong	.05
570 Sal Butera	.05
571 Jose Morales	.05

OAKLAND A'S

NO. PLAYER	MINT
572 Rick Langford	.05
573 Mike Norris	.05

NO. PLAYER	MINT
574 Rickey Henderson	1.50
575 Tony Armas	.15
576 Dave Revering	.05
577 Jeff Newman	.05
578 Bob Lacey	.05
579 Brian Kingman	.05
580 Mitchell Page	.05
581 Billy Martin (Mgr.)	.12
582 Rob Picciolo	.05
583 Mike Heath	.05
584 Mickey Klutts	.05
585 Orlando Gonzalez	.05
586 Mike Davis (R)	.25
587 Wayne Gross	.05
588 Matt Keough	.05
589 Steve McCatty	.05
590 Dwayne Murphy	.08
591 Mario Guerrero	.05
592 Dave McKay	.05
593 Jim Essian	.05
594 Dave Heaverlo	.05

SEATTLE MARINERS (Except 606)

NO. PLAYER	MINT
595 Maury Wills (Mgr.)	.10
596 Juan Beniquez	.05
597 Rodney Craig	.05
598 Jim Anderson	.05
599 Floyd Bannister	.08
600 Bruce Bochte	.05
601 Julio Cruz	.05
602 Ted Cox	.05
603 Dan Meyer	.05
604 Larry Cox	.05
605 Bill Stein	.05
606 Steve Garvey	.50
Most Hits, NL	
607 Dave Roberts	.05
608 Leon Roberts	.05
609 Reggie Walton	.05
610 Dave Edler	.05

NO. PLAYER	MINT
611 Larry Milbourne	.05
612 Kim Allen	.05
613 Mario Mendoza	.05
614 Tom Paciorek	.05
615 Glenn Abbott	.05
616 Joe Simpson	.05

TEXAS RANGERS

NO. PLAYER	MINT
617 Mickey Rivers	.08
618 Jim Kern	.05
619 Jim Sundberg	.05
620 Richie Zisk	.05
621 Jon Matlack	.05
622 Ferguson Jenkins	.12
623 Pat Corrales (Mgr.)	.05
624 Ed Figueroa	.05
625 Buddy Bell	.15
626 Al Oliver	.20
627 Doc Medich	.05
628 Bump Wills	.05
629 Rusty Staub	.12
630 Pat Putnam	.05
631 John Grubb	.05
632 Danny Darwin	.05
633 Ken Clay	.05
634 Jim Norris	.05
635 John Butcher	.20
636 Dave Roberts	.05
637 Billy Sample	.05

SPECIAL CARDS

NO. PLAYER	MINT
638 Carl Yastrzemski	.75
400 Home Run Club	
639 Cecil Cooper	.20
640 Mike Schmidt	1.25
(Third Base)	
Error—No. 5	
640 Mike Schmidt	1.00
(Home Run King)	
641 Checklist (1 to 50)*	.08
642 Checklist (51 to 109)	.08
643 Checklist (110 to 168)	.08

NO. PLAYER	MINT
644 Checklist (169 to 220)*	.08
645 Triple Threat:*	1.75
Schmidt, Rose, Bowa	
646 Checklist (221 to 267)	.08
647 Checklist (268 to 315)	.08
648 Checklist (316 to 359)	.08
649 Checklist (360 to 408)	.08
650 Reggie Jackson	1.00
Mr. Baseball	
Error—No. 79	
650 Reggie Jackson	.75
Mr. Baseball	
651 Checklist (409 to 458)	.08
652 Checklist (459 to 506)*	.08
653 Willie Wilson	.25
Most Hits, Most Runs	
Error—No. 29	
653 Willie Wilson	.25
Most Hits, Most Runs	
654 Checklist (507 to 550)*	.08
655 G. Brett (.390 Avg.)	1.25
Error—No. 28*	
656 Checklist (551 to 593)	.08
657 Tug McGraw	.08
Game Saver, Error—No. 7	
657 Tug McGraw	.08
Game Saver	
658 Checklist (594 to 637)	.08
659 Checklist (Specials)*	.08
660 Steve Carlton	.50
"Lefty"—The Golden Arm Errors—Card No.6 and "1066" Cardinals	
660 Steve Carlton	.50
"Lefty"—The Golden Arm Error—"1066" Cardinals	
660 Steve Carlton	1.50
"Lefty"—The Golden Arm Corrected—"1966" Cardinals	

1982 Fleer.... Complete Set of 660 Cards—Value $35.00

Features the rookie cards of Cal Ripken, Dave Stewart and George Bell. Several errors were corrected; none are scarce or worth much more than ordinary cards, except cards 438 and 576. If a *variety* (error) is significant, it is listed and explained; if it is minor it is noted by an *asterisk*.

LOS ANGELES DODGERS

NO. PLAYER	MINT
1 Dusty Baker	.10
2 Robert Castillo	.05
3 Roy Cey	.15
4 Terry Forster	.05
5 Steve Garvey	.40
6 Dave Goltz	.05
7 Pedro Guerrero	.30
8 Burt Hooton	.05
9 Steve Howe	.05
10 Jay Johnstone	.05
11 Ken Landreaux	.05
12 Davey Lopes	.05
13 Mike Marshall (R)	1.25
14 Bobby Mitchell	.09
15 Rick Monday	.10
16 Tom Niedenfuer (R)	.30
17 Ted Power (R)	.25

NO. PLAYER	MINT
18 Jerry Reuss	.10
19 Ron Roenicke	.05
20 Bill Russell	.05
21 Steve Sax (R)	2.50
22 Mike Scioscia	.05
23 Reggie Smith	.10
24 Dave Stewart (R)	2.50
25 Rick Sutcliffe	.20
26 Darrell Thomas	.05
27 Fernando Valenzuela	.50
28 Bob Welch	.12
29 Steve Yeager	.05

NEW YORK YANKEES

NO. PLAYER	MINT
30 Bobby Brown	.05
31 Rick Cerone	.05
32 Ron Davis	.05
33 Bucky Dent	.08
34 Barry Foote	.05

NO. PLAYER	MINT
35 George Frazier	.05
36 Oscar Gamble	.05
37 Rich Gossage	.20
38 Ron Guidry	.20
39 Reggie Jackson	.50
40 Tommy John	.15
41 Rudy May	.05
42 Larry Milbourne	.05
43 Jerry Mumphrey	.05
44 Bobby Murcer	.10
45 Gene Nelson (R)	.15
46 Graig Nettles	.15
47 Johnny Oates	.05
48 Lou Piniella	.10
49 Willie Randolph	.12
50 Rick Reuschel	.12
51 Dave Reverink	.05
52 Dave Righetti (R)	1.25

NO. PLAYER	MINT
53 Aurelio Rodriguez	.05
54 Bob Watson	.05
55 Dennis Werth	.05
56 Dave Winfield	.50

CINCINNATI REDS

NO. PLAYER	MINT
57 Johnny Bench	.60
58 Bruce Berenyi	.05
59 Larry Biittner	.05
60 Scott Brown	.09
61 Dave Collins	.05
62 Geoff Combe	.05
63 Dave Concepcion	.10
64 Dan Driessen	.05
65 Joe Edelen	.05
66 George Foster	.20
67 Ken Griffey	.10
68 Paul Householder	.05
69 Tom Hume	.05

NO. PLAYER	MINT
70 Junior Kennedy	.05
71 Ray Knight	.10
72 Mike LaCoss	.05
73 Rafael Landestoy	.05
74 Charlie Leibrandt	.05
75 Sam Mejias	.05
76 Paul Moskau	.05
77 Joe Nolan	.05
78 Mike O'Berry	.05
79 Ron Oester	.05
80 Frank Pastore	.05
81 Joe Price	.05
82 Tom Seaver	.45
83 Mario Soto	.10
84 Mike Vail	.05

OAKLAND A'S

NO. PLAYER	MINT
85 Tony Armas	.10
86 Shooty Babitt	.05
87 Dave Beard	.05
88 Rick Bosetti	.05
89 Keith Drumright	.05
90 Wayne Gross	.05
91 Mike Heath	.05
92 Rickey Henderson	.60
93 Cliff Johnson	.05
94 Jeff Jones	.05
95 Matt Keough	.05
96 Brian Kingman	.05
97 Mickey Klutts	.05
98 Rick Langford	.05
99 Steve McCatty	.05
100 Dave McKay	.05
101 Dwayne Murphy	.07
102 Jeff Newman	.05
103 Mike Norris	.05
104 Bob Owchinko	.05
105 Mitchell Page	.05
106 Rob Picciolo	.05
107 Jim Spencer	.05
108 Fred Stanley	.05
109 Tom Underwood	.05

ST. LOUIS CARDINALS

NO. PLAYER	MINT
110 Joaquin Andujar	.15
111 Steve Braun	.05
112 Bob Forsch	.05
113 George Hendrick	.08
114 Keith Hernandez	.30
115 Tom Herr	.15
116 Dane Iorg	.05
117 Jim Kaat	.10
118 Tito Landrum	.05
119 Sixto Lezcano	.05
120 Mark Littell	.05
121 John Martin	.05
122 Silvio Martinez	.05
123 Ken Oberkfell	.05
124 Darrell Porter	.05
125 Mike Ramsey	.05
126 Orlando Sanchez	.08
127 Bob Shirley	.05
128 Lary Sorensen	.05
129 Bruce Sutter	.20
130 Bob Sykes	.05
131 Garry Templeton	.15
132 Gene Tenace	.05

MILWAUKEE BREWERS

NO. PLAYER	MINT
133 Jerry Augustine	.05
134 Sal Bando	.05
135 Mark Brouhard	.08
136 Mike Caldwell	.05
137 Reggie Cleveland	.05
138 Cecil Cooper	.20
139 Jamie Easterly	.05
140 Marshall Edwards	.05
141 Rollie Fingers	.20
142 Jim Gantner	.05
143 Moose Haas	.05
144 Larry Hisle	.05
145 Roy Howell	.05
146 Rickey Keeton	.05
147 Randy Lerch	.05
148 Paul Molitor	.25
149 Don Money	.05
150 Charlie Moore	.05
151 Ben Oglivie	.10

NO. PLAYER	MINT
152 Ted Simmons	.10
153 Jim Slaton	.05
154 Gorman Thomas	.10
155 Robin Yount	.60
156 Pete Vuckovich	.10

BALTIMORE ORIOLES

NO. PLAYER	MINT
157 Benny Ayala	.05
158 Mark Belanger	.05
159 Al Bumbry	.05
160 Terry Crowley	.05
161 Rich Dauer	.05
162 Doug DeCinces	.10
163 Rick Dempsey	.05
164 Jim Dwyer	.05
165 Mike Flanagan	.10
166 Dave Ford	.05
167 Dan Graham	.05
168 Wayne Krenchicki	.05
169 John Lowenstein	.05
170 Dennis Martinez	.05
171 Tippy Martinez	.05
172 Scott McGregor	.10
173 Jose Morales	.05
174 Eddie Murray	.60
175 Jim Palmer	.30
176 Cal Ripken, Jr. (R)	7.50
177 Gary Roenicke	.05
178 Lenn Sakata	.05
179 Ken Singleton	.10
180 Sammy Stewart	.05
181 Tim Stoddard	.05
182 Steve Stone	.05

MONTREAL EXPOS

NO. PLAYER	MINT
183 Stan Bahnsen	.05
184 Ray Burris	.05
185 Gary Carter	.50
186 Warren Cromartie	.05
187 Andre Dawson	.35
188 Terry Francona (R)	.20
189 Woodie Fryman	.05
190 Bill Gullickson	.05
191 Grant Jackson	.05
192 Wallace Johnson	.05
193 Charlie Lea	.05
194 Bill Lee	.05
195 Jerry Manuel	.05
196 Brad Mills	.07
197 John Milner	.05
198 Rowland Office	.05
199 David Palmer	.05
200 Larry Parrish	.05
201 Mike Phillips	.05
202 Tim Raines	1.50
203 Bobby Ramos	.05
204 Jeff Reardon	.12
205 Steve Rogers	.10
206 Scott Sanderson	.05
207 Rodney Scott	.10
208 Elias Sosa	.05
209 Chris Speier	.05
210 Tim Wallach (R)	.75
211 Jerry White	.05

HOUSTON ASTROS

NO. PLAYER	MINT
212 Alan Ashby	.05
213 Cesar Cedeno	.10
214 Jose Cruz	.15
215 Kiko Garcia	.05
216 Phil Garner	.05
217 Danny Heep	.05
218 Art Howe	.05
219 Bob Knepper	.05
220 Frank LaCorte	.05
221 Joe Niekro	.10
222 Joe Pittman	.05
223 Terry Puhl	.05
224 Luis Pujols	.05
225 Craig Reynolds	.05
226 J.R. Richard	.10
227 Dave Roberts	.05
228 Vern Ruhle	.05
229 Nolan Ryan	.75
230 Joe Sambito	.05
231 Tony Scott	.05
232 Dave Smith	.05
233 Harry Spilman	.05

NO. PLAYER	MINT
234 Don Sutton	.25
235 Dickie Thon	.10
236 Denny Walling	.05
237 Gary Woods	.05

PHILADELPHIA PHILLIES

NO. PLAYER	MINT
238 Luis Aguayo	.05
239 Ramon Aviles	.05
240 Bob Boone	.05
241 Larry Bowa	.10
242 Warren Brusstar	.05
243 Steve Carlton	.50
244 Larry Christenson	.05
245 Dick Davis	.05
246 Greg Gross	.05
247 Sparky Lyle	.08
248 Garry Maddox	.10
249 Gary Matthews	.10
250 Bake McBride	.05
251 Tug McGraw	.10
252 Keith Moreland	.08
253 Dickie Noles	.05
254 Mike Proly	.05
255 Ron Reed	.05
256 Pete Rose	1.00
257 Dick Ruthven	.05
258 Mike Schmidt	.75
259 Lonnie Smith	.10
260 Manny Trillo	.05
261 Del Unser	.05
262 George Vukovich	.05

DETROIT TIGERS

NO. PLAYER	MINT
263 Tom Brookens	.05
264 George Cappuzzello	.05
265 Marty Castillo	.05
266 Al Cowens	.05
267 Kirk Gibson	.75
268 Richie Hebner	.05
269 Ron Jackson	.05
270 Lynn Jones	.05
271 Steve Kemp	.10
272 Rick Leach	.08
273 Aurelio Lopez	.05
274 Jack Morris	.30
275 Kevin Saucier	.05
276 Lance Parrish	.25
277 Rick Peters	.05
278 Dan Petry	.15
279 David Rozema	.05
280 Stan Papi	.05
281 Dan Schatzeder	.05
282 Champ Summers	.05
283 Alan Trammell	.30
284 Lou Whitaker	.20
285 Milt Wilcox	.05
286 John Wockenfuss	.05

BOSTON RED SOX

NO. PLAYER	MINT
287 Gary Allenson	.05
288 Tom Burgmeier	.05
289 Bill Campbell	.05
290 Mark Clear	.05
291 Steve Crawford	.05
292 Dennis Eckersley	.15
293 Dwight Evans	.15
294 Rich Gedman (R)	.40
295 Garry Hancock	.05
296 Glenn Hoffman	.05
297 Bruce Hurst	.50
298 Carney Lansford	.20
299 Rick Miller	.05
300 Reid Nichols	.05
301 Bob Ojeda (R)	.45
302 Tony Perez	.15
303 Chuck Rainey	.05
304 Jerry Remy	.05
305 Jim Rice	.35
306 Joe Rudi	.05
307 Bob Stanley	.05
308 Dave Stapleton	.05
309 Frank Tanana	.15
310 Mike Torrez	.05
311 John Tudor	.15
312 Carl Yastrzemski	.70

TEXAS RANGERS

NO. PLAYER	MINT
313 Buddy Bell	.15
314 Steve Comer	.05

NO. PLAYER	MINT
315 Danny Darwin	.05
316 John Ellis	.05
317 John Grubb	.05
318 Rick Honeycutt	.05
319 Charlie Hough	.05
320 Ferguson Jenkins	.15
321 John Henry Johnson	.05
322 Jim Kern	.05
323 Jon Matlack	.05
324 Doc Medich	.05
325 Mario Mendoza	.05
326 Al Oliver	.15
327 Pat Putnam	.05
328 Mickey Rivers	.05
329 Leon Roberts	.05
330 Billy Sample	.05
331 Bill Stein	.05
332 Jim Sundberg	.05
333 Mark Wagner	.05
334 Bump Wills	.05

CHICAGO WHITE SOX

NO. PLAYER	MINT
335 Bill Almon	.05
336 Harold Baines	.30
337 Ross Baumgarten	.05
338 Tony Bernazard	.05
339 Britt Burns	.10
340 Richard Dotson	.10
341 Jim Essian	.05
342 Ed Farmer	.05
343 Carlton Fisk	.20
344 Kevin Hickey	.05
345 LaMarr Hoyt	.10
346 Lamar Johnson	.05
347 Jerry Koosman	.05
348 Rusty Kuntz	.05
349 Dennis Lamp	.05
350 Ron LeFlore	.05
351 Chet Lemon	.08
352 Greg Luzinski	.10
353 Bob Molinaro	.05
354 Jim Morrison	.05
355 Wayne Nordhagen	.05
356 Greg Pryor	.05
357 Mike Squires	.05
358 Steve Trout	.05

CLEVELAND INDIANS

NO. PLAYER	MINT
359 Alan Bannister	.05
360 Len Barker	.05
361 Bert Blyleven	.15
362 Joe Charboneau	.05
363 John Denny	.10
364 Bo Diaz	.05
365 Miguel Dilone	.05
366 Jerry Dybzinski	.05
367 Wayne Garland	.05
368 Mike Hargrove	.05
369 Toby Harrah	.05
370 Ron Hassey	.05
371 Von Hayes (R)	.90
372 Pat Kelly	.05
373 Duane Kuiper	.05
374 Rick Manning	.05
375 Sid Monge	.05
376 Jorge Orta	.05
377 Dave Rosello	.05
378 Dan Spillner	.05
379 Mike Stanton	.05
380 Andre Thornton	.10
381 Tom Veryzer	.05
382 Rick Waits	.05

SAN FRANCISCO GIANTS

NO. PLAYER	MINT
383 Doyle Alexander	.05
384 Vida Blue	.05
385 Fred Breining	.07
386 Enos Cabell	.05
387 Jack Clark	.25
388 Darrell Evans	.10
389 Tom Griffin	.05
390 Larry Herndon	.05
391 Al Holland	.05
392 Gary Lavelle	.05
393 Johnnie LeMaster	.05
394 Jerry Martin	.05
395 Milt May	.05
396 Greg Minton	.05

NO.	PLAYER	MINT
397	Joe Morgan	.25
398	Joe Pettini	.05
399	Alan Ripley	.05
400	Billy Smith	.05
401	Rennie Stennett	.05
402	Ed Whitson	.05
403	Jim Wohlford	.05

KANSAS CITY ROYALS

NO.	PLAYER	MINT
404	Willie Aikens	.05
405	George Brett	.75
406	Ken Brett	.05
407	Dave Chalk	.05
408	Rich Gale	.05
409	Cesar Geronimo	.05
410	Larry Gura	.05
411	Clint Hurdle	.05
412	Mike Jones	.05
413	Dennis Leonard	.05
414	Renie Martin	.05
415	Lee May	.05
416	Hal McRae	.05
417	Darryl Motley (R)	.15
418	Rance Mulliniks	.05
419	Amos Otis	.05
420	Ken Phelps (R)	.60
421	Jamie Quirk	.05
422	Dan Quisenberry	.20
423	Paul Splittorff	.05
424	U.L. Washington	.05
425	John Wathan	.05
426	Frank White	.05
427	Willie Wilson	.20

ATLANTA BRAVES

NO.	PLAYER	MINT
428	Brian Asselstine	.05
429	Bruce Benedict	.05
430	Tom Boggs	.05
431	Larry Bradford	.05
432	Rick Camp	.05
433	Chris Chambliss	.05
434	Gene Garber	.05
435	Preston Hanna	.05
436	Bob Horner *	.25
438	"All" Hrabosky (error)	16.00
	"Al" misspelled	
438	Al Hrabosky	1.00
	(height 5'1"—error)	
438	Al Hrabosky	.12
	(height 5'10" correct)	
439	Rufino Linares	.05
440	Rick Mahler (R)	.25
441	Ed Miller	.05
442	John Montefusco	.05
443	Dale Murphy	1.00
444	Phil Niekro	.25
445	Gaylord Perry	.30
446	Biff Pocoroba	.05
447	Rafael Ramirez	.05
448	Jerry Royster	.05
449	Claudell Washington	.08

CALIFORNIA ANGELS

NO.	PLAYER	MINT
450	Don Aase	.05
451	Don Baylor	.15
452	Juan Beniquez	.05
453	Rick Burleson	.05
454	Bert Campaneris	.05
455	Rod Carew	.50
456	Bob Clark	.05
457	Brian Downing	.05
458	Dan Ford	.05
459	Ken Forsch	.05
460	Dave Frost *	.05
461	Bobby Grich	.10
462	Larry Harlow	.05
463	John Harris	.05
464	Andy Hassler	.05

NO.	PLAYER	MINT
465	Butch Hobson	.05
466	Jesse Jefferson	.05
467	Bruce Kison	.05
468	Fred Lynn	.25
469	Angel Moreno	.05
470	Ed Ott	.05
471	Fred Patek	.05
472	Steve Renko	.05
473	Mike Witt (R)	.75
474	Geoff Zahn	.05

PITTSBURGH PIRATES

NO.	PLAYER	MINT
475	Gary Alexander	.05
476	Dale Berra	.05
477	Kurt Bevacqua	.05
478	Jim Bibby	.05
479	John Candelaria	.05
480	Victor Cruz	.05
481	Mike Easler	.05
482	Tim Foli	.05
483	Lee Lacy	.05
484	Vance Law	.12
485	Bill Madlock	.15
486	Willie Montanez	.05
487	Omar Moreno	.05
488	Steve Nicosia	.05
489	Dave Parker	.25
490	Tony Pena	.20
491	Pascual Perez	.15
492	Johnny Ray (R)	.60
493	Rick Rhoden	.05
494	Bill Robinson	.05
495	Don Robinson	.05
496	Enrique Romo	.05
497	Rod Scurry	.05
498	Eddie Solomon	.05
499	Willie Stargell	.40
500	Kent Tekulve	.05
501	Jason Thompson	.05

SEATTLE MARINERS

NO.	PLAYER	MINT
502	Glenn Abbott	.05
503	Jim Anderson	.05
504	Floyd Bannister	.05
505	Bruce Bochte	.05
506	Jeff Burroughs	.05
507	Bryan Clark	.07
508	Ken Clay	.05
509	Julio Cruz	.05
510	Dick Drago	.05
511	Gary Gray	.05
512	Dan Meyer	.05
513	Jerry Narron	.05
514	Tom Paciorek	.05
515	Casey Parsons	.05
516	Lenny Randle	.05
517	Shane Rawley	.05
518	Joe Simpson	.05
519	Richie Zisk	.05

NEW YORK METS

NO.	PLAYER	MINT
520	Neil Allen	.05
521	Bob Bailor	.05
522	Hubie Brooks	.35
523	Mike Cubbage	.05
524	Pete Falcone	.05
525	Doug Flynn	.05
526	Tom Hausman	.05
527	Ron Hodges	.05
528	Randy Jones	.05
529	Mike Jorgensen	.05
530	Dave Kingman	.15
531	Ed Lynch	.10
532	Mike Marshall	.05
533	Lee Mazzilli	.05
534	Dyar Miller	.05
535	Mike Scott	.35
536	Rusty Staub	.10
537	John Stearns	.05

NO.	PLAYER	MINT
538	Craig Swan	.05
539	Frank Taveras	.05
540	Alex Trevino	.05
541	Ellis Valentine	.05
542	Mookie Wilson	.05
543	Joel Youngblood	.05
544	Pat Zachry	.05

MINNESOTA TWINS

NO.	PLAYER	MINT
545	Glenn Adams	.05
546	Fernando Arroyo	.05
547	John Verhoeven	.05
548	Sal Butera	.05
549	John Castino	.05
550	Don Cooper	.05
551	Doug Corbett	.05
552	Dave Engle	.05
553	Roger Erickson	.05
554	Danny Goodwin	.05
555	Darrell Jackson	1.25
	(error—black hat)	
555	Darrell Jackson	.10
	(correct—red hat)	
556	Pete Mackanin	.05
557	Jack O'Connor	.05
558	Hosken Powell	.05
559	Pete Redfern	.05
560	Roy Smalley	.05
561	Chuck Baker	.05
562	Gary Ward	.05
563	Rob Wilfong	.05
564	Al Williams	.05
565	Butch Wynegar	.05

SAN DIEGO PADRES

NO.	PLAYER	MINT
566	Randy Bass	.05
567	Juan Bonilla	.07
568	Danny Boone	.05
569	John Curtis	.05
570	Juan Eichelberger	.05
571	Barry Evans	.05
572	Tim Flannery	.05
573	Ruppert Jones	.05
574	Terry Kennedy	.10
575	Joe LeFebvre	.05
576	John Littlefield	125.00
	(left handed—error)	
576	John Littlefield	.10
	(right handed—corrected)	
577	Gary Lucas	.05
578	Steve Mura	.05
579	Broderick Perkins	.05
580	Gene Richards	.05
581	Luis Salazar	.05
582	Ozzie Smith	.30
583	John Urrea	.05
584	Chris Welsh	.07
585	Rick Wise	.05

CHICAGO CUBS

NO.	PLAYER	MINT
586	Doug Bird	.05
587	Tim Blackwell	.05
588	Bobby Bonds	.10
589	Bill Buckner	.10
590	Bill Caudill	.05
591	Hector Cruz	.05
592	Jody Davis (R)	.30
593	Ivan DeJesus	.05
594	Steve Dillard	.05
595	Leon Durham	.15
596	Rawly Eastwick	.05
597	Steve Henderson	.05
598	Mike Krukow	.05
599	Mike Lum	.05
600	Randy Martz	.05
601	Jerry Morales	.05
602	Ken Reitz	.05
603	Lee Smith (R) *	.75
604	Dick Tidrow	.05

NO.	PLAYER	MINT
605	Jim Tracy	.05
606	Mike Tyson	.05
607	Ty Waller	.08

TORONTO BLUE JAYS

NO.	PLAYER	MINT
608	Danny Ainge	.10
609	Jorge Bell (R)	7.00
610	Mark Bomback	.05
611	Barry Bonnell	.05
612	Jim Clancy	.05
613	Damaso Garcia	.10
614	Jerry Garvin	.05
615	Alfredo Griffin	.10
616	Garth Iorg	.05
617	Luis Leal	.05
618	Ken Macha	.05
619	John Mayberry	.05
620	Joey McLaughlin	.05
621	Lloyd Moseby	.15
622	Dave Stieb	.20
623	Jackson Todd	.05
624	Willie Upshaw	.15
625	Otto Velez	.05
626	Ernie Whitt	.05
627	Al Woods	.05

SPECIAL CARDS

NO.	PLAYER	MINT
628	All-Star Game	.05
629	All-Star Infielders:	.05
	Frank White, Bucky Dent	
630	Big Red Machine:	.10
	Driessen, Concepcion,	
	Foster	
631	Bruce Sutter	.10
	"Top NL Relief Pitcher"	
632	"Steve and Carlton"	.20
	Steve Carlton, Carlton Fisk	
633	Carl Yastrzemski	.30
	"3000th Game"	
634	"Dynamic Duo"	.25
	Johnny Bench, Tom Seaver	
635	"West Meets East"	.25
	Valenzuela, Carter	
636	Fernando Valenzuela:*	.30
	"NL Strikeout King"	
637	Mike Schmidt	.30
	"Home Run King"	
638	"NL All Stars"	.20
	Gary Carter, Dave Parker	
639	"Perfect Game"	.10
	Len Barker, Bo Diaz	
640	"Pete & Re-Pete"	1.00
	Pete Rose and Son	
641	"Phillies' Finest"	.30
	Carlton, Smith, Schmidt	
642	"Red Sox Reunion"	.10
	Fred Lynn, Dwight Evans	
643	Rickey Henderson	.30
	"Most Hits, Most Runs"	
644	Rollie Fingers	.10
	"Most 'Saves AL"	
645	Tom Seaver	.20
	"Most 1981 Wins"	
646	"Yankee Powerhouse"*	.50
	R. Jackson, D. Winfield	
647	Checklist No. 1	.08
648	Checklist No. 2	.08
649	Checklist No. 3	.08
650	Checklist No. 4	.08
651	Checklist No. 5	.08
652	Checklist No. 6	.08
653	Checklist No. 7	.08
654	Checklist No. 8	.08
655	Checklist No. 9	.08
656	Checklist No. 10	.08
657	Checklist No. 11	.08
658	Checklist No. 12	.08
659	Checklist No. 13	.08
660	Checklist No. 14	.08

1983 Fleer. . . . Complete Set of 660 Cards—Value $60.00

Features the rookie cards of Wade Boggs, Tony Gwynn, Howard Johnson and Ryne Sandberg. The back of the card is printed in two shades of brown.

Willie McGee

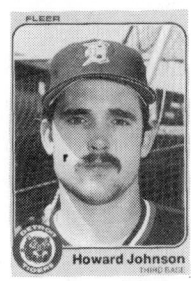
Howard Johnson

Wade Boggs

Tony Gwynn

Ryne Sandberg

NO.	PLAYER	MINT
ST. LOUIS CARDINALS		
1	Joaquin Andujar	.10
2	Doug Bair	.05
3	Steve Braun	.05
4	Glenn Brummer	.05
5	Bob Forsch	.05
6	David Green (R)	.15
7	George Hendrick	.10
8	Keith Hernandez	.30
9	Tom Herr	.10
10	Dane Iorg	.05
11	Jim Kaat	.10
12	Jeff Lahti	.10
13	Tito Landrum	.05
14	Dave LaPoint (R)	.35
15	Willie McGee (R)	1.50
16	Steve Mura	.05
17	Ken Oberkfell	.05
18	Darrell Porter	.05
19	Mike Ramsey	.05
20	Gene Roof	.05
21	Lonnie Smith	.10
22	Ozzie Smith	.30
23	John Stuper	.12
24	Bruce Sutter	.15
25	Gene Tenace	.05
MILWAUKEE BREWERS		
26	Jerry Augustin	.05
27	Dwight Bernard	.05
28	Mark Brouhard	.05
29	Mike Caldwell	.05
30	Cecil Cooper	.15
31	Jamie Easterly	.05
32	Marshall Edwards	.05
33	Rollie Fingers	.20
34	Jim Gantner	.05
35	Moose Haas	.05
36	Roy Howell	.05
37	Peter Ladd	.05
38	Bob McClure	.05
39	Doc Medich	.05
40	Paul Molitor	.20
41	Don Money	.05
42	Charlie Moore	.05
43	Ben Oglivie	.07
44	Ed Romero	.05
45	Ted Simmons	.10
46	Jim Slaton	.05
47	Don Sutton	.25
48	Gorman Thomas	.10
49	Pete Vuckovich	.05
50	Ned Yost	.05
51	Robin Yount	.40
BALTIMORE ORIOLES		
52	Benny Ayala	.05
53	Bob Bonner	.05
54	Al Bumbry	.05
55	Terry Crowley	.05
56	Storm Davis (R)	.50
57	Rich Dauer	.05
58	Rick Dempsey	.05
59	Jim Dwyer	.05
60	Mike Flanagan	.10
61	Dan Ford	.05
62	Glenn Gulliver	.12
63	John Lowenstein	.05

NO.	PLAYER	MINT
64	Dennis Martinez	.05
65	Tippy Martinez	.05
66	Scott McGregor	.10
67	Eddie Murray	.50
68	Joe Nolan	.05
69	Jim Palmer	.40
70	Cal Ripken Jr.	1.00
71	Gary Roenicke	.05
72	Lenn Sakata	.05
73	Ken Singleton	.05
74	Sammy Stewart	.05
75	Tim Stoddard	.05
CALIFORNIA ANGELS		
76	Don Aase	.05
77	Don Baylor	.10
78	Juan Beniquez	.05
79	Bob Boone	.05
80	Rick Burleson	.05
81	Rod Carew	.40
82	Bobby Clark	.05
83	Doug Corbett	.05
84	John Curtis	.05
85	Doug DeCinces	.10
86	Brian Downing	.05
87	Joe Ferguson	.05
88	Tim Foli	.05
89	Ken Forsch	.05
90	Dave Goltz	.05
91	Bobby Grich	.05
92	Andy Hassler	.05
93	Reggie Jackson	.50
94	Ron Jackson	.05
95	Tommy John	.15
96	Bruce Kison	.05
97	Fred Lynn	.20
98	Ed Ott	.05
99	Steve Renko	.05
100	Luis Sanchez	.05
101	Rob Wilfong	.05
102	Mike Witt	.15
103	Geoff Zahn	.05
KANSAS CITY ROYALS		
104	Willie Aikens	.05
105	Mike Armstrong	.05
106	Vida Blue	.10
107	Bud Black (R)	.15
108	George Brett	.50
109	Bill Castro	.05
110	Onix Concepcion	.12
111	Dave Frost	.05
112	Cesar Geronimo	.05
113	Larry Gura	.05
114	Steve Hammond	.12
115	Don Hood	.05
116	Dennis Leonard	.05
117	Jerry Martin	.05
118	Lee May	.05
119	Hal McRae	.05
120	Amos Otis	.05
121	Greg Pryor	.05
122	Dan Quisenberry	.20
123	Don Slaught (R)	.25
124	Paul Splittorff	.05
125	U.L. Washington	.05
126	John Wathan	.05
127	Frank White	.07

NO.	PLAYER	MINT
128	Willie Wilson	.20
ATLANTA BRAVES		
129	Steve Bedrosian	.30
130	Bruce Benedict	.05
131	Tommy Boggs	.05
132	Brett Butler	.05
133	Rick Camp	.05
134	Chris Chambliss	.05
135	Ken Dayley	.05
136	Gene Garber	.05
137	Terry Harper	.05
138	Bob Horner	.20
139	Glenn Hubbard	.05
140	Rufino Linares	.05
141	Rick Mahler	.05
142	Dale Murphy	.75
143	Phil Niekro	.20
144	Pascual Perez	.10
145	Biff Pocoroba	.05
146	Rafael Ramirez	.05
147	Jerry Royster	.05
148	Ken Smith	.12
149	Bob Walk	.05
150	Claudell Washington	.10
151	Bob Watson	.05
152	Larry Whisenton	.05
PHILADELPHIA PHILLIES		
153	Porfirio Altamirano	.12
154	Marty Bystrom	.05
155	Steve Carlton	.40
156	Larry Christenson	.05
157	Ivan DeJesus	.05
158	John Denny	.10
159	Bob Dernier	.05
160	Bo Diaz	.05
161	Ed Farmer	.05
162	Greg Gross	.05
163	Mike Krukow	.05
164	Garry Maddox	.05
165	Gary Matthews	.10
166	Tug McGraw	.08
167	Bob Molinaro	.05
168	Sid Monge	.05
169	Ron Reed	.05
170	Bill Robinson	.05
171	Pete Rose	1.00
172	Dick Ruthven	.05
173	Mike Schmidt	.70
174	Manny Trillo	.05
175	Ozzie Virgil	.05
176	George Vuckovich	.05
BOSTON RED SOX		
177	Gary Allenson	.05
178	Luis Aponte	.12
179	Wade Boggs (R)	17.50
180	Tom Burgmeier	.05
181	Mark Clear	.05
182	Dennis Eckersley	.10
183	Dwight Evans	.15
184	Rich Gedman	.05
185	Glenn Hoffman	.05
186	Bruce Hurst	.10
187	Carney Lansford	.10
188	Rick Miller	.05
189	Reid Nichols	.05
190	Bob Ojeda	.10

NO.	PLAYER	MINT
191	Tony Perez	.15
192	Chuck Rainey	.05
193	Jerry Remy	.05
194	Jim Rice	.35
195	Bob Stanley	.05
196	Dave Stapleton	.05
197	Mike Torrez	.05
198	John Tudor	.15
199	Julio Valdez	.05
200	Carl Yastrzemski	.75
LOS ANGELES DODGERS		
201	Dusty Baker	.10
202	Joe Beckwith	.05
203	Greg Brock (R)	.30
204	Roy Cey	.15
205	Terry Forster	.05
206	Steve Garvey	.40
207	Pedro Guerrero	.30
208	Burt Hooton	.05
209	Steve Howe	.05
210	Ken Landreaux	.05
211	Mike Marshall	.20
212	Candy Maldonado (R)	.50
213	Rick Monday	.05
214	Tom Niedenfuer	.05
215	Jorge Orta	.05
216	Jerry Reuss	.05
217	Ron Roenicke	.05
218	Vicente Romo	.05
219	Bill Russell	.05
220	Steve Sax	.35
221	Mike Scioscia	.05
222	Dave Stewart	.30
223	Derrel Thomas	.05
224	Fernando Valenzuela	.30
225	Bob Welch	.05
226	Ricky Wright	.12
227	Steve Yeager	.05
CHICAGO WHITE SOX		
228	Bill Almon	.05
229	Harold Baines	.25
230	Salome Barojas	.12
231	Tony Bernazard	.05
232	Britt Burns	.05
233	Richard Dotson	.05
234	Ernesto Escarrega	.12
235	Carlton Fisk	.20
236	Jerry Hairston	.05
237	Kevin Hickey	.05
238	LaMarr Hoyt	.15
239	Steve Kemp	.05
240	Jim Kern	.05
241	Ron Kittle (R)	.75
242	Jerry Koosman	.15
243	Dennis Lamp	.05
244	Rudy Law	.05
245	Vance Law	.05
246	Ron LeFlore	.05
247	Greg Luzinski	.10
248	Tom Paciorek	.05
249	Aurelio Rodriguez	.05
250	Mike Squires	.05
251	Steve Trout	.05
SAN FRANCISCO GIANTS		
252	Jim Barr	.05
253	Dave Bergman	.05

NO.	PLAYER	MINT
254	Fred Breining	.05
255	Bob Brenly	.05
256	Jack Clark	.30
257	Chili Davis	.20
258	Darrell Evans	.10
259	Alan Fowlkes	.12
260	Rich Gale	.05
261	Atlee Hammaker	.05
262	Al Holland	.05
263	Duane Kuiper	.05
264	Bill Laskey (R)	.15
265	Gary Lavelle	.05
266	Johnnie LeMaster	.05
267	Renie Martin	.05
268	Milt May	.05
269	Greg Minton	.05
270	Joe Morgan	.20
271	Tom O'Malley	.12
272	Reggie Smith	.10
273	Guy Sularz	.12
274	Champ Summers	.05
275	Max Venable	.05
276	Jim Wohlford	.05

MONTREAL EXPOS

NO.	PLAYER	MINT
277	Ray Burris	.05
278	Gary Carter	.35
279	Warren Cromartie	.05
280	Andre Dawson	.40
281	Terry Francona	.05
282	Doug Flynn	.05
283	Woody Fryman	.05
284	Bill Gullickson	.05
285	Wallace Johnson	.05
286	Charlie Lea	.05
287	Randy Lerch	.05
288	Brad Mills	.05
289	Dan Norman	.05
290	Al Oliver	.20
291	David Palmer	.05
292	Tim Raines	.40
293	Jeff Reardon	.10
294	Steve Rogers	.10
295	Scott Sanderson	.05
296	Dan Schatzeder	.05
297	Bryn Smith	.30
298	Chris Speier	.05
299	Tim Wallach	.15
300	Jerry White	.05
301	Joel Youngblood	.05

PITTSBURGH PIRATES

NO.	PLAYER	MINT
302	Ross Baumgarten	.05
303	Dale Berra	.05
304	John Candelaria	.05
305	Dick Davis	.05
306	Mike Easler	.05
307	Richie Hebner	.05
308	Lee Lacy	.05
309	Bill Madlock	.15
310	Larry McWilliams	.05
311	John Milner	.05
312	Omar Moreno	.05
313	Jim Morrison	.05
314	Steve Nicosia	.05
315	Dave Parker	.25
316	Tony Pena	.15
317	Johnny Ray	.15
318	Rick Rhoden	.05
319	Don Robinson	.05
320	Enrique Romo	.05
321	Manny Sarmiento	.05
322	Rod Scurry	.05
323	Jim Smith	.12
324	Willie Stargell	.30
325	Jason Thompson	.10
326	Kent Tekulve	.05

DETROIT TIGERS

NO.	PLAYER	MINT
327	Tom Brookens	.05
328	Enos Cabell	.05
329	Kirk Gibson	.40
330	Larry Herndon	.05
331	Mike Ivie	.05
332	Howard Johnson (R)	8.00
333	Lynn Jones	.05
334	Rick Leach	.05
335	Chet Lemon	.07
336	Jack Morris	.20
337	Lance Parrish	.25
338	Larry Pashnick	.12
339	Dan Petry	.15
340	Dave Rozema	.05
341	Dave Rucker	.05
342	Elias Sosa	.05
343	Dave Tobik	.05
344	Alan Trammell	.25
345	Jerry Turner	.05
346	Jerry Ujdur	.05
347	Pat Underwood	.05
348	Lou Whitaker	.20
349	Milt Wilcox	.05
350	Glenn Wilson (R)	.40
351	John Wockenfuss	.05

SAN DIEGO PADRES

NO.	PLAYER	MINT
352	Kurt Bevacqua	.05
353	Juan Bonilla	.05
354	Floyd Chiffer	.12
355	Luis DeLeon	.05
356	Dave Dravecky (R)	.40
357	Dave Edwards	.05
358	Juan Eichelberger	.05
359	Tim Flannery	.05
360	Tony Gwynn (R)	12.00
361	Ruppert Jones	.05
362	Terry Kennedy	.10
363	Joe Lefebvre	.05
364	Sixto Lezcano	.05
365	Tim Lollar	.05
366	Gary Lucas	.05
367	John Montefusco	.05
368	Broderick Perkins	.05
369	Joe Pittman	.05
370	Gene Richards	.05
371	Luis Salazar	.05
372	Eric Show (R)	.30
373	Garry Templeton	.10
374	Chris Welsh	.05
375	Alan Wiggins (R)	.15

NEW YORK YANKEES

NO.	PLAYER	MINT
376	Rick Cerone	.05
377	Dave Collins	.05
378	Roger Erickson	.05
379	George Frazier	.05
380	Oscar Gamble	.05
381	Goose Gossage	.20
382	Ken Griffey	.10
383	Ron Guidry	.20
384	Dave LaRoche	.05
385	Rudy May	.05
386	John Mayberry	.05
387	Lee Mazzilli	.05
388	Mike Morgan	.05
389	Jerry Mumphrey	.05
390	Bobby Murcer	.10
391	Graig Nettles	.15
392	Lou Piniella	.10
393	Willie Randolph	.05
394	Shane Rawley	.05
395	Dave Righetti	.15
396	Andre Robertson	.05
397	Roy Smalley	.05
398	Dave Winfield	.40
399	Butch Wynegar	.05

CLEVELAND INDIANS

NO.	PLAYER	MINT
400	Chris Bando	.05
401	Alan Bannister	.05
402	Len Barker	.05
403	Tom Brennan	.05
404	Carmelo Castillo (R)	.10
405	Miguel Dilone	.05
406	Jerry Dybzinski	.05
407	Mike Fischlin	.05
408	Ed Glynn	.05
409	Mike Hargrove	.05
410	Toby Harrah	.05
411	Ron Hassey	.05
412	Von Hayes	.15
413	Rick Manning	.05
414	Bake McBride	.05
415	Larry Milbourne	.05
416	Bill Nahorodny	.05
417	Jack Perconte	.05
418	Lary Sorensen	.05
419	Dan Spillner	.05
420	Rick Sutcliffe	.20
421	Andre Thornton	.10
422	Rick Waits	.05
423	Eddie Whitson	.05

TORONTO BLUE JAYS

NO.	PLAYER	MINT
424	Jesse Barfield	.60
425	Barry Bonnell	.05
426	Jim Clancy	.05
427	Damaso Garcia	.10
428	Jerry Garvin	.05
429	Alfredo Griffin	.05
430	Garth Iorg	.05
431	Roy Lee Jackson	.05
432	Luis Leal	.05
433	Buck Martinez	.05
434	Joey McLaughlin	.05
435	Lloyd Moseby	.15
436	Rance Mulliniks	.05
437	Dale Murray	.05
438	Wayne Nordhagen	.05
439	Gene Petralli	.12
440	Hosken Powell	.05
441	Dave Stieb	.20
442	Willie Upshaw	.10
443	Ernie Whitt	.05
444	Al Woods	.05

HOUSTON ASTROS

NO.	PLAYER	MINT
445	Alan Ashby	.05
446	Jose Cruz	.15
447	Kiko Garcia	.05
448	Phil Garner	.05
449	Danny Heep	.05
450	Art Howe	.05
451	Bob Knepper	.05
452	Alan Knicely	.05
453	Ray Knight	.05
454	Frank LaCorte	.05
455	Mike LaCoss	.05
456	Randy Moffitt	.05
457	Joe Niekro	.05
458	Terry Puhl	.05
459	Luis Pujols	.05
460	Craig Reynolds	.05
461	Bert Roberge	.05
462	Vern Ruhle	.05
463	Nolan Ryan	.75
464	Joe Sambito	.05
465	Tony Scott	.05
466	Dave Smith	.05
467	Harry Spilman	.05
468	Dickie Thon	.05
469	Denny Walling	.05

SEATTLE MARINERS

NO.	PLAYER	MINT
470	Larry Andersen	.05
471	Floyd Bannister	.08
472	Jim Beattie	.05
473	Bruce Bochte	.05
474	Manny Castillo	.05
475	Bill Caudill	.05
476	Bryan Clark	.05
477	Al Cowens	.05
478	Julio Cruz	.05
479	Todd Cruz	.05
480	Gary Gray	.05
481	Dave Henderson	.25
482	Mike Moore (R)	1.00
483	Gaylord Perry	.30
484	Dave Revering	.05
485	Joe Simpson	.05
486	Mike Stanton	.05
487	Rick Sweet	.05
488	Ed VandeBerg (R)	.15
489	Richie Zisk	.05

CHICAGO CUBS

NO.	PLAYER	MINT
490	Doug Bird	.05
491	Larry Bowa	.10
492	Bill Buckner	.10
493	Bill Campbell	.05
494	Jody Davis	.10
495	Leon Durham	.15
496	Steve Henderson	.05
497	Willie Hernandez	.20
498	Ferguson Jenkins	.15
499	Jay Johnstone	.05
500	Junior Kennedy	.05
501	Randy Martz	.05
502	Jerry Morales	.05
503	Keith Moreland	.05
504	Dickie Noles	.05
505	Mike Proly	.05
506	Allen Ripley	.05
507	Ryne Sandberg	6.00
508	Lee Smith	.10
509	Pat Tabler	.20
510	Dick Tidrow	.05
511	Bump Wills	.05
512	Gary Woods	.05

OAKLAND A'S

NO.	PLAYER	MINT
513	Tony Armas	.15
514	Dave Beard	.05
515	Jeff Burroughs	.05
516	John D'Acquisto	.05
517	Wayne Gross	.05
518	Mike Heath	.05
519	Rickey Henderson	.60
520	Cliff Johnson	.05
521	Matt Keough	.05
522	Brian Kingman	.05
523	Rick Langford	.05
524	Davey Lopes	.05
525	Steve McCatty	.05
526	Dave McKay	.05
527	Dan Meyer	.05
528	Dwayne Murphy	.05
529	Jeff Newman	.05
530	Mike Norris	.05
531	Bob Owchinko	.05
532	Joe Rudi	.05
533	Jimmy Sexton	.05
534	Fred Stanley	.05
535	Tom Underwood	.05

NEW YORK METS

NO.	PLAYER	MINT
536	Neil Allen	.05
537	Wally Backman	.05
538	Bob Bailor	.05
539	Hubie Brooks	.15
540	Carlos Diaz (R)	.15
541	Pete Falcone	.05
542	George Foster	.15
543	Ron Gardenhire	.05
544	Brian Giles	.12
545	Ron Hodges	.05
546	Randy Jones	.05
547	Mike Jorgensen	.05
548	Dave Kingman	.15
549	Ed Lynch	.05
550	Jesse Orosco	.10
551	Rick Ownbey	.12
552	Charlie Puleo	.05
553	Gary Rajsich	.12
554	Mike Scott	.30
555	Rusty Staub	.10
556	John Stearns	.05
557	Craig Swan	.05
558	Ellis Valentine	.05
559	Tom Veryzer	.05
560	Mookie Wilson	.10
561	Pat Zachry	.05

TEXAS RANGERS

NO.	PLAYER	MINT
562	Buddy Bell	.15
563	John Butcher	.05
564	Steve Comer	.05
565	Danny Darwin	.05
566	Bucky Dent	.05
567	John Grubb	.05
568	Rick Honeycutt	.05
569	Dave Hostetler	.12
570	Charlie Hough	.05
571	Lamar Johnson	.05
572	Jon Matlack	.05
573	Paul Mirabella	.05
574	Larry Parrish	.05
575	Mike Richardt	.12
576	Mickey Rivers	.05
577	Billy Sample	.05
578	Dave Schmidt	.10
579	Bill Stein	.05
580	Jim Sundberg	.05

1983 Fleer (Continued)

NO. PLAYER	MINT
581 Frank Tanana	.10
582 Mark Wagner	.05
583 George Wright (R)	.15
CINCINNATI REDS	
584 Johnny Bench	.50
585 Bruce Berenyi	.05
586 Larry Biittner	.05
587 Cesar Cedeno	.10
588 Dave Concepcion	.10
589 Dan Driessen	.05
590 Greg Harris	.05
591 Ben Hayes	.12
592 Paul Householder	.05
593 Tom Hume	.05
594 Wayne Krenchicki	.05
595 Rafael Landestoy	.05
596 Charlie Leibrandt	.05
597 Eddie Milner	.10
598 Ron Oester	.05
599 Frank Pastore	.05
600 Joe Price	.05
601 Tom Seaver	.50
602 Bob Shirley	.05
603 Mario Soto	.10
604 Alex Trevino	.05
605 Mike Vail	.05

NO. PLAYER	MINT
606 Duane Walker (R)	.15
MINNESOTA TWINS	
607 Tom Brunansky	.40
608 Bobby Castillo	.05
609 John Castino	.05
610 Ron Davis	.05
611 Lenny Gaetti	.05
612 Terry Felton	.12
613 Gary Gaetti (R)	4.00
614 Mickey Hatcher	.05
615 Brad Havens	.05
616 Kent Hrbek	.75
617 Randy Johnson	.05
618 Tim Laudner	.05
619 Jeff Little	.12
620 Bob Mitchell	.05
621 Jack O'Connor	.05
622 John Pacella	.05
623 Pete Redfern	.05
624 Jesus Vega	.12
625 Frank Viola (R)	4.00
626 Ron Washington	.12
627 Gary Ward	.05
628 Al Williams	.05
SPECIAL CARDS	
629 Red Sox All-Stars:	.20
Eckersley, Yaz, Clear	

NO. PLAYER	MINT
630 "300 Career Wins"	.15
Perry and Bulling	
631 Pride of Venezuela:	.10
Concepcion, Trillo	
632 All-Star Infielders:	.15
Yount and Bell	
633 Mr. Vet & Mr. Rookie:	.25
Winfield, Hrbek	
634 Fountain of Youth:	.60
Stargell, Rose	
635 Big Chiefs:	.10
Harrah, Thornton	
636 Smith Brothers:	.10
Ozzie and Lonnie	
637 Base Stealers' Threat:	.10
Diaz and Carter	
638 All-Star Catchers:	.15
Fisk, Carter	
639 The Silver Shoe:	.35
Rickey Henderson	
640 Home Run Threats:	.15
Oglivie, Jackson	
641 Two Teams on the	
Same Day:	.08
Joel Youngblood 8/4/82	

NO. PLAYER	MINT
642 Last Perfect Game:	.08
Hassey, Barker	
643 Black and Blue:	.08
Vida Blue	
644 Black and Blue:	.08
Bud Black	
645 Speed and Power:	.35
Reggie Jackson	
646 Speed and Power:	.35
Rickey Henderson	
647 Checklist No. 1	.08
648 Checklist No. 2	.08
649 Checklist No. 3	.08
650 Checklist No. 4	.08
651 Checklist No. 5	.08
652 Checklist No. 6	.08
653 Checklist No. 7	.08
654 Checklist No. 8	.08
655 Checklist No. 9	.08
656 Checklist No. 10	.08
657 Checklist No. 11	.08
658 Checklist No. 12	.08
659 Checklist No. 13	.08
660 Checklist No. 14	.08

1984 Fleer.... Complete Set of 660 Cards—Value $125.00

Features the rookie cards of Don Mattingly, Darryl Strawberry and Kevin McReynolds. For the first time a traded update set was issued.

NO. PLAYER	MINT
BALTIMORE ORIOLES	
1 Mike Boddicker	.20
2 Al Bumbry	.05
3 Todd Cruz	.05
4 Rich Dauer	.05
5 Storm Davis	.10
6 Rick Dempsey	.05
7 Jim Dwyer	.05
8 Mike Flanagan	.10
9 Dan Ford	.05
10 John Lowenstein	.05
11 Dennis Martinez	.10
12 Tippy Martinez	.05
13 Scott McGregor	.10
14 Eddie Murray	.50
15 Joe Nolan	.05
16 Jim Palmer	.35
17 Cal Ripken, Jr.	.75
18 Gary Roenicke	.05
19 Lenn Sakata	.05
20 John Shelby (R)	.35
21 Ken Singleton	.10
22 Sammy Stewart	.05
23 Tim Stoddard	.05
PHILADELPHIA PHILLIES	
24 Marty Bystrom	.05
25 Steve Carlton	.35
26 Ivon DeJesus	.05
27 John Denny	.10
28 Bob Dernier	.05
29 Bo Diaz	.05
30 Kiko Garcia	.05
31 Greg Gross	.05
32 Kevin Gross (R)	.30

NO. PLAYER	MINT
33 Von Hayes	.15
34 Willie Hernandez	.20
35 Al Holland	.05
36 Charles Hudson (R)	.35
37 Joe Lefebvre	.05
38 Sixto Lezcano	.05
39 Garry Maddox	.05
40 Gary Matthews	.10
41 Len Matuszek	.05
42 Tug McGraw	.10
43 Joe Morgan	.25
44 Tony Perez	.20
45 Ron Reed	.05
46 Pete Rose	1.00
47 Juan Samuel (R)	4.00
48 Mike Schmidt	1.00
49 Ozzie Virgil	.05
CHICAGO WHITE SOX	
50 Juan Agosto	.20
51 Howard Baines	.20
52 Floyd Bannister	.10
53 Salome Barojas	.05
54 Britt Burns	.05
55 Julio Cruz	.05
56 Richard Dotson	.10
57 Jerry Dybzinski	.05
58 Carlton Fisk	.20
59 Scott Fletcher	.05
60 Jerry Hairston	.05
61 Kevin Hickey	.05
62 Marc Hill	.05
63 LaMarr Hoyt	.10
64 Ron Kittle	.15
65 Jerry Koosman	.15

NO. PLAYER	MINT
66 Dennis Lamp	.05
67 Rudy Law	.05
68 Vance Law	.05
69 Greg Luzinski	.10
70 Tom Paciorek	.05
71 Mike Squires	.05
72 Dick Tidrow	.05
73 Greg Walker (R)	.45
DETROIT TIGERS	
74 Glenn Abbott	.05
75 Howard Bailey	.05
76 Doug Bair	.05
77 Juan Berenguer	.05
78 Tom Brookens	.05
79 Enos Cabell	.05
80 Kirk Gibson	.35
81 John Grubb	.05
82 Larry Herndon	.05
83 Wayne Krenchicki	.05
84 Rick Leach	.05
85 Chet Lemon	.10
86 Aurelio Lopez	.05
87 Jack Morris	.25
88 Lance Parrish	.25
89 Dan Petry	.15
90 Dave Rozema	.05
91 Alan Trammell	.30
92 Lou Whitaker	.30
93 Milt Wilcox	.05
94 Glenn Wilson	.10
95 John Wockenfuss	.05
LOS ANGELES DODGERS	
96 Dusty Baker	.10
97 Joe Beckwith	.05

NO. PLAYER	MINT
98 Greg Brock	.10
99 Jack Fimple	.12
100 Pedro Guerrero	.35
101 Rick Honeycutt	.05
102 Burt Hooton	.05
103 Steve Howe	.05
104 Ken Landreaux	.05
105 Mike Marshall	.15
106 Rick Monday	.05
107 Jose Morales	.05
108 Tom Niedenfuer	.05
109 Alejandro Pena (R)	.25
110 Jerry Reuss	.05
111 Bill Russell	.05
112 Steve Sax	.30
113 Mike Scioscia	.05
114 Derrel Thomas	.05
115 Fernando Valenzuela	.30
116 Bob Welch	.10
117 Steve Yeager	.05
118 Pat Zachry	.05
NEW YORK YANKEES	
119 Don Baylor	.10
120 Bert Campaneris	.05
121 Rick Cerone	.05
122 Ray Fontenot (R)	.15
123 George Frazier	.05
124 Oscar Gamble	.05
125 Goose Gossage	.15
126 Ken Griffey	.10
127 Ron Guidry	.15
128 Jay Howell	.25
129 Steve Kemp	.05
130 Matt Keough	.05

NO.	PLAYER	MINT
131	Don Mattingly (R)	30.00
132	John Montefusco	.05
133	Omar Moreno	.05
134	Dale Murray	.05
135	Graig Nettles	.10
136	Lou Piniella	.10
137	Willie Randolph	.10
138	Shane Rawley	.05
139	Dave Righetti	.15
140	Andre Robertson	.05
141	Bob Shirley	.05
142	Roy Smalley	.05
143	Dave Winfield	.35
144	Butch Wynegar	.05

TORONTO BLUE JAYS

NO.	PLAYER	MINT
145	Jim Acker (R)	.15
146	Doyle Alexander	.10
147	Jesse Barfield	.25
148	Jorge Bell	1.00
149	Barry Bonnell	.05
150	Jim Clancy	.05
151	Dave Collins	.05
152	Tony Fernandez (R)	3.75
153	Damaso Garcia	.10
154	Dave Geisel	.05
155	Jim Gott	.15
156	Alfredo Griffin	.05
157	Garth Iorg	.05
158	Roy Lee Jackson	.05
159	Cliff Johnson	.05
160	Luis Leal	.05
161	Buck Martinez	.05
162	Joey McLaughlin	.05
163	Randy Moffitt	.05
164	Lloyd Moseby	.15
165	Rance Mulliniks	.05
166	Jorge Orta	.05
167	Dave Stieb	.20
168	Willie Upshaw	.15
169	Ernie Whitt	.05

ATLANTA BRAVES

NO.	PLAYER	MINT
170	Len Barker	.05
171	Steve Bedrosian	.10
172	Bruce Benedict	.05
173	Brett Butler	.10
174	Rick Camp	.05
175	Chris Chambliss	.05
176	Ken Dayley	.05
177	Pete Falcone	.05
178	Terry Forster	.05
179	Gene Garber	.05
180	Terry Harper	.05
181	Bob Horner	.20
182	Glenn Hubbard	.05
183	Randy Johnson	.05
184	Craig McMurtry	.10
185	Donnie Moore	.05
186	Dale Murphy	.75
187	Phil Niekro	.20
188	Pascual Perez	.05
189	Biff Pocoroba	.05
190	Rafael Ramirez	.05
191	Jerry Royster	.05
192	Claudell Washington	.10
193	Bob Watson	.05

MILWAUKEE BREWERS

NO.	PLAYER	MINT
194	Jerry Augustine	.05
195	Mark Brouhard	.05
196	Mike Caldwell	.05
197	Tom Candiotti (R)	.35
198	Cecil Cooper	.15
199	Rollie Fingers	.15
200	Jim Gantner	.05
201	Bob Gibson	.12
202	Moose Haas	.05
203	Roy Howell	.05
204	Pete Ladd	.05
205	Rick Manning	.05
206	Bob McClure	.05
207	Paul Molitor	.20
208	Don Money	.05
209	Charlie Moore	.05
210	Ben Oglivie	.10
211	Chuck Porter	.05
212	Ed Romero	.05
213	Ted Simmons	.10
214	Jim Slaton	.05
215	Don Sutton	.15
216	Tom Tellmann	.05
217	Pete Vuckovich	.05
218	Ned Yost	.05
219	Robin Yount	.50

HOSTON ASTROS

NO.	PLAYER	MINT
220	Alan Ashby	.05
221	Kevin Bass	.25
222	Jose Cruz	.10
223	Bill Dawley (R)	.20
224	Frank DiPino	.05
225	Bill Doran (R)	.70
226	Phil Garner	.05
227	Art Howe	.05
228	Bob Knepper	.10
229	Ray Knight	.10
230	Frank LaCorte	.05
231	Mike LaCoss	.05
232	Mike Madden (R)	.15
233	Jerry Mumphrey	.05
234	Joe Niekro	.10
235	Terry Puhl	.05
236	Luis Pujols	.05
237	Craig Reynolds	.05
238	Vern Ruhle	.05
239	Nolan Ryan	1.00
240	Mike Scott	.35
241	Tony Scott	.05
242	Dave Smith	.05
243	Dickie Thon	.08
244	Denny Walling	.05

PITTSBURGH PIRATES

NO.	PLAYER	MINT
245	Dale Berra	.05
246	Jim Bibby	.05
247	John Candelaria	.05
248	Jose DeLeon (R)	.50
249	Mike Easler	.08
250	Cecilio Guante	.05
251	Richie Hebner	.05
252	Lee Lacy	.05
253	Bill Madlock	.15
254	Milt May	.05
255	Lee Mazzilli	.05
256	Larry McWilliams	.05
257	Jim Morrison	.05
258	Dave Parker	.25
259	Tony Pena	.15
260	Johnny Ray	.15
261	Rick Rhoden	.05
262	Don Robinson	.05
263	Manny Sarmiento	.05
264	Rod Scurry	.05
265	Kent Tekulve	.05
266	Gene Tenace	.05
267	Jason Thompson	.10
268	Lee Tunnell (R)	.15
269	Marvell Wynne (R)	.15

MONTREAL EXPOS

NO.	PLAYER	MINT
270	Ray Burris	.05
271	Gary Carter	.35
272	Warren Cromartie	.05
273	Andre Dawson	.30
274	Doug Flynn	.05
275	Terry Francona	.05
276	Bill Gullickson	.05
277	Bob James (R)	.25
278	Charlie Lea	.05
279	Bryan Little	.05
280	Al Oliver	.15
281	Tim Raines	.45
282	Bobby Ramos	.05
283	Jeff Reardon	.10
284	Steve Rogers	.05
285	Scott Sanderson	.05
286	Dan Schatzeder	.05
287	Bryn Smith	.05
288	Chris Speier	.05
289	Manny Trillo	.05
290	Mike Vail	.05
291	Tim Wallach	.10
292	Chris Welsh	.05
293	Jim Wohlford	.05

SAN DIEGO PADRES

NO.	PLAYER	MINT
294	Kurt Bevacqua	.05
295	Juan Bonilla	.05
296	Bobby Brown	.05
297	Luis DeLeon	.05
298	Dave Dravecky	.10
299	Tim Flannery	.05
300	Steve Garvey	.40
301	Tony Gwynn	2.50
302	Andy Hawkins (R)	.45
303	Ruppert Jones	.05
304	Terry Kennedy	.10
305	Tim Lollar	.05
306	Gary Lucas	.05
307	Kevin McReynolds (R)	6.00
308	Sid Monge	.05
309	Mario Ramirez	.05
310	Gene Richards	.12
311	Luis Salazar	.05
312	Eric Show	.05
313	Elias Sosa	.05
314	Garry Templeton	.10
315	Mark Thurmond (R)	.20
316	Ed Whitson	.05
317	Alan Wiggins	.10

ST. LOUIS CARDINALS

NO.	PLAYER	MINT
318	Neil Allen	.05
319	Joaquin Andujar	.10
320	Steve Braun	.05
321	Glenn Brummer	.05
322	Bob Forsch	.10
323	David Green	.05
324	George Hendrick	.08
325	Tom Herr	.10
326	Dane Iorg	.05
327	Jeff Lahti	.05
328	Dave LaPoint	.05
329	Willie McGee	.40
330	Ken Oberkfell	.05
331	Darrell Porter	.05
332	Jamie Quirk	.05
333	Mike Ramsey	.05
334	Floyd Rayford	.05
335	Lonnie Smith	.10
336	Ozzie Smith	.40
337	John Stuper	.05
338	Bruce Sutter	.15
339	Andy Van Slyke (R)	2.50
340	Dave Von Ohlen	.12

KANSAS CITY ROYALS

NO.	PLAYER	MINT
341	Willie Aikens	.05
342	Mike Armstrong	.05
343	Bud Black	.05
344	George Brett	.65
345	Onix Concepcion	.05
346	Keith Creel	.05
347	Larry Gura	.05
348	Don Hood	.05
349	Dennis Leonard	.05
350	Hal McRae	.05
351	Amos Otis	.05
352	Gaylord Perry	.30
353	Greg Pryor	.05
354	Dan Quisenberry	.20
355	Steve Renko	.05
356	Leon Roberts	.05
357	Pat Sheridan (R)	.25
358	Joe Simpson	.05
359	Don Slaught	.05
360	Paul Splittorff	.05
361	U.L. Washington	.05
362	John Wathan	.05
363	Frank White	.05
364	Willie Wilson	.15

SAN FRANCISCO GIANTS

NO.	PLAYER	MINT
365	Jim Barr	.05
366	Dave Bergman	.05
367	Fred Breining	.05
368	Bob Brenly	.05
369	Jack Clark	.30
370	Chili Davis	.15
371	Mark Davis	.35
372	Darrell Evans	.10
373	Atlee Hammaker	.05
374	Mike Krukow	.05
375	Duane Kuiper	.05
376	Bill Laskey	.05
377	Gary Lavelle	.05
378	Johnnie LeMaster	.05
379	Jeff Leonard	.05
380	Randy Lerch	.05
381	Renie Martin	.05
382	Andy McGaffigan	.05
383	Greg Minton	.05
384	Tom O'Malley	.05
385	Max Venable	.05
386	Brad Wellman	.05
387	Joel Youngblood	.12

BOSTON RED SOX

NO.	PLAYER	MINT
388	Gary Allenson	.05
389	Luis Aponte	.05
390	Tony Armas	.15
391	Doug Bird	.05
392	Wade Boggs	7.00
393	Dennis Boyd (R)	.40
394	Mike Brown	.12
395	Mark Clear	.05
396	Dennis Eckersley	.05
397	Dwight Evans	.15
398	Rich Gedman	.10
399	Glenn Hoffman	.05
400	Bruce Hurst	.15
401	John Henry Johnson	.05
402	Ed Jurak	.12
403	Rick Miller	.05
404	Jeff Newman	.05
405	Reid Nichols	.05
406	Bob Ojeda	.10
407	Jerry Remy	.05
408	Jim Rice	.30
409	Bob Stanley	.05
410	Dave Stapleton	.05
411	John Tudor	.15
412	Carl Yastrzemski	.75

TEXAS RANGERS

NO.	PLAYER	MINT
413	Buddy Bell	.15
414	Larry Biittner	.05
415	John Butcher	.05
416	Danny Darwin	.05
417	Bucky Dent	.05
418	Dave Hostetler	.05
419	Charlie Hough	.05
420	Bobby Johnson	.05
421	Odell Jones	.05
422	Jon Matlack	.05
423	Pete O'Brien (R)	1.00
424	Larry Parrish	.05
425	Mickey Rivers	.10
426	Billy Sample	.05
427	Dave Schmidt	.05
428	Mike Smithson (R)	.15
429	Bill Stein	.05
430	Dave Stewart	.30
431	Jim Sundberg	.05
432	Frank Tanana	.10
433	Dave Tobik	.05
434	Wayne Tolleson	.05
435	George Wright	.05

OAKLAND A'S

NO.	PLAYER	MINT
436	Bill Almon	.05
437	Keith Atherton	.12
438	Dave Beard	.05
439	Tom Burgmeier	.05
440	Jeff Burroughs	.05
441	Chris Codiroli	.10
442	Tim Conroy	.12
443	Mike Davis	.10
444	Wayne Gross	.05
445	Garry Hancock	.05
446	Mike Heath	.05
447	Rickey Henderson	.60
448	Don Hill	.12
449	Bob Kearney	.05
450	Bill Krueger	.12
451	Rick Langford	.05
452	Carney Lansford	.10
453	Davey Lopes	.10
454	Steve McCatty	.05
455	Dan Meyer	.05
456	Dwayne Murphy	.05

NO.	PLAYER	MINT
457	Mike Norris	.05
458	Ricky Peters	.05
459	Tony Phillips	.12
460	Tom Underwood	.05
461	Mike Warren (R)	.15

CINCINNATI REDS

NO.	PLAYER	MINT
462	Johnny Bench	.60
463	Bruce Berenyi	.05
464	Dann Bilardello	.05
465	Cesar Cedeno	.05
466	Dave Concepcion	.10
467	Dan Driessen	.05
468	Nick Esasky (R)	2.00
469	Rich Gale	.05
470	Ben Hayes	.05
471	Paul Householder	.05
472	Tom Hume	.05
473	Alan Knicely	.05
474	Eddie Milner	.05
475	Ron Oester	.05
476	Kelly Paris	.10
477	Frank Pastore	.05
478	Ted Power	.05
479	Joe Price	.05
480	Charlie Puleo	.05
481	Gary Redus (R)	.25
482	Bill Scherrer	.12
483	Mario Soto	.10
484	Alex Trevino	.05
485	Duane Walker	.05

CHICAGO CUBS

NO.	PLAYER	MINT
486	Larry Bowa	.05
487	Warren Brusstar	.05
488	Bill Buckner	.10
489	Bill Campbell	.05
490	Ron Cey	.15
491	Jody Davis	.05
492	Leon Durham	.15
493	Mel Hall	.25
494	Ferguson Jenkins	.15
495	Jay Johnstone	.05
496	Craig Lefferts (R)	.20
497	Carmelo Martinez (R)	.25
498	Jerry Morales	.05
499	Keith Moreland	.05
500	Dickie Noles	.05
501	Mike Proly	.05
502	Chuck Rainey	.05
503	Dick Ruthven	.05
504	Ryne Sandberg	2.00
505	Lee Smith	.12
506	Steve Trout	.05
507	Gary Woods	.05

CALIFORNIA ANGELS

NO.	PLAYER	MINT
508	Juan Beniquez	.05
509	Bob Boone	.05
510	Rick Burleson	.10
511	Rod Carew	.40
512	Bobby Clark	.05
513	John Curtis	.05
514	Doug DeCinces	.10
515	Brian Downing	.05
516	Tim Foli	.05
517	Ken Forsch	.05
518	Bobby Grich	.05
519	Andy Hassler	.05
520	Reggie Jackson	.60
521	Ron Jackson	.05
522	Tommy John	.15
523	Bruce Kison	.05
524	Steve Lubratich	.12
525	Fred Lynn	.15
526	Gary Pettis (R)	.30
527	Luis Sanchez	.05
528	Daryl Sconiers	.05
529	Ellis Valentine	.05
530	Rob Wilfong	.05
531	Mike Witt	.10
532	Geoff Zahn	.05

CLEVELAND INDIANS

NO.	PLAYER	MINT
533	Bud Anderson	.05
534	Chris Bando	.05
535	Alan Bannister	.05
536	Bert Blyleven	.10
537	Tom Brennan	.05
538	Jamie Easterly	.05
539	Juan Eichelberger	.05
540	Jim Essian	.05
541	Mike Fischlin	.05
542	Julio Franco	1.50
543	Mike Hargrove	.05
544	Toby Harrah	.05
545	Ron Hassey	.05
546	Neal Heaton (R)	.15
547	Bake McBride	.05
548	Broderick Perkins	.12
549	Lary Sorensen	.05
550	Dan Spillner	.05
551	Rick Sutcliffe	.20
552	Pat Tabler	.10
553	Gorman Thomas	.10
554	Andre Thornton	.10
555	George Vukovich	.05

MINNESOTA TWINS

NO.	PLAYER	MINT
556	Darrell Brown	.05
557	Tom Brunansky	.25
558	Randy Bush	.15
559	Bobby Castillo	.05
560	John Castino	.05
561	Ron Davis	.05
562	Dave Engle	.05
563	Lenny Faedo	.05
564	Pete Filson	.12
565	Gary Gaetti	.75
566	Mickey Hatcher	.05
567	Kent Hrbek	.40
568	Rusty Kuntz	.05
569	Tim Laudner	.05
570	Rick Lysander	.12
571	Bobby Mitchell	.05
572	Ken Schrom	.05
573	Ray Smith	.12
574	Tim Teufel (R)	.30
575	Frank Viola	1.00
576	Gary Ward	.05
577	Ron Washington	.05
578	Len Whitehouse	.05
579	Al Williams	.05

NEW YORK METS

NO.	PLAYER	MINT
580	Bob Bailor	.05
581	Mark Bradley	.10
582	Hubie Brooks	.15
583	Carlos Diaz	.05
584	George Foster	.15
585	Brian Giles	.05
586	Danny Heep	.05
587	Keith Hernandez	.30
588	Ron Hodges	.05
589	Scott Holman	.05
590	Dave Kingman	.15
591	Ed Lynch	.05
592	Jose Oquendo	.50
593	Jesse Orosco	.10
594	Junior Ortiz	.12
595	Tom Seaver	.50
596	Doug Sisk	.15
597	Rusty Staub	.10
598	John Stearns	.05
599	Darryl Strawberry (R)	20.00
600	Craig Swan	.05
601	Walt Terrell (R)	.35
602	Mike Torrez	.05
603	Mookie Wilson	.10

SEATTLE MARINERS

NO.	PLAYER	MINT
604	Jamie Allen	.12
605	Jim Beattie	.05
606	Tony Bernazard	.05
607	Manny Castillo	.05
608	Bill Caudill	.05
609	Bryan Clark	.05
610	Al Cowens	.05
611	Dave Henderson	.05
612	Steve Henderson	.05
613	Orlando Mercado	.12
614	Mike Moore	.05
615	Ricky Nelson	.12
616	Spike Owen (R)	.20
617	Pat Putnam	.05
618	Ron Roenicke	.05
619	Mike Stanton	.05
620	Bob Stoddard	.05
621	Rick Sweet	.05
622	Roy Thomas	.05
623	Ed Vande Berg	.05
624	Matt Young (R)	.15

NO.	PLAYER	MINT
625	Richie Zisk	.05

SPECIAL CARDS

NO.	PLAYER	MINT
626	Fred Lynn: "All-Star Record Breaker"	.15
627	Manny Trillo: "All-Star Record Breaker"	.05
628	Steve Garvey: "NL Iron Man"	.25
629	Rod Carew: "AL Batting Runner-Up"	.20
630	Wade Boggs: "AL Batting Champion"	.50
631	Tim Raines: "Letting Go Of The Raines"	.15
632	Al Oliver: "Double Trouble"	.15
633	Steve Sax: "All-Star Second Base"	.10
634	Dickie Thon: "All-Star Shortstop"	.10
635	Quisenberry & Martinez: "Ace Fireman"	.10
636	Perez, Rose, & Morgan "Reds Reunited"	.40
637	Parrish & Boone: "Backstop Stars"	.10
638	Brett & Perry: "Pine Tar Incident"	.25
639	Forsch, Warren & Righetti "1983 No-Hitters"	.10
640	Bench and Yaz: "Retiring Superstars"	.25
641	Gaylord Perry: "Going Out In Style"	.15
642	Steve Carlton: 300 Club and Strikeout Record	.20
643	Altobelli and Owens: "World Series Managers"	.05
644	Rick Dempsey: "World Series MVP"	.05
645	Mike Boddicker: "Rookie Winner"	.10
646	Scott McGregor: "The Clincher"	.10
647	Checklist No. 1	.08
648	Checklist No. 2	.08
649	Checklist No. 3	.08
650	Checklist No. 4	.08
651	Checklist No. 5	.08
652	Checklist No. 6	.08
653	Checklist No. 7	.08
654	Checklist No. 8	.08
655	Checklist No. 9	.08
656	Checklist No. 10	.08
657	Checklist No. 11	.08
658	Checklist No. 12	.08
659	Checklist No 13	.08
660	Checklist No. 14	.08

1984 Fleer Traded Update.... Complete Set of 132 Cards— Value $350.00

This was Fleer's first traded update set. It updates the main 1984 card set with players who had changed teams during the season and rookies. This set features Fleer's first card of Dwight Gooden, Roger Clemens, Bret Saberhagen and Kirby Puckett. Production was extremely limited. The complete set was packaged in its own printed box and distributed exclusively through card hobby dealers.

Card values shown here fluctuate considerably

NO. PLAYER	MINT
U1 Willie Aikens	.25
U2 Luis Aponte	.20
U3 Mark Bailey	.25
U4 Bob Bailor	.20
U5 Dusty Baker	.25
U6 Steve Balboni	.40
U7 Alan Bannister	.20
U8 Marty Barrett (RR)	3.00
U9 Dave Beard	.20
U10 Joe Beckwith	.20
U11 Dave Bergman	.20
U12 Tony Bernazard	.20
U13 Bruce Bochte	.20
U14 Barry Bonnell	.20
U15 Phil Bradley (RR)	4.00
U16 Fred Breining	.20
U17 Mike Brown	.35
U18 Bill Buckner	.30
U19 Ray Burris	.20
U20 John Butcher	.20
U21 Brett Butler	.40
U22 Enos Cabell	.20
U23 Bill Campbell	.20
U24 Bill Caudill	.20
U25 Bobby Clark	.20
U26 Brian Clark	.20
U27 R. Clemens (RR)	80.00
U28 Jaime Cocanower	.40
U29 Ron Darling (RR)	10.00
U30 Alvin Davis (RR)	8.00
U31 Bob Dernier	.25
U32 Carlos Diaz	.20
U33 Mike Easler	.20

NO. PLAYER	MINT
U34 Dennis Eckersley	.20
U35 Jim Essian	.20
U36 Darrell Evans	.40
U37 Mike Fitzgerald	.35
U38 Tim Foli	.20
U39 John Franco (RR)	5.00
U40 George Frazier	.20
U41 Rich Gale	.20
U42 Barbaro Garbey	.40
U43 Dwight Gooden (RR)	65.00
U44 Goose Gossage	.50
U45 Wayne Gross	.20
U46 Mark Gubicza	4.00
U47 Jackie Gutierrez	.40
U48 Toby Harrah	.20
U49 Ron Hassey	.20
U50 Richie Hebner	.20
U51 Willie Hernandes	.60
U52 Ed Hodge	.35
U53 Ricky Horton	.60
U54 Art Howe	.75
U55 Dane Iorg	.20
U56 Brook Jacoby (RR)	2.50
U57 Dion James	.50
U58 Mike Jeffcoat	.30
U59 Ruppert Jones	.20
U60 Bob Kearney	.20
U61 Jimmy Key (RR)	4.50
U62 Dave Kingman	.35
U63 B. Komminsk (RR)	.35
U64 Jerry Koosman	.50
U65 Wayne Krenchicki	.20
U66 Rusty Kuntz	.20

NO. PLAYER	MINT
U67 Frank LaCorte	.20
U68 Dennis Lamp	.20
U69 Tito Landrum	.20
U70 Mark Langston (RR)	15.00
U71 Rick Leach	.20
U72 Craig Lefferts	.20
U73 Gary Lucas	.20
U74 Jerry Martin	.20
U75 Carmelo Martinez	.25
U76 Mike Mason	.30
U77 Gary Matthews	.20
U78 Andy McGaffigan	.20
U79 Joey McLaughlin	.20
U80 Joe Morgan	2.50
U81 Darryl Motley	.25
U82 Graig Nettles	.60
U83 Phil Niekro	2.00
U84 Ken Oberkfell	.20
U85 Al Oliver	.40
U86 Jorge Orta	.20
U87 Amos Otis	.35
U88 Bob Owchinko	.20
U89 Dave Parker	2.00
U90 Jack Perconte	.20
U91 Tony Perez	1.50
U92 Gerald Perry	2.50
U93 Kirby Puckett (RR)	80.00
U94 Shane Rawley	.30
U95 Floyd Rayford	.20
U96 Ron Reed	.20
U97 R.J. Reynolds (RR)	1.25
U98 Gene Richards	.20
U99 Jose Rijo	2.00

NO. PLAYER	MINT
U100 Jeff Robinson	.50
U101 R. Romanick (RR)	.50
U102 Pete Rose	20.00
U103 B. Saberhagen (RR)	20.00
U104 Scott Sanderson	.25
U105 Dick Schofield	.50
U106 Tom Seaver	7.50
U107 Jim Slaton	.20
U108 Mike Smithson	.20
U109 Lary Sorensen	.20
U110 Tim Stoddard	.20
U111 Jeff Stone (RR)	.40
U112 Champ Summers	.20
U113 Jim Sundberg	.20
U114 Rick Sutcliffe	.75
U115 Craig Swan	.20
U116 Derrel Thomas	.20
U117 Gorman Thomas	.25
U118 Alex Trevino	.20
U119 Manny Trillo	.20
U120 John Tudor	.60
U121 Tom Underwood	.20
U122 Mike Vail	.20
U123 Tom Waddell	.35
U124 Gary Ward	.20
U125 Terry Whitfield	.20
U126 Curtis Wilkerson	.35
U127 Frank Williams	.40
U128 Glenn Wilson	.30
U129 John Wockenfuss	.20
U130 Ned Yost	.20
U131 Mike Young (RR)	.50
U132 Checklist	.50

1985 Fleer.... Complete Set of 660 Cards--Value $110.00

Features the rookie cards of Dwight Gooden, Roger Clemens, Bret Saberhagen, Eric Davis, Orel Hershiser and Kirby Puckett. The frames on the front of the cards are color coded to the player's team. The back is printed in two shades of black and red ink. A new feature was "Major League Prospect" cards—each featuring two rookies.

NO. PLAYER	MINT
DETROIT TIGERS	
1 Doug Bair	.10
2 Juan Berenguer	.05
3 Dave Bergman	.05
4 Tom Brookens	.05
5 Marty Castillo	.05
6 Darrell Evans	.10

NO. PLAYER	MINT
7 Barbaro Garbey (R)	.15
8 Kirk Gibson	.40
9 John Grubb	.05
10 Willie Hernandez	.15
11 Larry Herndon	.05
12 Howard Johnson	1.25
13 Ruppert Jones	.05

NO. PLAYER	MINT
14 Rusty Kuntz	.05
15 Chet Lemon	.05
16 Aurelio Lopez	.05
17 Sid Monge	.05
18 Jack Morris	.20
19 Lance Parrish	.20
20 Dan Petry	.15

NO. PLAYER	MINT
21 Dave Rozema	.05
22 Bill Scherrer	.05
23 Alan Trammell	.25
24 Lou Whitaker	.20
25 Milt Wilcox	.05
SAN DIEGO PADRES	
26 Curt Bevacqua	.05

NO.	PLAYER	MINT
27	Greg Booker (R)	.10
28	Bobby Brown	.05
29	Luis DeLeon	.05
30	Dave Dravecky	.05
31	Tim Flannery	.05
32	Steve Garvey	.40
33	Goose Gossage	.15
34	Tony Gwynn	1.25
35	Greg Harris	.05
36	Andy Hawkins	.05
37	Terry Kennedy	.05
38	Craig Lefferts	.05
39	Tim Lollar	.05
40	Carmelo Martinez	.05
41	Kevin McReynolds	.75
42	Graig Nettles	.10
43	Luis Salazar	.05
44	Eric Show	.05
45	Garry Templeton	.12
46	Mark Thurmond	.05
47	Ed Whitson	.05
48	Alan Wiggins	.10

CHICAGO CUBS

NO.	PLAYER	MINT
49	Rich Bordi	.05
50	Larry Bowa	.10
51	Warren Brusster	.05
52	Ron Cey	.15
53	Henry Cotto (R)	.15
54	Jody Davis	.10
55	Bob Dernier	.05
56	Leon Durham	.15
57	Dennis Eckersley	.10
58	George Frazier	.05
59	Richie Hebner	.05
60	Dave Lopes	.10
61	Gary Matthews	.10
62	Keith Moreland	.05
63	Rick Reuschel	.10
64	Dick Ruthven	.05
65	Ryne Sandberg	.50
66	Scott Sanderson	.05
67	Lee Smith	.10
68	Tim Stoddard	.05
69	Rick Sutcliffe	.20
70	Steve Trout	.05
71	Gary Woods	.05

NEW YORK METS

NO.	PLAYER	MINT
72	Wally Backman	.05
73	Bruce Berenyi	.05
74	Hubie Brooks	.10
75	Kelvin Chapman (R)	.15
76	Ron Darling	1.00
77	Sid Fernandez	1.00
78	Mike Fitzgerald	.05
79	George Foster	.15
80	Brent Gaff	.05
81	Ron Gardenhire	.05
82	Dwight Gooden (R)	10.00
83	Tom Gorman	.05
84	Danny Heep	.05
85	Keith Hernandez	.30
86	Ray Knight	.10
87	Ed Lynch	.05
88	Jose Oquendo	.12
89	Jesse Orosco	.10
90	Rafael Santana (R)	.35
91	Doug Sisk	.05
92	Rusty Staub	.10
93	Darryl Strawberry	4.00
94	Walt Terrell	.05
95	Mookie Wilson	.05

TORONTO BLUE JAYS

NO.	PLAYER	MINT
96	Jim Acker	.05
97	Willie Aikens	.05
98	Doyle Alexander	.05
99	Jesse Barfield	.35
100	George Bell	.50
101	Jim Clancy	.05
102	Dave Collins	.05
103	Tony Fernandez	.40
104	Damaso Garcia	.10
105	Jim Gott	.05
106	Alfredo Griffin	.05
107	Garth Iorg	.05
108	Roy Lee Jackson	.05
109	Cliff Johnson	.05
110	Jimmy Key (R)	1.00
111	Dennis Lamp	.05
112	Rick Leach	.05
113	Luis Leal	.05
114	Buck Martinez	.05
115	Lloyd Moseby	.15
116	Rance Mulliniks	.05
117	Dave Stieb	.15
118	Willie Upshaw	.10
119	Ernie Whitt	.05

NEW YORK YANKEES

NO.	PLAYER	MINT
120	Mike Armstrong	.05
121	Don Baylor	.10
122	Marty Bystrom	.05
123	Rick Cerone	.05
124	Joe Cowley	.05
125	Brian Dayett	.05
126	Tim Foli	.05
127	Ray Fontenot	.05
128	Ken Griffey	.10
129	Ron Guidry	.15
130	Toby Harrah	.05
131	Jay Howell	.05
132	Steve Kemp	.05
133	Don Mattingly	12.00
134	Bobby Meacham	.05
135	John Montefusco	.05
136	Omar Moreno	.05
137	Dale Murray	.05
138	Phil Niekro	.30
139	Mike Pagliarulo (R)	.80
140	Willie Randolph	.05
141	Dennis Rasmussen	.25
142	Dave Righetti	.15
143	Jose Rijo (R)	.40
144	Andre Robertson	.05
145	Bob Shirley	.05
146	Dave Winfield	.35
147	Butch Wynegar	.05

BOSTON RED SOX

NO.	PLAYER	MINT
148	Gary Allenson	.05
149	Tony Armas	.10
150	Marty Barrett	.35
151	Wade Boggs	3.50
152	Dennis Boyd	.10
153	Bill Buckner	.10
154	Mark Clear	.05
155	Roger Clemens (R)	11.00
156	Steve Crawford	.05
157	Mike Easler	.05
158	Dwight Evans	.20
159	Rich Gedman	.10
160	Jackie Gutierrez (R)	.15
161	Bruce Hurst	.15
162	John H. Johnson	.05
163	Rick Miller	.05
164	Reid Nichols	.05
165	Al Nipper (R)	.15
166	Bob Ojeda	.10
167	Jerry Remy	.05
168	Jim Rice	.35
169	Bob Stanley	.05

BALTIMORE ORIOLES

NO.	PLAYER	MINT
170	Mike Boddicker	.10
171	Al Bumbry	.05
172	Todd Cruz	.05
173	Rich Dauer	.05
174	Storm Davis	.05
175	Rick Dempsey	.05
176	Jim Dwyer	.05
177	Mike Flanagan	.05
178	Dan Ford	.05
179	Wayne Gross	.05
180	John Lowenstein	.05
181	Dennis Martinez	.10
182	Tippy Martinez	.05
183	Scott McGregor	.05
184	Eddie Murray	.50
185	Joe Nolan	.05
186	Floyd Rayford	.05
187	Cal Ripken, Jr.	.50
188	Gary Roenicke	.05
189	Lenn Sakata	.05
190	John Shelby	.05
191	Ken Singleton	.05

NO.	PLAYER	MINT
192	Sammy Stewart	.05
193	Bill Swaggerty (R)	.15
194	Tom Underwood	.05
195	Mike Young	.10

KANSAS CITY ROYALS

NO.	PLAYER	MINT
196	Steve Balboni	.10
197	Joe Beckwith	.05
198	Bud Black	.05
199	George Brett	.50
200	Onix Concepcion	.05
201	Mark Gubicza (R)	1.00
202	Larry Gura	.05
203	Mark Huismann	.05
204	Dane Iorg	.05
205	Danny Jackson	1.25
206	Charlie Leibrandt	.05
207	Hal McRae	.05
208	Darryl Motley	.05
209	Jorge Orta	.05
210	Greg Pryor	.05
211	Dan Quisenberry	.15
212	Bret Saberhagen (R)	6.00
213	Pat Sheridan	.05
214	Don Slaught	.05
215	U.L. Washington	.05
216	John Wathan	.05
217	Frank White	.05
218	Willie Wilson	.15

ST. LOUIS CARDINALS

NO.	PLAYER	MINT
219	Neil Allen	.05
220	Joaquin Andujar	.10
221	Steve Braun	.05
222	Danny Cox	.05
223	Bob Forsch	.10
224	David Green	.05
225	George Hendrick	.08
226	Tom Herr	.10
227	Ricky Horton (R)	.25
228	Art Howe	.05
229	Mike Jorgensen	.05
230	Kurt Kepshire (R)	.15
231	Jeff Lahti	.05
232	Tito Landrum	.05
233	Dave LaPoint	.05
234	Willie McGee	.30
235	Tom Nieto	.15
236	Terry Pendleton (R)	.50
237	Darrell Porter	.05
238	Dave Rucker	.05
239	Lonnie Smith	.12
240	Ozzie Smith	.30
241	Bruce Sutter	.15
242	Andy Van Slyke	.40
243	Dave Von Ohlen	.05

PHILADELPHIA PHILLIES

NO.	PLAYER	MINT
244	Larry Andersen	.05
245	Bill Campbell	.05
246	Steve Carlton	.35
247	Tim Corcoran	.05
248	Ivan DeJesus	.05
249	John Denny	.05
250	Bo Diaz	.05
251	Greg Gross	.05
252	Kevin Gross	.05
253	Von Hayes	.15
254	Al Holland	.05
255	Charles Hudson	.05
256	Jerry Koosman	.10
257	Joe Lefebvre	.05
258	Sixto Lezcano	.05
259	Garry Maddox	.05
260	Len Matuszek	.05
261	Tug McGraw	.10
262	Al Oliver	.10
263	Shane Rawley	.05
264	Juan Samuel	.30
265	Mike Schmidt	.60
266	Jeff Stone (R)	.30
267	Ozzie Virgil	.05
268	Glenn Wilson	.10
269	John Wockenfuss	.05

MINNESOTA TWINS

NO.	PLAYER	MINT
270	Darrell Brown	.05
271	Tom Brunansky	.25
272	Randy Bush	.05

NO.	PLAYER	MINT
273	John Butcher	.05
274	Bobby Castillo	.05
275	Ron Davis	.05
276	Dave Engle	.05
277	Pete Filson	.05
278	Gary Gaetti	.40
279	Mickey Hatcher	.05
280	Ed Hodge	.15
281	Kent Hrbek	.35
282	Houston Jimenez	.05
283	Tim Laudner	.05
284	Rick Lysander	.05
285	Dave Meier (R)	.15
286	Kirby Puckett (R)	13.00
287	Pat Putnam	.05
288	Ken Schrom	.05
289	Mike Smithson	.05
290	Tim Teufel	.05
291	Frank Viola	.45
292	Ron Washington	.05

CALIFORNIA ANGELS

NO.	PLAYER	MINT
293	Don Aase	.05
294	Juan Beniquez	.05
295	Bob Boone	.05
296	Mike Brown	.05
297	Rod Carew	.35
298	Doug Corbett	.05
299	Doug DeCinces	.05
300	Brian Downing	.10
301	Ken Forsch	.05
302	Bobby Grich	.05
303	Reggie Jackson	.40
304	Tommy John	.15
305	Curt Kaufman (R)	.15
306	Bruce Kison	.05
307	Fred Lynn	.15
308	Gary Pettis	.10
309	Ron Romanick (R)	.20
310	Luis Sanchez	.05
311	Dick Schofield	.10
312	Daryl Sconiers	.05
313	Jim Slaton	.05
314	Derrel Thomas	.05
315	Rob Wilfong	.05
316	Mike Witt	.10
317	Geoff Zahn	.05

ATLANTA BRAVES

NO.	PLAYER	MINT
318	Len Barker	.05
319	Steve Bedrosian	.10
320	Bruce Benedict	.05
321	Rick Camp	.05
322	Chris Chambliss	.10
323	Jeff Dedmon (R)	.10
324	Terry Forster	.05
325	Gene Garber	.05
326	Albert Hall (R)	.15
327	Terry Harper	.05
328	Bob Horner	.15
329	Glenn Hubbard	.05
330	Randy Johnson	.05
331	Brad Komminsk	.05
332	Rick Mahler	.05
333	Craig McMurtry	.05
334	Donnie Moore	.05
335	Dale Murphy	.60
336	Ken Oberkfell	.05
337	Pascual Perez	.05
338	Gerald Perry	.40
339	Rafael Ramirez	.05
340	Jerry Royster	.05
341	Alex Trevino	.05
342	Claudell Washington	.08

HOUSTON ASTROS

NO.	PLAYER	MINT
343	Alan Ashby	.05
344	Mark Bailey	.10
345	Kevin Bass	.10
346	Enos Cabell	.05
347	Jose Cruz	.10
348	Bill Dawley	.05
349	Frank DiPino	.05
350	Bill Doran	.05
351	Phil Garner	.05
352	Bob Knepper	.10
353	Mike LaCoss	.05
354	Jerry Mumphrey	.05
355	Joe Niekro	.10

NO.	PLAYER	MINT
356	Terry Puhl	.05
357	Craig Reynolds	.05
358	Vern Ruhle	.05
359	Nolan Ryan	.75
360	Joe Sambito	.05
361	Mike Scott	.25
362	Dave Smith	.05
363	Julio Solano (R)	.10
364	Dickie Thon	.05
365	Denny Walling	.05
LOS ANGELES DODGERS		
366	Dave Anderson	.05
367	Bob Bailor	.05
368	Greg Brock	.05
369	Carlos Diaz	.05
370	Pedro Guerrero	.25
371	Orel Hershiser (R)	10.00
372	Rick Honeycutt	.05
373	Burt Hooton	.05
374	Ken Howell (R)	.20
375	Ken Landreaux	.05
376	Candy Maldonado	.15
377	Mike Marshall	.10
378	Tom Niedenfuer	.05
379	Alejandro Pena	.05
380	Jerry Reuss	.10
381	R.J. Reynolds (R)	.30
382	German Rivera (R)	.15
383	Bill Russell	.05
384	Steve Sax	.30
385	Mike Scioscia	.05
386	Franklin Stubbs (R)	.40
387	Fernando Valenzuela	.30
388	Bob Welch	.10
389	Terry Whitfield	.05
390	Steve Yeager	.05
391	Pat Zachry	.05
MONTREAL EXPOS		
392	Fred Breining	.05
393	Gary Carter	.30
394	Andre Dawson	.30
395	Miguel Dilone	.05
396	Dan Driessen	.05
397	Doug Flynn	.05
398	Terry Francona	.05
399	Bill Gullickson	.05
400	Bob James	.05
401	Chrlie Lea	.05
402	Bryan Little	.05
403	Gary Lucas	.05
404	David Palmer	.05
405	Tim Raines	.30
406	Mike Ramsey	.05
407	Jeff Reardon	.10
408	Steve Rogers	.05
409	Dan Schatzeder	.05
410	Bryn Smith	.05
411	Mike Stenhouse	.05
412	Tim Wallach	.12
413	Jim Wohlford	.05
OAKLAND A'S		
414	Bill Almon	.05
415	Keith Atherton	.05
416	Bruce Bochte	.05
417	Tom Burgmeier	.05
418	Ray Burris	.05
419	Bill Caudill	.05
420	Chris Codiroli	.05
421	Tim Conroy	.05
422	Mike Davis	.05
423	Jim Essian	.05
424	Mike Heath	.05
425	Rickey Henderson	.50
426	Donnie Hill	.05
427	Dave Kingman	.10
428	Bill Krueger	.05
429	Carney Lansford	.10
430	Steve McCatty	.05
431	Joe Morgan	.20
432	Dwayne Murphy	.05
433	Tony Phillips	.05
434	Lary Sorensen	.05
435	Mike Warren	.05
436	Curt Young (R)	.35
CLEVELAND INDIANS		
437	Luis Aponte	.05
438	Chris Bando	.05
439	Tony Bernazard	.05
440	Bert Blyleven	.10
441	Brett Butler	.05
442	Ernie Camacho	.05
443	Joe Carter	2.50
444	Carmelo Castillo	.05
445	Jamie Easterly	.05
446	Steve Farr (R)	.25
447	Mike Fischlin	.05
448	Julio Franco	.30
449	Mel Hall	.10
450	Mike Hargrove	.05
451	Neal Heaton	.05
452	Brook Jacoby	.25
453	Mike Jeffcoat	.05
454	Don Schulze (R)	.15
455	Roy Smith (R)	.15
456	Pat Tabler	.05
457	Andre Thornton	.05
458	George Vukovich	.05
459	Tom Waddell (R)	.15
460	Jerry Willard	.05
PITTSBURGH PIRATES		
461	Dale Berra	.05
462	John Candelaria	.10
463	Jose DeLeon	.05
464	Doug Frobel	.05
465	Cecilio Guante	.05
466	Brian Harper	.05
467	Lee Lacy	.05
468	Bill Madlock	.10
469	Lee Mazzilli	.05
470	Larry McWilliams	.05
471	Jim Morrison	.05
472	Tony Pena	.10
473	Johnny Ray	.10
474	Rick Rhoden	.10
475	Don Robinson	.05
476	Rod Scurry	.05
477	Kent Tekulve	.05
478	Jason Thompson	.05
479	John Tudor	.10
480	Lee Tunnell	.05
481	Marvell Wynne	.05
SEATTLE MARINERS		
482	Salome Barojas	.05
483	Dave Beard	.05
484	Jim Beattie	.05
485	Barry Bonnell	.05
486	Phil Bradley (R)	1.00
487	Al Cowens	.05
488	Alvin Davis (R)	2.00
489	Dave Henderson	.05
490	Steve Henderson	.05
491	Bob Kearney	.05
492	Mark Langston (R)	2.50
493	Larry Milbourne	.05
494	Paul Mirabella	.05
495	Mike Moore	.05
496	Edwin Nunez	.05
497	Spike Owen	.05
498	Jack Perconte	.05
499	Ken Phelps	.05
500	Jim Presley (R)	.75
501	Mike Stanton	.05
502	Bob Stoddard	.05
503	Gorman Thomas	.10
504	Ed VandeBerg	.05
505	Matt Young	.05
CHICAGO WHITE SOX		
506	Juan Agosto	.05
507	Harold Baines	.20
508	Floyd Bannister	.10
509	Britt Burns	.05
510	Julio Cruz	.05
511	Richard Dotson	.05
512	Jerry Dybzinski	.05
513	Carlton Fisk	.20
514	Scott Fletcher	.05
515	Jerry Hairston	.05
516	Marc Hill	.05
517	LaMarr Hoyt	.10
518	Ron Kittle	.15
519	Rudy Law	.05
520	Vance Law	.05
521	Greg Luzinski	.10
522	Gene Nelson	.05
523	Tom Paciorek	.05
524	Ron Reed	.05
525	Bert Roberge	.05
526	Tom Seaver	.35
527	Roy Smalley	.05
528	Dan Spillner	.05
529	Mike Squires	.05
530	Greg Walker	.10
CINCINNATI REDS		
531	Cesar Cedeno	.10
532	Dave Concepcion	.10
533	Eric Davis (R)	15.00
534	Nick Esasky	.05
535	Tom Foley	.05
536	John Franco (R)	1.00
537	Brad Guden	.05
538	Tom Hume	.05
539	Wayne Krenchicki	.05
540	Andy McGaffigan	.05
541	Eddie Milner	.05
542	Ron Oester	.05
543	Bob Owchinko	.05
544	Dave Parker	.15
545	Frank Pastore	.05
546	Tony Perez	.15
547	Ted Power	.05
548	Joe Price	.05
549	Gary Redus	.05
550	Pete Rose	.75
551	Jeff Russell	.20
552	Mario Soto	.10
553	Jay Tibbs (R)	.20
554	Duane Walker	.05
TEXAS RANGERS		
555	Alan Bannister	.05
556	Buddy Bell	.10
557	Danny Darwin	.05
558	Charlie Hough	.05
559	Bobby Jones	.05
560	Odell Jones	.05
561	Jeff Kunkel (R)	.15
562	Mike Mason (R)	.15
563	Pete O'Brien	.10
564	Larry Parrish	.05
565	Mickey Rivers	.10
566	Billy Sample	.05
567	Dave Schmidt	.05
568	Donnie Scott (R)	.15
569	Dave Stewart	.25
570	Frank Tanana	.10
571	Wayne Tolleson	.05
572	Gary Ward	.05
573	Curtis Wilkerson	.05
574	George Wright	.05
575	Ned Yost	.05
MILWAUKEE BREWERS		
576	Mark Brouhard	.05
577	Mike Caldwell	.05
578	Bobby Clark	.05
579	Jaime Cocanower (R)	.15
580	Cecil Cooper	.10
581	Rollie Fingers	.15
582	Jim Gantner	.05
583	Moose Haas	.05
584	Dion James	.20
585	Pete Ladd	.05
586	Rick Manning	.05
587	Bob McClure	.05
588	Paul Molitor	.20
589	Charlie Moore	.05
590	Ben Oglivie	.05
591	Chuck Porter	.05
592	Randy Ready (R)	.25
593	Ed Romero	.05
594	Bill Schroeder	.05
595	Ray Searage	.05
596	Ted Simmons	.10
597	Jim Sundberg	.05
598	Don Sutton	.20
599	Tom Tellmann	.05
600	Rick Waits	.05
601	Robin Yount	.50
SAN FRANCISCO GIANTS		
602	Dusty Baker	.05
603	Bob Brenly	.05
604	Jack Clark	.25
605	Chili Davis	.10
606	Mark Davis	.20
607	Dan Gladden (R)	.50
608	Atlee Hammaker	.05
609	Mike Krukow	.05
610	Duane Kuiper	.05
611	Bob Lacey	.05
612	Bill Laskey	.05
613	Gary Lavelle	.05
614	Johnnie LeMaster	.05
615	Jeff Leonard	.15
616	Randy Lerch	.05
617	Greg Minton	.05
618	Steve Nicosia	.05
619	Gene Richards	.05
620	Jeff Robinson (R)	.35
621	Scot Thompson	.05
622	Manny Trillo	.05
623	Brad Wellman	.05
624	Frank Williams (R)	.15
625	Joel Youngblood	.05
SPECIAL CARDS		
626	Ripken-In-Action	.25
627	Schmidt-In-Action	.25
628	Giving The Signs: Sparky Anderson	.05
629	AL Pitcher's Nightmare: Henderson & Winfield	.25
630	NL Pitcher's Nightmare: Schmidt & Sandberg	.25
631	NL All-Stars: Strawberry, Carter, Garvey, Smith	.25
632	All-Star Game Winning Battery: Carter, Lea	.10
633	NL Pennant Clinchers: Garvey, Gossage	.15
634	NL Rookie Phenoms: Samuel, Gooden	.75
635	Toronto's Big Guns: Willie Upshaw	.10
636	Toronto's Big Guns: Lloyd Moseby	.10
637	Al Holland	.05
638	Lee Tunnell	.05
639	500th Homer: Reggie Jackson	.25
640	4,000th Hit: Pete Rose	.50
641	Father and Son: Cal Ripken & Cal, Jr.	.25
642	Cubs: Division Champs	.05
643	Two Perfect Games and One No-Hitter: Witt, Palmer, Morris	.10
644	Willie Lozado (R), Vic Mata (R)	.15
645	Kelly Gruber (R), Randy O'Neal (R)	.75
646	Jose Roman (R), Joel Skinner (R)	.20
647	Steve Kiefer (R), Danny Tartabull (R)	5.00
648	Rob Deer (R), Alejandro Sanchez (R)	1.25
649	Bill Hatcher (R), Shawon Dunston (R)	1.50
650	Ron Robinson (R), Mike Bielecki (R)	.50
651	Zane Smith (R), Paul Zuvella (R)	.40
652	Joe Hesketh (R), Glenn Davis (R)	8.00
653	John Russell (R), Steve Jeltz (R)	.20
654	Checklist No. 1	.08
655	Checklist No. 2	.08
656	Checklist No. 3	.08
657	Checklist No. 4	.08
658	Checklist No. 5	.08
659	Checklist No. 6	.08
660	Checklist No. 7	.08

1985 Fleer Traded Update. . . . Complete Set of 132 Cards— Value $20.00

This set updates the main 1985 card with players who had changed teams during the season, and rookies. This set features Fleer's first card of Vince Coleman, Tom Browning and Teddy Higuera. The set was packaged in a printed box and distributed exclusively through card hobby dealers.

NO.	PLAYER	MINT
U1	Don Aase	.15
U2	Bill Almon	.07
U3	Dusty Baker	.10
U4	Dale Berra	.07
U5	Karl Best	.15
U6	Tim Birtsas	.20
U7	Vida Blue	.07
U8	Rich Bordi	.07
U9	Daryl Boston	.15
U10	Hubie Brooks	.25
U11	Chris Brown (RR)	.25
U12	T. Browning	1.00
U13	Al Bumbry	.07
U14	Tim Burke	.40
U15	Ray Burris	.07
U16	Jeff Burroughs	.07
U17	Ivan Calderon	.75
U18	Jeff Calhoun	.15
U19	Bill Campbell	.07
U20	Don Carman	.30
U21	Gary Carter	.60
U22	Bobby Castillo	.07
U23	Bill Caudill	.07
U24	Rick Cerone	.07
U25	Jack Clark	.40
U26	Pat Clement	.20
U27	Stewart Cliburn	.15
U28	V. Coleman (RR)	4.00
U29	Dave Collins	.07
U30	Fritz Connally	.15
U31	Henry Cotto	.07
U32	Danny Darwin	.07
U33	Darren Daulton	.25

NO.	PLAYER	MINT
U34	Jerry Davis	.15
U35	Brian Dayett	.15
U36	Ken Dixon (RR)	.25
U37	Tommy Dunbar	.20
U38	M. Duncan (RR)	.30
U39	Bob Fallon	.15
U40	Brian Fisher (RR)	.35
U41	Mike Fitzgerald	.07
U42	Ray Fontenot	.07
U43	Greg Gagne	.35
U44	Oscar Gamble	.07
U45	Jim Gott	.07
U46	David Green	.07
U47	Alfredo Griffin	.07
U48	Ozzie Guillen (RR)	.75
U49	Toby Harrah	.07
U50	Ron Hassey	.07
U51	Rickey Hendersen	1.00
U52	Steve Henderson	.07
U53	George Hendrick	.07
U54	Teddy Higuera (RR)	2.00
U55	Al Holland	.07
U56	Burt Hooton	.07
U57	Jay Howell	.15
U58	LaMarr Hoyt	.12
U59	Tim Hulett	.15
U60	Bob James	.07
U61	Cliff Johnson	.05
U62	Howard Johnson	2.00
U63	Ruppert Jones	.07
U64	Steve Kemp	.07
U65	Bruce Kison	.07
U66	Mike LaCoss	.07

NO.	PLAYER	MINT
U67	Lee Lacy	.07
U68	Dave LaPoint	.07
U69	Gary Lavelle	.07
U70	Vance Law	.07
U71	Manny Lee	.15
U72	Sixto Lezcano	.07
U73	Tim Lollar	.07
U74	Urbano Lugo	.12
U75	Fred Lynn	.20
U76	Steve Lyons	.20
U77	Mickey Mahler	.07
U78	Ron Mathis	.15
U79	Len Matuszek	.10
U80	O. McDowell (RR)	.75
U81	R. McDowell (RR)	.90
U82	Donnie Moore	.10
U83	Ron Musselman	.12
U84	Al Oliver	.15
U85	Joe Orsulak	.20
U86	Dan Pasqua	.45
U87	Chris Pittaro	.15
U88	Rick Reuschel	.12
U89	Earnie Riles (RR)	.30
U90	Jerry Royster	.07
U91	Dave Rozema	.07
U92	Dave Rucker	.07
U93	Vern Ruhle	.07
U94	Mark Salas	.15
U95	Luis Salazar	.07
U96	Joe Sambito	.07
U97	Billy Sample	.07
U98	Alex Sanchez	.07
U99	Calvin Schiraldi	.25

NO.	PLAYER	MINT
U100	Rick Schu	.25
U101	Larry Sheets	.50
U102	Ron Shephard	.15
U103	Nelson Simmons	.15
U104	Don Slaught	.10
U105	Roy Smalley	.10
U106	Lonnie Smith	.10
U107	Nate Snell	.10
U108	Lary Sorensen	.07
U109	Chris Speier	.07
U110	Mike Stenhouse	.07
U111	Tim Stoddard	.07
U112	John Stuper	.07
U113	Jim Sundberg	.07
U114	Bruce Sutter	.25
U115	Don Sutton	.50
U116	Bruce Tanner	.15
U117	Kent Tekulve	.10
U118	Walt Terrell	.10
U119	Mickey Tettleton	1.00
U120	Rich Thompson	.10
U121	Louis Thornton	.10
U122	Alex Trevino	.07
U123	John Tudor	.20
U124	Jose Uribe	.25
U125	Dave Valle	.12
U126	Dave Von Ohlen	.07
U127	Curt Wardle	.12
U128	U.L. Washington	.07
U129	Ed Whitson	.07
U130	Herm Winningham	.15
U131	Rich Yett	.12
U132	Update Checklist	.20

1986 Fleer. . . . Complete Set of 660 Cards—Value $100.00

Features the rookie cards of Vince Coleman, Jose Canseco, Andres Galarraga, Kal Daniels and Cory Snyder.

NO.	PLAYER	MINT
KANSAS CITY ROYALS		
1	Steve Balboni	.10
2	Joe Beckwith	.05
3	Buddy Biancalana	.05
4	Bud Black	.05
5	George Brett	.45
6	Onix Concepcion	.05
7	Steve Farr	.05

NO.	PLAYER	MINT
8	Mark Gubicza	.05
9	Dane Iorg	.05
10	Danny Jackson	.30
11	Lynn Jones	.05
12	Mike Jones	.05
13	Charlie Leibrandt	.05
14	Hal McRae	.05
15	Omar Moreno	.05

NO.	PLAYER	MINT
16	Darryl Motley	.05
17	Jorge Orta	.05
18	Dan Quisenberry	.15
19	Bret Saberhagen	.75
20	Pat Sheridan	.05
21	Lonnie Smith	.05
22	Jim Sundberg	.05
23	John Wathan	.05

NO.	PLAYER	MINT
24	Frank White	.05
25	Willie Wilson	.15
ST. LOUIS CARDINALS		
26	Joaquin Andejar	.10
27	Steve Braun	.05
28	Bill Campbell	.05
29	Cesar Cedeno	.05
30	Jack Clark	.25

NO.	PLAYER	MINT
31	Vince Coleman (R)	2.00
32	Danny Cox	.10
33	Ken Dayley	.05
34	Ivan DeJesus	.05
35	Bob Forsch	.05
36	Brian Harper	.05
37	Tom Herr	.10
38	Ricky Horton	.05
39	Kurt Kepshire	.05
40	Jeff Lahti	.05
41	Tito Landrum	.05
42	Willie McGee	.20
43	Tom Nieto	.05
44	Terry Pendleton	.05
45	Darrell Porter	.05
46	Ozzie Smith	.30
47	John Tudor	.15
48	Andy Van Slyke	.30
49	Todd Worrell (R)	.75

TORONTO BLUE JAYS

NO.	PLAYER	MINT
50	Jim Acker	.05
51	Doyl Alexander	.05
52	Jesse Barfield	.20
53	George Bell	.25
54	Jeff Burroughs	.05
55	Bill Caudill	.05
56	Jim Clancy	.05
57	Tony Fernandez	.20
58	Tom Filer	.05
59	Damaso Garcia	.10
60	Tom Henke	.20
61	Garth Iorg	.05
62	Cliff Johnson	.05
63	Jimmy Key	.10
64	Dennis Lamp	.05
65	Gary Lavelle	.05
66	Buck Martinez	.05
67	Lloyd Moseby	.10
68	Rance Mulliniks	.05
69	Al Oliver	.10
70	Dave Stieb	.15
71	Louis Thornton	.15
72	Willie Upshaw	.10
73	Ernie Whitt	.05

NEW YORK METS

NO.	PLAYER	MINT
74	Rick Aguilera (R)	.30
75	Wally Backman	.05
76	Gary Carter	.30
77	Ron Darling	.30
78	Len Dykstra (R)	.75
79	Sid Fernandez	.15
80	George Foster	.15
81	Dwight Gooden	2.00
82	Tom Gorman	.05
83	Danny Heep	.05
84	Keith Hernandez	.25
85	Howard Johnson	.50
86	Ray Knight	.05
87	Terry Leach	.15
88	Ed Lynch	.05
89	Roger McDowell (R)	.45
90	Jesse Orosco	.05
91	Tom Paciorek	.05
92	Ronn Reynolds	.15
93	Rafael Santana	.05
94	Doug Sisk	.05
95	Rusty Staub	.10
96	Darryl Strawberry	1.50
97	Mookie Wilson	.05

NEW YORK YANKEES

NO.	PLAYER	MINT
98	Neil Allen	.05
99	Don Baylor	.10
100	Dale Berra	.05
101	Rich Bordi	.05
102	Marty Bystrom	.05
103	Joe Cowley	.05
104	Brian Fisher (R)	.25
105	Ken Griffey	.05
106	Ron Guidry	.15
107	Ron Hassey	.05
108	Rickey Henderson	.45
109	Dan Mattingly	4.00
110	Bobby Meacham	.05
111	John Montefusco	.05
112	Phil Niekro	.20
113	Mike Pagliarulo	.10
114	Dan Pasqua	.15
115	Willie Randolph	.05
116	Dave Righetti	.10
117	Andre Robertson	.05
118	Billy Sample	.05
119	Bob Shirley	.05
120	Ed Whitson	.05
121	Dave Winfield	.30
122	Butch Wynegar	.05

LOS ANGELES DODGERS

NO.	PLAYER	MINT
123	Dave Anderson	.05
124	Bob Bailor	.05
125	Greg Brock	.05
126	Enos Cabell	.05
127	Bobby Castillo	.05
128	Carlos Diaz	.05
129	Mariano Duncan (R)	.25
130	Pedro Guerrero	.25
131	Orel Hershiser	1.50
132	Rick Honeycutt	.05
133	Ken Howell	.05
134	Ken Landreaux	.05
135	Bill Madlock	.10
136	Candy Maldonado	.10
137	Mike Marshall	.10
138	Len Matuszek	.05
139	Tom Niedenfuer	.05
140	Alejandro Pena	.05
141	Jerry Reuss	.05
142	Bill Russell	.05
143	Steve Sax	.15
144	Mike Scioscia	.05
145	Fernando Valenzuela	.30
146	Bob Welch	.05
147	Terry Whitfield	.05

CALIFORNIA ANGELS

NO.	PLAYER	MINT
148	Juan Beniquez	.05
149	Bob Boone	.05
150	John Candelaria	.05
151	Rod Carew	.30
152	Stewart Cliburn (R)	.20
153	Doug DeCinces	.10
154	Brian Downing	.05
155	Ken Forsch	.05
156	Craig Gerber (R)	.15
157	Bobby Grich	.10
158	George Hendrick	.05
159	Al Holland	.05
160	Reggie Jackson	.35
161	Ruppert Jones	.05
162	Urbano Lugo (R)	.15
163	Kirk McCaskill (R)	.50
164	Donnie Moore	.05
165	Gary Pettis	.05
166	Ron Romanick	.05
167	Dick Schofield	.05
168	Darly Sconiers	.05
169	Jim Slaton	.05
170	Don Sutton	.20
171	Mike Witt	.10

CINCINNATI REDS

NO.	PLAYER	MINT
172	Buddy Bell	.10
173	Tom Browning	.20
174	Dave Concepcion	.10
175	Eric Davis	3.00
176	Bo Diaz	.05
177	Nick Esasky	.05
178	John Franco	.25
179	Tom Hume	.05
180	Wayne Krenchicki	.05
181	Andy McGaffigan	.05
182	Eddie Milner	.05
183	Ron Oester	.05
184	Dave Parker	.15
185	Frank Pastore	.05
186	Tony Perez	.10
187	Ted Power	.05
188	Joe Price	.05
189	Gary Redus	.05
190	Ron Robinson	.05
191	Pete Rose	.60
192	Mario Soto	.10
193	John Stuper	.05
194	Jay Tibbs	.05
195	Dave Van Gorder	.05
196	Max Venable	.05

CHICAGO WHITE SOX

NO.	PLAYER	MINT
197	Juan Agosto	.05
198	Harold Baines	.15
199	Floyd Bannister	.05
200	Britt Burns	.05
201	Julio Cruz	.05
202	Joel Davis (R)	.20
203	Richard Dotson	.05
204	Carlton Fisk	.15
205	Scott Fletcher	.05
206	Ozzie Guillen (R)	.50
207	Jerry Hairston	.05
208	Tim Hulett	.05
209	Bob James	.05
210	Ron Kittle	.10
211	Rudy Law	.05
212	Bryan Little	.05
213	Gene Nelson	.05
214	Reid Nichols	.05
215	Luis Salazar	.05
216	Tom Seaver	.35
217	Dan Spillner	.05
218	Bruce Tanner (R)	.15
219	Greg Walker	.10
220	Dave Wehrmeister	.05

DETROIT TIGERS

NO.	PLAYER	MINT
221	Juan Berenguer	.05
222	Dave Bergman	.05
223	Tom Brookens	.05
224	Darrell Evans	.10
225	Barbaro Garbey	.05
226	Kirk Gibson	.30
227	John Grubb	.05
228	Willie Hernandez	.15
229	Larry Herndon	.05
230	Chet Lemon	.05
231	Aurelio Lopez	.05
232	Jack Morris	.20
233	Randy O'Neal	.05
234	Lance Parrish	.15
235	Dan Petry	.15
236	Alex Sanchez	.05
237	Bill Scherrer	.05
238	Nelson Simmons (R)	.10
239	Frank Tanana	.05
240	Walt Terrell	.05
241	Alan Trammell	.20
242	Lou Whitaker	.15
243	Milt Wilcox	.05

MONTREAL EXPOS

NO.	PLAYER	MINT
244	Hubie Brooks	.10
245	Tim Burke (R)	.25
246	Andre Dawson	.25
247	Mike Fitzgerald	.05
248	Terry Francona	.05
249	Bill Gullickson	.05
250	Joe Hesketh	.10
251	Bill Laskey	.05
252	Vance Law	.05
253	Charlie Lea	.05
254	Gary Lucas	.05
255	David Palmer	.05
256	Tim Raines	.25
257	Jeff Reardon	.10
258	Bert Roberge	.05
259	Dan Schatzeder	.05
260	Bryn Smith	.05
261	Randy St. Claire	.05
262	Scot Thompson	.05
263	Tim Wallach	.10
264	U.L. Washington	.05
265	Mitch Webster (R)	.35
266	Herm Winningham (R)	.15
267	Floyd Youmans (R)	.30

BALTIMORE ORIOLES

NO.	PLAYER	MINT
268	Don Aase	.05
269	Mike Boddicker	.10
270	Rich Dauer	.05
271	Storm Davis	.05
272	Rick Dempsey	.05
273	Ken Dixon	.05
274	Jim Dwyer	.05
275	Mike Flanagan	.05
276	Wayne Gross	.05
277	Lee Lacy	.05
278	Fred Lynn	.15
279	Tippy Martinez	.05
280	Dennis Martinez	.05
281	Scott McGregor	.05
282	Eddie Murray	.30
283	Floyd Rayford	.05
284	Cal Ripken, Jr.	.35
285	Gary Roenicke	.05
286	Larry Sheets	.25
287	John Shelby	.05
288	Nate Snell	.15
289	Sammy Stewart	.05
290	Alan Wiggins	.05
291	Mike Young	.10

HOUSTON ASTROS

NO.	PLAYER	MINT
292	Alan Ashby	.05
293	Mark Bailey	.05
294	Kevin Bass	.05
295	Jeff Calhoun (R)	.15
296	Jose Cruz	.10
297	Glenn Davis	1.00
298	Bill Dawley	.05
299	Frank DiPino	.05
300	Bill Doran	.05
301	Phil Garner	.05
302	Jeff Heathcock (R)	.15
303	Charlie Kerfeld (R)	.20
304	Bob Knepper	.05
305	Ron Mathis (R)	.15
306	Jerry Mumphrey	.05
307	Jim Pankovits	.05
308	Terry Puhl	.05
309	Craig Reynolds	.05
310	Nolan Ryan	.60
311	Mike Scott	.25
312	Dave Smith	.05
313	Dickie Thon	.05
314	Denny Walling	.05

SAN DIEGO PADRES

NO.	PLAYER	MINT
315	Kurt Bevacqua	.05
316	Al Bumbry	.05
317	Jerry Davis	.05
318	Luis DeLeon	.05
319	Dave Dravecky	.05
320	Tim Flannery	.05
321	Steve Garvey	.35
322	Goose Gossage	.15
323	Tony Gwynn	.60
324	Andy Hawkins	.05
325	LaMarr Hoyt	.05
326	Roy Lee Jackson	.05
327	Terry Kennedy	.05
328	Craig Lefferts	.05
329	Carmelo Martinez	.05
330	Lance McCullers (R)	.30
331	Kevin McReynolds	.25
332	Graig Nettles	.10
333	Jerry Royster	.05
334	Eric Show	.05
335	Tim Stoddard	.05
336	Garry Templeton	.08
337	Mark Thurmond	.05
338	Ed Wojna (R)	.15

BOSTON RED SOX

NO.	PLAYER	MINT
339	Tony Armas	.10
340	Marty Barrett	.05
341	Wade Boggs	2.50
342	Dennis Boyd	.10
343	Bill Buckner	.10
344	Mark Clear	.05
345	Roger Clemens	2.50
346	Steve Crawford	.05
347	Mike Easler	.05
348	Dwight Evans	.12
349	Rich Gedman	.08
350	Jackie Gutierrez	.05
351	Glenn Hoffman	.05
352	Bruce Hurst	.10
353	Bruce Kison	.05
354	Tim Lollar	.05
355	Steve Lyons	.05
356	Al Nipper	.05
357	Bob Ojeda	.05
358	Jim Rice	.25
359	Bob Stanley	.05
360	Mike Trujillo (R)	.10

NO.	PLAYER	MINT

CHICAGO CUBS
361	Thad Bosley	.05
362	Warren Brusstar	.05
363	Ron Cey	.10
364	Jody Davis	.07
365	Bob Dernier	.05
366	Shawon Dunston	.20
367	Leon Durham	.15
368	Dennis Eckersley	.05
369	Ray Fontenot	.05
370	George Frazier	.05
371	Bill Hatcher	.15
372	Dave Lopes	.05
373	Gary Matthews	.05
374	Ron Meredith (R)	.15
375	Keith Moreland	.05
376	Reggie Patterson	.05
377	Dick Ruthven	.05
378	Ryne Sandberg	.25
379	Scott Sanderson	.05
380	Lee Smith	.10
381	Lary Sorensen	.05
382	Chris Speier	.05
383	Rick Sutcliffe	.15
384	Steve Trout	.05
385	Gary Woods	.05

MINNESOTA TWINS
386	Bert Blyleven	.10
387	Tom Brunansky	.15
388	Randy Bush	.05
389	John Butcher	.05
390	Ron Davis	.05
391	Dave Engle	.05
392	Frank Eufemia	.15
393	Pete Filson	.05
394	Gary Gaetti	.20
395	Greg Gagne	.10
396	Mickey Hatcher	.05
397	Kent Hrbek	.20
398	Tim Laudner	.05
399	Rick Lysander	.05
400	Dave Meier	.05
401	Kirby Puckett	2.50
402	Mark Salas	.05
403	Ken Schrom	.05
404	Roy Smalley	.05
405	Mike Smithson	.05
406	Mike Stenhouse	.05
407	Tim Teufel	.05
408	Frank Viola	.30
409	Ron Washington	.05

OAKLAND A'S
410	Keith Atherton	.05
411	Dusty Baker	.05
412	Tim Birtsas (R)	.15
413	Bruce Bochte	.05
414	Chris Codiroli	.05
415	Dave Collins	.05
416	Mike Davis	.05
417	Alfredo Griffin	.05
418	Mike Heath	.05
419	Steve Henderson	.05
420	Donnie Hill	.05
421	Jay Howell	.10
422	Tommy John	.10
423	Dave Kingman	.10
424	Bill Krueger	.05
425	Rick Langford	.05
426	Carney Lansford	.10
427	Steve McCatty	.05
428	Dwayne Murphy	.05
429	Steve Ontiveros (R)	.15
430	Tony Phillips	.05
431	Jose Rijo	.05
432	Mickey Tettleton (R)	.70

PHILADELPHIA PHILLIES
433	Luis Aguayo	.05
434	Larry Andersen	.05
435	Steve Carlton	.30
436	Don Carman (R)	.25
437	Tim Corcoran	.05
438	Darren Daulton (R)	.15
439	John Denny	.08
440	Tom Foley	.05
441	Greg Gross	.05
442	Kevin Gross	.05
443	Von Hayes	.15

444	Charles Hudson	.05
445	Garry Maddox	.05
446	Shane Rawley	.05
447	Dave Rucker	.05
448	John Russell	.05
449	Juan Samuel	.15
450	Mike Schmidt	.60
451	Rick Schu	.05
452	Dave Shipanoff (R)	.15
453	Dave Stewart	.20
454	Jeff Stone	.05
455	Kent Tekulve	.05
456	Ozzie Virgil	.05
457	Glenn Wilson	.10

SEATTLE MARINERS
458	Jim Beattie	.05
459	Karl Best	.10
460	Barry Bonnell	.05
461	Phil Bradley	.20
462	Ivan Calderon (R)	.50
463	Al Cowens	.05
464	Alvin Davis	.20
465	Dave Henderson	.05
466	Bob Kearney	.05
467	Mark Langston	.35
468	Bob Long	.05
469	Mike Moore	.05
470	Edwin Nunez	.05
471	Spike Owen	.05
472	Jack Perconte	.05
473	Jim Presley	.25
474	Donnie Scott	.05
475	Bill Swift	.05
476	Danny Tartabull	.65
477	Gorman Thomas	.10
478	Roy Thomas	.05
479	Ed VandeBerg	.05
480	Frank Wills (R)	.15
481	Matt Young	.05

MILWAUKEE BREWERS
482	Ray Burris	.05
483	Jaime Cocanower	.05
484	Cecil Cooper	.15
485	Danny Darwin	.05
486	Rollie Fingers	.15
487	Jim Gantner	.05
488	Bob Gibson	.05
489	Moose Haas	.05
490	Teddy Higuera (R)	1.25
491	Paul Householder	.05
492	Pete Ladd	.05
493	Rick Manning	.05
494	Bob McClure	.05
495	Paul Molitor	.20
496	Charlie Moore	.05
497	Ben Oglivie	.05
498	Randy Ready	.05
499	Earnie Riles (R)	.30
500	Ed Romero	.05
501	Bill Schroeder	.05
502	Ray Searage	.05
503	Ted Simmons	.10
504	Pete Vuckovich	.05
505	Rick Waits	.05
506	Robin Yount	.30

ATLANTA BRAVES
507	Len Barker	.05
508	Steve Bedrosian	.15
509	Bruce Benedict	.05
510	Rick Camp	.05
511	Rick Cerone	.05
512	Chris Chambliss	.05
513	Jeff Dedmon	.05
514	Terry Forster	.05
515	Gene Garber	.05
516	Terry Harper	.05
517	Bob Horner	.15
518	Glenn Hubbard	.05
519	Joe Johnson (R)	.15
520	Brad Komminsk	.05
521	Rick Mahler	.05
522	Dale Murphy	.50
523	Ken Oberkfell	.05
524	Pascual Perez	.05
525	Gerald Perry	.20
526	Rafael Ramirez	.05

527	Steve Shields (R)	.15
528	Zane Smith	.10
529	Bruce Sutter	.15
530	Milt Thompson (R)	.35
531	Claudell Washington	.05
532	Paul Zuvella	.05

S.F. GIANTS
533	Vida Blue	.05
534	Bob Brenly	.05
535	Chris Brown (R)	.30
536	Chili Davis	.10
537	Mark Davis	.05
538	Rob Deer	.30
539	Dan Driessen	.05
540	Scott Garrelts	.30
541	Dan Gladden	.05
542	Jim Gott	.05
543	David Green	.05
544	Atlee Hammaker	.05
545	Mike Jeffcoat	.05
546	Mike Krukow	.05
547	Dave LaPoint	.05
548	Jeff Leonard	.05
549	Greg Minton	.05
550	Alex Trevino	.05
551	Manny Trillo	.05
552	Jose Uribe (R)	.35
553	Brad Wellman	.05
554	Frank Williams	.05
555	Joel Youngblood	.05

TEXAS RANGERS
556	Alan Bannister	.05
557	Glenn Brummer	.05
558	Steve Buechele (R)	.25
559	Jose Guzman (R)	.25
560	Toby Harrah	.05
561	Greg Harris	.05
562	Dwayne Henry (R)	.15
563	Burt Hooton	.05
564	Charlie Hough	.05
565	Mike Mason	.05
566	Oddibe McDowell	.25
567	Dickie Noles	.05
568	Pete O'Brien	.15
569	Larry Parrish	.05
570	Dave Rozema	.05
571	Dave Schmidt	.05
572	Don Slaught	.05
573	Wayne Tolleson	.05
574	Duane Walker	.05
575	Gary Ward	.05
576	Chris Welsh	.05
577	Curtis Wilkerson	.05
578	George Wright	.05

CLEVELAND INDIANS
579	Chris Bando	.05
580	Tony Bernazard	.05
581	Brett Butler	.10
582	Ernie Camacho	.05
583	Joe Carter	.40
584	Carmello Castillo	.05
585	Jamie Easterly	.05
586	Julio Franco	.15
587	Mel Hall	.05
588	Mike Hargrove	.05
589	Neal Heaton	.05
590	Brook Jacoby	.10
591	Otis Nixon (R)	.20
592	Jerry Reed (R)	.15
593	Vern Ruhle	.05
594	Pat Tabler	.05
595	Rich Thompson (R)	.15
596	Andre Thornton	.05
597	Dave Von Ohlen	.05
598	George Vuckovich	.05
599	Tom Waddell	.05
600	Curt Wardle (R)	.15
601	Jerry Willard	.05

PITTSBURGH PIRATES
602	Bill Almon	.05
603	Mike Bielecki	.05
604	Sid Bream	.05
605	Mike Brown	.05
606	Pat Clements (R)	.15
607	Jose DeLeon	.05
608	Denny Gonzalez	.05

609	Cecilio Guante	.05
610	Steve Kemp	.05
611	Sam Khalifa (R)	.15
612	Lee Mazzilli	.05
613	Larry McWilliams	.05
614	Jim Morrison	.05
615	Joe Orsulak (R)	.20
616	Tony Pena	.10
617	Johnny Ray	.10
618	Rick Reuschel	.05
619	R.J. Reynolds	.05
620	Rick Rhoden	.05
621	Don Robinson	.05
622	Jason Thompson	.05
623	Lee Tunnell	.05
624	Jim Winn	.05
625	Marvell Wynne	.05

SPECIAL CARDS
626	Gooden in Action	.50
627	Mattingly in Action	1.25
628	Pete Rose—4,192	.50
629	3,000 Career Hits: Rod Carew	.25
630	300 Career Wins: Tom Seaver, Phil Niekro	.20
631	Ouch: Don Baylor	.15
632	Instant Offense: Raines and Strawberry	.30
633	Shortstops Supreme: Trammell & Ripken	.25
634	Boggs and "Hero" Wade Boggs, George Brett	.50
635	Braves Dynamic Duo: Horner and Murphy	.30
636	Cardinal Ignitors: Coleman & McGee	.35
637	Terror on Basepaths: Vince Coleman	.35
638	Charlie Hustle and Dr. K: Rose and Gooden	.75
639	1984 and 1985 AL Batting Champs: Mattingly and Boggs	1.50
640	NL West Sluggers: Murphy, Garvey, Parker	.30
641	Staff Aces: Valenzuela & Gooden	.35
642	Blue Jay Stoppers: Key and Stieb	.10
643	AL All-Star Backstops Fisk & Gedman	.10
644	Benito Santiago (R) and Gene Walter (R)	4.50
645	Mike Woodard (R) and Colin Ward (R)	.15
646	Kal Daniels (R) and Paul O'Neill (R)	4.00
647	Fred Toliver (R) and Andres Galarraga (R)	3.50
648	Bob Kipper (R) and Curt Ford (R)	.20
649	Eric Plunk (R) and Jose Canseco (R)	36.00
650	Gus Polidor (R) and Mark McLemore (R)	.20
651	Rob Woodward (R) and Mickey Brantley (R)	.35
652	Billy Joe Robidoux (R) and Mark Funderburk (R)	.20
653	Cecil Fielder (R) and Cory Snyder	3.00
654	Checklist No. 1	.08
655	Checklist No. 2	.08
656	Checklist No. 3	.08
657	Checklist No. 4	.08
658	Checklist No. 5	.08
659	Checklist No. 6	.08
660	Checklist No. 7	.08

1986 Fleer Traded Update. . . Complete Set of 132 Cards—Value $30.00

This set updates the main 1986 card set with players who had changed teams during the season, and rookies. This set features Fleer's first card of Jose Canseco, Ruben Sierra, Kevin Mitchell and Will Clark. The set was packaged in a printed box and distributed exclusively through card dealers.

NO. PLAYER	MINT	NO. PLAYER	MINT	NO. PLAYER	MINT	NO. PLAYER	MINT
U1 Mike Aldrete (RR)	.30	U34 John Denny	.07	U67 Dennis Leonard	.07	U100 Angel Salazar	.12
U2 Andy Allanson	.20	U35 Jim DeShaies	.40	U68 Steve Lombardozzi	.20	U101 Joe Sambito	.07
U3 Nell Allen	.07	U36 Doug Drabek	.35	U69 Aurelio Lopez	.07	U102 Billy Sample	.07
U4 Joaquin Andujar	.07	U37 Mike Easler	.07	U70 Miceky Mahler	.07	U103 Dave Schmidt	.07
U5 Paul Assenmacher	.20	U38 Mark Eichhorn	.20	U71 Candy Maldonado	.20	U104 Ken Schrom	.07
U6 Scott Bailes	.15	U39 Dave Engle	.07	U72 Roger Mason	.15	U105 Ruben Sierra (RR)	5.00
U7 Jay Baller	.15	U40 Mike Fischlin	.07	U73 Greg Mathews	.30	U106 Ted Simmons	.10
U8 Scott Bankhead	.30	U41 Scott Fletcher	.07	U74 Andy McGaffigan	.10	U107 Sammy Stewart	.07
U9 Bill Bathe	.15	U42 Terry Forster	.07	U75 Joel McKeon	.15	U108 Kurt Stillwell (RR)	.40
U10 Don Baylor	.12	U43 Terry Francona	.07	U76 Kevin Mitchell (RR)	7.00	U109 Dale Sveum	.35
U11 Billy Beane	.15	U44 Andres Galarraga	1.00	U77 Bill Mooneyham	.12	U110 Tim Teufel	.07
U12 Steve Bedrosian	.15	U45 Lee Guetterman	.25	U78 Omar Moreno	.07	U111 Bob Tewksbury	.20
U13 Juan Beniquez	.10	U46 Bill Gullickson	.07	U79 Jerry Mumphrey	.07	U112 Andres Thomas	.20
U14 Barry Bonds (RR)	1.25	U47 Jackie Gutierrez	.07	U80 Al Newman	.12	U113 Jason Thompson	.12
U15 Bobby Bonilla (RR)	1.00	U48 Moose Haas	.07	U81 Phil Niekro	.35	U114 Milt Thompson	.07
U16 Rich Bordi	.07	U49 Bily Hatcher	.20	U82 Randy Niemann	.07	U115 Rob Thompson	.40
U17 Bill Campbell	.07	U50 Mike Heath	.10	U83 Juan Nieves	.25	U116 Jay Tibbs	.07
U18 Tom Candiotti	.10	U51 Guy Hofman	.07	U84 Bob Ojeda	.20	U117 Fred Toliver	.07
U19 John Cangelosi	.20	U52 Tom Hume	.07	U85 Rick Ownbey	.07	U118 Wayne Tolleson	.07
U20 Jose Canseco (RR)	8.00	U53 Pete Incaviglia (RR)	.75	U86 Tom Paciorek	.07	U119 Alex Trevino	.07
U21 Chuck Cary	.20	U54 Dane Iorg	.07	U87 David Palmer	.07	U120 Manny Trillo	.07
U22 Juan Castillo	.15	U55 Chris James (RR)	.75	U88 Jeff Parrett	.35	U121 Ed Vande Berg	.07
U23 Rick Cerone	.07	U56 Stan Javier	.35	U89 Pat Perry	.20	U122 Ozzie Virgil	.07
U24 John Cerutti	.25	U57 Tommy John	.15	U90 Dan Plesac	.35	U123 Tony Walker	.20
U25 Will Clark (RR)	9.00	U58 Tracy Jones	.35	U91 Darrell Porter	.07	U124 Gene Walter	.15
U26 Marc Clear	.07	U59 Wally Joyner (RR)	2.25	U92 Luis Quinones	.15	U125 Duane Ward	.25
U27 Darnell Coles	.15	U60 Wayne Krenchicki	.07	U93 Rey Quinonez	.20	U126 Jerry Willard	.07
U28 Dave Collins	.07	U61 John Kruk (RR)	.50	U94 Gary Redus	.12	U127 Mitch Williams	.50
U29 Tim Conroy	.07	U62 Mike LaCoss	.07	U95 Jeff Reed	.12	U128 Reggie Williams	.20
U30 Ed Correa	.25	U63 Pete Ladd	.07	U96 Bip Roberts	.20	U129 Bobby Witt (RR)	.60
U31 Joe Cowley	.07	U64 Dave LaPoint	.07	U97 Billy Joe Robidoux	.20	U130 Marvell Wynne	.07
U32 Bill Dawley	.07	U65 Mike LaValliere	.25	U98 Gary Roenicke	.07	U131 Steve Yeager	.10
U33 Rob Deer	.40	U66 Rudy Law	.07	U99 Ron Roenicke	.07	U132 Checklist	.15

1987 Fleer. . . . Complete Set of 660 Cards—Value $90.00

Features the rookie cards of Kevin Mitchell, Will Clark, Bo Jackson and Ruben Sierra. The back of each card features a *Scouting Report*. A high gloss version of the set was issued in a tin box.

NO. PLAYER	MINT	NO. PLAYER	MINT	NO. PLAYER	MINT	NO. PLAYER	MINT
NEW YORK METS		10 Ed Hearn (R)	.15	20 Jesse Orosco	.07	29 Wade Boggs	1.50
1 Rick Aguilera	.15	11 Danny Heep	.05	21 Rafael Santana	.07	30 Oil Can Boyd	.12
2 R. Anderson (R)	.15	12 Keith Hernandez	.25	22 Doug Sisk	.07	31 Bill Buckner	.08
3 Wally Backman	.07	13 Howard Johnson	.35	23 Darryl Strawberry	.75	32 Roger Clemens	1.25
4 Gary Carter	.25	14 Ray Knight	.07	24 Tim Teufel	.07	33 Steve Crawford	.07
5 Ron Darling	.20	15 Lee Mazzilli	.07	25 Mookie Wilson	.07	34 Dwight Evans	.10
6 Len Dykstra	.20	16 Roger McDowell	.15	**BOSTON RED SOX**		35 Rich Gedman	.07
7 Kevin Elster (R)	.75	17 Kevin Mitchell (R)	7.50	26 Toni Armas	.07	36 Dave Henderson	.07
8 Sid Fernandez	.20	18 Randy Niemann	.05	27 Marty Barrett	.12	37 Bruce Hurst	.10
9 Dwight Gooden	1.00	19 Bob Ojeda	.15	28 Don Baylor	.12	38 Tim Lollar	.07

148

NO.	PLAYER	MINT
39	Al Nipper	.07
40	Spike Owen	.07
41	Jim Rice	.30
42	Ed Romero	.07
43	Joe Sambito	.07
44	Calvin Schiraldi	.15
45	Tom Seaver	.30
46	Jeff Sellers (R)	.15
47	Bob Stanley	.07
48	Sammy Stewart	.07

HOUSTON ASTROS

NO.	PLAYER	MINT
49	Larry Andersen	.05
50	Alan Ashby	.05
51	Keven Bass	.05
52	Jeff Calhoun	.05
53	Jose Cruz	.10
54	Danny Darwin	.05
55	Glenn Davis	.35
56	Jim Deshaies (R)	.35
57	Bill Doran	.05
58	Phil Garner	.05
59	Billy Hatcher	.10
60	Charlie Kerfeld	.12
61	Bob Knepper	.08
62	Dave Lopes	.08
63	Aurelio Lopez	.05
64	Jim Pankovits	.05
65	Terry Puhl	.08
66	Craig Reynolds	.08
67	Nolan Ryan	.60
68	Mike Scott	.20
69	Dave Smith	.05
70	Dickie Thon	.05
71	Tony Walker (R)	.15
72	Denny Walling	.05

CALIFORNIA ANGELS

NO.	PLAYER	MINT
73	Bob Boone	.05
74	Rick Burleson	.05
75	John Candelaria	.08
76	Doug Corbett	.05
77	Doug DeCinces	.08
78	Brian Downing	.05
79	Chuck Finley (R)	.50
80	Terry Forster	.05
81	Bobby Grich	.05
82	George Hendrick	.05
83	Jack Howell	.10
84	Reggie Jackson	.35
85	Ruppert Jones	.05
86	Wally Joyner (R)	2.00
87	Gary Lucas	.05
88	Kirk McCaskill	.12
89	Donnie Moore	.05
90	Gary Pettis	.05
91	Vern Ruhle	.05
92	Dick Schofield	.05
93	Don Sutton	.12
94	Rob Wilfong	.05
95	Mike Witt	.12

NEW YORK YANKEES

NO.	PLAYER	MINT
96	Doug Drabek (R)	.40
97	Mike Easler	.07
98	Mike Fischlin	.07
99	Brian Fisher	.07
100	Ron Guidry	.15
101	Rickey Henderson	.40
102	Tommy John	.15
103	Ron Kittle	.10
104	Don Mattingly	2.25
105	Bobby Meacham	.07
106	Joe Niekro	.12
107	Mike Pagliarulo	.15
108	Dan Pasqua	.15
109	Willie Randolph	.10
110	Dennis Rasmussen	.10
111	Dave Righetti	.15
112	Gary Roenicke	.07
113	Rod Scurry	.07
114	Bob Shirley	.07
115	Joel Skinner	.07
116	Tim Stoddard	.07
117	Bob Tewksbury (R)	.15
118	Wayne Tolleson	.07
119	C. Washington	.07
120	Dave Winfield	.30

TEXAS RANGERS

NO.	PLAYER	MINT
121	Steve Buechele	.05
122	Ed Correa (R)	.20
123	Scott Fletcher	.05
124	Joe Guzman	.15
125	Toby Harrah	.05
126	Greg Harris	.05
127	Charlie Hough	.05
128	Pete Incaviglia (R)	1.00
129	Mike Mason	.05
130	Oddibe McDowell	.15
131	Dale Mohorcic (R)	.15
132	Pete O'Brien	.10
133	Tom Paciorek	.05
134	Larry Parrish	.05
135	Geno Petralli	.05
136	Darrell Porter	.05
137	Jeff Russell	.05
138	John Sierra (R)	7.00
139	Don Slaught	.05
140	Gary Ward	.05
141	Curtis Wilkerson	.05
142	Mitch Williams (R)	.75
143	Bobby Witt (R)	.35

DETROIT TIGERS

NO.	PLAYER	MINT
144	Dave Bergman	.05
145	Tom Brookens	.05
146	Bill Campbell	.05
147	Chuck Cary (R)	.25
148	Darnell Coles	.05
149	Dave Collins	.05
150	Darrell Evans	.12
151	Kirk Gibson	.30
152	John Grubb	.05
153	Willie Hernandez	.05
154	Larry Herndon	.05
155	Eric King (R)	.15
156	Chet Lemon	.07
157	Dwight Lowry (R)	.15
158	Jack Morris	.15
159	Randy O'Neal	.05
160	Lance Parrish	.15
161	Dan Petry	.10
162	Pat Sheridan	.05
163	Jim Slaton	.05
164	Frank Tanana	.05
165	Walt Terrell	.05
166	Mark Thurmond	.05
167	Alan Trammell	.20
168	Lou Whitaker	.12

PHILADELPHIA PHILLIES

NO.	PLAYER	MINT
169	Luis Aguayo	.05
170	Steve Bedrosian	.15
171	Don Carman	.05
172	Darren Daulton	.05
173	Greg Gross	.05
175	Von Hayes	.12
176	Charles Hudson	.05
177	Tom Hume	.05
178	Steve Jeltz	.05
179	Mike Maddux (R)	.25
180	Shane Rawley	.05
181	Gary Redus	.05
182	Ron Roenicke	.05
183	Bruce Ruffin (R)	.20
184	John Russell	.05
185	Juan Samuel	.15
186	Dan Schatzeder	.05
187	Mike Schmidt	.60
188	Rick Schu	.05
189	Jeff Stone	.05
190	Kent Tekulve	.05
191	Milt Thompson	.05
192	Glenn Wilson	.05

CINCINNATI REDS

NO.	PLAYER	MINT
193	Buddy Bell	.10
194	Tom Browning	.07
195	Sal Butera	.05
196	Dave Concepcion	.07
197	Kal Daniels	.75
198	Eric Davis	1.50
199	John Denny	.05
200	Bo Diaz	.05
201	Nick Esasky	.05
202	John Franco	.10
203	Bill Gullickson	.05
204	Barry Larkin (R)	3.00
205	Eddie Milner	.05
206	Rob Murphy (R)	.20

NO.	PLAYER	MINT
207	Ron Oester	.05
208	Dave Parker	.15
209	Tony Perez	.12
210	Ted Power	.05
211	Joe Price	.05
212	Ron Robinson	.05
213	Pete Rose (Mgr.)	.50
214	Mario Soto	.05
215	Kurt Stillwell (R)	.40
216	Max Venable	.05
217	Chris Welsh	.05
218	Carl Willis (R)	.15

TORONTO BLUE JAYS

NO.	PLAYER	MINT
219	Jesse Barfield	.15
220	George Bell	.30
221	Bill Caudill	.05
222	John Cerutti (R)	.30
223	Jim Clancy	.05
224	Mark Eichhorn (R)	.25
225	Tony Fernandez	.15
226	Damaso Garcia	.07
227	Kelly Gruber	.05
228	Tom Henke	.10
229	Garth Iorg	.05
230	Joe Johnson	.07
231	Cliff Johnson	.05
232	Jimmy Key	.10
233	Dennis Lamp	.05
234	Rick Leach	.05
235	Buck Martinez	.05
236	Lloyd Moseby	.07
237	Rance Mulliniks	.05
238	Dave Stieb	.10
239	Willie Upshaw	.05
240	Ernie Whitt	.05

CLEVELAND INDIANS

NO.	PLAYER	MINT
241	Andy Allanson (R)	.15
242	Scott Bailes (R)	.15
243	Chris Bando	.05
244	Tony Bernazard	.05
245	John Butcher	.05
246	Brett Butler	.05
247	Ernie Camacho	.05
248	Tom Candiotti	.05
249	Joe Carter	.25
250	Carmen Castillo	.05
251	Julio Franco	.10
252	Mel Hall	.05
253	Brook Jacoby	.05
254	Phil Niekro	.15
255	Otis Nixon	.05
256	Dickie Noles	.05
257	Bryan Oelkers	.05
258	Ken Schrom	.05
259	Don Schulze	.05
260	Cory Snyder	.75
261	Pat Tabler	.10
262	Andre Thornton	.05
263	Rich Yett (R)	.10

SAN FRANCISCO GIANTS

NO.	PLAYER	MINT
264	Mike Aldrete (R)	.30
265	Juan Berenguer	.05
266	Vida Blue	.05
267	Bob Brenly	.05
268	Chris Brown	.15
269	Will Clark (R)	30.00
270	Chili Davis	.10
271	Mark Davis	.05
272	Kelly Downs (R)	.30
273	Scott Garrelts	.05
274	Dan Gladden	.05
275	Mike Krukow	.05
276	Randy Kutcher (R)	.15
277	Mike LaCoss	.05
278	Jeff Leonard	.05
279	Candy Maldonado	.15
280	Roger Mason	.05
281	Bob Melvin	.05
282	Greg Minton	.05
283	Jeff Robinson	.05
284	Harry Spilman	.05
285	Rob Thompson (R)	.35
286	Jose Uribe	.05
287	Frank Williams	.05
288	Joel Youngblood	.05

ST. LOUIS CARDINALS

NO.	PLAYER	MINT
289	Jack Clark	.20
290	Vince Coleman	.40
291	Tim Conroy	.05
292	Danny Cox	.05
293	Ken Dayley	.05
294	Curt Ford	.08
295	Bob Forsch	.05
296	Tom Herr	.05
297	Ricky Horton	.05
298	Clint Hurdle	.05
299	Jeff Lahti	.05
300	Steve Lake	.05
301	Tito Landrum	.05
302	Mike LaValliere (R)	.25
303	Greg Mathews (R)	.25
304	Willie McGee	.15
305	Jose Oquendo	.05
306	Terry Pendleton	.05
307	Pat Perry	.10
308	Ozzie Smith	.20
309	Ray Soff (R)	.15
310	John Tudor	.10
311	Andy Van Slyke	.20
312	Todd Worrell	.25

MONTREAL EXPOS

NO.	PLAYER	MINT
313	Dann Bilardello	.05
314	Hubie Brooks	.10
315	Tim Burke	.05
316	Andre Dawson	.25
317	Mike Fitzgerald	.05
318	Tom Foley	.05
319	Andres Galarraga	.35
320	Joe Hesketh	.05
321	Wallace Johnson	.05
322	Wayne Krenchicki	.05
323	Vance Law	.05
324	Dennis Martinez	.05
325	Bob McClure	.05
326	Andy McGaffigan	.05
327	Al Newman	.15
328	Tim Raines	.30
329	Jeff Reardon	.10
330	Luis Rivera (R)	.15
331	Bob Sebra (R)	.15
332	Bryn Smith	.05
333	Jay Tibbs	.05
334	Tim Wallach	.12
335	Mitch Webster	.12
336	John Wohlford	.05
337	Floyd Youmans	.15

MILWAUKEE BREWERS

NO.	PLAYER	MINT
338	Chris Bosio (R)	.40
339	Glenn Braggs (R)	.50
340	Rick Cerone	.05
341	Mark Clear	.05
342	B. Clutterbuck (R)	.15
343	Cecil Cooper	.15
344	Rob Deer	.35
345	Jim Gantner	.05
346	Ted Higuera	.20
347	J.H. Johnson	.05
348	Tim Leary	.30
349	Rick Manning	.05
350	Paul Molitor	.15
351	Charlie Moore	.05
352	Juan Nieves	.15
353	Ben Oglivie	.05
354	Dan Plesac (R)	.35
355	Ernest Riles	.05
356	Billy Joe Robidoux	.10
357	Bill Schroeder	.05
358	Dale Sveum (R)	.20
359	Gorman Thomas	.10
360	Bill Wegman	.05
361	Robin Yount	.40

KC ROYALS

NO.	PLAYER	MINT
362	Steve Balboni	.07
363	Scott Bankhead	.20
364	Buddy Biancalana	.05
365	Bud Black	.05
366	George Brett	.40
367	Steve Farr	.05
368	Mark Gubicza	.05
369	Bo Jackson (R)	15.00
370	Danny Jackson	.20
371	Mike Kingery (R)	.15
372	Rudy Law	.05
373	Charlie Leibrandt	.05

NO.	PLAYER	MINT
374	Dennis Leonard	.05
375	Hal McRae	.05
376	Jorge Orta	.05
377	Jamie Quirk	.05
378	Dan Quisenberry	.10
379	Bret Saberhagen	.30
380	Angel Salazar	.05
381	Lonnie Smith	.05
382	Jim Sundberg	.05
383	Frank White	.05
384	Willie Wilson	.12

OAKLAND A's

NO.	PLAYER	MINT
385	Joaquin Andujar	.05
386	Doug Bair	.05
387	Dusty Baker	.05
388	Bruce Bochte	.05
389	Jose Canseco	7.50
390	Chris Codiroli	.05
391	Mike Davis	.05
392	Alfredo Griffin	.05
393	Moose Haas	.05
394	Donnie Hill	.05
395	Jay Howell	.05
396	Dave Kingman	.12
397	Carney Lansford	.05
398	David Leiper	.12
399	B. Mooneyham (R)	.15
400	Dwayne Murphy	.05
401	Steve Ontiveros	.05
402	Tony Phillips	.05
403	Eric Plunk	.05
404	Jose Rijo	.05
405	Terry Steinbach (R)	1.00
406	Dave Stewart	.20
407	Mickey Tettleton	.20
408	Dave Von Ohlen	.05
409	Jerry Willard	.05
410	Curt Young	.05

SAN DIEGO PADRES

NO.	PLAYER	MINT
411	Bruce Bochy	.05
412	Dave Dravecky	.05
413	Tim Flannery	.05
414	Steve Garvey	.30
415	Goose Gossage	.12
416	Tony Gwynn	.50
417	Andy Hawkins	.05
418	LaMarr Hoyt	.05
419	Terry Kennedy	.05
420	John Kruk (R)	.50
421	Dave LaPoint	.05
422	Craig Letters	.05
423	Carmelo Martinez	.05
424	Lance McCullers	.12
425	Kevin McReynolds	.30
426	Graig Nettles	.10
427	Bip Roberts (R)	.15
428	Jerry Royster	.05
429	Benito Santiago	.75
430	Eric Show	.07
431	Bob Stoddard	.05
432	Garry Templeton	.05
433	Gene Walter	.10
434	Ed Whitson	.05
435	Marvell Wynne	.05

LA DODGERS

NO.	PLAYER	MINT
436	Dave Anderson	.05
437	Greg Brock	.05
438	Enos Cabell	.05
439	Mariano Duncan	.12
440	Pedro Guerrero	.20
441	Orel Hershiser	.40
442	Rick Honeycutt	.05
443	Ken Howell	.05
444	Ken Landreaux	.05
445	Bill Madlock	.08
446	Mike Marshall	.08
447	Len Matuszek	.05
448	Tom Niedenfuer	.05
449	Alejandro Pena	.05
450	Dennis Powell	.05
451	Jerry Reuss	.05
452	Bill Russell	.05
453	Steve Sax	.12
454	Mike Scioscia	.05
455	Franklin Stubbs	.05
456	Alex Trevino	.05
457	F. Valenzuela	.25
458	Ed Vande Berg	.05

NO.	PLAYER	MINT
459	Bob Welch	.05
460	Reggie Williams (R)	.15

BALTIMORE ORIOLES

NO.	PLAYER	MINT
461	Don Aase	.05
462	Juan Beniquez	.05
463	Mike Boddicker	.05
464	Juan Bonilla	.05
465	Rich Bordi	.05
466	Storm Davis	.05
467	Rick Dempsey	.05
468	Ken Dixon	.05
469	Jim Dwyer	.05
470	Mike Flanagan	.05
471	Jackie Gutierrez	.05
472	Brad Havens	.05
473	Lee Lacy	.05
474	Fred Lynn	.15
475	Scott McGregor	.08
476	Eddie Murray	.30
477	Tom O'Malley	.05
478	Cal Ripken, Jr.	.30
479	Larry Sheets	.10
480	John Shelby	.05
481	Nate Snell	.05
482	Jim Traber	.10
483	Mike Young	.05

CHICAGO WHITE SOX

NO.	PLAYER	MINT
484	Neil Allen	.05
485	Harold Baines	.15
486	Floyd Bannister	.05
487	Daryl Boston	.05
488	Ivan Calderon	.20
489	John Cangelosi (R)	.20
490	Steve Carlton	.25
491	Joe Cowley	.05
492	Julio Cruz	.05
493	Bill Dawley	.05
494	Jose DeLeon	.05
495	Richard Dotson	.05
496	Carlton Fisk	.20
497	Ozzie Guillen	.12
498	Jerry Hairston	.05
499	Ron Hassey	.05
500	Tim Hulett	.05
501	Bob James	.05
502	Steve Lyons	.05
503	Joel McKeon (R)	.15
504	Gene Nelson	.05
505	Dave Schmidt	.05
506	Ray Searage	.05
507	Bobby Thigpen (R)	.30
508	Greg Walker	.05

ATLANTA BRAVES

NO.	PLAYER	MINT
509	Jim Acker	.05
510	Doyle Alexander	.05
511	P. Assenmacher (R)	.15
512	Bruce Benedict	.05
513	Chris Chambliss	.08
514	Jeff Dedmon	.05
515	Gene Garber	.05
516	Ken Griffey	.08
517	Terry Harper	.05
518	Bob Horner	.15
519	Glenn Hubbard	.05
520	Rick Mahler	.05
521	Omar Moreno	.05
522	Dale Murphy	.40
523	Ken Oberkfell	.05
524	Ed Olwine (R)	.15
525	David Palmer	.05
526	Rafael Ramirez	.05
527	Billy Sample	.05
528	Ted Simmons	.05
529	Zane Smith	.05
530	Bruce Sutter	.12
531	Andres Thomas (R)	.25
532	Ozzie Virgil	.05

MINNESOTA TWINS

NO.	PLAYER	MINT
533	A. Anderson (R)	.50
534	Keith Atherton	.05
535	Billy Beane	.05
536	Bert Blyleven	.05
537	Tom Brunansky	.20
538	Randy Bush	.05
539	George Frazier	.05
540	Gary Gaetti	.25
541	Greg Gagne	.05
542	Mickey Hatcher	.05

NO.	PLAYER	MINT
543	Neal Heaton	.05
544	Kent Hrbek	.15
545	Roy Lee Jackson	.05
546	Tim Laudner	.05
547	Steve Lombardozzi	.05
548	Mark Portugal (R)	.25
549	Kirby Puckett	1.00
550	Jeff Reed	.05
551	Mark Salas	.05
552	Roy Smalley	.05
553	Mike Smithson	.05
554	Frank Viola	.20

CHICAGO CUBS

NO.	PLAYER	MINT
555	Thad Bosley	.05
556	Ron Cey	.05
557	Jody Davis	.10
558	Ron Davis	.05
559	Bob Dernier	.05
560	Frank DiPino	.05
561	Shawon Dunston	.07
562	Leon Durham	.10
563	Dennis Eckersley	.05
564	Terry Francona	.05
565	Dave Gumpert	.05
566	Guy Hoffman	.05
567	Ed Lynch	.05
568	Gary Matthews	.05
569	Keith Moreland	.05
570	Jamie Moyer (R)	.20
571	Jerry Mumphrey	.05
572	Ryne Sandberg	.25
573	Scott Sanderson	.05
574	Lee Smith	.05
575	Chris Speier	.05
576	Rick Sutcliffe	.07
577	Manny Trillo	.05
578	Steve Trout	.05

SEATTLE MARINERS

NO.	PLAYER	MINT
579	Karl Best	.05
580	Scott Bradley	.10
581	Phil Bradley	.05
582	Mickey Brantley	.05
583	Mike Brown	.05
584	Alvin Davis	.10
585	L. Guetterman (R)	.20
586	Mark Huismann	.05
587	Bob Kearney	.05
588	Pete Ladd	.05
589	Mark Langston	.25
590	Mike Moore	.05
591	Mike Morgan	.05
592	John Moses	.05
593	Ken Phelps	.05
594	Jim Presley	.20
595	Rey Quinonez (R)	.20
596	Harold Reynolds	.05
597	Billy Swift	.05
598	Danny Tartabull	.40
599	Steve Yeager	.05
600	Matt Young	.05

PITTSBURGH PIRATES

NO.	PLAYER	MINT
601	Bill Almon	.05
602	Rafael Belliard (R)	.15
603	Mike Bielecki (R)	.05
604	Barry Bonds (R)	1.00
605	Bobby Bonilla (R)	1.25
606	Sid Bream	.05
607	Mike Brown	.05
608	Pat Clements	.05
609	Mike Diaz (R)	.15
610	Cecilio Guante	.05
611	Barry Jones (R)	.15
612	Bob Kipper	.05
613	Larry McWilliams	.05
614	Jim Morrison	.05
615	Joe Orsulak	.05
616	Junior Ortiz	.05
617	Tony Pena	.05
618	Johnny Ray	.05
619	Rick Reuschel	.05
620	R.J. Reynolds	.05
621	Rick Rhoden	.05
622	Don Robinson	.05
623	Bob Walk	.05
624	Jim Winn	.05

SPECIAL CARDS

NO.	PLAYER	MINT
625	Youthful Power: P. Incaviglia, J. Canseco	.60

NO.	PLAYER	MINT
626	300 Game Winners: D. Sutton, P. Niekro	.15
627	A.L. Firemen: D. Righetti, D. Asse	.15
628	Rookie All-Stars: W. Joyner, J. Canseco	1.25
629	Magic Mets: G. Carter, S. Fernandez, D. Gooden, K. Hernandez, D. Strawberry	.50
630	N.L. Best Righties: M. Scott, M. Krukow	.15
631	Sensational Southpaws: F. Venezuela, J. Franco	.15
632	4 HR's in Game: Bob Horner	.15
633	Pitcher's Nightmare: J. Canseco, J. Rice, K. Puckett	.60
634	All-Star Battery: G. Carter, R. Clemens	.30
635	4,000 Strikeouts: S. Carlton	.20
636	Big Bats at First Sack: G. Davis, E. Murray	.20
637	On Base: W. Boggs, K. Hernandez	.25
638	Sluggers from Left Side: D. Mattingly, D. Strawberry	1.00
639	Former MVP's: D. Parker, R. Sandberg	.20
640	Dr. K. & Super K: D. Gooden, R. Clemens	.50
641	A.L. West Stoppers: M. Witt, C. Hough	.15
642	Doubles & Triples: J. Samuel, T. Raines	.15
643	Outfielders with Punch: H. Baines, J. Barfield	.15

No. 644 to 653—Major League Prospects

NO.	PLAYER	MINT
644	D. Clark (R) and G. Swindell (R)	2.00
645	Ron Karkovice (R) and Russ Morman (R)	.20
646	Devon White (R) and Willie Fraser (R)	1.25
647	Mike Stanley (R) and Jerry Browne (R)	.40
648	Dave Magadan (R) and Phil Lombardi (R)	.60
649	Jose Gonzalez (R) and Ralph Bryant (R)	.30
650	Jimmy Jones (R) and Randy Asadoor (R)	.25
651	Tracy Jones (R) and Marvin Freeman (R)	.30
652	John Stefero (R) and Kevin Seitzer (R)	5.00
653	Rob Nelson (R) and Steve Fireovid (R)	.25
654	Checklist No. 1	.08
655	Checklist No. 2	.08
656	Checklist No. 3	.08
657	Checklist No. 4	.08
658	Checklist No. 5	.08
659	Checklist No. 6	.08
660	Checklist No. 7	.08

1987 Fleer Traded Update. . . . Complete Set of 132 Cards— Value $16.00

This set updates the main 1987 card set with players who had changed teams during the season, and rookies. This set features Fleer's first card of Ellis Burks, Mike Greenwell, Mark McGwire, and Matt Williams. The set was packaged in a printed box and distributed exclusively through card dealers. A high gloss version of the set was issued in a tin box.

NO. PLAYER	MINT	NO. PLAYER	MINT	NO. PLAYER	MINT	NO. PLAYER	MINT
U1 Scott Bankhead	.07	U34 Ken Gerhart	.15	U67 Mike Loynd	.15	J100 Randy Ready	.07
U2 Eric Bell	.15	U35 Jim Gott	.07	U68 Greg Maddux (RR)	.75	U101 Jeff Reardon	.15
U3 Juan Beniquez	.07	U36 Dan Gladden	.07	U69 Bill Madlock	.07	U102 Gary Redus	.07
U4 Juan Berenguer	.07	U37 Mike Greenwell (RR)	4.00	U70 Dave Magadan	.20	U103 Rick Rhoden	.15
U5 Mike Birkbeck	.20	U38 Cecilio Guante	.07	U71 Joe Magrane (RR)	1.00	U104 Wally Ritchie	.12
U6 Randy Bockus	.12	U39 Albert Hall	.07	U72 Fred Manrique	.15	U105 Jeff Robinson (RR)	.50
U7 Rod Booker	.07	U40 Atlee Hammaker	.07	U73 Mike Mason	.07	U106 Mark Salas	.07
U8 Thad Bosley	.07	U41 Mickey Hatcher	.07	U74 Lloyd McClendon	.25	U107 Dave Schmidt	.07
U9 Greg Brock	.10	U42 Mike Heath	.07	U75 Fred McGriff (RR)	2.50	U108 Kevin Seitzer	1.00
U10 Bob Brower	.15	U43 Neal Heaton	.07	U76 Mark McGwire (RR)	2.50	U109 John Shelby	.07
U11 Chris Brown	.10	U44 Mike Henneman	.30	U77 Mark McLemore	.07	U110 John Smiley (RR)	.40
U12 Jerry Browne	.07	U45 Guy Hoffman	.07	U78 Kevin McReynolds	.30	U111 Lary Sorensen	.07
U13 Ralph Bryant	.07	U46 Charlie Hudson	.07	U79 Dave Meads	.15	U112 Chris Speier	.07
U14 De Wayne Buice	.10	U47 Chuck Jackson	.15	U80 Greg Minton	.12	U113 Randy St. Claire	.07
U15 Ellis Burks (RR)	2.00	U48 Mike Jackson	.25	U81 John Mitchell	.12	U114 Jim Sundberg	.07
U16 Casey Candaele	.15	U49 Reggie Jackson	.35	U82 Kevin Mitchell	2.00	U115 B.J. Surhoff (RR)	.40
U17 Steve Carlton	.30	U50 Chris James	.30	U83 John Morris	.10	U116 Greg Swindell	.50
U18 Juan Castillo	.07	U51 Dian James	.15	U84 Jeff Musselman	.20	U117 Danny Tartabull	.35
U19 Chuck Crim	.15	U52 Stan Javier	.07	U85 Randy Myers (RR)	.50	U118 Dorn Taylor	.10
U20 Mark Davidson	.15	U53 Stan Jefferson	.25	U86 Gene Nelson	.07	U119 Lee Tunnell	.07
U21 Mark Davis	.07	U54 Jimmy Jones	.10	U87 Joe Niekro	.15	U120 Ed Vande Berg	.07
U22 Storm Davis	.15	U55 Tracy Jones	.20	U88 Tom Nieto	.07	U121 Andy Van Slyke	.25
U23 Bill Dawley	.07	U56 Terry Kennedy	.07	U89 Reid Nichols	.07	U122 Gary Ward	.07
U24 Andre Dawson	.35	U57 Mike Kingery	.07	U90 Matt Nokes (RR)	.75	U123 Devon White	.40
U25 Brian Dayett	.07	U58 Ray Knight	.07	U91 Dickie Noles	.07	U124 Alan Wiggins	.07
U26 Rick Dempsay	.07	U59 Gene Larkin	.30	U92 Edwin Nunez	.07	U125 Bill Wilkinson	.12
U27 Ken Dowell	.12	U60 Mike La Valliere	.07	U93 Jose Nunez	.15	U126 Jim Winn	.07
U28 Dave Dravecky	.07	U61 Jack Lazorko	.12	U94 Paul O'Neill	.20	U127 Frank Williams	.07
U29 Mike Dunne (RR)	.30	U62 Terry Leach	.12	U95 Jim Paciorek	.15	U128 Kenny Williams (RR)	.20
U30 Dennis Eckersley	.15	U63 Rick Leach	.07	U96 Lance Parrish	.20	U129 Matt Williams (RR)	2.50
U31 Cecil Fielder	.07	U64 Craig Lefferts	.07	U97 Bill Pecota	.15	U130 Herm Winningham	.07
U32 Brian Fisher	.07	U65 Jim Lindeman (RR)	.15	U98 Tony Pena	.07	U131 Matt Young	.07
U33 Willie Fraser	.07	U66 Bill Long	.20	U99 Luis Polonia	.25	U132 Checklist	.08

1988 Fleer. . . . Complete Set of 660 Cards—Value $40.00

Features the rookie cards of Mark Grace, Gregg Jefferies, Ellis Burks and Matt Williams. A new feature on the back of the card is "At Their Best." It reveals the player's record regarding day/night and home/road games.

NO. PLAYER	MINT	NO. PLAYER	MINT	NO. PLAYER	MINT	NO. PLAYER	MINT
MINNESOTA TWINS		8 Mark Davidson (R)	.15	16 Steve Lombardozzi	.05	24 Les Straker (R)	.20
1 Keith Atherton	.05	9 George Frazier	.05	17 Al Newman	.05	25 Frank Viola	.15
2 Don Baylor	.08	10 Gary Gaetti	.15	18 Joe Niekro	.08	**ST. LOUIS CARDINALS**	
3 Juan Berenguer	.05	11 Greg Gagne	.05	19 Kirby Puckett	.40	26 Jk. Clark	.25
4 Bert Blyleven	.10	12 Dan Gladden	.05	20 Jeff Reardon	.05	27 Vince Coleman	.20
5 Tom Brunansky	.15	13 Kent Hrbek	.15	21 Dan Schatzader	.05	28 Danny Cox	.05
6 Randy Bush	.05	14 Gene Larkin (R)	.30	22 Roy Smalley	.05	29 Bill Dawley	.05
7 Steve Carlton	.20	15 Tim Laudner	.05	23 Mike Smithson	.05	30 Ken Dayley	.05

NO.	PLAYER	MINT
31	Doug DeCinces	.05
32	Curt Ford	.05
33	Bob Forsch	.05
34	David Green	.05
35	Tom Herr	.05
36	Ricky Horton	.05
37	Lance Johnson (R)	.25
38	Steve Lake	.05
39	Jim Lindeman	.12
40	Joe Magrane (R)	.75
41	Greg Mathews	.05
42	Willie McGee	.15
43	John Morris	.12
44	Jose Oquendo	.05
45	Tony Pena	.05
46	Terry Pendleton	.05
47	Ozzie Smith	.15
48	John Tudor	.10
49	Lee Tunnell	.05
50	Todd Worrell	.10

DETROIT TIGERS

NO.	PLAYER	MINT
51	Doyle Alexander	.05
52	Dave Bergman	.05
53	Tom Brookens	.05
54	Darrell Evans	.05
55	Kirk Gibson	.20
56	Mike Heath	.05
57	Mike Henneman (R)	.25
58	Willie Hernandez	.10
59	Larry Herndon	.05
60	Eric King	.05
61	Chet Lemon	.05
62	Scott Lusader (R)	.20
63	Bill Madlock	.15
64	Jack Morris	.15
65	Jim Morrison	.05
66	Matt Nokes (R)	.50
67	Dan Petry	.05
68	Jeff Robinson (R)	.40
68	J. Robinson (error)	1.25
69	Pat Sheridan	.05
70	Nate Snell	.05
71	Frank Tanana	.05
72	Walt Terrell	.05
73	Mark Thurmond	.05
74	Alan Trammell	.15
75	Lou Whitaker	.20

SAN FRANCISCO GIANTS

NO.	PLAYER	MINT
76	Mike Aldrete	.05
77	Bob Brenly	.05
78	Will Clark	2.00
79	Chili Davis	.10
80	Kelly Downs	.05
81	Dave Dravecky	.05
82	Scott Garrelts	.05
83	Atlee Hammaker	.05
84	Dave Henderson	.05
85	Mike Krukow	.05
86	Mike LaCoss	.05
87	Craig Lefferts	.05
88	Jeff Leonard	.10
89	Candy Maldonado	.10
90	Bob Melvin	.05
91	Ed Milner	.05
92	Kevin Mitchell	1.00
93	Jon Perlman (R)	.12
94	Rick Reuschel	.05
95	Don Robinson	.05
96	Chris Speier	.05
97	Harry Spilman	.05
98	Robbie Thompson	.05
99	Jose Uribe	.05
100	Mark Wasinger (R)	.25
101	Matt Williams (R)	2.00

TORONTO BLUE JAYS

NO.	PLAYER	MINT
102	Jesse Barfield	.15
103	George Bell	.25
104	Juan Beniquez	.05
105	John Cerutti	.05
106	Jim Clancy	.05
107	Rob Ducey (R)	.20
108	Mark Eichhorn	.05
109	Tony Fernandez	.12
110	Cecil Fielder	.05
111	Kelly Gruber	.05
112	Tom Henke	.05
113	Garth Iorg	.05
114	Jimmy Key	.10
115	Rick Leach	.05
116	Manny Lee	.08
117	Nelson Liriano (R)	.30
118	Fred McGriff	1.50
119	Lloyd Moseby	.10
120	Rance Mulliniks	.05
121	Jeff Musselman	.12
122	Jose Nunez	.25
123	Dave Stieb	.05
124	Willie Upshaw	.05
125	Duane Ward	.08
126	Ernie Whitt	.05

NEW YORK METS

NO.	PLAYER	MINT
127	Rick Aguilera	.05
128	Wally Backman	.05
129	Mark Carreon (R)	.20
130	Gary Carter	.20
131	David Cone	1.25
132	Ron Darling	.15
133	Len Dykstra	.15
134	Sid Fernandez	.08
135	Dwight Gooden	.60
136	Keith Hernandez	.20
137	Gregg Jefferies (R)	5.00
138	Howard Johnson	.35
139	Terry Leach	.05
140	Barry Lyons (R)	.25
141	Dave Magadan	.15
142	Roger McDowell	.05
143	Kevin McReynolds	.15
144	Keith Miller (R)	.25
145	John Mitchell (R)	.20
146	Randy Myers	.25
147	Bob Ojeda	.10
148	Jesse Orosco	.05
149	Rafael Santana	.05
150	Doug Sisk	.05
151	Darryl Strawberry	.60
152	Tim Teufel	.05
153	Gene Walter	.05
154	Mookie Wilson	.08

MILWAUKEE BREWERS

NO.	PLAYER	MINT
155	Jay Aldrich (R)	.15
156	Chris Bosio	.05
157	Glenn Braggs	.10
158	Greg Brock	.05
159	Juan Castillo	.08
160	Mark Clear	.05
161	Cecil Cooper	.08
162	Chuck Crim (R)	.15
163	Rob Deer	.10
164	Mike Felder	.05
165	Jim Gantner	.05
166	Ted Higuera	.12
167	Steve Kiefer	.05
168	Rick Manning	.05
169	Paul Molitor	.15
170	Juan Nieves	.10
171	Dan Plesac	.05
172	Earnest Riles	.05
173	Bill Schroeder	.05
174	Steve Stanicek (R)	.20
175	B.J. Surhoff	.20
176	Dale Sveum	.08
177	Bill Wegman	.05
178	Robin Yount	.25

MONTREAL EXPOS

NO.	PLAYER	MINT
179	Hubie Brooks	.10
180	Tim Burke	.05
181	Casey Candaele	.10
182	Mike Fitzgerald	.05
183	Tom Foley	.05
184	Andres Galarraga	.30
185	Neal Heaton	.05
186	Wallace Johnson	.05
187	Vance Law	.05
188	Dennis Martinez	.08
189	Bob McClure	.05
190	Andy McGaffigan	.05
191	Reid Nichols	.05
192	Pascual Perez	.05
193	Tim Raines	.20
194	Jeff Reed	.05
195	Bob Sebra	.05
196	Bryn Smith	.05
197	Randy St. Claire	.05
198	Tim Wallach	.10
199	Mitch Webster	.05
200	Herm Winningham	.05
201	Floyd Youmans	.08

N.Y. YANKEES

NO.	PLAYER	MINT
202	Brad Arnsberg (R)	.15
203	Rick Cerone	.05
204	Pat Clements	.05
205	Henry Cotto	.05
206	Mike Easler	.05
207	Ron Guidry	.10
208	Bill Gullickson	.05
209	Rickey Henderson	.35
210	Charles Hudson	.05
211	Tommy John	.10
212	Roberto Kelly (R)	.75
213	Ron Kittle	.08
214	Don Mattingly	1.50
215	Bobby Meacham	.05
216	Mike Pagliarulo	.15
217	Dan Pasqua	.10
218	Willie Randolph	.12
219	Rick Rhoden	.05
220	Dave Righetti	.10
221	Jerry Royster	.05
222	Tim Stoddard	.05
223	Wayne Tolleson	.05
224	Gary Ward	.05
225	Claudell Washington	.05
226	Dave Winfield	.20

CINCINNATI REDS

NO.	PLAYER	MINT
227	Buddy Bell	.15
228	Tom Browning	.05
229	Dave Concepcion	.05
230	Kal Daniels	.25
231	Eric Davis	.75
232	Bo Diaz	.05
233	Nick Esasky	.05
234	John Franco	.08
235	Guy Hoffman	.05
236	Tom Hume	.05
237	Tracy Jones	.10
238	Bill Landrum (R)	.20
239	Barry Larkin	.30
240	Terry McGriff	.12
241	Rob Murphy	.05
242	Ron Oester	.05
243	Dave Parker	.15
244	Pat Perry	.05
245	Ted Power	.05
246	Dennis Rasmussen	.05
247	Ron Robinson	.05
248	Kurt Stillwell	.08
249	Jeff Treadway (R)	.40
250	Frank Williams	.05

K.C. ROYALS

NO.	PLAYER	MINT
251	Steve Balboni	.05
252	Bud Black	.05
253	Thad Bosley	.05
254	George Brett	.35
255	John Davis (R)	.25
256	Steve Farr	.05
257	Gene Garber	.05
258	Jerry Gleaton	.05
259	Mark Gubicza	.05
260	Bo Jackson	1.50
261	Danny Jackson	.10
262	Ross Jones (R)	.12
263	Charlie Leibrandt	.05
264	Bill Pecota (R)	.15
265	Melido Perez (R)	.25
266	Jamie Quirk	.05
267	Dan Quisenberry	.10
268	Bret Saberhagen	.20
269	Angel Salazar	.05
270	Kevin Seitzer	.50
271	Danny Tartabull	.25
272	Gary Thurman (R)	.30
273	Frank White	.05
274	Willie Wilson	.10

OAKLAND A'S

NO.	PLAYER	MINT
275	Tony Bernazard	.05
276	Jose Canseco	2.00
277	Mike Davis	.05
278	Storm Davis	.05
279	Dennis Eckersley	.05
280	Alfredo Griffin	.05
281	Rick Honeycutt	.05
282	Jay Howell	.05
283	Reggie Jackson	.30
284	Dennis Lamp	.05
285	Carney Lansford	.05
286	Mark McGwire	2.00
287	Dwayne Murphy	.05
288	Gene Nelson	.05
289	Steve Ontiveros	.05
290	Tony Philips	.05
291	Eric Plunk	.05
292	Luis Polonia (R)	.20
293	Rick Rodriguez (R)	.15
294	Terry Steinbach	.10
295	Dave Stewart	.15
296	Curt Young	.05

PHILADELPHIA PHILLIES

NO.	PLAYER	MINT
297	Luis Aguayo	.05
298	Steve Bedrosian	.05
299	Jeff Calhoun	.05
300	Don Carman	.05
301	Todd Frohwirth (R)	.20
302	Greg Gross	.05
303	Kevin Gross	.05
304	Von Hayes	.05
305	Keith Hughes (R)	.20
306	Mike Jackson (R)	.15
307	Chris James	.15
308	Steve Jeltz	.05
309	Mike Maddux	.05
310	Lance Parrish	.12
311	Shane Rawley	.05
312	Wally Ritchie (R)	.15
313	Bruce Ruffin	.05
314	Juan Samuel	.10
315	Mike Schmidt	.35
316	Rick Schu	.05
317	Jeff Stone	.05
318	Kent Tekulve	.05
319	Milt Thompson	.05
320	Glenn Wilson	.08

PITTSBURGH PIRATES

NO.	PLAYER	MINT
321	Rafael Belliard	.05
322	Barry Bonds	.25
323	Bobby Bonilla	.20
324	Sid Bream	.05
325	John Cangelosi	.05
326	Mike Diaz	.05
327	Doug Drabek	.05
328	Mike Dunne	.25
329	Brian Fisher	.05
330	Brett Gideon (R)	.15
331	Terry Harper	.05
332	Bob Kipper	.05
333	Mike LaValliere	.05
334	Jose Lind (R)	.25
335	Junior Ortiz	.05
336	Vincente Palacios (R)	.20
337	Bob Patterson (R)	.15
338	Al Pedrique (R)	.15
339	R.J. Reynolds	.05
340	John Smiley (R)	.25
341	Andy Van Slyke	.15
342	Bob Walk	.05

BOSTON RED SOX

NO.	PLAYER	MINT
343	Marty Barrett	.10
344	Todd Benzinger (R)	.50
345	Wade Boggs	1.00
346	Tom Bolton (R)	.15
347	Oil Can Boyd	.05
348	Ellis Burks (R)	1.50
349	Roger Clemens	.75
350	Steve Crawford	.15
351	Dwight Evans	.10
352	Wes Gardner (R)	.25
353	Rich Gedman	.05
354	Mike Greenwell	2.00
355	Sam Horn (R)	.30
356	Bruce Hurst	.10
357	John Marzano	.20
358	Al Nipper	.05
359	Spike Owen	.05
360	Jody Reed (R)	.40
361	Jim Rice	.20
362	Ed Romero	.05
363	Kevin Romine	.10
364	Joe Sambito	.05
365	Calvin Schiraldi	.05

NO.	PLAYER	MINT
366	Jeff Sellers	.05
367	Bob Stanley	.05

SEATTLE MARINERS

NO.	PLAYER	MINT
368	Scott Bankhead	.05
369	Phil Bradley	.08
370	Scott Bradley	.05
371	Mickey Brantley	.10
372	Mike Campbell (R)	.25
373	Alvin Davis	.08
374	Lee Guetterman	.05
375	Dave Hengel (R)	.20
376	Mike Kingery	.05
377	Mark Langston	.08
378	Edgar Martinez (R)	.25
379	Mike Moore	.05
380	Mike Morgan	.05
381	John Moses	.05
382	Donnell Nixon (R)	.15
383	Edwin Nunez	.05
384	Ken Phelps	.05
385	Jim Presley	.05
386	Rey Quinones	.05
387	Jerry Reed	.05
388	Harold Reynolds	.05
389	Dave Valle	.08
390	Bill Wilkinson (R)	.15

CHICAGO WHITE SOX

NO.	PLAYER	MINT
391	Harold Baines	.10
392	Floyd Bannister	.05
393	Daryl Boston	.05
394	Ivan Calderon	.05
395	Jose DeLeon	.05
396	Richard Dotson	.05
397	Carlton Fisk	.15
398	Ozzie Guillen	.05
399	Ron Hassey	.05
400	Donnie Hill	.05
401	Bob James	.05
402	Dave LaPoint	.05
403	Bill Lindsey (R)	.15
404	Bill Long (R)	.20
405	Steve Lyons	.05
406	Fred Manrique (R)	.15
407	Jack McDowell (R)	.30
408	Gary Redus	.05
409	Ray Searage	.05
410	Bobby Thigpen	.05
411	Greg Walker	.05
412	Kenny Williams (R)	.20
413	Jim Winn	.05

CHICAGO CUBS

NO.	PLAYER	MINT
414	Jody Davis	.05
415	Andre Dawson	.25
416	Brian Dayett	.05
417	Bob Dernier	.05
418	Frank DiPino	.05
419	Shawon Dunston	.05
420	Leon Durham	.10
421	Les Lancaster (R)	.20
422	Ed Lynch	.05
423	Greg Maddux	.60
424	Dave Martinez	.15
425	K. Moreland (error)	3.50
	(photo of Jody Davis)	
425	K. Moreland (correct)	.25
426	Jamie Moyer	.05
427	Jerry Mumphrey	.05
428	Paul Noce (R)	.20
429	Rafael Palmeiro	.75
430	Wade Rowdon	.10
431	Ryne Sandberg	.20
432	Scott Sanderson	.05
433	Lee Smith	.10
434	Jim Sundberg	.05
435	Rick Sutcliffe	.10
436	Manny Trillo	.05

HOUSTON ASTROS

NO.	PLAYER	MINT
437	Juan Agosto	.05
438	Larry Andersen	.05
439	Alan Ashby	.05
440	Kevin Bass	.05
441	Ken Caminiti (R)	.30
442	Rocky Childress (R)	.15
443	Jose Cruz	.05
444	Danny Darwin	.05
445	Glenn Davis	.15
446	Jim Deshaies	.05

NO.	PLAYER	MINT
447	Bill Doran	.05
448	Ty Gainey	.05
449	Billy Hatcher	.10
450	Jeff Heathcock	.05
451	Bob Knepper	.05
452	Rob Mallicoat (R)	.15
453	Dave Meads (R)	.15
454	Craig Reynolds	.05
455	Nolan Ryan	.45
456	Mike Scott	.15
457	Dave Smith	.05
458	Denny Walling	.05
459	Robbie Wine (R)	.20
460	Gerald Young (R)	.35

TEXAS RANGERS

NO.	PLAYER	MINT
461	Bob Brower	.10
462	J. Browne (error)	3.50
	(photo of Bob Brower)	
462	J. Browne (correct)	.25
463	Steve Buechele	.05
464	Edwin Correa	.05
465	Cecil Espy (R)	.20
466	Scott Fletcher	.05
467	Jose Guzman	.05
468	Greg Harris	.05
469	Charlie Hough	.05
470	Pete Incaviglia	.15
471	Mike Kilgus (R)	.20
472	Mike Loynd	.08
473	Oddibe McDowell	.10
474	Dale Mohorcic	.05
475	Pete O'Brien	.10
476	Larry Parrish	.05
477	Geno Petralli	.05
478	Jeff Russell	.05
479	Ruben Sierra	.60
480	Mike Stanley	.05
481	Curtis Wilkerson	.05
482	Mitch Williams	.05
483	Bobby Witt	.05

CALIFORNIA ANGELS

NO.	PLAYER	MINT
484	Tony Armas	.05
485	Bob Boone	.05
486	Bill Buckner	.05
487	DeWayne Buice (R)	.15
488	Brian Downing	.05
489	Chuck Finley	.05
490	Willie Fraser	.05
491	Jack Howell	.05
492	Ruppert Jones	.05
493	Wally Joyner	.50
494	Jack Lazorko	.10
495	Gary Lucas	.05
496	Kirk McCaskill	.05
497	Mark McLemore	.05
498	Darrell Miller	.05
499	Greg Minton	.05
500	Donnie Moore	.05
501	Gus Polidor	.05
502	Johnny Ray	.05
503	Mark Ryal	.05
504	Dick Schofield	.05
505	Don Sutton	.15
506	Devon White	.20
507	Mike Witt	.10

LOS ANGELES DODGERS

NO.	PLAYER	MINT
508	Dave Anderson	.05
509	Tim Belcher	.50
510	Ralph Bryant	.05
511	Tim Crews (R)	.15
512	Mike Devereaux (R)	.30
513	Mariano Duncan	.05
514	Pedro Guerrero	.20
515	Jeff Hamilton	.15
516	Mickey Hatcher	.05
517	Brad Havens	.05
518	Orel Hershiser	.30
519	Shawn Hillegas (R)	.20
520	Ken Howell	.05
521	Tim Leary	.05
522	Mike Marshall	.10
523	Steve Sax	.15
524	Mike Scioscia	.05
525	Mike Sharperson	.05
526	John Shelby	.05
527	Franklin Stubbs	.05

NO.	PLAYER	MINT
528	Fernando Valenzuela	.20
529	Bob Welch	.05
530	Matt Young	.05

ATLANTA BRAVES

NO.	PLAYER	MINT
531	Jim Acker	.05
532	Paul Assenmacher	.05
533	Jeff Blauser (R)	.30
534	Joe Boever (R)	.20
535	Martin Clary	.05
536	Kevin Coffman	.15
537	Jeff Dedmon	.05
538	Ron Gant (R)	.75
539	Tom Glavine (R)	.35
540	Ken Griffey	.05
541	Al Hall	.05
542	Glenn Hubbard	.05
543	Dion James	.05
544	Dale Murphy	.35
545	Ken Oberkfell	.05
546	David Palmer	.05
547	Gerald Perry	.15
548	Charlie Puleo	.05
549	Ted Simmons	.05
550	Zane Smith	.05
551	Andres Thomas	.05
552	Ozzie Virgil	.05

BALTIMORE ORIOLES

NO.	PLAYER	MINT
553	Don Aase	.05
554	Jeff Ballard (R)	.35
555	Eric Bell	.05
556	Mike Boddicker	.05
557	Ken Dixon	.05
558	Jim Dwyer	.05
559	Ken Gehart	.05
560	Rene Gonzales (R)	.15
561	Mike Griffin	.05
562	John Hayban	.10
563	Terry Kennedy	.05
564	Ray Knight	.05
565	Lee Lacy	.05
566	Fred Lynn	.15
567	Eddie Murray	.25
568	Tom Niedenfuer	.05
569	Bill Ripken (R)	.25
570	Cal Ripken, Jr.	.25
571	Dave Schmidt	.05
572	Larry Sheets	.10
573	Pete Stanicek (R)	.25
574	Mark Williamson (R)	.15
575	Mike Young	.05

SAN DIEGO PADRES

NO.	PLAYER	MINT
576	Shawn Abner	.20
577	Greg Booker	.05
578	Chris Brown	.10
579	Keith Comstock (R)	.20
580	Joey Cora (R)	.15
581	Mark Davis	.05
582	Tim Flannery	.05
583	Goose Gossage	.10
584	Mark Grant	.05
585	Tony Gwynn	.30
586	Andy Hawkins	.05
587	Stan Jefferson	.15
588	Jimmy Jones	.05
589	John Kruk	.20
590	Shane Mack	.20
591	Carmelo Martinez	.05
592	Lance McCullers	.05
593	Eric Nolte (R)	.15
594	Randy Ready	.05
595	Luis Salazar	.05
596	Benito Santiago	.40
597	Eric Show	.05
598	Garry Templeton	.05
599	Ed Whitson	.05

CLEVELAND INDIANS

NO.	PLAYER	MINT
600	Scott Bailes	.05
601	Chris Bando	.05
602	Jay Bell (R)	.20
603	Brett Butler	.05
604	Tom Candiotti	.10
605	Joe Carter	.15
606	Carmen Castillo	.05
607	Brian Dorsett (R)	.15
608	John Farrell (R)	.25
609	Julio Franco	.10

NO.	PLAYER	MINT
610	Mel Hall	.05
611	Tommy Hinzo (R)	.15
612	Brook Jacoby	.10
613	Doug Jones (R)	.35
614	Ken Schrom	.05
615	Cory Snyder	.20
616	Sammy Stewart	.05
617	Greg Swindell	.15
618	Pat Tabler	.05
619	Ed Vande Berg	.05
620	Eddie Williams (R)	.20
621	Rich Yett	.05

SPECIAL CARDS

NO.	PLAYER	MINT
622	Slugging Sophomores	.25
623	Dominican Dynamite	.10
624	Oakland's Power Team	.75
625	Classic Relief	.10
626	All Star Righties	.10
627	Game Closers	.10
628	Masters of Double Play	.10
629	Rookie Record Setter	.50
630	Changing the Guard	.60
631	N.L. Batting Champs	.25
632	Pitching Magic	.10
633	Big Bats At First	.30
634	Hitting King and Thief	.20
635	Slugging Shortstop	.10
636	Tried and True Sluggers	.20
637	Crunch Time	.30
638	A.L. All Stars	.20
639	N.L. All-Stars	.15
640	The "O's" Brothers	.10

No. 641 to 653— Major League Prospects

NO.	PLAYER	MINT
641	Mark Grace (R) and Darrin Jackson (R)	5.00
642	Damon Berryhill (R) and Jeff Montgomery (R)	1.00
643	Felix Fermin (R) and Jessie Reid (R)	.20
644	Greg Myers (R) and Greg Tabor (R)	.20
645	Joey Meyer and Jim Eppard (R)	.25
646	Adam Peterson (R) and Randy Velarde (R)	.25
647	Peter Smith (R) and Chris Gwynn (R)	.40
648	Tom Newell (R) and Greg Jelks (R)	.25
649	Mario Diaz (R) and Clay Parker (R)	.30
650	Jack Savage (R) and Todd Simmons (R)	.25
651	John Burkett (R) and Kirt Manwaring (R)	.30
652	Dave Otto (R) and Walt Weiss (R)	1.50
653	Jeff King (R) and Randell Byers (R)	.30
654	Checklist No. 1	.08
655	Checklist No. 2	.08
656	Checklist No. 3	.08
657	Checklist No. 4	.08
658	Checklist No. 5	.08
659	Checklist No. 6	.08
660	Checklist No. 7	.08

1988 Fleer Traded Update.... Complete Set of 132 Cards— Value $13.00

This set updates the main 1988 card set with players who had changed teams during the season, and rookies. This set features Fleer's first card of Chris Sabo and Ricky Jordan. This set was packaged in a printed box and distributed primarily through card dealers. For the first time Fleer arranged the cards of its update set in alphabetical order, by team.

NO. PLAYER	MINT	NO. PLAYER	MINT	NO. PLAYER	MINT	NO. PLAYER	MINT
U1 Jose Bautista	.12	U34 Israel Sanchez	.12	U67 Mike Flanagan	.07	U100 Brian Holman	.20
U2 Jose Orsulak	.10	U35 Kurt Stillwelll	.07	U68 Todd Stottlemyre	.20	U101 Rex Hudler	.15
U3 Doug Sisk	.07	U36 Pat Tabler	.07	U69 David Wells	.15	U102 Jeff Parrett	.07
U4 Craig Worthington	.50	U37 Don August	.15	U70 Jose Alvarez	.20	U103 Nelson Santovenia	.30
U5 Mike Boddiker	.07	U38 Darryl Hamilton	.20	U71 Paul Runge	.07	U104 Kevin Elster	.15
U6 Rick Cerone	.07	U39 Jeff Leonard	.07	U72 Cesar Jimenez	.15	U105 Jeff Innis	.20
U7 Larry Parrish	.07	U40 Joey Meyer	.30	U73 Pete Smith	.15	U106 Mackey Sasser	.25
U8 Lee Smith	.07	U41 Allan Anderson	.07	U74 John Smoltz	1.25	U107 Phil Bradley	.07
U9 Mike Smithson	.07	U42 Brian Harper	.07	U75 Damon Berryhill	.25	U108 Danny Clay	.12
U10 John Trautwein	.12	U43 Tom Herr	.07	U76 Goose Gossage	.07	U109 Greg Harris	.07
U11 Sherman Corbett	.15	U44 Charlie Lea	.07	U77 Mark Grace	3.00	U110 Ricky Jordan (RR)	2.50
U12 Chili Davis	.10	U45 John Moses	.07	U78 Darrin Jackson	.25	U111 David Palmer	.07
U13 Jim Eppard	.15	U46 John Candelaria	.10	U79 Vance Law	.07	U112 Jim Gott	.07
U14 Bryan Harvey	.35	U47 Jack Clark	.12	U80 Jeff Pico	.15	U113 Tommy Gregg	.25
U15 John Davis	.07	U48 Richard Dotson	.07	U81 Gary Varsho	.20	U114 Barry Jones	.07
U16 Dave Gallagher	.30	U49 Al Leiter	.40	U82 Tim Birtsas	.07	U115 Randy Miligan	.25
U17 Ricky Horton	.07	U50 Rafael Santana	.07	U83 Rob Dibble	.50	U116 Luis Alicea	.15
U18 Dan Pasqua	.07	U51 Dons Slaught	.07	U84 Danny Jackson	.20	U117 Tom Brunansky	.15
U19 Melido Perez	.07	U52 Todd Burns	.35	U85 Paul O'Neill	.07	U118 John Costello	.20
U20 Jose Segura	.12	U53 Dave Henderson	.07	U86 Jose Rijo	.07	U119 Jose DeLeon	.07
U21 Andy Allanson	.07	U54 Doug Jennings	.20	U87 Chris Sabo (RR)	1.00	U120 Bob Horner	.07
U22 John Perlman	.07	U55 Dave Parker	.20	U88 John Fishel	.25	U121 Scott Terry	.20
U23 Domingo Ramos	.07	U56 Walt Weiss	.60	U89 Craig Biggio	.75	U122 Roberto Alomar (RR)	.50
U24 Rick Rodriquez	.07	U57 Bob Welch	.07	U90 Terry Puhl	.07	U123 Dave Leiper	.07
U25 Willie Upshaw	.10	U58 Henry Cotto	.07	U91 Rafael Ramirez	.07	U124 Keith Moreland	.07
U26 Phil Gibson	.12	U59 Mario Diaz	.07	U92 Louie Meadows	.15	U125 Mark Parent	.20
U27 Don Heinkel	.15	U60 Mike Jackson	.07	U93 Kirk Gibson	.25	U126 Dennis Rasmussen	.07
U28 Ray Knight	.07	U61 Bill Swift	.07	U94 Alfredo Griffin	.07	U127 Randy Bockus	.07
U29 Gary Pettis	.07	U62 Jose Cecena	.12	U95 Jay Howell	.12	U128 Brett Butler	.07
U30 Luis Salazar	.07	U63 Ray Haywad	.15	U96 Jesse Orosco	.07	U129 Donnell Nixon	.07
U31 Mike MacFarlane	.15	U64 Jim Steels	.12	U97 Alejandro Pena	.07	U130 Ernest Riles	.07
U32 Jeff Montgomery	.15	U65 Pat Borders	.15	U98 Tracy Woodson	.25	U131 Roger Samuels	.15
U33 Ted Power	.07	U66 Sil Campusano	.25	U99 John Dopson	.25	U132 Checklist	.07

1989 Fleer.... Complete Set of 660 Cards—Value $35.00

Features the rookie cards of Gary Sheffield, Tom Gordon, Sandy Alomar, Jr. and Ken Griffey, Jr. A new feature on the back is a comparison of each player's statistics before and after the All-Star break.

NO. PLAYER	MINT	NO. PLAYER	MINT	NO. PLAYER	MINT	NO. PLAYER	MINT
OAKLAND A'S		8 Mike Gallego	.05	16 Carney Lansford	.08	24 Walt Weiss	.30
1 Don Baylor	.08	9 Ron Hassey	.05	17 Mark McGwire	.60	25 Bob Welch	.08
2 Lance Blankenship (R)	.25	10 Dave Henderson	.05	18 Gene Nelson	.05	26 Curt Young	.05
3 Todd Burns (R)	.35	11 Rick Honeycutt	.05	19 Dave Parker	.10	**NEW YORK METS**	
4 Greg Cadaret	.05	12 Glenn Hubbard	.05	20 Eric Plunk	.05	27 Rick Aguilera	.05
5 Jose Canseco	1.25	13 Stan Javier	.05	21 Luis Polonia	.05	28 Wally Backman	.05
6 Storm Davis	.05	14 Doug Jennings (R)	.25	22 Terry Steinbach	.15	29 Mark Carreon	.05
7 Dennis Eckersley	.12	15 Felix Jose (R)	.30	23 Dave Stewart	.10	30 Gary Carter	.20

154

NO.	PLAYER	MINT
31	Dave Cone	.30
32	Ron Darling	.10
33	Len Dykstra	.20
34	Kevin Elster	.08
35	Sid Fernandez	.10
36	Dwight Gooden	.30
37	Keith Hernandez	.20
38	Gregg Jefferies	1.50
39	Howard Johnson	.20
40	Terry Leach	.05
41	Dave Magadan	.10
42	Bob McClure	.05
43	Roger McDowell	.05
44	Kevin McReynolds	.20
45	Keith Miller	.05
46	Randy Myers	.08
47	Bob Ojeda	.08
48	Mackey Sasser	.10
49	Darryl Strawberry	.50
50	Tim Teufel	.05
51	Dave West (R)	.35
52	Mookie Wilson	.08

LOS ANGELES DODGERS

NO.	PLAYER	MINT
53	Dave Anderson	.05
54	Tim Belcher	.15
55	Mike Davis	.05
56	Mike Devereaux	.20
57	Kirk Gibson	.20
58	Alfredo Griffin	.05
59	Chris Gwynn	.10
60	Jeff Hamilton	.05
61	Danny Heep	.15
62	Orel Hershiser	.30
63	Brian Holton	.05
64	Jay Howell	.08
65	Tim Leary	.10
66	Mike Marshall	.08
67	Ramon Martinez (R)	.45
68	Jess Orosco	.05
69	Alejandro Pena	.08
70	Steve Sax	.12
71	Mike Scioscia	.05
72	Mike Sharperson	.05
73	John Shelby	.05
74	Fanklin Stubbs	.05
75	John Tudor	.05
76	Fernando Velenzuela	.12
77	Tracy Woodson	.10

BOSTON RED SOX

NO.	PLAYER	MINT
78	Marty Barrett	.05
79	Todd Benzinger	.15
80	Mike Boddicker	.08
81	Wade Boggs	.60
82	"Oil Can" Boyd	.08
83	Ellis Burks	.40
84	Rick Cerone	.05
85	Roger Clemens	.35
86	Steve Curry (R)	.20
87	Dwight Evans	.15
88	Wes Gardner	.05
89	Rich Gedman	.05
90	Mike Greenwell	1.00
91	Bruce Hurst	.15
92	Dennis Lamp	.05
93	Spike Owen	.05
94	Larry Parrish	.10
95	Carlos Quintana (R)	.40
96	Jody Reed	.15
97	Jim Rice	.15
98	Kevin Romine	.50
98	K. Romine (error)	1.00
99	Lee Smith	.08
100	Mike Smithson	.05
101	Bob Stanley	.05

MINNESOTA TWINS

NO.	PLAYER	MINT
102	Allan Anderson	.08
103	Keith Atherton	.05
104	Juan Berenguer	.05
105	Bert Blyleven	.15
106	Eric Bullock	.15
107	Randy Bush	.05
108	John Christensen	.05
109	Mark Davidson	.05
110	Gary Gaetti	.10
111	Greg Gagne	.05
112	Dan Gladden	.05
113	German Gonzalez (R)	.15
114	Brian Harper	.05
115	Tom Herr	.05

NO.	PLAYER	MINT
116	Kent Hrbek	.15
117	Gene Larken	.05
118	Tim Laudner	.05
119	Charlie Lea	.05
120	Steve Lombardozzi	.05
121	J. Moses (Phoenix)	.25
121	J. Moses (Tempe)	1.00
122	Al Newman	.05
123	Mark Portugal	.05
124	Kirby Puckett	.30
125	Jeff Reardon	.08
126	Fred Toliver	.05
127	Frank Viola	.15

DETROIT TIGERS

NO.	PLAYER	MINT
128	Doyle Alexander	.05
129	Dave Bergman	.05
130	Tom Brookens	.25
130	T. Brookens (error)	2.50
131	Paul Gibson (R)	.15
132	Mike Heath	.25
132	M. Heath (error)	2.50
133	Don Heinkel (R)	.15
134	Mike Henneman	.05
135	Guillermo Hernandez	.05
136	Eric King	.05
137	Chet Lemon	.05
138	Fred Lynn	.08
139	Jack Morris	.10
140	Matt Nokes	.10
141	Gary Pettis	.05
142	Ted Power	.05
143	Jeff M. Robinson	.20
144	Luis Salazar	.05
145	Steve Searcy (R)	.30
146	Pat Sheridan	.05
147	Frank Tanana	.08
148	Alan Trammell	.12
149	Walt Terrell	.08
150	Jim Walewander	.10
151	Lou Whitaker	.08

CINCINNATI REDS

NO.	PLAYER	MINT
152	Tim Birtsas	.05
153	Tom Browning	.08
154	Keith Brown (R)	.20
155	Norm Charlton (R)	.20
156	Dave Concepcion	.05
157	Kal Daniels	.15
158	Eric Davis	.30
159	Bo Diaz	.05
160	Rob Dibble	.40
161	Nick Esasky	.10
162	John Franco	.08
163	Danny Jackson	.12
164	Barry Larkin	.12
165	Rob Murphy	.05
166	Paul O'Neil	.05
167	Jeff Reed	.10
168	Jose Rijo	.08
169	Ron Robinson	.08
170	Chris Sabo (R)	.50
171	Candy Sierra (R)	.20
172	Van Snider (R)	.20
173	Jeff Treadway	.08
174	Frank Williams	.05
175	Herm Winningham	.05

MILWAUKEE BREWERS

NO.	PLAYER	MINT
176	Jim Adduci	.08
177	Don August	.15
178	Mike Birkbeck	.05
179	Chris Bosio	.05
180	Glenn Braggs	.05
181	Greg Brock	.05
182	Mark Clear	.05
183	Chuck Crim	.05
184	Rob Deer	.08
185	Tom Filer	.05
186	Jim Gantner	.05
187	Darryl Hamilton (R)	.25
188	Ted Higuera	.10
189	Odell Jones	.05
190	Jeffrey Leonard	.05
191	Joey Meyer	.05
192	Paul Mirabella	.05
193	Paul Molitor	.08
194	Charlie O'Brien	.05
195	Dan Plesac	.05
196	Gary Sheffield (R)	2.00
197	B.J. Surhoff	.08
198	Dale Sveum	.08

NO.	PLAYER	MINT
199	Bill Wegman	.05
200	Robin Yount	.15

PITTSBURGH PIRATES

NO.	PLAYER	MINT
201	Rafael Belliard	.05
202	Barry Bonds	.15
203	Bobby Bonilla	.15
204	Sid Bream	.05
205	Benny Distefano	.10
206	Doug Drabek	.10
207	Mike Dunne	.05
208	Felix Fermin	.05
209	Brian Fisher	.05
210	Jim Gott	.05
211	Bob Kipper	.05
212	Dave LaPoint	.05
213	Mike LaValliere	.05
214	Jose Lind	.05
215	Junior Ortiz	.05
216	Vincente Palacios	.05
217	Tom Prince	.10
218	Gary Redus	.05
219	R.J. Reynolds	.05
220	Jeff Robinson	.05
221	John Smiley	.08
222	Andy Van Slyke	.15
223	Bob Walk	.05
224	Glenn Wilson	.05

TORONTO BLUE JAYS

NO.	PLAYER	MINT
225	Jesse Barfield	.12
226	George Bell	.15
227	Pat Borders (R)	.20
228	John Cerutti	.05
229	Jim Clancy	.05
230	Mark Eichhorn	.05
231	Tony Fernandez	.15
232	Cecil Fielder	.05
233	Mike Flanagan	.05
234	Kelly Gruber	.05
235	Tom Henke	.05
236	Jimmy Key	.15
237	Rick Leach	.05
238	Manny Lee	.05
239	Nelson Liriano	.05
240	Fred McGriff	.25
241	Lloyd Moseby	.12
242	Rance Mulliniks	.05
243	Jeff Musselman	.05
244	Dave Stieb	.08
245	Todd Stottlemyre	.15
246	Duane Ward	.05
247	David Wells	.10
248	Ernie Whitt	.05

NEW YORK YANKEES

NO.	PLAYER	MINT
249	Luis Aguayo	.05
250	Neil Allen (N.Y.)	.35
250	Neil Allen (Fla.)	2.50
251	John Candelaria	.08
252	Jack Clark	.10
253	Richard Dotson	.08
254	Rickey Henderson	.25
255	Tommy John	.10
256	Roberto Kelly	.15
257	Al Leiter	.20
258	Don Mattingly	1.00
259	Dale Mohorcic	.05
260	Hal Morris	.20
261	Scott Nielsen	.05
262	Mike Pagliarulo	.10
263	Hipolito Peno (R)	.15
264	Ken Phelps	.05
265	Willie Randolph	.08
266	Rick Rhoden	.05
267	Dave Righetti	.10
268	Rafael Santana	.05
269	Steve Shields	.05
270	Joel Skinner	.05
271	Don Slaught	.05
272	Claudell Washington	.05
273	Gary Ward	.05
274	Dave Winfield	.15

KC ROYALS

NO.	PLAYER	MINT
275	Luis Aquino	.05
276	Floyd Bannister	.05
277	George Brett	.30
278	Bill Buckner	.08
279	Nick Capra (R)	.15
280	Jose DeJesus (R)	.15
281	Steve Farr	.05

NO.	PLAYER	MINT
282	Jerry Don Gleaton	.05
283	Mark Gubicza	.10
284	Tom Gordon (R)	3.00
285	Bo Jackson	.75
286	Charlie Leibrandt	.08
287	Mike MacFarlane (R)	.20
288	Jeff Montgomery	.05
289	Bill Pecota	.05
290	Jamie Quirk	.05
291	Bret Saberhagen	.12
292	Kevin Seitzer	.20
293	Kurt Stillwell	.05
294	Pat Tabler	.08
295	Danny Tartabull	.15
296	Gary Thurman	.05
297	Frank White	.05
298	Willie Wilson	.08

SAN DIEGO PADRES

NO.	PLAYER	MINT
299	Roberto Alomar	.40
300	Sandy Alomar Jr. (R)	1.50
301	Chris Brown	.08
302	Mike Brumley	.10
303	Mark Davis	.05
304	Mark Grant	.05
305	Tony Gwynn	.25
306	Greg W. Harris (R)	.20
307	Andy Hawkins	.05
308	Jimmy Jones	.05
309	John Kruk	.10
310	Dave Leiper	.05
311	Carmelo Martinez	.05
312	Lance McCullers	.08
313	Keith Moreland	.05
314	Dennis Rasmussen	.05
315	Randy Ready	.05
316	Benito Santiago	.15
317	Eric Show	.05
318	Todd Simmons	.05
319	Garry Templeton	.05
320	Dickie Thon	.05
321	Ed Whitson	.05
322	Marvell Wynne	.05

SF GIANTS

NO.	PLAYER	MINT
323	Mike Aldrete	.05
324	Bret Butler	.05
325	Will Clark	1.00
326	Kelly Downs	.05
327	Dave Dravecky	.05
328	Scott Garrelts	.05
329	Atlee Hammaker	.05
330	Charlie Hayes (R)	.25
331	Mike Krukow	.08
332	Craig Lefferts	.05
333	Candy Maldonado	.10
334	Kirt Manwaring	.05
335	Bob Melvin	.05
336	Kevin Mitchell	.45
337	Donell Nixon	.05
338	Tony Perezchica (R)	.20
339	Joe Price	.05
340	Rick Reuschel	.05
341	Ernest Riles	.05
342	Don Robinson	.05
343	Chris Speier	.05
344	Robby Thompson	.05
345	Jose Uribe	.08
346	Matt Williams	.35
347	Trevor Wilson (R)	.15

HOUSTON ASTROS

NO.	PLAYER	MINT
348	Juan Agosto	.05
349	Larry Anderson	.10
350	Alan Ashby	.05
351	Kevin Bass	.08
352	Buddy Bell	.08
353	Craig Biggio (R)	.50
354	Danny Darwin	.05
355	Glenn Davis	.10
356	Jim Deshaies	.05
357	Bill Doran	.08
358	John Fisher (R)	.20
359	Billy Hatcher	.05
360	Bob Knepper	.05
361	Louie Meadows (R)	.15
362	Dave Meads	.05
363	Jim Pankovits	.05
364	Terry Puhl	.05
365	Rafael Ramirez	.05

NO.	PLAYER	MINT
366	Craig Reynolds	.05
367	Mike Scott	.15
368	Nolan Ryan	.40
369	Dave Smith	.05
370	Gerald Young	.08

MONTREAL EXPOS

NO.	PLAYER	MINT
371	Hubie Brooks	.05
372	Tim Burke	.05
373	John Dopson (R)	.30
374	Mike Fitzgerald	.05
375	Tom Foley	.05
376	Andres Galarraga	.15
377	Neal Heaton	.05
378	Joe Hesketh	.05
379	Brian Holman (R)	.15
380	Rex Hudler	.10
381	Randy Johnson (R)	.30
382	Wallace Johnson	.05
383	Tracy Jones	.05
384	Dave Martinez	.05
385	Dennis Martinez	.05
386	Andy McGaffigan	.05
387	Otis Nixon	.05
388	Johnny Padres (R)	.15
389	Jeff Parrett	.08
390	Pascual Perez	.05
391	Tim Raines	.20
392	Luis Rivera	.05
393	Nelson Santovenia (R)	.20
394	Bryn Smith	.05
395	Tim Wallach	.08

CLEVELAND INDIANS

NO.	PLAYER	MINT
396	Andy Allanson	.05
397	Rod Allen (R)	.20
398	Scott Bailes	.05
399	Tom Candiotti	.08
400	Joe Carter	.10
401	Carmen Castillo	.05
402	Dave Clark	.05
403	John Farrell	.10
404	Julio Franco	.08
405	Don Gordon	.10
406	Mel Hall	.05
407	Brad Havens	.05
408	Brook Jacoby	.05
409	Doug Jones	.05
410	Jeff Kaiser (R)	.15
411	Luis Medina (R)	.35
412	Cory Snyder	.15
413	Greg Swindell	.10
414	Ron Tingley	.15
415	Willie Upshaw	.05
416	Ron Washington	.05
417	Rich Yett	.05

CHICAGO CUBS

NO.	PLAYER	MINT
418	Damon Berryhill	.15
419	Mike Bielecki	.05
420	Doug Dascenzo (R)	.25
421	Jody Davis	.05
422	Andre Dawson	.20
423	Frank Dipino	.05
424	Shawon Dunston	.10
425	"Goose" Gossage	.08
426	Mark Grace	1.75
427	Mike Harkey (R)	.30
428	Darrin Jackson	.08
429	Les Lancaster	.05
430	Vance Law	.05
431	Greg Maddux	.15
432	Jamie Moyer	.05
433	Al Nipper	.05
434	Rafael Palmeiro	.15
435	Pat Perry	.05
436	Jeff Pico (R)	.20
437	Ryne Sandberg	.15
438	Calvin Schiraldi	.05
439	Rick Sutcliffe	.10
440	Manny Trillo	.05
441	Gary Varsho	.20
442	Mitch Webster	.05

ST. LOUIS CARDINALS

NO.	PLAYER	MINT
443	Luis Alicea (R)	.15
444	Tom Brunansky	.08
445	Vince Coleman	.15
446	John Costello (R)	.15
447	Danny Cox	.05
448	Ken Dayley	.05
449	Jose Deleon	.05
450	Curt Ford	.05
451	Pedro Guerrero	.15
452	Bob Horner	.05
453	Tim Jones (R)	.15
454	Steve Lake	.05
455	Joe Magrane	.10
456	Greg Mathews	.05
457	Willie McGee	.08
458	Larry McWilliams	.05
459	Jose Oquendo	.05
460	Tony Pena	.08
461	Terry Pendleton	.08
462	Steve Peters (R)	.15
463	Ozzie Smith	.15
464	Scott Terry	.05
465	Denny Walling	.05
466	Todd Worrell	.08

CALIFORNIA ANGELS

NO.	PLAYER	MINT
467	Tony Armas	.05
468	Dante Bichette (R)	.25
469	Bob Boone	.05
470	Terry Clark (R)	.15
471	Stew Cliburn	.05
472	Mike Cook (R)	.15
473	Sherman Corbett (R)	.15
474	Chili Davis	.08
475	Brian Downing	.08
476	Jim Eppard	.05
477	Chuck Finley	.05
478	Willie Fraser	.05
479	Bryan Harvey (R)	.30
480	Jack Howell	.08
481	Wally Joyner	.20
482	Jack Lazorko	.05
483	Kirk McCaskill	.05
484	Mark McLemore	.05
485	Greg Minton	.05
486	Dan Petry	.05
487	Johnny Ray	.10
488	Dick Schofield	.05
489	Devon White	.10
490	Mike Witt	.08

CHICAGO WHITE SOX

NO.	PLAYER	MINT
491	Harold Baines	.10
492	Daryl Boston	.05
493	Ivan Calderon	.10
494	Mike Diaz	.05
495	Carlton Fisk	.10
496	Dave Gallagher (R)	.30
497	Ozzie Guillen	.08
498	Shawn Hillegas	.05
499	Lance Johnson	.05
500	Barry Jones	.05
501	Bill Long	.05
502	Steve Lyons	.05
503	Fred Manrique	.05
504	Jack McDowell	.10
505	Donn Pall	.15
506	Kelly Paris	.05
507	Dan Pasqua	.08
508	Ken Patterson (R)	.15
509	Melido Perez	.10
510	Jerry Reuss	.05
511	Mark Salas	.05
512	Bobby Thigpen	.05
513	Mike Woodard	.05

TEXAS RANGERS

NO.	PLAYER	MINT
514	Bob Brower	.05
515	Steve Buechele	.05
516	Jose Cecena (R)	.15
517	Cecil Espy	.05
518	Scott Fletcher	.05
519	Cecilio Guante	.05
520	Jose Guman	.05
521	Ray Hayward	.05
522	Charlie Hough	.08
523	Pete Incaviglia	.10
524	Mike Jeffcoat	.05
525	Paul Kilgus	.05
526	Chad Kreuter (R)	.20
527	Jeff Kunkel	.05
528	Oddibe McDowell	.08
529	Pete O'Brien	.10
530	Geno Petralli	.05
531	Jeff Russell	.05
532	Ruben Sierra	.25
533	Mike Stanley	.05
534	Ed VandeBerg	.05
535	Curtis Wilkerson	.05
536	Mitch Williams	.05
537	Bobby Witt	.05

SEATTLE MARINERS

NO.	PLAYER	MINT
538	Steve Balboni	.05
539	Scott Bankhead	.05
540	Scott Bradley	.05
541	Mickey Brantley	.08
542	Jay Buhner	.25
543	Mike Campbell	.05
544	Darnell Coles	.05
545	Henry Cotto	.05
546	Alvin Davis	.08
547	Mario Diaz	.05
548	Ken Griffey Jr. (R)	6.00
549	Erik Hanson (R)	.25
550	Mike Jackson	.05
551	Mark Langston	.12
552	Edgar Martinez	.15
553	Bill McGuire (R)	.15
554	Mike Moore	.05
555	Jim Presley	.05
556	Rey Quinones	.05
557	Jerry Reed	.05
558	Harold Reynolds	.08
559	Mike Schooler (R)	.35
560	Bill Swift	.05
561	Dave Valle	.05

PHILADELPHIA PHILLIES

NO.	PLAYER	MINT
562	Steve Bedrosian	.08
563	Phil Bradley	.08
564	Don Carman	.05
565	Bob Dernier	.05
566	Marvin Freeman	.05
567	Todd Frohwirth	.05
568	Greg Gross	.05
569	Kevin Gross	.05
570	Greg Harris	.12
571	Von Hayes	.08
572	Chris James	.08
573	Steve Jeltz	.05
574	Ron Jones (R)	.35
575	Ricky Jordan (R)	2.00
576	Mike Maddux	.05
577	David Palmer	.05
578	Lance Parrish	.10
579	Shane Rawley	.05
580	Bruce Ruffin	.05
581	Juan Samuel	.10
582	Mike Schmidt	.35
583	Kent Tekulve	.05
584	Milt Thompson	.05

ATLANTA BRAVES

NO.	PLAYER	MINT
585	Jose Alvarez (R)	.15
586	Paul Assenmacher	.05
587	Bruce Benedict	.05
588	Jeff Blauser	.05
589	Terry Blocker (R)	.15
590	Ron Gant	.20
591	Tom Glavine	.05
592	Tommy Gregg	.15
593	Albert Hall	.05
594	Dion James	.05
595	Rich Mahler	.05
596	Dale Murphy	.30
597	Gerald Perry	.12
598	Charlie Puleo	.05
599	Ted Simmons	.05
600	Pete Smith	.08
601	Zane Smith	.05
602	John Smoltz (R)	.50
603	Bruce Sutter	.08
604	Andres Thomas	.05
605	Ozzie Virgil	.05

BALTIMORE ORIOLES

NO.	PLAYER	MINT
606	Brady Anderson (R)	.30
607	Jeff Ballard	.05
608	Jose Bautista (R)	.15
609	Ken Gerhart	.05
610	Terry Kennedy	.05
611	Eddie Murray	.20
612	Carl Nichols	.15
613	Tom Niedenfeuer	.05
614	Joe Orsulak	.05
615	Oswaldo Perraza (R)	.15
616	Billy Ripken	.75
	obscenity blocked out in black	
616	Billy Ripken	20.00
	obscenity on bat	
616	Billy Ripken	36.00
	obscenity blocked out in white	
617	Cal Ripken Jr.	.20
618	Dave Schmidt	.35
619	Rich Schu	.05
620	Larry Sheets	.05
621	Doug Sisk	.05
622	Pete Stanicek	.05
623	Mickey Tettleton	.05
624	Jay Tibbs	.05
625	Jim Traber	.05
626	Mark Williamson	.05
627	Craig Worthington (R)	.40

SPECIAL CARDS

NO.	PLAYER	MINT
628	Speed/Power	.50
629	Pitcher Perfect	.08
630	Like Father-Like Son	.25
631	N.L. All Stars	.25
632	Homeruns-Coast to Coast	.25
633	Hot Corners-Hot Hitters	.25
634	Triple A's	.35
635	Dual Heat	.25
636	N.L. Pitching Power	.15
637	Cannon Arms	.15
638	Double Trouble	.15
639	Power Center	.25

No. 640 to 653—
Major League Prospects

NO.	PLAYER	MINT
640	S. Wilson (R)/C. Drew (R)	.25
641	K.Brown (R)/K. Reimer (R)	.25
642	B.Pounders (R)/J.Clark (R)	.25
643	M. Capel (R)/D. Hall	.15
644	J.Girardi (R)/R. Roomes (R)	.45
645	L. Harris (R)/M. Brown (R)	.25
646	L.Santos(R)/J.Campbell(R)	.25
647	R.Kramer (R)/M.Garcia (R)	.25
648	T.Lovullo (R)/R.Palacios(R)	.25
649	J. Corsi (R)/B. Milacki (R)	.25
650	G.Hall (R)/M.Rochford (R)	.25
651	T.Taylor(R)/V.Lovelace (R)	.25
652	K. Hill (R)/D. Cook (R)	.50
653	S. Service (R)/S. Turner (R)	.25
654	Checklist No. 1	.08
655	Checklist No. 2	.08
656	Checklist No. 3	.08
657	Checklist No. 4	.08
658	Checklist No. 5	.08
659	Checklist No. 6	.08
660	Checklist No. 7	.08

1989 Fleer Traded Update.... Complete Set of 132 Cards—Value $20.00

This set updates the main 1989 card set with players who had changed teams during the season, and rookies. This set features the first card of Jim Abbott, Greg Vaughn, Jerome Walton and Todd Zeile. The set was packaged in a printed box and distributed primarily through card hobby dealers.

NO. PLAYER	MINT	NO. PLAYER	MINT	NO. PLAYER	MINT	NO. PLAYER	MINT
U1 Phil Bradley	.06	U34 Frank Williams	.06	U67 Nolan Ryan	1.00	U100 Don Aase	.06
U2 Mike Devereaux	.08	U35 Kevin Appier	.25	U68 Francisco Cabrera	.25	U101 Barry Lyons	.06
U3 Steve Finley	.35	U36 Bob Boone	.06	U69 Junior Felix (RR)	1.00	U102 Juan Samuel	.06
U4 Kevin Hickey	.06	U37 Luis del los Santos	.15	U70 Al Leiter	.06	U103 Wally Whitehurst	.30
U5 Brian Holton	.10	U38 Jim Eisenreich	.10	U71 Alex Sanchez	.25	U104 Dennis Cook	.20
U6 Bob Milacki	.25	U39 Jaime Navarro	.06	U72 Geronimo Berroa	.08	U105 Lenny Dykstra	.25
U7 Randy Milligan	.10	U40 Bill Spiers	.35	U73 Derek Lilliquist	.20	U106 Charlie Hayes	.10
U8 John Dopson	.10	U41 Greg Vaughn (RR)	2.25	U74 Lonnie Smith	.08	U107 Tommy Herr	.06
U9 Nick Esasky	.20	U42 Randy Veres	.25	U75 Jeff Treadway	.06	U108 Ken Howell	.06
U10 Rob Murphy	.06	U43 Wally Backman	.06	U76 Paul Kilgus	.06	U109 John Kruk	.06
U11 Jim Abbott (RR)	2.50	U44 Shane Rawley	.06	U77 Lloyd McClendon	.25	U110 Roger McDowell	.06
U12 Bert Blyleven	.06	U45 Steve Balboni	.06	U78 Scott Sanderson	.06	U111 Terry Mulholland	.10
U13 Jeff Manto	.30	U46 Jesse Barfield	.06	U79 Dwight Smith (RR)	1.50	U112 Jeff Parrett	.06
U14 Bob McClure	.06	U47 Alvaro Espinosa	.25	U80 Jerome Walton (RR)	5.00	U113 Neal Heaton	.06
U15 Lance Parrish	.06	U48 Bob Geren	.40	U81 Mitch Williams	.25	U114 Jeff King	.12
U16 Lee Stevens	.40	U49 Mel Hall	.06	U82 Steve Wilson	.15	U115 Randy Kramer	.06
U17 Claudell Washington	.06	U50 Andy Hawkins	.06	U83 Todd Benzinger	.06	U116 Bill Landrum	.06
U18 Mark Davis	.06	U51 Hensley Muelens (RR)	.50	U84 Ken Griffey	.25	U117 Cris Carpenter	.25
U19 Eric King	.06	U52 Steve Sax	.20	U85 Rick Mahler	.06	U118 Frank DiPino	.06
U20 Ron Kittle	.06	U53 Deion Sanders (RR)	1.00	U86 Rolando Roomes	.15	U119 Ken Hill	.12
U21 Matt Murullo	.20	U54 Rickey Henderson	.35	U87 Scott Scudder	.25	U120 Dan Quisenberry	.06
U22 Steve Rosenberg	.06	U55 Mike Moore	.06	U88 Jim Clancy	.06	U121 Milt Thompson	.06
U23 Robin Ventura (RR)	1.50	U56 Tony Phillips	.06	U89 Rick Rhoden	.06	U122 Todd Zeile (RR)	3.00
U24 Keith Atherton	.06	U57 Greg Briley (RR)	1.00	U90 Dan Schatzeder	.06	U123 Jack Clark	.12
U25 Joey Belle (RR)	1.25	U58 Gene Harris	.20	U91 Mike Morgan	.06	U124 Bruce Hurst	.06
U26 Jerry Browne	.06	U59 Randy Johnson	.06	U92 Eddie Murray	.15	U125 Mark Parent	.06
U27 Felix Fermin	.06	U60 Jeffrey Leonard	.06	U93 Willie Randolph	.06	U126 Bip Roberts	.06
U28 Brad Komminsk	.06	U61 Dennis Powell	.06	U94 Ray Searage	.06	U127 Jeff Brantley	.20
U29 Pete O'Brien	.06	U62 Omar Vizquel	.25	U95 Mike Aldrete	.06	U128 Terry Kennedy	.06
U30 Mike Brumley	.06	U63 Kevin Brown	.15	U96 Kevin Gross	.06	U129 Mike LaCoss	.06
U31 Tracy Jones	.06	U64 Julio Franco	.15	U97 Mark Langston	.20	U130 Greg Litton	.25
U32 Mike Schwabe	.25	U65 Jamie Moyer	.06	U98 Spike Owen	.06	U131 Mike Schmidt	1.00
U33 Gary Ward	.06	U66 Rafael Palmeiro	.15	U99 Zane Smith	.06	U132 Checklist	.06

1990 Fleer.... Complete Set of 660 Cards—Value $30.00

A new feature is a 10 card subset "Players of the Decade." New features on the back are "Vital Signs" and some cards feature "Did You Know."

NO. PLAYER	MINT	NO. PLAYER	MINT	NO. PLAYER	MINT	NO. PLAYER	MINT
OAKLAND A'S		8 Ron Hassey	.06	16 Mike Moore	.08	24 Curt Young	.06
1 Lance Blankenship	.08	9 Dave Henderson	.08	17 Gene Nelson	.06	**CHICAGO CUBS**	
2 Todd Burns	.05	10 Rickey Henderson	.25	18 Dave Parker	.10	25 Paul Assenmacher	.06
3 Jose Canseco	.60	11 Rick Honeycutt	.06	19 Tony Phillips	.06	26 Damon Beryhill	.08
4 Jim Corsi	.06	12 Stan Javier	.06	20 Terry Steinbach	.15	27 Mike Bielecki	.06
5 Storm Davis	.06	13 Felix Jose	.06	21 Dave Stewart	.10	28 Kevin Blankenship	.08
6 Dennis Eckersley	.10	14 Carney Lansford	.08	22 Walt Weiss	.10	29 Andre Dawson	.12
7 Mike Gallego	.06	15 Mark McGwire	.35	23 Bob Welch	.06	30 Shawon Dunston	.08

NO.	PLAYER	MINT
31	Joe Girardi	.10
32	Mark Grace	.35
33	Mike Harkey	.10
34	Paul Kilgus	.06
35	Les Lancaster	.06
36	Vance Law	.06
37	Greg Maddux	.12
38	Lloyd McClendon	.06
39	Jeff Pico	.06
40	Ryne Sandberg	.15
41	Scott Sanderson	.06
42	Dwight Smith	.70
43	Rick Sutcliffe	.06
44	Jerome Walton	1.50
45	Mitch Webster	.06
46	Curt Wilkerson	.06
47	Dean Wilkins (R)	.20
48	Mitch Williams	.08
49	Steve Wilson	.06

SAN FRANCISCO GIANTS

NO.	PLAYER	MINT
50	Steve Bedrosian	.06
51	Mike Benjamin (R)	.20
52	Jeff Brantley (R)	.15
53	Brett Butler	.06
54	Will Clark	.60
55	Kelly Downs	.08
56	Scott Garrelts	.08
57	Atlee Hammaker	.06
58	Terry Kennedy	.06
59	Mike LaCoss	.06
60	Craig Lefferts	.06
61	Greg Litton (R)	.25
62	Candy Maldonado	.06
63	Kirt Manwaring	.08
64	Randy McCament (R)	.20
65	Kevin Mitchell	.25
66	Donell Nixon	.06
67	Ken Okberkfell	.06
68	Rick Reuschel	.08
69	Ernest Riles	.06
70	Don Robinson	.06
71	Pat Sheridan	.06
72	Chris Speler	.06
73	Robby Thompson	.10
74	Jose Uribe	.06
75	Matt Williams	.20

TORONTO BLUE JAYS

NO.	PLAYER	MINT
76	George Bell	.15
77	Pat Borders	.06
78	John Cerutti	.06
79	Junior Felix (R)	.40
80	Tony Fernandez	.10
81	Mike Flanagan	.06
82	Mauro Gozzo (R)	.25
83	Kelly Gruber	.08
84	Tom Henke	.06
85	Jimmy Key	.08
86	Manny Lee	.06
87	Nelson Liriano	.06
88	Lee Mazzilli	.06
89	Fred McGriff	.15
90	Lloyd Moseby	.08
91	Rance Mulniks	.06
92	Alex Sanchez	.15
93	Dave Stieb	.06
94	Todd Stottlemyre	.10
95	Duane Ward	.06
96	David Wells	.06
97	Ernie Whitt	.06
98	Frank Wills	.06
99	Mookie Wilson	.08

KANSAS CITY ROYALS

NO.	PLAYER	MINT
100	Kevin Appler (R)	.20
101	Luis Aquino	.06
102	Bob Boone	.06
103	George Brett	.15
104	Jose DeJesus	.06
105	Luis de los Santos	.06
106	Jim Eisenreich	.06
107	Steve Farr	.06
108	Tom Gordon	.45
109	Mark Gubicza	.06
110	Bo Jackson	.50
111	Terry Leach	.06

NO.	PLAYER	MINT
112	Charlie Leibrandt	.06
113	Rich Luecken (R)	.20
114	Mike Macfarlane	.06
115	Jeff Montgomery	.08
116	Bret Saberhagen	.12
117	Kevin Seitzer	.08
118	Kurt Stillwell	.06
119	Pat Tabler	.06
120	Danny Tartabull	.06
121	Gary Thurman	.06
122	Frank White	.06
123	Willie Wilson	.08
124	Matt Winters (R)	.20

CALIFORNIA ANGELS

NO.	PLAYER	MINT
125	Jim Abbott	.75
126	Tony Armas	.06
127	Dante Bichette	.06
128	Bert Blyleven	.08
129	Chill Davis	.06
130	Brian Downing	.06
131	Mike Fetters (R)	.20
132	Chuck Finley	.08
133	Willie Fraser	.06
134	Bryan Harvey	.06
135	Jack Howell	.06
136	Wally Joyner	.15
137	Jeff Manto (R)	.20
138	Kirk McCaskill	.08
139	Bob McClure	.06
140	Greg Minton	.06
141	Lance Parrish	.06
142	Dan Petry	.06
143	Johnny Ray	.08
144	Dick Schofield	.06
145	Lee Stevens (R)	.25
146	Claudell Washington	.06
147	Devon White	.10
148	Mike Witt	.08

SAN DIEGO PADRES

NO.	PLAYER	MINT
149	Roberto Alomar	.10
150	Sandy Alomar, Jr.	.40
151	Andy Benes	.60
152	Jack Clark	.08
153	Pat Clements	.06
154	Joey Cora	.06
155	Mark Davis	.08
156	Mark Grant	.06
157	Tony Gwynn	.20
158	Greg Harris	.06
159	Bruce Hurst	.06
160	Darrin Jackson	.06
161	Chris James	.06
162	Carmelo Martinez	.06
163	Mike Pagliarulo	.08
164	Mark Parent	.06
165	Dennis Rasmussen	.06
166	Bip Roberts	.06
167	Benito Santiago	.15
168	Calvin Schiraldi	.06
169	Eric Show	.06
170	Garry Templeton	.06
171	Ed Whitson	.06

BALTIMORE ORIOLES

NO.	PLAYER	MINT
172	Brady Anderson	.06
173	Jeff Ballard	.08
174	Phil Bradley	.08
175	Mike Devereaux	.08
176	Steve Finley	.20
177	Pete Harnisch	.08
178	Kevin Hickey	.10
179	Brian Holton	.06
180	Ben McDonald (R)	2.00
181	Bob Melvin	.06
182	Bob Milacki	.15
183	Randy Milligan	.10
184	Gregg Olson	.25
185	Joe Orsulak	.06
186	Bill Ripken	.08
187	Cal Ripken, Jr.	.15
188	Dave Schmidt	.08
189	Larry Sheets	.06
190	Mickey Tettleton	.06
191	Mark Thurmond	.06
192	Jay Tibbs	.06

NO.	PLAYER	MINT
193	Jim Traber	.06
194	Mark Williamson	.06
195	Craig Worthington	.12

NEW YORK METS

NO.	PLAYER	MINT
196	Don Aase	.06
197	Blaine Beatty (R)	.25
198	Mark Carreon	.06
199	Gary Carter	.10
200	David Cone	.10
201	Ron Darling	.10
202	Kevin Elster	.08
203	Sid Fernandez	.08
204	Dwight Gooden	.25
205	Keith Hernandez	.10
206	Jeff Innis	.10
207	Gregg Jefferies	.40
208	Howard Johnson	.15
209	Barry Lyons	.06
210	Dave Magadan	.06
211	Kevin McReynolds	.12
212	Jeff Musselman	.06
213	Randy Myers	.10
214	Bob Ojeda	.06
215	Juan Samuel	.08
216	Mackey Sasser	.06
217	Darryl Strawberry	.30
218	Tim Teufel	.06
219	Frank Viola	.10

HOUSTON ASTROS

NO.	PLAYER	MINT
220	Juan Agosto	.06
221	Larry Andersen	.06
222	Eric Anthony (R)	1.75
223	Kevin Bass	.06
224	Craig Biggio	.15
225	Ken Caminiti	.06
226	Jim Clancy	.06
227	Danny Darwin	.06
228	Glenn Davis	.15
229	Jim Deshaies	.06
230	Bill Doran	.06
231	Bob Forsch	.10
232	Brian Meyer	.08
233	Terry Puhl	.06
234	Rafael Ramirez	.06
235	Rick Rhoden	.06
236	Dan Schatzeder	.06
237	Mike Scott	.08
238	Dave Smith	.08
239	Alex Trevino	.06
240	Glenn Wilson	.06
241	Gerald Young	.06

ST. LOUIS CARDINALS

NO.	PLAYER	MINT
242	Tom Brunansky	.06
243	Cris Carpenter	.06
244	Alex Cole (R)	.25
245	Vince Coleman	.12
246	John Costello	.06
247	Ken Dayley	.06
248	Jose DeLeon	.06
249	Frank Depino	.06
250	Pedro Guerrero	.15
251	Ken Hill	.08
252	Joe Magrane	.08
253	Willie McGee	.08
254	John Morris	.06
255	Jose Oquendo	.06
256	Tony Pena	.08
257	Terry Pendleton	.06
258	Ted Power	.06
259	Dan Quisenberry	.06
260	Ozzie Smith	.10
261	Scott Terry	.06
262	Milt Thompson	.06
263	Denny Walling	.06
264	Todd Worrell	.08
265	Todd Zelle (R)	1.50

BOSTON RED SOX

NO.	PLAYER	MINT
266	Marty Barrett	.06
267	Mike Boddicker	.08
268	Wade Boggs	.35
269	Ellis Burks	.20
270	Rick Cerone	.06
271	Roger Clemens	.30
272	John Dopson	.08

NO.	PLAYER	MINT
273	Nick Esasky	.08
274	Dwight Evans	.10
275	Wes Gardner	.08
276	Rich Gedman	.06
277	Mike Greenwell	.25
278	Danny Heep	.06
279	Eric Hetzel	.08
280	Dennis Lamp	.06
281	Rob Murphy	.06
282	Joe Price	.06
283	Carlos Quintana	.08
284	Jody Reed	.06
285	Luis Rivera	.06
286	Kevin Romine	.06
287	Lee Smith	.08
288	Mike Smithson	.06
289	Bob Stanley	.06

TEXAS RANGERS

NO.	PLAYER	MINT
290	Harold Baines	.08
291	Kevin Brown	.06
292	Steve Buechele	.06
293	Scott Coolbaugh (R)	.30
294	Jack Daugherty (R)	.20
295	Cecil Espy	.06
296	Julio Franco	.12
297	Juan Gonalez (R)	.45
298	Cecilio Guante	.06
299	Drew Hall	.06
300	Charlie Hough	.06
301	Pete Incaviglia	.12
302	Mike Jeffcoat	.06
303	Chad Kreuter	.06
304	Jeff Kunkel	.06
305	Rich Leach	.06
306	Fred Manrique	.06
307	Jamie Moyer	.06
308	Rafael Palmeiro	.10
309	Geno Petralli	.06
310	Kevin Reimer	.08
311	Kenny Rogers (R)	.15
312	Jeff Russell	.06
313	Nolan Ryan	.30
314	Ruben Sierra	.25
315	Bobby Witt	.08

MILWAUKEE BREWERS

NO.	PLAYER	MINT
316	Chris Bosio	.06
317	Glenn Braggs	.06
318	Greg Brock	.06
319	Chuck Crim	.06
320	Rob Deer	.06
321	Mike Felder	.06
322	Tom Filer	.06
323	Tony Fossas (R)	.15
324	Jim Gantner	.06
325	Darryl Hamilton	.06
326	Ted Higuera	.06
327	Mark Knudson	.12
328	Bill Krueger	.06
329	Tim McIntosh (R)	.25
330	Paul Molitor	.12
331	Jaime Navarro (R)	.25
332	Charlie O'Brien	.06
333	Jeff Peterek (R)	.20
334	Dan Plesac	.06
335	Jerry Reuss	.06
336	Gary Sheffield	.30
337	Billy Spiers (R)	.25
338	B.J. Surhoff	.06
339	Greg Vaughn (R)	1.25
340	Robin Yount	.20

MONTREAL EXPOS

NO.	PLAYER	MINT
341	Hubie Brooks	.06
342	Tim Burke	.06
343	Mike Fitzgerald	.06
344	Tom Foley	.06
345	Andres Galarraga	.15
346	Damaso Garcia	.06
347	Marquis Grissom (R)	.60
348	Kevin Gross	.06
349	Joe Hesketh	.06
350	Jeff Huson (R)	.20
351	Wallace Johnson	.06
352	Mark Langston	.10
353	Dave Martinez	.06

NO.	PLAYER	MINT
354	Dennis Martinez	.06
355	Andy McGaffigan	.06
356	Otis Nixon	.06
357	Spike Owen	.06
358	Pascual Perez	.06
359	Tim Raines	.15
360	Nelson Santovenia	.06
361	Bryn Smith	.06
362	Zane Smith	.06
363	Larry Walker (R)	.20
364	Tim Wallach	.06

MINNESOTA TWINS

NO.	PLAYER	MINT
365	Rick Aguilera	.06
366	Allan Anderson	.08
367	Wally Backman	.06
368	Doug Baker	.06
369	Juan Berenguer	.06
370	Randy Bush	.06
371	Carmen Castillo	.06
372	Mike Dyer (R)	.20
373	Gary Gaetti	.10
374	Greg Gagne	.06
375	Dan Gladden	.06
376	German Gonzalez	.06
377	Brian Harper	.06
378	Kent Hrbek	.12
379	Gene Larkin	.06
380	Tim Laudner	.06
381	John Moses	.06
382	Al Newman	.06
383	Kirby Puckett	.30
384	Shane Rawley	.06
385	Jeff Reardon	.08
386	Roy Smith	.06
387	Gary Wayne (R)	.15
388	Dave West	.08

LOS ANGELES DODGERS

NO.	PLAYER	MINT
389	Tim Belcher	.08
390	Tim Crews	.06
391	Mike Davis	.06
392	Rick Dempsey	.06
393	Kirk Gibson	.10
394	Jose Gonzalez	.06
395	Alfredo Griffin	.08
396	Jeff Hamilton	.06
397	Lenny Harris	.06
398	Mickey Hatcher	.06
399	Orel Hershiser	.15
400	Jay Howell	.08
401	Mike Marshall	.08
402	Ramon Martinez	.10
403	Mike Morgan	.06
404	Eddie Murray	.15
405	Alejandro Pena	.08
406	Willie Randolph	.12
407	Mike Scioscia	.08
408	Ray Searage	.06
409	Fernando Valenzuela	.12
410	Jose Vizcaino (R)	.15
411	John Wetteland (R)	.30

CINCINNATI REDS

NO.	PLAYER	MINT
412	Jack Armstrong	.10
413	Todd Benzinger	.08
414	Tim Birtsas	.06
415	Tom Browning	.06
416	Norm Charlton	.06
417	Eric Davis	.25
418	Rob Dibble	.12
419	John Franco	.08
420	Ken Griffey, Sr.	.20
421	Chris Hammond (R)	.20
422	Danny Jackson	.10
423	Barry Larkin	.10
424	Tim Leary	.08
425	Rick Mahler	.06
426	Joe Oliver (R)	.15
427	Paul O'Neill	.06
428	Luis Quinones	.06
429	Jeff Reed	.06
430	Jose Rijo	.06
431	Ron Robinson	.06
432	Rolando Roomes	.08
433	Chris Sabo	.12
434	Scott Scudder (R)	.20

NO.	PLAYER	MINT
435	Herm Winningham	.06

NEW YORK YANKEES

NO.	PLAYER	MINT
436	Steve Balboni	.06
437	Jesse Barfield	.06
438	Mike Blowers (R)	.20
439	Tom Brookens	.06
440	Greg Cadaret	.06
441	Alvaro Espinoza	.06
442	Bob Geren (R)	.20
443	Lee Guetterman	.06
444	Mel Hall	.06
445	Andy Hawkins	.06
446	Roberto Kelly	.12
447	Don Mattingly	.50
448	Lance McCullers	.06
449	Hensley Meulens	.25
450	Dale Mohorcic	.06
451	Clay Parker	.06
452	Eric Plunk	.06
453	Dave Righetti	.12
454	Deion Sanders (R)	.60
455	Steve Sax	.12
456	Don Slaught	.06
457	Walt Terrell	.06
458	Dave Winfield	.15

PITTSBURGH PIRATES

NO.	PLAYER	MINT
459	Jay Bell	.06
460	Rafael Belliard	.06
461	Barry Bonds	.10
462	Bobby Bonilla	.10
463	Sid Bream	.06
464	Benny Distefano	.06
465	Doug Drabek	.06
466	Jim Gott	.06
467	Billy Hatcher	.06
468	Neal Heaton	.06
469	Jeff King	.08
470	Bob Kipper	.06
471	Randy Kramer	.06
472	Bill Landrum	.06
473	Mike LaValliere	.06
474	Jose Lind	.06
475	Junior Ortiz	.06
476	Gary Redus	.06
477	Rick Reed (R)	.20
478	R.J. Reynolds	.06
479	Jeff Robinson	.10
480	John Smiley	.08
481	Andy Van Slyke	.08
482	Bob Walk	.06

CLEVELAND INDIANS

NO.	PLAYER	MINT
483	Andy Allanson	.06
484	Scott Bailes	.06
485	Joey Belle (R)	.65
486	Bud Black	.06
487	Jerry Browne	.06
488	Tom Candiotti	.06
489	Joe Carter	.12
490	David Clark	.06
491	John Farrell	.08
492	Felix Fermin	.06
493	Brook Jacoby	.06
494	Dion James	.06
495	Doug Jones	.06
496	Brad Komminsk	.06
497	Rod Nichols	.06
498	Pete O'Brien	.12
499	Steven Ofin (R)	.15
500	Jesse Orosco	.06
501	Joel Skinner	.06
502	Cory Snyder	.10
503	Greg Swindell	.12
504	Rich Yett	.06

SEATTLE MARINERS

NO.	PLAYER	MINT
505	Scott Bankhead	.06
506	Scott Bradley	.06
507	Greg Briley	.20
508	Jay Buhner	.08
509	Darnell Coles	.06
510	Keith Comstock	.06
511	Henry Cotto	.06
512	Alvin Davis	.12
513	Ken Griffey, Jr.	.75
514	Erik Hanson	.08

NO.	PLAYER	MINT
515	Gene Harris (R)	.20
516	Brian Holman	.06
517	Mike Jackson	.06
518	Randy Johnson	.10
519	Jeffrey Leonard	.06
520	Edgar Martinez	.06
521	Dennis Powell	.06
522	Jim Presley	.06
523	Jerry Reed	.06
524	Harold Reynolds	.06
525	Mike Schooler	.12
526	Bill Swift	.06
527	David Valle	.06
528	Omar Vizquel (R)	.20

CHICAGO WHITE SOX

NO.	PLAYER	MINT
529	Ivan Calderon	.06
530	Carlton Fisk	.12
531	Scott Fletcher	.06
532	Dave Gallagher	.06
533	Ozzie Guillen	.08
534	Greg Hibbard (R)	.20
535	Shawn Hillegas	.06
536	Lance Johnson	.06
537	Eric King	.06
538	Ron Kittle	.06
539	Steve Lyons	.06
540	Carlos Marinez (R)	.20
541	Tom McCarthy (R)	.15
542	Matt Merullo (R)	.15
543	Donn Pall	.06
544	Dan Pasqua	.06
545	Ken Patterson	.06
546	Melido Perez	.06
547	Steve Rosenberg	.06
548	Sammy Sosa (R)	.50
549	Bobby Thigpen	.06
550	Robin Ventura	.60
551	Greg Walker	.06

PHILADELPHIA PHILLIES

NO.	PLAYER	MINT
552	Don Carman	.06
553	Pat Combs (R)	.40
554	Dennis Cook	.06
555	Darren Daulton	.06
556	Lenny Dykstra	.08
557	Curt Ford	.06
558	Charlie Hayes	.06
559	Von Hayes	.08
560	Tom Herr	.08
561	Ken Howell	.06
562	Steve Jeltz	.06
563	Ron Jones	.06
564	Ricky Jordan	.50
565	John Kruk	.06
566	Steve Lake	.06
567	Roger McDowell	.06
568	Terry Mulholland	.06
569	Dwayne Murphy	.06
570	Jeff Parrett	.06
571	Randy Ready	.06
572	Bruce Ruffin	.06
573	Dickie Thon	.06

ATLANTA BRAVES

NO.	PLAYER	MINT
574	Jose Alvarez	.06
575	Geronimo Berroa	.07
576	Jeff Blauser	.06
577	Joe Boever	.06
578	Marty Clary	.06
579	Jody Davis	.06
580	Mark Eichhorn	.06
581	Darrell Evans	.06
582	Ron Gant	.06
583	Tom Glavine	.12
584	Tommy Greene (R)	.40
585	Tommy Gregg	.06
586	David Justice (R)	.20
587	Mark Lemke	.08
588	Derek Lilliquist	.10
589	Oddibe McDowell	.06
590	Ken Mercher (R)	.35
591	Dale Murphy	.15
592	Gerald Perry	.06
593	Lonnie Smith	.06
594	Pete Smith	.06
595	John Smoltz	.10

NO.	PLAYER	MINT
596	Mike Stanton (R)	.20
597	Andres Thomas	.06
598	Jeff Treadway	.06

DETROIT TIGERS

NO.	PLAYER	MINT
599	Doyle Alexander	.08
600	Dave Bergman	.06
601	Brian Dubois (R)	.15
602	Paul Gibson	.06
603	Mike Heath	.06
604	Mike Henneman	.06
605	Guillermo Hernandez	.06
606	Shawn Holman (R)	.20
607	Tracy Jones	.06
608	Chet Lemon	.06
609	Fred Lynn	.08
610	Jack Morris	.08
611	Matt Nokes	.10
612	Gary Pettis	.06
613	Kevin Ritz (R)	.20
614	Jeff Robinson	.08
615	Steve Searcy	.08
616	Frank Tanana	.06
617	Alan Trammell	.15
618	Gary Ward	.06
619	Lou Whitaker	.08
620	Frank Williams	.06

PLAYERS OF THE DECADE

NO.	PLAYER	MINT
621	1980—George Brett	.15
622	1981—F. Valenzuela	.10
623	1982—Dale Murphy	.15
624	1983—Cal Ripken, Jr.	.15
625	1984—Ryne Sandberg	.05
626	1985—Don Mattingly	.35
627	1986—Roger Clemens	.15
628	1987—George Bell	.10
629	1988—Jose Canseco	.35
630	1989—Will Clark	.45

SPECIAL CARDS

NO.	PLAYER	MINT
631	Game Savers	.15
632	Boston Igniters	.25
633	Starter & Stopper	.15
634	League's Best Shortstops	.15
635	Human Dynamos	.25
636	300 Strikeout Club	.20
637	Dynamic Duo	.35
638	A.L. All-Stars	.25
639	N.L. East Rivals	.25

No. 640 to 653—
Major League Prospects

NO.	PLAYER	MINT
640	R. Seanez (R) and C. Charland (R)	.25
641	G. Canale (R) and K. Mass (R)	.25
642	K. Mann (R) and D. Hansen (R)	.25
643	G. Smith (R) and S. Tate (R)	.25
644	T. Drees (R) and D. Howitt (R)	.25
645	M. Roesler (R) and D. May (R)	.25
646	S. Hemond (R) and M. Gardner (R)	.25
647	J. Orlan (R) and S. Leuis (R)	.25
648	R. Monteleone (R) and D. Williams (R)	.20
649	M. Huff (R) and S. Frey (R)	.25
650	C. McElroy (R) and M. Alou (R)	.30
651	B. Rose (R) and M. Hartley (R)	.20
652	M. Kinzer (R) and W. Edwards (R)	.25
653	D. Deshields (R) and J. Grimsley (R)	.45
654	Checklist No. 1	.10
655	Checklist No. 2	.10
656	Checklist No. 3	.10
657	Checklist No. 4	.10
658	Checklist No. 5	.10
659	Checklist No. 6	.10
660	Checklist No. 7	.10

1988 Score. . . . Complete Set of 660 Cards—Value $25.00

This was Score's *first* baseball card set. It was issued by the same company that produced the Sportsflic card sets. Features the rookie cards of Gregg Jefferies, Ellis Burks and Matt Williams.

NO.	PLAYER	MINT	NO.	PLAYER	MINT	NO.	PLAYER	MINT	NO.	PLAYER	MINT
1	Don Mattingly	1.25	67	Mike Boddicker	.05	133	Larry Andersen	.05	199	John Grubb	.05
2	Wade Boggs	.65	68	Vince Coleman	.20	134	Bob Brenley	.08	200	Bill Ripken (R)	.25
3	Tim Raines	.20	69	Howard Johnson	.15	135	Mike Marshall	.10	201	Sam Horn (R)	.25
4	Andre Dawson	.20	70	Tim Wallach	.08	136	Gerald Perry	.15	202	Todd Worrell	.10
5	Mark McGwire	1.00	71	Keith Moreland	.05	137	Bobby Meacham	.05	203	Terry Leach	.05
6	Kevin Seitzer	.60	72	Barry Larkin	.12	138	Larry Herndon	.05	204	Garth Iorg	.05
7	Wally Joyner	.40	73	Alan Ashby	.05	139	Fred Manrique (R)	.15	205	Brian Dayett	.05
8	Jesse Barfield	.20	74	Rick Rhoden	.05	140	Charlie Hough	.05	206	Bo Diaz	.05
9	Pedro Guerrero	.15	75	Darrell Evans	.08	141	Ron Darling	.10	207	Craig Reynolds	.05
10	Eric Davis	.75	76	Dave Stieb	.08	142	Herm Winningham	.05	208	Brian Holton	.15
11	George Brett	.30	77	Dan Plesac	.08	143	Mike Diaz	.05	209	Marvelle Wynne	.05
12	Ozzie Smith	.20	78	Will Clark	1.00	144	Mike Jackson (R)	.10	210	Dave Concepcion	.10
13	Rickey Henderson	.30	79	Frank White	.05	145	Denny Walling	.05	211	Mike Davis	.05
14	Jim Rice	.20	80	Joe Carter	.15	146	Rob Thompson	.05	212	Devon White	.20
15	Matt Nokes (R)	.40	81	Mike Witt	.08	147	Franklin Stubbs	.05	213	Mickey Brantley	.08
16	Mike Schmidt	.30	82	Terry Steinbach	.25	148	Albert Hall	.05	214	Greg Gagne	.05
17	Dave Parker	.15	83	Alvin Davis	.08	149	Bobby Witt	.05	215	Oddibe McDowell	.08
18	Eddie Murray	.20	84	Tom Herr	.05	150	Lance McCullers	.08	216	Jimmy Key	.10
19	Andres Galarraga	.25	85	Vance Law	.05	151	Scott Bradley	.05	217	Dave Bergman	.05
20	Tony Fernandez	.08	86	Kal Daniels	.20	152	Mark McLemore	.08	218	Calvin Schiraldi	.05
21	Kevin McReynolds	.12	87	Rick Honeycutt	.05	153	Tim Laudner	.05	219	Larry Sheets	.10
22	B.J. Surhoff	.15	88	Alfredo Griffin	.05	154	Greg Swindell	.10	220	Mike Easler	.05
23	Pat Tabler	.05	89	Bret Saberhagen	.15	155	Marty Barrett	.10	221	Kurt Stillwell	.05
24	Kirby Puckett	.35	90	Bert Blyleven	.08	156	Mike Heath	.05	222	Chuck Jackson (R)	.15
25	Benito Santiago	.40	91	Jeff Reardon	.05	157	Gary Ward	.05	223	Dave Martinez	.05
26	Ryn Sandberg	.15	92	Cory Snyder	.20	158	Lee Mazzilli	.10	224	Tim Leary	.05
27	Kelly Downs	.05	93	Greg Walker	.08	159	Tom Foley	.05	225	Steve Garvey	.20
28	Jose Cruz	.05	94	Joe Magrane (R)	.50	160	Robin Yount	.20	226	Greg Mathews	.05
29	Pete O'Brien	.08	95	Rob Deer	.10	161	Steve Bedrosian	.08	227	Doug Sisk	.05
30	Mark Langston	.08	96	Ray Knight	.05	162	Bob Walk	.05	228	Dave Henderson	.05
31	Lee Smith	.08	97	Casey Candaele	.05	163	Nick Esasky	.05	229	Jimmy Dwyer	.05
32	Juan Samuel	.10	98	John Cerutti	.05	164	Ken Caminiti (R)	.25	230	Larry Owen	.05
33	Kevin Bass	.08	99	Buddy Bell	.10	165	Jose Uribe	.05	231	Andre Thornton	.05
34	R.J. Reynolds	.08	100	Jack Clark	.20	166	Dave Anderson	.05	232	Mark Salas	.05
35	Steve Sax	.15	101	Eric Bell (R)	.05	167	Ed Whitson	.05	233	Tom Brookens	.05
36	John Kruk	.10	102	Willie Wilson	.10	168	Ernie Whitt	.05	234	Greg Brock	.05
37	Alan Trammell	.15	103	Dave Schmidt	.05	169	Cecil Cooper	.10	235	Rance Mulliniks	.05
38	Chris Bosio	.05	104	Dennis Eckersley	.10	170	Mike Pagliarulo	.10	236	Bob Brower	.08
39	Brook Jacoby	.08	105	Don Sutton	.10	171	Pat Sheridan	.05	237	Joe Niekro	.10
40	Willie McGee	.10	106	Danny Tartabull	.20	172	Chris Bando	.05	238	Scott Bankhead	.05
41	Dave Magadan	.15	107	Fred McGriff	1.00	173	Lee Lacy	.05	239	Doug DeCinces	.05
42	Fred Lynn	.10	108	Les Straker (R)	.15	174	Steve Lombardozzi	.05	240	Tommy John	.10
43	Kent Hrbek	.15	109	Lloyd Moseby	.15	175	Mike Greenwell	1.25	241	Rich Gedman	.05
44	Brian Downing	.05	110	Roger Clemens	.50	176	Greg Minton	.05	242	Ted Power	.05
45	Jose Canseco	1.25	111	Glenn Hubbard	.05	177	Moose Haas	.05	243	Dave Meads (R)	.15
46	Jim Presley	.05	112	Ken Williams (R)	.25	178	Mike Kingery	.05	244	Jim Sundberg	.05
47	Mike Stanley	.10	113	Ruben Sierra	.30	179	Greg Harris	.05	245	Ken Oberkfell	.05
48	Tony Pena	.05	114	Stan Jefferson	.15	180	Bo Jackson	.75	246	Jimmy Jones	.10
49	David Cone	.75	115	Milt Thompson	.05	181	Carmelo Martinez	.05	247	Ken Landreaux	.05
50	Rick Sutcliffe	.10	116	Bobby Bonilla	.20	182	Alex Trevino	.05	248	Jose Oquendo	.05
51	Doug Drabeck	.05	117	Wayne Tolleson	.05	183	Ron Oester	.05	249	John Mitchell (R)	.15
52	Bill Doran	.05	118	Matt Williams (R)	1.00	184	Danny Darwin	.05	250	Don Baylor	.05
53	Mike Scioscia	.05	119	Chet Lemon	.05	185	Mike Krukow	.05	251	Scott Fletcher	.05
54	Candy Maldonado	.08	120	Dale Sveum	.05	186	Rafael Palmeiro	.50	252	Al Newman	.05
55	Dave Winfield	.20	121	Dennis Boyd	.05	187	Tim Burke	.05	253	Carney Lansford	.05
56	Lou Whitaker	.10	122	Brett Butler	.05	188	Roger McDowell	.05	254	Johnny Ray	.08
57	Tom Henke	.05	123	Terry Kennedy	.05	189	Garry Templeton	.05	255	Gary Pettis	.05
58	Ken Gerhardt	.08	124	Jack Howell	.05	190	Terry Pendleton	.05	256	Ken Phelps	.05
59	Glenn Braggs	.08	125	Curt Young	.05	191	Larry Parrish	.05	257	Rick Leach	.05
60	Julio Franco	.08	126	Dale Valle	.08	192	Rey Quinones	.05	258	Tim Stoddard	.05
61	Charlie Leibrandt	.05	127	Curt Wilkerson	.05	193	Joaquin Andujar	.05	259	Ed Romero	.05
62	Gary Gaetti	.15	128	Tim Teufel	.05	194	Tom Brunansky	.10	260	Sid Bream	.05
63	Bob Boone	.05	129	Ozzie Virgil	.05	195	Donnie Moore	.05	261	Tom Niedenfuer	.05
64	Luis Polonia (R)	.20	130	Brian Fisher	.05	196	Dan Pasqual	.10	262	Rick Dempsey	.05
65	Dwight Evans	.10	131	Lance Parrish	.10	197	Jim Gantner	.05	263	Lonnie Smith	.05
66	Phil Bradley	.08	132	Tom Browning	.05	198	Mark Eichhorn	.05	264	Bob Forsch	.05

NO. PLAYER	MINT	NO. PLAYER	MINT	NO. PLAYER	MINT	NO. PLAYER	MINT
265 Barry Bonds	.20	349 Ernest Riles	.05	433 Wallace Johnson	.05	517 Ken Dayley	.05
266 Willie Randolph	.10	350 Dwight Gooden	.50	434 Jack O'Connor	.05	518 Don Aase	.05
267 Mike Ramsey	.10	351 Dave Righetti	.10	435 Steve Jeltz	.05	519 Rick Reuschel	.05
268 Don Slaught	.05	352 Pat Dodson	.12	436 Donnell Nixon (R)	.15	520 Mike Henneman (R)	.20
269 Mickey Tettleton	.05	353 John Habyan	.08	437 Jack Lazorko	.05	521 Rick Aguilera	.05
270 Jerry Reuss	.05	354 Jim Deshaies	.05	438 Keith Comstock (R)	.12	522 Jay Howell	.05
271 Marc Sullivan	.05	355 Butch Wynegar	.05	439 Jeff Robinson	.05	523 Ed Correa	.05
272 Jim Morrison	.05	356 Bryn Smith	.05	440 Graig Nettles	.10	524 Manny Trillo	.05
273 Steve Balboni	.05	357 Matt Young	.05	441 Mel Hall	.05	525 Kirk Gibson	.25
274 Dick Schofield	.05	358 Tom Pagnozzi (R)	.15	442 Gerald Young (R)	.25	526 Wally Ritchie (R)	.15
275 John Tudor	.10	359 Floyd Rayford	.05	443 Gary Redus	.05	527 Al Nipper	.05
276 Gene Larkin (R)	.25	360 Darryl Strawberry	.50	444 Charlie Moore	.05	528 Atlee Hammaker	.05
277 Harold Reynolds	.05	361 Sal Butera	.05	445 Bill Madlock	.08	529 Shawon Dunston	.05
278 Jerry Browne	.05	362 Domingo Ramos	.05	446 Mark Clear	.05	530 Jim Clancy	.05
279 Willie Upshaw	.05	363 Chris Brown	.10	447 Greg Booker	.05	531 Tom Paciorek	.05
280 Ted Higuera	.15	364 Jose Gonzalez	.10	448 Rick Schu	.05	532 Joel Skinner	.05
281 Terry McGriff	.10	365 Dave Smith	.05	449 Ron Kittle	.10	533 Scott Garrelts	.05
282 Terry Puhl	.05	366 Andy McGaffigan	.05	450 Dale Murphy	.25	534 Tom O'Malley	.05
283 Mark Wasinger (R)	.20	367 Stan Javier	.05	451 Bob Dernier	.05	535 John Franco	.10
284 Luis Salazar	.05	368 Henry Cotto	.05	452 Dale Mohorcic	.05	536 Paul Kilgus (R)	.20
285 Ted Simmons	.08	369 Mike Birkbeck	.05	453 Rafael Belliard	.05	537 Darrell Porter	.05
286 John Shelby	.05	370 Len Dykstra	.15	454 Charlie Puleo	.05	538 Walt Terrell	.05
287 John Smiley (R)	.25	371 Dave Collins	.05	455 Dwayne Murphy	.05	539 Bill Long (R)	.12
288 Curt Ford	.05	372 Spike Owen	.05	456 Jim Eisenreich	.05	540 George Bell	.15
289 Steve Crawford	.05	373 Geno Petralli	.05	457 David Palmer	.05	541 Jeff Sellers	.05
290 Dan Quisenberry	.08	374 Ron Karkovice	.05	458 Dave Stewart	.10	542 Joe Boever (R)	.15
291 Alan Wiggins	.05	375 Shane Rawley	.05	459 Pasqual Perez	.05	543 Steve Howe	.05
292 Randy Bush	.05	376 Dewayne Buice (R)	.15	460 Glenn Davis	.12	544 Scott Sanderson	.05
293 John Candelaria	.08	377 Bill Pecota (R)	.15	461 Dan Petry	.05	545 Jack Morris	.10
294 Tony Phillips	.05	378 Leon Durham	.05	462 Jim Winn	.05	546 Todd Benzinger (R)	.30
295 Mike Morgan	.05	379 Ed Olwine	.05	463 Darrell Miller	.05	547 Steve Henderson	.05
296 Bill Wegman	.05	380 Bruce Hurst	.10	464 Mike Moore	.05	548 Eddie Milner	.05
297 Terry Francona	.05	381 Bob McClure	.05	465 Mike LaCoss	.05	549 Jeff Robinson (R)	.40
298 Mickey Hatcher	.05	382 Mark Thurmond	.05	466 Steve Farr	.05	550 Cal Ripken, Jr.	.20
299 Andres Thomas	.05	383 Buddy Biancalana	.05	467 Jerry Mumphrey	.05	551 Jody Davis	.08
300 Bob Stanley	.05	384 Tim Conroy	.05	468 Kevin Gross	.05	552 Kirk McCaskill	.05
301 Alfredo Pedrique (R)	.12	385 Tony Gwynn	.35	469 Bruce Bochy	.05	553 Craig Lefferts	.05
302 Jim Lindeman	.10	386 Greg Gross	.05	470 Orel Hershiser	.20	554 Darnell Coles	.05
303 Wally Backman	.05	387 Barry Lyons (R)	.20	471 Eric King	.05	555 Phil Niekro	.15
304 Paul O'Neill	.10	388 Mike Felder	.05	472 Ellis Burks (R)	1.00	556 Mike Aldrete	.05
305 Hubie Brooks	.08	389 Pat Clements	.05	473 Darren Daulton	.05	557 Pat Perry	.05
306 Steve Buechele	.05	390 Ken Griffey	.08	474 Mookie Wilson	.05	558 Juan Agosto	.05
307 Bobby Thigpen	.05	391 Mark Davis	.05	475 Frank Viola	.15	559 Rob Murphy	.05
308 George Hendrick	.05	392 Jose Rijo	.05	476 Ron Robinson	.05	560 Dennis Rasmussen	.05
309 John Moses	.05	393 Mike Young	.05	477 Bob Melvin	.05	561 Manny Lee	.05
310 Ron Guidry	.08	394 Willie Fraser	.10	478 Jeff Musselman	.12	562 Jeff Blauser (R)	.20
311 Bill Schroeder	.05	395 Dion James	.05	479 Charlie Kerfeld	.05	563 Bob Ojeda	.05
312 Jose Nunez (R)	.15	396 Steve Shields	.12	480 Richard Dotson	.05	564 Dave Dravecky	.05
313 Bud Black	.05	397 Randy St. Claire	.05	481 Kevin Mitchell	.50	565 Gene Garber	.05
314 Joe Sambito	.05	398 Danny Jackson	.10	482 Gary Roenicke	.05	566 Ron Roenicke	.05
315 Scott McGregor	.05	399 Cecil Fielder	.05	483 Tim Flannery	.05	567 Tommy Hinzo (R)	.15
316 Rafael Santana	.05	400 Keith Hernandez	.25	484 Rich Yett	.05	568 Eric Nolte (R)	.12
317 Frank Williams	.05	401 Don Carman	.05	485 Pete Incaviglia	.20	569 Ed Hearn	.05
318 Mike Fitzgerald	.05	402 Chuck Crim (R)	.15	486 Rick Cerone	.05	570 Mark Davidson (R)	.15
319 Rick Mahler	.05	403 Rob Woodward	.05	487 Tony Armas	.05	571 Jim Walewander (R)	.15
320 Jim Gott	.05	404 Junior Ortiz	.05	488 Jerry Reed	.05	572 Donnie Hill	.05
321 Marinao Duncan	.05	405 Glenn Wilson	.05	489 Davey Lopes	.05	573 Jamie Moyer	.05
322 Jose Guzman	.05	406 Ken Howell	.05	490 Frank Tanana	.05	574 Ken Schrom	.05
323 Lee Guetterman	.05	407 Jeff Kunkel	.05	491 Mike Loynd	.10	575 Nolan Ryan	.40
324 Dan Gladden	.05	408 Jeff Reed	.05	492 Bruce Ruffin	.05	576 Jim Acker	.05
325 Gary Carter	.20	409 Chris James	.15	493 Chris Speier	.05	577 Jamie Quirk	.05
326 Tracy Jones	.08	410 Zane Smith	.05	494 Tom Hume	.05	578 Jay Alrich (R)	.12
327 Floyd Youmans	.05	411 Ken Dixon	.05	495 Jesse Orosco	.05	579 Claudell Washington	.05
328 Bill Dawley	.05	412 Rickey Horton	.05	496 Robbie Wine, Jr. (R)	.20	580 Jeff Leonard	.08
329 Paul Noce (R)	.15	413 Frank Dipino	.05	497 Jeff Montgomery (R)	.30	581 Carmen Castillo	.05
330 Angel Salazar	.05	414 Shane Mack	.15	498 Jeff Dedmon	.05	582 Darryl Boston	.05
331 Goose Gossage	.10	415 Danny Cox	.05	499 Luis Aguayo	.05	583 Jeff DeWillis (R)	.12
332 George Frazier	.05	416 Andy Van Slyke	.12	500 Reggie Jackson #1	.20	584 John Marzano (R)	.10
333 Ruppert Jones	.05	417 Danny Heep	.05	501 Reggie Jackson #2	.20	585 Bill Gullickson	.05
334 Billy Jo Robidoux	.05	418 John Cangelosi	.05	502 Reggie Jackson #3	.20	586 Andy Allanson	.05
335 Mike Scott	.10	419 John Christensen	.05	503 Reggie Jackson #4	.20	587 Lee Tunnell	.05
336 Randy Myers	.20	420 Joey Cora (R)	.15	504 Reggie Jackson #5	.20	588 Gene Nelson	.05
337 Bob Sebra	.05	421 Mike Lavalliere	.05	505 Billy Hatcher	.10	589 Dave LaPoint	.05
338 Eric Show	.05	422 Kelly Gruber	.05	506 Ed Lynch	.05	590 Harold Baines	.10
339 Mitch Williams	.05	423 Bruce Benedict	.05	507 Willie Hernandez	.05	591 Bill Buckner	.05
340 Paul Molitor	.15	424 Len Matuszek	.05	508 Jose DeLeon	.05	592 Carlton Fisk	.10
341 Gus Polidor	.05	425 Kent Tekulve	.05	509 Joel Youngblood	.05	593 Rick Manning	.05
342 Steve Trout	.05	426 Rafael Ramirez	.05	510 Bob Welch	.05	594 Doug Jones (R)	.25
343 Jerry Don Gleaton	.05	427 Mike Flanagan	.05	511 Steve Ontiveros	.05	595 Tom Candiotti	.08
344 Bob Knepper	.05	428 Mike Gallego	.05	512 Randy Ready	.05	596 Steve Lake	.05
345 Mitch Webster	.05	429 Juan Castillo	.05	513 Juan Nieves	.05	597 Jose Lind (R)	.20
346 John Morris	.05	430 Neal Heaton	.05	514 Jeff Russell	.05	598 Ross Jones (R)	.15
347 Andy Hawkins	.05	431 Phil Garner	.05	515 Von Hayes	.10	599 Gary Matthews	.05
348 Dave Leiper	.05	432 Mike Dunne (R)	.20	516 Mark Gubicza	.05	600 Fernando Valenzuela	.20

NO.	PLAYER	MINT
601	Dennis Martinez	.05
602	Les Lancaster (R)	.12
603	Ozzie Guillen	.05
604	Tony Bernazard	.05
605	Chili Davis	.05
606	Roy Smalley	.05
607	Ivan Calderon	.15
608	Jay Tibbs	.05
609	Guy Hoffman	.05
610	Doyle Alexander	.05
611	Mike Bielecki	.05
612	Shawn Hillegas (R)	.15
613	Keith Atherton	.05
614	Eric Plunk	.05
615	Sid Fernandez	.10
616	Dennis Lamp	.05
617	Dave Engle	.05
618	Harry Spilman	.05

NO.	PLAYER	MINT
619	Don Robinson	.05
620	John Farrell (R)	.30
621	Nelson Liriano (R)	.20
622	Floyd Bannister	.05
623	Randy Milligan (R)	.40
624	Kevin Elster	.25
625	Jody Reed (R)	.30
626	Shawn Abner	.25
627	Kurt Manwaring (R)	.25
628	Pete Stanicek (R)	.25
629	Rob Ducey (R)	.30
630	Steve Kiefer	.10
631	Gary Thurman (R)	.20
632	Darrel Akerfelds (R)	.15
633	Dave Clark	.15
634	Roberto Kelly (R)	.50
635	Keith Hughes (R)	.15

NO.	PLAYER	MINT
636	John Davis (R)	.20
637	Mike Devereaux (R)	.25
638	Tom Glavine (R)	.25
639	Keith Miller (R)	.25
640	Chris Gwynn (R)	.35
641	Tim Crews (R)	.15
642	Mackey Sasser (R)	.30
643	Vincente Palacios (R)	.15
644	Kevin Romine (R)	.15
645	Gregg Jefferies (R)	3.00
646	Jeff Treadway (R)	.35
647	Ronnie Gant (R)	.40
648	M. McGwire/M. Nokes	.35
649	E. Davis/T. Raines	.25
650	D. Mattingly/J. Clark	.35
651	A. Trammell/T. Fernandez/ C. Ripken	.15

NO.	PLAYER	MINT
652	Highlights: Coleman 100 SB	.15
653	Highlights: Puckett 10 Hits	.25
654	Highlights: Santiago Hit Streak	.15
655	Highlights: Nieves No-Hitter	.10
656	Highlights: Bedrosian Saves	.10
657	Highlights: Schmidt 500 HR's	.20
658	Highlights: Mattingly HR's	.40
659	Highlights: McGwire HR's	.35
660	Highlights: Molitor Hit Streak	.35

1988 Score Traded & Rookie.... Complete Set of 110 Cards—Value $35.00

Updates the main 1988 card set with players who changed teams during the season, and rookies. Features the first Score card of Mark Grace, Chris Sabo, Ricky Jordan and Craig Biggio. The set was packaged in a printed box and distributed primarily through card hobby dealers.

NO.	PLAYER	MINT
1	Jack Clark	.12
2	Danny Jackson	.15
3	Brett Butler	.06
4	Kurt Stillwell	.06
5	Tom Brunansky	.10
6	Dennis Lamp	.06
7	Jose DeLeon	.06
8	Tom Herr	.06
9	Keith Moreland	.06
10	Kirk Gibson	.15
11	Bud Black	.06
12	Rafael Ramirez	.06
13	Luis Salazar	.06
14	Goose Gossage	.06
15	Bob Welch	.06
16	Vance Law	.06
17	Ray Knight	.06
18	Dan Quisenberry	.06
19	Don Slaught	.06
20	Lee Smith	.06
21	Rick Cerone	.06
22	Pat Tabler	.06
23	Larry McWilliams	.06
24	Rick Horton	.06
25	Graig Nettles	.06
26	Dan Petry	.06
27	Jose Rijo	.06
28	Chili Davis	.06

NO.	PLAYER	MINT
29	Dickie Thon	.06
30	Mackey Sasser	.12
31	Mickey Tettleton	.06
32	Rick Dempsey	.06
33	Ron Hassey	.06
34	Phil Bradley	.06
35	Jay Howell	.06
36	Bill Buckner	.06
37	Alfredo Griffin	.06
38	Gary Pettis	.06
39	Calvin Schiraldi	.06
40	John Candelaria	.06
41	Joe Orsulak	.06
42	Willie Upshaw	.06
43	Herm Winningham	.06
44	Ron Kittle	.06
45	Bob Dernier	.06
46	Steve Balboni	.06
47	Steve Shields	.06
48	Henry Cotto	.06
49	Dave Henderson	.06
50	Dave Parker	.12
51	Mike Young	.06
52	Mark Salas	.06
53	Mike Davis	.06
54	Rafael Santana	.06
55	Don Baylor	.06

NO.	PLAYER	MINT
56	Dan Pasqua	.06
57	Ernest Riles	.06
58	Glenn Hubbard	.06
59	Mike Smithson	.06
60	Richard Dotson	.06
61	Jerry Reuss	.06
62	Mike Jackson	.06
63	Floyd Bannister	.06
64	Jesse Orosco	.06
65	Larry Parrish	.06
66	Jeff Bittiger	.15
67	Ray Hayward	.10
68	Ricky Jordan (RR)	3.50
69	Tommy Gregg	.25
70	Brady Anderson	.40
71	Jeff Montgomery	.06
72	Darryl Hamilton	.20
73	Cecil Espy	.25
74	Greg Briley (RR)	2.00
75	Joey Meyer (RR)	.20
76	Mike Macfarlane	.15
77	Oswald Peraza	.15
78	Jack Armstrong	.25
79	Don Heinkel	.15
80	Mark Grace (RR)	5.00
81	Steve Curry	.25
82	Damon Barryhill (RR)	.50

NO.	PLAYER	MINT
83	Steve Ellsworth	.15
84	Pete Smith	.15
85	Jack McDowell	.25
86	Rob Dibble	.75
87	Bryan Harvey (RR)	.35
88	John Dopson	.25
89	Dave Gallagher	.50
90	Todd Stottlemyre	.30
91	Mike Schooler	.45
92	Don Gordon	.15
93	Sil Campusano	.25
94	Jeff Pico	.15
95	Jay Buhner	.35
96	Nelson Santovenia	.30
97	Al Leiter (RR)	.25
98	Luis Alicea	.20
99	Pat Borders	.20
100	Chris Sabo (RR)	1.50
101	Tim Belcher	.35
102	Walt Weiss	1.00
103	Craig Biggio	1.50
104	Don August	.20
105	Roberto Alomar (RR)	.60
106	Todd Burns	.40
107	John Costello	.15
108	Melodo Perez	.35
109	Darrin Jackson	.25
110	Orestes Destrade	.25

1989 Score. . . . Complete Set of 660 Cards—Value $25.00

Features the rookie cards of Sandy Alomar, Jr., Ricky Jordan, Tom Gordon and Gary Sheffield. The set includes 9 Highlight cards and 32 Rookie Prospect cards.

NO.	PLAYER	MINT	NO.	PLAYER	MINT	NO.	PLAYER	MINT	NO.	PLAYER	MINT
1	Jose Canseco	1.00	69	Steve Sax	.12	136	Howard Johnson	.20	204	Pat Sheridan	.05
2	Andre Dawson	.15	70	Rickey Henderson	.20	137	Terry Pendleton	.08	205	Don Baylor	.08
3	Mark McGwire	.50	71	Mitch Webster	.05	138	Andy McGaffigan	.05	206	Paul O'Neill	.05
4	Benny Santiago	.10	72	Rob Deer	.08	139	Ken Oberkfell	.05	207	Pete Smith	.12
5	Rick Reuschel	.05	73	Jim Presley	.05	140	Butch Wynegar	.05	208	Mark McLemore	.05
6	Fred McGriff	.30	74	Albert Hall	.05	141	Rob Murphy	.05	209	Henry Cotto	.05
7	Kal Daniels	.15	75	G. Brett (correct)	.25	142	Rich Renteria	.10	210	Kirk Gibson	.20
8	Gary Gaetti	.10	75	G. Brett (error)	.75	143	Jose Guzman	.05	211	Claudell Washington	.05
9	Ellis Burks	.35	76	Brian Downing	.08	144	Andres Galarraga	.15	212	Randy Bush	.05
10	Darryl Strawberry	.45	77	Dave Martinez	.05	145	Rick Horton	.05	213	Joe Carter	.15
11	Julio Franco	.08	78	Scott Fletcher	.05	146	Frank DiPino	.05	214	Bill Buckner	.08
12	Lloyd Moseby	.12	79	Phil Bradley	.08	147	Glenn Braggs	.05	215	Bert Blyleven	.15
13	Jeff Pico (R)	.15	80	Ozzie Smith	.15	148	John Kruk	.15	216	Brett Butler	.05
14	Johnny Ray	.10	81	Larry Sheets	.05	149	Mike Schmidt	.30	217	Lee Mazzilli	.05
15	Cal Ripken, Jr.	.20	82	Mike Aldrete	.05	150	Lee Smith	.08	218	Spike Owen	.05
16	Dick Schofield	.05	83	Darnell Coles	.05	151	Robin Yount	.15	219	Bill Swift	.05
17	Mel Hall	.05	84	Len Dykstra	.10	152	Mark Eichhorn	.05	220	Tim Wallach	.08
18	Bill Ripken	.05	85	Jim Rice	.12	153	DeWayne Buice	.05	221	David Cone	.15
19	Brook Jacoby	.05	86	Jeff Treadway	.05	154	B.J. Surhoff	.08	222	Don Carman	.05
20	Kirby Puckett	.25	87	Jose Lind	.05	155	Vince Coleman	.15	223	Rich Gossage	.08
21	Bill Doran	.08	88	Willie McGee	.08	156	Tony Phillips	.05	224	Bob Walk	.05
22	Pete O'Brien	.10	89	Mickey Brantley	.08	157	Willie Fraser	.05	225	Dave Righetti	.10
23	Matt Nokes	.10	90	Tony Gwynn	.20	158	Lance McCullers	.08	226	Kevin Bass	.08
24	Brian Fisher	.05	91	R.J. Reynolds	.05	159	Greg Gagne	.05	227	Kevin Gross	.05
25	Jack Clark	.10	92	Milt Thompson	.05	160	Jesse Barfield	.12	228	Tim Burke	.05
26	Gary Petis	.05	93	Kevin McReynolds	.15	161	Mark Langston	.10	229	Rick Mahler	.05
27	Dave Valle	.05	94	Eddie Murray	.15	162	Kurt Stillwell	.05	230	Lou Whitaker	.08
28	Willie Wilson	.08	95	Lance Parrish	.10	163	Dion James	.05	231	Luis Alicea (R)	.15
29	Curt Young	.05	96	Ron Kittle	.08	164	Glenn Davis	.10	232	Roberto Alomar	.30
30	Dale Murphy	.25	97	Gerald Young	.08	165	Walt Weiss	.30	233	Bob Boone	.05
31	Barry Larkin	.10	98	Ernie Whitt	.05	166	Dave Concepcion	.05	234	Dickie Thon	.05
32	Dave Stewart	.10	99	Jeff Reed	.05	167	Alfredo Griffin	.05	235	Shawon Dunston	.10
33	Mike LaValliere	.05	100	Don Mattingly	.75	168	Don Heinkel (R)	.15	236	Pete Stanicek	.05
34	Glen Hubbard	.05	101	Gerald Perry	.10	169	Luis Rivera	.10	237	Craig Biggio (R)	.40
35	Ryne Sandberg	.12	102	Vance Law	.05	170	Shane Rawley	.05	238	Dennis Boyd	.08
36	Tony Pena	.08	103	John Shelby	.05	171	Darrell Evans	.05	239	Tom Candiotti	.08
37	Greg Walker	.05	104	Chris Sabo (R)	.50	172	Robby Thompson	.05	240	Gary Carter	.15
38	Von Hayes	.08	105	Danny Tartabull	.15	173	Jody Davis	.05	241	Mike Stanley	.05
39	Kevin Mitchell	.08	106	Glenn Wilson	.05	174	Andy Van Slyke	.12	242	Ken Phelps	.05
40	Tim Raines	.15	107	Mark Davidson	.05	175	Wade Boggs	.50	243	Chris Bosio	.05
41	Keith Hernandez	.15	108	Dave Parker	.10	176	Garry Templeton	.05	244	Les Straker	.05
42	Keith Moreland	.05	109	Eric Davis	.30	177	Gary Redus	.05	245	Dave Smith	.05
43	Ruben Sierra	.15	110	Alan Trammell	.10	178	Craig Lefferts	.05	246	John Candelaria	.05
44	Chet Lemon	.05	111	Ozzie Virgil	.05	179	Carney Lansford	.08	247	Joe Orsulak	.05
45	Willie Randolph	.08	112	Frank Tanana	.08	180	Ron Darling	.10	248	Storm Davis	.05
46	Andy Allanson	.05	113	Rafael Ramirez	.05	181	Kirk McCaskill	.05	249	Floyd Bannister	.05
47	Candy Maldonado	.10	114	Dennis Martinez	.05	182	Tony Armas	.05	250	Jack Morris	.10
48	Sid Bream	.05	115	Jose DeLeon	.05	183	Steve Farr	.05	251	Bret Saberhagen	.15
49	Denny Walling	.05	116	Bob Ojeda	.08	184	Tom Brunansky	.08	252	Tom Niedenfuer	.05
50	Dave Winfield	.15	117	Doug Drabek	.10	185	Bryan Harvey (R)	.20	253	Neal Heaton	.05
51	Alvin Davis	.08	118	Andy Hawkins	.05	186	Mike Marshall	.08	254	Eric Show	.05
52	Cory Snyder	.10	119	Greg Maddux	.15	187	Bo Diaz	.05	255	Juan Samuel	.10
53	Hubie Brooks	.05	120	Cecil Fielder	.05	188	Willie Upshaw	.05	256	Dale Sveum	.08
54	Chili Davis	.08	121	Mike Scioscia	.05	189	Mike Pagliarulo	.10	257	Jim Gott	.05
55	Kevin Seitzer	.15	122	Dan Petry	.05	190	Mike Krukow	.08	258	Scott Garrelts	.05
56	Jose Uribe	.05	123	Terry Kennedy	.05	191	Tommy Herr	.05	259	Larry McWilliams	.05
57	Tony Fernandez	.10	124	Kelly Downs	.05	192	Jim Pankovits	.05	260	Steve Bedrosian	.08
58	Tim Teufel	.05	125	Greg Gross	.05	193	Dwight Evans	.15	261	Jack Howell	.08
59	Oddibe McDowell	.08	126	Fred Lynn	.08	194	Kelly Gruber	.05	262	Jay Tibbs	.05
60	Les Lancaster	.05	127	Barry Bonds	.12	195	Bobby Bonilla	.10	263	Jamie Moyer	.05
61	Billy Hatcher	.05	128	Harold Baines	.10	196	Wallace Johnson	.05	264	Doug Sisk	.05
62	Dan Gladden	.05	129	Doyle Alexander	.05	197	Dave Stieb	.08	265	Todd Worrell	.08
63	Marty Barrett	.05	130	Kevin Elster	.08	198	Pat Borders (R)	.15	266	John Farrell	.10
64	Nick Esasky	.10	131	Mike Heath	.05	199	Rafael Palmeiro	.12	267	Dave Collins	.05
65	Wally Joyner	.15	132	Teddy Higuera	.10	200	Doc Gooden	.30	268	Sid Fernandez	.10
66	Mike Greenwell	.50	133	Charlie Leibrandt	.08	201	Pete Incaviglia	.10	269	Tom Brookens	.05
67	Ken Williams	.05	134	Tim Laudner	.05	202	Chris James	.08	270	Shane Mack	.05
68	Bob Horner	.05	135	Ray Knight (correct)	.15	203	Marvell Wynne	.05	271	Paul Kilgus	.05
			135	Ray Knight (error)	.75						

NO.	PLAYER	MINT	NO.	PLAYER	MINT	NO.	PLAYER	MINT	NO.	PLAYER	MINT
272	Chuck Crim	.05	354	Bob Kipper	.05	437	Fernando Valenzuela	.10	520	Dan Quisenberry	.08
273	Bob Knepper	.05	355	Steve Jeltz	.05	438	Jeff Russell	.05	521	Lloyd McClendon	.08
274	Mike Moore	.05	356	Jesse Orosco	.05	439	Cecilio Guante	.05	522	Steve Trout	.05
275	Guillermo Hernandez	.05	357	Bob Dernier	.05	440	Don Robinson	.05	523	Larry Andersen	.05
276	Dennis Eckersley	.10	358	Mickey Tettleton	.05	441	Rick Anderson	.05	524	Don Aase	.05
277	Craig Nettles	.10	359	Duane Ward	.05	442	Tom Glavine	.05	525	Bob Forsch	.05
278	Rich Dotson	.08	360	Darrin Jackson	.12	443	Daryl Boston	.05	526	Geno Petralli	.05
279	Larry Herndon	.05	361	Rey Quinones	.05	444	Joe Price	.05	527	Angel Salazar	.05
280	Gene Larkin	.05	362	Mark Grace	1.25	445	Stewart Cliburn	.05	528	Mike Schooler (R)	.25
281	Roger McDowell	.05	363	Steve Lake	.05	446	Manny Trillo	.05	529	Jose Oquendo	.05
282	Greg Swindell	.10	364	Pat Perry	.05	447	Joel Skinner	.05	530	Jay Buhner	.25
283	Juan Agosto	.05	365	Terry Steinbach	.12	448	Charlie Puleo	.05	531	Tom Bolton	.05
284	Jeff Robinson	.15	366	Alan Ashby	.05	449	Carlton Fisk	.10	532	Al Nipper	.05
285	Mike Dunne	.05	367	Jeff Montgomery	.05	450	Will Clark	.50	533	Dave Henderson	.05
286	Greg Mathews	.05	368	Steve Buechele	.05	451	Otis Nixon	.05	534	John Costello (R)	.15
287	Kent Tekulve	.05	369	Chris Brown	.08	452	Rick Schu	.05	535	Donnie Moore	.05
288	Jerry Mumphrey	.05	370	Orel Hershiser	.25	453	Todd Stottlemyre	.15	536	Mike Laga	.05
289	Jack McDowell	.15	371	Todd Benzinger	.10	454	Tim Birtsas	.05	537	Mike Gallego	.05
290	Frank Viola	.15	372	Ron Gant	.15	455	Dave Gallagher (R)	.25	538	Jim Clancy	.05
291	Mark Gubicza	.10	373	Paul Assenmacher	.05	456	Barry Lyons	.05	539	Joel Youngblood	.05
292	Dave Schmidt	.05	374	Joey Meyer	.10	457	Fred Manrique	.05	540	Rick Leach	.05
293	Mike Henneman	.05	375	Neil Allen	.05	458	Ernest Riles	.05	541	Kevin Romine	.05
294	Jimmy Jones	.05	376	Mike Davis	.05	459	Doug Jennings (R)	.25	542	Mark Salas	.05
295	Charlie Hough	.08	377	Jeff Parrett	.08	460	Joe Magrane	.10	543	Greg Minton	.05
296	Rafael Santana	.05	378	Jay Howell	.08	461	Jamie Quirk	.05	544	Dave Palmer	.05
297	Chris Speier	.05	379	Rafael Belliard	.05	462	Jack Armstrong (R)	.20	545	Dwayne Murphy	.05
298	Mike Witt	.08	380	Luis Polonia	.05	463	Bobby Witt	.05	546	Jim Deshaies	.05
299	Pascual Perez	.05	381	Keith Atherton	.05	464	Keith Miller	.05	547	Don Gordon	.10
300	Nolan Ryan	.35	382	Kent Hrbek	.10	465	Todd Burns (R)	.35	548	Ricky Jordan (R)	1.50
301	Mitch Williams	.05	383	Bob Stanley	.05	466	John Dopson (R)	.15	549	Mike Boddicker	.08
302	Mookie Wilson	.08	384	Dave LaPoint	.05	467	Rich Yett	.05	550	Mike Scott	.15
303	Mackey Sasser	.08	385	Rance Mulliniks	.05	468	Craig Reynolds	.05	551	Jeff Ballard	.12
304	John Cerutti	.05	386	Melido Perez	.10	469	Dave Bergman	.05	552	Jose Rijo	.15
305	Jeff Reardon	.08	387	Doug Jones	.05	470	Rex Hudler	.10	552	Jose Rijo (error)	.75
306	Randy Myers	.08	388	Steve Lyons	.05	471	Eric King	.05	553	Danny Darwin	.05
307	Greg Brock	.05	389	Alejandro Pena	.08	472	Joaquin Andujar	.05	554	Tom Browning	.08
308	Bob Welch	.08	390	Frank White	.05	473	Sil Campusano (R)	.20	555	Danny Jackson	.10
309	Jeff Robinson	.05	391	Pat Tabler	.08	474	Terry Mulholland	.05	556	Rick Dempsey	.05
310	Harold Reynolds	.08	392	Eric Plunk	.05	475	Mike Flanagan	.05	557	Jeffrey Leonard	.05
311	Jim Walewander	.05	393	Mike Maddux	.05	476	Greg Harris	.15	558	Jeff Musselman	.05
312	Dave Magadan	.10	394	Allan Anderson	.08	477	Tommy John	.10	559	Ron Robinson	.08
313	Jim Gantner	.05	395	Bob Brenly	.05	478	Dave Anderson	.05	560	John Tudor	.05
314	Walt Terrell	.05	396	Rick Cerone	.05	479	Fred Toliver	.05	561	Don Slaught	.05
315	Wally Backman	.05	397	Scott Terry	.05	480	Jimmy Key	.12	562	Dennis Rasmussen	.05
316	Luis Salazar	.05	398	Mike Jackson	.05	481	Donell Nixon	.05	563	Brady Anderson (R)	.20
317	Rick Rhoden	.05	399	Bobby Thigpen	.05	482	Mark Portugal	.05	564	Pedro Guerrero	.15
318	Tom Henke	.05	400	Don Sutton	.10	483	Tom Pagnozzi	.05	565	Paul Molitor	.08
319	Mike Macfarlane (R)	.15	401	Cecil Espy	.10	484	Jeff Kunkel	.05	566	Terry Clark (R)	.15
320	Dan Plesac	.05	402	Junior Ortiz	.05	485	Frank Williams	.05	567	Terry Puhl	.05
321	Calvin Schiraldi	.05	403	Mike Smithson	.05	486	Jody Reed	.10	568	Mike Campbell	.05
322	Stan Javier	.05	404	Bud Black	.05	487	Roberto Kelly	.25	569	Paul Mirabella	.05
323	Devon White	.10	405	Tom Foley	.05	488	Shawn Hillegas	.05	570	Jeff Hamilton	.05
324	Scott Bradley	.05	406	Andres Thomas	.05	489	Jerry Reuss	.05	571	Oswald Peraza (R)	.15
325	Bruce Hurst	.15	407	Rick Sutcliffe	.10	490	Mark Davis	.05	572	Bob McClure	.05
326	Manny Lee	.05	408	Brian Harper	.05	491	Jeff Sellers	.05	573	Jose Bautista (R)	.15
327	Rick Aguilera	.05	409	John Smoley	.08	492	Zane Smith	.05	574	Alex Trevino	.05
328	Bruce Ruffin	.05	410	Juan Nieves	.05	493	Al Newman	.05	575	John Franco	.08
329	Ed Whitson	.05	411	Shawn Abner	.05	494	Mike Young	.05	576	Mark Parent (R)	.15
330	Bo Jackson	.50	412	Wes Gardner	.05	495	Larry Parrish	.05	577	Nelson Liriano	.05
331	Ivan Calderon	.10	413	Darren Daulton	.05	496	Herm Winningham	.05	578	Steve Shields	.05
332	Mickey Hatcher	.05	414	Juan Berenguer	.05	497	Carmen Castillo	.05	579	Odell Jones	.05
333	Barry Jones	.05	415	Charles Hudson	.08	498	Joe Hesketh	.05	580	Al Leiter	.20
334	Ron Hassey	.05	416	Rick Honeycutt	.05	499	Darrell Miller	.05	581	Dave Stapleton	.05
335	Bill Wegman	.05	417	Greg Booker	.05	500	Mike LaCoss	.05	582	'88 World Series	.25
336	Damon Berryhill	.20	418	Tim Belcher	.15	501	Charlie Lea	.05	583	Donnie Hill	.05
337	Steve Ontiveros	.05	419	Don August	.15	502	Bruce Benedict	.05	584	Chuck Jackson	.05
338	Dan Pasqua	.08	420	Dale Mohorcic	.05	503	Chuck Finley	.05	585	Rene Gonzales	.05
339	Bill Pecota	.05	421	Steve Lombardozzi	.05	504	Brad Wellman	.05	586	Tracy Woodson	.10
340	Greg Cadaret	.08	422	Atlee Hammaker	.05	505	Tim Crews	.05	587	Jim Adduci	.08
341	Scott Bankhead	.05	423	Jerry Don Gleaton	.05	506	Ken Gerhart	.05	588	Mario Soto	.05
342	Ron Guidry	.08	424	Scott Bailes	.05	507	Brian Holton	.05	589	Jeff Blauser	.05
343	Danny Heep	.05	425	Bruce Sutter	.08	508	Dennis Lamp	.05	590	Jim Traber	.05
344	Bob Brower	.05	426	Randy Ready	.05	509	Bobby Meacham	.05	591	Jon Perlman	.05
345	Rich Gedman	.05	427	Jerry Reed	.05	510	Tracy Jones	.05	592	Mark Williamson	.05
346	Nelson Santovenia (R)	.15	428	Bryn Smith	.05	511	Mike Fitzgerald	.05	593	Dave Meads	.05
347	George Bell	.15	429	Tim Leary	.10	512	Jeff Bittiger (R)	.15	594	Jim Eisenreich	.05
348	Ted Power	.05	430	Mark Clear	.05	513	Tim Flannery	.05	595	Paul Gibson (R)	.15
349	Mark Grant	.05	431	Terry Leach	.05	514	Ray Hayward	.05	596	Mike Birkbeck	.05
350	R. Clemens (correct)	.50	432	John Moses	.05	515	Dave Leiper	.05	597	Terry Francona	.05
350	R. Clemens (error)	2.50	433	Ozzie Guillen	.08	516	Rod Scurry	.05	598	Paul Zuvella	.05
351	Bill Long	.05	434	Gene Nelson	.05	517	Carmelo Martinez	.05	599	Franklin Stubbs	.05
352	Jay Bell	.10	435	Gary Ward	.05	518	Curtis Wilkerson	.05	600	Gregg Jefferies	1.00
353	Steve Balboni	.05	436	Luis Aguayo	.05	519	Stan Jefferson	.08	601	John Cangelosi	.05

NO.	PLAYER	MINT
602	Mike Sharperson	.05
603	Mike Diaz	.05
604	Gary Varsho (R)	.20
605	Terry Blocker (R)	.15
606	Charlie O'Brien	.05
607	Jim Eppard	.10
608	John Davis	.05
609	Ken Griffey, Sr.	.10
610	Buddy Bell	.05
611	Ted Simmons	.05
612	Matt Williams	.20
613	Danny Cox	.05
614	Al Pedrique	.05
615	Ron Oester	.05
616	John Smoltz (R)	.35
617	Bob Melvin	.05
618	Rob Dibble (R)	.20

NO.	PLAYER	MINT
619	Kirt Manwaring	.05
No. 620 to 651 (Rookie Prospects)		
620	Felix Fermin	.10
621	Doug Dascenzo (R)	.20
622	Bill Brennan (R)	.20
623	Carlos Quintana (R)	.35
624	Mike Harkey (R)	.30
625	Gary Sheffield (R)	1.25
626	Tom Prince	.10
627	Steve Searcy (R)	.20
628	Charlie Hayes (R)	.20
629	Felix Jose (R)	.25
630	Sandy Alomar (R)	.75
631	Derek Lilliquist (R)	.25
632	Geronimo Berroa	.15
633	Luis Medina (R)	.35
634	Tom Gordon (R)	1.50

NO.	PLAYER	MINT
635	Ramon Martinez (R)	.35
636	Craig Worthington (R)	.35
637	Edgar Martinez (R)	.15
638	Chad Krueter (R)	.20
639	Ron Jones (R)	.40
640	Van Snider (R)	.25
641	Lance Blankenship (R)	.20
642	Dwight Smith (R)	2.50
643	Cameron Drew (R)	.25
644	Jerald Clark (R)	.15
645	Randy Johnson (R)	.25
646	Norm Charlton (R)	.20
647	Todd Frohwirth (R)	.12
648	Luis De los Santos (R)	.25
649	Tim Jones (R)	.20
650	Dave West (R)	.35
651	Bob Milacki (R)	.25

NO.	PLAYER	MINT
652	Highlight—Wrigley Field— night opener	.15
653	Highlight—Hershiser— scoreless inning record	.20
654	Highlight—Boggs—6 yrs. consecutive 200 hits	.50
654	HL Boggs (error)	2.50
655	Highlight—Canseco 40 hr's, 40 stolen bases	.50
656	Highlight—Jones—saves	.05
657	Highlight—Henderson— lead off homers	.15
658	Highlight—Browning— perfect game	.10
659	Highlight—Greenwell—A.L. game-winning record	.30
660	Highlight—Red Sox—24 home game-winning streak	.15

1989 Score Traded & Rookie. . . . Complete Set of 110 Cards—Value $15.00

Updates the main 1989 card set with players who changed teams during the season, and rookies. Features the first Score card of Jerome Walton, Jim Abbott and Ken Griffey, Jr.

NO.	PLAYER	MINT
1	Rafael Palmeiro	.10
2	Nolan Ryan	1.25
3	Jack Clark	.15
4	Dave LaPoint	.05
5	Mike Moore	.05
6	Pete O'Brien	.05
7	Jeffrey Leonard	.05
8	Rob Murphy	.05
9	Tom Herr	.05
10	Claudell Washington	.05
11	Mike Pagliarulo	.05
12	Steve Lake	.05
13	Spike Owen	.05
14	Andy Hawkins	.05
15	Todd Benzinger	.05
16	Mookie Wilson	.05
17	Bert Blyleven	.10
18	Jeff Treadway	.05
19	Bruce Hurst	.05
20	Steve Sax	.15
21	Juan Samuel	.05
22	Jesse Barfield	.05
23	Carmelo Castillo	.05
24	Terry Leach	.05
25	Mark Langston	.20
26	Eric King	.05
27	Steve Balboni	.05
28	Len Dykstra	.05

NO.	PLAYER	MINT
29	Keith Moreland	.05
30	Terry Kennedy	.05
31	Eddie Murray	.12
32	Mitch Williams	.15
33	Jeff Parrett	.05
34	Wally Backman	.05
35	Julio Franco	.10
36	Lance Parrish	.05
37	Nick Esasky	.10
38	Luis Polonia	.05
39	Kevin Gross	.05
40	John Dopson	.05
41	Willie Randolph	.05
42	Jim Clancy	.05
43	Tracy Jones	.05
44	Phil Bradley	.05
45	Milt Thompson	.05
46	Chris James	.05
47	Scott Fletcher	.05
48	Kal Daniels	.10
49	Steve Bedrosian	.05
50	Rickey Henderson	.40
51	Dion James	.05
52	Tim Leary	.05
53	Roger Mcdowell	.05
54	Mel Hall	.05
55	Dickie Thon	.05

NO.	PLAYER	MINT
56	Zane Smith	.05
57	Danny Heep	.05
58	Bob McClure	.05
59	Brian Holton	.05
60	Randy Ready	.05
61	Bob Melvin	.05
62	Harold Baines	.05
63	Lance McCullers	.05
64	Jody Davis	.05
65	Darrell Evans	.05
66	Joel Youngblood	.05
67	Frank Viola	.10
68	Mike Aldrete	.05
69	Greg Cadaret	.05
70	John Kruk	.05
71	Pat Sheridan	.05
72	Oddibe McDowell	.05
73	Tom Brookens	.05
74	Bob Boone	.05
75	Walt Terrell	.05
76	Joel Skinner	.05
77	Randy Johnson	.05
78	Felix Fermin	.05
79	Rick Mahler	.05
80	Rich Dotson	.05
81	Cris Carpenter	.25
82	Bill Spiers	.30

NO.	PLAYER	MINT
83	Junior Felix (RR)	1.25
84	Joe Girardi	.30
85	Jerome Walton (RR)	4.00
86	Greg Litton	.25
87	Greg Harris	.20
88	Jim Abbott (RR)	2.00
89	Kevin Brown	.20
90	John Wetteland	.50
91	Gary Wayne	.20
92	Rich Monteleone	.25
93	Bob Geren	.40
94	Clay Parker	.20
95	Steve Finley	.35
96	Gregg Olson (RR)	1.00
97	Ken Patterson	.12
98	Ken Hill	.20
99	Scott Scudder	.30
100	Ken Griffey, Jr. (RR)	3.00
101	Jeff Brantley	.20
102	Donn Pall	.15
103	Carlos Martinez	.25
104	Joe Oliver	.30
105	Omar Vizquel	.25
106	Joey Belle (RR)	1.25
107	Kenny Rogers	.20
108	Mark Carreon	.15
109	Rolando Roomes	.35
110	Pete Harnisch	.20

1990 Score.... Complete Set of 704 Cards—Value $25.00

The set was increased from 660 to 704 cards. New features this year include 22 First Round Draft Pick cards, 13 Dream Team cards (styled after the 1911 T-206 cards), 4 World Series cards and 5 Highlight cards.

NO.	PLAYER	MINT
1	Don Mattingly	.65
2	Cal Ripken, Jr.	.12
3	Dwight Evans	.08
4	Barry Bonds	.10
5	Kevin McReynolds	.10
6	Ozzie Guillen	.08
7	Terry Kennedy	.05
8	Bryan Harvey	.05
9	Alan Trammell	.08
10	Cory Snyder	.10
11	Jody Reed	.05
12	Roberto Alomar	.10
13	Pedro Guerrero	.10
14	Gary Redus	.05
15	Marty Barrett	.05
16	Ricky Jordan	.25
17	Joe Magrane	.10
18	Sid Fernandez	.08
19	Rich Dotson	.05
20	Jack Clark	.08
21	Bob Walk	.05
22	Ron Karkovice	.05
23	Lenny Harris	.08
24	Phil Bradley	.08
25	Andres Galarraga	.12
26	Brian Downing	.05
27	Dave Martinez	.05
28	Eric King	.05
29	Barry Lyons	.05
30	Dave Schmidt	.08
31	Mike Boddicker	.08
32	Tom Foley	.05
33	Brady Anderson	.05
34	Jim Presley	.05
35	Lance Parrish	.08
36	Von Hayes	.08
37	Lee Smith	.08
38	Herm Winningham	.05
39	Alejandro Pena	.05
40	Mike Scott	.08
41	Joe Orsulak	.05
42	Rafael Ramirez	.05
43	Gerald Young	.10
44	Dick Schofield	.05
45	Dve Smith	.08
46	Dave Magadan	.08
47	Dennis Martinez	.05
48	Greg Minton	.05
49	Milt Thompson	.05
50	Orel Hershiser	.12
51	Bip Roberts	.05
52	Jerry Browne	.08
53	Bob Ojeda	.05
54	Fernando Valenzuela	.10
55	Matt Nokes	.08
56	Brook Jacoby	.05
57	Frank Tanana	.05
58	Scott Fletcher	.05
59	Ron Oester	.05
60	Bob Boone	.05
61	Dan Gladden	.05
62	Darnell Coles	.05
63	Gregg Olson	.25
64	Todd Burns	.05

NO.	PLAYER	MINT
65	Todd Benzinger	.08
66	Dale Murphy	.12
67	Mike Flanagan	.05
68	Jose Oquendo	.05
69	Cecil Espy	.05
70	Chris Sabo	.10
71	Shane Rawley	.05
72	Tom Brunansky	.05
73	Vance Law	.05
74	B.J. Surhoff	.05
75	Lou Whitaker	.08
76	Ken Caminiti	.05
77	Nelson Liriano	.05
78	Tommy Gregg	.05
79	Don Slaught	.05
80	Eddie Murray	.10
81	Joe Boever	.05
82	Charlie Leibrandt	.05
83	Jose Lind	.05
84	Tony Phillips	.05
85	Mitch Webster	.05
86	Dan Plesac	.05
87	Rick Mahler	.05
88	Steve Lyons	.05
89	Tony Fernandez	.10
90	Ryne Sandberg	.10
91	Nick Esasky	.05
92	Luis Salazar	.05
93	Pete Incaviglia	.10
94	Ivan Calderon	.05
95	Jeff Treadway	.05
96	Kurt Stillwell	.05
97	Gary Sheffield	.35
98	Jeffrey Leonard	.05
99	Andres Thomas	.05
100	Roberto Kelly	.12
101	Alvaro Espinoza	.05
102	Greg Gagne	.05
103	John Farrell	.08
104	Willie Wilson	.08
105	Glenn Braggs	.05
106	Chet Lemon	.05
107	Jamie Moyer	.05
108	Chuck Crim	.05
109	Dave Valle	.05
110	Walt Weiss	.10
111	Larry Sheets	.05
112	Don Robinson	.05
113	Danny Heep	.05
114	Carmelo Martinez	.05
115	Dave Gallagher	.05
116	Mike LaValliere	.05
117	Bob McClure	.05
118	Rene Gonzales	.05
119	Mark Parent	.05
120	Wally Joyner	.10
121	Mark Gubicza	.05
122	Tony Pena	.08
123	Carmelo Castillo	.05
124	Howard Johnson	.10
125	Steve Sax	.08
126	Tim Belcher	.08
127	Tim Burke	.05
128	Al Newman	.05

NO.	PLAYER	MINT
129	Dennis Rasmussen	.05
130	Doug Jones	.05
131	Fred Lynn	.08
132	Jeff Hamilton	.05
133	German Gonzalez	.05
134	John Morris	.05
135	Dave Parker	.10
136	Gary Pettis	.05
137	Dennis Boyd	.05
138	Candy Maldonado	.05
139	Rick Cerone	.05
140	George Brett	.15
141	Dave Clark	.05
142	Dickie Thon	.05
143	Junior Ortiz	.05
144	Don August	.08
145	Gary Gaetti	.10
146	Kirt Manwaring	.05
147	Jeff Reed	.05
148	Jose Alvarez	.05
149	Mike Schooler	.10
150	Mark Grace	.35
151	Geronimo Berroa	.07
152	Barry Jones	.05
153	Geno Petralli	.05
154	Jim Deshaies	.05
155	Barry Larkin	.12
156	Alfredo Griffin	.08
157	Tom Henke	.05
158	Mike Jeffcoat	.05
159	Bob Welch	.05
160	Julio Franco	.10
161	Henry Cotto	.05
162	Terry Steinbach	.10
163	Damon Berryhill	.08
164	Tim Crews	.05
165	Tom Browning	.05
166	Fred Manrique	.05
167	Harold Reynolds	.05
168	Ron Hassey	.05
169	Shawon Dunston	.08
170	Bobby Bonilla	.10
171	Tom Herr	.05
172	Mike Heath	.05
173	Rich Gedman	.05
174	Bill Ripken	.08
175	Pete O'Brien	.08
176	Lloyd McClendon	.08
177	Brian Holton	.05
178	Jeff Blauser	.05
179	Jim Eisenreich	.05
180	Bert Blyleven	.08
181	Rob Murphy	.05
182	Bill Doran	.05
183	Curt Ford	.05
184	Mike Henneman	.05
185	Eric Davis	.25
186	Lance McCullers	.05
187	Steve Davis (R)	.15
188	Bill Wegman	.05
189	Brian Harper	.05
190	Mike Moore	.08
191	Dale Mohorcic	.05
192	Tim Wallach	.05

NO.	PLAYER	MINT
193	Keith Hernandez	.08
194	Dave Righetti	.10
195	Bret Saberhagen	.10
196	Paul Kilgus	.05
197	Bud Black	.05
198	Juan Samuel	.08
199	Kevin Seitzer	.10
200	Darryl Strawberry	.30
201	Dave Stieb	.05
202	Charlie Hough	.05
203	Jack Morris	.10
204	Rance Mulliniks	.05
205	Alvin Davis	.08
206	Jack Howell	.05
207	Ken Patterson	.05
208	Terry Pendleton	.05
209	Craig Lefferts	.05
210	Kevin Brown	.05
211	Dan Petry	.05
212	Dave Leiper	.05
213	Daryl Boston	.05
214	Kevin Hickey	.15
215	Mike Krukow	.08
216	Terry Francona	.05
217	Mirk McCaskill	.08
218	Scott Bailes	.05
219	Bob Forsch	.05
220	Mike Aldrete	.10
221	Steve Buechele	.05
222	Jesse Barfield	.05
223	Juan Berenguer	.05
224	Andy McGaffigan	.05
225	Pete Smith	.05
226	Mike Witt	.08
227	Jay Howell	.08
228	Scott Bradley	.05
229	Jerome Walton	1.50
230	Greg Swindell	.10
231	Atlee Hammaker	.05
232	Mike Devereaux	.08
233	Ken Hill	.08
234	Craig Worthington	.08
235	Scott Terry	.05
236	Brett Butler	.05
237	Doyle Alexander	.08
238	Dave Anderson	.05
239	Bob Milacki	.08
240	Dwight Smith	.30
241	Otis Nixon	.05
242	Pat Tabler	.05
243	Derek Lilliquist	.08
244	Danny Tartabull	.10
245	Wade Boggs	.30
246	Scott Garrelts	.08
247	Spike Owen	.05
248	Norm Charlton	.05
249	Gerald Perry	.05
250	Nolan Ryan	.25
251	Kevin Gross	.05
252	Randy Milligan	.05
253	Mike LaCoss	.05
254	Dave Bergman	.05
255	Tony Gwynn	.15
256	Felix Fermin	.05

NO.	PLAYER	MINT
257	Greg Harris	10
258	Junior Felix	30
259	Mark Davis	08
260	Vince Coleman	08
261	Paul Gibson	05
262	Mitch Williams	08
263	Jeff Russell	05
264	Omar Vizquel (R)	15
265	Andre Dawson	12
266	Storm Davis	05
267	Guillermo Hernandez	05
268	Mike Felder	05
269	Tom Candiotti	05
270	Bruce Hurst	05
271	Fred McGriff	15
272	Glenn Davis	10
273	John Franco	08
274	Rich Yett	08
275	Craig Biggio	10
276	Gene Larkin	05
277	Rob Dibble	10
278	Randy Bush	05
279	Kevin Bass	05
280	Bo Jackson	50
281	Wally Backman	05
282	Larry Andersen	05
283	Chris Bosio	05
284	Juan Agosto	05
285	Ozzie Smith	08
286	George Bell	08
287	Rex Hudler	05
288	Pat Borders	05
289	Danny Jackson	10
290	Carlton Fisk	10
291	Tracy Jones	05
292	Allan Anderson	08
293	Johnny Ray	08
294	Lee Guetterman	05
295	Paul O'Neill	05
296	Carney Lansford	08
297	Tom Brookens	05
298	Claudell Washington	05
299	Hubie Brooks	05
300	Will Clark	60
301	Kenny Rogers (R)	10
302	Darrell Evans	05
303	Greg Briley	15
304	Donn Pall	08
305	Teddy Higuera	05
306	Dan Pasqua	05
307	Dave Winfield	12
308	Dennis Powell	05
309	Jose DeLeon	05
310	Roger Clemens	25
311	Melido Perez	05
312	Devon White	10
313	Doc Gooden	25
314	Carlos Martinez (R)	20
315	Dennis Eckersley	08
316	Clay Parker	10
317	Rick Honeycutt	05
318	Tim Laudner	05
319	Joe Carter	10
320	Robin Yount	25
321	Felix Jose	05
322	Mickey Tettleton	05
323	Mike Gallego	05
324	Edgar Martinez	05
325	Dave Henderson	08
326	Chili Davis	05
327	Steve Balboni	05
328	Jody Davis	05
329	Shawn Hillegas	05
330	Jim Abbott	75
331	John Dopson	08
332	Mark Williamson	05
333	Jeff Robinson	08
334	John Smiley	08
335	Bobby Thigpen	05
336	Garry Templeton	05
337	Marvell Wynne	05
338	Ken Griffey, Sr.	05
339	Steve Finley (R)	20
340	Ellis Burks	20
341	Frank Williams	05
342	Mike Morgan	05
343	Kevin Mitchell	20
344	Joel Youngblood	05
345	Mike Greenwell	25
346	Glenn Wilson	05
347	John Costello	05
348	Wes Gardner	05
349	Jeff Ballard	08
350	Mark Thurmond	05
351	Randy Myers	08
352	Shawn Abner	05
353	Jesse Orosco	05
354	Greg Walker	05
355	Pete Harnisch	08
356	Steve Farr	05
357	Dave LaPoint	05
358	Willie Fraser	05
359	Mickey Hatcher	08
360	Rickey Henderson	20
361	Mike Fitzgerald	05
362	Bill Schroeder	05
363	Mark Carreon	05
364	Ron Jones	05
365	Jeff Montgomery	08
366	Bill Krueger	05
367	John Cangelosi	05
368	Jose Gonzalez	05
369	Greg Hibbard (R)	15
370	John Smoltz	10
371	Jeff Brantley (R)	15
372	Frank White	05
373	Ed Whitson	05
374	Willie McGee	08
375	Jose Canseco	60
376	Randy Ready	05
377	Don Aase	05
378	Tony Armas	05
379	Steve Bedrosian	05
380	Chuck Finley	08
381	Kent Hrbek	08
382	Jim Gantner	05
383	Mel Hall	05
384	Mike Marshall	08
385	Mark McGwire	25
386	Wayne Tolleson	05
387	Brian Homan	05
388	John Wetteland (R)	20
389	Darren Daulton	05
390	Rob Deer	05
391	John Moses	05
392	Todd Worrell	08
393	Chuck Cary	05
394	Stan Javier	05
395	Willie Randolph	08
396	Bill Buckner	05
397	Robby Thompson	10
398	Mike Scioscia	08
399	Lonnie Smith	05
400	Kirby Puckett	25
401	Mark Langston	10
402	Danny Darwin	05
403	Greg Maddux	12
404	Lloyd Moseby	08
405	Rafael Palmeiro	10
406	Chad Kreuter	05
407	Jimmy Key	08
408	Tim Birtsas	05
409	Tim Raines	12
410	Dave Stewart	10
411	Eric Yelding (R)	10
412	Kent Anderson (R)	10
413	Les Lancaster	05
414	Rick Dempsey	05
415	Randy Johnson	08
416	Gary Carter	08
417	Rolando Roomes	08
418	Dan Schatzeder	05
419	Bryn Smith	05
420	Ruben Sierra	20
421	Steve Jeltz	08
422	Ken Oberkfell	05
423	Sid Bream	05
424	Jim Clancy	05
425	Kelly Gruber	08
426	Rick Leach	05
427	Lenny Dykstra	08
428	Jeff Pico	05
429	John Cerutti	05
430	David Cone	12
431	Jeff Kunkel	05
432	Luis Aquino	05
433	Ernie Whitt	05
434	Bo Diaz	05
435	Steve Lake	05
436	Pat Perry	05
437	Mike Davis	05
438	Cecilio Guante	05
439	Duane Ward	05
440	Andy Van Slyke	10
441	Gene Nelson	05
442	Luis Polonia	05
443	Kevin Elster	08
444	Keith Moreland	05
445	Roger McDowell	05
446	Ron Darling	10
447	Ernest Riles	05
448	Mookie Wilson	08
449	Bill Spiers (R)	20
450	Rick Sutcliffe	05
451	Nelson Santovenia	05
452	Andy Allanson	05
453	Bob Melvin	05
454	Benny Santiago	10
455	Jose Uribe	05
456	Bill Landrum	05
457	Bobby Witt	08
458	Kevin Romine	05
459	Lee Mazzilli	05
460	Paul Molitor	10
461	Ramon Martinez	10
462	Frank DiPino	05
463	Walt Terrell	05
464	Bob Geren (R)	15
465	Rick Reuschel	08
466	Mark Grant	05
467	John Kruk	05
468	Gregg Jefferies	35
469	R.J. Reynolds	05
470	Harold Baines	08
471	Dennis Lamp	05
472	Tom Gordon	35
473	Terry Puhl	05
474	Curtis Wilkerson	05
475	Dan Quisenberry	05
476	Oddibe McDowell	05
477	Zane Smith	05
478	Franklin Stubbs	05
479	Wallace Johnson	05
480	Jay Tibbs	05
481	Tom Glavine	08
482	Manny Lee	05
483	Joe Hesketh	05
484	Mike Bielecki	05
485	Greg Brock	05
486	Pascual Perez	05
487	Kirk Gibson	08
488	Scott Sanderson	05
489	Domingo Ramos	05
490	Kal Daniels	10
491	David Wells	05
492	Jerry Reed	05
493	Eric Show	05
494	Mike Pagliarulo	08
495	Ron Robinson	05
496	Brad Komminsk	05
497	Greg Litton (R)	15
498	Chris James	05
499	Luis Quinones	05
500	Frank Viola	10
501	Tim Teufel	05
502	Terry Leach	05
503	Matt Williams	15
504	Tim Leary	08
505	Doug Drabek	08
506	Mariano Duncan	05
507	Charlie Hayes	05
508	Joey Belle (R)	50
509	Pat Sheridan	05
510	Mackey Sasser	05
511	Jose Rijo	05
512	Mike Smithson	05
513	Gary Ward	05
514	Dion James	05
515	Jim Gott	05
516	Drew Hall	05
517	Doug Bair	05
518	Scott Scudder (R)	15
519	Rick Aguilera	05
520	Rafael Belliard	05
521	Jay Buhner	08
522	Jeff Reardon	08
523	Steve Rosenberg	05
524	Randy Velarde	05
525	Jeff Musselman	05
526	Bill Long	05
527	Gary Wayne (R)	10
528	Dave Johnson (R)	10
529	Ron Kittle	05
530	Erik Hanson	08
531	Steve Wilson	10
532	Joey Meyer	05
533	Curt Young	05
534	Kelly Downs	08
535	Joe Girardi	15
536	Lance Blankenship	05
537	Greg Mathews	05
538	Donell Nixon	05
539	Mark Knudson	08
540	Jeff Wetherby (R)	15
541	Darrin Jackson	05
542	Terry Mulholland	05
543	Eric Hetzel	05
544	Rick Reed (R)	15
545	Dennis Cook	10
546	Mike Jackson	05
547	Brian Fisher	05
548	Gene Harris (R)	15
549	Jeff King	12
550	Dave Dravecky	05
551	Randy Kutcher	05
552	Mark Portugal	05
553	Jim Corsi	08
554	Todd Stottlemyre	08
555	Scott Bankhead	05
556	Ken Dayley	05
557	Rick Wrona (R)	15
558	Sammy Sosa (R)	45
559	Keith Miller	05
560	Ken Griffey, Jr.	50
561	HL: Ryne Sandberg	40
562	Billy Hatcher	05
563	Jay Bell	05
564	Jack Daugherty (R)	15
565	Rich Monteleone (R)	10
566	Bo Jackson (MVP)	40
567	Tony Fossas (R)	15
568	Roy Smith	05
569	Jaime Navarro (R)	25
570	Lance Johnson	05
571	Mike Dyer (R)	15
572	Kevin Ritz (R)	15
573	Dave West	10
574	Gary Mielke (R)	15
575	Scott Lusader	05
576	Joe Oliver (R)	15
577	Sandy Alomar, Jr.	30
578	Andy Benes	50
579	Tim Jones	05
580	Randy McCament (R)	15
581	Curt Schilling	10
582	John Orton (R)	25
583	Milt Cuyler (R)	15
584	Eric Anthony (R)	1.50
585	Greg Vaughn (R)	1.50
586	Deion Sanders (R)	60
587	Jose DeJesus	05
588	Chip Hale (R)	15
589	John Olerud (R)	2.00
590	Steve Olin (R)	15
591	Marquis Grissom (R)	50
592	Moises Alou (R)	30

NO.	PLAYER	MINT
593	Mark Lemke	.05
594	Dean Palmer (R)	.20
595	Robin Ventura	.40
596	Tino Martinez (R)	.35
597	Mike Huff (R)	.25
598	Scott Hemond (R)	.25
599	Wally Whitehurst	.15
600	Todd Zeile (R)	1.25
601	Hill Glenallen	.08
602	Hal Morris	.15
603	Juan Bell	.15
604	Bobby Rose (R)	.25
605	Matt Merullo (R)	.15
606	Kevin Maas (R)	.25
607	Randy Nosek (R)	.15
608	Billy Bates (R)	.20
609	Mike Stanton (R)	.15
610	Goose Gozzo (R)	.15
611	Charles Nagy (R)	.20
612	Scott Coolbaugh (R)	.35
613	Jose Vizcaino (R)	.20
614	Greg Smith (R)	.25
615	Jeff Huson (R)	.20
616	Mickey Weston (R)	.15
617	John Pawlowski	.10
618	Joe Skalski (R)	.15
619	Bernie Williams (R)	.50
620	Shawn Holman (R)	.20
621	Gary Eave (R)	.15
622	Darrin Fletcher (R)	.20
623	Pat Combs	.40
624	Mike Blowers (R)	.20
625	Kevin Appier (R)	.15
626	Pat Austin (R)	.20
627	Kelly Mann (R)	.15
628	Matt Kinzer (R)	.20
629	Chris Hammond (R)	.20
630	Dean Wilkins (R)	.15
631	Larry Walker (R)	.20
632	Blaine Beatty (R)	.20
633	Tom Barrett	.08
634	Stan Belinda (R)	.15
635	Mike Smith (Tex) (R)	.15
636	Hensley Meulens	.20
637	Juan Gonzalez (R)	.50
638	Lenny Webster (R)	.15
639	Mark Gardner (R)	.15
640	Tommy Greene (R)	.40
641	Mike Hartley (R)	.15
642	Phil Stephenson (R)	.10
643	Kevin Mmahat (R)	.20
644	Ed Whited (R)	.15
645	Delino DeShields (R)	.25
646	Kevin Blankenship	.08
647	Paul Sorrento (R)	.15
648	Mike Roesler (R)	.15
649	Jason Brimsely (R)	.20
650	Dave Justice (R)	.20
651	Scott Cooper (R)	.25
652	Dave Eiland	.10
653	Mike Munoz (R)	.20
654	Jeff Fischer (R)	.25
655	Terry Jorgenson (R)	.15
656	George Canale (R)	.20
657	Brian Dubois (R)	.15
658	Carlos Quintana	.08
659	Luis De Los Santos	.05
660	Jerald Clark	.05
661	Donald Harris (R)	.30
662	Paul Coleman (R)	.35
663	Frank Thomas (R)	.35
664	Brent Mayne (R)	.25
665	Eddie Zosky (R)	.20
666	Steve Hosey (R)	.25
667	Scott Bryant (R)	.25
668	Tom Goodwin (R)	.50
669	Cal Eldred (R)	.25
670	Earl Cunningham (R)	.40
671	Alan Zinter (R)	.15
672	Chuck Knoblauch (R)	.20
673	Kyle Abbott (R)	.25
674	Roger Salkeld (R)	.25
675	Maurice Vaughn (R)	.30
676	Keith Jones (Kiki) (R)	.40
677	Tyler Houston (R)	.50
678	Jeff Jackson (R)	.25
679	Greg Gohr (R)	.25
680	Ben McDonald (R)	2.00
681	Greg Blosser (R)	.25
682	Willie Green (R)	.25
683	Wade Boggs	.25
684	Will Clark	.40
685	Tony Gwynn	.15
686	Rickey Henderson	.20
687	Bo Jackson	.40
688	Mark Langston	.12
689	Barry Larkin	.12
690	Kirby Puckett	.25
691	Ryne Sandberg	.10
692	Mike Scott	.08
693	Terry Steinbach	.10
694	Bobby Thigpen	.05
695	Mitch Williams	.08
696	Nolan Ryan	.25
697	Bo Jackson	.60
698	Rickey Henderson	.20
699	Will Clark	.40
700	WS Games 1,2	.10
701	Candlestick Park	.10
702	WS Game 3	.10
703	WS Wrap-up	.10
704	HL: Wade Boggs	.20

1986 Sportflics. . . . Complete Set of 200 Cards—Value $40.00

Sportflics entered the baseball card market in 1986. Each card can be tilted to show three different photos. The set includes 139 cards, each featuring three poses of the same player; 50 "Tri-Stars"—each card featuring three players; 10 "Big Six" cards—each featuring six players; 1 World Series card—featuring 12 players.

Dwight Gooden—Phase 1

Dwight Gooden—Phase 2

Dwight Gooden—Phase 3

NO.	PLAYER	MINT
1	George Brett	1.00
2	Don Mattingly	4.00
3	Wade Boggs	2.00
4	Eddie Murray	.50
5	Dale Murphy	1.00
6	Rickey Henderson	.75
7	Harold Baines	.25
8	Cal Ripken, Jr.	.60
9	Orel Hershiser	.60
10	Bret Saberhagen	.30
11	Tim Raines	.35
12	Fernando Valenzuela	.30
13	Tony Gwynn	.75
14	Pedro Guerrero	.30
15	Keith Hernandez	.30
16	Ernest Riles	.20
17	Jim Rice	.35
18	Ron Guidry	.30
19	Willie McGee	.35
20	Ryne Sandberg	.60
21	Kirk Gibson	.50
22	Ozzie Guillen (R)	.25
23	Dave Parker	.30
24	Vince Coleman (R)	1.75
25	Tom Seaver	.60
26	Bret Butler	.15
27	Steve Carlton	.50
28	Gary Carter	.40
29	Cecil Cooper	.25
30	Jose Cruz	.20
31	Alvin Davis	.20
32	Dwight Evans	.25
33	Julio Franco	.15
34	Damaso Garcia	.15
35	Steve Garvey	.60
36	Kent Hrbek	.35
37	Reggie Jackson	.75
38	Fred Lynn	.25
39	Paul Molitor	.30
40	Jim Presley	.30
41	Dave Righetti	.25
42	Robin Yount	.50
43	Nolan Ryan	1.00
44	Mike Schmidt	1.00
45	Lee Smith	.20
46	Rick Sutcliffe	.20
47	Bruce Sutter	.20
48	Lou Whitaker	.20
49	Dave Winfield	.50
50	Pete Rose	1.25

No. 51 to 75—TRI-STARS

NO.	PLAYER	MINT
51	Nat'l. League MVPs:	.75
	Ryn Sandberg, Steve Garvey, Pete Rose	
52	Slugging Stars:	.30
	Harold Baines, George Brett, Jim Rice	
53	No-Hitters:	.25
	Mike Witt, Phil Niekro, Jerry Reuss	
54	Big Hitters:	1.00
	Robin Yount, Don Mattingly, Cal Ripken, Jr.	
55	Bullpen Aces:	.25
	Dan Quisenberry, Lee Smith, Goose Gossage	
56	Rookies of The Year:	.75
	Pete Rose, Steve Sax, Darryl Strawberry	
57	Am. League MVP's:	.40
	Cal Ripken, Jr., Don Baylor, Reggie Jackson	
58	Batting Champs:	.60
	Bill Madlock, Pete Rose, Dave Parker	
59	Cy Young Winners:	.20
	LaMarr Hoyt, Mike Flanagan, Ron Guidry	
60	Double Award Winners:	.30
	Fernando Valenzuela, Rick Sutcliffe, Tom Seaver	
61	Home Run Champs:	.60
	Tony Armas, Reggie Jackson, Jim Rice	
62	Nat'l League MVP's:	.75
	Keith Hernandez, Mike Schmidt, Dale Murphy	
63	Am. League MVP's:	.50
	George Brett, Robin Yount, Fred Lynn	
64	Comeback Players:	.20
	Bert Blyleven, Jerry Koosman, John Denny	
65	Cy Young Relievers:	.25
	Willie Hernandez, Rollie Fingers, Bruce Sutter	
66	Rookies of The Year:	.25
	Bob Horner, Andre Dawson, G. Matthews	
67	Rookies of The Year:	.35
	Ron Kittle, Carlton Fisk, Tom Seaver	
68	Home Run Champs:	.30
	Dave Kingman, Mike Schmidt, George Foster	
69	Dbl. Award Winners:	.75
	Cal Ripken, Jr., Pete Rose, Rod Carew	
70	Cy Young Winners:	.30
	Rick Sutcliffe, Steve Carlton, Tom Seaver	
71	Top Sluggers:	.35
	Reggie Jackson, Fred Lynn, Robin Yount	
72	Rookies of The Year:	.25
	Rick Sutcliffe, Dave Righetti, F. Valenzuela	
73	Rookies of The Year:	.50
	Fred Lynn, Eddie Murray, Cal Ripken, Jr.	
74	Rookies of The Year:	.25
	Alvin Davis, Lou Whitaker, Rod Carew	
75	Batting Champs:	1.50
	Don Mattingly, Carney Lansford, Wade Boggs	

NO.	PLAYER	MINT
76	Jesse Barfield	.35
77	Phil Bradley	.25
78	Chris Brown (R)	.35
79	Tom Browning	.25
80	Tom Brunansky	.25
81	Bill Buckner	.15
82	Chili Davis	.15
83	Mike Davis	.15
84	Rich Gedman	.15
85	Willie Hernandez	.15
86	Ron Kittle	.15
87	Lee Lacy	.15
88	Bill Madlock	.15
89	Mike Marshall	.15
90	Keith Moreland	.15
91	Graig Nettles	.15
92	Lance Parrish	.25
93	Kirby Puckett	1.00
94	Juan Samuel	.25
95	Steve Sax	.30
96	Dave Stieb	.25
97	Darryl Strawberry	1.00
98	Willie Upshaw	.15
99	Frank Viola	.35
100	Dwight Gooden	1.25
101	Joaquin Andujar	.15
102	George Bell	.45
103	Bert Blyleven	.20
104	Mike Boddicker	.15
105	Britt Burns	.15
106	Rod Carew	.50
107	Jack Clark	.30
108	Danny Cox	.15
109	Ron Darling	.30
110	Andre Dawson	.40
111	Leon Durham	.15
112	Tony Fernandez	.25
113	Tom Herr	.15
114	Teddy Higuera (R)	.60
115	Bob Horner	.20
116	Dave Kingman	.15
117	Jack Morris	.25
118	Dan Quisenberry	.20
119	Jeff Reardon	.20
120	Bryn Smith	.15
121	Ozzie Smith	.35
122	John Tudor	.15
123	Tim Wallach	.15
124	Willie Wilson	.15
125	Carlton Fisk	.30

No. 126 to 150—TRI-STARS

NO.	PLAYER	MINT
126	RBI Sluggers:	.20
	George Foster, Gary Carter, Al Oliver	
127	Run Scorers:	.50
	Keith Hernandez, Tim Raines, Ryne Sandberg	
128	Run Scorers:	.35
	Willie Wilson, Paul Molitor, Cal Ripken, Jr.	
129	No-Hitters:	.20
	J. Candelaria, B. Forsch, D. Eckersley	

NO.	PLAYER	MINT
130	World Series MVP's:	.50
	Rollie Fingers, Pete Rose, Ron Cey	
131	All-Star Game MVP's:	.20
	George Foster, Dave Concepcion, Bill Madlock	
132	Cy Young Winners:	.20
	Vida Blue, John Denny, Fernando Valenzuela	
133	Comeback Players:	.20
	Richard Dotson, Joaquin Andujar, Doyle Alexander	
134	Big Winners:	.30
	Rick Sutcliffe, Tom Seaver, John Denny	
135	Veteran Pitchers:	.35
	Tom Seaver, Phil Niekro, Don Sutton	
136	Rookies of The Year:	.75
	Dwight Gooden, Vince Coleman, Alfredo Griffin	
137	All-Star Game MVP's	.35
	Steve Garvey, Gary Carter, Fred Lynn	
138	Veteran Hitters:	.50
	Tony Perez, Pete Rose, Rusty Staub	
139	Power Hitters:	.50
	Mike Schmidt, Jim Rice, George Foster	
140	Batting Champs:	.35
	Tony Gwynn, Al Oliver, Bill Buckner	
141	No-Hitters:	.35
	Jack Morris, Dave Righetti, Nolan Ryan	
142	No-Hitters:	.30
	Tom Seaver, Bert Blyleven, Vida Blue	
143	Strikeout Kings:	1.00
	Nolan Ryan, Fernando Valenzuela, Dwight Gooden	
144	Base Stealers:	.25
	Willie Wilson, Tim Raines, Davey Lopes	
145	RBI Sluggers:	.35
	Tony Armas, Cecil Cooper, Eddie Murray	
146	Am. League MVP's:	.25
	Rod Carew, Jim Rice, Rollie Fingers	
147	World Series MVP's:	.30
	Alan Trammell, Rick Dempsey, Reggie Jackson	
148	World Series MVP's:	.35
	Darrell Porter, Mike Schmidt, Pedro Guerrero	
149	ERA Leaders:	.20
	Mike Boddicker, Rick Sutcliffe, Ron Guidry	
150	Comeback Players:	.40
	Reggie Jackson, Dave Kingman, Fred Lynn	

1986 Sportflics (Continued)

NO. PLAYER	MINT
151 Buddy Bell	.15
152 Dennis Boyd	.15
153 Dave Concepcion	.15
154 Brian Downing	.15
155 Shawon Dunston	.20
156 John Franco	.25
157 Scott Garrelts	.15
158 Bob James	.15
159 Charlie Leibrandt	.15
160 Oddibe McDowell	.30
161 Roger McDowell (R)	.35
162 Mike Moore	.15
163 Phil Niekro	.35
164 Al Oliver	.15
165 Tony Pena	.20
166 Ted Power	.15
167 Mike Scioscia	.15
168 Mario Soto	.15
169 Bob Stanley	.15
170 Gary Templeton	.15
171 Andre Thornton	.15
172 Alan Trammell	.35
173 Doug DeCinces	.20
174 Greg Walker	.20
175 Don Sutton	.35

NO. PLAYER	MINT
No. 176 to 185—THE BIG SIX	
176 1985 Award Winners:	1.00
Vince Coleman, Ozzie	
Guillen, Bret Saberhagen,	
Don Mattingly, Dwight	
Gooden, Willie McGee	
177 1985 Hot Rookies:	.50
Mark Salas, Stew Cliburn,	
Brian Fisher, Joe Hesketh,	
Joe Orsulak, Larry Sheets	
178 Future Stars:	15.00
Steve Lombardozzi, Jose	
Canseco, Mark Funderburk,	
Mike Greenwell, Billy Joe	
Robidoux, Dan Tartabull	
179 1985 Gold Glovers:	1.00
George Brett, Don	
Mattingly, Ron Guidry,	
Keith Hernandez, Willie	
McGee, Dale Murphy	
180 Active .300 Hitters	1.00
Wade Boggs, George Brett,	
Rod Carew, Cecil Cooper,	
Don Mattingly, W. Wilson	

NO. PLAYER	MINT
181 Active .300 Hitters	.75
Tony Gwynn, Bill Madlock,	
Pedro Guerrero,	
Dave Parker, Pete Rose,	
Keith Hernandez	
182 1985 Milestones:	.75
Rod Carew, Phil Niekro,	
Pete Rose, Tom Seaver,	
Nolan Ryan, Matt Tallman	
183 1985 Triple Crown:	.75
Willie McGee, Dave Parker,	
Wade Boggs, Darrell Evans,	
D. Mattingly, D. Murphy	
184 1985 Highlights:	1.25
Wade Boggs, Rickey	
Henderson, Don Mattingly,	
Willie McGee, Dwight	
Gooden, John Tudor	
185 20 Game Winners:	.75
Dwight Gooden,	
Ron Guidry, John Tudor,	
Joaquin Andujar,	
Bret Saberhagen,	
Tom Browning	

NO. PLAYER	MINT
186 W. Series Champions:	.50
D. Iorg, W. Wilson,	
C. Leibrandt, L. Smith,	
G. Brett, B. Saberhagen,	
D. Motley, D. Quisenberry,	
J. Sundberg, S. Balboni,	
F. White, D. Jackson	
187 Hubie Brooks	.20
188 Glenn Davis	.50
189 Darrell Evans	.15
190 Rich Gossage	.15
191 Andy Hawkins	.15
192 Jay Howell	.15
193 LaMarr Hoyt	.15
194 Davey Lopes	.15
195 Mike Scott	.35
196 Ted Simmons	.20
197 Gary Ward	.15
198 Bob Welch	.15
199 Mike Young	.15
200 Buddy Blancalana	.15

1987 Sportflics. . . . Complete Set of 200 Cards—Value $35.00

Each card can be tilted to show three different photos. The set included 165 individual players, 20 "Tri-Star" cards and 15 other cards. There are three different copyright on the back—1986, 1987 and no copyright.

NO. PLAYER	MINT
1 Don Mattingly	3.00
2 Wade Boggs	1.75
3 Dale Murphy	.75
4 Rickey Henderson	.60
5 George Brett	.60
6 Eddie Murray	.50
7 Kirby Puckett	.75
8 Ryne Sandberg	.35
9 Cal Ripken Jr.	.40
10 Roger Clemens	1.00
11 Teddy Higuera	.25
12 Steve Sax	.25
13 Chris Brown	.15
14 Jesse Barfield	.25
15 Kent Hrbek	.25
16 Robin Yount	.35
17 Glenn Davis	.35
18 Hubie Brooks	.15
19 Mike Scott	.25
20 Darryl Strawberry	.75
21 Alvin Davis	.20
22 Eric Davis	1.00
23 Danny Tartabull	.35
24 Cory Snyder (correct)	1.50
24 C. Snyder (error)	1.50
(photo of Pat Tabler)	
25 Pete Rose	1.00
26 Wally Joiner (R)	1.25
27 Pedro Guerrero	.25
28 Tom Seaver	.50
29 Bob Knepper	.15
30 Mike Schmidt	.75
31 Tony Gwynn	.75
32 Don Slaught	.15
33 Todd Worrell	.25
34 Tim Raines	.40
35 Dave Parker	.25
36 Bob Ojeda	.15
37 Pete Incaviglia (R)	.50
38 Bruce Hurst	.20
39 Bobby Witt (R)	.20
40 Steve Garvey	.50
41 Dave Winfield	.40
42 Jose Cruz	.15
43 Orel Hershiser	.50
44 Reggie Jackson	.40
45 Chili Davis	.20

NO. PLAYER	MINT
46 Robby Thompson	.20
47 Dennis Boyd	.15
48 Kirk Gibson	.35
49 Fred Lynn	.25
50 Gary Carter	.40
51 George Bell	.35
52 Pete O'Brien	.15
53 Ron Darling	.25
54 Paul Molitor	.25
55 Mike Pagliarulo	.15
56 Mike Boddicker	.15
57 Dave Righetti	.20
58 Len Dykstra	.20
59 Mike Witt	.15
60 Tony Bernazard	.15
61 John Kruk	.25
62 Mike Krukow	.15
63 Sid Fernandez	.25
64 Gary Gaetti	.25
65 Vince Coleman	.50
66 Pat Tabler	.15
67 Mike Scioscia	.15
68 Scott Garrelts	.15
69 Brett Butler	.15
70 Bill Buckner	.15
71 Dennis Rasmussen	.40
72 Tim Wallach	.15
73 Bob Horner	.15
74 Willie McGee	.20
75 Tri-Stars:	1.25
Mattingly, Joyner, Murray	
76 Jesse Orosco	.15
77 Tri-Stars:	.15
Worrell, Reardon, Smith	
78 Candy Maldonado	.15
79 Tri-Stars:	.25
Smith, Brooks, Dunston	
80 Tri-Stars:	1.25
Bell, Canseco, Rice	
81 Bert Blyleven	.15
82 Mike Marshall	.15
83 Ron Guidry	.15
84 Julio Franco	.15
85 Willie Wilson	.15
86 Lee Lacy	.15

NO. PLAYER	MINT
87 Jack Morris	.25
88 Ray Knight	.15
89 Phil Bradley	.20
90 Jose Canseco	3.00
91 Gary Ward	.15
92 Mike Easler	.15
93 Tony Pena	.15
94 Dave Smith	.15
95 Will Clark (R)	7.00
96 Lloyd Moseby	.15
97 Jim Rice	.30
98 Shawon Dunston	.20
99 Don Sutton	.25
100 Dwight Gooden	1.00
101 Lance Parrish	.15
102 Mark Langston	.25
103 Floyd Youmans	.20
104 Lee Smith	.20
105 Willie Hernandez	.15
106 Doug DeCinces	.15
107 Ken Schrom	.15
108 Don Carman	.15
109 Brook Jacoby	.15
110 Steve Bedrosian	.25
111 Tri-Stars:	.50
Clemens, Morris, Higuera	
112 Tri-Stars:	.20
Barrett, Bernazard, Whitaker	
113 Tri-Stars:	.25
Ripken, Fletcher, Fernandez	
114 Tri-Stars:	.75
Boggs, Brett, Gaetti	
115 Tri-Stars:	.40
Schmidt, Brown, Wallach	
116 Tri-Stars:	.25
Sandberg, Ray, Doran	
117 Tri-Stars:	.25
Parker, Gwynn, Bass	
118 Big 6 Rookies:	2.00
Ty Gainey, Terry Steinbach,	
David Clark, Pat Dodson,	
Phil Lombardi, B. Santiago	
119 Hi-Lite Tri-Stars:	.25
Righetti, Valenzuela, Scott	

NO. PLAYER	MINT
120 Tri-Stars:	.50
Valenzuela, Scott, Gooden	
121 Johnny Ray	.15
122 Keith Moreland	.15
123 Juan Samuel	.15
124 Wally Backman	.15
125 Nolan Ryan	1.00
126 Greg Harris	.15
127 Kirk McCaskill	.15
128 Dwight Evans	.25
129 Rick Rhoden	.15
130 Bill Madlock	.15
131 Oddibe McDowell	.15
132 Darrell Evans	.15
133 Keith Hernandez	.25
134 Tom Brunansky	.20
135 Kevin McReynolds	.50
136 Scott Fletcher	.15
137 Lou Whitaker	.15
138 Carney Lansford	.15
139 Andre Dawson	.30
140 Carlton Fisk	.25
141 Buddy Bell	.15
142 Ozzie Smith	.35
143 Dan Pasqua	.15
144 Kevin Mitchell (R)	2.00
145 Bret Saberhagen	.30
146 Charlie Kerfeld	.15
147 Phil Niekro	.30
148 John Candelaria	.15
149 Rich Gedman	.15
150 Fernando Valenzuela	.30
151 Tri-Stars:	.20
Carter, Scioscia, Pena	
152 Tri-Stars:	.40
Raines, Cruz, Coleman	
153 Tri-Stars:	.30
Barfield, Baines, Winfield	
154 Tri-Stars:	
Parrish, Slaught, Gedman	
155 Tri-Stars:	.60
Murphy, McReynolds, Davis	
156 Hi-Lite Tri-Stars:	.40
Sutton, Schmidt, Deshaies	

NO.	PLAYER	MINT
157	Speedburners:............35	
	Henderson, Cangelosi, Pettis	
158	Big 6 Rookies: 2.50	
	Randy Asadoor, C. Candaele,	
	K. Seitzer, Rafael Palmeiro,	
	Tim Pyznarski, D. Cochrane	
159	Big 6: 1.50	
	Mattingly, Henderson,	
	Clemens, Murphy,	
	Murray, Gooden	
160	Roger McDowell 15	
161	Brian Downing 15	
162	Bill Doran 15	
163	Don Baylor...............20	
164	Alfredo Griffin 15	

NO.	PLAYER	MINT
165	Don Aase 15	
166	Glenn Wilson 15	
167	Dan Quisenberry 20	
168	Frank White 15	
169	Cecil Cooper 15	
170	Jody Davis 15	
171	Harold Baines 25	
172	Rob Deer 20	
173	John Tudor 20	
174	Larry Parrish 15	
175	Kevin Bass 15	
176	Joe Carter 35	
177	Mitch Webster 15	
178	Dave Kingman..........20	

NO.	PLAYER	MINT
179	Jim Presley 25	
180	Mel Hall 15	
181	Shane Rawley 15	
182	Marty Barrett 25	
183	Damaso Garcia 15	
184	Bobby Grich 15	
185	Leon Durham 15	
186	Ozzie Guillen 15	
187	Tony Fernandez 25	
188	Alan Trammell..........25	
189	Jim Clancy 15	
190	Bo Jackson (R) 3.50	
191	Bob Forsch 15	
192	John Franco 25	

NO.	PLAYER	MINT
193	Von Hayes 15	
194	Tri-Stars:.............15	
	Aase, Righetti, Eichhorn	
195	Tri-Stars:...........1.50	
	Hernandez, Clark, Davis	
196	Hi-Lite Tri-Stars:........40	
	Clemens, Cowley, Horner	
197	Big 6: 75	
	Brett, Brooks, Gwynn,	
	Sandberg, Raines, Boggs	
198	Tri-Stars:..........50	
	Puckett, Henderson, Lynn	
199	Speedburners:..........50	
	Raines, Coleman, Davis	
200	Steve Carlton.............35	

1988 Sportflics. . . . Complete Set of 255 Cards—Value $35.00

Each card can be tilted to show three different photos. The set includes 219 individual players, 3 Highlights and 3 Rookie Prospects.

NO.	PLAYER	MINT
1	Don Mattingly 2.50	
2	Tim Raines 40	
3	Andre Dawson 35	
4	George Bell 25	
5	Joe Carter 25	
6	Matt Nokes (R) 45	
7	Dave Winfield..........35	
8	Kirby Puckett 60	
9	Will Clark 1.00	
10	Eric Davis 75	
11	Rickey Henderson.......50	
12	Ryne Sandberg 35	
13	Jesse Barfield 25	
14	Ozzie Guillen 15	
15	Bret Saberhagen 20	
16	Tony Gwynn 50	
17	Kevin Seitzer 60	
18	Jack Clark 15	
19	Danny Tartabull 30	
20	Ted Higuera 20	
21	Charlie Liebrandt, Jr. 10	
22	Benny Santiago 50	
23	Fred Lynn 20	
24	Rob Thompson 10	
25	Alan Trammell 30	
26	T. Fernandez 20	
27	Rick Sutcliffe 20	
28	Gary Carter 30	
29	Cory Snyder 35	
30	Lou Whitaker 15	
31	Keith Hernandez 25	
32	Mike Witt 15	
33	Harold Baines 15	
34	Robin Yount 40	
35	Mike Schmidt 60	
36	Dion James 10	
37	Tom Candiotti 10	
38	Tracy Jones 10	
39	Nolan Ryan 75	
40	Fernando Valenzuela 30	
41	Vance Law 10	
42	Roger McDowell 15	
43	Carlton Fisk 25	
44	Scott Garrelts 10	
45	Lee Guetterman 10	
46	Mark Langston 30	
47	Willie Randolph 20	
48	Bill Doran..............10	
49	Larry Parrish 10	
50	Wade Boggs 1.50	
51	Shan Rawley 10	
52	Alvin Davis 10	
53	Jeff Reardon 10	
54	Jim Presley 15	
55	Kevin Bass 15	
56	Kevin McReynolds 35	
57	B.J. Surhoff 15	
58	Julio Franco 15	
59	Eddie Murray 40	

NO.	PLAYER	MINT
60	Jody Davis 12	
61	Todd Worrell 20	
62	Von Hayes 20	
63	Billy Hatcher 15	
64	John Kruk 20	
65	Tom Henke 12	
66	Mike Scott 25	
67	Vince Coleman 40	
68	Ozzie Smith 45	
69	Ken Williams 20	
70	Steve Bedrosian 15	
71	Luis Polonia 20	
72	Brook Jacoby 15	
73	Ron Darling 25	
74	Lloyd Moseby 20	
75	Wally Joyner 50	
76	Dan Quisenberry 15	
77	Scott Fletcher 12	
78	Kirk McKaskill 12	
79	Paul Molitor 30	
80	Mike Aldrete 20	
81	Neal Heaton 12	
82	Jeffrey Leonard 12	
83	Dave Magadan 20	
84	Danny Cox 15	
85	Lance McCullers 12	
86	Jay Howell 12	
87	Charlie Hough 12	
88	Gene Garber 12	
89	Jesse Orosco 12	
90	Don Robinson 12	
91	Willie McGee 25	
92	Bert Blyleven 20	
93	Phil Bradley 20	
94	Terry Kennedy 12	
95	Kent Hrbek 35	
96	Juan Samuel 25	
97	Pedro Guerrero 25	
98	Sid Bream 12	
99	Devon White 25	
100	Mark McGwire 1.25	
101	Dave Parker 30	
102	Glen Davis 25	
103	Greg Walker 20	
104	Rick Rhoden 15	
105	Mitch Webster 15	
106	Lenny Dykstra 15	
107	Gene Larkin 15	
108	Floyd Youmans 15	
109	Andy Van Slyke 30	
110	Mike Scioscia 12	
111	Kirk Gibson 35	
112	Kal Daniels 35	
113	Ruben Sierra 40	
114	Sam Horn (R) 30	
115	Ray Knight 12	
116	Jimmy Key 15	
117	Bo Diaz 12	
118	Mike Greenwell 1.25	

NO.	PLAYER	MINT
119	Barry Bonds 30	
120	Reggie Jackson 50	
121	Mike Pagliarulo 20	
122	Tommy John 25	
123	Bill Madlock 20	
124	Ken Caminiti 20	
125	Gary Ward 15	
126	Candy Maldonado.......15	
127	Harold Reynolds 15	
128	Joe Magrane 40	
129	Mike Henneman 20	
130	Jim Gantner 12	
131	Bobby Bonilla 30	
132	John Farrell 30	
133	Frank Tanana 15	
134	Zane Smith 20	
135	Dave Righetti 20	
136	Rick Reuschel 25	
137	Dwight Evans 25	
138	Howard Johnson 35	
139	Terry Leach 20	
140	Casey Candaele 12	
141	Tom Herr 15	
142	Tony Pena 15	
143	Lance Parrish 20	
144	Ellis Burks (R) 1.25	
145	Pete O'Brien 20	
146	Mike Boddicker 15	
147	Buddy Bell 25	
148	Bo Jackson 75	
149	Frank White 15	
150	George Brett 50	
151	Tim Wallach 15	
152	Cal Ripken, Jr. 40	
153	Brett Butler 20	
154	Gary Gaetti 25	
155	Darryl Strawberry 75	
156	Alredo Griffin 15	
157	Marty Barrett 20	
158	Jim Rice 30	
159	Terry Pendleton 15	
160	Orel Hershiser 60	
161	Larry Sheets 20	
162	Dave Stewart 25	
163	Shawon Dunston 20	
164	Keith Moreland 15	
165	Ken Oberkfell 15	
166	Ivan Calderon 20	
167	Bob Welch 20	
168	Fred McGriff 60	
169	Pete Incaviglia 30	
170	Dale Murphy 60	
171	Mike Dunne 25	
172	Chili Davis 20	
173	Milt Thompson 15	
174	Terry Steinbach 25	
175	Oddibe McDowell 20	
176	Jack Morris 20	
177	Sid Fernandez 25	

NO.	PLAYER	MINT
178	Ken Griffey 15	
179	Lee Smith 15	
180	Hi-Lite Tri-Stars:..........30	
	Puckett, Nieves, Schmidt	
181	Brian Downing 15	
182	Andres Galarraga 40	
183	Rob Deer 20	
184	Greg Brock 12	
185	Doug DeCinces 12	
186	Johnny Ray 12	
187	Hubie Brooks 12	
188	Darrell Evans 20	
189	Mel Hall 15	
190	Jim Deshaies 12	
191	Dan Plesac 20	
192	Willie Wilson 12	
193	Mike LaValliere 12	
194	Tom Brunansky 20	
195	John Franco 20	
196	Frank Viola 35	
197	Bruce Hurst 25	
198	John Tudor 15	
199	Bob Forsch 15	
200	Dwight Gooden 75	
201	Jose Canseco 2.00	
202	Carney Lansford 15	
203	Kelly Downs 15	
204	Glenn Wilson 15	
205	Pat Tabler 15	
206	Mike Davis 15	
207	Roger Clemens 1.00	
208	Dave Smith 15	
209	Curt Young 15	
210	Mark Eichhorn 15	
211	Juan Nieves 15	
212	Bob Boone 15	
213	Don Sutton 35	
214	Cecil Upshaw 10	
215	Jim Clancy 10	
216	Bill Ripken (R) 25	
217	Ozzie Virgil 15	
218	Dave Concepcion 10	
219	Alan Ashby 15	
220	Mike Marshall 25	
221	Hi-Lite Tri-Stars:..........75	
	McGwire, Molitor, Coleman	
222	Hi-Lite Tri-Stars: 75	
	Santiago, Bedrosian,	
	Mattingly	
223	Rookies: 1.00	
	Shawn Abner, Jay Buhner,	
	Gary Thurman	
224	Rookies: 35	
	Tim Crews, Vincente	
	Palacios, John Davis	
225	Rookies: 75	
	Jody Reed, Jeff Treadway,	
	Keith Miller	

1989 Sportflics.... Complete Set of 225 Cards—Value $35.00

Each card can be tilted to show three different photos. The set includes 219 individual players, 2 Highlights and 3 Rookie Prospects.

NO.	PLAYER	MINT	NO.	PLAYER	MINT	NO.	PLAYER	MINT	NO.	PLAYER	MINT
1	Jose Canseco	1.75	58	Steve Sax	.20	114	Tim Wallach	.15	170	Will Clark	.75
2	Wally Joyner	.35	59	Lance Parrish	.15	115	Nolan Ryan	.50	171	Chet Lemon	.12
3	Roger Clemens	.75	60	Keith Hernandez	.25	116	Walt Weiss	.35	172	Pat Tabler	.12
4	Greg Swindell	.20	61	Jose Uribe	.12	117	Brian Downing	.12	173	Jim Rice	.20
5	Jack Morris	.20	62	Jose Lind	.12	118	Melido Perez	.15	174	Billy Hatcher	.12
6	Mickey Brantley	.12	63	Steve Bedrosian	.12	119	Terry Steinbach	.20	175	Bruce Hurst	.20
7	Jim Presley	.12	64	George Brett	.40	120	Mike Scott	.20	176	John Franco	.15
8	Pete O'Brien	.15	65	Kirk Gibson	.25	121	Tim Belcher	.15	177	Van Snider	.20
9	Jesse Barfield	.20	66	Cal Ripken Jr.	.30	122	Mike Boddicker	.15	178	Ron Jones	.30
10	Frank Viola	.20	67	Mitch Webster	.12	123	Len Dykstra	.20	179	Jerald Clark	.20
11	Kevin Bass	.12	68	Fred Lynn	.15	124	Fernando Valenzuela	.20	180	Tom Browning	.15
12	Glenn Wilson	.12	69	Eric Davis	.75	125	Gerald Young	.15	181	Von Hayes	.12
13	Chris Sabo	1.00	70	Bo Jackson	.75	126	Tom Henke	.12	182	Bobby Bonilla	.25
14	Fred McGriff	.50	71	Kevin Elster	.15	127	Dave Henderson	.15	183	Todd Worrell	.12
15	Mark Grace	1.50	72	Rick Reuschel	.12	128	Dan Plesac	.12	184	John Kruk	.12
16	Devon White	.15	73	Tim Burke	.12	129	Chili Davis	.12	185	Scott Fletcher	.12
17	Juan Samuel	.15	74	Mark Davis	.12	130	Bryan Harvey	.30	186	Willie Wilson	.15
18	Lou Whitaker	.15	75	Claudell Washington	.15	131	Don August	.20	187	Jody Davis	.12
19	Greg Walker	.12	76	Lance McCullers	.15	132	Mike Harkey	.50	188	Kent Hrbek	.15
20	Roberto Alomar	.30	77	Mike Moore	.12	133	Luis Polonia	.12	189	Ruben Sierra	.20
21	Mike Schmidt	.60	78	Robby Thompson	.12	134	Craig Worthington	.25	190	Shawon Dunston	.15
22	Benny Santiago	.30	79	Roger McDowell	.15	135	Joey Meyer	.12	191	Ellis Burks	.50
23	Dave Stewart	.20	80	Danny Jackson	.20	136	Barry Larkin	.15	192	Brook Jacoby	.12
24	Dave Winfield	.35	81	Tim Leary	.15	137	Glenn Davis	.20	193	Jeff Robinson	.20
25	George Bell	.20	82	Bobby Witt	.12	138	Mike Scioscia	.12	194	Rich Dotson	.15
26	J. Clark	.20	83	Jim Gott	.12	139	Andres Galarraga	.35	195	Johnny Ray	.15
27	Doug Drabek	.15	84	Andy Hawkins	.12	140	Dwight Gooden	.50	196	Cory Snyder	.20
28	Ron Gant	.25	85	Ozzie Guillen	.15	141	Keith Moreland	.12	197	Mike Witt	.12
29	Glenn Braggs	.12	86	John Tudor	.12	142	Kevin Mitchell	.15	198	Marty Barrett	.12
30	Rafael Palmeiro	.25	87	Todd Burns	.25	143	Mike Greenwell	1.75	199	Robin Yount	.35
31	Brett Butler	.12	88	Dave Gallagher	.20	144	Mel Hall	.12	200	Mark McGwire	1.00
32	Ron Darling	.20	89	Jay Buhner	.20	145	Rickey Henderson	.50	201	Ryne Sandberg	.25
33	Alvin Davis	.20	90	Gregg Jefferies	1.50	146	Barry Bonds	.20	202	John Candelaria	.15
34	Bob Walk	.12	91	Bob Welch	.15	147	Eddie Murray	.35	203	Matt Nokes	.15
35	Dave Stieb	.15	92	Charlie Hough	.15	148	Lee Smith	.15	204	Dwight Evans	.20
36	Orel Hershiser	.50	93	Tony Fernandez	.20	149	Julio Franco	.15	205	Darryl Strawberry	.75
37	John Farrell	.15	94	Ozzie Virgil	.12	150	Tim Raines	.25	206	Willie McGee	.15
38	Doug Jones	.12	95	Andre Dawson	.25	151	Mitch Williams	.12	207	Bobby Thigpen	.12
39	Kelly Downs	.12	96	Hubie Brooks	.12	152	Tim Laudner	.12	208	B.J. Surhoff	.12
40	Bob Boone	.12	97	Kevin McReynolds	.30	153	Mike Pagliarulo	.15	209	Paul Molitor	.15
41	Gary Sheffield	1.50	98	Mike LaValliere	.12	154	Floyd Bannister	.12	210	Jody Reed	.20
42	Doug Dascenzo	.25	99	Terry Pendleton	.12	155	Gary Carter	.30	211	Doyle Alexander	.15
43	Chad Krueter	.20	100	Wade Boggs	1.00	156	Kirby Puckett	.75	212	Dennis Rasmussen	.12
44	Ricky Jordan	1.50	101	Dennis Eckersley	.15	157	Harold Baines	.15	213	Kevin Gross	.12
45	Dave West	.50	102	Mark Gubicza	.20	158	Dave Righetti	.20	214	Kirk McCaskill	.12
46	Danny Tartabull	.25	103	Frank Tanana	.15	159	Mark Langston	.15	215	Alan Trammell	.25
47	Teddy Higuera	.20	104	Joe Carter	.25	160	Tony Gwynn	.50	216	Damon Berryhill	.20
48	Gary Gaetti	.20	105	Ozzie Smith	.25	161	Tom Brunansky	.15	217	Rick Sutcliffe	.15
49	Dave Parker	.20	106	Dennis Martinez	.15	162	Vance Law	.15	218	Don Slaught	.12
50	Don Mattingly	1.50	107	Jeff Treadway	.15	163	Kelly Gruber	.12	219	Carlton Fisk	.20
51	David Cone	.35	108	Greg Maddux	.20	164	Gerald Perry	.15	220	Allan Anderson	.20
52	Kal Daniels	.20	109	Bret Saberhagen	.20	165	Harold Reynolds	.12	221	Boggs, Canseco, Greenwell	1.50
53	Carney Lansford	.15	110	Dale Murphy	.35	166	Andy Van Slyke	.15	222	Hershiser, Eckersley, Browning	.35
54	Mike Marshall	.15	111	Rob Deer	.15	167	Jimmy Key	.15	223	Sheffield, Jefferies, Alomar	.50
55	Kevin Seitzer	.30	112	Pete Incaviglia	.20	168	Jeff Reardon	.15	224	Milacki, Johnson, Martinez	.75
56	Mike Henneman	.15	113	Vince Coleman	.25	169	Milt Thompson	.12	225	Drew, Berroa, Jones	.40
57	Bill Doran	.12									

1990 Sportflics.... Complete Set of 225 Cards—Value $35.00

Each card can be tilted to show three different photos.

NO.	PLAYER	MINT	NO.	PLAYER	MINT	NO.	PLAYER	MINT	NO.	PLAYER	MINT
1	Kevin Mitchell	.50	16	Ozzie Smith	.20	31	Bryan Harvey	.15	46	Kevin Seitzer	.25
2	Wade Boggs	.50	17	George Bell	.40	32	Jim Deshaies	.15	47	Bruce Hurst	.15
3	Cory Snyder	.20	18	Robin Yount	.25	33	Terry Steinbach	.25	48	Ozzie Guillen	.15
4	Paul O'Neill	.15	19	Glenn Davis	.25	34	Tom Glavine	.20	49	Wally Joyner	.25
5	Will Clark	.75	20	Jeffrey Leonard	.15	35	Bob Welch	.15	50	Mike Greenwell	.60
6	Tony Fernandez	.25	21	Chili Davis	.15	36	Charlie Hayes	.15	51	Gary Gaetti	.25
7	Ken Griffey, Jr.	.50	22	Craig Biggio	.25	37	Jeff Reardon	.15	52	Gary Sheffield	.50
8	Nolan Ryan	.40	23	Jose Canseco	.75	38	Joe Orsulak	.15	53	Dennis Martinez	.15
9	Rafael Palmeiro	.25	24	Derek Lilliquist	.20	39	Scott Garrelts	.15	54	Ryne Sandberg	.25
10	Jesse Barfield	.15	25	Chris Bosio	.15	40	Bob Boone	.15	55	Mike Scott	.15
11	Kirby Puckett	.40	26	Dave Stieb	.15	41	Scott Bankhead	.15	56	Todd Benzinger	.15
12	Steve Sax	.20	27	Bobby Thigpen	.15	42	Tom Henke	.15	57	Kelly Gruber	.15
13	Fred McGriff	.40	28	Jack Clark	.08	43	Greg Briley	.15	58	Jose Lind	.15
14	Gregg Jefferies	.50	29	Kevin Ritz (R)	.35	44	Teddy Higuera	.15	59	Allan Anderson	.15
15	Mark Grace	.50	30	Tom Gordon	.60	45	Pat Borders	.15	60	Robby Thompson	.20

172

NO.	PLAYER	MINT
61	John Smoltz	.30
62	Mark Davis	.25
63	Tom Herr	.15
64	Randy Johnson	.20
65	Lonnie Smith	.15
66	Pedro Guerrero	.25
67	Jerome Walton	2.00
68	Ramon Martinez	.25
69	Tim Raines	.25
70	Matt Williams	.60
71	Joe Oliver	.40
72	Nick Esasky	.15
73	Kevin Brown	.15
74	Walt Weiss	.25
75	Roger McDowell	.15
76	Jose DeLeon	.15
77	Brian Downing	.15
78	Jay Howell	.15
79	Jose Uribe	.15
80	Ellis Burks	.40
81	Sammy Sosa (R)	.60
82	Johnny Ray	.15
83	Danny Darwin	.15
84	Carney Lansford	.15
85	Jose Oquendo	.15
86	John Cerutti	.15
87	Dave Winfield	.25
88	Dave Righetti	.20
89	Danny Jackson	.25
90	Andy Benes	.75
91	Tom Browning	.15
92	Pete O'Brien	.20
93	Roberto Alomar	.20
94	Bret Saberhagen	.25
95	Phil Bradley	.15
96	Doug Jones	.15
97	Eric Davis	.50
98	Tony Gwynn	.35
99	Jim Abbott	1.00
100	Cal Ripken, Jr.	.15
101	Andy Van Slyke	.20
102	Dan Plesac	.15
103	Lou Whitaker	.15
104	Steve Bedrosian	.15
105	Dave Gallagher	.15
106	Keith Hernandez	.20
107	Duane Ward	.15
108	Andre Dawson	.25
109	Howard Johnson	.20
110	Mark Langston	.25
111	Jerry Browne	.15
112	Alvin Davis	.20
113	Sid Fernandez	.15
114	Mike Devereaux	.15
115	Benny Santiago	.25
116	Bip Roberts	.15
117	Craig Worthington	.20
118	Kevin Elster	.15
119	Harold Reynolds	.15
120	Joe Carter	.25
121	Brian Harper	.15
122	Frank Viola	.25
123	Jeff Ballard	.15
124	John Kruk	.20
125	Harold Baines	.15
126	Tom Candiotti	.15
127	Kevin McReynolds	.25
128	Mookie Wilson	.15
129	Danny Tartabull	.20
130	Craig Lefferts	.15
131	Jose DeJesus	.15
132	John Orton	.40
133	Curt Schilling	.25
134	Marquis Grissom	.40
135	Greg Vaughn	1.00
136	Brett Butler	.15
137	Rob Deer	.15
138	John Franco	.20
139	Keith Moreland	.15
140	Dave Smith	.15
141	Mark McGwire	.60
142	Vince Coleman	.20
143	Barry Bonds	.25
144	Mike Henneman	.15
145	Doc Gooden	.40
146	Darryl Strawberry	.50
147	Von Hayes	.15
148	Andres Galarraga	.25
149	Roger Clemens	.40
150	Don Mattingly	.75
151	Joe Magrane	.25
152	Dwight Smith	.75
153	Ricky Jordan	.50
154	Alan Trammell	.25
155	Brook Jacoby	.15
156	Lenny Dykstra	.15
157	Mike LaValliere	.15
158	Julio Franco	.20
159	Joey Belle	.50
160	Barry Larkin	.20
161	Rick Reuschel	.15
162	Nelson Santovenia	.15
163	Mike Scioscia	.15
164	Damon Berryhill	.15
165	Todd Worrell	.15
166	Jim Eisenreich	.15
167	Ivan Calderon	.15
168	Goose Gozzo	.25
169	Kirk McCaskill	.15
170	Dennis Eckersley	.20
171	Mickey Tettleton	.15
172	Chuck Finley	.15
173	Dave Magadan	.15
174	Terry Pendleton	.15
175	Willie Randolph	.20
176	Jeff Huson	.35
177	Todd Zeile	1.75
178	Steve Olin	.35
179	Eric Anthony	1.50
180	Scott Coolbaugh	.35
181	Rick Sutcliffe	.15
182	Tim Wallach	.15
183	Paul Molitor	.15
184	Roberto Kelly	.25
185	Mike Moore	.15
186	Junior Felix	.50
187	Mike Schooler	.20
188	Ruben Sierra	.30
189	Dale Murphy	.25
190	Dan Gladden	.15
191	John Smiley	.20
192	Jeff Russell	.15
193	Burt Blyleven	.15
194	Dave Stewart	.25
195	Bobby Bonilla	.25
196	Mitch Williams	.15
197	Orel Hershiser	.25
198	Kevin Bass	.15
199	Tim Burke	.15
200	Bo Jackson	.75
201	David Cone	.25
202	Gary Pettis	.15
203	Kent Hrbek	.20
204	Carlton Fisk	.20
205	Bob Geren	.30
206	Bill Spiers	.30
207	Oddibe McDowell	.15
208	Rickey Henderson	.30
209	Ken Caminiti	.15
210	Devon White	.25
211	Greg Maddux	.25
212	Ed Whitson	.15
213	Carlos Martinez	.30
214	George Brett	.35
215	Gregg Olson	.25
216	Kenny Rogers	.35
217	Dwight Evans	.20
218	Pat Tabler	.15
219	Jeff Treadway	.15
220	Scott Fletcher	.15
221	Deion Sanders	1.00
222	Robin Ventura	.50
223	Chip Hale (R)	.25
224	Tommy Greene	.40
225	Dean Palmer	.35

1989 Upper Deck.... Complete Set of 700 Cards—Value $60.00

This was the premier issue of Upper Deck—the sixth major card manufacturer. Features the rookie cards of Gary Sheffield and Ken Griffey, Jr. A special feature is a small hologram on the card's back to discourage counterfeiting. The first 26 cards feature Upper Deck's selection of star rookies. Each team checklist features a drawing of a player on the team.

Ricky Jordan

Craig Biggio

Gary Sheffield

Sandy Alomar Jr.

Ken Griffey Jr.

NO.	PLAYER	MINT
1	Ken Griffey Jr. (R)	8.00
2	Luis Medina (R)	.50
3	Tony Chance (R)	.20
4	Dave Otto	.15
5	Sandy Alomar, Jr. (R)	1.50
6	Rolando Roomes (R)	.35
7	David West (R)	.60
8	Cris Carpenter (R)	.30
9	Gregg Jefferies	3.00
10	Doug Dascenzo (R)	.25
11	Ron Jones (R)	.35
12	Luis De Los Santos (R)	.30
13	Gary Sheffield	2.50
13	Gary Sheffield (error)	7.50
14	Mike Harkey (R)	.50
15	Lance Blankenship (R)	.30
16	William Brennan (R)	.15
17	John Smoltz (R)	.75
18	Ramon Martinez (R)	.40
19	Mark Lemke (R)	.15
20	Juan Bell (R)	.35
21	Rey Palacios	.15
22	Felix Jose (R)	.30
23	Van Snider (R)	.25
24	Dante Bichete (R)	.20
25	Randy Johnson (R)	.35
26	Carlos Quintana (R)	.45
27	Star Rookie Checklist	.10
28	Mike Schooler (R)	.25
29	Randy St. Claire	.12
30	Gerald Clark (R)	.20
31	Kevin Gross	.08
32	Dan Firova (R)	.15
33	Jeff Calhoun	.08
34	Tommy Hinze	.08
35	Ricky Jordan (R)	2.00
36	Larry Parrish	.10
37	Bret Saberhagen	.15
38	Mike Smithson	.08
39	Dave Dravecky	.08
40	Ed Romero	.08
41	Jeff Musselman	.08
42	Ed Hearn	.08
43	Rance Mulliniks	.08
44	Jim Eisenreich	.08
45	Sil Campusano (R)	.20
46	Mike Krukow	.10
47	Paul Gibson (R)	.15
48	Mike LaCoss	.08
49	Larry Herndon	.08
50	Scott Garreits	.08
51	Duane Henry	.08
52	Jim Acker	.08
53	Steve Sax	.12
54	Pete O'Brien	.08
55	Paul Runge	.08
56	Rick Rhoden	.08
57	John Dopson (R)	.25
58	Casey Candaele	.08
59	Dave Righetti	.08
60	Joe Hesketh	.08
61	Frank DiPino	.08
62	Tim Laudner	.08
63	Jamie Moyer	.08
64	Fred Toliver	.08
65	Mitch Webster	.08
66	John Tudor	.12
67	John Cangelosi	.08

NO.	PLAYER	MINT
68	Mike Devereaux	.12
69	Brian Fisher	.08
70	Mike Marshall	.10
71	Zane Smith	.08
72	Brian Holton	.30
72	B. Holton (error)	2.00
73	Jose Guzman	.08
74	Rick Mahler	.10
75	John Shelby	.08
76	Jim Deshaies	.08
77	Bobby Meacham	.08
78	Bryn Smith	.08
79	Joaquin Andujar	.08
80	Richard Dotson	.08
81	Charlie Lea	.08
82	Calvin Schiraldi	.08
83	Les Straker	.08
84	Les Lancaster	.08
85	Allan Anderson	.08
86	Junior Oritz	.08
87	Jesse Orosco	.08
88	Felix Fermin	.08
89	Dave Anderson	.08
90	Rafael Belliard	.08
91	Franklin Stubbs	.08
92	Cecil Espy	.08
93	Albert Hall	.08
94	Tim Leary	.08
95	Mitch Williams	.08
96	Tracy Jones	.08
97	Danny Darwin	.08
98	Gary Ward	.08
99	Neal Heaton	.08
100	Jim Pankovits	.08
101	Bill Doran	.08
102	Tim Wallach	.08
103	Joe Magrane	.08
104	Ozzie Virgil	.08
105	Alvin Davis	.08
106	Tom Brookens	.08
107	Shawon Dunston	.10
108	Tracy Woodson	.08
109	Nelson Liriano	.08
110	Devon White	.12
111	Steve Balboni	.10
112	Buddy Bell	.08
113	German Jimenez (R)	.15
114	Ken Dayley	.08
115	Andres Galarraga	.08
116	Mike Scioscia	.08
117	Gary Pettis	.08
118	Ernie Whitt	.08
119	Bob Boone	.08
120	Ryne Sandberg	.15
121	Bruce Benedict	.08
122	Hubie Brooks	.08
123	Mike Moore	.08
124	Wallace Johnson	.08
125	Bob Horner	.08
126	Chili Davis	.08
127	Manny Trillo	.08
128	Chet Lemon	.10
129	John Cerutti	.08
130	Orel Hershiser	.25
131	Terry Pendleton	.08
132	Jeff Blauser	.08
133	Mike Fitzgerald	.08
134	Henry Cotto	.08

NO.	PLAYER	MINT
135	Gerald Young	.08
136	Luis Salazar	.08
137	Alejandro Pena	.08
138	Jack Howell	.08
139	Tony Fernandez	.08
140	Mark Grace	1.50
141	Ken Caminiti	.08
142	Mike Jackson	.08
143	Larry McWilliams	.08
144	Andres Thomas	.08
145	Nolan Ryan	2.00
146	Mike Davis	.08
147	DeWayne Buice	.08
148	Jody Davis	.08
149	Jesse Barfield	.12
150	Matte Nokes	.10
151	Jerry Reuss	.08
152	Rick Cerone	.08
153	Storm Davis	.08
154	Marvell Wynee	.08
155	Will Clark	1.00
156	Luis Aguayo	.08
157	Willie Upshaw	.08
158	Randy Bush	.08
159	Ron Darling	.12
160	Kal Daniels	.15
161	Spike Owen	.08
162	Luis Polonia	.08
163	Kevin Mitchell	.50
164	Dave Gallagher (R)	.30
165	Benito Santiago	.15
166	Greg Gagne	.08
167	Ken Phelps	.08
168	Sid Fernandez	.08
169	Bo Diaz	.08
170	Cory Snyder	.20
171	Eric Show	.10
172	Ron Thompson	.08
173	Marty Barrett	.10
174	Dave Henderson	.08
175	Ozzie Guillen	.08
176	Barry Lyons	.08
177	Kelvin Torve (R)	.12
178	Don Slaught	.08
179	Steve Lombardozzi	.08
180	Chris Sabo (R)	1.00
181	Jose Uribe	.08
182	Shane Mack	.08
183	Ron Karkovice	.08
184	Todd Benzinger	.10
185	Dave Stewart	.10
186	Julio Franco	.08
187	Ron Robinson	.08
188	Wally Backman	.08
189	Randy Velarde	.08
190	Joe Carter	.10
191	Bob Welch	.08
192	Kelly Paris	.08
193	Chris Brown	.08
194	Rick Reuschel	.10
195	Roger Clemens	.50
196	Dave Concepcion	.08
197	Al Newman	.08
198	Brook Jacoby	.08
199	Mookie Wilson	.08
200	Don Mattingly	1.00
201	Dick Schofield	.08
202	Mark Gubicza	.08

NO.	PLAYER	MINT
203	Gary Gaetti	.12
204	Dan Pasqua	.08
205	Andre Dawson	.15
206	Chris Speier	.08
207	Kent Tekulve	.08
208	Rod Scurry	.08
209	Scott Bailes	.08
210	Rickey Henderson	.25
211	Harold Baines	.08
212	Tony Armas	.08
213	Kent Hrbek	.10
214	Darrin Jackson	.20
215	George Brett	.30
216	Rafael Santana	.08
217	Andy Allanson	.08
218	Brett Butler	.08
219	Steve Jeltz	.08
220	Jay Buhner	.20
221	Bo Jackson	1.00
222	Angel Salazar	.08
223	Kirk McCaskill	.08
224	Steve Lyons	.08
225	Bert Blyleven	.08
226	Scott Bradley	.08
227	Bob Melvin	.08
228	Ron Kittle	.08
229	Phil Bradley	.08
230	Tommy John	.08
231	Greg Walker	.08
232	Juan Berenguer	.08
233	Pat Tabler	.08
234	Terry Clark (R)	.15
235	Rafael Palmeiro	.12
236	Paul Zuvella	.08
237	Willie Randolph	.10
238	Bruce Fields	.08
239	Mike Aldrete	.08
240	Lance Parrish	.10
241	Gregg Maddux	.20
242	John Moses	.08
243	Melido Perez	.15
244	Willie Wilson	.08
245	Mark McLemore	.08
246	Von Hayes	.10
247	Matt Williams	.30
248	John Candelaria	.12
249	Harold Reynolds	.08
250	Greg Swindell	.08
251	Juan Agosto	.08
252	Mike Felder	.08
253	Vince Coleman	.15
254	Larry Sheets	.08
255	George Bell	.15
256	Terry Steinbach	.08
257	Jack Armstrong (R)	.20
258	Dickie Thon	.08
259	Ray Knight	.08
260	Darryl Strawberry	.50
261	Doug Sisk	.08
262	Alex Trevino	.08
263	Jeff Leonard	.08
264	Tom Henke	.08
265	Ozzie Smith	.20
266	Dave Bergman	.08
267	Tony Phillips	.08
268	Mark Davis	.08
269	Kevin Elster	.08
270	Barry Larkin	.15

NO.	PLAYER	MINT	NO.	PLAYER	MINT	NO.	PLAYER	MINT	NO.	PLAYER	MINT
271	Manny Lee	.08	357	Dale Murphy (cor.)	1.00	442	Rob Deer	.08	529	Jerry Reed	.08
272	Tom Brunansky	.10	357	Dale Murphy (err.) reversed negative	150.00	443	Glenn Davis	.15	530	Jack McDowell	.08
273	Craig Biggio (R)	.50	358	Mark Portugal	.08	444	Dave Martinez	.08	531	Greg Mathews	.08
274	Jim Gantner	.08	359	Andy McGaffigan	.08	445	Bill Wegman	.08	532	John Russell	.08
275	Eddie Murray	.15	360	Tom Glavine	.08	446	Loyd McClendon	.12	533	Dan Quisenberry	.08
276	Jeff Reed	.08	361	Keith Moreland	.08	447	Dave Schmidt	.08	534	Greg Gross	.08
277	Tim Teufel	.08	362	Todd Stottlemyre	.12	448	Darren Daulton	.08	535	Danny Cox	.08
278	Rick Honeycutt	.08	363	Dave Leiper	.08	449	Frank Williams	.08	536	Terry Francona	.08
279	Guillermo Hernandez	.08	364	Cecil Fielder	.08	450	Dan Aase	.08	537	Andy Van Slyke	.12
280	John Kruk	.08	365	Carmelo Martinez	.08	451	Lou Whitaker	.08	538	Mel Hall	.08
281	Luis Alice (R)	.15	366	Dwight Evans	.08	452	Goose Gossage	.08	539	Jim Gott	.08
282	Jim Clancy	.08	367	Kevin McReynolds	.15	453	Ed Whitson	.08	540	Doug Jones	.08
283	Billy Ripken	.10	368	Rich Gedman	.08	454	Jim Walewander	.08	541	Craig Lefferts	.08
284	Craig Reynolds	.08	369	Len Dykstra	.08	455	Damon Berryhill	.20	542	Mike Boddicker	.08
285	Robin Yount	.25	370	Jody Reed	.08	456	Tim Burke	.08	543	Greg Brock	.08
286	Jimmy Jones	.08	371	Jose Canseco	1.50	457	Barry Jones	.08	544	Atlee Hammaker	.08
287	Ron Oester	.08	372	Rob Murphy	.08	458	Joel Youngblood	.08	545	Tom Bolton	.08
288	Terry Leach	.08	373	Mike Henneman	.08	459	Floyd Youmans	.08	546	Mike MacFarlane (R)	.15
289	Dennis Eckersley	.08	374	Walt Weiss	.75	460	Mark Salas	.08	547	Rich Rentiera	.15
290	Alan Trammel	.15	375	Bob Dibble (R)	.30	461	Jeff Russell	.08	548	John Davis	.08
291	Jimmy Key	.08	376	Kirby Puckett	.50	462	Darrell Miller	.08	549	Floyd Bannister	.08
292	Chris Bosio	.08	377	Denny Martinez	.08	463	Jeff Kunkel	.08	550	Mickey Tettleton	.08
293	Jose DeLeon	.08	378	Ron Gant	.35	464	Sherman Corbett (R)	.15	551	Duane Ward	.08
294	Jim Traber	.08	379	Brian Harper	.08	465	Curtis Wilkerson	.08	552	Dan Petry	.08
295	Mike Scott	.15	380	Nelson Santovenia (R)	.15	466	Bud Black	.08	553	Mickey Tettleton	.08
296	Roger McDowell	.08	381	Lloyd Moseby	.10	467	Cal Ripken Jr.	.15	554	Rick Leach	.08
297	Gary Templeton	.08	382	Lance McCullers	.08	468	John Farrell	.08	555	Mike Witt	.08
298	Doyle Alexander	.08	383	Dave Stieb	.10	469	Terry Kennedy	.08	556	Sid Bream	.08
299	Nick Esasky	.08	384	Tony Gwynn	.30	470	Tom Candiotti	.08	557	Bobby Witt	.08
300	Mark McGwire	.75	385	Mike Flanagan	.08	471	Roberto Alomar	.40	558	Tommy Herr	.08
301	Darryl Hamilton (R)	.30	386	Bob Ojeda	.08	472	Jeff Robinson	.08	559	Randy Milligan	.12
302	Dave Smith	.08	387	Bruce Hurst	.08	473	Vance Law	.08	560	Jose Cecena	.12
303	Rick Sutcliffe	.08	388	Dave Magadan	.08	474	Randy Ready	.08	561	Mackey Sasser	.08
304	Dave Stapleton	.10	389	Wade Boggs	.75	475	Walt Terrell	.08	562	Carney Lansford	.08
305	Alan Ashby	.08	390	Gary Carter	.15	476	Kelly Downs	.08	563	Rick Aguilera	.08
306	Pedro Guerrero	.12	391	Frank Tanana	.08	477	Johnny Paredes (R)	.15	564	Ron Hassey	.08
307	Ron Guidry	.08	392	Curt Young	.08	478	Shawn Hillegas	.08	565	Dwight Gooden	.40
308	Steve Farr	.08	393	Jeff Treadway	.08	479	Bob Brenly	.08	566	Paul Assenmacher	.08
309	Curt Ford	.08	394	Darrell Evans	.08	480	Otis Nixon	.08	567	Neil Allen	.08
310	Claudell Washington	.08	395	Glenn Hubbard	.08	481	Johnny Ray	.08	568	Jim Morrison	.08
311	Tom Prince	.08	396	Chuck Cary	.08	482	Geno Petralli	.08	569	Mike Pagliarulo	.10
312	Chad Kreuter (R)	.15	397	Frank Viola	.12	483	Stu Cliburn	.08	570	Tedd Simmons	.08
313	Ken Oberkfell	.08	398	Jeff Parrett	.08	484	Pete Incaviglia	.12	571	Mark Thurmond	.08
314	Jerry Browne	.08	399	Terry Blocker (R)	.15	485	Bria Downing	.08	572	Fred McGriff	.35
315	R.J. Reynolds	.08	400	Dan Gladden	.08	486	Jeff Stone	.08	573	Wally Joyner	.25
316	Scott Bankhead	.08	401	Louis Meadows (R)	.15	487	Carmen Castillo	.08	574	Jose Bautista (R)	.15
317	Milt Thompson	.08	402	Tim Raines	.15	488	Tom Niedenfuer	.08	575	Kelly Gruber	.08
318	Mario Diaz	.08	403	Joey Meyer	.10	489	Jay Bell	.10	576	Cecilo Guante	.08
319	Bruce Ruffin	.08	404	Larry Anderson	.08	490	Rick Schu	.10	577	Mark Davidson	.08
320	Dave Valle	.08	405	Rex Hudler	.08	491	Jeff Pico (R)	.15	578	Bobby Bonilla	.15
321	Gary Varsho (R)	.25	406	Mike Schmidt	.50	492	Mark Parent (R)	.15	579	Mike Stanley	.08
321	Gary Varsho (error)	2.00	407	John Franco	.08	493	Eric King	.08	580	Gene Larkin	.08
322	Paul Mirabella	.08	408	Brady Anderson (R)	.30	494	Al Nipper	.08	581	Stan Javier	.08
323	Chuck Jackson	.08	409	Don Carmen	.08	495	Andy Hawkins	.08	582	Howard Johnson	.20
324	Drew Hall	.08	410	Eric Davis	.30	496	Daryl Boston	.08	583	Mike Gallego	.30
325	Don August	.08	411	Bob Stanley	.08	497	Ernie Riles	.08	583	M. Gallego (error)	2.50
326	Israel Sanchez (R)	.15	412	Pete Smith	.08	498	Pascual Perez	.08	584	David Cone	.40
327	Denny Walling	.08	413	Jim Rice	.12	499	Bill Long	.08	585	Doug Jennings (R)	.20
328	Joel Skinner	.08	414	Bruce Sutter	.10	500	Kirt Manwaring	.08	586	Charlie Hudson	.08
329	Danny Tartabull	.12	415	Oil Can Boyd	.08	501	Chuck Crim	.08	587	Dion James	.08
330	Tony Pena	.08	416	Ruben Sierra	.30	502	Candy Maldonado	.08	588	Al Leiter	.20
331	Jim Sundberg	.08	417	Mike LaValiere	.08	503	Dennis Lamp	.08	589	Charlie Puleo	.08
332	Jeff Robinson	.08	418	Steve Buechele	.08	504	Glenn Braggs	.08	590	Roberto Kelly	.25
333	Odibbe McDowell	.08	419	Gary Redus	.08	505	Joe Price	.08	591	Thad Bosley	.08
334	Jose Lind	.08	420	Scott Fletcher	.08	506	Ken Williams	.08	592	Pete Stanicek	.08
335	Paul Kilgus	.08	421	Dale Sveum	.08	507	Bill Pecota	.08	593	Pat Borders (R)	.15
336	Juan Samuel	.08	422	Bob Knepper	.08	508	Rey Quinones	.08	594	Bryan Harvey (R)	.20
337	Mike Campbell	.10	423	Luis Rivera	.08	509	Jeff Bittiger (R)	.15	595	Jeff Ballard	.15
338	Mike Maddux	.08	424	Ted Higuera	.08	510	Kevin Seitzer	.15	596	Jeff Reardon	.08
339	Darnell Coles	.08	425	Kevin Bass	.08	511	Steve Bedrosian	.08	597	Doug Drabek	.08
340	Bob Dernier	.08	426	Ken Gerhart	.08	512	Todd Worrell	.10	598	Edwin Correa	.08
341	Rafael Ramierez	.08	427	Shane Rawley	.08	513	Chris James	.08	599	Keith Atherton	.08
342	Scott Sanderson	.08	428	Paul O'Neill	.08	514	Jose Oquendo	.08	600	Dave LaPoint	.08
343	B.J. Surhoff	.08	429	Joe Orsulak	.08	515	David Palmer	.08	601	Don Baylor	.08
344	Billy Hatcher	.08	430	Jack Gutierrez	.08	516	John Smiley	.08	602	Tom Pagnozzi	.08
345	Pat Perry	.08	431	Gerald Perry	.08	517	Dave Clark	.08	603	Tim Flannery	.08
346	Jack Clark	.12	432	Mike Greenwell	.75	518	Mike Dunne	.08	604	Gene Walter	.08
347	Gary Thurman	.08	433	Jerry Royster	.08	519	Ron Washington	.08	605	Dave Parker	.12
348	Timmy Jones (R)	.15	434	Ellis Burks	.40	520	Bob Kipper	.08	606	Mike Diaz	.08
349	Dave Winfield	.15	435	Ed Olwine	.08	521	Lee Smith	.08	607	Chris Gwynn	.12
350	Frank White	.08	436	Dave Rucker	.08	522	Juan Castillo	.08	608	Odell Jones	.08
351	Dave Collins	.08	437	Charlie Hough	.08	523	Don Robinson	.08	609	Carlton Fisk	.08
352	Jack Morris	.08	438	Bob Walk	.08	524	Kevin Romine	.08	610	Jay Howell	.08
353	Eric Plunk	.08	439	Bob Brower	.08	525	Paul Molitor	.12	611	Tim Crews	.08
354	Leon Durham	.08	440	Bobby Bonds	.08	526	Mark Langston	.10	612	Keith Hernandez	.15
355	Ivan DeJesus	.15	441	Tom Foley	.08	527	Donnie Hill	.08	613	Willie Fraser	.08
356	Brian Holman (R)	.15				528	Larry Owen	.08	614	Jim Eppard	.08

NO.	PLAYER	MINT
615	Jeff Hamilton	.08
616	Kurt Stilwell	.08
617	Tom Browning	.08
618	Jeff Montgomery	.15
619	Jose Rijo	.08
620	Jamie Quirk	.08
621	Willie McGee	.15
622	Mark Grant	.08
623	Bill Swift	.08
624	Orlando Mercado	.08
625	John Costello (R)	.15
626	Jose Gonzalez	.08
627	Bill Schroeder	.30
627	B. Schroeder (error)	2.00
628	Fred Manrique	.30
628	F. Manrique (error)	2.00
629	Ricky Horton	.08
630	Dan Plesac	.08
631	Alfredo Griffin	.08
632	Chuck Finley	.08
633	Kirk Gibson	.20
634	Randy Myers	.08
635	Greg Minton	.08

NO.	PLAYER	MINT
636	Herm Winningham	.08
637	Charlie Leibrandt	.08
638	Tim Birtsas	.08
639	Bill Buckner	.08
640	Danny Jackson	.10
641	Greg Booker	.08
642	Jim Presley	.08
643	Gene Nelson	.08
644	Rod Booker	.08
645	Dennis Rasmussen	.08
646	Juan Nieves	.08
647	Bobby Thigpen	.08
648	Tim Belcher	.15
649	Mike Young	.08
650	Ivan Calderon	.08
651	Oswaldo Peraza (R)	.15
652	Pat Sheridan (cor.)	.25
652	Pat Sheridan (err.)	35.00
652	Pat Sheridan	.08
653	Mike Morgan	.08
654	Mike Heath	.08
655	Jay Tibbs	.08

NO.	PLAYER	MINT
656	Fernando Valenzuela	.15
657	Lee Mazzilli	.10
658	AL Cy Young	.12
659	AL MVP	.50
660	AL Rookie of the Year	.20
661	NL Cy Young	.25
662	NL MVP	.15
663	NL Rookie of the Year	.20
664	ALCS MVP	.15
665	NLCS MVP	.25
666	World Series Moment	.15
667	World Series MVP	.20
668	Angels Checklist	.15
669	Astros Checklist	.30
670	Athletics Checklist	.60
671	Blue Jays Checklist	.08
672	Braves Checklist	.25
673	Brewers Checklist	.08
674	Cardinals Checklist	.08
675	Cubs Checklist	.08
676	Dodgers Checklist	.15
677	Expos Checklist	.08
678	Giants Checklist	.40

NO.	PLAYER	MINT
679	Indians Checklist	.08
680	Mariners Checklist	.08
681	Mets Checklist	.50
682	Orioles Checklist	.15
683	Padres Checklist	.15
684	Phillies Checklist	.20
685	Pirates Checklist	.08
686	Rangers Checklist	.08
687	Red Sox Checklist	.40
688	Reds Checklist	.35
689	Royals Checklist	.15
690	Tigers Checklist	.12
691	Twins Checklist	.08
692	White Sox Checklist	.08
693	Yankees Checklist	.50
694	Checklist 1-100	.08
695	Checklist 101-200	.08
696	Checklist 201-300	.08
697	Checklist 301-400	.08
698	Checklist 401-500	.08
699	Checklist 501-600	.08
700	Checklist 601-700	.08

1989 Upper Deck Extended.... Complete Set of 100 Cards—Value $50.00

This set updates the main 1989 card set with players who had changed teams during the season, and rookies. The set was packaged in a printed box and also included with the factory sets. Features the first Upper Deck card of Gregg Olson, Tom Gordon, Todd Zeile, Jim Abbott and Jerome Walton.

Gregg Olson — Todd Zeile — Dwight Smith — Jim Abbott — Tom Gordon

NO.	PLAYER	MINT
701	Checklist 701-800	.15
702	Jesse Barfield	.20
703	Walt Terrell	.15
704	Dickie Thon	.15
705	Al Leiter	.15
706	Dave LaPoint	.15
707	Charlie Hayes	.40
708	Andy Hawkins	.15
709	Mickey Hatcher	.15
710	Lance McCullers	.15
711	Ron Kittle	.15
712	Bert Blyleven	.20
713	Rick Dempsey	.15
714	Ken Williams	.15
715	Steve Rosenberg	.25
716	Joe Skalski	.15
717	Spike Owen	.15
718	Todd Burns	.15
719	Kevin Gross	.15
720	Tommy Herr	.15
721	Rob Ducey	.25
722	Gary Green	.20
723	Gregg Olson (RR)	4.00
724	Greg W. Harris	.30
725	Craig Worthington	.50

NO.	PLAYER	MINT
726	Tom Howard	.40
727	Dale Mohorcic	.15
728	Rich Yett	.15
729	Mel Hall	.15
730	Floyd Youmans	.20
731	Lonnie Smith	.15
732	Wally Backman	.15
733	Trevor Wilson	.30
734	Jose Alvarez	.20
735	Bob Milacki	.15
736	Tom Gordon (RR)	5.00
737	Wally Whitehurst	.30
738	Mike Aldrete	.15
739	Keith Miller	.20
740	Randy Milligan	.15
741	Jeff Parrett	.15
742	Steve Finley	.50
743	Junior Felix (RR)	2.00
744	Pate Harnisch	.15
745	Bill Spiers	.60
746	Hensley Meulens	.75
747	Juan Bell	.15
748	Steve Sax	.20
749	Phil Bradley	.15
750	Rey Quinones	.15

NO.	PLAYER	MINT
751	Tommy Gregg	.15
752	Kevin Brown	.60
753	Derek Lilliquist	.25
754	Todd Zeile (RR)	7.00
755	Jim Abbott (RR)	8.00
756	Ozzie Canseco (RR)	2.00
757	Nick Esasky	.25
758	Mike Moore	.15
759	Rob Murphy	.15
760	Rick Mahler	.15
761	Fred Lynn	.15
762	Kevin Blankenship	.20
763	Eddie Murray	.25
764	Steve Searcy	.20
765	Jerome Walton (RR)	12.00
766	Erik Hanson	.25
767	Bob Boone	.15
768	Edgar Martinez	.30
769	Jose DeJesus	.15
770	Greg Briley (RR)	2.00
771	Steve Peters	.25
772	Rafael Palmeiro	.20
773	Jack Clark	.25
774	Nolan Ryan	5.00
775	Lance Parrish	.15

NO.	PLAYER	MINT
776	Joe Girardi	.40
777	Willie Randolph	.20
778	Mitch Williams	.15
779	Dennis Cook	.35
780	Dwight Smith (RR)	3.00
781	Lenny Harris	.25
782	Torey Lovullo	.25
783	Norm Charlton	.25
784	Chris Brown	.15
785	Todd Benzinger	.15
786	Shane Rawley	.15
787	Omar Vizquel	.30
788	LaVel Freeman	.50
789	Jeffrey Leonard	.20
790	Eddie Williams	.15
791	Jamie Moyer	.15
792	Bruce Hurst	.15
793	Julio Franco	.20
794	Claudell Washington	.15
795	Jody Davis	.15
796	Odibbe McDowell	.15
797	Paul Kilgus	.15
798	Tracy Jones	.15
799	Steve Wilson	.20
800	Pete O'Brien	.15

1990 Upper Deck.... Complete Set of 700 Cards—Value $60.00

Features the rookie cards of Greg Vaughn, Eric Anthony, Ben McDonald, John Olerud and Todd Zeile.

David Cone

Eric Davis

Junior Felix

Julio Machado

Chris Hammond

NO. PLAYER	MINT	NO. PLAYER	MINT	NO. PLAYER	MINT	NO. PLAYER	MINT
1 Star Rookie checklist	.10	67 Matt Merullo (R)	.15	133 Marty Barrett	.08	200 Checklist 101-200	.08
2 Randy Nosek (R)	.20	68 Cardinals checklist	.08	134 Nelson Liriano	.08	201 Terry Puhl	.08
3 Tom Dress (R)	.30	69 Ron Karkovice	.08	135 Mark Carreon	.08	202 Frank DiPino	.08
4 Curt Young	.08	70 Kevin Mass (R)	.45	136 Candy Maldonado	.08	203 Jim Clancy	.08
5 Angels checklist	.08	71 Dennis Cook	.12	137 Tim Birtsas	.08	204 Bob Ojeda	.08
6 Luis Salazar	.08	72 Juan Gonzalez (R)	.12	138 Tom Brookens	.08	205 Alex Trevino	.08
7 Phillies checklist	.08	73 Cubs checklist	.08	139 John Franco	.10	206 Dave Henderson	.10
8 Jose Bautista	.08	74 Dean Palmer (R)	.35	140 Mike LaCoss	.08	207 Henry Cotto	.08
9 Marquis Grissom (R)	.75	75 Special card-Jackson	.50	141 Jeff Treadway	.08	208 Rafael Belliard	.08
10 Dodgers checklist	.08	76 Rob Richie (R)	.20	142 Pat Tabler	.08	209 Stan Javier	.08
11 Rick Aguilera	.08	77 Bobby Rose	.35	143 Darrell Evans	.08	210 Jerry Reed	.08
12 Padres checklist	.08	78 Brian DuBois (R)	.20	144 Rafael Ramirez	.08	211 Doug Dascenzo	.08
13 Deion Sanders (R)	.60	79 White Sox checklist	.08	145 Odibbe McDowell	.08	212 Andres Thomas	.08
14 Marvell Wynne	.08	80 Gene Nelson	.08	146 Brian Downing	.08	213 Greg Maddux	.10
15 David West	.10	81 Bob McClure	.08	147 Curtis Wilkerson	.08	214 Mike Schooler	.10
16 Pirates checklist	.08	82 Rangers checklist	.08	148 Ernie Whitt	.08	215 Lonnie Smith	.08
17 Sammy Sosa (R)	.60	83 Greg Minton	.08	149 Bill Schroeder	.08	216 Jose Rijo	.08
18 Yankees checklist	.08	84 Braves checklist	.08	150 Domingo Ramos	.08	217 Greg Gagne	.08
19 Jack Howell	.08	85 Willie Fraser	.08	151 Rick Honeycutt	.08	218 Jim Gantner	.08
20 Special card-Schmidt	.40	86 Neal Heaton	.08	152 Don Slaught	.08	219 Allan Anderson	.08
21 Robin Ventura	.75	87 Kevin Tapani (R)	.20	153 Mitch Webster	.10	220 Rick Mahler	.08
22 Brian Meyer	.15	88 Astros checklist	.08	154 Tony Phillips	.08	221 Jim Deshaies	.08
23 Blaine Beatty (R)	.25	89 Jim Gott	.15	155 Paul Kilgus	.08	222 Keith Hernandez	.12
24 Mariners checklist	.08	90 Lance Johnson	.12	156 Ken Griffey, Jr.	1.50	223 Vince Colman	.15
25 Greg Vaughn (R)	1.50	91 Brewers checklist	.08	157 Gary Sheffield	.50	224 David Cone	.15
26 Xavier Hernandez (R)	.20	92 Jeff Parrett	.08	158 Wally Backman	.08	225 Ozzie Smith	.12
27 Jason Grimsley (R)	.20	93 Julio Machado (R)	.25	159 B.J. Surhoff	.08	226 Matt Nokes	.10
28 Eric Anthony (R)	2.25	94 Ron Jones	.08	160 Louie Meadows	.08	227 Barry Bonds	.12
29 Expos checklist	.08	95 Blue Jays checklist	.08	161 Paul O'Neill	.08	228 Felix Jose	.08
30 David Wells	.08	96 Jerry Reuss	.08	162 Jeff McKnight (R)	.25	229 Dennis Powell	.08
31 Hal Morris	.10	97 Brian Fisher	.08	163 Alvaro Espinoza (R)	.25	230 Mike Gallego	.08
32 Royals checklist	.08	98 Kevin Ritz (R)	.20	165 Jeff Reed	.08	231 Shawon Dunston	.08
33 Kelly Mann (R)	.15	99 Reds checklist	.08	166 Gregg Jefferies	.50	232 Ron Gant	.08
34 Special card-Ryan	.50	100 Checklist 1-100	.08	167 Barry Larkin	.10	233 Omar Vizquel (R)	.20
35 Scott Service	.20	101 Gerald Perry	.08	168 Gary Carter	.15	234 Derek Lilliquist	.12
36 Athletics checklist	.20	102 Kevin Appier (R)	.20	169 Robby Thompson	.15	235 Erik Hanson	.12
37 Tino Martinez	.45	103 Julio Franco	.10	170 Rolando Roomes	.12	236 Kirby Puckett	.35
38 Chili Davis	.08	104 Craig Biggio	.15	171 Mark McGwire	.35	237 Bill Spiers (R)	.30
39 Scott Sanderson	.08	105 Bo Jackson	.60	172 Steve Sax	.15	238 Dan Gladden	.08
40 Giants checklist	.20	106 Junior Felix (R)	.40	173 Mark Williamson	.08	239 Bryan Clutterbuck	.08
41 Tigers checklist	.08	107 Mike Markey	.35	174 Mitch Williams	.08	240 John Moses	.08
42 Scott Coolbaugh (R)	.35	108 Fred McGriff	.20	175 Brian Holton	.08	241 Ron Darling	.12
43 Jose Cano (R)	.35	109 Rick Sutcliffe	.08	176 Rob Deer	.08	242 Joe Magrane	.10
44 Jose Vizcaino (R)	.25	110 Pete O'Brien	.10	177 Tim Raines	.20	243 Dave Magadan	.10
45 Bob Hamelin (R)	.75	111 Kelly Gruber	.08	178 Mike Felder	.08	244 Pedro Guerrero	.12
46 Jose Offerman (R)	1.25	112 Pat Borders	.08	179 Harold Reynolds	.08	245 Glenn Davis	.12
47 Kevin Blankenship	.12	113 Dwight Evans	.12	180 Terry Francona	.08	246 Terry Steinbach	.10
48 Twins checklist	.15	114 Dwight Gooden	.30	181 Chris Sabo	.15	247 Fred Lynn	.10
49 Tommy Greene (R)	.50	115 Kevin Batiste (R)	.20	182 Darryl Strawberry	.35	248 Gary Redus	.08
50 Special card-Clark	.35	116 Eric Davis	.25	183 Willie Randolph	.15	249 Kenny Williams	.08
51 Rob Nelson	.08	117 Kevin Mitchell	.25	184 Billy Ripken	.20	250 Sid Bream	.08
52 Chris Hammond (R)	.25	118 Ron Oester	.08	185 Mackey Sasser	.08	251 Bob Welch	.08
53 Indians checklist	.08	119 Brett Butler	.08	186 Todd Benzinger	.08	252 Bill Buckner	.08
54 Ben McDonald (R)	3.00	120 Danny Jackson	.12	187 Kevin Elster	.12	253 Carney Lansford	.08
55 Andy Benes	.75	121 Tommy Gregg	.08	188 Jose Uribe	.08	254 Paul Molitor	.12
56 John Olerud (R)	3.50	122 Ken Caminiti	.08	189 Tom Browning	.08	255 Jose DeJesus	.08
57 Red Sox checklist	.15	123 Kevin Brown	.15	190 Keith Miller	.08	256 Orel Hershiser	.15
58 Tony Armas	.08	124 George Brett	.20	191 Don Mattingly	.60	257 Tom Brunansky	.08
59 George Canale (R)	.20	125 Mike Scott	.12	192 Dave Parker	.15	258 Mike Davis	.08
60 Orioles checklist	.15	126 Cory Snyder	.15	193 Roberto Kelly	.12	259 Jeff Ballard	.08
61 Mike Stanton (R)	.20	127 George Bell	.10	194 Phil Bradley	.08	260 Scott Terry	.08
62 Mets checklist	.20	128 Mark Grace	.45	195 Ron Hassey	.08	261 Sid Fernandez	.08
63 Kent Mercker (R)	.50	129 Devon White	.10	196 Gerald Young	.08	262 Mike Marshall	.08
64 Francisco Cabrera (R)	.20	130 Tony Fernandez	.10	197 Hubie Brooks	.08	263 Howard Johnson	.15
65 Steve Avery	.40	131 Don Aase	.08	198 Bill Doran	.08	264 Kirk Gibson	.12
66 Jose Canseco	.60	132 Rance Mulliniks	.08	199 Al Newman	.08		

NO.	PLAYER	MINT
265	Kevin McReynolds	.10
266	Cal Ripken, Jr.	.15
267	Ozzie Guillen	.08
268	Jim Traber	.08
269	Bobby Thigpen	.08
270	Joe Orsulak	.08
271	Bob Boone	.08
272	Dave Stewart	.12
273	Tim Wallach	.08
274	Luis Aquino	.08
275	Mike Moore	.08
276	Tony Pena	.08
277	Eddie Murray	.15
278	Milt Thompson	.08
279	Alejandro Pena	.08
280	Ken Dayley	.08
281	Carmen Castillo	.08
282	Tom Henke	.08
283	Mickey Hatcher	.08
284	Roy Smith	.08
285	Manny Lee	.08
286	Dan Pasqua	.08
287	Larry Sheets	.08
288	Garry Templeton	.08
289	Eddie Williams	.15
290	Brady Anderson	.08
291	Spike Owen	.08
292	Storm Davis	.08
293	Chris Bosio	.08
294	Jim Eisenreich	.08
295	Don August	.10
296	Jeff Hamilton	.08
297	Mickey Tettleton	.08
298	Mike Scioscia	.12
299	Kevin Hickey	.10
300	Checklist 201-300	.08
301	Shawn Abner	.08
302	Kevin Bass	.08
303	Bip Roberts	.08
304	Joe Girardi	.15
305	Danny Darwin	.08
306	Mike Heath	.08
307	Mike MacFarlane	.08
308	Ed Whitson	.08
309	Tracy Jones	.08
310	Scott Fletcher	.08
311	Darnell Coles	.08
312	Mike Brumley	.08
313	Bill Swift	.08
314	Charlie Hough	.08
315	Jim Presley	.08
316	Luis Polonia	.08
317	Mike Morgan	.08
318	Lee Guetterman	.08
319	Jose Oquendo	.08
320	Wayne Tolleson	.08
321	Jody Reed	.08
322	Damon Berryhill	.12
323	Roger Clemens	.25
324	Ryne Sandberg	.15
325	Benito Santiago	.10
326	Bret Saberhagen	.10
327	Lou Whitaker	.08
328	Dave Gallagher	.08
329	Mike Pagliarulo	.08
330	Doyle Alexander	.08
331	Jeffrey Leonard	.08
332	Torey Lovullo	.10
333	Pete Incaviglia	.10
334	Rickey Henderson	.30
335	Rafael Palmeiro	.10
336	Ken Hill	.12
337	Dave Winfield	.15
338	Alfredo Griffin	.08
339	Andy Hawkins	.08
340	Ted Power	.08
341	Steve Wilson	.15
342	Jack Clark	.08
343	Ellis Burks	.20
344	Tony Gwynn	.25
345	Jerome Walton	1.50
346	Roberto Alomar	.12
347	Carlos Martinez (R)	.25
348	Chet Lemon	.08

NO.	PLAYER	MINT
349	Willie Wilson	.08
350	Greg Walker	.08
351	Tom Bolton	.08
352	German Gonzalez	.08
353	Harold Baines	.08
354	Mike Greenwell	.30
355	Ruben Sierra	.25
356	Andres Galarraga	.10
357	Andre Dawson	.12
358	Jeff Brantley	.15
359	Mike Bielecki	.08
360	Ken Oberkfell	.08
361	Kurt Stillwell	.08
362	Brian Homan	.08
363	Kevin Seitzer	.12
364	Alvin Davis	.10
365	Tom Gordon	.75
366	Bobby Bonilla	.10
367	Carlton Fisk	.12
368	Steve Carter (R)	.20
369	Joel Skinner	.08
370	John Cangelosi	.08
371	Cecil Espy	.08
372	Gary Wayne (R)	.15
373	Jim Rice	.15
374	Mike Dyer (R)	.20
375	Joe Carter	.15
376	Dwight Smith	.75
377	John Wetteland (R)	.35
378	Ernie Riles	.08
379	Otis Nixon	.08
380	Vance Law	.08
381	Dave Bergman	.08
382	Frank White	.08
383	Scott Bradley	.08
384	Israel Sanchez	.08
385	Gary Pettis	.08
386	Donn Pall	.08
387	John Smiley	.08
388	Tom Candiotti	.08
389	Junior Ortiz	.08
390	Steve Lyons	.08
391	Brian Harper	.08
392	Fred Manrique	.10
393	Lee Smith	.08
394	Jeff Kunkel	.08
395	Claudell Washington	.08
396	John Tudor	.08
397	Terry Kennedy	.08
398	Lloyd McClendon	.08
399	Craig Lefferts	.08
400	Checklist 301-400	.08
401	Keith Moreland	.08
402	Rich Gedman	.08
403	Jeff Robinson	.12
404	Randy Ready	.08
405	Rick Cerone	.08
406	Jeff Blauser	.08
407	Larry Andersen	.08
408	Joe Boever	.08
409	Felix Fermin	.08
410	Glenn Wilson	.08
411	Rex Hudler	.08
412	Mark Grant	.08
413	Dennis Martinez	.08
414	Darrin Jackson	.08
415	Mike Aldrete	.08
416	Roger McDowell	.08
417	Jeff Reardon	.08
418	Darren Daulton	.08
419	Tim Laudner	.08
420	Don Carman	.08
421	Lloyd Moseby	.08
422	Doug Drabek	.08
423	Lenny Harris	.10
424	Jose Lind	.08
425	Dave Johnson	.12
426	Jerry Browne	.12
427	Eric Yelding (R)	.15
428	Brad Komminsk	.08
429	Jody Davis	.08
430	Mariano Duncan	.08
431	Mark Davis	.10
432	Nelson Santovenia	.08

NO.	PLAYER	MINT
433	Bruce Hurst	.08
434	Jeff Huson (R)	.20
435	Chris James	.08
436	Mark Guthrie (R)	.15
437	Charlie Hayes	.10
438	Shane Rawley	.08
439	Dickie Thon	.08
440	Juan Berenguer	.08
441	Kevin Romine	.08
442	Bill Landrum	.08
443	Todd Frohwirth	.08
444	Craig Worthington	.08
445	Fernando Valenzuela	.15
446	Joey Belle (R)	.75
447	Ed Whited (R)	.20
448	Dave Smith	.08
449	Dave Clark	.08
450	Juan Agosta	.08
451	Dave Valle	.08
452	Kent Hrbek	.10
453	Von Hayes	.08
454	Gary Gaetti	.12
455	Greg Briley	.25
456	Glenn Braggs	.08
457	Kirt Manwaring	.08
458	Mel Hall	.08
459	Brook Jacoby	.08
460	Pat Sheridan	.08
461	Rob Murphy	.08
462	Jimmy Key	.08
463	Nick Esasky	.08
464	Rob Ducey	.08
465	Carlos Quintana	.08
466	Larry Walker (R)	.30
467	Todd Worrell	.08
468	Kevin Gross	.08
469	Terry Pendleton	.08
470	Dave Martinez	.08
471	Gene Larkin	.08
472	Len Dykstra	.08
473	Barry Lyons	.08
474	Terry Mulholland	.08
475	Chip Hale (R)	.20
476	Jesse Barfield	.08
477	Dan Plesac	.08
478	Scott Garrelts	.10
479	Dave Righetti	.15
480	Gus Polidor	.08
481	Mookie Wilson	.10
482	Luis Rivera	.08
483	Mike Falangan	.08
484	Dennis "Oil Can" Boyd	.08
485	John Cerutti	.08
486	John Costello	.08
487	Pascual Perez	.08
488	Tommy Herr	.10
489	Tom Foley	.08
490	Curt Ford	.08
491	Steve Lake	.08
492	Tim Teufel	.08
493	Randy Bush	.08
494	Mike Jackson	.08
495	Steve Jeitz	.08
496	Paul Gibson	.08
497	Steve Balboni	.08
498	Bud Black	.08
499	Dale Sveum	.08
500	Checklist 401-500	.08
501	Timmy Jones	.08
502	Mark Portugal	.08
503	Ivan Calderon	.08
504	Rick Rhoden	.08
505	Willie McGee	.10
506	Kirk McCaskill	.10
507	Dave LaPoint	.08
508	Jay Howell	.08
509	Johnny Ray	.08
510	Dave Anderson	.08
511	Chuck Crim	.08
512	Joe Hesketh	.08
513	Dennis Eckersley	.12
514	Greg Brock	.08
515	Tim Burke	.08
516	Frank Tanana	.08

NO.	PLAYER	MINT
517	Jay Bell	.08
518	Guillermo Hernandez	.08
519	Randy Kramer	.08
520	Charles Hudson	.08
521	Jim Corsi	.08
522	Steve Rosenberg	.08
523	Cris Carpeter	.08
524	Matt Winters (R)	.20
525	Melido Perez	.08
526	Chris Gwynn	.12
527	Bert Blyleven	.12
528	Chuck Cary	.08
529	Daryl Boston	.08
530	Dale Mohorcic	.08
531	Geronomi Berroa	.10
532	Edgar Martinez	.08
533	Dale Murphy	.20
534	Jay Buhner	.12
535	John Smoltz	.30
536	Andy Van Slyke	.12
537	Mike Henneman	.08
538	Miguel Garcia	.08
539	Frank Williams	.08
540	R.J. Reynolds	.08
541	Shawn Hillegas	.08
542	Walt Weiss	.12
543	Greg Hibbard (R)	.20
544	Nolan Ryan	.45
545	Todd Zeile (R)	2.00
546	Hensley Meulens	.30
547	Tim Belcher	.12
548	Mike Witt	.12
549	Greg Cadaret	.08
550	Franklin Stubbs	.08
551	Tony Castillo	.08
552	Jeff Robinson	.12
553	Steve Olin (R)	.15
554	Alan Trammell	.10
555	Wade Boggs	.35
556	Will Clark	.65
557	Jeff King	.15
558	Mike Fitzgerald	.08
559	Ken Howell	.08
560	Bob Kipper	.08
561	Scott Bankhead	.08
562	Jeff Innis	.12
563	Randy Johnson	.10
564	Wally Whitehurst (R)	.20
565	Gene Harris (R)	.15
566	Norm Charlton	.12
567	Robin Yount	.30
568	Joe Oliver (R)	.20
569	Mark Parent	.08
570	John Farrell	.10
571	Tom Glavine	.12
572	Rod Nichols	.10
573	Jack Morris	.10
574	Greg Swindell	.10
575	Steve Searcy	.15
576	Ricky Jordan	.25
577	Matt Williams	.15
578	Mike LaValliere	.12
579	Bryn Smith	.08
580	Bruce Ruffin	.08
581	Randy Myers	.12
582	Rick Wrona (R)	.20
583	Juan Samuel	.10
584	Les Lancaster	.08
585	Jeff Musselman	.08
586	Rob Dibble	.12
587	Eric Show	.08
588	Jesse Orosco	.08
589	Herm Winningham	.08
590	Andy Allanson	.08
591	Dion James	.08
592	Carmelo Martinez	.08
593	Luis Quinones	.08
594	Dennis Rasmussen	.08
595	Rich Yett	.08
596	Bob Walk	.08
597	Andy McGaffigan	.08
598	Billy Hatcher	.08
599	Bob Knepper	.08
600	Checklist 501-600	.08

NO.	PLAYER	MINT	NO.	PLAYER	MINT	NO.	PLAYER	MINT	NO.	PLAYER	MINT
601	Joey Cora	12	626	Frank Viola	12	651	Eric King	08	676	Mark Gubicza	08
602	Steve Finley (R)	15	627	Ted Higuera	08	652	Mike Boddicker	08	677	Greg Litton (R)	30
603	Kal Daniels	10	628	Marty Pevey (R)	20	653	Duane Ward	08	678	Greg Mathews	08
604	Gregg Olson	35	629	Bill Wegman	08	654	Bob Stanley	08	679	Dave Dravecky	08
605	Dave Stieb	08	630	Eric Plunk	08	655	Sandy Alomar, Jr.	40	680	Steve Farr	08
606	Kenny Rogers (R)	15	631	Drew Hall	08	656	Danny Tartabull	12	681	Mike Devereaux	08
607	Zane Smith	08	632	Doug Jones	08	657	Rick McCament (R)	20	682	Ken Griffey, Sr.	08
608	Bob Geren (R)	25	633	Geno Petralli	08	658	Charlie Leibrandt	08	683	Jamie Weston (R)	35
609	Chad Kreuter	08	634	Jose Alvarez	08	659	Dan Quisenberry	08	684	Jack Armstrong	08
610	Mike Smithson	08	635	Bob Milacki	12	660	Paul Assenmacher	08	685	Steve Buechele	08
611	Jeff Wetherby (R)	25	636	Bobby Witt	12	661	Walt Terrell	08	686	Bryan Harvey	08
612	Gary Mielke (R)	15	637	Trevor Wilson	08	662	Tim Leary	08	687	Lance Blankenship	08
613	Pete Smith	08	638	Jeff Russell	08	663	Randy Milligan	10	688	Dante Bichette	08
614	Jack Daugherty (R)	20	639	Mike Krukow	08	664	Bo Diaz	08	689	Todd Burns	15
615	Lance McCullers	08	640	Rick Leach	08	665	Mark Lemke	08	690	Dan Petry	08
616	Don Robinson	08	641	Dave Schmidt	08	666	Jose Gonzalez	08	691	Kent Anderson (R)	20
617	Jose Guzman	08	642	Terry Leach	08	667	Chuck Finley	10	692	Todd Stottlemyre	10
618	Steve Bedrosian	08	643	Calvin Schiraldi	08	668	John Kruk	08	693	Wally Joyner	15
619	Jamie Moyer	08	644	Bob Melvin	08	669	Dick Schofield	08	694	Mike Rochford	15
620	Atlee Hammaker	08	645	Jim Abbott	1.50	670	Tim Crews	08	695	Floyd Bannister	08
621	Rick Luecken (R)	20	646	Jaime Navarro (R)	25	671	John Dopson	08	696	Rick Reuschel	12
622	Greg W. Harris	12	647	Mark Langston	15	672	John Orton (R)	25	697	Jose DeLeon	08
623	Pete Harnisch	12	648	Juan Nieves	08	673	Eric Hetzel	08	698	Jeff Montgomery	10
624	Jerald Clark	08	649	Damaso Garcia	08	674	Lance Parrish	08	699	Kelly Downs	10
625	Jack McDowell	10	650	Charlie O'Brien	08	675	Ramon Martinez	20	700	Checklist 601-700	08

1989 BOWMAN.... Complete Set of 484 Cards (2½″ x 3¾″)—Value $25.00

This was the first Bowman card set since 1955 when Topps bought the Bowman Gum Co. The set which was released in July includes hot rookie stars from Spring training '89, traded players in their new uniforms, and all of the top stars of the game. The cards are the same size as the classic '53 Bowmans, 2½″ x 3¾″. Features the rookie cards of Ken Griffey, Jr., Jerome Walton, Gary Sheffield and Ricky Jordan.

NO. PLAYER	MINT	NO. PLAYER	MINT	NO. PLAYER	MINT	NO. PLAYER	MINT
1 Oswald Peraza (R)	.15	67 Dan Pasqua	.08	133 Dan Plesac	.05	199 Glenn Hubbard	.05
2 Briand Holton	.10	68 Ivan Calderon	.08	134 Chris Bosio	.05	200 Dave Henderson	.08
3 Jose Bautista (R)	.15	69 Ron Kittle	.05	135 Bill Wegman	.05	201 Jose Canseco	1.00
4 Pete Harnisch (R)	.25	70 Daryl Boston	.05	136 Chuck Crim	.05	202 Dave Parker	.08
5 Dave Schmidt	.05	71 Dave Gallagher (R)	.25	137 B.J. Surhoff	.08	203 Scott Bankhead	.12
6 Gregg Olson (R)	.40	72 Harold Baines	.08	138 Joey Meyer	.10	204 Tom Niedenfuer	.05
7 Jeff Ballard	.15	73 Charles Nagy (R)	.25	139 Dale Sveum	.05	205 Mark Langston	.10
8 Bob Melvin	.05	74 John Farrell	.05	140 Paul Molitor	.08	206 Erik Hanson (R)	.20
9 Cal Ripken	.15	75 Kevin Wickander (R)	.20	141 Jim Gantner	.05	207 Mike Jackson	.05
10 Randy Milligan	.12	76 Greg Swindell	.10	142 Gary Sheffield (R)	1.00	208 Dave Valle	.05
11 Juan Bell (R)	.30	77 Mike Walker (R)	.20	143 Greg Brock	.05	209 Scott Bradley	.05
12 Billy Ripken	.08	78 Doug Jones	.05	144 Robin Yount	.12	210 Harold Reynolds	.08
13 Jim Traber	.05	79 Rich Yett	.05	145 Glenn Braggs	.05	211 Tino Martinez (R)	.60
14 Pete Stanicek	.10	80 Tom Candiotti	.05	146 Rob Deer	.08	212 Rich Renteria (R)	.15
15 Steve Finley (R)	.35	81 Jesse Orosco	.05	147 Fred Toliver	.05	213 Rey Quinones	.05
16 Larry Sheets	.05	82 Bud Black	.05	148 Jeff Reardon	.08	214 Jim Presley	.05
17 Phil Bradley	.08	83 Andy Allanson	.05	149 Allan Anderson	.12	215 Alvin Davis	.08
18 Brady Anderson (R)	.25	84 Pete O'Brien	.10	150 Frank Viola	.12	216 Edgar Martinez	.10
19 Lee Smith	.08	85 Jerry Browne	.05	151 Shane Rawley	.05	217 Darnell Coles	.05
20 Tom Fischer (R)	.15	86 Brook Jacoby	.05	152 Juan Berenguer	.05	218 Jeffrey Leonard	.05
21 Mike Boodicker	.05	87 Mark Lewis (R)	.30	153 Johnny Ard (R)	.15	219 Jay Buhner	.20
22 Rob Murphy	.05	88 Luis Aguayo	.05	154 Tim Laudner	.05	220 Ken Griffey, Jr. (R)	3.00
23 Wes Gardner	.05	89 Cory Snyder	.15	155 Brian Harper	.05	221 Drew Hall	.05
24 John Dopson (R)	.25	90 Oddibe McDowell	.05	156 Al Newman	.05	222 Bobby Witt	.08
25 Bob Stanley	.05	91 Joe Carter	.15	157 Kent Hrbek	.12	223 Jamie Moyer	.05
26 Roger Clemens	.35	92 Frank Tanana	.05	158 Gary Gaetti	.12	224 Charlie Hough	.05
27 Rich Gedman	.05	93 Jack Morris	.10	159 Wally Backman	.05	225 Nolan Ryan	.40
28 Marty Barrett	.05	94 Doyle Alexander	.05	160 Gene Larkin	.05	226 Jeff Russell	.05
29 Luis Rivera	.05	95 Steve Searcy (R)	.25	161 Greg Gagne	.05	227 Jim Sundberg	.05
30 Jody Reed	.08	96 Randy Bockus (R)	.15	162 Kirby Puckett	.35	228 Julio Franco	.08
31 Nick Esasky	.08	97 Jeff Robinson	.08	163 Danny Gladden	.05	229 Buddy Bell	.05
32 Wade Boggs	.65	98 Mike Henneman	.05	164 Randy Bush	.05	230 Scott Fletcher	.05
33 Jim Rice	.12	99 Paul Gibson (R)	.15	165 Dave LaPoint	.05	231 Jeff Kunkel	.05
34 Mike Greenwell	.75	100 Frank Williams	.05	166 Andy Hawkins	.05	232 Steve Buechele	.05
35 Dwight Evans	.10	101 Matt Nokes	.10	167 Dave Righetti	.08	233 Monty Fariss ((R)	.25
36 Ellis Burks	.30	102 Ricco Brogna (R)	.15	168 Lance McCullers	.08	234 Rick Leach	.05
37 Chuck Finley	.12	103 Lou Whitaker	.08	169 Jimmy Jones	.08	235 Ruben Sierra	.20
38 Kirk McCaskill	.10	104 Al Pedrique	.05	170 Al Leiter	.10	236 Cecil Espy	.08
39 Jim Abbott (R)	2.00	105 Alan Trammell	.15	171 John Candelaria	.08	237 Rafael Palmeiro	.15
40 Bryan Harvey (R)	.25	106 Chris Brown	.05	172 Don Slaught	.05	238 Pete Incaviglia	.08
41 Bert Blyleven	.08	107 Pat Sheridan	.05	173 Jamie Quirk	.05	239 Dave Stieb	.05
42 Mike Witt	.08	108 Chet Lemon	.05	174 Rafael Santana	.05	240 Jeff Musselman	.05
43 Bob McClure	.05	109 Keith Moreland	.05	175 Mike Pagliarulo	.10	241 Mike Flanagan	.05
44 Bill Schroeder	.05	110 Mel Stottlemyre, Jr. (R)	.25	176 Don Mattingly	1.00	242 Todd Stottlemyre	.15
45 Lance Parrish	.10	111 Bret Saberhagen	.10	177 Ken Phelps	.08	243 Jimmy Key	.08
46 Dick Schofield	.05	112 Floyd Bannister	.05	178 Steve Sax	.10	244 Tony Castillo (R)	.15
47 Wally Joyner	.20	113 Jeff Montgomery	.10	179 Dave Winfield	.15	245 Alex Sanchez (R)	.20
48 Jack Howell	.05	114 Steve Farr	.05	180 Stan Jefferson	.05	246 Tom Henke	.05
49 Johnny Ray	.10	115 Tom Gordon (R)	1.50	181 Rickey Henderson	.20	247 John Cerutti	.05
50 Chili Davis	.08	116 Charlie Leibrandt	.08	182 Bob Brower	.05	248 Ernie Whitt	.05
51 Tony Armas	.05	117 Mark Gubicza	.08	183 Roberto Kelly	.20	249 Bob Brenly	.05
52 Claudell Washington	.05	118 Mike Macfarlane (R)	.15	184 Curt Young	.05	250 Rance Mulliniks	.05
53 Brian Downing	.08	119 Bob Boone	.05	185 Gene Nelson	.05	251 Kelly Gruber	.08
54 Devon White	.10	120 Kurt Stillwell	.05	186 Bob Welch	.08	252 Ed Sprague	.15
55 Bobby Thigpen	.05	121 George Brett	.20	187 Rick Honeycutt	.05	253 Fred McGriff	.15
56 Bill Long	.05	122 Frank White	.05	188 Dave Stewart	.08	254 Tony Fernandez	.08
57 Jerry Reuss	.05	123 Kevin Seitzer	.20	189 Mike Moore	.05	255 Tom Lawless	.05
58 Shawn Hillegas	.05	124 Willie Wilson	.08	190 Dennis Eckersley	.05	256 George Bell	.10
59 Melido Perez	.10	125 Pat Tabler	.05	191 Eric Plunk	.05	257 Jesse Barfield	.08
60 Jeff Bittiger (R)	.15	126 Bo Jackson	.50	192 Storm Davis	.05	258 S. Alomar, Jr./Sr.	.25
61 Jack McDowell	.12	127 Hugh Walker (R)	.15	193 Terry Steinbach	.10	259 Griffey, Jr./Sr.	.75
62 Carlton Fisk	.10	128 Danny Tartabull	.15	194 Ron Hassey	.05	260 Cal Ripken, Sr.,	.05
63 Steve Lyons	.05	129 Teddy Higuera	.08	195 Stan Royer (R)	.15	261 Mel Stottlemyre	.05
64 Ozzie Guillen	.08	130 Don August	.08	196 Walt Weiss	.20	262 Zane Smith	.05
65 Robin Ventura (R)	1.00	131 Juan Nieves	.05	197 Mark McGwire	.60	263 Charlie Puleo	.05
66 Fred Manrique	.05	132 Mike Birkbeck	.05	198 Carney Lansford	.08	264 Derek Lilliquist (R)	.35

NO.	PLAYER	MINT	NO.	PLAYER	MINT	NO.	PLAYER	MINT	NO.	PLAYER	MINT
265	Paul Assenmacher	.05	320	Jim Deshaies	.05	375	David Cone	.25	430	Brad DuVall (R)	.15
266	John Smoltz (R)	.35	321	Juan Agosto	.05	376	Doc Gooden	.30	431	Jose DeLeon	.05
267	Tom Glavine	.10	322	Mike Scott	.08	377	Sid Fernandez	.05	432	Joe Magrane	.08
268	Steve Avery (R)	.25	323	Rick Rhoden	.05	378	Dave Proctor (R)	.15	433	John Ericks (R)	.15
269	Pete Smith	.08	324	Jim Clancy	.05	379	Gary Carter	.08	434	Frank DiPino	.05
270	Jody Davis	.05	325	Larry Andersen	.05	380	Keith Miller	.05	435	Tony Pena	.08
271	Bruce Benedict	.05	326	Alex Trevino	.05	381	Gregg Jefferies	1.00	436	Ozzie Smith	.15
272	Andres Thomas	.05	327	Alan Ashby	.05	382	Tim Teufel	.05	437	Terry Pendleton	.05
273	Gerald Perry	.08	328	Craig Reynolds	.05	383	Kevin Elster	.05	438	Jose Oquendo	.05
274	Ron Gant	.10	329	Bill Doran	.05	384	Dave Magadan	.05	439	Tim Jones (R)	.15
275	Darrell Evans	.05	330	Rafael Ramirez	.05	385	Keith Hernandez	.10	440	Pedro Guerrero	.10
276	Dale Murphy	.15	331	Glenn Davis	.08	386	Mookie Wilson	.05	441	Milt Thompson	.08
277	Dion James	.05	332	Willie Ansley (R)	.25	387	Darryl Strawberry	.40	442	Willie McGee	.08
278	Lonnie Smith	.05	333	Gerald Young	.05	388	Kevin McReynolds	.10	443	Vince Coleman	.15
279	Geronimo Berroa	.10	334	Cameron Drew (R)	.25	389	Mark Carreon	.05	444	Tom Brunansky	.05
280	Steve Wilson (R)	.15	335	Jay Howell	.05	390	Jeff Parrett	.05	445	Walt Terrell	.05
281	Rick Sutcliffe	.08	336	Tim Belcher	.15	391	Mike Maddux	.05	446	Eric Show	.05
282	Kevin Coffman	.05	337	Fernando Valenzuela	.08	392	Don Carman	.05	447	Mark Davis	.08
283	Mitch Williams	.08	338	Ricky Horton	.05	393	Bruce Ruffin	.05	448	Andy Benes (R)	.45
284	Greg Maddux	.08	339	Tim Leary	.05	394	Ken Howell	.05	449	Eddie Whitson	.05
285	Paul Kilgus	.05	340	Bill Bene (R)	.15	395	Steve Bedrosian	.10	450	Dennis Rasmussen	.05
286	Mike Harkey (R)	.40	341	Orel Hershiser	.20	396	Floyd Youmans	.05	451	Bruce Hurst	.08
287	Lloyd McClendon	.10	342	Mike Scioscia	.05	397	Larry McWilliams	.05	452	Pat Clements	.05
288	Damon Berryhill	.15	343	Rick Dempsey	.05	398	Pat Combs (R)	.25	453	Benny Santiago	.10
289	Ty Griffin (R)	.75	344	Willie Randolph	.08	399	Steve Lake	.05	454	Sandy Alomar, Jr. (R)	1.00
290	Ryne Sandberg	.12	345	Alfredo Griffin	.05	400	Dickie Thon	.05	455	Garry Templeton	.05
291	Mark Grace	.75	346	Eddie Murray	.12	401	Ricky Jordan (R)	1.25	456	Jack Clark	.10
292	Curt Wilkerson	.05	347	Mickey Hatcher	.05	402	Mike Schmidt	.25	457	Tim Flannery	.05
293	Vance Law	.05	348	Mike Sharperson	.05	403	Tom Herr	.08	458	Roberto Alomar	.25
294	Shawon Dunston	.08	349	John Shelby	.05	404	Chris James	.08	459	Carmelo Martinez	.05
295	Jerome Walton (R)	2.50	350	Mike Marshall	.08	405	Juan Samuel	.05	460	John Kruk	.08
296	Mitch Webster	.05	351	Kirk Gibson	.15	406	Von Hayes	.08	461	Tony Gwynn	.25
297	Dwight Smith (R)	1.25	352	Mike Davis	.05	407	Ron Jones (R)	.30	462	Jerald Clark (R)	.15
298	Andre Dawson	.10	353	Bryn Smith	.05	408	Curt Ford	.05	463	Don Robinson	.05
299	Jeff Sellers	.05	354	Pascual Perez	.05	409	Bob Walk	.05	464	Craig Lefferts	.05
300	Jose Rijo	.10	355	Kevin Gross	.05	410	Jeff Robinson	.05	465	Kelly Downs	.05
301	John Franco	.08	356	Andy McGaffigan	.05	411	Jim Gott	.05	466	Rick Reuschel	.05
302	Rick Mahler	.05	357	Brian Holman (R)	.12	412	Scott Medvin	.08	467	Scott Garrelts	.05
303	Ron Robinson	.05	358	Dave Wainhouse (R)	.12	413	John Smiley	.08	468	Wil Tejada	.05
304	Danny Jackson	.08	359	Denny Martinez	.05	414	Bob Kipper	.05	469	Kirt Manwaring	.05
305	Rob Dibble (R)	.25	360	Tim Burke	.05	415	Brian Fisher	.05	470	Terry Kennedy	.05
306	Tom Browning	.05	361	Nelson Santovenia (R)	.12	416	Doug Drabek	.08	471	Jose Uribe	.05
307	Bo Diaz	.05	362	Tim Wallach	.08	417	Mike LaValliere	.05	472	Royce Clayton (R)	.15
308	Manny Trillo	.05	363	Spike Owen	.05	418	Ken Oberkfell	.05	473	Robby Thompson	.05
309	Chris Sabo (R)	.60	364	Rex Hudler	.05	419	Sid Bream	.05	474	Kevin Mitchell	.30
310	Ron Oester	.05	365	Andres Galarraga	.10	420	Austin Manahan (R)	.15	475	Ernie Riles	.05
311	Barry Larkin	.10	366	Otis Nixon	.05	421	Jose Lino	.05	476	Will Clark	.60
312	Todd Benzinger	.08	367	Hubie Brooks	.05	422	Bobby Bonilla	.10	477	Donell Nixon	.05
313	Paul O'Neill	.08	368	Mike Aldrete	.05	423	Glenn Wilson	.05	478	Candy Maldonado	.08
314	Kal Daniels	.12	369	Tim Raines	.15	424	Andy Van Slyke	.10	479	Tracy Jones	.05
315	Joel Youngblood	.05	370	Dave Martinez	.05	425	Gary Redus	.05	480	Brett Butler	.08
316	Eric Davis	.30	371	Bob Ojeda	.05	426	Barry Bonds	.10	481	Checklist	.05
317	Dave Smith	.05	372	Ron Darling	.10	427	Don Heinkel (R)	.15	482	Checklist	.05
318	Mark Portugal	.05	373	Wally Whitehurst (R)	.15	428	Ken Dayley	.05	483	Checklist	.05
319	Brian Meyer (R)	.12	374	Randy Myers	.05	429	Todd Worrell	.05	484	Checklist	.05

RARE & FAMOUS BASEBALL CARDS

1910 Honus Wagner

1933 Goudey Gum

1933 Goudey Gum

1911 Sherry "Magie"

Year	Manufacturer	Player	Value Near Mint
1910	T-206 Tobacco	Honus Wagner (Pitt)	$115,00.00
1910	T-206 Tobacco	Eddie Plank (Phil)	10,000.00
1910	T-206 Tobacco	Ray Demmitt (St. L)	2,500.00
1911	T-206 Tobacco	Sherry "Magie" (misspelled)	9,000.00
1911	T-206 Tobacco	Joy Doyle	15,000.00
1911	T-3 Tobacco	Ty Cobb	3,000.00
1911	T-3 Tobacco	Walter Johnson	2,000.00
1911	T-3 Tobacco	Christy Mathewson	2,000.00
1911	T-205 Tobacco	Ty Cobb	1,200.00
1912	T-207 Tobacco	Duffy Lewis (Boston N.)	2,000.00
1914	Cracker Jack	Ty Cobb	3,000.00
1933	Goudey Gum	Napoleon Lajoie	15,000.00
1933	Goudey Gum	Babe Ruth (4 diff. cards)	3,500.00 each
1933	De Long Gum	Lou Gehrig	2,000.00
1934	Goudey Gum	Lou Gehrig (2 diff. cards)	2,000.00 each
1938	Goudey Gum	Joe DiMaggio (2 diff. cards)	1,500.00 each
1940	Play Ball (Gum, Inc.)	Joe DiMaggio	1,250.00
1941	Play Ball (Gum, Inc.)	Joe DiMaggio	1,100.00
1948	Leaf Gum	Satchel Paige	1,250.00
1951	Topps All-Stars	Jim Konstanty	5,000.00
1951	Topps All-Stars	Robin Roberts	5,000.00
1951	Topps All-Stars	Eddie Stanky	5,000.00
1951	Bowman Gum	Mickey Mantle	5,000.00
1951	Bowman Gum	Willie Mays	1,750.00
1952	Topps	Mickey Mantle	6,750.00
1954	Bowman Gum	Ted Williams	2,000.00
1968	Topps 3-D	Roberto Clemente	2,000.00

1910 Eddie Plank

1938 Goudey Gum

1912 Duffy Lewis